PRINCIPAL SUBJECTS
IN THIS VOLUME

METALS HANDBOOK

8th Edition

VOL. 10

Failure Analysis and Prevention

prepared under the direction of the
ASM HANDBOOK COMMITTEE

Howard E. Boyer, Editor
William J. Carnes, Managing Editor – Copy and Production

Senior Editors:
Hugh Baker, Edward A. Durand,
Philip D. Harvey and Paul M. Unterweiser
Consulting Editor: John A. Fellows
Associate Editor: David Benjamin
Chief Copy Editor: Ian A. Anderson
Assistant Editors:
Helen V. Bukovics and Craig W. Kirkpatrick
Editorial Assistance: Lois L. Engintunca and
Helen Lawton Waldorf

Jack W. Kothera, Manager – Production Art
Sandra L. Craig, Assistant Manager – Production Art
Illustrators:
Charlene M. Christopher, Richard J. Czentorycki,
Peter T. Schwerko and William C. Seamon

AMERICAN SOCIETY FOR METALS

Metals Park, Ohio 44073

Contributors to This Volume

Each number that follows a name in this list refers to the first page of an article in which a contributor participated. Names not followed by numbers are those of contributors not identified with specific articles; titles and affiliations of these contributors are given on the facing page. Names of committee chairmen in the list below are printed in capital letters.

John W. Abar, 437
Shaffiq Ahmed, 95
L. E. Alban, 507
Leopold Albertin, 373
Joseph Aliotta, 249
Wayne L. Amber, 134
Pierre V. Andreae, 525, 545, 558
Lynn Arnold, 507
Edward L. Aul, 373
Robert T. Ault, 30, 44, 61, 125
CHARLES H. AVERY, 205, 228, 230, 240
Howard S. Avery, 134
Donald L. Bagnoli, 249
Robert M. Baker, 507
Bani R. Banerjee, 95
Bruce P. Bardes, 95, 449
Ralph D. Barer
Thomas E. Barker, 315
Harold J. Bates
Cedric D. Beachem, 205, 228, 230, 240
H. D. Bewley
James G. Bielenberg, 168
Jack J. Bodzin, 525, 545, 558
Gary L. Boerman
A. P. Bond, 205, 228, 230, 240
Donald L. Borden, 507
Walter K. Boyd, 205, 228, 230, 240
A. S. Brar
Nick F. Bratkovich, 333, 369
Frank C. Brautigam
P. H. Brotzman
I. Brough, 10
Kenneth G. Budinski, 134
Richard H. Burns
Spencer H. Bush
Donald P. Buswell, 507
James W. Butler, Jr., 397, 417
J. G. Byrne, 249
S. R. Callaway, 373
Charles O. Cambridge, 315
J. L. Cannon
D. A. Canonico, 525, 545, 558
J. Chandler, 30, 44, 61, 125
Philip J. Charley, 205, 228, 230, 240
James L. Chevalier, 397, 417
A. J. Cienkus, 134
W. L. Clarke, Jr.
Craig D. Clauser, 333, 369
John F. Clayton, 525, 545, 558
Ernest D. Coberly, Jr., 315
Franklin H. Cocks, 205, 228, 230, 240
Louis F. Coffin, Jr., 525, 545, 558
Vito J. Colangelo, 291
V. W. Comstock, 397, 417
Herbert F. Conrad
C. Howard Craft
Carl J. Cron, 205, 228, 230, 240
Hugh Crowder, 26, 168
E. Philip Dahlberg, 525, 545, 558
T. J. Davies, 10
Richard S. DeFries, 249

C. R. Denaburg, 168
James E. Denton, 507
STEWART M. DePOY, 333, 369
Owen F. Devereux, 205, 228, 230, 240
John Dodd, 134
W. J. Doelker, 315
T. J. Dolan
Matthew J. Donachie, Jr., 249, 333, 369
John H. Dumbleton, 205, 228, 230, 240, 571
C. W. Dunstan
D. J. Duquette, 205, 228, 230, 240
Richard P. Edwards, 507
John D. Eyestone, 333, 369
A. L. Fabens, 397, 417
H. A. Fabert, Jr., 134
H. Edward Fairman, 95
A. M. Federico
C. Feng, 30, 44, 61, 125
A. O. Fisher
Stephen Floreen, 205, 228, 230, 240
Frederick J. Fraikor, 30, 44, 61, 125
William G. Fricke, Jr., 30, 44, 61, 125
Glenn A. Fritzlen, 249
John H. Frome, Jr.
Henry O. Fuchs, 95
Robert F. Gamer
Amal Ganguli
Robert H. Gassner
W. A. Glaeser, 134
J. V. Gluck, 525, 545, 558
Edward J. Goldman
HERMAN D. GREENBERG, 373
WILSON T. GROVES, 507
John D. Gruner
Henry T. Hadley, 315
M. W. Hagadorn, 30, 44, 61, 125
D. William Hall, 134
Frederick G. Hammitt, 160
Albert Hanson, 168
Louis A. Hartcorn
T. W. Heaslip
George A. Hendry, 333, 369
Gary H. Henger
Frank J. Heymann, 160
John F. Hildebrand
J. A. Hildebrandt, 507
William L. Holshouser
Ralph M. Horton
V. F. Horvath
Robert L. Huddleston, 30, 44, 61, 125
Herbert B. Hummer
F. R. Hutchings, 10
Erwin M. Ichiyasu, 397, 417
Clarence E. Jackson, 333, 369
Lyle R. Jacobs
F. L. Jamieson, 95, 455
Walter L. Jensen, 470
Sam R. Kegley
Ralph Keidel, 333, 369
E. G. Kendall
John M. Kiefer, Jr.

Joseph A. Kies, 30, 44, 61, 125
John Kildsig, 249
Virgil J. Knierim, 168
Gabor Koves
Leslie D. Kramer, 205, 228, 230, 240
J. F. Krieg
F. Eric Krueger, 154, 373
E. R. Kuch
Loren L. Lanier, 205, 228, 230, 240
James T. Larkin
James S. Laub, 95
Jesse Le Coff, 525, 545, 558
Robert L. Littler
Oles Lomacky, 30, 44, 61, 125
Saul H. Lowe, 373
K. C. Lowstetter, 249
Robert N. Lukat
William C. Mack
James Maker, 30, 44, 61, 125, 487
Gunvant N. Maniar, 30, 44, 61, 125
E. M. Marski
JAMES L. McCALL, 95
Donald E. McGarrigan, 525, 545, 558
Sherwood W. McGee, 507
Daniel F. McGrath, 373
Michael F. McGuire, 397, 417
Bruce W. McLeod, 249
Richard W. Meek, 397, 417
Wilton F. Melhorn, 525, 545, 558
Alan H. Miller, 168
Edward H. Miller, 571
W. L. Mitchell, 397, 417
Jerome Mogul, 95
Ronald C. Moorhead, 249
Donald R. Neruda
Daniel F. Newman, 507
Daniel M. Noble, 525, 545, 558
Telfer E. Norman, 134
T. L. Oberle, 333, 369
Kenneth F. Packer, 333, 369
Vito Palombella, 168
E. C. Pearson
GEORGE E. PELLISSIER, 30, 44, 61, 125
Thoni V. Philip, 134
Robert T. Picha
M. L. Pickelsimer, 30, 44, 61, 125
Lawrence G. Platt
Conrad J. Polk, 397, 417
James Pugh
R. Quattrone, 333, 369
Thomas L. Ramsey
A. H. RAUCH, 315
I. W. Reese
Robert G. Reeves
Lewis H. Reid, 525, 545, 558
E. H. Rennhack
STUART L. RICE, 397, 417
John A. Richter, 315
B. W. Roberts, 134
Hugh R. Roberts, 397, 417
Dennis D. Rogers, 30, 44, 61, 125

Robert M. Rose, 168
Marion Russo, 95
D. A. Ryder, 10
S. Sarkar
L. W. Sarver, 134
Woodrow A. Schilling, 315
James C. Schluckbier
ERNEST A. SCHOEFER, 249
William A. Schrader
Paul E. Schwiegerling
Charles N. Scott, 397, 417
Charles C. Seastrom, 525, 545, 558
Ray Shahani, 95
John P. Sheehan, 95
Robert Sherman, 249
T. R. Shives, 30, 44, 61, 125
N. H. Simpson
G. M. SLAUGHTER, 525, 545, 558
Robert M. Slepian
Robert E. Smallwood, 168
Charles O. Smith

Whitney Snyder, 95
Donald O. Sprowls, 205, 228, 230, 240
ROGER W. STAEHLE, 205, 228, 230, 240
James K. Stanley
J. E. Steiner, 373
Joseph R. Stephens
Ralph W. Stevenson, 397, 417
James H. Stewart, 249
John W. Sullivan, 373
Earl C. Sutherland, 205, 228, 230, 240
William A. Svekric, 333, 369
D. O. Taylor, 168
William J. Teaford, 95
Peter A. Thornton, 291
R. C. Tucker, Jr., 134
R. J. Urban
George F. Vander Voort, 30, 44, 61, 125
Larry J. Vande Walle, 315
Edward T. Vitcha, 249
Frederick R. Wagner, 95

William L. Walker, 168
David Wallace, 134
W. Wallace
Richard Waltein, 373
RAYMOND WARD, 168
Ray E. Warnock, 315
Peter R. Weihsmann, 397, 417
Theodore R. Weins, 507
Sidney Weisman
D. E. Wenschhof, 249
David E. Werstler, 373
P. R. White, 333, 369
David E. Wicks
William Wiebe, 205, 228, 230, 240
Richard A. Wilde, 507
Samuel L. Williams, 315
Arthur L. Wills
Thomas M. Wolfe
Richard A. Wright, 455
Donald J. Wulpi, 373
Noble C. York, 373

Contributors to This Volume Not Identified With Specific Articles

RALPH D. BARER, Head, Materials Engineering, Defence Research Establishment Pacific; HAROLD J. BATES (deceased), formerly Superintendent, Metallurgy and Inspection, Fairfield Manufacturing Co., Inc.; H. D. BEWLEY, Nuclear Div., Union Carbide Corp.; GARY L. BOERMAN, Chief Metallurgist, Ordnance Engineering Div., FMC Corp.; A. S. BRAR, Senior Scientist, Normandale Div., Control Data Corp.

FRANK C. BRAUTIGAM, Manager, Metallurgical Engineering, Sharples-Stokes Div., Penwalt Corp.; P. H. BROTZMAN (retired), formerly Chief Metallurgist, Firestone Tire & Rubber Co.; RICHARD H. BURNS, Manager of Quality Assurance, Worthington Turbine International, Inc.; SPENCER H. BUSH, Senior Staff Consultant, Battelle – Pacific Northwest Laboratories; J. L. CANNON, Metallurgy Dept., Goodyear Atomic Corp.

W. L. CLARKE, JR., Metallurgical Engineer, Metallurgy Development, Vallecitos Nuclear Center, General Electric Co.; HERBERT F. CONRAD, Consulting Engineer; C. HOWARD CRAFT, Senior Metallurgist, Magnaflux Testing Laboratories, Magnaflux Corp.; T. J. DOLAN (retired), formerly Professor, Dept. of Theoretical and Applied Mechanics, Talbot Laboratory, University of Illinois.

C. W. DUNSTAN, Metallurgist, Test and Development Laboratory, Bristol Aerospace (1968) Ltd.; A. M. FEDERICO, Metallurgist, Metals Laboratory, Missile Systems Div., Rockwell International Corp.; A. O. FISHER, Materials Consultant, Central Engineering Dept., Monsanto Co.; JOHN H. FROME, JR., Metallurgist, W. B. Coleman Co.

ROBERT F. GAMER, Professional Affairs Director, Zimmer Manufacturing Co.; AMAL GANGULI, Head, Microanalysis Section, Metal-Ceramic Engineering Dept., Energy Controls Div., Bendix Corp.; ROBERT H. GASSNER, Assistant Manager, Metallics, Douglas Aircraft Co. Div., McDonnell Douglas Corp.

EDWARD J. GOLDMAN, Vice President, Foster-Miller Associates, Inc.; JOHN D. GRUNER, Senior Materials Engineer, Materials and Electronic Equipment and Cabling Engineering Section, Jet Propulsion Laboratory, California Institute of Technology; LOUIS A. HARTCORN, Manager, Microstructural Analysis Section, Hanford Engineering Development Laboratory, Westinghouse Hanford Co.

T. W. HEASLIP, Supervisor, Materials Failure Analysis, Aircraft Accident Investigation Engineering Laboratory, Canadian Department of Transport; GARY H. HENGER, General Supervising Metallurgist, Metallurgical Dept., Inland Steel Co.; JOHN F. HILDEBRAND, Staff Metallurgical Engineer, Gulf General Atomic, Inc.; WILLIAM L. HOLSHOUSER (retired), formerly Chief, Laboratory Services Staff, Bureau of Aviation Safety, National Transportation Safety Board.

RALPH M. HORTON, Associate Professor, Dept. of Materials Science and Engineering, Washington State University; V. F. HORVATH, Metallurgical Engineer, Wyatt Div., U. S. Industries, Inc.; HERBERT B. HUMMER, Director of Engineering, Durametallic Corp.; LYLE R. JACOBS, Executive Vice President, Taussig Associates, Inc.; SAM R. KEGLEY, Director of Quality Assurance, Denison Div., Abex Corp.; E. G. KENDALL, Head, Metallurgy and Ceramics Dept., Aerospace Corp.

JOHN M. KIEFER, JR., Metallurgical Engineer, Cuyahoga Plant, United States Steel Corp.; GABOR KOVES, Manager, Materials and Process Engineering, International Business Machines Corp.; J. F. KRIEG, Senior Group Engineer, Metallurgical Laboratory, McDonnell Aircraft Co. Div., McDonnell Douglas Corp.; E. R. KUCH, Chief Metallurgist, Metallurgical Dept., Gardner-Denver Co.

JAMES T. LARKIN, Engineer, Alfred Heller Heat Treating Co.; ROBERT L. LITTLER, Senior Corrosion Engineer, Mobil Chemical Co.; ROBERT N. LUKAT, Metallurgist, Southern Saw Service, Inc.; WILLIAM C. MACK, Senior Metallurgist, Technical Services, Tubular Products Div., Babcock & Wilcox Co.

E. M. MARSKI, Research Engineer, Cast Iron Pipe and Foundry Div., Clow Corp.; DONALD R. NERUDA, Senior Engineer, Materials Engineering Dept., Hawthorn Works, Western Electric Co., Inc.; E. C. PEARSON, Metallurgist, Alcan International Ltd.

ROBERT T. PICHA, Consulting Metallurgical Engineer, R. T. Picha Co.; LAWRENCE G. PLATT, Laboratory Supervisor, Gardner-Denver Co.; JAMES PUGH, Director, Biomechanics Laboratory, Hospital for Joint Diseases and Medical Center; THOMAS L. RAMSEY, Metallurgist, Libbey-Owens-Ford Co.; I. W. REESE, Supervisor, Metallurgical and Chemical Laboratory, Research and Advanced Product Development Div., DeLaval Turbine, Inc.; ROBERT G. REEVES, Senior Metallographer, Technical Center, Gould Corp.

E. H. RENNHACK, Research Specialist, Manufacturing Research, Lockheed Missiles & Space Co.; S. SARKAR, Bramalea Laboratory, Bell Canada Northern Electric Research Ltd.; JAMES C. SCHLUCKBIER, Manufacturing Engineer, Cummins Engine Co., Inc.; WILLIAM A. SCHRADER, Metallurgist, Woodward Governor Co.; PAUL E. SCHWIEGERLING, Consultant, Conax Corp.

N. H. SIMPSON, Manager, Metallurgy and Quality Control, Macwhyte Co.; ROBERT M. SLEPIAN, Supervisor, Metallography, Research and Development Center, Westinghouse Electric Corp.; CHARLES O. SMITH, Professor of Mechanical Engineering, University of Detroit; JAMES K. STANLEY (deceased), formerly Head, Applied Metallurgy, Materials Sciences Laboratory, Aerospace Corp.

JOSEPH R. STEPHENS, Research Metallurgist, Lewis Research Center, NASA; R. J. URBAN, Metallurgist, Texas Div., Menasco Manufacturing Co.; W. WALLACE, Research Officer, National Research Council of Canada; SIDNEY WEISMAN, Senior Metallurgical Research Associate, Howmedica, Inc.; DAVID E. WICKS, Manager, Dansville Welding Laboratory, Foster-Wheeler Corp.; ARTHUR L. WILLS, Process Engineer, Cadillac Motor Car Div., General Motors Corp.; THOMAS M. WOLFE, Manager, Metallurgy and Welding Engineering, Materials and Processes Dept., Grumman Aerospace Corp.

FOREWORD

THIS TENTH VOLUME of the 8th Edition of METALS HAND-BOOK, "Failure Analysis and Prevention", represents the realization of an ambitious, long-range plan to include in the Handbook series a volume that would provide definitive, objective and technically reliable coverage of all aspects of the investigative and corrective science of failure analysis. Although the word "failure" bears the burden of negative connotation, the practice of failure analysis is, above all else, the systematic pursuit of the positive — the pursuit of technological progress.

Consistent with an editorial policy that has applied to all previous volumes in this 8th Edition, major emphasis has again been directed toward providing the reader with practical information that will guide and assist him in solving problems. Such emphasis is uniquely appropriate in a comprehensive treatment of failure analysis — a science dedicated to the principle that the extension of product improvement and reliability depends in large part on the recognition of shortcomings that can usually be corrected and on the identification of problems that, when fully explored and understood, can usually be solved.

Once again, the Handbook Committee, author committees, other contributors, and editorial staff have joined ranks to produce a book without precedent both in content and in breadth of coverage — a book that proceeds in orderly sequence, beginning with a review of the engineering aspects of failure, then following with in-depth studies of the various failure mechanisms and related environmental factors, and concluding with extensive analyses of hundreds of actual service failures. To all who contributed to this successful completion of a challenging assignment, we extend our sincere thanks.

DEAN K. HANINK
President, ASM

ALLAN RAY PUTNAM
Managing Director, ASM

PREFACE

THIS IS THE TENTH in a series of volumes that will supersede the single-volume 7th edition of METALS HANDBOOK and greatly enlarge its scope.

The title of the present volume, "Failure Analysis and Prevention", was adopted by the ASM Handbook Committee and the editors during the early stages of planning because it connotes a balanced presentation of subject matter — a presentation that deals not only with analysis of failures but also with effective measures for failure prevention by improving product performance and reliability. In common with all previous volumes in this series, the present volume is intended to provide comprehensive, reliable and objective technical information that will be of maximum usefulness to the reader. Much of the information has not been published previously, and no collection of such magnitude is to be found in any other single volume.

The adoption of technical terms for use in this volume has been predicated solely on current technical usage. It is recognized that the term "failure", in particular, has many meanings and potentially carries with it innumerable implications, most of them non-technical and ranging in scope from the trivial to the calamitous. In this volume, the term "failure" is employed as a technical term — as are many other terms relating to failure. As a technical term, "failure" means cessation of function or usefulness. Failures may stem from many causes, but the term carries no implication of negligence or malfeasance.

"Failure Analysis and Prevention" provides a basic reference on analysis of failures and corrective procedures for failure prevention; a greater understanding of its scope and contents may be derived from the following summary of the four principal sections or subdivisions of this volume.

Engineering Aspects of Failure and Failure Analysis. This 56-page section, which comprises four articles that present a total of 116 illustrations and eight examples, begins with a systematic review of the fundamental sources of failure of metallic components and considers such contributory factors as deficiencies in design, deficiencies in selection of material, imperfections in material, deficiencies in processing, errors in assembly, and improper service conditions (including improper procedures at start-up and shutdown and inadequate maintenance). The general procedures, techniques and precautions employed in the investigation and analysis of service failures are covered in the 20-page article "General Practice in Failure Analysis", which carries an appendix describing a portable metallographic laboratory suited for on-site failure analysis.

Of major interest to the metallurgical community in recent years have been the subjects treated comprehensively in the concluding articles of this section, "Toughness and Fracture Mechanics" and "Ductile-to-Brittle Fracture Transition". The first of these articles, which provides in-depth coverage of the roles of notch toughness, fracture toughness and fracture mechanics in component design and failure analysis, also contains appendixes on notch-toughness and fracture-toughness testing and evaluation. "Ductile-to-Brittle Fracture Transition" reviews the methods for determining transition temperature, describes the effects of temperature, metallurgical factors, composition and microstructure, allotropic transformation and other variables on transition, and concludes with a review of transition behavior in major alloy systems.

Failures From Various Mechanisms and Related Environmental Factors. Analysis of a failure of a metal structure or part usually requires identification of the type of failure. Identification of failure type is the general subject of the introductory article in this 228-page section, which then delineates each of the major types of failures in a series of 12 additional articles. (Augmenting this section are 615 illustrations and 105 examples of failed parts or structures.) Of the 12 articles, two are concerned with fracture-type failures — ductile and brittle failures, and failures resulting from fatigue. The remaining articles in the section separately treat each of the following failure mechanisms and environmental factors that contribute to failure: wear, fretting, distortion, liquid erosion, corrosion, stress-corrosion cracking, liquid-metal embrittlement, hydrogen damage, corrosion fatigue, and elevated temperature. These articles, each profusely illustrated and reinforced by examples reporting on actual failure analyses, can greatly simplify many tasks of the failure analyst in pinpointing types of failure with which he is unfamiliar or in confirming his judgment regarding types of failure with which he is familiar.

Analysis and Prevention of Service Failures: Products of Principal Metalworking Processes. This 87-page section, which contains five articles, 291 illustrations and 89 examples, relates types and causes of failure of metal products, as well as techniques in failure prevention, to characteristics derived from, or associated with, principal primary and secondary metalworking processes. The products considered are those produced by cold forming, forging, casting, welding and brazing.

The contributions of a metalworking process to product performance and reliability are often as important as those of design and material selection. For example, in the article "Failures of Cold Formed Parts" (the first article in this section), it is explained that, for a given set of service conditions, certain unique characteristics of cold formed parts may significantly increase or decrease their susceptibility to failure. Cold forming of a metal part causes deformation of grains — a condition that, depending on service factors, may increase vulnerability to corrosion and fatigue. Conversely, the imposition of compressive stresses at the part surface during cold forming may enhance resistance to fatigue failure by counteracting residual tensile stresses. Forgings may inherit imperfections from the initial ingot or billet, or may develop defects or deficiencies in microstructure during the forging process, that give rise to problems in service. Service life of iron and steel castings can be affected by a variety of imperfections and discontinuities associated with casting processes, including cold shuts, gas porosity and hot tears. Characteristics, both beneficial and deleterious, acquired during welding and brazing also affect product performance and service life.

Analysis and Prevention of Service Failures: Manufactured Components and Assemblies. The final section of the volume, which occupies 208 pages, probably will be the section most often referred to, because it deals exclusively with analysis and prevention of failures of specific classes of manufactured components and assemblies. The section consists of 14 articles, 664 illustrations and 140 examples of failure analyses.

That the scope and contents of this section are without precedent in the literature of failure analysis can be demonstrated by a review of any one of its articles. Consider "Failures of Sliding Bearings", an article that deals with a commonly encountered class of mechanical components. This article begins with a review of fundamentals (which is of particular value to the reader who is not a bearing specialist), such as types of sliding bearings, significance of bearing-characteristic number, bearing lubrication, engineering requirements for selection of bearing materials, and preferred applications for specific sliding-bearing materials. The procedures for analyzing bearing failures are then set forth in detail, including preliminary examination, metallographic examination, and the study and identification of embedded particles. Next are comprehensive reviews of each of the mechanisms by which sliding bearings fail — fatigue, wear, fretting, corrosion, corrosion fatigue and cavitation. Finally, the causes of bearing damage are considered: presence of foreign particles between bearing and shaft surfaces, inadequate or improper lubrication, extremes in operating temperature, overloading, improper assembly, surface and subsurface discontinuities, and improper design of shaft or bearing. Throughout the article, the reader is afforded an overview of preventive measures in design, materials selection, assembly, operation and maintenance that contribute to improved performance, reliability and long service life.

The same detailed coverage is given the other manufactured components and assemblies that comprise the subject matter of this section — including shafts, rolling-element bearings, lifting equipment, mechanical fasteners, springs, dies, gears, boilers, heat exchangers and pressure vessels.

That the information presented in "Failure Analysis and Prevention" will be of great benefit to those concerned with modern technology fulfills the mission of the 245 contributors to this volume, upon whose collective experience and high competence the accuracy and authority of the book are based.

HOWARD E. BOYER
Editor – Metals Handbook

TABLE OF CONTENTS

Engineering Aspects of Failure and Failure Analysis

Failures From Various Mechanisms and Related Environmental Factors

Analysis and Prevention of Service Failures:
Products of Principal Metalworking Processes

Analysis and Prevention of Service Failures:
Manufactured Components and Assemblies

ENGINEERING ASPECTS OF FAILURE AND FAILURE ANALYSIS

CONTENTS

Fundamental Sources of Failures

A PART or assembly is considered to have failed under one of three conditions: (*a*) when it becomes completely inoperable, (*b*) when it is still operable but is no longer able to perform its intended function satisfactorily, or (*c*) when serious deterioration has made it unreliable or unsafe for continued use, thus necessitating its immediate removal from service for repair or replacement.

The fundamental sources of failure include many aspects of design, material selection, material imperfections, fabrication and processing, reworking, assembly, inspection, testing, quality control, storage and shipment, service conditions, maintenance, and unanticipated exposure to overload or mechanical or chemical damage in service. Often, more than one source contributes to the occurrence of a given failure.

Deficiencies in Design

Some failures result from design deficiencies of a nature indicating that little engineering effort was made to avoid design features known to be conducive to failure. At the other extreme, sometimes even a carefully conceived and thoroughly evaluated design may still be deficient and contribute to early failure in service.

Mechanical Notches. Perhaps the most frequently observed and often easily avoided deficiency in design is the presence of mechanical notches at points of high stress. The use of too sharp a fillet radius at a change in section of a shaft or similar part that is subject to bending or torsional loading exemplifies this type of deficiency in design.

Example 1 on page 376 in the article on Failures of Shafts describes the contribution of a 0.010-in.-radius fillet at a change in section to failure of shafts that were part of a tube-bending assembly. The shafts, which were subjected to a cyclic unidirectional bending load, fractured in fatigue at the fillet. Recurrence of failure of this type was prevented by redesigning the shafts to have a smooth $\frac{3}{32}$-in. radius at the change in section where fracture had formerly originated.

A design feature that is especially conducive to failure and should always be avoided is the intersection of two mechanical notches, such as a keyway and a fillet in a shaft.

Changes in design are sometimes made without adequate consideration of the possible introduction of stress raisers in the form of mechanical notches. In the example that follows, the maximum permissible depth of a weight-reducing hole in a stationary spindle that supported a roller wheel for the tracks on a military vehicle was not specified when the design of the spindle was changed to add the hole. The hole was drilled too deep, and the result was early failure of the spindle by fatigue, with fracture originating at the bottom of the hole, the sharp corner of which was an internal stress raiser.

Example 1. Fatigue Fracture of a Hardened 4340 Steel Spindle at the Bottom of an Improperly Dimensioned Axial Weight-Reducing Hole (Fig. 1)

The spindle in one of two similar spindle assemblies (see Fig. 1a) on a military tracked vehicle broke off completely in transverse fracture after the vehicle had traveled about 1400 miles. The track, which was supported on a roller wheel mounted on bearings seated on the spindle assembly, came off, causing other damage to the vehicle.

The vehicle on which the fracture occurred was one of a pilot lot being operated under expected-use conditions at a proving ground before volume manufacture of these vehicles was begun.

Material and Fabrication. Starting material for the spindle was specified to be an annealed or normalized 4340 steel forging. After rough machining, the part was to be hardened (using an oil quench), tempered to a final hardness of Rockwell C 34 to 40, and finish machined on the critical areas for shrink fitting to the support member. Before assembly, the outer surface of the spindle was shot peened in the region that would be most highly stressed in service (see detail A in Fig. 1a).

Macroexamination. The fracture region and fracture surfaces were examined both with the unaided eye and at low magnification. As indicated in detail A in Fig. 1, the fracture extended radially from the bottom of a drilled weight-reducing hole to the periphery of the spindle, at about $\frac{1}{8}$ in. beyond the end of the contacting portion of the support member. No service damage or material defects that could be related to the failure were detected.

The appearance of the fracture surfaces, one of which is shown in Fig. 1(b), was characteristic of fatigue fracture resulting from the combination of a cyclic one-way bending load, low to moderate overload and high stress concentration. The fatigue zone of the fracture was defined by clearly visible clamshell marks and covered more than half of the fracture surface.

The location and orientation of the clamshell marks established that the fracture origin was at the periphery of the conical bottom of the weight-reducing hole, where indicated by the arrow in Fig. 1(b). The entire bottom surface of the hole was deeply scored by drilling tool marks. Less-severe tool marks were evident on the wall of the hole.

Conformance to Specifications. The composition of the broken spindle, as determined by chemical analysis, met the requirements for 4340 steel.

No indications of imperfections that could be related to the fracture were detected by magnetic-particle inspection of the part.

Hardness measurements and examination of microstructure on a cross section taken through the spindle near the fracture verified that the part conformed to the specified material requirements in both respects. The hardness measurements ranged from Rockwell C 38 to 40, and metallographic examination of a polished and etched (2% nital) specimen at a magnification of 500 diameters revealed a normal structure of tempered martensite. There was no measurable decarburization at the spindle surface, and no harmful inclusions or other abnormalities were detected.

Conclusions. The fracture occurred by fatigue as a direct result of the presence of a circumferential internal notch at the most highly stressed portion of the spindle. The fracture origin was at the periphery of the conical bottom of the weight-reducing hole, at a point just beyond the end of the surrounding support member (see detail A in Fig. 1a, and Fig. 1b). The presence of this notch was estimated as being equivalent to a reduction in strength of the spindle of approximately 40%.

A weight-reducing hole was not called for in the original design of the spindle; when this design modification was made, the depth of the hole was not specified. Failure to recognize the importance of the depth of the drilled hole was apparently an oversight in making the design change, inasmuch as shot peening of the critical area of the spindle had been specified because of the expected presence of high cyclic bending stresses on this part in service.

Corrective Action. It was specified that the bottom of the weight-reducing hole be at least 1 in. short of the end of the contacting portion of the support member, thus removing the notch from the area of the spindle that was subject to severe cyclic bending stresses.

Also, instructions were issued to check for any nonconforming spindles in stock on unused vehicles and vehicles in proving-ground service, and to scrap any spindles that did not conform to the new requirements on depth of the weight-reducing hole.

Upgrading of a part to a new application in which the part must withstand service conditions more severe than in its former use sometimes results in early failure, revealing that the original design is deficient in the new application. Some of the more common reasons for early failure in a new application include: improper material and heat treatment specifications for the new application, complex stress fields that become critical factors upon upgrading, and (as in the example that follows) stress raisers that were not important in the original application.

Example 2. Fatigue Fracture of a 1010 Steel Valve-Spring Retainer Cap During Engine Test Run, Because of a Deficiency in Design (Fig. 2)

A valve-spring retainer cap for a high-performance eight-cylinder automobile engine failed prematurely during a qualification run on a production engine. The cap had a long history of completely satisfactory

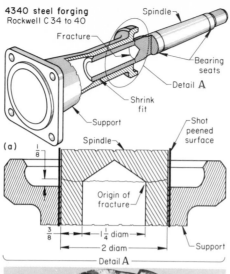

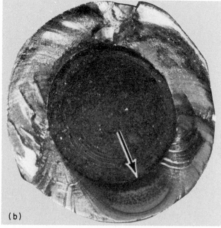

The origin of the fracture, at the periphery of a conical weight-reducing hole, is indicated by arrows in detail A, and in the fractograph (b) of one of the fracture surfaces at about 2⅓×. The portion of the spindle illustrated in detail A was shot peened (indicated by broad line) on its outer surface. Bearings (not shown) were mounted on the bearing seats on the spindle to support the roller wheel for the track.

Fig. 1. Spindle assembly, of 4340 steel, that fractured by fatigue in service on a military tracked vehicle (Example 1)

service in a less powerful engine. The retainer cap, valve spring, and related parts are illustrated in Fig. 2(a); the region in which the failure occurred is shown in greater detail in Fig. 2(b).

Description of Failure. Most of the flange on the retainer cap broke off shortly before completion of 200 hr of test operation at 4100 to 4600 rpm, or after about 26 million cycles. One indication of the occurrence of the fracture was a sudden drop in dynamometer reading, which signaled a decrease in engine power.

The test described was equivalent to driving an automobile equipped with this engine continuously for 200 hr at a speed of 140 mph. Although it constituted a severe test for a commercial passenger-car engine, this test was used routinely to detect deficiencies in a relatively short time.

Manufacturing Procedure and Specifications. The retainer cap was to be manufactured from 0.650-in.-diam commercial-quality cold drawn 1010 steel wire in the

annealed condition, by the following sequence of operations:

1. Forge and trim
2. Case harden by carbonitriding for 30 min at 843 C (1550 F) and quenching in oil
3. Temper in air at 260 C (500 F).

Total case depth was specified to be 0.005 to 0.010 in., and the cap was to be file resistant (specified as a hardness of Rockwell 15-N 86 minimum).

Conformance to Specifications. Chemical analysis of the core material of the fractured cap gave a carbon content of 0.11% and a manganese content of 0.48%, which were within the normal range for 1010 steel.

Microscopic examination of a polished and picral-etched cross section showed total case depth to be 0.008 in., which was within the acceptable range. The average hardness at the surface of the cap was Rockwell 15-N 84 (slightly below the specified minimum), with a range of 83 to 86.

Macroexamination. The fractured retainer cap was examined visually and at a magnification of 10 to 50 diameters. The flange had broken off along about ¾ of the periphery of the cap (Fig. 2c). The smooth area on the fracture surface (at the left in Fig. 2c) had the characteristic appearance of a fatigue zone. The examination established that the fatigue fracture had originated at the outside surface of the cap, along the sharp fillet (0.020-in. radius; see Fig. 2b) between the pilot and flange portions. No clamshell indications or beach marks were visible in the fatigue zone.

The irregular, ragged areas of the fracture surface (Fig. 2c) were the zones of final, fast fracture. There were no signs of plastic deformation or of a shear lip in the zones of final fracture, indicating that final fracture was of a brittle nature.

Metallographic Examination. Examination (at 250 diameters) of the polished and picral-etched cross section used for checking case depth revealed that the microstructure of both the case and the core regions was normal for 1010 steel processed as described above under "Manufacturing Procedure and Specifications". No harmful inclusions or other significant imperfections or abnormalities were detected.

Conclusions. Examination and testing of the failed part, together with the nature and conditions of the cyclic loading to which it had been subjected, established that fracture had been initiated by fatigue and had propagated by this mechanism until final, brittle fracture occurred. No significant imperfections in material or processing or other abnormalities were observed. However, the sharp fillet between the pilot and flange portions of the retainer cap (see Fig. 2b) had provided a line of stress concentration along which fracture originated under the severe conditions of the engine test.

Corrective Action. The design of the retainer cap was changed by increasing the radius of the fillet at which the fracture had originated from 0.020 to 0.050 in., to distribute the stress more uniformly. Retainer caps made to the new design performed satisfactorily both in engine test runs and in actual service, and no further changes in the part were needed.

An additional advantage of the new design was that the increase in fillet radius could be made at relatively little expense, especially when compared with the cost of upgrading the material. Also, the increase in fillet radius made fabrication easier and presented no new problems.

Insufficient Design Criteria. Deficiencies in design may result from the impossibility of making reliable stress calculations for complex parts and from insufficient information about the types and magnitude of the loads to which a part will be exposed in service (as with hoisting, earthmoving, excavating, farming, and other off-the-road equipment).

Failures related to lack of information about loading in service are described in Example 3 on page 475 in the article on Failures of Mechanical Fasteners.

Complex parts for which stress calculations present extreme difficulties are exemplified by the hollow splined shaft described in Example 1 on page 241 in the article on Corrosion-Fatigue Failures, and by the crankshaft described in Example 5 on page 296 in the article on Failures of Forgings.

However, in the examples listed in the preceding two paragraphs, other factors, such as corrosion and the presence of imperfections in the material, may also have contributed to susceptibility to early failure.

Even with parts for which loading in service is known accurately and stress analysis is straightforward, gross deficiencies in design may arise from reliance on static load-carrying capacity based on tensile-strength and yield-strength data without taking into account the possibility of failure by such mechanisms as brittle fracture, low-cycle fatigue, stress corrosion, and corrosion fatigue.

Deficiencies in Selection of Material

Because material selection, as part of the over-all design of a product, must be made in relation to the dimensional and geometrical aspects of design, the preceding discussion, under "Deficiencies in Design", applies to material selection as well as to design.

Inadequacy of Tensile-Test Data. Although most standard specifications require tensile-test data, these data are only partly indicative of inherent mechanical resistance to specific service conditions. The wide use of standard tensile tests is useful primarily as a routine check of the relative quality of different lots of a given material; the data resulting from the tests serve primarily as an index of batch-to-batch variability of the material.

Except for those few situations in which ductile fracture or gross yielding may be the limiting condition for failure, tensile strength and yield strength not only are inadequate criteria for avoidance of failure but also may actually lead

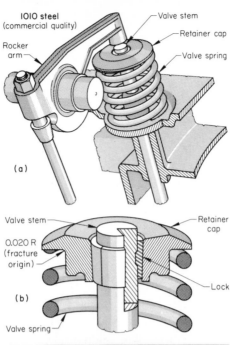

Smooth area at left in the fracture surface in (c) is the fatigue zone; the fracture origin was at the 0.020-in.-radius fillet on the retainer cap; irregular, ragged areas are zones of final, fast fracture; magnification is 2×.

Fig. 2. Retainer cap, valve spring and related parts in an automobile-engine head in which the retainer cap failed prematurely by fatigue fracture during an engine test run (Example 2)

to the selection of an unsatisfactory material. High tensile strength is frequently detrimental in parts in which severe stress raisers are present and for which the potential mechanism of failure is likely to be fatigue or brittle fracture or to involve corrosion in combination with static or cyclic loading.

Criteria for Selection of Material. For each foreseeable mechanism of failure, there are only a few criteria of primary importance for selection of an optimum material; these are the specific characteristics of the material that quantitatively measure its resistance to failure by a given mechanism. In some instances a trade-off will be necessary among these material characteristics and also among factors such as cost, fabricability, availability and expected service life in the intended application.

No generalizations can be made that will be valid for all material-selection problems; each problem must be considered individually or on the basis of closely related experience. Table 1, however, provides general guidance as to the criteria that ordinarily are most significant in selecting a material in relation to possible failure mechanisms, types of loading, types of stress and operating temperatures.

The most troublesome areas of material selection are those related to mechanical behavior in which properties of the material are influenced by the effect of time in service. Some of these characteristics are: (*a*) resistance to wear; (*b*) effect of elevated temperature on properties; and (*c*) resistance to corrosion, stress corrosion, corrosion fatigue and radiation. These applications require a great deal of judgment in the interpretation of laboratory test data and their extrapolation to long periods of time in service; closely simulated service testing may be necessary.

Example 4 on page 179 in the article on Corrosion Failures discusses a failure that was detected only as a result of customer complaints about relatively infrequent contamination of the end product — a soft drink dispensed from a vending machine. This failure was related to the selection of type 303 stainless steel for ease of machining of a dispensing valve, instead of using type 304 stainless steel, which is usually specified for such an application.

The failure of a malleable iron latch in contact with a copper alloy clapper in water in an automatic sprinkler system is described in Example 5 on page 183 in the article on Corrosion Failures. This failure should have been predictable in advance on the basis of susceptibility of the malleable iron latch to galvanic attack.

The possible difference in resistance to cavitation-erosion between low-carbon steels of different carbon content was not considered in making the change in material described in the next example.

Example 3. Cavitation-Erosion Failure of Carbon Steel Spray Ring From Which Superheated Water Was Discharged (Fig. 3)

Several low-carbon steel spray rings that supplied superheated water for curing automobile tires failed prematurely by severe wearing away of the angled exit ends of the water channels. The rings, one of which is illustrated in Fig. 3(a), were machined from seamless low-carbon steel pipe.

Operating Conditions. Curing was done by injecting water at 193 C (380 F) into a flexible rubber bladder inside the uncured tire carcass, which had been placed in a metal mold. In normal operation, narrow, high-velocity jets of superheated water from the spray ring provided vigorous agitation and efficient heat transfer by impinging on the upper surface of the curing bladder several inches from the spray ring. While the bladder was being filled at the beginning of the curing cycle, the superheated water flashed to steam as it exited from the spray ring into the bladder, in which the pressure remained only slightly above atmospheric pressure until the bladder was filled with water.

Detection of the failures resulted from the loss of ability to maintain the curing temperature of 177 to 182 C (350 to 360 F) in several presses in one plant, in which the spray rings had been used for only four to six months. Similar presses in this plant and several other plants were performing satisfactorily, using supposedly identical spray rings that had been in service for more than four years.

Examination of Failure Region. The exit ends of water channels in an as-manufactured spray ring, a malfunctioning spray ring, and a spray ring that was still functioning properly after more than four years were examined visually and at low magnification, and were then sectioned.

The surface appearance of the exit ends of channels from each of the three spray rings is shown in the upper views in Fig. 3(d), and longitudinal sections through the exit ends are shown immediately below these views, as sections A-A, B-B and C-C. As compared to that in the as-manufactured spray ring, the exit opening in the failed ring had been extensively enlarged whereas the opening in the satisfactory ring had been only slightly enlarged, despite its much longer service.

Pitting was also visible on the eroded surfaces at low magnification, but high-magnification examination of these surfaces and of

sections through them showed no evidence that the pitting was caused by corrosion. There were no indications of intergranular attack or of selective leaching.

Chemical analysis showed that both of the used spray rings were made of low-carbon steel having a very low content of residual metallic and nonmetallic elements. However, the steel used for the ring that failed had a carbon content about half that of the steel used for the ring that proved satisfactory:

Alloying element	Failed ring	Satisfactory ring
Carbon	0.11%	0.20%
Manganese	0.42	0.45
Phosphorus	0.011	0.011
Sulfur	0.010	0.019
Silicon	0.01	0.01
Nickel	0.01	0.01
Chromium	0.01	0.01
Molybdenum	0.01	0.01
Copper	0.05	0.03

Metallographic Examination and Hardness Tests. The microstructures of the two used spray rings are shown at a magnification of 100 diameters in Fig. 3(b) and (c), as etched in 2% nital.

The specimen from the failed ring (Fig. 3b) appeared to be fully recrystallized, having a very coarse-grained (ASTM grain size No. 3) equiaxed structure. The black grains are pearlite (not resolved at the 100-diameter magnification). The hardness of this specimen was Rockwell B 40.

The specimen from the satisfactory ring (Fig. 3c) had a much finer grain size (ASTM No. 7) and showed pronounced grain orientation. Although the ferrite grains in this specimen had been equiaxed, probably by subcritical annealing, pearlite stringers formed in previous working were

identified on examination at high magnification and are visible in Fig. 3(c) as stringers of black grains. This specimen had a hardness of Rockwell B 55.

Conclusions. For satisfactory heat transfer during the curing operation, only minor enlargement of the exit ends of the water channels in the spray rings (as shown in section C-C in Fig. 3d) could be tolerated. However, the drastic change in size and contour of the openings in the failed spray ring (section B-B in Fig. 3d) allowed the superheated water to fan out and also changed its direction and lowered its velocity, thus greatly reducing the agitation and hence the over-all rate of heat transfer to the curing bladder.

The erosion at the water-channel openings and the pitting on the eroded surfaces apparently resulted from cavitation effects associated with the change in direction of the water flow during the curing operation and with the flashing of the superheated water into steam as it exited from the spray ring into the bladder at the beginning of each curing cycle.

The lower carbon content, lower hardness and coarser grain size of the steel used for the spray ring that failed resulted in a much lower resistance to cavitation-erosion than was needed for adequate life in this application.

Corrective Action. Use of the lower-carbon material was discontinued. Replacement spray rings were required to have a fine grain size and a composition like that of the satisfactory spray ring, and only a subcritical anneal was permitted so that the final hardness would not be less than Rockwell B 55 and the final grain size not larger than ASTM grain size No. 7.

Table 1. Guide to Criteria Generally Useful for Selection of Material in Relation to Possible Failure Mechanisms, Types of Loading, Types of Stress, and Intended Operating Temperatures(a)

Failure mechanisms	Types of loading Static	Repeated	Impact	Types of stress Tension	Compression	Shear	Operating temperatures Low	Room	High	Criteria generally useful for selection of material
Brittle fracture	X	X	X	X	..	..	X	X	..	Charpy V-notch transition temperature. Notch toughness. K_{Ic} toughness measurements.
Ductile fracture(b)	X	..	..	X	..	X	..	X	X	Tensile strength. Shearing yield strength.
High-cycle fatigue(c)	..	X	..	X	..	X	X	X	X	Fatigue strength for expected life, with typical stress raisers present.
Low-cycle fatigue	..	X	..	X	..	X	X	X	X	Static ductility available and the peak cyclic plastic strain expected at stress raisers during prescribed life.
Corrosion fatigue	..	X	..	X	..	X	..	X	X	Corrosion-fatigue strength for the metal and contaminant and for similar time(d).
Buckling	X	..	X	..	X	..	X	X	X	Modulus of elasticity and compressive yield strength.
Gross yielding(b)	X	..	..	X	X	X	X	X	X	Yield strength.
Creep	X	..	..	X	X	X	..	..	X	Creep rate or sustained stress-rupture strength for the temperature and expected life(d).
Caustic or hydrogen embrittlement	X	..	..	X	..	..	..	X	X	Stability under simultaneous stress and hydrogen or other chemical environment(d).
Stress-corrosion cracking	X	..	..	X	..	X	..	X	X	Residual or imposed stress and corrosion resistance to the environment. K_{Iscc} measurements(d).

(a) Adapted from T. J. Dolan, *Experimental Mechanics*, Jan 1970, p 1-14. (b) Applies to ductile metals only. (c) Millions of cycles. (d) Items strongly dependent on elapsed time.

The excessively eroded spray rings were replaced with spray rings made from steel having the properties specified above. No additional erosion failures occurred on either the new spray rings or the satisfactory used spray rings during the ensuing period of about four years, representing continuing satisfactory performance after at least eight years by the original rings in the presses in which the rings had not malfunctioned, and after four years by the replacement rings.

Imperfections in Material

Many failures originate at imperfections in material. Both internal and surface imperfections may reduce the over-all strength of the material, provide preferential paths for the propagation of cracks, act as notches, serve as sites for preferential pitting-type attack, or provide paths for intergranular corrosion.

Failures related to segregation, lamination, inclusions, porosity, voids and other types of imperfections are described in the articles on various types and mechanisms of failure and on failure of specific products and product forms in this volume.

Castings. Cold shuts, inclusions, porosity, voids and shrinkage cavities can present special problems in castings. For example, an aluminum alloy pump-fitting casting that contained a steel insert failed by brittle fracture because of a pre-existing imperfection. Discontinuity of the microstructure on the two sides of the crack in this casting, the glossy appearance of the mating fracture surfaces, the presence of gas porosity and the absence of any other abnormality in the cast metal identified the imperfection at which the fracture originated as a cold shut that was produced during the casting operation.

Forgings. Laps, seams, shrinkage, cavities and flow-line pattern frequently are related to failure in forgings, as discussed in detail in the article on Failures of Forgings. The effects of these imperfections are discussed and illustrated in several failure-analysis examples in that article and other articles in this volume (see Directory of Examples, inside back cover).

The next example describes the fatigue failure of a forging in which severe segregation in the billet had produced a notch-sensitive banded structure.

Example 4. Fatigue Fracture That Originated on Ground Surface of a Medium-Carbon Steel Forging With a Notch-Sensitive Banded Structure (Fig. 4)

The broken connecting end of a forged medium-carbon steel rod used in an application in which it was subjected to severe low-frequency loading is illustrated in Fig. 4(a); the part shown is from one of two identical rods that failed in service by fracture. In each instance, fracture extended

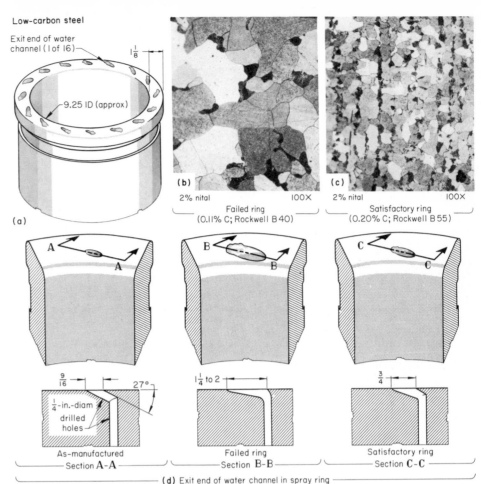

Fig. 3. Low-carbon steel spray ring that failed by cavitation-erosion of angled exit ends of water channels by discharge and flashing of superheated water. Failure was influenced by carbon content, microstructure and hardness. (Example 3)

completely through the connecting end in two places. The two fractured rods, together with two similar unused forged rods, were examined to determine the mechanism and cause of fracture.

Preliminary Examination. The material of the four forged rods was found by spectrographic analysis to be within the normal limits for the specified medium-carbon steel. Except for the fractures on the connecting ends of the two failed rods, no significant imperfections or evidence of damage were found by visual examination.

Surface hardness of the four rods, as measured at various points with a Rockwell tester, was equivalent to 140 Bhn — substantially lower than the specified hardness of 160 to 205 Bhn.

The fractures in the two failed rods were in areas of the transition regions that had been rough ground to remove flash along the parting line (see Fig. 4a). The fracture surfaces were fairly flat and were radial with respect to the annular connecting ends.

Low-magnification examination of the fracture surfaces revealed the presence of beach marks, indicating that the fractures had originated and propagated by fatigue. The location and curvature of the beach marks on the fracture surfaces of the two broken rods (see Fig. 4b) established that the fracture origin in each rod was at the rough-ground surface. The fatigue region of the fracture surface, which was quite

smooth, extended about halfway through the thickness of the rod end.

The remainder of the area of the fracture surfaces, corresponding to final, fast fracture, had the typical appearance of brittle fracture, exhibiting little or no evidence of plastic deformation.

Liquid-Penetrant Examination. The four rods were checked for the presence of imperfections in the general vicinity of rough-ground areas, using liquid-penetrant inspection. This examination revealed an incipient crack about 3/8 in. long (see view A-A in Fig. 4) on one of the fractured rods. The crack was apparently a fatigue crack in the initiation stage and was located at a rough-ground area. Liquid-penetrant indications of several other incipient cracks that were smaller in size were also detected on the fractured rods in this examination; several were on rough-ground areas.

Metallographic Examination. Cross sections for metallographic examination were taken through the annular connecting ends of the two fractured rods and of the two unused rods, and were polished and then etched with nital. At a magnification of 80 diameters, the microstructure of the unused rods (Fig. 4c) and that of the fractured rods (Fig. 4d) appeared greatly different.

The two unused rods had a fairly fine-grained, homogeneous structure containing approximately equal amounts of ferrite and pearlite — a normal structure for good-qual-

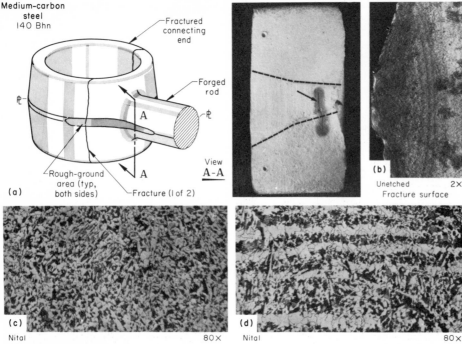

Medium-carbon
steel
140 Bhn

Fractured
connecting
end

Forged
rod

Rough-ground
area (typ,
both sides)

Fracture (1 of 2)

(a)

View
A-A

(b)
Unetched   2×
Fracture surface

(c)
Nital   80×

(d)
Nital   80×

(a) Rod end showing locations of fractures at rough-ground areas at the parting line; in view A-A, dashed lines denote a rough-ground area, arrow points to a liquid-penetrant indication of an incipient crack. (b) Fracture surface, with beach marks indicating fracture origin at rough-ground surface. (c) Normal, homogeneous structure of an unused rod examined for comparison; this structure contains equal amounts of ferrite (light) and pearlite (dark). (d) Unsatisfactory structure of the fractured rod, which contains alternating bands of ferrite and pearlite.

Fig. 4. Connecting end of a forged rod that fractured by fatigue in service (Example 4)

ity medium-carbon steel forgings of this composition that had been properly heat treated after forging.

The two fractured rods had a banded structure consisting of zones of ferrite (light) and pearlite (dark). Microhardness of the banded region was 140 Bhn in the light areas and 145 Bhn in the dark areas (converted from Vickers dph readings, 100-gram load).

Examination at 320 diameters of sections through the rough-ground areas of the fractured rods established that the incipient cracks found in liquid-penetrant inspection had originated at the surface in the banded region, in areas of ferrite where this constituent had been visibly deformed by grinding.

Discussion. The loads applied to the annular connecting ends of the rods were apparently complex, consisting of torsional, bending and axial loads from the forged rods; these loads caused cyclic tensile circumferential stresses and bending stresses in the connecting ends.

The microhardness readings on the ferrite and pearlite bands were not considered to represent true hardness values, because of the small size and shallowness of the bands. However, the following observations were considered to be significant with respect to the failures:

1 The forged rods that had a normal microstructure (see Fig. 4c) did not fail.
2 The forged rods that had a banded microstructure (see Fig. 4d) did fail.
3 The hardness of all four rods, as measured on the surface using a Rockwell hardness tester, was the same and was equivalent to 140 Bhn — substantially below the specified range of 160 to 205 Bhn.
4 The fractures originated in rough-ground areas, and incipient cracks were found in an area of ferrite that had been visibly deformed by grinding.

Conclusions. The rod-end fractures had originated and propagated by fatigue during continued exposure of the rods to severe cyclic loads in service. The loads on the rods developed tensile and bending stresses in the connecting ends.

Contributory factors were (a) the presence of a notch-sensitive banded structure containing alternately soft (ferrite) and hard (pearlite) layers; (b) the presence of stress raisers produced by rough grinding to remove the forging flash along the highly stressed transition area between the rod and the connecting end; and (c) hardness (and, accordingly, strength) below the range specified for the part. The banded microstructure of the two fractured rods apparently resulted from severe segregation in the billet from which they were forged.

Corrective Action. It was recommended that closer control be exercised over the microstructure and hardness of the forgings, that the connecting end be finished more smoothly in the critical area, and that consideration be given to increasing the thickness (diametral with respect to the ring) of the connecting end in the transition area.

Deficiencies in Processing

Susceptibility to failure is sometimes related to specification of unsuitable processing procedures, incomplete or ambiguous specifications, changes made in specifications without complete evaluation, failure to follow specified procedures, and operator error or accidental damage.

Cold forming and related operations, such as deep drawing, stretching, expanding, reducing and bending, produce high residual stresses. These operations sometimes also alter gross or local mechanical properties, produce microcracks or macrocracks, and cause localized depletion of ductility.

Surface effects and metallurgical changes caused by processing have an influence on fatigue strength, resistance to brittle fracture, and corrosion resistance. Anisotropic properties, zones of dissimilar material, and changes in orientation of residual stresses also can be introduced, with possible harmful effects on susceptibility of the finished product to failure in service.

Shearing, blanking and piercing leave residual stresses; they often also introduce rough or torn edges that constitute stress raisers.

Machining and grinding often leave residual stresses and stress-raising roughness. Hot trimming and snag grinding initiated fatigue cracking in a forged 4140 steel crankshaft, as described in Example 7 on page 387 in the article on Failures of Shafts. Severe grinding is a source of overheating and consequent local softening; it has been known to produce cracking, usually of the crazing type, in hardened steels.

Identification marking by impact indentation or by electroetching is a potential source of failure if done on a highly stressed region of a part. Electrical discharge machining produces fusion and a heat-affected zone; these are likely to cause cracking in service if not properly controlled, especially in stressed areas of steel harder than about Rockwell C 50 to 55 (see discussion under "Electrical Discharge Machining", and Examples 6 and 7, on page 505 in the article on Failures of Dies).

Improper heat treatment occurs in a variety of forms, such as overheating, undertempering, use of unacceptably low hardening temperatures, introduction of excessive temperature gradients, and use of quenching, tempering, annealing and aging conditions unsuitable for a specific alloy or part.

Decarburization during heat treatment sometimes induces failure by (a) fatigue, because it greatly reduces the endurance limit of the surface; and (b) by distortion, for small parts, on which it reduces the average strength of the section.

Decarburization is particularly detrimental to the service life of springs and small shafts, on which surface stresses ordinarily are quite high. Figure 7 on page 129 in the article on Distortion Failures illustrates the failure of a spring on which the surface had been decarburized.

Acid pickling and electroplating (especially at low cathode efficiency) are well known for their ability to cause hydrogen charging and consequent hydrogen-damage failure of high-strength steels. Chemical or electrolytic cleaning and etching in which hydrogen is generated produce similar effects, especially when these processes are followed immediately by deposition of a metallic coating that hinders the escape of absorbed hydrogen from the base metal. Processing procedures must be carefully developed in applications of this sort to minimize hydrogen absorption and, if necessary, to remove absorbed hydrogen by subsequent suitable heating procedures (for details, see the article on Hydrogen-Damage Failures, which begins on page 230 in this volume).

Welding can lead to failure by a variety of mechanisms unless suitable precautions are taken as discussed in the article on Failures of Weldments, which begins on page 333 in this volume.

One of the more serious types of weld-related failure is stress-corrosion cracking of welded austenitic stainless steels, especially in boilers, heat exchangers and pressure vessels. In some instances, the welding operation itself, if it entails a very high heat input, can render the metal susceptible to stress-corrosion cracking; in other situations, stress relief after welding may be the sensitizing factor leading to failure.

Reworking. When welding is done under conditions of severe restraint, such as on large parts or with improper fixturing, contraction of the weld metal and heat-affected zone during cooling induces residual tensile stresses that can cause cracking at once or promote cracking in service. Selection of an unsuitable filler metal or use of excessive heat input during welding can cause similar effects.

Unless done by carefully developed and closely controlled procedures, build-up by welding of undersize or worn parts such as large shafts (particularly those made of high-strength steel) is likely to cause cracking at once or to reduce fatigue endurance.

Reworking of a part that has been rejected during some stage of manufacture takes the part out of normal production channels and may thus make errors in processing more likely. In the example that follows, a pinion failed in service because rehardening had inadvertently been omitted after the pinion was tempered to a lowered hardness for remachining of a defective keyway.

Example 5. Fatigue-Cracking Failure of a 4817H Steel Forged Pinion That Was Not Rehardened After Being Tempered to Machinable Hardness (Fig. 5)

A spiral-bevel gear set was returned from service because cracks were discovered in the pinion teeth (see Fig. 5) during replacement of a bearing that had failed. The pinion was machined from a 4817H steel forging. The ring gear that mated with the pinion was in good condition and showed no evidence of cracks or damage; the teeth of the gear were file hard.

The pinion had a crack in every tooth (some of the more severe cracks are shown in Fig. 5); each crack originated about 1 in. from the heel end of the tooth near the root fillet on the concave side. The hardness of the teeth of the pinion was considerably lower than that specified.

Metallographic examination of the microstructure of both the case and the core indicated that the pinion had been carburized and hardened as specified, but had been tempered for remachining of the keyway and not rehardened. This was confirmed by a review of manufacturing records. Hardness results of the metallurgical examination performed on the pinion are given in the table that accompanies Fig. 5.

Conclusion. The pinion failed by fatigue cracking that originated near the root at the concave side of the tooth. Normal usage produced a cyclic bending stress on the pinion tooth that resulted in fatigue failure. The strength of the tooth was not sufficient to withstand normal loads because the pinion had not been rehardened after the keyway had been reworked by machining.

Errors in Assembly

Failures in service sometimes result from errors in assembly that were not detected in inspection by the manufacturer or the purchaser and that did not prevent apparently normal operation when the assembled products were first put into service.

This kind of failure is most frequently associated with moving parts of mechanical assemblies or with electrical assemblies, but many failures caused by assembly errors also have occurred in structural components. For example, small errors in the placement of rivet holes have caused fatigue failures in structural members of airplane wings.

Deficiencies of this type are sometimes related to inaccurate, incomplete or ambiguous assembly specifications, but they also occur frequently as a consequence of operator error or negligence.

Operator negligence can occur in a wide variety of commonplace and novel forms and can result in costly damage, as well as interruption of production, as illustrated in the following example.

Example 6. Breakdown of an Air-Compressor Engine That Resulted From Carelessness in Assembly of Components (Fig. 6)

A serious breakdown was sustained by a vertical four-cylinder oil engine driving an air compressor in a quarry. A piston had been broken, a connecting rod had been bent, and a hole measuring 8 by 3 in. had been knocked in the side of the crankcase by the connecting rod.

Disassembly and examination showed that the breakdown had been caused by the failure of two connecting-rod bolts, which are shown in Fig. 6. The bolts had been inserted from the piston end of the connecting rod, as is usual with this type of engine, and one bolt (bolt A in Fig. 6) had not been fitted with a nut. Wear marks and damage visible on this bolt showed that it had been moving relative to the connecting rod for a considerable period.

Discussion. Not only was much of the thread on bolt A worn away where it had been rubbing on the bore of the hole, but also the shank of this bolt was appreciably worn in places, and a groove had been cut in it at one point by shims used to adjust the bearing clearance.

The connecting-rod cap had been retained in position by the other bolt (bolt B in Fig. 6) only until this bolt finally failed, first bending and then tearing apart in ductile fracture, with substantial necking in the fracture region. Like bolt A, bolt B showed marks indicative of movement between it and the connecting rod. As shown in Fig. 6, the bearing face of the working nut had been worn and the adjacent threads on the bolt had been stretched.

Conclusions. The threaded end of each bolt was to have been fitted with a castellated nut to hold the connecting-rod bearing assembly in place. Actually, both nuts had been threaded onto bolt B, with one nut properly tightened against the bearing assembly and the second nut then threaded onto the same bolt upside down. Apparently, the fitter who last assembled the bearing screwed the second nut onto the end of bolt B as a convenient place to hold it temporarily and then forgot to remove it and screw it onto bolt A.

No complaint about malfunction of the engine had been reported prior to the mishap, perhaps because of generally high noise level in the vicinity, although the engine undoubtedly had been knocking severely for some time before it finally broke down.

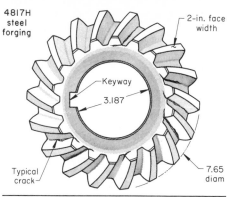

Item	Specified	Actual(a)
Case hardness, R_C	58-63	40-41
Core hardness, R_C, on tooth center:		
At midpoint	None	33
At root	None	28.5
Case depth, in.	0.050-0.065	...
Case depth, in., at:		
Midpoint of tooth	...	0.052
Tooth-root fillet	...	0.036

(a) Determined by laboratory examination of pinion. (b) Total case depth as observed with Brinell glass on sectioned and etched tooth. Results of Tukon traverse are not recorded in table because case hardness was less than Rockwell C 50.

Fig. 5. Spiral-tooth pinion, machined from a 4817H steel forging, that failed by fatigue cracking because it was not rehardened after being tempered for reworking of the keyway (Example 5)

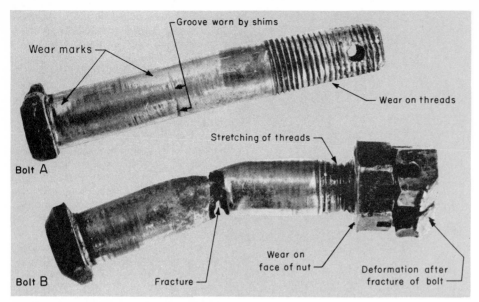

Fig. 6. Connecting-rod bolts on which incorrect assembly of nuts caused failure of the bolts and breakdown and severe damage to an air-compressor engine. After properly tightening one nut on bolt B, the assembler apparently threaded the nut intended for bolt A on bolt B for temporary storage and forgot to transfer it to bolt A. (Example 6)

Inadequate specification of procedures for assembly sometimes contributes to the occurrence of service failures. Example 1 on page 473 in the article on Failures of Fasteners describes the failure of wheel studs on a semitrailer because of insufficient and nonuniform tightening of wheel nuts on the studs. Implementation of a procedure of tightening the nuts to a specified torque and checking the torque at normal maintenance periods eliminated the failures.

Misalignment of shafts, gears, bearings, seals, and couplings is quite frequently a factor contributing to service failures. Example 6 on page 521 in the article on Failures of Gears shows how improper alignment of a pinion and mating gear resulted in early fatigue failure of an otherwise satisfactory assembly in normal service.

Improper Service Conditions

The operation of equipment under abnormally severe conditions of speed, loading, temperature, and chemical environment, or without regularly scheduled maintenance, inspection and monitoring is often a major contribution to the occurrence of service failures.

Inspection and monitoring procedures may be of little or no value unless they are based on a thorough consideration of the various mechanisms of failure that may be possible for the part in question. Such procedures should be capable of detecting significant deterioration during normal inspection and maintenance operations at regularly scheduled intervals.

Start-up of various types of equipment — especially when complex equipment is put into operation for the first time, but

also when equipment has been shut down for maintenance or where intermittent operation is the normal procedure — is a particularly critical aspect of operation. During start-up, equipment may be subjected to conditions that are not encountered in normal operation, including rapid changes in operating parameters, extreme gradients in temperature, and other abnormal conditions. The unexpected is frequently encountered despite thorough analysis and advance planning.

Without well-controlled implementation of properly planned start-up procedures, malfunction and possible failure of some components should not be unexpected. Example 2 on page 530 in the article on Failures of Boilers and Related Steam-Power-Plant Equipment describes the deformation and rupture of two carbon steel tubes in a marine reheat boiler because of extreme and rapid local overheating during start-up. Failure of these tubes caused extensive boiler damage.

Shutdown procedures, and maintenance of proper conditions for the duration of the shutdown period (again, especially with complex equipment), have essentially the same potential for contributing to failure as do start-up procedures. The next example describes cumulative severe pitting corrosion of medium-carbon steel tubes in a vent-tube boiler that developed during several annual shutdowns for overhaul.

Example 7. Failure of Medium-Carbon Steel Superheater Tubes by Differential-Aeration Corrosion During Annual Shutdown (Fig. 7)

During hydrostatic testing of a 15-year-old vent-tube boiler designed for a capacity of 100,000 lb per hr at 700 psi and 400 C (750 F), several superheater tubes began leaking. These tubes had been in service

for nine years at 650 psi and temperatures approaching 400 C (750 F). The tubes were 2 in. in outside diameter, had 0.165-in. wall thickness, and were made of medium-carbon steel (ASTM A210).

Figure 7(a) is a schematic illustration of the boiler that indicates the location of the area of failure. One representative section of a leaking tube was removed and split longitudinally for examination.

Visual inspection of the tube section revealed a black, adherent magnetic scale over the entire interior surface. In local areas, a loose, powdery, nonmagnetic brown deposit was found on the black scale; no distinctive pattern of the brown deposit was detected. Removal of the scale and deposits from the inside surface of the tube revealed severe pitting attack (see Fig. 7b) that was confined exclusively to the areas covered by the loose brown deposit.

Analysis of Deposits. Composite samples of the black scale and the brown deposit were removed from the pitted areas and analyzed by x-ray fluorescence and x-ray diffraction techniques. The samples were found to contain Fe_3O_4 (black iron oxide), Fe_2O_3 (red rust) and FeO (ferrous oxide). No chlorides were detected.

Metallographic Examination. A section through a major pit (see section A-A in Fig. 7) showed a normal microstructure for medium-carbon steel with no significant impurities or segregations that might have promoted local attack.

Discussion. The absence of chlorides in the deposits indicated that pitting was not caused by inhibited hydrochloric acid used in periodic tube cleanings. The presence of oxygen in the deposit over the pitted areas strongly suggested that oxygen was the cause of attack.

The presence of the magnetic black oxide (Fe_3O_4) as a tightly adherent scale on the interior of the pits and the entire tube surface suggested that this scale was formed under conditions when little oxygen was present, such as under operating conditions.

The localization of the loose, powdery, nonmagnetic brown deposit of red rust (Fe_2O_3) over the pits suggested that this corrosion product was formed, and that the pitting attack occurred, in the presence of excess oxygen, such as during shutdown conditions. In the normal course of corrosion in the presence of moisture, this oxide would be in a hydrated condition ($Fe_2O_3 \cdot xH_2O$) as initially produced and would form Fe_2O_3 on drying.

An investigation of the history of the boiler revealed that it had been given yearly overhauls for the past 15 years. The overhauls usually lasted two weeks, during which time any necessary repairs were made. The boiler was then hydrostatically tested before being placed back in service. The tubes that leaked had been subjected to eight such cycles.

Conclusions. Failure of the tubes was by corrosion pitting caused by an oxygen-rich condensate in the low points of the return bends. Pitting attack took place during overhaul periods, when vacuum conditions were created within the boiler by shutdown procedures. Under these conditions, air was drawn into the system and mixed with the condensing steam. The oxygen-rich condensate settled in the low points of the

Fig. 7. Schematic illustration of a vent-tube boiler in which the medium-carbon steel superheater tubes corroded during annual shutdowns; view of pitted area on inside of tube; and photomicrograph of a section through a pit (Example 7)

superheater section (return bends), causing pitting by differential aeration corrosion.

Corrective Measures. Shutdown and storage procedures for overhauls were changed, and additions of soluble sulfite salt to the boiler feed water were increased to tie up dissolved oxygen during operating periods. The latter was accomplished by maintaining a residual sulfite (SO_3^{--}) level of 20 to 30 ppm.

The modified shutdown and storage procedure included feeding of nitrogen gas into the boiler from cylinders connected through a regulator valve on the superheated header. When the boiler pressure dropped to 50 psi, nitrogen was automatically fed into the boiler. The following day, the boiler was prepared for storage by dissolving a filming amine in hot deaerated zeolite-softened water. This solution was fed to the boiler, displacing the nitrogen. The concentration of the amine in the hot make-up water was less than 22 ppm.

During the ensuing ten years, satisfactory boiler performance and inhibition of the pitting corrosion previously experienced at the return bends in the superheater section showed the effectiveness of the new shutdown procedures.

Inadequate maintenance frequently is a contributory factor in service failures. Maintenance procedures should be thoroughly reevaluated when failures recur despite regularly scheduled maintenance.

In the example that follows, the splined ends of five drive shafts failed before a thorough analysis established the cause of failure and led to the specification of mandatory relubrication at each 300-hr inspection instead of only at initial installation.

Example 8. Wear Failure of External Splines on a 4350 Steel Shaft Because of Lubricant Breakdown (Fig. 8)

The splined end of the drive shaft of a starter-generator on an aircraft failed after a total operating time of 907 hr. Previous engineering reports indicated that the splined ends of four other drive shafts had failed after 700 to 900 hr of operation.

The shaft was made of 4350 steel with a specified core hardness of Rockwell C 34 to 38, and the splined end was to be induction hardened to Rockwell C 48 to 52 at a minimum depth of $\frac{1}{32}$ in. The splined end, which mated with an internally splined member having a hardness of Rockwell C 58 to 63, was coated with a molybdenum-disulfide-base lubricant at the time of initial installation.

The starter-generator drive shaft was submitted to a laboratory to determine the cause of failure.

Investigation. Visual examination revealed that the crowns of the spline teeth had worn away as shown in section B-B in Fig. 8. Oxidized debris was found in the root areas of the spline teeth. No residual lubricant could be detected on the surface of

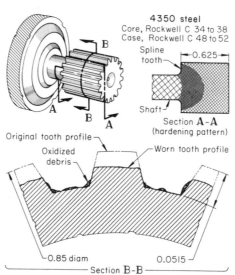

Section A-A is a schematic view of the hardening pattern; the hemispherical area was softer than the remainder of the splined end of the shaft because of the heat-sink effect of the adjacent portion of the shaft proper (see text). Section B-B shows details of original and worn tooth profiles.

Fig. 8. Splined end of a 4350 steel drive shaft for an aircraft starter-generator, which failed by excessive wear and lubricant breakdown (Example 8)

the splined end when the shaft was received at the laboratory.

Magnetic-particle inspection of the shaft and the remaining portions of the worn splined end did not reveal the presence of any imperfections.

Microscopic examination of the splined end did not show the presence of any surface deformation of the teeth. However, the splines had failed in service and thus any surface features produced by the failure could have been obliterated before the part was submitted for examination.

Metallographic examination of a longitudinal section revealed that the splines had been through-hardened. As shown in section A-A in Fig. 8, a hemispherical area at the inner end of the splined portion of the shaft was softer than the outer end, as a result of the heat-sink effect of the adjoining portion of the shaft proper.

The manufacturing drawing showed that the splined end of the shaft, including the root surfaces and fillets, should have been induction hardened to a minimum depth of $\frac{1}{32}$ in. instead of being through-hardened.

The hardness of the shaft proper was Rockwell C 34 to 36 and that of the surface of the splined end was Rockwell C 50 to 51, as specified. However, contrary to specifications, the core hardness of the splined end of the shaft was Rockwell C 48 to 52, except for the hemispherical area (section A-A in Fig. 8), which was somewhat lower in hardness.

Chemical composition and microstructure of the part were satisfactory.

Conclusion. Failure of the splines was the result of excessive wear or fretting against the mating internally splined member and the breakdown of the lubricating film during operation. The through-hardening of the splined end of the shaft, although contrary to specifications, did not contribute to the failure.

Recommendations. The splines should be lubricated during each 300-hr inspection instead of only at initial installation. To increase wear resistance, the surface hardness of the splined end of the shaft should be increased from Rockwell C 48 to 52 to Rockwell C 58 to 63 — the surface hardness of the mating internally splined member.

General Practice in Failure Analysis

By D. A. RYDER, T. J. DAVIES, I. BROUGH and F. R. HUTCHINGS*

THIS ARTICLE is concerned primarily with general procedures, techniques and precautions employed in the investigation and analysis of metallurgical failures that occur in service. The stages of investigation are discussed, and the various features of the more common causes of failure are indicated. Types of failure characteristics are described, and, where appropriate, several of the fundamental mechanisms involved are explained (Ref 1).

For information on procedures and techniques specific to the analysis of failures by various mechanisms and related environmental factors, failures of principal product forms, and failures of manufactured components and assemblies, the reader is referred to the individual articles in the three main sections of this volume that follow. The reader is referred also to the article on Use of Fractography for Failure Analysis, on pages 106 to 124 in Volume 9 of this Handbook, and to the Atlas section on Failure-Analysis Fractographs, on pages 377 to 475 in Volume 9.

Objectives of Failure Investigation

A failure investigation and subsequent analysis should determine the primary cause of a failure, and, based on the determination, corrective action should be initiated that will prevent similar failures. Frequently, the importance of contributory causes to the failure must be assessed; new experimental techniques may have to be developed, or an unfamiliar field of engineering or science explored. A complex accident investigation, such as investigation into aircraft accidents (Ref 2), usually requires the services of experts in several branches of engineering and the physical sciences, as well as metallurgy.

Stages of an Analysis

Although the sequence is subject to variation depending on the nature of a specific failure, the principal stages that

*Mr. Ryder is Senior Lecturer, Dr. Davies is Lecturer, and Mr. Brough is Senior Experimental Officer, Department of Metallurgy, The University of Manchester Institute of Science and Technology, Manchester, England. Mr. Hutchings is Manager, Research Dept., British Engine, Boiler and Electrical Insurance Co., Ltd., Manchester, England.

comprise the investigation and analysis of a failure are as follows:

1 Collection of background data and selection of samples
2 Preliminary examination of the failed part (visual examination and record keeping)
3 Nondestructive testing
4 Mechanical testing (including hardness and toughness testing)
5 Selection, identification, preservation and/or cleaning of all specimens
6 Macroscopic examination and analysis (fracture surfaces, secondary cracks and other surface phenomena)
7 Microscopic examination and analysis
8 Selection and preparation of metallographic sections
9 Examination and analysis of metallographic sections
10 Determination of failure mechanism
11 Chemical analyses (bulk, local, surface corrosion products, deposits or coatings, and microprobe analysis)
12 Analysis of fracture mechanics
13 Testing under simulated service conditions (special tests)
14 Analysis of all the evidence, formulation of conclusions, and writing the report (including recommendations).

Time employed in ascertaining all the circumstances of a failure is time well spent. When a broken component is received for examination, the investigator is sometimes inclined to prepare specimens immediately without devising an investigation procedure. Such a lack of forethought should be avoided, since in the end a large amount of time and effort may be wasted, whereas by first carefully considering the background of the failure and studying the general features, a more informative procedure will be indicated.

In the investigation of failures of some components, it may be impractical or impossible for the failure analyst to visit the failure site. Under these circumstances, data and samples may be collected by field engineers or by other personnel at the site. A field failure report sheet or check list can be used to ensure that all pertinent information regarding the failure is recorded.

Collection of Background Data and Selection of Samples

Initially, the failure investigation should be directed toward gaining an acquaintance with all pertinent details relating to the failure, collecting the available information regarding the manufacturing, processing and service

histories of the failed component or structure, and reconstructing insofar as possible the sequence of events leading to the failure. The collection of background data on the manufacturing and fabricating history of a component should begin with obtaining specifications and drawings, and should encompass all the design aspects of the component. Data relating to manufacturing and fabrication may be grouped into (a) mechanical processing, which should include cold forming, stretching, bending, machining, polishing and grinding; (b) thermal processing, which should include details of hot forming; heat treating, welding, brazing or soldering; and (c) chemical processing, which should provide details of cleaning, electroplating and application of coatings by chemical alloying or diffusion.

Service History. Obtaining a complete service history depends a great deal on how detailed and thorough the record keeping was prior to the occurrence of the failure. The availability of complete service records greatly simplifies the assignment of the failure analyst. In collecting service histories, special attention should be given to environmental details, such as normal and abnormal loading, accidental overloads, cyclic loads, variations in temperature, temperature gradients, and operation in a corrosive environment. In most instances, however, complete service records are not available, forcing the analyst to work from fragmentary service information. When service data are sparse, the analyst must, to the best of his ability, deduce the service conditions. Much depends on his skill and judgment, because a misleading deduction can be more harmful than the absence of information.

Photographic Records. The analyst should decide if photographs of the failed component or structure are required. A failure that appears almost inconsequential in a preliminary investigation may later be found to have serious consequences; thus a complete photographic record of the investigation can be important. If the photographs are to be provided to the analyst from another source, the analyst should be certain that these will be suitable for his purpose — that is, that they will adequately detail the characteristics of the failure.

It usually is desirable to have all photographs taken by a professional photographer using a large (4-by-5-in. minimum) camera, in order to permit detailed enlargements to be made at a later date should they be deemed necessary.

For the failure analyst who chooses to do his own photography, a single-lens-reflex 35-mm camera with a variety of lenses and an extension bellows and with a battery-operated flash unit is capable of producing excellent results. It is desirable to supplement the 35-mm equipment with a Polaroid camera and close-up and portrait lenses. The quality of Polaroid prints will generally be lower than that of prints made from 35-mm film, yet Polaroid prints may be quite adequate for the intended purpose.

When accurate color rendition is required, the subject should be photographed against a gray background, and a sample of the actual background provided to the photographic studio for use as a guide in developing and printing.

Selection of samples should be done prior to starting the examination proper, especially if the investigation is to be lengthy or involved. As with photographs, the analyst is responsible for ensuring that the samples will be suitable for the intended purpose and that they adequately represent the characteristics of the failure. It is advisable to look for additional evidence of damage beyond that which is immediately apparent.

It is often necessary to compare failed components with similar components that did not fail, to determine whether the failure was brought about by service conditions or was the result of an error in manufacture. For example, if a boiler tube fails and overheating is suspected to be the cause, and if investigation reveals a spheroidized structure in the boiler tube (which is indicative of overheating in service), then comparison with another tube, remote from the region exposed to high temperature, will determine if the tubes were supplied in the spheroidized condition.

As another example, assume that examination of a bolt shows a fatigue fracture that is typical of the type caused by repeated application of excessive bending stresses. Loss of clamping force is the major reason for fatigue fractures of bolts. Generally, it is also necessary to examine nuts or other components associated with the bolt, since errors in machining, or wear, of associated components can result in nonaxial loading in service, which could not be established from an examination of the bolt alone. Also, in failures involving corrosion, stress corrosion, or corrosion fatigue, a sample of the fluid that has been in contact with the metal, or of any deposits that have been formed, will often be required for analysis.

Abnormal Conditions. In addition to developing a general history of the failed component or structure, it is also ad-visable to determine if any abnormal conditions prevailed or events occurred in service that may have contributed to the cause of failure, and also to determine if any recent repairs or overhauls have been carried out and why they were carried out. It is also necessary to inquire if the failure under investigation is an isolated example, or if others have occurred, either in the component under consideration or in another of a similar design. In routine examination of a brittle fracture, it is important to know if at the time of the accident or failure the prevailing temperature was low, and if some measure of shock loading was involved. When dealing with failures of crankshafts or other shafts, it is generally desirable to ascertain the conditions of the bearings, and whether any misalignment existed, either within the machine concerned or between the driving and driven components.

Wreckage Analysis. Although detailed treatment of the procedures employed in wreckage analysis exceeds the scope of this article, some of the precautions to be observed, as well as a few of the techniques, will be discussed.

Possibly the most important precaution to be observed in wreckage analysis is that the position of each and every piece of the wreckage should be recorded before any of the pieces are touched or moved. Such recording usually requires extensive photography, the preparation of suitable sketches, and the taking and tabulation of appropriate measurements of the pieces.

Next, it is essential that an inventory be taken to ensure that all of the pieces or fragments are present at the site of the accident. An investigation of an aircraft accident involves the development of a considerable inventory, including listing the number of engines, flaps, landing gear, and the various parts of the fuselage and wings. Obviously, it is essential to establish whether all the necessary parts of the aircraft were aboard at the time that it crashed. Providing an inventory, although painstaking, is often invaluable. For example, one complex aircraft-accident investigation was readily solved by an experienced investigating officer when he observed that a portion of one wing tip was missing from the wreckage. This fragment was subsequently located several miles back along the flight path of the aircraft. The fragment provided evidence of a fatigue failure, thus accounting for the crash.

Assuming that all the component parts are at the wreckage site, it is also important to establish, insofar as possible, whether the control systems were in working order at the time of the accident. In an aircraft accident, this involves checking not only the control systems but also the power sources on which they de-pend for their operation. Obviously, in a catastrophic aircraft accident, many control systems break up as a result of the accident itself, and a great deal of time is spent in examining overstress fractures produced on impact. These must be carefully segregated from fractures and other types of failures that occurred prior to the moment of impact. The problem, therefore, becomes one of analysis of sequence.

In the investigation of one aircraft accident, it was necessary to determine whether a failure of an electric power supply, involving several small generators, had occurred before the crash, and to establish which of the generators were operative at the time of the crash. Several of the generators were air-cooled by small fans mounted at the ends of the main generator shafts; the fan blades were protected by mesh guards. It was observed that all of the guards had been forced back onto the fans, bending the fan blades. There was no evidence of circumferential scoring of the blades or the mesh, so at first it was assumed that the fans, and hence the generators, were stationary (inoperative) when the crash occurred. However, more detailed examination disproved this theory.

Each fan consisted of a central bushing to which the blades were attached; the bushing was press fitted to the generator shaft, and a pin — passing diametrically through the bushing and shaft — secured the fan to the shaft. Examination of a polished-and-etched section taken through the bushing, shaft and pin revealed that, in some of the generators, the pins had failed in shear, accompanied by localized deformation and overheating. Thus, it was apparent that although impact and mesh deformation had stopped some of the fans by fouling the blades, the shafts of some generators continued to rotate after the bushing pin failed. This procedure has been helpful in the analysis of other accidents involving fans or pulleys secured to rotating shafts with pins, keys or splines.

A second technique was developed to determine whether a radio direction-finding instrument was switched on at the time an aircraft crashed into high ground. The radio direction finder contained thermionic tubes having tungsten filaments. Experiments with electric light bulbs established that the fracture appearance of tungsten filaments differed markedly, depending on whether the fracture occurred when the filament was hot or cold. This information was applied successfully to the direction finder, and has been used widely in the investigation of automobile accidents.

The most common problem encountered in wreckage analysis involves the establishment of the sequence of fractures so as to determine the origin of the initial failure. Usually, the direction of crack growth can be detected from marks on a fracture surface, such as chevron marks (see Fig. 3, and related text, on page 16). The typical sequence of fractures is shown in Fig. 1, where A and B represent fractures that intersect at a point, and fracture B grew in the direction indicated by the arrow. Here the sequence of fractures is clearly discernible. Obviously, fracture A must have occurred prior to fracture B because the presence of fracture A served to arrest cracking at fracture B. This method of sequencing is called the T-junction procedure and is an important technique in wreckage analysis.

Provided the fragments are not permitted to contact each other, it is also helpful to carefully fit together the fragments of broken components which, when assembled, may indicate the sequence in which fractures occurred. Figure 2 shows a lug that was part of a pin-joint assembly; failure occurred when the pin broke out of the lug. With the broken pieces of the lug fitted together as shown in Fig. 2, it is apparent from the deformation that fracture A must have preceded fractures B and C.

Preliminary Examination of the Failed Part

The failed part, including all its fragments, should be subjected to a thorough visual examination before any cleaning is undertaken. Often, soils and debris found on the part provide useful evidence in establishing the cause of failure or in determining a sequence of events leading to the failure. For example, traces of paint found on a portion of a fracture surface may provide evidence that a crack, into which some paint seeped, was present in the surface for some time before through-fracture occurred. Such evidence should be noted and recorded.

Visual Inspection. The preliminary examination should begin with unaided visual inspection. The unaided eye has exceptional depth of focus, and the ability to examine large areas rapidly and to detect subtle changes of color and texture. Some of these advantages are lost when any optical or electron-optical device is used. Particular attention should be given to the surfaces of fractures and to the paths of cracks. The significance of any indications of abnormal conditions or abuse in service should be observed and assessed, and a general assessment of the basic design and workmanship of the part should also be made. All important features, including dimensions, should be recorded, either in writing or by sketches or photographs.

It cannot be emphasized too strongly that the examination should be performed as searchingly and effectively as

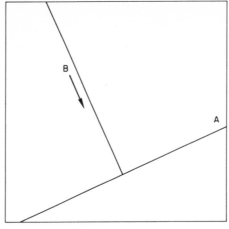

Fig. 1. Schematic illustration of the sequencing of cracking by the T-junction procedure (a technique used in wreckage analysis), where fracture A precedes and arrests fracture B

possible, because clues to the cause of breakdown often are present but may be missed if the observer is not vigilant enough to notice them. In this connection, a low-power microscope (about 6 to 25 diameters), preferably of a binocular type, will be invaluable.

Photographing Fractures. Where fractures are involved, the next step in preliminary examination should be general photography of the entire fractured part, including broken pieces, to record their size and condition and to show how the fracture is related to the components of the part. This should be followed by careful examination of the fracture by studying its image on the ground-glass back of the camera or through the viewfinder. The examination should begin with the use of direct lighting and proceed using various angles of oblique lighting and dark-field illumination, to assess how the fracture characteristics can best be delineated and emphasized. This should also assist in determining which areas of the fracture are of prime interest and which magnifications will be possible (for a given picture size) to bring out fine details. When this evaluation has been completed, it is appropriate to proceed with photography of the fracture, recording what each photograph shows, its magnification, and how it relates to the other photographs.

For information on photographic equipment, materials and techniques, the reader is referred to the article entitled "Photography of Fractured Parts and Fracture Surfaces", on pages 11 to 24 in Volume 9 of this Handbook.

Nondestructive Testing

Several nondestructive tests are extremely useful in failure investigation and analysis — notably, magnetic-particle inspection of ferrous metals, liquid-

penetrant inspection, ultrasonic inspection, and electromagnetic (eddy-current) inspection of materials that conduct electricity. All these tests are used to detect surface cracks and discontinuities. Other nondestructive tests used are radiography, mainly for internal examination, and experimental stress analysis, for determining machine loads and component stresses that can cause failure.

Magnetic-particle inspection utilizes magnetic fields to locate surface and subsurface discontinuities in ferromagnetic materials. When the material or part to be tested is magnetized, discontinuities that lie generally transverse to the direction of the magnetic field will cause a leakage field to be formed at and above the surface of the part. This leakage field, and therefore the presence of the discontinuity, is detected by means of fine ferromagnetic particles applied over the surface, some of these particles being gathered and held by the leakage field. The magnetically held collection of particles forms an outline of the discontinuity and indicates its size, shape and extent. Frequently, a fluorescent material is combined with the particles so that discontinuities can be readily detected visually under ultraviolet light. Magnetic lines of force (or flux) can be set up (a) by passing a large current of electricity through the component to be inspected, (b) by use of a magnetizing yoke, and (c) by use of a magnetizing coil. Following magnetic-particle inspection, the component is demagnetized.

Among the advantages of magnetic-particle inspection are the following:

1 It is the best and most reliable method available for detecting surface cracks — especially, very fine and shallow cracks and cracks filled with foreign matter.
2 Techniques are easy to learn, and the process is rapid, simple and inexpensive to perform.
3 Indications are produced directly on the surface of the part and are a magnetic picture of the actual discontinuity. There is no electric circuitry or electronic readout to be calibrated or kept in proper operating condition.
4 There is little or no limitation on size or shape of the part to be tested.
5 No elaborate precleaning is ordinarily necessary, and the process will work well through a thin coating of paint or other nonmetallic coverings.

Limitations of magnetic-particle inspection are as follows:

1 It is not completely reliable for locating discontinuities that lie entirely below the surface.
2 The magnetic field must be in a direction that will intercept the principal plane of the discontinuity.
3 Care is required in order to avoid local heating and burning of surfaces at the points of electrical contact.

Liquid-penetrant inspection is used to detect surface flaws in materials. It is used mainly, but not exclusively, with nonmagnetic materials, on which magnetic-particle inspection cannot be used. The technique of liquid-penetrant inspection involves the spreading of a liquid penetrant on the sample. This liquid has wetting characteristics, so that it will seep into small cracks and flaws in the surface of the sample. The excess liquid is wiped from the surface, and a developer is applied that causes the liquid to be drawn from the cracks or flaws that are open at the surface. The liquid itself is usually a very bright color or contains fluorescent particles that, under ultraviolet light, cause discontinuities in the material to stand out.

The main advantages of the liquid-penetrant method are its ability to be used on nonmagnetic materials, its low cost, its portability, and the ease with which results can be interpreted.

The principal limitations of the liquid-penetrant method are:

1 Discontinuities must be open to the surface.
2 Test pieces must be cleaned before and after testing, because the liquid penetrant may corrode the metal.
3 Surface films may prevent detection of discontinuities.

Electromagnetic inspection, sometimes called eddy-current inspection, can be used on all materials that conduct electricity. If a coil conducting an alternating current is placed around or near the surface of the sample, it will set up eddy currents within the material by electromagnetic induction. These eddy currents affect the impedance in the exciting coil or any other pickup coil that is nearby. Cracks or flaws within the sample will cause distortions in the eddy current, which in turn cause distortion in the impedance of the coil. The resulting change in impedance can be detected by attaching the appropriate electrical circuits and a meter. Flaws or cracks will show up as some deflection or fluctuation on the meter.

The advantages of electromagnetic inspection are:

1 Both surface and subsurface defects are detectable.
2 No special operator skills are required.
3 The process is adaptable to continuous monitoring.
4 The process may be substantially automated and is capable of high speeds.
5 No probe contact is needed.

Limitations of electromagnetic inspection include:

1 Depth of penetration is shallow.
2 Materials to be inspected must be electrically conductive.
3 Indications are influenced by more than one variable.
4 Reference standards are required.

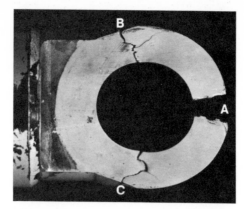

Fig. 2. Fractured lug, part of a pin-joint assembly, showing sequence of fracture. Fracture A preceded fractures B and C.

Ultrasonic-inspection methods depend on sound waves of very high frequency being transmitted through metal and reflected at any boundary — such as a metal-air boundary at the surface of the metal, or a metal-crack boundary at a defect. High-frequency sound waves can detect small irregularities, but they are easily absorbed, particularly by coarse-grained materials.

The advantages of ultrasonic tests are as follows:

1 High sensitivity, which permits the detection of minute cracks
2 Great penetrating power, which allows the examination of extremely thick sections
3 Accuracy in measurement of flaw position and estimation of flaw size.

Ultrasonic tests have the following limitations:

1 Size-contour complexity and unfavorable discontinuity orientation can pose problems in interpretation of the echo pattern.
2 Undesirable internal structure (for example, grain size, structure, porosity, inclusion content, or fine, dispersed precipitates) can similarly hinder interpretation.
3 Reference standards are required.

Radiography involves the use of x-rays or gamma rays, which are directed through the sample to a photographic film. After the film has been developed, it can be examined by placing it in front of a light source. The intensity of the light coming through the film will be proportional to the density of the sample and the path length of the radiation. Thus, lighter areas on the plate would correspond to the denser areas of the sample, whereas darker areas would indicate an area where there is a crack or defect running in the direction of the incident beam.

The main advantages of radiography are its ability to detect internal variations and defects, and that it provides permanent records in the form of photographic films.

Experimental stress analysis can be done by several methods, all of which may be valuable in determining machine loads and component stresses that can cause failures.

Stress-coating can be used effectively for (*a*) locating small areas of high strains, (*b*) determining the directions of the principal strains, and (*c*) measuring the approximate magnitude of tensile and compressive strains. Gages can then be placed at the high-strain areas and in the principal-strain directions to accurately measure the strain on gage lengths of 0.02 to 6 in. Although there are many mechanical, optical and electrical devices capable of accurate strain measurements, the bonded, electrical-resistance strain gage has become the standard tool for general laboratory and field use.

Photoelastic coatings also have been used for laboratory stress measurements. For this technique, a birefringent coating of controlled thickness is bonded to the test part with a reflective cement. Optical analysis is similar to conventional analysis but requires special equipment. The analysis may be recorded on color film with single-frame or movie cameras.

X-ray diffraction is the only available method for direct, nondestructive measurement of surface residual stresses in crystalline materials. Stresses are determined by measuring the angle by which the stressed material crystal diffracts an x-ray beam.

Mechanical Testing

Hardness testing is the simplest of the mechanical tests and is often the most versatile tool available to the failure analyst. Among its many applications, hardness testing can be used (*a*) to assist in evaluating heat treatment (comparing the hardness of the failed component with that prescribed by specification); (*b*) to provide an approximation of the tensile strength of steel; and (*c*) to detect work hardening, or to detect softening or hardening caused by overheating, by decarburization, or by carbon or nitrogen pickup. Hardness testing is also essentially nondestructive, except when preparation of a special hardness-test specimen is required, as in microhardness testing.

Other mechanical tests are useful in confirming that the failed component conforms to specification or in evaluating the effects of surface conditions on mechanical properties. Where appropriate, tensile and impact tests should be carried out, provided sufficient material for the fabrication of test specimens is available. The determination of plane-strain fracture-toughness values may also be justifiable. It may be necessary to make some tests either at slightly elevated or at low temperatures to simulate service conditions. Also, it may be helpful to test specimens after they have been subjected to particular heat treatments that simulate the thermal treatment of the failed component in service, to determine how this treatment has modified mechanical properties. For example, treating a steel at a temperature in the embrittling range for about 1 hr prior to impact testing will indicate any tendency to strain-age embrittlement, and the determination of the ductile-to-brittle transition temperature may be useful in investigating brittle fracture of a low-carbon steel.

The failure analyst should exercise care in interpreting mechanical-test results; for instance, because a material has a tensile strength 5 to 10% below the minimum specified value does not mean that this is the prime cause of its failure in service. Also, it should be understood that laboratory tests on small specimens may not adequately represent the behavior of a much larger structure or component in service. For instance, it is possible for brittle fracture of a large structure to occur at or near ordinary temperature, while subsequent laboratory tests of Charpy or Izod specimens show a transition temperature well below −18 C (0 F). The effects of size in fatigue, stress-corrosion, and hydrogen-embrittlement testing are not well understood. However, on the basis of the limited evidence available, it appears that resistance to these failure processes decreases as specimen size increases.

Limitations of Tensile Tests. In the majority of service-failure investigations, the tensile test does not provide much useful information, because relatively few failures result from the use of a material that is deficient in tensile strength or from a tensile load that is applied until rupture occurs. Furthermore, samples cut from components that have failed in a brittle manner generally show adequate ductility under the conditions imposed during a tensile test.

Tensile tests are essential during production, to ascertain if the material conforms to specification requirements. There is also some justification for tensile testing of components that have failed in service, to eliminate poor-quality material as a possible cause of failure. Often, these tensile tests for determining material quality are carried out by manufacturers and suppliers when examining defective components that have been returned to them for analysis.

Preparation of specimens for tensile tests is expensive and time consuming; the amount of material available also may be insufficient, even if only substandard test specimens are to be prepared. When steels are involved, sufficient information regarding the approxi-

mate tensile strength can generally be obtained from Brinell tests or other hardness tests. A simple bend test usually shows whether or not a material possesses adequate ductility. The amount of ductility, as shown by the elongation value in a tensile test, is not related directly to the behavior of metals in service. For instance, a crankshaft failure could not be attributed to the fact that the crankshaft showed only 20% elongation on a standard sample, as opposed to the 26% required by the specification.

It is usually sufficient during the initial stages of an investigation to determine whether the material is essentially ductile or brittle, and this can be ascertained from a simple bend test. The reduction of area, thought by some to be related to the ability of the material to deform plastically at a notch and so to relieve stress intensification, gives a much more realistic measure of ductility, but is often omitted from a tensile test. Testing of cast irons and most nonferrous alloys for tensile strength is almost essential, although some indication of the tensile strength is obtainable from hardness tests.

Results of tensile tests on specimens from components that have failed in service sometimes show that the material is slightly inferior in strength and ductility compared to results of acceptance tests done when the components were made. However, acceptance tests are often carried out on test specimens provided specially for the purpose. Consequently, some discrepancy is to be expected, either because of differences in the amount of forging or cold work to which the component and the test specimens have been subjected during the course of manufacture, or because a difference in section thickness has resulted in variations in cooling rate either at the time of casting or during heat treatment. Therefore, such disparities in results should not necessarily be interpreted as an indication that the particular properties of the material have deteriorated in service.

The role of directionality in tensile testing should also be considered. Specimens cut transversely to the longitudinal axis of a component such as a shaft should be expected to give lower yield-strength values and lower elongation values than those cut along the longitudinal axis, because of the marked directionality and the resulting anisotropy produced during rolling or forging.

Selection, Preservation and Cleaning of Fracture Surfaces

The proper selection, preservation and cleaning of fracture surfaces are vital to prevent important evidence from being destroyed or obscured. Surfaces of frac-

tures may suffer either mechanical or chemical damage. Mechanical damage may arise from several sources, including the striking of the surface of the fracture by other objects. This can occur during actual fracture in service or when removing or transporting a fractured part for analysis. Information regarding the selection and preservation of surfaces that have been degraded by wear or corrosion is provided in this volume in the articles on Wear Failures (see page 134) and on Corrosion Failures (see page 168).

Usually, the surface of a fracture can be protected during shipment by a covering of cloth or cotton, but this may remove some loosely adhering material, which often contains the primary clue to the cause of the fracture. Touching or rubbing the surface of a fracture with the fingers should definitely be avoided. Also, no attempt should be made to fit together the sections of a fractured part by placing them in contact. This generally accomplishes nothing and almost always causes damage to the fracture surface.

Chemical (corrosion) damage to a fracture specimen can be prevented in several ways. For instance, because the identification of foreign material present on a fracture surface may be important in the over-all interpretation of the cause of the fracture, many laboratories prefer not to use corrosion-preventive coatings on a fracture specimen. When possible, it is best to dry the fracture specimen, preferably by use of a jet of dry compressed air (which will also blow extraneous foreign material from the surface), and then to place it in a desiccator or pack it with a suitable desiccant.

Whenever possible, washing the fracture surface with water should be avoided. However, specimens contaminated with seawater or with fire-extinguishing fluids require thorough washing, usually with water, followed by rinsing with acetone or alcohol before storage in a desiccator or coating with a desiccant.

Cleaning. Surfaces of fractures should be cleaned only when absolutely necessary. Cleaning may be required for removal of obliterating debris and dirt, or to prepare for electron-microscope examination. Cleaning procedures include (a) use of a dry-air blast or of a soft-hair artist's brush; (b) treating with inorganic solvents, either by immersion or by jet; (c) treating with mild acid or alkaline solutions (depending on the metal) that will attack deposits but to which the base metal is essentially inert; (d) ultrasonic cleaning; and (e) application and stripping of plastic replicas.

Cleaning with a cellulose acetate replica is one of the most useful methods, particularly when the surface of a fracture has been affected by corrosion. A strip of acetate sheet about 1 mm thick and of suitable size is softened by immersion in acetone and placed on the surface of the fracture. The initial strip is backed by a piece of unsoftened acetate, and then the replica is pressed hard onto the surface of the fracture using a vise or suitable clamps. The drying time will depend on the extent to which the replicating material was softened, and this in turn will be governed by the texture of the surface of the fracture. Drying times of not less than 1 hr are recommended, and overnight drying is desirable if time permits. The dry replica is lifted from the fracture, using a scalpel or tweezers. The replicating procedure can be repeated several times if the fracture is badly contaminated. When a clean and uncontaminated replica is obtained, the process is complete. An advantage of this method is that the debris removed from the fracture is preserved for any subsequent examination that may be necessary for identification of the type of debris.

Sectioning. Because examination tools, including hardness testers and optical and electron microscopes, are limited as to the size of specimen they can accept, it is often necessary to remove from a failed component a fracture-containing portion or section that is of a size convenient to handle and examine.

It is important that records, either sketches or photographs, be kept to show the locations of the cuts made during sectioning.

Before cutting or sectioning, the fracture area should be carefully protected. All cutting should be done so that surfaces of fractures and areas adjacent to them are not damaged or altered; this includes keeping the fracture surface dry, whenever possible. For large parts, the common method of removing specimens is by flame cutting. Cutting must be done at a sufficient distance from the fracture site so that the microstructure of the metal underlying the surface of the fracture is not altered by the heat of the flame, and so that none of the molten metal from flame cutting is deposited on the surface of the fracture.

Sawing and cutoff-wheel cutting can be used for a wide range of part sizes. Dry cutting is preferable, because coolants may corrode the fracture site or may wash away foreign matter from the surface of the fracture. A coolant may be required, however, if a dry cut cannot be made at a sufficient distance from the fracture site to avoid heat damage to the area of the fracture.

Opening Secondary Cracks. When the primary fracture has been damaged or corroded to such a degree that most of the information on the cause of fracture is obliterated, it is desirable to open any secondary cracks to expose their fracture surfaces for examination and study. These cracks may provide more information than the primary fracture. If the cracks are tightly closed, they may have been protected from corrosive conditions, and if they have existed for less time than the primary fracture, they may have corroded less. Also, primary cracks that have not been propagated to total fracture may have to be opened.

In opening cracks for examination, care must be exercised to prevent damage, primarily mechanical, to the surface of the fracture. This can usually be accomplished if opening is done in such a way that the two surfaces of the fracture are moved in opposite directions, normal to the fracture plane. Generally, a saw cut can be made from the back of the fractured part to a point near the tip of the crack, using extreme care to avoid actually reaching the tip of the crack. This saw cut will reduce the amount of solid metal that must be broken. The final breaking of the specimen can be done in several ways: (a) by clamping the two sides of the fractured part in a tensile-testing machine, if the shape permits, and pulling; (b) by placing the specimen in a vise and bending one half away from the other by striking it with a hammer in a manner that will avoid damage to the surfaces of the crack; or (c) by gripping the halves of the fracture in pliers or vise grips and bending or pulling them apart.

It is desirable to be able to distinguish between a fracture surface produced during opening of a primary or secondary crack and the surface produced by primary or secondary cracking. This can be accomplished by making sure that a different fracture mechanism is active in making the new break, such as by opening the crack at a very low temperature. During opening at low temperature, care should be taken to avoid condensation of water, because this could cause corrosion of the fracture surface.

It is recommended that both crack separations and crack lengths be measured prior to opening. Often, the amount of strain that occurred in the specimen can be determined from a measurement of the separation between the adjacent halves of a fracture. This should be done before preparation for opening a secondary crack has begun. The lengths of cracks may also be important for analyses of fatigue fractures or for consideration of fracture mechanics.

Macroscopic Examination of Fracture Surfaces

The detailed examination of fracture surfaces at magnifications ranging from 1 to 100 diameters may be done with the unaided eye, a hand lens or a low-power stereoscopic microscope. Occasionally, it may also be advantageous to employ a scanning electron microscope at low magnification. Photography of specimens requires a high-quality camera for magnifications up to 20 diameters, and a metallograph with macro objectives and illuminating systems for magnifications from 20 to 50 diameters. The ordinary incident (vertical and oblique) light system and objectives used in standard metallography are generally best for magnifications of 50 to 100 diameters. Frequently, a specimen may be too large or too heavy for the stage of the metallograph, and cutting or sectioning the specimen may be difficult or undesirable. In these instances, excellent results can be achieved by examining, and where appropriate, photographing, replicas made by the method for cleaning fractures (see discussion under "Cleaning" in column 3, opposite page). These replicas can be coated with a thin layer (about 200 angstroms thick) of vacuum-evaporated gold or aluminum to improve their reflectivity, or they may be shadowed at an angle to increase the contrast of fine detail. The replicas may be examined by incident-light or transmitted-light microscopy. Because they are electrically conductive, the replicas may also be examined by scanning electron microscopy.

The amount of information that can be obtained from examination of a fracture surface at low-power magnification is surprisingly extensive. Consideration of the configuration of the fracture surfaces may give an indication of the stress system that produced failure. Failure in monotonic tension produces a "flat" ("square") fracture normal to the maximum tensile stress under plane-strain conditions and a "slant" ("shear") fracture at about 45° if plane-stress conditions prevail. Because pure plane-strain and pure plane-stress conditions are ideal situations that seldom occur in service, many fractures are "flat" at the center, but surrounded by a "picture frame" of "slant" fracture. The slant fracture occurs because conditions approximating plane strain operate at the center of the specimen but relax toward plane stress near free surfaces. An example of this behavior is to be found in the familiar "cup-and-cone" tensile fracture.

In thin sheets or small-diameter rods, full-slant fracture may occur because through-the-thickness stresses are relaxed by plastic deformation and a stress state approximating plane strain cannot develop. The term "shear lip" is often used to describe an area of slant fracture between a flat area and a free surface. This term should be avoided, because it seems unlikely that slant fractures are the result of pure shear. The term "45° fracture" for a slant fracture is somewhat misleading, because the angle between principal axis and fracture surface may vary several degrees from this value, and

Fig. 3. Chevron marks on the fracture surface of a steel tube (J. Schijve)

Fig. 4. Surfaces of a fatigue fracture that initiated in the vicinity of a drilled hole and progressed to final overstress fracture. Shown are the advancing crack front and the chevron marks that point to the region of final fracture.

in addition the fracture surface may be a curved plane. Torsional stresses may produce fractures having spiral surfaces, especially if they are generated by fatigue.

Macroscopic examination can usually determine the direction of crack growth and hence the origin of failure. With brittle flat fractures, determination depends largely on the fracture surface showing "chevron marks" of the type shown in Fig. 3. The direction of crack growth is almost always away from the tips of the chevrons.

Chevron marks occur because nearly all cracks are stepped at an early stage in their development, and as the crack front expands, the traces of the steps form chevron marks. In plate and sheet, chevron marks may result from the nucleation of new cracks ahead of a main crack front.

Occasionally, chevron marks may not follow the general pattern and their tips may point to the last region to fail rather than to the origin, as in the fracture surfaces shown in Fig. 4; in that fracture, the condition resulted from fatigue-crack initiation along the whole length of a drilled hole due to fretting. When the crack front contracts in the latter stages of fracture (rather than expanding, as is usually the case), the chevron marks, being normal to the crack front at any given position, indicate the region of final fracture. This behavior is unusual; however, chevron marks of this type should be looked for when determining crack-growth directions.

Where fracture surfaces show both flat and slant fractures, it may be generally concluded that the flat fracture occurred first. Crack extension, often with crack-front tunneling, relaxes the plane-strain state of stress so that final fracture occurs by slant fracture under plane-stress conditions. Conversely, if a fracture has begun at a free surface, the fracture-origin area is usually characterized by a total absence of slant fracture or "shear lip".

Low-power examination of fracture surfaces often reveals regions having a texture different from the region of final fracture; fatigue, stress-corrosion and hydrogen-embrittlement fractures may all show these differences.

Figure 5(a) shows the fracture surface of a steel tube and is an excellent example of the type of information that can be obtained by macroscopic examination. In Fig. 5(a), the chevron marks clearly indicate that the fracture origin is at the point marked by the arrow. This region, unlike the rest of the fracture, has no "shear lip". The flat fracture surface suggests that the stress causing the failure was tension parallel to the length of the tube. The origin of the fracture as seen at higher magnification in Fig. 5(b) shows several small fracture nuclei having a texture different from that of the remainder of the fracture surface.

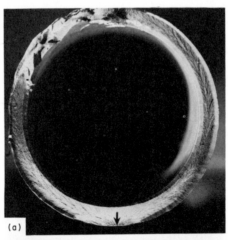

(a)

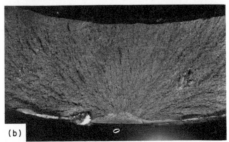

(b)

Fig. 5. (a) Fracture surface of a steel tube, at approximately actual size, showing point of crack initiation (at arrow), chevron marks, and development of shear lips. (b) Fracture-origin area, at 5×; note that fracture nuclei differ in texture from the main fracture surface.

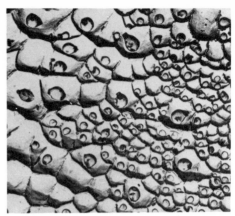

Fig. 6. TEM fractograph, at 40,000×, of a carbon replica of the surface of a ductile-tensile fracture, showing dimpled pattern typical in overstress fractures of ductile metals and alloys (Henry and Plateau)

Microscopic Examination of Fracture Surfaces

The microscopic examination of fracture surfaces, sometimes called microfractography, is discussed in detail in Volume 9 of this Handbook and in other references (Ref 3 to 8).

A light microscope can be used for fractography, although its limit of resolution (approximately 0.5 micron) and depth of field do impose restrictions.

The use of plastic replicas, with or without evaporated reflective metal coatings, is recommended for light microscopy. Replicas permit detailed examination of selected regions without the necessity for cutting up the specimen. They also are convenient to handle, and they avoid the risk of damage to the front lens of the microscope objective. (Techniques employed for producing single-stage and two-stage replicas, and for shadowing and coating of replicas, are described on pages 56 to 60 in Volume 9 of this Handbook.)

Compared to a light microscope, a transmission electron microscope (TEM) offers much better limits of resolution (approximately 10 angstroms) and magnifications as high as 300,000 diameters. (In fractography, however, the useful upper limit is perhaps 30,000 diameters.) Furthermore, the low numerical aperture of electron-optical objectives gives the instruments great depth of field.

With a transmission electron microscope, fracture surfaces cannot be examined directly; this requires that suitable replicas be made (see pages 56 to 60 in Volume 9), and be shadowed to improve contrast. The limit of resolution obtained generally is not governed by the instrument but by the quality of the replica, and this limit of resolution is about 50 angstroms for direct, or single-stage, replicas and about 100 to 150 angstroms for two-stage replicas.

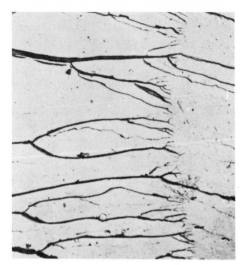

Fig. 7. Fractograph, at 16,000×, of a fracture surface in a zinc specimen, showing a cleavage facet containing river marks generated by a subgrain boundary

A useful ancillary technique that can be employed with extraction replicas is particle identification by electron diffraction. Transmission-electron-microscope microanalyzers, which incorporate a "mini lens" to produce an electron beam less than 1000 angstroms in diameter, and which have facilities for analyzing the x-rays generated by the probe, also are becoming available for use in failure investigation.

Scanning electron microscopes (SEM) are gaining wider use in fractography, because they permit direct examination of the actual fracture surface without the need for a replica. Most modern instruments claim limits of resolution of better than 150 angstroms; "first generation" instruments, many of which are currently in use, have limits of resolution of about 250 angstroms. In practice, these limits are seldom achieved with fracture surfaces, and in consequence magnifications of more than 10,000 diameters are seldom used. The great advantage of the SEM is its ability to examine specimens at low magnifications of about 50 diameters, then enlarge regions of special interest to very high magnifications. It is also extremely useful when examining fractures in fine wire or thin sheet that are difficult to replicate. Examination of electrically nonconductive specimens, such as nonmetallic materials or replicas of metal fractures, necessitates coating the samples with a conducting material, and about 50 angstroms of evaporated gold is satisfactory for this purpose.

It should be emphasized that the instruments and techniques described here are complementary to each other, and they should be used when they are available. The use of stereographic pairs of fractographs is extremely valuable. The angle of tilt used when making stereographic pairs must correctly recreate the topography of the fracture surface, neither overemphasizing nor underemphasizing the features that are present. This requires calibration of the tilting stage of the microscope with respect to the focal length of the stereographic viewer — a process that can be carried out algebraically or experimentally. Measurement on electron-optical stereographic pairs of a microhardness indentation taken over a range of specimen tilt angles provides a useful experimental calibration procedure (Ref 9).

Although the interpretation of microfractographs requires practice and understanding of fracture mechanisms, there are only a small number of basic features that are clearly recognizable and indicative of a particular mode of failure. These are as follows:

1 Dimpled fracture, typical of overstress failures of ductile metals and alloys (see Fig. 6)
2 Cleavage facets, typical of transgranular brittle fracture of body-centered-cubic and close-packed, hexagonal metals and alloys (see Fig. 7)
3 Brittle intergranular fracture typical of temper-brittle steel, where fracture is due to segregation of an embrittling species to grain boundaries (such as oxygen in iron or nickel), to intergranular stress-corrosion cracking (see Fig. 8), or to hydrogen embrittlement
4 Stage II striations, typical of fatigue failure (see Fig. 9).

Selection and Preparation of Metallographic Sections

Metallographic examination of polished and of polished-and-etched sections by optical microscopy and by electron-optical techniques is a vital part of failure investigation, and should be car-

Fig. 8. TEM fractograph, at 6000×, of a plastic-carbon replica of the surface of a brittle fracture in steel that resulted from intergranular stress-corrosion cracking, showing a pattern of small angle tilts and an absence of deformation (D. Broek)

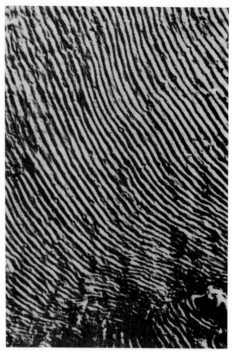

Fig. 9. Fractograph, at 3500×, of a fracture surface showing stage II striations, typical of fatigue failure (R. J. Forsyth)

ried out as a routine procedure. Metallographic examination provides the investigator with a good indication of the class of material involved and whether it has the desired structure. If abnormalities are present, these may not be associated with undesirable characteristics that predispose to early failure. It is sometimes possible to relate them to an unsuitable composition or to the effects of service, such as aging in low-carbon steel that has caused precipitation of iron nitride, or gassing in copper. The microscope may also provide information as to the method of manufacture of the part under investigation and the heat treatment to which it has been subjected, either intentionally during manufacture or accidentally during service. Other service effects, such as corrosion, oxidation, and severe work hardening of surfaces, also are revealed, and their extent can be investigated. Also, the characteristics of any cracks that may be present, particularly their mode of propagation, provide information regarding the factors responsible for their initiation and development.

Only a few general directions can be given as to the best location from which to take specimens for microscopic examination, because almost every failure has individual features that must be taken into account. In most examinations, however, it must be determined whether the structure of a specimen taken adjacent to a fracture surface or a region at which a service defect has developed is representative of the component as a whole. This can be done only by the ex-

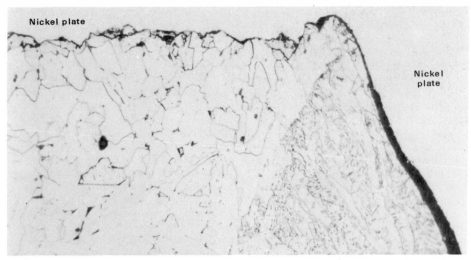

Fig. 10. Metallographic specimen on which nickel plate (smooth light-gray areas along top and right side) was used to protect edges during preparation. Specimen shows profile of a stress-corrosion crack in welded low-carbon steel pipe. Fracture surface is at top; weld, at right; pipe surface, far right. (Picral etch; 500×)

amination of specimens taken from other locations, and in general it is recommended that the number selected for examination should be too many rather than too few. For instance, in the case of ruptured or bulged boiler tubes in which failure is usually restricted to one portion only, it is desirable to examine specimens taken from both sides of the fracture, from a location opposite the affected zone, and also from an area as remote from the failure as the size of sample permits, so as to determine whether the failure has been due to a defect in the material or to overheating — and, if the latter, whether this was of a general or localized nature. In investigations involving general overheating, sometimes the original condition of the material can be ascertained only from a sample cut from a part of the tube many feet away from the affected zone.

When examining cracks microscopically, the most valuable information may sometimes be gained from a study of specimens that include the extremities of the cracks. In general, the parts of cracks that are visible to the unaided eye are too wide, ragged, or corroded for their paths to be revealed with certainty under the microscope, but at their extremities they are finer and examination of specimens from these regions generally enables the paths to be positively identified as either intergranular or transgranular.

In the investigation of fatigue cracks, it is advisable to take a specimen from the region where the fracture originated to ascertain if the initial development was associated with an abnormality, such as a weld defect, a decarburized surface, a zone rich in inclusions or, in castings, a zone containing severe porosity. Where multiple-origin cracks are concerned, however, such a procedure is not practicable; in these instances, it is most

unlikely that the cracks were due to local inhomogeneities. Multiple fatigue-crack initiation is very typical of both fretting and corrosion fatigue. Similarly, with surface marks, where their origin is impossible to identify from outward appearances, a microscopic examination will show whether they occurred in rolling or arose from ingot defects, such as scabs, laps or seams. In brittle fractures, it is useful to examine a specimen cut from where the failure originated, if this can be located with certainty, because failures by brittle fracture are frequently associated with locally work-hardened surfaces, particularly if the steel is of the strain-aging type.

It is usually best to plate the fracture surface of a specimen with a metal, such as nickel, prior to mounting and sectioning, so that the fracture edge is supported and can be included in the examination. Figure 10, which shows a section through a welded low-carbon steel pipe, is an example of the plating technique. The section is bordered at the top by the surface of a stress-corrosion crack and at the right by the outside surface of the pipe (both shown in profile). Both of these surfaces were nickel plated to prevent rounding of the edges during polishing. This section shows the intergranular nature of the crack and the location of the crack relative to the end of a weld deposit (at right), which suggests that the heat of welding caused the stress; the source of the corrosion is not known.

Examination and Analysis of Metallographic Sections

As with hardness testing and macroscopic examination, the examination of metallographic sections with a microscope is standard practice in most failure analyses, because of the outstanding ca-

pability of the microscope of revealing material imperfections caused during processing and of detecting the results of a variety of in-service operating conditions and environments that may have contributed to failure. Inclusions, microstructural segregation, decarburization, carbon pickup, improper heat treatment, untempered "white" martensite, and intergranular corrosion are among the many metallurgical imperfections and undesirable conditions that can be detected and analyzed by microscopic examination of metallographic sections.

Volume 7 of this Handbook presents a comprehensive selection of micrographs of wrought and cast ferrous and nonferrous alloys, illustrating 214 undesirable or abnormal microstructures, 143 defects or significant surface conditions, and 174 microstructures after service or exposure, supplementing the many pertinent failure-related micrographs presented in the present volume.

Figures 11 and 12 exemplify the usefulness of metallographic sectioning in failure analysis.

Figure 11 shows localized structural transformation, in the form of a layer of untempered "white" martensite, at the surface of a ball-bearing steel (1% C, 1% Cr) component that resulted from etching identification letters on the surface with an electric-arc pencil. These martensite layers are always extremely brittle and hard (Rockwell C 65) and often contain cracks that can initiate fatigue failure.

Figure 12 shows a section through a nitrided steel gear in which excessive grinding removed enough of the case at the roots of teeth to lower fatigue strength and cause failure.

Even in the absence of a specific metallurgical imperfection, examination of metallographic sections is invaluable to the investigator in the measurement of parameters, such as case depth, thickness of plated coatings, grain size, and heat-affected zone — all of which may have a bearing on the cause of failure.

Metallographic sections are also useful when quantitative metallographic techniques, such as point counting, lineal analysis, or electron-probe microanalysis, are employed in failure analysis.

Determination of Fracture Type

To use the information obtained from examination of the failure region, the fracture surfaces and metallographic sections to determine the cause of fracture, it is usually necessary to determine the fracture type. However, a satisfactory logical classification of failures involving fracture does not exist. For instance, the extensive elongation of a low-carbon steel specimen followed by cleavage might be classified as either brittle or ductile fracture. The low-energy catastrophic fracture of a high-strength aluminum alloy by microvoid coalescence is also difficult to classify, because, although the fracture energy is low and failure will have initiated by fracture or decohesion of brittle particles, the growth and coalescence of the microvoids will have occurred by plastic deformation. Another difficulty is that cleavage fracture may be initiated by dislocation interactions that, by definition, involve plasticity.

For the purposes of this article, fractures will be classified in terms of their growth mechanism, and crack initiation will not be considered. Thus, cleavage-crack extension is "brittle" regardless of the plastic deformation that may have accompanied or preceded crack initiation, and any fracture mainly by microvoid coalescence will be regarded as "ductile" because the mechanism of crack extension necessarily involves plastic deformation. The fracture classifications used in this article are described below. For further discussion of failure classification, see the article on Identification of Types of Failure, which begins on page 57 in this volume.

Ductile Fracture

Overload fractures of many metals and alloys occur by ductile fracture. Overloading in tension is perhaps the least complex of the overload fractures, although essentially the same processes operate in bending and torsion as well as under the complex states of stress that may have produced a given service failure. Classically, ductile-tensile fracture of a cylindrical specimen involves plastic extension, initially without necking. During this extension, cracking of included particles, which are present in even the purest metals, or decohesion of particle-matrix interfaces occurs, creating microvoids. When the ability of the material to work harden is exhausted, necking begins and triaxial stresses are set up that cause lateral extension of the microvoids, which coalesce to form a central crack. Fracture of the remaining section to produce an annulus of "slant" fracture, often incorrectly called "shear", is less well understood but probably occurs by a crack growing circumferentially around the specimen under plane-stress conditions. The total absence of second-phase particles would result in fracture by 100% reduction of area, but this rarely occurs in service failures.

Sheet specimens fracture by similar mechanisms and if they are thick enough for plane-strain conditions to operate, a "flat" fracture with "shear lips" is produced. Full-slant fracture may occur in thin sections (that is, under plane-stress conditions). Exceptions occur in materials that show marked discontinuous

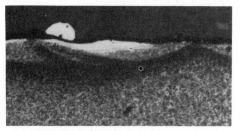

Fig. 11. Micrograph, at 500×, of a section through a component made of ball-bearing steel (1% C, 1% Cr). At surface is localized structural transformation ("white" martensite) caused by etching with an electric-arc pencil.

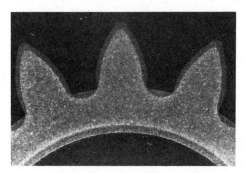

Fig. 12. Macrograph, at 10×, of a section through a nitrided steel spur gear that failed in fatigue. An incorrect grinding allowance resulted in localized thinning of the nitrided case, with a consequent reduction in fatigue strength.

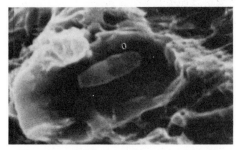

Fig. 13. SEM fractograph, at 5000×, showing an equiaxed dimple pattern produced in a ductile-tensile fracture

Fig. 14. TEM fractograph of a carbon replica, at 6000×, showing elongated dimples that resulted from a ductile fracture involving a shear-stress component (D. Broek)

yielding accompanied by the generation of Lüders bands across the whole cross section of the specimen. It is possible for fracture to occur by microvoid coalescence within a Lüders band, producing a full-slant fracture in thick sections — that is, under nominally plane-strain conditions (Ref 10).

Fractography of Ductile Fractures. Fractographic examination of flat ductile-fracture surfaces usually reveals approximately equiaxed "dimples", generally with evidence of the particles that originated the fracture (see Fig. 13). Slant fracture, or ductile fracture involving shear-stress components (such as torsion), generates elongated dimples (see Fig. 14). When the elongated dimples are produced by a shear component, the dimples in the mating fracture surfaces point in opposite directions. In ductile-fracture surfaces produced by tearing, the crack produces elongated dimples on mating surfaces that are mirror images.

Fractures that are ductile as seen macroscopically are usually transgranular, but electron fractography has shown dimple patterns on tensile-fracture surfaces of aluminum-copper alloys when metallographic sections have shown that the fracture path was apparently intergranular and nominally "brittle" (Ref 10). Isolated dimples on brittle intergranular-fracture surfaces of aluminum-zinc-magnesium alloys have been observed (Ref 10); this situation is generally confined to precipitation-hardened alloys with grain-boundary zones that are precipitate-free.

Transgranular Brittle Fracture

Transgranular cleavage of iron and low-carbon steel is the most commonly encountered process of brittle fracture — so common, in fact, that the term "brittle fracture" is sometimes misinterpreted as meaning only transgranular cleavage of iron and low-carbon steel. Transgranular cleavage can also occur in several other body-centered-cubic metals and their alloys (for example, tungsten, molybdenum and chromium) and some hexagonal, close-packed metals (for example, zinc, magnesium and beryllium), but face-centered-cubic metals and alloys are usually regarded as immune from this mechanism of fracture. Iron and low-carbon steel show a ductile-to-brittle transition with decreasing temperature that arises from a strong dependence of the yield stress to temperature.

Transition temperature is not really a physical constant, but depends on several physical factors, including specimen shape and size, and strain rate. Thus, a component or structure that has given satisfactory service may fracture unexpectedly; the catastrophic brittle fracture of ships in heavy seas and the failure

Fig. 15. Light fractograph, at 750×, showing the surface of a cleavage fracture in zinc that was broken at −196 C (−321 F)

of bridges on unusually cold days are examples. Metallurgical changes, especially strain aging, may cause the brittle fracture of such items as crane hooks and chain links after long periods of satisfactory operation.

Cleavage fracture is not difficult to diagnose, because the fracture path is by definition crystallographic and usually, but not invariably, occurs on {100} cube planes in body-centered-cubic metals and alloys and on {0001} basal planes in hexagonal, close-packed metals and alloys. In polycrystalline specimens, this often produces a pattern of brightly reflecting crystal facets, and such fractures are often described as "crystalline". The general plane of fracture is approximately normal to the axis of maximum tensile stress, and a "shear lip" is often present as a "picture frame" around the fracture. The local absence of a shear lip or slant fracture suggests a possible location for initiation of the fracture.

Fractography of Transgranular Brittle Fractures. The fractography of cleavage fracture in low-carbon steels, iron, zinc and other single-phase body-centered-cubic metals and alloys, is fairly well established. In polycrystalline specimens, numerous fan-shaped cleavage plateaus, usually showing a high degree of geometric perfection, are present (see Fig. 15). The most characteristic feature of these plateaus is the presence of a pattern of river marks, which consist of cleavage steps and indicate the local direction of crack growth. The rule is that, if the tributaries are regarded as flowing into the main stream, then the direction of crack growth is downstream. This is in contrast to macroscopic chevron marks,

where the direction of crack growth, using the river analogy, would be upstream. Figure 16 shows the generation of river marks on a fracture surface as a cleavage crack crosses a subgrain boundary, and the merging of the tributaries to form rivers.

Other fractographic features that may be observed include the presence of cleavage on conjugate planes, ductile tears joining cleavage planes at different levels, and "tongues", which result from fracture in mechanical twins formed ahead of the advancing crack. Cleavage fracture in pearlitic and martensitic steels is less easily interpreted, because microstructure tends to modify the fracture surface.

Intergranular Brittle Fracture

Intergranular brittle fracture can usually be easily recognized but determining the primary cause of the fracture may be difficult. Fractographic examination can readily identify the presence of large fractions of second-phase particles at grain boundaries. Unfortunately, the segregation of a layer a few atoms thick of some element or compound that produces intergranular fracture often cannot

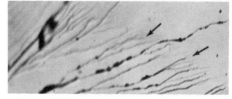

Fig. 16. Surface of a cleavage fracture, at 1000×, showing the generation of river marks as the crack crosses a subgrain boundary (at arrows)

be detected by fractography. Some causes of intergranular brittle fracture are given below, but the list is not exhaustive. The list does, however, indicate some of the possibilities that need to be considered, and either eliminated or confirmed, as contributing to the fracture.

1 Absence of sufficient deformation systems to satisfy the Taylor – von Mises criterion, which states that five independent systems (slip or slip-plus-twinning) are necessary for a grain to deform to an arbitrary shape imposed by its neighbors. The fracture of polycrystalline ceramics at low temperature is a good example, but this mechanism of fracture is not usual in face-centered-cubic metals and alloys.
2 The presence at a grain boundary of a large area of second-phase particles (such as carbides in iron-nickel-chromium alloys)
3 Segregation of a specific element or compound to a grain boundary where a layer a few atoms thick is sufficient to cause embrittlement. Embrittlement caused by the presence of oxygen in high-purity iron, oxygen in nickel, or antimony in copper, and temper embrittlement of certain steels, are examples of intergranular embrittlement where detection of a second phase at grain boundaries is difficult.

The conditions under which a slowly growing crack may follow an intergranular path before final overload fracture occurs include fatigue fracture, stress-corrosion cracking, embrittlement by liquid metals, hydrogen embrittlement, and creep and stress-rupture failures. These are discussed below.

Fatigue Fracture

Fatigue fracture results from the application of repeated or cyclic stresses, each of which may be substantially below the nominal yield strength of the material. Because the laboratory fatigue behavior of many metals and alloys is well established, it is perhaps surprising that so many service failures still occur by this mechanism. The difficulty is that there are a great many variables that influence fatigue behavior; these include the magnitude and frequency of application of the fluctuating stress, the presence of a mean stress, temperature, environment, specimen size and shape, state of stress, the presence of residual stresses, surface finish, microstructure and the presence of fretting damage. This list is not comprehensive, and an additional problem is that one variable may be more important with respect to one material than another. For example, the noble metals are insensitive to most corrosive environments, titanium alloys are especially susceptible to fretting, and high-strength, low-toughness materials, such as high-strength steels, are more susceptible to the effect of surface finish than are low-strength, tougher alloys.

General Features of Fatigue Fractures.
Because most of the surface area of a fatigue crack is generated by a process that is tensile-stress dependent, the stress system responsible for fracture can often be deduced from the configuration of the fracture. The article on Fatigue Failures, which begins on page 95 in this volume, describes the way in which fatigue-fracture configuration is influenced by the stress system, the magnitude of stress, and part shape.

The most noticeable macroscopic features of classic fatigue-fracture surfaces are the progression marks (also known as beach marks, clamshell marks or tide marks) that indicate successive positions of the advancing crack front (see Fig. 17).

Fatigue-fracture surfaces are smooth textured near their origins and generally show slight roughening as the crack grows. There is little macroscopic ductility associated with fatigue fracture, and there may be some evidence that the crack has followed specific crystal planes during early growth, thus giving a faceted appearance. Unfortunately, a great many fatigue fractures do not show the classic progression marks.

Most fatigue cracks are transcrystalline without marked branching, although intercrystalline fatigue is not particularly uncommon. Corrosion fatigue in most materials is also transcrystalline; its most striking feature usually is the multiplicity of crack origins, only one of which extends catastrophically. Fatigue initiated by fretting has similar characteristics and is generally diagnosed by the presence of a fretting product filling the multiplicity of cracks and by the presence of a fretting product on the surface of the component. On aluminum alloys, the fretting product is often a hard black deposit; on steels, considerable quantities of a substance resembling cocoa in appearance is produced. Fretting product appears to be a mixture of finely divided particles of the base metal, its oxides, and its hydrated oxides.

Microscopically, surfaces of fatigue fractures are characterized by the presence of striations, each of which is produced by a single cycle of stress (Ref 11). It is not true, however, that every cycle of stress produces a striation; in fact, the complete absence of striations does not rule out fatigue fracture. Also, there are a number of fractographic features that may be confused with fatigue striations — notably, Wallner lines, produced by shock-wave – crack-front interactions (see Fig. 18); rub marks; and microstructural features such as pearlite.

Stress-Corrosion Cracking

Stress-corrosion cracking is a mechanical-environmental failure process in which mechanical stress and chemical attack combine in the initiation and

Fig. 17. A classic fatigue-fracture surface, showing progression marks (beach marks) that indicate successive positions of the advancing crack front (J. Schijve)

propagation of fracture in a metal part. It is produced by the synergistic action of a sustained tensile stress and a specific corrosive environment, causing failure in less time than would the sum of the separate effects of the stress and the corrosive environment.

Failure by stress-corrosion cracking is frequently caused by exposure to a seemingly mild chemical environment while subject to a tensile stress that is well below the yield strength of the metal. Under such conditions, fine cracks can penetrate deeply into the part, although the surface may show only apparently insignificant amounts of corrosion. Hence there may be no macroscopic indications of impending failure. The most common instances of failure by stress-corrosion cracking in service are probably those associated with the following metals and alloys:

1 High-strength aluminum alloys, especially of the aluminum-zinc-magnesium type, under atmospheric-corrosion conditions. Internal and assembly stresses are often important.
2 Austenitic stainless steels and nickel alloys of the Inconel type in the presence of very low concentrations of chloride ions. The hydroxyl ion is also reported as causing failure, but this is disputed by some authors (Ref 12).
3 Low-carbon structural steels, usually in the presence of hot concentrated-nitrate or caustic-alkali solutions
4 High-strength steels (tensile strengths of 180,000 psi and above) in a variety of environments, probably with hydrogen embrittlement playing a dominant part

5 Copper alloys, notably 70Cu-30Zn cartridge brass in ammoniacal environments, usually in the presence of internal stresses.

General Features of Stress-Corrosion Cracking. Stress-corrosion cracks may be intergranular, transgranular, or a combination of both. In aluminum alloys and low-carbon steels, intergranular fracture is usual, although the fracture path may be immediately adjacent to the grain boundary rather than precisely along it. High-strength steels and alpha brasses also usually show grain-boundary fracture, with some cracking along matrix-twin interfaces in alpha brasses. Transgranular fractures showing extensive branching are typical of stress-corrosion cracking in austenitic stainless steels of the 18Cr-8Ni type (Fig. 19), and similar transgranular cracks with branches that follow crystallographic planes have been observed in magnesium alloys.

When stress-corrosion cracking is transgranular, deviations may occur on a microscopic scale so that the crack may follow microstructural features, such as grain and twin boundaries or specific crystal planes. When stress-corrosion cracking is intergranular, the presence of flat elongated grains means that there is an easy stress-corrosion path normal to the short-transverse direction, which produces "woody" stress-corrosion fracture surfaces. This behavior is typical of extrusions of high-strength aluminum alloys where solution treatment does not cause recrystallization. Some stress-corrosion fractures show progression marks and alternating regions of stress-corrosion cracking and overload fracture, with changes of shape of the crack front. The progression marks in the fracture surface shown in Fig. 20 could very easily be confused with fatigue. This fracture occurred in a forging that had not been

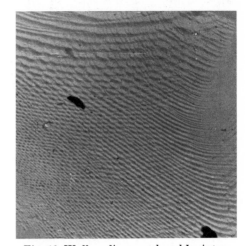

Fig. 18. Wallner lines produced by interaction of the primary crack with transverse shock waves. A TEM fractograph, at 5000×, of a plastic-carbon replica of the fracture surface of an aluminum alloy specimen. (H. van Leuwen)

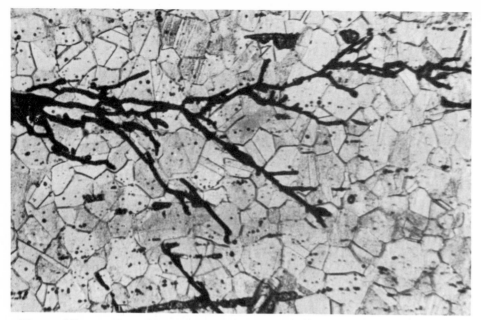

Fig. 19. Micrograph, at 200×, of a longitudinal section from a specimen of austenitic stainless steel, showing a branching stress-corrosion crack (R. Proctor)

used in service, and the fracture was due entirely to residual internal stress and atmospheric corrosion.

Other features observed on stress-corrosion-cracking fractures include striations, cleavage facets and tongues, which can easily be confused with similar features on cleavage and fatigue fractures.

When intergranular fracture occurs with only superficial corrosion, a "rock candy" appearance of the fracture surface is typical (see Fig. 21). Unfortunately, only in the high-strength aluminum alloys does this clearly define stress-corrosion fracture, because in high-strength steels, this pattern is also characteristic of hydrogen-induced slow crack growth.

The fractographic features of transgranular stress-corrosion cracking are numerous and varied. They are described and discussed in the article that begins on page 205 in this volume.

Embrittlement by Liquid Metals

Metallurgical failure by penetration of liquid metal, usually around grain boundaries, can perhaps be regarded as a special type of either corrosion or stress-corrosion cracking, because applied or residual stress accelerates fracture. The penetration of copper alloys by mercury and the penetration of steels by molten tin and cadmium are typical examples. Such penetration can usually be detected by microscopic examination of polished, or polished-and-etched, sections. Positive identification of the penetrant may be more difficult, but electron-microprobe analysis usually can solve this problem.

Features of liquid-metal embrittlement are discussed in the article that begins on page 228 in this volume.

Hydrogen Embrittlement

Hydrogen embrittles several metals and alloys, but its deleterious effect on steels, particularly when the strength of the steel is in excess of about 180,000 psi, is most important. A few parts per million of hydrogen dissolved in steel can cause hairline cracking and loss of tensile ductility. Even when the quantity of gas in solution is too small to reduce ductility, hydrogen-induced delayed fracture (sometimes called static fatigue) may occur. Gaseous environments containing hydrogen are also damaging. Hairline cracking usually follows prior-austenite grain boundaries and seems to occur when the damaging effect of dissolved hydrogen is superimposed on the stresses that accompany the austenite-to-martensite transformation. Affected areas are recognized on fracture surfaces by their brittle appearance and high reflectivity, which usually contrasts with the matte appearance of surrounding regions of ductile fracture. This has led to such areas being described as "flakes" or "fisheyes".

Hairline cracking is readily recognizable metallographically and is most common near the center of fairly bulky components where constraint of plastic deformation is high, but its incidence may be minimized by modification of steelmaking and heat treating practices. Hairline cracking is important with respect to service failures, because such a crack may extend by fatigue and so initiate catastrophic fracture.

Fractography of Hydrogen-Embrittled Steels. Hydrogen-embrittled steels, especially those that have suffered delayed fracture, show fracture surfaces very similar to those typical of stress-corrosion-cracking fracture in aluminum alloys and high-strength steels. In delayed fracture, there is always a region of fracture surface produced by hydrogen-assisted slow crack growth; this crack growth typically follows austenite grain boundaries, as shown in Fig. 22. Out-of-plane branch cracking along such boundaries is also common. In some steels, hydrogen may promote cleavage fracture. Positive identification is often difficult, and it is frequently impossible to differentiate between hydrogen-induced delayed fracture and stress-corrosion-cracking fracture.

Hydrogen embrittlement is discussed in greater detail in the article that begins on page 230 in this volume.

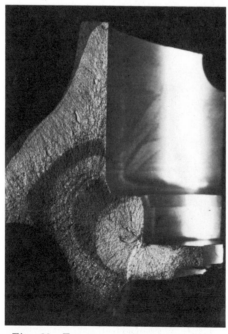

Fig. 20. Fracture surface of a high-strength aluminum alloy forging that failed from stress corrosion, showing progression marks similar to those observed in fatigue fractures (Ref 11)

Fig. 21. Fracture surface with a "rock candy" appearance caused by stress corrosion. A TEM fractograph, at 4000×, of a germanium-shadowed plastic-carbon replica of a fracture surface of an aluminum alloy specimen.

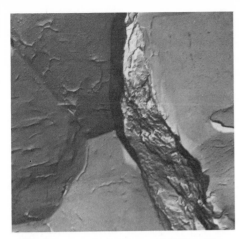

The intergranular fracture, with little evidence of plastic deformation, is typical of hydrogen-induced slow crack growth. A TEM fractograph, at 8000×, of a germanium-shadowed plastic-carbon replica.

Fig. 22. Fracture surface of a 4340 steel specimen that failed in a hydrogen environment (S. A. Ahmad)

Creep and Stress-Rupture Failures

Creep is the change in dimension of a metal or alloy under an applied stress at a temperature in excess of about 0.5 T_M, where T_M is the melting point measured on the absolute scale. Thus, lead, tin and superpure aluminum may deform by creep at room temperature or a little above, whereas temperatures near 1000 C (1832 F) may be necessary to permit creep in refractory body-centered-cubic metals such as tungsten and molybdenum and in nickel-base superalloys used in gas turbines. Clearly, creep strain may produce sufficiently large changes in the dimensions of a component to render it useless for further service before fracture occurs. In other situations, the creep strain may lead to fracture; this type of failure is called stress rupture.

Creep and stress-rupture failures generally are easy to identify; often, they can be recognized by the local ductility and multiplicity of intergranular cracks that are usually present (see Fig. 23). Stress-rupture failure often can be identified by optical examination of microsections, because there is generally a multiplicity of creep voids adjacent to the main fracture (see Fig. 24).

Creep and stress-rupture failures are best understood by considering the two general types of creep processes that occur. In the first type, grain-boundary sliding is thought to generate a stress concentration at a triple point that cannot be relieved by plastic deformation in an adjacent grain. This produces a wedge-shaped grain-boundary crack. The second type involves the initiation of voids at grain boundaries, especially those grain boundaries oriented transversely to a tensile stress, and the growth

of the voids by the migration and precipitation of vacancies. This process is called "cavitation creep". Stress-rupture fracture due to cavitation creep produces voids that are detectable by fractography, but use of fractography is seldom required for identification of stress-rupture failure. However, fractography does show that the cavities produced by the voids are not usually spherical, but have complex crystallographic shapes (Fig. 25), and that striations and terraced patterns may also be observed (Fig. 26).

Complex Failures

Occasionally, a service failure may occur by the sequential operation of two quite different fracture mechanisms. When conducting a failure analysis, this possibility should always be considered. An example of two types of fracture

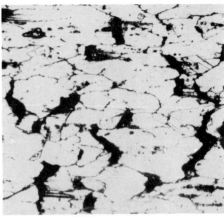

Fig. 24. Micrograph, at 300×, of structure adjacent to a stress-rupture surface in austenitic stainless steel creep tested at 618 C (1144 F). Stress axis is in a horizontal plane. (M. Harris)

Fig. 25. Creep cavities on a fracture surface of a high-purity iron specimen fractured by impact at low temperature after creep testing. A TEM fractograph, at 5000×. (D. Taplin)

Fracture surface is that of an austenitic stainless steel specimen that was tested at 750 C (1382 F) and subsequently broken at −196 C (−321 F). A TEM fractograph, at 20,000×, of a carbon-shadowed carbon replica.

Fig. 26. Striations and terracing produced previously by creep (G. Henry and J. Plateau)

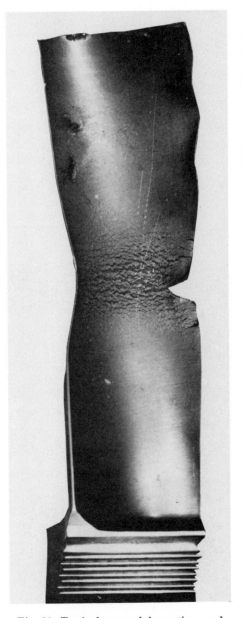

Fig. 23. Typical creep deformation, and intergranular cracking, in a jet-engine turbine blade (J. Schijve)

mechanism occurring together is shown in Fig. 27. The fractures originated on the inside surface of a diametrically drilled hole in an aluminum alloy lug at the points indicated by arrows A and B in Fig. 27.

Fractographic examination revealed that the initial cracking was by stress corrosion (A and B in Fig. 27) but that crack extension by this mechanism stopped, probably because of internal stress relief. Crack propagation continued by fatigue, as evidenced by beach marks in a band on one of the fracture surfaces (indicated by arrow C in Fig. 27), until catastrophic fracture of the remaining section occurred.

Chemical Analysis

In a failure investigation, routine analysis to ensure that the material is the one that was specified is recommended. Slight deviations from specified compositions are not likely to be of major importance in failure analysis. In fact, because only a minority of service failures result from unsuitable or defective material, rarely will the reason for failure be revealed by the results of chemical analysis. In specific investigations, particularly where corrosion and stress corrosion are involved, chemical analysis of any deposit, scale or corrosion product, or the medium with which the affected material has been in contact, is required to assist in establishing the primary cause of failure.

Where analysis shows that the content of a particular element is slightly greater than that required in the specifications, it should not be concluded that such deviation is responsible for the failure. Often, it is doubtful whether such a deviation has played even a contributory part toward failure. For example, sulfur and phosphorus contents in structural steels are limited to 0.04% in many specifications, but rarely can a failure in service be attributed to a sulfur content slightly in excess of 0.04%. Within limits, the distribution of the microstructural constituents in a material is of more importance than their exact proportions. A chemical analysis (excepting a spectrographic analysis restricted to a limited region of the surface) is usually made on drillings representing a considerable volume of material and therefore providing no indication of possible local deviation due to segregation and similar effects.

Also, certain gaseous elements, or interstitials, that normally are not reported in a chemical analysis have profound effects on the mechanical properties of some metals. In steel, for example, the effects of oxygen, nitrogen and hydrogen are of major importance. Oxygen and nitrogen may give rise to strain aging and

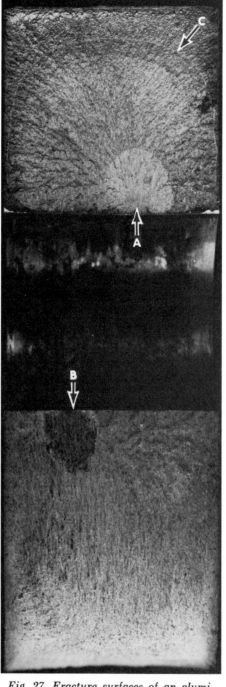

Fig. 27. Fracture surfaces of an aluminum alloy lug. Fractures originated by stress-corrosion cracking on the surface of a diametrical hole, at A and B. The crack propagated by fatigue, as evidenced by the presence of beach marks, at C.

quench aging. Hydrogen may induce brittleness, particularly when absorbed during welding, cathodic cleaning, electroplating, or pickling. Hydrogen is also responsible for the characteristic "halos" or "fisheyes" on the fracture surfaces of welds in steels, in which instance the presence of hydrogen often is due to the use of damp electrodes. These halos are indications of local rupture that has taken place under the bursting stresses induced by the molecular hydrogen,

which diffuses through the metal in the atomic state and collects under pressure in pores and other discontinuities. Various effects due to gas absorption are found in other metals and alloys.

Analysis of Bulk Materials. Various analytical techniques can be used to determine elemental concentrations, and to identify compounds, in alloys, bulky deposits, and samples of environmental fluids, lubricants and suspensions.

Semiquantitative emission spectrography, spectrophotometry and atomic-absorption spectroscopy can be used to determine dissolved metals (as in analysis of an alloy), with wet chemical methods used where greater accuracy is needed in determining the concentration of metals present in substantial concentrations. Combustion methods ordinarily are used for determining the concentration of carbon, sulfur, nitrogen, hydrogen and oxygen.

Wet chemical analysis methods are employed for determining the presence and concentration of anions such as Cl^-, NO_3^- and S^{--}. These methods are very sensitive.

X-ray diffraction identifies crystalline compounds either on the metal surface or as a mass of particles, and can be used to analyze corrosion products and other surface deposits. Minor and trace elements that are capable of being dissolved can be determined by atomic-absorption spectroscopy of the solution.

The x-ray fluorescence spectrographic technique can be used to analyze both crystalline and amorphous solids, as well as liquids and gases.

Infrared and ultraviolet spectroscopy are used in analyzing organic materials. When the organic materials are present in a complex mixture (such as, for example, solvents, oils, greases, rubber and plastics), the mixture is first separated into its individual components by gas chromatography.

Analysis of Surfaces and Deposits. Concurrent with the many developments in the analysis and interpretation of fractures by examination of fracture-surface topographies have been the development and application of certain analytical techniques for providing information regarding the chemical composition of surface constituents.

Dispersive and nondispersive x-ray spectrometers have been used for this purpose. They are employed as accessories to scanning electron microscopes and permit simultaneous viewing and chemical analysis of a surface. If it is desirable to detect the elements in extremely thin surface layers, the Auger electron spectrometer, the Mossbauer spectrometer and the ion-scattering spectrometer are useful.

The Auger electron spectrometer can provide semiquantitative determinations of elements with atomic numbers down to three (lithium). The size of the area examined varies greatly with the test conditions; it may be from 1 to 50 microns in diameter.

Mossbauer spectrometry is primarily applicable to identifying compounds such as oxides, sulfides, nitrides and carbides on ferrous alloys. It examines a depth of 3000 angstroms or less when measuring back-scattered electrons, and a depth of as much as 0.0005 in. when measuring emitted gamma rays.

For chemical analysis of surface areas as small as one micron in diameter, the electron-microprobe analyzer is widely used. The electron-microprobe analyzer can determine the concentration of all but the low-atomic-number elements, with a limit of detection of about 0.1%. The area examined with the ion-microprobe analyzer is slightly larger (a few microns in diameter) than that examined with the electron-microprobe analyzer. The ion-microprobe analyzer has the advantage of being able to detect nearly all elements (including those of low atomic weights) in concentrations as low as 100 ppm. It is sometimes used to volatilize materials, which are then passed through a mass spectrometer.

Spectrometers and microprobe analyzers are described in greater detail on pages 51 and 52 in Volume 9 of this Handbook.

The instruments discussed above are used for direct analysis of surfaces; other techniques can be used for analyzing material that has been removed from the surface. For example, if material is removed in a replica (perhaps chemically extracted), it can be analyzed structurally by x-ray diffraction or electron diffraction. Also, depending on the quantity of material extracted, many of the routine chemical-analysis techniques may be applicable.

Spot tests are relatively simple, qualitative chemical tests that can be used to identify the metal in the failed part, the alloying elements present, deposits, corrosion products, and soil. These tests require little equipment — none of which is complicated or expensive — and can be performed quickly. Spot tests can be performed both in the laboratory and in the field; they do not require extensive training in analytical chemistry. The only requirement is that the substance to be tested be dissolvable; hydrochloric acid or even aqua regia may be used to dissolve the substance.

Spot tests for metallic elements such as chromium, nickel, cobalt, iron and molybdenum are usually carried out by dissolving a small amount of the alloy in acid and mixing a drop of the resulting solution with a drop of a specific reagent on absorbent paper or a porcelain plate. Spot colorings produced in this way indicate the presence or absence of the metallic radical under test. Samples may be removed from gross surfaces by spotting the specimen with a suitable acid, allowing time for solution and collecting the acid spot with an eyedropper.

Methods for detecting and identifying both metallic and nonmetallic elements and radicals are described in "Spot Tests, Vol I, Inorganic Applications", by Fritz Feigl, 4th Edition, Elsevier Publishing Co., 1954. ASTM STP 550, "Nondestructive Rapid Identification of Metals by Spot Test", by M. L. Wilson, gives procedures for spot testing nearly all engineering metals and alloys with a minimum of equipment.

Application of Fracture Mechanics

The mechanics of fracture in metal parts and specimens under load, and the application of fracture-mechanics concepts to the design and prediction of service life of parts and components, are often both pertinent to the investigation of failures due to fracture and to the formulation of corrective measures that will prevent similar failures. The concepts of fracture mechanics are useful in measuring fracture toughness and other toughness parameters, and in providing a quantitative framework for evaluating structural reliability.

Fracture-mechanics concepts and applications are dealt with in the article "Toughness and Fracture Mechanics", beginning on page 30. The article also provides detailed consideration of notch effects and of toughness testing and evaluation. Among the subjects dealt with in connection with notch effects are stress concentration, triaxiality, plastic constraint and local strain rate. Test methods that are considered in connection with toughness testing and evaluation are the plane-strain fracture-toughness test, the dynamic tear test, the crack-opening displacement test, and instrumented impact testing.

Simulated-Service Testing

During the concluding stages of an investigation, it may be necessary to conduct tests that attempt to simulate the conditions under which failure is believed to have occurred. Often, simulated-service testing is not practicable because elaborate equipment is required, and even when practicable, it is possible that not all of the service conditions are fully known or understood. Corrosion failures, for example, are difficult to reproduce in a laboratory, and many attempts to reproduce them have given misleading results. Serious errors can arise when attempts are made to reduce the time required for a test by artificially increasing the severity of one of the factors — such as the corrosive medium or the operating temperature.

On the other hand, when its limitations are clearly understood, the simulated testing of the effects of certain selected variables encountered in service may be helpful in planning corrective action that will avoid similar failure or, at least, extend service life. The evaluation of the efficacy of special additives to lubricants to counteract wear is an example of the successful application of simulated-service testing employing a selected number of service variables. The aircraft industry has made successful use of devices, such as the wind tunnel, to simulate some of the conditions encountered in flight, and naval architects have employed tank tests to evaluate hull modifications, power requirements, steerage and other variables that might forestall component failure or promote safety at sea.

Taken singly, most of the metallurgical phenomena involved in failures can be satisfactorily reproduced on a laboratory scale, and the information derived from such experiments can be helpful to the investigator, provided the limitations of the tests are fully recognized.

Analyzing the Evidence, Formulating Conclusions, and Writing the Report

At a certain stage in every investigation, the evidence revealed by examinations and tests that are outlined in this article is analyzed and collated, and preliminary conclusions are formulated. Obviously, many investigations will not involve a series of clear-cut stages. If the probable cause of failure is apparent early in the examination, the pattern and extent of subsequent investigation will be directed toward confirmation of the probable cause and the elimination of other possibilities. Other investigations will follow a logical series of stages, as outlined in this article, and the findings at each stage will determine the manner in which the investigation proceeds. As new facts modify first impressions, different hypotheses of failure will develop and will be retained or abandoned as dictated by the findings. Where extensive laboratory facilities are available to the investigator, maximum effort will be devoted to amassing the results of mechanical tests, chemical analysis, fractography and microscopy before the formulation of preliminary conclusions is attempted. Finally, in those investigations in which the cause of failure is particularly elusive, a search through published reports of similar instances may be required to suggest possible clues.

Some of the work performed during the course of an investigation may be thought to be unnecessary. It is important, however, to distinguish between work that is unnecessary and that which does not bear fruitful results. During an examination, it is to be expected that some of the work done will not assist directly in determining the cause of failure; nevertheless, some "negative" evidence may be helpful in dismissing some causes of failure from consideration.

On the other hand, any tendency to curtail work essential to an investigation should be guarded against. In some instances, it is possible to form an opinion regarding the cause of failure from a single aspect of the investigation, such as visual examination of a fracture surface or examination of a single metallographic specimen. However, before final conclusions are reached, supplementary data confirming the original opinion, if available, should be sought. Total dependence on the conclusions that can be drawn from a single specimen, such as a metallographic section, may be readily challenged unless a history of similar failures can be drawn upon.

The following check list, which is in the form of a series of questions, has been proposed as an aid in analyzing the evidence derived from examinations and tests and in formulating conclusions (Ref 13). The questions are also helpful in calling attention to details of the over-all investigation that may have been overlooked.

Has failure sequence been established?

If failure involved cracking or fracture, have the initiation sites been determined?

Did cracks initiate at the surface or below the surface?

Was cracking associated with a stress concentrator?

How long was the crack present?

What was the intensity of the load?

What was the type of loading: static, cyclic or intermittent?

How were the stresses oriented?

What was the failure mechanism?

What was the approximate service temperature at the time of failure?

Did temperature contribute to failure?

Did wear contribute to failure?

Did corrosion contribute to failure? What type of corrosion?

Was the proper material used? Is a better material required?

Was the cross section adequate for class of service?

Was the quality of the material acceptable in accordance with specification?

Were the mechanical properties of the material acceptable in accordance with specification?

Was the component that failed properly heat treated?

Was the component that failed properly fabricated?

Was the component properly assembled or installed?

Was the component repaired during service and, if so, was the repair correctly performed?

Was the component properly run in?

Was the component properly maintained? Properly lubricated?

Was failure related to abuse in service?

Can the design of the component be improved to prevent similar failures?

Are failures likely to occur in similar components now in service, and what can be done to prevent their failure?

In general, the answers to these questions will be derived from a combination of records and the examinations and tests previously outlined in this article. However, the cause or causes of failure cannot always be determined with certainty. In this instance, the investigation should determine the most probable cause or causes of failure, distinguishing findings based on demonstrated fact from conclusions based on conjecture.

Writing the Report. The failure-analysis report should be written clearly, concisely and logically. One experienced investigator has proposed that the report be divided into the following principal sections:

1 Description of the failed component
2 Service conditions at time of failure
3 Prior service history
4 Manufacturing and processing history of component
5 Mechanical and metallurgical study of failure
6 Metallurgical evaluation of quality
7 Summary of mechanisms that caused failure
8 Recommendations for prevention of similar failures or for correction of similar components in service.

Obviously, not every report will require coverage under every one of these sections. Lengthy reports should begin with an abstract. Because readers of failure-analysis reports are often purchasing, operating and accounting personnel, the avoidance of technical jargon wherever possible is highly desirable. A glossary of terms may also be helpful. The use of appendixes, containing detailed calculations, equations and tables of chemical and metallurgical data, can serve to keep the body of the report clear and uncluttered.

References

1. F. R. Hutchings, "The Laboratory Examination of Service Failures", Technical Report, Vol III, British Engine, Boiler and Electrical Insurance Co., Ltd., London, May 1957
2. Ministry of Transport and Civil Aviation Report of Court of Enquiry into the Accidents to Comet Aircraft, HMSO, London, 1955
3. G. Henry and J. Plateau, "La Microfractographie", Éditions Métaux, Institute de Récherche de la Siderurgie Française (English translation), 1967
4. A. Phillips, V. Kerlins and B. V. Whiteson, Electron-fractography Handbook, USAAF Technical Report, ML-TDR-64-416, Air Force Material Laboratory, Wright Patterson Air Force Base, Ohio, 1965
5. D. A. Ryder, "The Elements of Fractography", AGARD-AG-155-71, AGARD/NATO, Neuilly-Sur-Seine, 1971
6. C. Zapffe and M. Clogg, Fractography — A New Tool for Metallurgical Research, Trans Am Soc Metals, Vol 34, 1945, p 71
7. H. de Leiris, "L'analyse Morphologique de Cassures", Cours à l'École de Genie Maritime, Paris, 1956
8. J. Plateau, G. Henry and C. Crussard, Métaux, Vol 33, 1958, p 141
9. M. Martin, D. Ryder and T. Davies, A Tilt Calibration for Stereomicroscopy (submitted for publication in Metallography, Vol 8, 1975)
10. D. A. Ryder and A. Smale, Fracture of Solids, Interscience, New York, 1963
11. P. J. Forsyth and D. A. Ryder, Metallurgia, Vol 63, 1961, p 117
12. R. Staehle, "Fundamental Aspects of Stress Corrosion Cracking", Ohio State University, 1967
13. G. F. Vander Voort, Conducting the Failure Examination, Met Eng Quart, May 1975

APPENDIX

A Portable Metallographic Laboratory Suited for On-Site Failure Analysis

By Hugh Crowder*

The portable laboratory described here has been used over a period of several years for on-site metallographic examination in investigating service failures. It can be readily transported almost anywhere in the world.

All the components of the portable laboratory fit into two standard pieces of luggage, each measuring about 28 by 20 by 8 in. (over-all) and each weighing about 40 lb when loaded with the equipment. Intended primarily for use in remote locations, the equipment operates either on direct current or on 50- or 60-Hz, 110-volt alternating current and requires in addition only a bucket of water and a reasonably clean place in which to work.

Capabilities of the unit include grinding, mechanical polishing, etching, and examination and photographing of macrostructure and microstructure and other features on selected areas of large parts or assemblies. In addition, small specimens can be cut from a part on the site for preparation, examination and photography at once or after return to a fully equipped laboratory. Either unmounted or mounted specimens can be used.

Equipment and Operation

The major components of the portable laboratory include the following:

1 A custom-made machine, plus auxiliary materials, for grinding and polishing small mounted or unmounted metal specimens
2 A right-angle-head electric-drill motor with attachments and materials for grinding and polishing selected spots on large parts or assemblies without the need for removing a specimen. The drill motor also is used for driving the

*Research Metallurgist, Production Research Div., Continental Oil Co.

grinding and polishing machine described in item 1.

3 A microscope, with Polaroid camera attachment and Polaroid film for use in photographing parts or metallographic specimens

4 Equipment and materials for mounting and etching specimens

5 A hand Polaroid camera, with close-up lenses and film

6 A pocket-size magnifier

7 A hacksaw and blades for cutting specimens.

Grinding and Polishing Machine. Figure 28 shows the machine used for grinding and polishing small metal specimens. The machine has four interchangeable wheels to enable the use of separate wheels for grinding with silicon carbide and for polishing with diamond abrasive, aluminum oxide, and magnesium oxide. The wheels are 8 in. in diameter so that standard abrasive disks and polishing cloths can be used. The splash guard is easily removable for convenience in cleaning and changing wheels.

The machine is belt-driven by an electric-drill motor arranged for a 9-to-1 speed reduction. The motor is one used in a 1/4-in. portable drill rated at 2000 rpm and 2 amp. Power for the machine as first built was supplied by a quarter-horsepower electric motor, and if such a motor is available at the work site, it can be used in place of the drill motor.

When driven with the drill motor, the machine does not have the full capacity of a regular laboratory polisher, but it can process a 1½-in.-diam specimen through four grades of silicon carbide paper and the usual polishing steps in about 20 min.

Where 110-volt power is not available but an alternator-equipped automotive vehicle can reach the site, the electric-drill motor can be driven by connecting it to the alternator on the vehicle through a commercially available converter to provide 110-volt direct-current power (see Ref 1). Converters of this type weigh about 1 lb and measure 2 by 3 by 4 in. With a heavy-duty extension cord, the drill motor can be operated at 100 ft or more from the alternator-equipped vehicle.

Spot-Polishing Equipment. The electric-drill motor that drives the grinding and polishing machine is also used to grind and polish selected areas on large parts or assemblies without removing specimens. Figure 29 shows the equipment and materials included for this work. Small, adhesive-backed abrasive disks and polishing cloths — all of which are commercially available — are applied to the rubber polishing wheels. Occasionally, the adhesive on these disks is not satisfactory, but ordinary rubber cement applied to both surfaces and allowed to dry for a few minutes before assembly will provide an adequate bond.

Fig. 28. Portable shop-built metallographic grinding and polishing machine, belt-driven by an electric-drill motor having a right-angle head

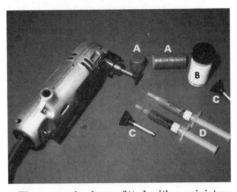

The motor is shown fitted with a miniature wheel for grinding or polishing small areas of parts or assemblies. Also shown are packages of abrasive disks (A), aluminum oxide suspension (B), extra grinding and polishing wheels (C), and diamond polishing paste (D).

Fig. 29. Electric-drill motor used for driving the grinding and polishing machine in Fig. 1

Fig. 30. Portable microscope – camera unit mounted on tubular feet, arranged for examining and photographing a polished spot on the surface of 8⅝-in.-OD line pipe, on which the unit is resting

A surface about 1 in. in diameter usually can be ground and polished to a condition suitable for metallographic examination in 30 to 40 min.

Microscope – Camera Unit. The microscope is a compact, lightweight, depth-measuring type suitable for both visual and photographic work; it has the standard through-the-lens lighting arrangement used on all metallurgical microscopes to permit reflected-light microscopy. The microscope is mounted on tubular feet, and thus can be used on large parts that are flat as well as on small parts and conventional metallographic specimens. Visual examination of polished specimens can be made at magnifications up to 1500 diameters. For additional details about the microscope, see Ref 1 and 2.

Using the camera attachment, photographs can be taken at magnifications of 30 to 1000 diameters. Polaroid film is ordinarily used, but the camera has been modified to permit the use of conventional film and plates if desired. Figure 30 shows the microscope – camera unit in position for examining and photographing a polished spot on a length of 8⅝-in.-OD line pipe.

In studying large objects, it is often helpful to clamp the microscope assembly in place. A web belt provides the necessary clamping action on most parts; it may be necessary to fasten two or more belts together to hold the microscope securely on extremely large parts. Web belts can be drawn up tightly, but have enough elasticity to permit small movements needed to change the field of view.

Two modifications that would add to the usefulness of the microscope are: (a) attachment of leveling support screws at three points on the base, to increase the versatility of the unit for use on surfaces that are irregular in contour; and (b) addition of an adjustable mechanical stage, to make handling of small specimens more convenient.

Mounting and etching equipment and materials in the kit are simple and versatile. For specimens that must be mounted, a cold-mounting technique is used, and for this purpose the kit contains six 1½-in.-diam reusable rubber casting molds and an adjustable rectangular metal mold. The liquid component for the cold-mounting mixture was repackaged for the kit in small metal cans having screw-type lids that provided a tight seal.

Six etchants that have been found to be satisfactory for etching the most frequently encountered metals are included in the kit. These etchants are listed with their compositions and usual applications in Table 1.

When it is known that metals for which the six standard etchants are not suitable will be encountered, other etchants that

Table 1. Standard Etchants Included in the Portable Metallographic Kit, and Their Usual Applications(a)

Etchant	Composition	Usual application
Nital, 3%	3 ml conc HNO_3, 100 ml ethanol (95%)	Carbon and low-alloy steels
Vilella's reagent . . .	5 ml conc HCl, 1 g picric acid, 100 ml ethanol (95%)	Some alloy steels resistant to nital; also to show grain boundaries in quenched-and-tempered steel
Carapella's etch . . .	5 g $FeCl_3$, 2 ml conc HCl, 100 ml ethanol (95%)	Some alloy steels and copper alloys
Marble's reagent . . .	10 g $CuSO_4$, 50 ml conc HCl, 50 ml H_2O	Chromium-nickel alloys
Oxalic acid(b)	Oxalic acid (to saturation), 100 ml H_2O	Austenitic stainless steels
Keller's reagent . . .	2 ml conc HF, 3 ml conc HCl, 5 ml conc HNO_3, 190 ml H_2O	Aluminum alloys

(a) See Volume 8 of this Handbook for selection of etchants for specific purposes. (b) For electrolytic etching. Use two or three 1½-volt dry-cell batteries in series.

will meet the special requirements are substituted or added. (See Volume 8 of this Handbook or other standard references on selection of etchants.)

The etchants are packaged in tightly capped 4-oz or 8-oz plastic bottles, and each bottle is enclosed in a heat-sealed plastic bag for additional protection against leakage in transit. Small plastic refrigerator dishes are used as etchant containers; their tight lids prevent evaporation between etching operations.

The hand Polaroid camera equipped with close-up lenses is a useful adjunct to the microscope – camera unit previously described. It permits photographing of the failure region, of adjacent areas on the failed part, and of entire large parts at any desired orientation, using magnifications of about ⅔ diameter or less. Such photographs can be used to show the location and orientation of the failure with respect to adjacent areas of the failed part and to related components.

To provide a complete record, photographs for later study can be taken before, during and after disassembly, as well as before, during and after removal of specimens. A photographic record of this type is of substantial value as part of a complete failure analysis.

The pocket-size magnifier is extremely useful in examining areas that cannot be viewed satisfactorily using the microscope – camera unit or the hand Polaroid camera.

Hacksaw. A hacksaw and an ample supply of blades are included for cutting specimens to be examined on the site or returned to the laboratory for study.

Having only the hacksaw for cutting specimens sometimes presents special difficulties at a remote site. To obtain suitable specimens, it sometimes may be necessary to obtain oxyacetylene cutting equipment, make use of mobile repair equipment or use the facilities of local machine shops.

Packaging. The arrangement of the major items of equipment that comprise the portable metallographic laboratory is shown in Fig. 31.

In the suitcase at left in Fig. 31 are the components of the grinding and polishing machine, including the splash guard, basic frame, electric-drill motor, and three grinding and polishing wheels. There is still room in this suitcase for the fourth 8-in. grinding and polishing wheel, small wheels for spot grinding and polishing, abrasive paper, polishing cloths, etchants, etching dishes, hacksaw and blades, and other small items.

In the suitcase at right in Fig. 31 are the microscope, microscope-light power supply, microscope camera, hand Polaroid camera with close-up lenses, camera accessories, film for both cameras, and a flashlight. Space is also available in this suitcase for the ac/dc power converter, the pocket-size magnifier, and other small items.

The various pieces of equipment are protected from damage in transit by wrapping them in foam rubber and enclosing some of the wrapped items in cardboard boxes, which are further protected by placing additional foam rubber packing around them where needed.

Modification and Improvement. The components and arrangement of the portable laboratory shown in Fig. 28 to 31 and described in this Appendix represent the equipment as it was generally used (see Ref 1). To meet the differing needs of specific failure-analysis investigations, suitable substitutions and additions of equipment and material have been made on numerous occasions. Improving details of equipment design, and the phasing-in, as they became available, of new equipment and materials with

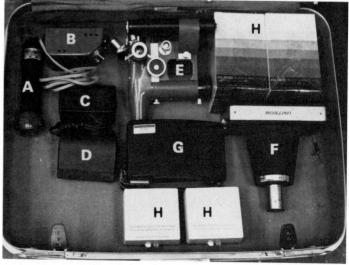

At left, equipment and materials for grinding and polishing: A, splash guard; B, basic frame for grinding and polishing machine; C, electric-drill motor; and D, 8-in.-diam grinding and polishing wheels. At right, equipment and materials for examination and photography: A, flashlight; B, power supply for microscope light; C, flash charger; D, flash attachment; E, microscope; F, microscope camera; G, hand Polaroid camera; and H, film.

Fig. 31. Arrangement of major components of portable metallographic laboratory in two standard pieces of luggage, each weighing about 40 lb fully loaded and measuring about 28 by 20 by 8 in. over-all

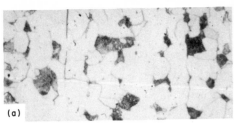 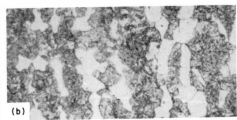 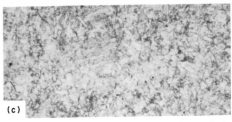

(a) Normal structure of pearlite and ferrite at about 3 ft from the rupture. (b) Mixture of ferrite and martensite at about 3 in. from the rupture, where the tube had begun to bulge. (c) Completely martensitic structure at the edge of the rupture.

Fig. 32. Microstructure of transverse sections at various distances from the point of failure of a carbon steel boiler tube that ruptured because of severe local overheating. The sections, etched in 3% nital and shown at 400×, were prepared, examined and photographed using the portable metallographic laboratory.

additional capabilities, were adopted as a continuing program. Other types of microscopes, cameras, film, accessories and additional small tools offer certain special advantages and may be preferred by other investigators for on-site failure analysis.

Application of the Portable Laboratory to Failure Analysis

The portable equipment is not intended to be a substitute for a fully equipped metallographic laboratory, but rather for use in on-site investigations and for examination (either in a conventional laboratory or in the field) of large parts and assemblies without disassembly.

It is of special value where cutting of specimens is not practicable or might entail the possibly unnecessary and costly repair or replacement of equipment (see "Electrolytic Etching of a Large Pump" in this Appendix).

Start-Up Problems at Overseas Refinery. The portable laboratory was of special value in helping to solve a number of problems encountered in start-up of an overseas refinery. One of these problems was the rupture of a carbon steel boiler tube. A major factor in analyzing the failure was determination of microstructure by examining transverse sections cut with a hacksaw from the failed tube at various locations with respect to the failure region, using the portable grinding and polishing machine (Fig. 28) and the portable microscope – camera unit (Fig. 30). Micrographs of three of the sections are presented in Fig. 32.

Figure 32(a) shows a normal structure of pearlite and ferrite at about 3 ft from the rupture; this micrograph provided evidence that the tube material was satisfactory.

The mixture of ferrite and martensite evident in Fig. 32(b), at about 3 in. from the rupture, showed that the metal in this area (where the tube had begun to bulge) had reached, and cooled from, a temperature between the lower and upper transformation temperatures.

Figure 32(c), taken at the edge of the rupture, revealed a completely martensitic structure, establishing that the tube

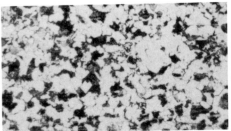 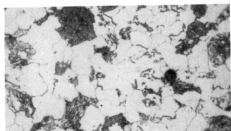

Fig. 33. Microstructure of spot-polished and etched (3% nital) surface of a longitudinal resistance weld in carbon steel line pipe. Micrographs, at 400× (left) and 1000× (right), were made using the portable metallographic laboratory.

had been severely overheated at this point and had reached a temperature substantially above the upper limit (about 870 C, or 1600 F) of the transformation range prior to cooling. At such a temperature, the tensile strength of the steel would be expected to decrease to such a degree that failure would occur by rupture at normal operating pressure (600 psi) in a few minutes.

Another problem for which the portable equipment was used during the same refinery start-up was the failure by cracking of a large austenitic stainless steel fan, which was exposed to chlorides and moisture in operation.

At first it was suspected that the fan had been improperly heat treated, causing precipitation of carbides at the grain boundaries and thus permitting intergranular corrosion to develop. However, metallographic studies using the portable equipment showed no evidence of improper heat treatment and established that the failure had been caused by stress-corrosion cracking.

Examination of Welds in Line Pipe. The usefulness of the portable equipment for local spot polishing and etching for metallographic studies on oil and gas line pipe on the site or in the laboratory is demonstrated by the quality of the micrographs (at 400 and 1000 diameters) in Fig. 33. These micrographs of the surface of a longitudinal resistance weld on 8⅝-in.-OD, 0.219-in.-wall API X-52 carbon steel line pipe, taken using the portable laboratory, show a relatively fine-grained structure of pearlite and ferrite, which would be expected for a resistance weld in this carbon steel after properly

done induction normalizing at the mill. If the weld had not been normalized, it would have a coarse structure and a hardness excessive for this application.

Extensive on-site studies of field welds in line pipe have been made in locations remote from conventional laboratories, with the portable laboratory being set up in any available facility, such as a janitor's storage room or a nearby machine shop.

Electrolytic Etching of a Large Pump. Electrolytic etching in a saturated solution of oxalic acid (see Table 1), after mechanical spot polishing, was used in the examination of cracked areas in the type 316 stainless steel housing of a large pump that had been dismantled for repairs.

An improvised arrangement was used to carry out the electrolytic etching. The electrolyte was retained within a dam constructed of paper-base masking tape. Power at an applied potential of 3 volts was provided from two D-size dry-cell batteries in series. The pump body served as the anode, and a stainless steel wire immersed in the electrolyte was used as the cathode.

The examination established that crack penetration was shallow and that the cracked areas could be ground out and repaired to make the housing serviceable again.

References Cited in This Appendix

1. Hugh Crowder, A Portable Laboratory for Field Metallography, *Metal Progress*, Apr 1974, p 76 and 79
2. Inspection Microscope Tackles Variety of Problem Assignments, *Metal Progress*, Aug 1972, p 69

Toughness and Fracture Mechanics

By the ASM Committee on Analysis of Ductile and Brittle Fractures*

TOUGHNESS is the capacity of a material to absorb energy by deforming plastically before fracture. Toughness is determined by the combined strength and ductility of a material and usually is measured by the amount of work absorbed during the propagation of a crack through a structural member or a standard specimen. The consideration of toughness during design of a part will permit selection of materials with low probability of failure by fracture, and its consideration during failure analysis often is necessary to establish the conditions that led to fracture.

One measure of toughness is the area under a standard tension stress-strain curve taken to fracture, but toughness is more commonly measured under high-strain-rate loading conditions, such as in an impact test. Although smooth specimens can be used to measure toughness, notched or precracked specimens are ordinarily used, because the more generally accepted meaning of toughness is resistance to rapid crack propagation, or the absence of brittleness.

Notch Toughness

Notch toughness is usually evaluated by testing prescribed notched-bar specimens at known temperatures in a single-blow pendulum-type impact machine. Results are reported in foot-pounds of impact energy absorbed by the test specimen. Both the Charpy and Izod methods of notched-bar impact testing make use of a swinging pendulum.

The Charpy and Izod impact tests are refinements of test methods developed early in the 20th century. These sufficed until World War II, when attention was focused on the problem of notch toughness because of the brittle failure of plates in some 250 welded transport ships, 19 of which broke in two. Inasmuch as these failures seriously jeopardized the Allied war effort, several extensive and costly investigations were initiated under

direction of the National Bureau of Standards and the Naval Research Laboratory in Washington, D. C.

In the course of these and other parallel investigations, several new test methods were developed for the evaluation of notch toughness. The most prominent of these were the drop-weight test, the explosion-bulge test, the Navy (or Kahn) tear test and various slow-bend tests, including the Lehigh bend test. A brief description of the various tests and illustrations of the specimens are included in Appendix 1 at the end of this article (see page 37). Techniques of notched-bar impact testing are discussed in detail in ASTM E23.

Although many widely different tests were used by the various laboratories investigating the ship-failure problem, an over-all review of test data clearly indicated that the transition temperature of the Charpy V-notch impact test correlated well with the temperature at which the failures occurred. All the examined plates in which fracture originated had a low Charpy V-notch energy value (less than 11 ft-lb) at the temperature at which the ship failures occurred. Because of this correlation and some subsequent correlations, the Charpy V-notch impact test is generally considered the preferred method for measuring the notch toughness of steel. As a result, industry has moved toward standardizing on the Charpy V-notch impact test as an indicator of notch toughness in materials specifications. Requirements may call for a minimum impact strength at a given temperature or a maximum temperature at which the fractured specimens shall exhibit 50% shear fracture. The latter is the more conservative requirement.

Reproducibility of Test Results. The Watertown Arsenal Laboratory conducted a closely controlled experiment that established the fact that the Charpy V-notch impact test is reliable and reproducible. A single heat of aircraft-quality 4340 steel was used to provide

18,000 blanks that were divided into three groups and heat treated to three different levels of hardness: Rockwell C 44.5, 34.5 and 27.5. Two hundred specimens at each hardness level were impact tested in each of two Charpy machines manufactured by two companies; the average impact-energy values and distribution of results are shown in Fig. 1. Of the 400 specimens of low hardness level that were tested, energy values for 364 specimens fell within ±1 ft-lb of the average value.

The test program just described clearly demonstrated the narrow spread of results that can be obtained under carefully controlled testing conditions. However, the experience of other laboratories indicates that even when the preparation and testing of impact specimens are closely controlled, minor variations often will increase the spread of test results. When the effects of these variables are added to the inherent scatter that occurs among different heats of steel, the distribution of test results is broadened appreciably. Thus, judging notch toughness on the basis of one or two tests for a specific set of conditions is unwise without voluminous data on prior production heats of the material.

Some specifications designate the number of specimens to be tested at a particular temperature or over a range of temperatures. In other instances, the number of specimens with minimum or average values, or both, is negotiated. The accuracy and usefulness of results vary directly with the number of specimens tested.

The scatter of results found in testing large numbers of specimens from 75 production heats of 1026 steel is shown in Fig. 2. These test results represent an extensive investigation made in one plant to evaluate the effects of several variables. The primary variable was section size; other factors included normal variations in composition and grain size that would be expected among 75 heats of the

*George E. Pellissier, *Chairman*, Manager, RRC International, Inc.; Robert T. Ault, Chief, Bar, Plate and Tubular Products Section, Research Center, Republic Steel Corp.; J. Chandler, Research Officer, National Research Council of Canada; C. Feng, Research Metallurgist, Metals and Polymers Branch, Picatinny Arsenal.

Frederick J. Fraikor, Consultant; William G. Fricke, Jr., Group Leader, Alcoa Technical Center; M. W. Hagadorn, Senior Engineer, Metallurgy and Metals Processing Dept., Westinghouse Electric Corp.; Robert L. Huddleston, Chief, Materials Evaluation Unit, Physical Test Section, Materiel Testing Directorate, U. S. Army Aberdeen Proving

Ground; Joseph A. Kies, U. S. Naval Research Laboratory; Oles Lomacky, Naval Ship Research and Development Center, Department of the Navy; James Maker, Chief Metallurgist, Wallace Barnes Div., Associated Spring Corp.; Gunvant N. Maniar, Manager, Physical Metallurgy, Research and Development, Carpenter Technology Corp.

M. L. Picklesimer, Division of Reactor Safety Research, U. S. Atomic Energy Commission; Dennis D. Rogers, Staff Materials Engineer, Saginaw Steering Gear Div., General Motors Corp.; T. R. Shives, Metallurgical Div., National Bureau of Standards; George Vander Voort, Homer Research Laboratory, Bethlehem Steel Corp.

same grade of steel, in addition to variations in the forged and heat treated product resulting from different equipment and operating personnel.

Three bars were selected at random from each of 75 heats of the 1026 steel and step forged to the three diameters shown in Fig. 2. The forgings were then cut so that each of the section sizes could be heat treated for the optimum length of time. All sections were normalized at 900 C (1650 F), but in different charges and equipment. All were tempered at 620 C (1150 F) in the same laboratory furnace. Test specimens were machined from half-radius locations from each section size and tested in the same impact machine after cooling to −45 C (−50 F) in acetone and dry ice.

Analysis of the results of these 2025 tests discloses that 99.4% had energy values of 15 ft-lb or higher. Eight specimens (0.4%) showed values below 15 ft-lb, and four (0.2%) were below 10 ft-lb. All specimens that had energy values of less than 15 ft-lb were from the larger sections.

Factors Affecting Notch Toughness. Notch toughness is influenced by the chemical composition and physical properties of the material. Alloying elements, gas content and impurities are the chemical factors affecting this property. The physical factors include hardness, microstructure, homogeneity, grain size, section size, rolling direction, hot and cold working temperatures, and method of fabrication. Surface conditions, such as carburization or decarburization, are also important. These factors are discussed extensively for steel on pages 227 to 234 in Volume 1 of this Handbook.

Use of Notch Toughness. Few service parts are subjected to the drastic shock conditions inherent in notched-bar impact testing. In addition, as stated above, section size also affects notch-toughness values. For these reasons, notch-toughness-test results cannot always be correlated with service experience and cannot be used directly in engineering-design calculations. The values become significant for design only when correlated with a particular type of structure in a particular kind of service. For example, many machinery components made of steel operate successfully in extreme cold without special consideration for notch-toughness values or the temperatures at which ductile-to-brittle fracture transition occurs. Steels with higher transition temperatures can be tolerated when maximum shear stress approaches maximum principal tensile stress, as in torsion or in the simple tension test under conditions of moderate strain and temperature. Where stress concentration and rate of strain are high and service temperatures are low, steels having low transition temperatures must be selected.

The correlation of notch-toughness-test results with service experience is discussed further on pages 235 to 238 in Volume 1 of this Handbook.

Fracture Toughness

The investigations of brittle fracture of World War II ship plates mentioned earlier in this article led to new methods for evaluation of notch toughness. The toughness parameters measured by these tests, however, have the same limitations as the older notched-bar impact tests in that the parameters are not material constants. Instead, they are affected by the size and shape of the specimen and its notch. Thus, a new parameter was needed — one that *was* a material constant. Through application of the concepts of fracture mechanics, a parameter called fracture toughness was developed.

Fracture-mechanics concepts provide a quantitative framework for evaluating structural reliability in terms of applied stress, crack length, and stress intensity at the crack tip. The linear-elastic fracture-mechanics approach to fracture analysis includes three major assumptions:

1 Cracks and similar flaws are inherently present in parts or specimens.
2 A crack is a flat, internal free surface in a linear elastic-stress field — a purely elastic stress field in an isotropic continuum (featureless solid).
3 The quantity of stored energy released from a cracking specimen or part during rapid crack propagation is a basic material property, independent of specimen or part size.

Many failure analyses have confirmed the validity of the first assumption. Cracks are often present in sizes below the limit of sensitivity of nondestructive-inspection tests. For example, a 260-in.-diam solid-propellant rocket-motor case fractured prematurely during hydrostatic testing because of a cracklike flaw (about 1.6 in. long) that was located within a practice weld and was undetected by x-ray inspection of the weld because the flaw was too shallow (see Fig. 3). The fracture toughness of the weld metal was inadequate to tolerate a flaw of this size.

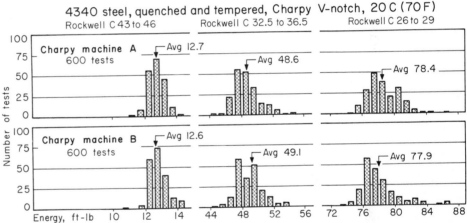

Fig. 1. Correlation of test results from two Charpy impact machines manufactured by two companies. All 1200 specimens were from a single heat of aircraft-quality 4340 steel. The specimens were heat treated to three hardness levels, and 200 specimens at each of the three hardness levels were tested on each of the two impact machines. (Ref 1)

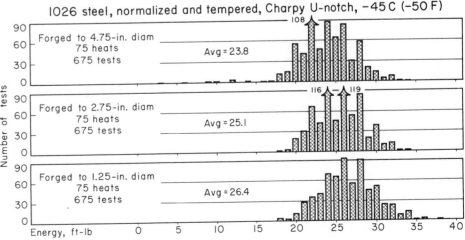

Fig. 2. Distribution of test results for different section sizes (different forging reductions) from 75 heats of 1026 steel. After air cooling from 900 C (1650 F) in different charges, all forged sections were tempered at 620 C (1150 F) in the same laboratory furnace.

Fig. 3. Fracture surface, at about 1¼×, of a 260-in.-diam solid-propellant rocket-motor case that fractured prematurely during hydrostatic testing. Fracture originated at a cracklike flaw (between arrows) that was produced by practice repair welding using the submerged-arc process. Ends of the bright flaw are dark because of their unfavorable angle to the light. Note the chevron patterns pointing toward the fracture origin from both sides. (Ref 2)

The second assumption is introduced to allow mathematical description of the stresses in the vicinity of the crack tip. The assumption of a linear elastic-stress field at first appears contradictory to what is known about fracture of metals. However, when the linear elastic-stress-field region is large compared with the size of the plastic zone at the crack tip, which often is the situation with large structures and with high-strength materials, this is a good assumption. Using linear-elastic theory, the stresses at a point, P, near the crack tip (Fig. 4) can be expressed as:

$$\sigma_y = \frac{K}{\sqrt{2\pi r}} \cos\frac{\theta}{2}\left(1 + \sin\frac{\theta}{2}\sin\frac{3\theta}{2}\right) \quad \text{(Eq 1)}$$

and as:

$$\sigma_x = \frac{K}{\sqrt{2\pi r}} \cos\frac{\theta}{2}\left(1 - \sin\frac{\theta}{2}\sin\frac{3\theta}{2}\right) \quad \text{(Eq 2)}$$

where σ_y is the stress perpendicular to the crack plane, σ_x is the stress perpendicular to the crack tip and in the plane of the crack, r is the distance from the crack tip to point P, θ is the angle between the crack plane and a line from point P to the crack tip, and K is a constant. The important points here are: (*a*) a crack in a loaded part or specimen generates its own stress field, a stress field that differs from another crack-tip stress field only by a scaling factor represented by K; and (*b*) the factor K expresses how much the stress intensifies at the crack tip, and thereby enables the external-loading and geometric factors that influence fracture in a specimen or a part to be described on a uniform basis.

Stress-Intensity Factors. The third assumption states that rapid crack propagation is controlled solely by a material constant. This constant, which is called the critical stress-intensity factor, K_c, is that value of the stress-intensity factor, K, at which crack propagation becomes rapid. The greater the value of K_c, the greater the stress required to produce rapid propagation and the greater the resistance of the material to brittle fracture. The critical stress-intensity factor is determined with relatively simple laboratory specimens, which are described in Appendix 2, which begins on page 40.

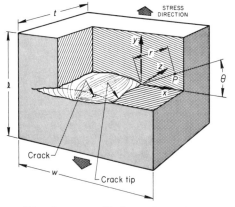

x = Direction perpendicular to the crack tip and in the plane of the crack
y = Direction perpendicular to the plane of the crack
z = Direction parallel to the crack tip
P = A point near the crack tip
r = Distance from the crack tip to point P
θ = Angle between the plane of the crack and a line from point P to the crack tip

Fig. 4. Schematic illustration of a through-thickness crack

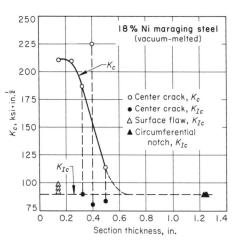

Data were obtained with three types of specimens: center-cracked (pop-in) rectangular, surface-flawed rectangular, and circumferentially notched cylindrical specimens. At thicknesses greater than about 0.6 in., the stress-intensity factor, K_c, drops to the critical plane-strain stress-intensity factor, K_{Ic}.

Fig. 5. Effect of section thickness of fracture-toughness specimens of vacuum-melted 18% Ni maraging steel (300-ksi min yield strength) on measured values of critical stress-intensity factor, K_{Ic}
(Redrawn from Ref 3)

The relation between applied stress and crack size for the laboratory specimens is known from a suitable stress analysis. Component fracture can be predicted in terms of applied stress and probable flaw size by application of Eq 1 and 2 to real structures. The critical stress-intensity factor, which also is called the plane-stress fracture toughness and is expressed in units of MPa·m^½ or psi·in.^½, is directly related to the energy required for rapid crack propagation by the formula:

$$K_c^2 = EG_c \quad \text{(Eq 3)}$$

where E is the elastic modulus (in MPa or in psi) and G_c is the critical strain-energy-release rate for unstable crack propagation (in megajoules/m^2 or in in.-lb/in.^{2}).

Fracture of thin sections usually produces both shear-face (or high-energy) and flat-face (or low-energy) types of fracture surfaces. In general, as specimen thickness increases, the percentage of shear-face fracture surface, the energy needed to propagate a crack, and K_c all decrease. As shown in Fig. 5 and 6, at some specific section thickness (which is different for each material and heat treatment condition), crack propagation is governed by plane-strain conditions (strain is zero in the through-thickness, or z-direction) and the critical stress-intensity factor reaches a minimum value designated as the critical plane-strain stress-intensity factor (K_{Ic}). This factor, also called plane-strain fracture toughness, is particularly pertinent in materials evaluation because, unlike other toughness parameters, it is essentially independent of specimen dimensions, provided plane-strain conditions are met. In addition, initiation of slow crack growth generally is governed by plane-strain conditions, so that K_{Ic} not only characterizes total fracture in thick sections, where plane-strain conditions prevail, but also indicates the stress at which cracks propagate in thinner sections. When K_{Ic} is considered in design and in material selection, the likelihood of choosing the correct material, of properly evaluating the potential danger of a flaw, and of preventing catastrophic fracture are improved.

In order to determine values of K_{Ic} in the laboratory, it is necessary to use specimens that are designed to produce mode I, or opening mode, crack deformation (see Fig. 7). There are two valid types of specimens that can be used — bend specimens and compact-tension (CT) specimens. The details of the specimens and test methods are described in ASTM E399-72. The specimens are further discussed in Appendix 2 of this article, which begins on page 40.

Effect of Material Strength. Material strength can, of course, have a pronounced effect on the fracture toughness of a given material; in general, as strength increases, fracture toughness decreases. This is illustrated for tensile strength in Fig. 8 (Ref 5). Although Fig. 8 presents data for only three types of steel, it is sufficient to show that, for a given strength requirement, the materials engineer and designer can select different materials to achieve different levels of crack or flaw tolerance for a given engineering structure. (The influence of strength on fracture toughness of several commercial high-strength steels, aluminum alloys and titanium alloys is illustrated in Fig. 31, 32 and 33, in the

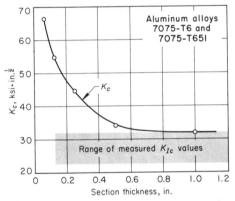

Fig. 6. Effect of section thickness of fatigue-precracked center-notched specimens of aluminum alloy 7075-T6 sheet and 7075-T651 plate on measured values of critical stress-intensity factor, K_c. At thicknesses greater than about 0.6 in., the value drops to the critical plane-strain stress-intensity factor, K_{Ic}. (Redrawn from Ref 4)

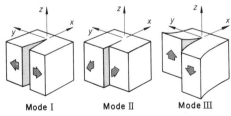

Mode I (opening mode) — tension stress in y direction (perpendicular to crack surfaces)

Mode II (edge-sliding mode) — shear stress in x direction (perpendicular to crack tip)

Mode III (screw-sliding mode) — shear stress in z direction (parallel to crack tip).

Fig. 7. Modes of crack deformation

section of Appendix 2 of this article that describes the dynamic tear test. Also included in Fig. 31, 32 and 33 are dynamic-tear-test energy values for lower-strength alloys, which have such high toughness properties that plane-strain conditions cannot be met, and valid K_{Ic} values cannot be obtained, with specimens of normal thickness.) In addition to the effect of strength level on values of K_{Ic}, material-processing operations such as melting, forging, rolling and welding can significantly influence the magnitude and degree of anisotropy of K_{Ic} values for any given material.

Although many attempts have been made to correlate K_{Ic} with other material properties, such as tensile properties and Charpy V-notch impact properties, the correlations have, in general, been poor ones, and are useful only for rough estimates of K_{Ic} (Ref 6).

Effect of Loading Rate. In ASTM E399-72, for plane-strain fracture-toughness testing, it is recommended that loading rate be controlled to maintain the rate of increase of the stress-intensity factor $(dK/dt$, or $\dot{K})$ within the range 0.55 to 2.75 MPa·m$^{\frac{1}{2}}$/sec (30 to 150 ksi·in.$^{\frac{1}{2}}$/min, or 0.5 to 2.5 ksi·in.$^{\frac{1}{2}}$/sec). Stress-intensity rates above this range will influence the value of K_{Ic}, depending on the strain-rate sensitivity of the material. For low-strength steels such as ASTM A533, grade B, dynamic fracture toughness (K_{Id}) is considerably lower than the static (normal-loading-rate) K_{Ic} values, as shown in Fig. 9 (Ref 7 and 8). The work of Priest *et al* (Ref 9 and 10) has demonstrated that K_{Ic} values can be determined over a wide range of stress-intensity rates $(10^{-1} < \dot{K} < 10^4$ ksi·in.$^{\frac{1}{2}}$/sec) using standard fracture-toughness techniques. At high stress-intensity rates $(\dot{K} > 10^5$ ksi·in.$^{\frac{1}{2}}$/sec), such as are encountered in the instrumented impact test, difficulties arise in interpretation of load-time records because of inertial-loading effects. The relationship between plane-strain fracture toughness (K_{Ic}) and stress-intensity rate $(\dot{K})$ can differ considerably for different heats and heat treatments of a material, as illustrated in Fig. 10 for a cast Cr-Ni-Mo high-strength steel. Loading rate (and resulting strain rate) also affects the fracture toughness and fracture behavior of parts in service. (See "Effect of Strain Rate on Toughness", page 44 in the article on Ductile-to-Brittle Fracture Transition.)

Effect of Temperature. The effects of testing temperature on plane-strain fracture-toughness values for two different high-strength steels and for a high-strength aluminum alloy are shown in Fig. 11 and 12. In contrast to the significant drop in K_{Ic} with decreasing temperature that occurs for the two steels, Fig. 12 illustrates a lack of dependence of K_{Ic} on temperature, down to −196 C

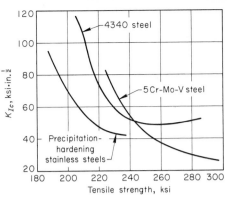

Fig. 8. Variation of plane-strain fracture toughness, K_{Ic}, with tensile strength for three steels (Redrawn from Ref 5)

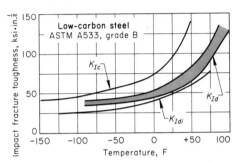

Fig. 9. Comparison of static (K_{Ic}), dynamic (K_{Id}) and dynamic-instrumented (K_{Idi}) impact fracture toughness of precracked specimens of ASTM A533, grade B, steel, as a function of test temperature. The stress-intensity rate, $\dot{K}$, was about 10^4 ksi·in.$^{\frac{1}{2}}$/sec for the dynamic tests and about 10^6 ksi·in.$^{\frac{1}{2}}$/sec for the dynamic-instrumented tests. (Redrawn from Ref 8)

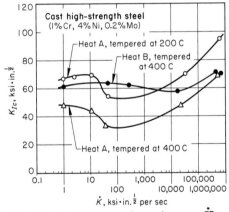

Fig. 10. Effect of stress-intensity rate, $\dot{K}$, on plane-strain fracture toughness, K_{Ic}, of two heats of cast 1Cr-4Ni-0.2Mo high-strength steel austenitized at 830 C (1526 F), oil quenched, and tempered as noted (Redrawn from Ref 9)

(−321 F) for the aluminum alloy. The drop in K_{Ic} with decreasing temperature shown in Fig. 11 and 12 for the two steels is typical of most of the iron-base alloys that have a body-centered-cubic crystal structure, and reflects a transition in their fracture behavior from ductile to brittle. This effect of tempera-

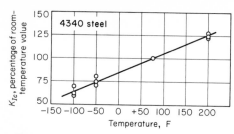

Fig. 11. *Effect of test temperature on plane-strain fracture toughness,* K_{Ic}, *of 4340 steel having a tensile strength of 260 ksi at room temperature (Redrawn from Ref 5)*

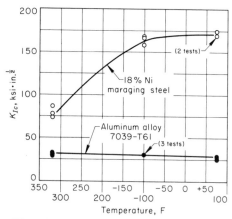

Fig. 12. *Effect of test temperature on plane-strain fracture toughness,* K_{Ic}, *of 18% Ni maraging steel (200-ksi min yield strength) and aluminum alloy 7039-T61 (Taken from Ref 11)*

ture on K_{Ic} and fracture behavior also is observed with titanium and some other metals and alloys that have a hexagonal, close-packed crystal structure. Aluminum and most other metals and alloys that have a face-centered-cubic crystal structure do not show a drop in K_{Ic} or a clear transition in fracture behavior.

The effect of temperature on other toughness properties for a given material is similar to these effects on K_{Ic}. For further discussion of the temperature dependence of K_{Ic} and the ductile-to-brittle fracture transition, see the article beginning on page 44 in this volume.

Applications of Fracture Mechanics

Fracture mechanics can be utilized in designing, and predicting service life of, pressure vessels and other engineering structures in which subcritical flaw growth, or time-dependent fractures such as those stemming from stress-corrosion cracking or fatigue, are important. Conventional fatigue data generally are obtained with small laboratory specimens and are plotted as *S-N* curves, but the absolute value of the stress required to produce fracture at a given number of cycles is dependent on specimen configuration. However, if fatigue data are ex-

pressed in terms of the stress-intensity factor (K) as a function either of cycles to fracture or of crack-growth rate, the basic curve obtained is independent of specimen configuration.

The application of fracture mechanics still is largely restricted to conditions in which general yielding is absent, and thus it cannot be used to analyze mechanical fracturing of tough, low-strength alloys, which yield throughout the component or specimen long before fracture is initiated. But when stress-corrosion cracking or fatigue cracking occurs in these alloys, it often occurs at such low stresses that it can be analyzed by linear-elastic fracture mechanics.

Pressure-Vessel Life. It is generally recognized that fabricated structures contain flaws of various kinds, including weld cracks, quench cracks and laps and seams, which may not be detected before the structure is placed in service. The service life of any such structure depends on (*a*) the size of flaw required to cause rapid fracture (that is, critical flaw size) at operating stress levels, (*b*) the initial size of flaws, and (*c*) the subcritical-flaw-growth characteristics of the material.

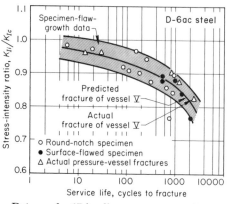

Data are for 17-in.-diam pressure vessels, and for round-notch and surface-flawed specimens, of D-6ac steel with a yield strength of 246,000 psi. Pressure was cycled between zero and that required for producing the indicated stress-intensity ratio.

Fig. 13. *Comparison of observed and predicted service lives of D-6ac steel pressure vessels (Redrawn from Ref 3)*

Table 1. Comparison of Measured and Predicted Stress at Fracture of Pressure Vessels Tested in Low-Cycle Fatigue(a)

Pressure-vessel material	Yield strength, ksi(b)	K_{Ic}, ksi·in.$^{\frac{1}{2}}$	Stress at fracture, ksi Measured	Predicted
17-7 PH stainless steel:				
Plate	168.0	49.0	124.0	132.0
Forging	165.0	48.7	116.0	99.0
Forged head	162.0	53.2	110.0	117.5
Aluminum alloy 2219-T87				
plate(c)	27.0	18.0	27.0	26.3

(a) Data from C. F. Tiffany. (b) 0.2% offset. (c) Values for K_{Ic}, and for measured and predicted stress, are at −253 C (−423 F).

The types of flaws encountered in fabricated structures can be categorized as surface flaws, embedded flaws, and through-thickness flaws. For surface and embedded flaws, the degree of constraint at the flaw (crack) tip is high and plane-strain conditions generally prevail. Whether or not initial flaws reach critical size prior to propagating through the entire thickness of a part depends on plane-strain fracture toughness (K_{Ic}), applied stress levels, and material thickness. If critical flaw size is less than wall thickness, formation of a through-thickness flaw prior to fracture is not likely. If rapid fracture does occur before a flaw propagates completely through the thickness, the flaw at time of rapid fracture very often has an elliptical or semi-elliptical shape.

The fracture-mechanics approach was used by Tiffany and Masters (Ref 3), and later by Bjeletich and Morton (Ref 12), to design, and predict the low-cycle-fatigue life of, pressure vessels. Tiffany and Masters obtained fatigue data from precracked specimens of several pressure-vessel materials and plotted these data, in terms of the ratio of initial stress-intensity factor (K_{Ii}) to critical stress-intensity factor (K_{Ic}), against cycles to fracture. Pressure vessels made of these same materials were then tested in low-cycle fatigue. The agreement between observed service life and the life predicted from specimen data was excellent (see Fig. 13 and Table 1).

Fatigue-Crack-Growth Rate. Fracture of structural components as a result of cyclic loading has long been a major design problem and has resulted in numerous investigations into the growth of cracks by fatigue. Although a considerable amount of fatigue data are available, the majority are concerned with the nominal stress required to produce fracture in a given number of cycles — namely, *S-N* curves. Such data usually are obtained from laboratory endurance tests on smooth specimens and, although of some qualitative use in guiding material selection, they do not indicate the effects of stress raisers on over-all fracture resistance. As noted previously, an adequate fracture-mechanics analysis of a structure subjected to cyclic loading or to a hostile environment, or to both, requires data on the rate at which a flaw of subcritical size will grow to critical size under prescribed loading and environmental conditions.

The fatigue life of a structure can be thought of as comprising three distinct stages — namely, (*a*) crack initiation, (*b*) crack propagation, and (*c*) final, fast fracture. The presence of a pre-existing flaw (crack) will reduce or eliminate the initiation stage. For many design considerations, the second stage, fatigue-crack growth, is of utmost importance,

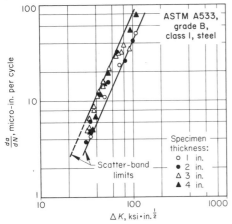

Fig. 14. Fatigue-crack-growth rate, da/dN, as a function of range of stress-intensity factor, ΔK, for 11¾-in.-thick ASTM A533, grade B, class 1, pressure-vessel steel plate. Data were obtained in air at room temperature using T-type wedge-opening-loading (WOL) specimens. (Redrawn from Ref 13)

because it is realistic to assume that some form of flaw is initially present in any structure. As a fatigue crack grows under a cyclic load of constant amplitude and mean value, the stress intensity at the crack tip increases as a result of increases in crack size. Eventually, the crack may grow to a length sufficient for the stress-intensity factor to reach the critical value (K_{Ic}), at which time final, fast fracture occurs. (For tough, low-strength alloys, for which K_{Ic} cannot be obtained in the size of structure involved, final, fast fracture occurs in the plane-stress mode and is ductile.)

The dependence of fatigue-crack-growth rate on the stress-intensity factor (K) has been verified by many investigations, and a generalized fatigue-crack-growth-rate exponential-power law has evolved as follows:

$$da/dN = C_0(\Delta K)^n \qquad (Eq 4)$$

where da/dN is the fatigue-crack-growth rate; C_0 and n are constants that depend on material, relative mean load, and frequency of loading; and ΔK (sometimes expressed as ΔK_I) is the range of the stress-intensity factor during one loading cycle. Fatigue-crack-growth-rate data of this type for ASTM A533, grade B, class 1, pressure-vessel steel plate are shown in Fig. 14. Extensive data for various high-strength martensitic steels show that the primary parameter affecting rate of fatigue-crack growth is the range of the stress-intensity factor, and that other mechanical and metallurgical properties of these steels have negligible effects on fatigue-crack-growth rates in air at room temperature. The fatigue-crack-growth-rate data for these steels fall within a single narrow band, as Fig. 15 shows.

The constants in Eq 4 can be determined for a material by constructing straight lines at the scatter-band limits in a plot of da/dN versus ΔK for the material, such as those in Fig. 14 and 15. The validity of Eq 4 has been established using published data from various investigations, and its applicability to martensitic steels with yield strengths from 80 to 300 ksi has been established also (Ref 14).

The advantage of the fracture-mechanics approach to crack-growth studies is that the variables — applied load and crack length — can be incorporated into the parameter ΔK, which describes the stress-intensity conditions corresponding to a given crack-growth rate under cyclic loading. By this approach it is therefore possible to apply crack-growth-rate data to a wide variety of initial crack lengths, applied loads, specimen shapes, and stress patterns.

Crack growth may be caused by cyclic stresses in a benign environment (fatigue), sustained loading in an aggressive environment (stress corrosion), or the combined effects of cyclic stresses and an aggressive environment (corrosion fatigue). A comparison of the corrosion-fatigue-crack-growth behavior in a 3% sodium chloride solution, and the fatigue-crack-growth behavior in air, of 4340 steel heat treated to a yield strength of 180 ksi and loaded sinusoidally at six cycles per minute is shown in Fig. 16 (Ref 14). In these experiments, the corro-

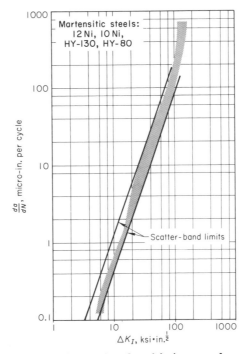

Fig. 15. Composite plot of fatigue-crack-growth rate, da/dN, versus range of stress-intensity factor, ΔK_I, for four high-strength martensitic steels (12 Ni, 10 Ni, HY-130, HY-80). Data (shaded band) were obtained in 280 tests in air at room temperature using 1-in.-wide T-type wedge-opening-loading (WOL) specimens. (Redrawn from Ref 14)

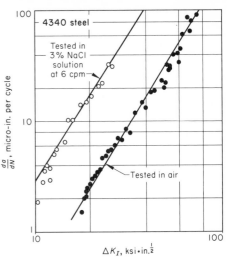

Fig. 16. Comparison of corrosion-fatigue-crack-growth-rate data obtained in a 3% sodium chloride solution with fatigue-crack-growth-rate data obtained in air for 4340 steel heat treated to a yield strength of 180 ksi. The stress-corrosion-cracking threshold, K_{Iscc}, of this steel in 3% sodium chloride is 26.0 ksi·in.¹. (Redrawn from Ref 14)

sion-fatigue-crack-growth rate in the sodium chloride solution was five to six times as high as the fatigue-crack-growth rate in air. Environmentally induced acceleration of fatigue-crack growth increases with increasing yield strength and is related to the stress-corrosion-cracking threshold, K_{Iscc}, of the environment-material system under consideration. (See next section for discussion of K_{Iscc}.) This emphasizes the need to conduct fracture-toughness and fatigue-crack-growth-rate tests under environments similar to those in actual service.

Stress-Corrosion-Crack-Growth Rate. Susceptibility to stress-corrosion cracking often is assessed by measuring time to fracture in a corrosive environment of stressed specimens — either bend specimens or smooth or notched tensile specimens. In these tests, time to fracture includes the time required to initiate a stress-corrosion crack, which can account for a large portion of the test duration. Fracture mechanics, on the other hand, deals only with crack growth, and thus does not consider the initiation phase of stress-corrosion cracking. Therefore, fracture mechanics is most useful for evaluating resistance to the growth of stress-corrosion cracks in materials that contain pre-existing flaws or for research on crack-growth kinetics.

Specimens suitable for the study of stress-corrosion cracking using fracture mechanics are similar to those used in conventional fracture-toughness testing. A simple fracture-mechanics stress-corrosion test using a fatigue-precracked specimen loaded as a cantilever beam has been developed by Brown at the U. S. Naval Research Laboratories (Ref 15)

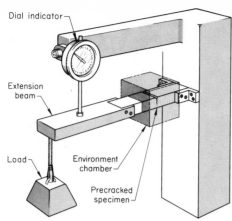

Fig. 17. Fixture for a cantilever-beam test. This test is used for monitoring stress-corrosion-crack-growth rate in fatigue-precracked fracture-mechanics specimens. (Ref 15)

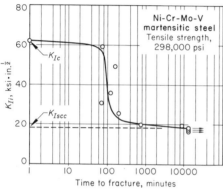

Data are for an experimental Ni-Cr-Mo-V steel with tensile strength of 298,000 psi, tested in a 3½% NaCl solution. The arrows indicate that three of the tests were stopped before fracture. The plane-strain fracture toughness, K_{Ic}, of the steel is 61.3 ksi·in.$^{\frac{1}{2}}$; the stress-corrosion-cracking. threshold, K_{Iscc}, is 18.0 ksi·in.$^{\frac{1}{2}}$.

Fig. 18. Curve of time to fracture by stress-corrosion cracking versus initial stress-intensity factor, K_{Ii} (Ref 16)

and has subsequently been used by many investigators. The setup for this test is shown schematically in Fig. 17. The initiation of cracking and the extent of crack growth are indicated by movement of the

extension beam, which can be monitored continuously. From the stress-intensity factor, K, for the particular specimen shape and loading direction, the relationship between crack-growth rate and stress intensity can be determined. The stress intensity at the start of the test, K_{Ii}, is governed by the load and by the depth of the fatigue precrack. As the load or the applied initial stress-intensity factor, K_{Ii}, is decreased, a plateau or threshold level of stress intensity is found, above which stress-corrosion cracking will definitely occur, and below which stress-corrosion cracking will not occur within a reasonably long period of time.

The results of a typical series of fracture-mechanics stress-corrosion tests on an experimental ultrahigh-strength Ni-Cr-Mo-V martensitic steel are shown in Fig. 18. It can be seen that, at an initial stress intensity corresponding to the K_{Ic} value of the material, the specimen fractures almost immediately. With decreasing values of K_{Ii}, time to fracture increases until, below a stress-intensity level of 18 ksi·in.$^{\frac{1}{2}}$, stress-corrosion cracking does not occur in 10,000 min and the stress-corrosion-cracking threshold, K_{Iscc}, is determined. It is important to select, for each class of materials, a sufficiently long cutoff or runout time to determine an accurate K_{Iscc} value. For lower-strength steels, which have high fracture-toughness levels, runout times required for accurate K_{Iscc} measurements may be as long as several thousand hours. In addition to constant-load, increasing-K_I, cantilever-beam specimens for determining K_{Iscc}, there are constant-displacement, decreasing-K_I specimens (bolt-loaded wedge-opening-loading, or WOL, specimens) and constant-K_I specimens of the tapered, double-cantilever-beam (DCB) type (Ref 17).

As shown previously for the plane-strain fracture-toughness parameter, K_{Ic}, the plane-strain stress-corrosion-cracking parameter, K_{Iscc}, often varies markedly with alloy composition, strength, and orientation of stress with respect to

wrought texture. Values of K_{Iscc} determined for specimens of various configurations are readily applied to the design of a structural member having a surface crack by use of suitable equations (Ref 18). Figure 19 shows K_{Iscc} values for 11 commercial steels tested in salt water, plotted as a function of yield strength. Shown on the graph are plots calculated for two assumed values of surface-crack depth, b. The use of such plots is as follows:

1　Assume some value of crack depth considered detectable (and therefore removable) in a given design.
2　For the assumed crack depth, calculate K values that correspond to several assumed values of stress equal to the yield strength.

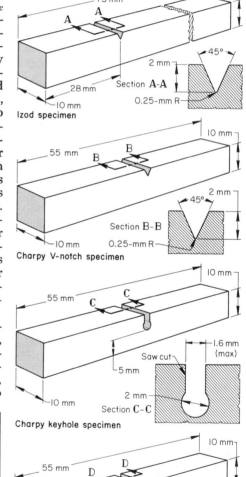

Fig. 20. Dimensional details of Izod and Charpy test specimens most commonly used for evaluation of notch toughness (ASTM E23)

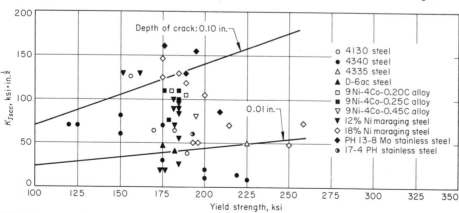

Fig. 19. Stress-corrosion-cracking threshold, K_{Iscc}, as a function of yield strength, for 11 commercial steels tested in salt water. Also plotted are lines calculated for specimens under tension containing surface cracks of two assumed values of depth. (Ref 18)

3 Plot a line through the points calculated in step 2 on a graph of measured values of K_{Iscc} versus yield strength for the alloys being considered for use in the design (see Fig. 19).

4 Select from those alloys having values above the line plotted in step 3.

In this manner, the fracture-mechanics stress-corrosion-cracking parameter, K_{Iscc}, can be utilized quantitatively in design and material selection.

Fracture-Toughness Data. Many current aircraft, nuclear, and pressure-vessel programs employ fracture toughness as an evaluation parameter. As a result, a large amount of information is being assembled that can aid in the effective presentation of reliable data in handbook form. A good example of this is the recently published "Damage Tolerant Design Handbook" (Ref 19). This handbook is a compilation of crack-growth and fracture data for high-strength alloys and includes the following types of information: plane-stress fracture toughness, K_c; plane-strain fracture toughness, K_{Ic}; fatigue-crack-growth rate, da/dN; and stress-corrosion-cracking threshold, K_{Iscc}.

APPENDIX 1

Notch-Toughness Testing and Evaluation

This Appendix describes in detail, and gives references to, a variety of tests for determination of notch toughness — both with impact loading and with slow loading.

The Charpy and Izod Tests. The Charpy machine has a total available striking energy of 220 ft-lb. The test specimen, supported at both ends, is broken by a single blow of the pendulum applied at the middle of the specimen on its unnotched side. The specimen breaks at the notch, the two halves fly away and the pendulum passes between the two parts of the anvil. Height of fall minus height of rise gives the amount of energy absorption involved in deforming and breaking the specimen. To this is added frictional and other losses amounting to 1 or 2 ft-lb. The instrument is calibrated to record directly the energy absorbed by the test specimen.

The Izod machine is similar in principle, but the test specimen is held rigidly in a vise as a cantilever beam, with the center of the notch coinciding with the upper face of the jaws. The capacity of the machine is usually 220 ft-lb. Half the test specimen is broken off and the impact value is determined as with the Charpy test.

Dimensional details are given in Fig. 20 for four standard Izod and Charpy specimens (see ASTM E23). The Charpy V-notch specimen is widely used for structural steels, as is the keyhole speci-

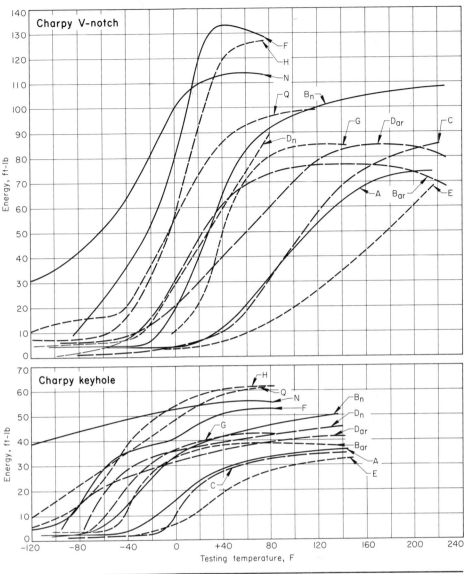

Steel	C	Mn	Si	P	S	Ni	Al	Cu	Cr	Mo	Sn	N
A	0.26	0.50	0.03	0.012	0.039	0.20	0.012	0.03	0.03	0.006	0.003	0.004
B	0.18	0.73	0.07	0.008	0.030	0.05	0.015	0.07	0.03	0.006	0.012	0.005
C	0.24	0.48	0.05	0.012	0.026	0.02	0.016	0.03	0.03	0.005	0.003	0.009
D	0.22	0.55	0.21	0.013	0.024	0.16	0.020	0.22	0.12	0.022	0.023	0.005
E	0.20	0.33	0.01	0.013	0.020	0.15	0.009	0.18	0.09	0.018	0.024	0.005
F	0.18	0.82	0.15	0.012	0.031	0.04	0.054	0.05	0.03	0.008	0.021	0.006
G	0.20	0.86	0.19	0.020	0.020	0.08	0.045	0.15	0.04	0.018	0.012	0.006
H	0.18	0.76	0.16	0.012	0.019	0.05	0.053	0.09	0.04	0.006	0.004	0.004
N	0.17	0.53	0.25	0.011	0.020	3.39	0.077	0.19	0.06	0.025	0.017	0.005
Q	0.22	1.13	0.05	0.011	0.030	0.05	0.008	0.13	0.03	0.006	0.018	0.006

Steel	Condition	Yield point, psi	Tensile strength, psi	Elongation in 2 in., %	Elongation in 8 in., %	Reduction of area, %	Rockwell B hardness
A	As rolled	36,000	59,000	41	34	58	60
B_{ar}	As rolled	33,000	57,500	44	34	64	61
B_n	Normalized	36,000	57,000	44	34	63	60
C	As rolled	36,000	65,000	39	30	56	67
D_{ar}	As rolled	37,500	65,000	..	30	54	..
D_n	Normalized	35,000	60,000	..	32	59	..
E_{ar}	As rolled	30,000	57,000	..	32	56	..
E_n	Normalized	35,000	57,500	..	31	56	..
F	As rolled	34,000	61,000	..	31	62	..
G	As rolled	41,500	70,000	..	28	56	..
H	As rolled	36,000	63,500	42	30	63	70
N	As rolled	58,000	80,000	35	26	65	84
Q	Quenched and tempered	46,000	72,000	45	23	62	81

Steels A, B and C, semikilled; D, F, G and H, fully deoxidized; E, rimmed.

Fig. 21. Comparison of energy-temperature curves obtained by Charpy V-notch and Charpy keyhole tests of the same 12 steels (Ref 20)

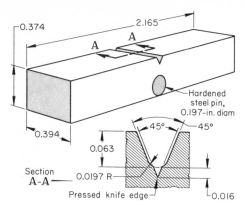

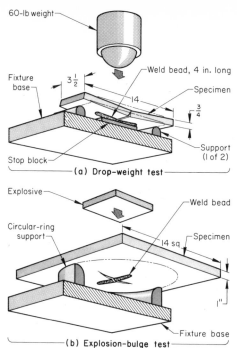

Fig. 22. Details of the Schnadt notched-bar impact-test specimen (Ref 21)

men. The Izod test can record higher values than the Charpy but is difficult to use for testing at reduced temperature. For testing heat treated steels, both the V-notch specimen and the keyhole specimen are used, with most users of the test showing a preference for the V-notch. Comparisons of results with Charpy V and keyhole notches for the same steels, tested over a range of temperature, are shown in Fig. 21.

The Schnadt specimen, details of which are shown in Fig. 22, has been used primarily in Europe for testing ship plate (see Ref 21). In the Schnadt test, five test pieces are used with different notch radii, ranging from no notch to a severe notch made by pressing a sharp knife into the bottom of a milled groove. A hardened steel pin is inserted in a hole parallel to and behind the notch, replacing the material normally under compression in the Charpy or Izod tests. The specimen is broken by impact as a three-point-loaded beam.

The drop-weight test (DWT) specimen and procedure are shown in Fig. 23(a) (see also ASTM E208). The crack inducer is a bead of hard-facing metal about 3 in. long. The specimen, $3\frac{1}{2}$ by 14 by $\frac{3}{4}$ in., is placed, weld down, on rounded end supports and is struck by a 60-lb falling weight with sufficient energy to bend the specimen about 5°. A cleavage crack forms in the bead as soon as incipient yield occurs (at about 3° deflection), thus forming the sharpest possible notch, a cleavage crack in the test specimen. A series of specimens is tested over a range of temperatures to find the nil-ductility transition temperature. This is the temperature below which steel, in the presence of a cleavage crack, will not deform plastically before fracturing, but will fracture at the moment of yielding.

This is a "go, no-go" test in that the specimen will either break or fail to break. It is surprisingly reproducible. For example, Pellini made 82 tests of specimens from one plate of semikilled low-carbon steel. At 30 and 40 F, all specimens remained unbroken. At 20 F,

The drop-weight test is used for determining the nil-ductility transition temperature by testing a series of specimens over a range of temperatures. In the explosion-bulge test, steel does not deform before fracturing below this temperature. Test results obtained by the explosion-bulge method are illustrated in Fig. 24.

Fig. 23. Drop-weight and explosion-bulge methods of testing (W. S. Pellini)

only one of 14 specimens broke; however, at 10 F, 13 of the 14 specimens broke. At temperatures below 10 F, all specimens broke.

The explosion-bulge test is shown in Fig. 23(b). The specimen is 14 in. square by about 1 in. thick. A crack-starter weld similar to the one in the drop-weight test

is applied to the lower surface of the specimen. The specimen is placed over a die with the weld bead on the tension side and is loaded by the force of a controlled explosion.

Typical results are shown in Fig. 24. At temperatures lower than the nil-ductility transition temperature, determined by the drop-weight test (about 20 F for this steel, as shown at the upper left corner of Fig. 24), the steel does not deform before fracturing. The specimens break flat under explosive impact, because fracture is readily initiated. Fractures also propagate through the very lightly loaded edge regions supported by the die.

Just above the nil-ductility transition temperature, considerable plastic deformation (bulging) precedes fracture. At this point it is more difficult to initiate fracture, but cracks propagate to the edges when fracture occurs. As the testing temperature is raised to where fracture is partly in shear, cracks are confined to the area of bulging (forcing); they do not run through the lightly loaded edge regions. Some shearing is evident along the edges of the fracture. At still higher temperatures, brittle fractures are no longer possible and all fractures occur in shear.

Notched Slow-Bend Test. Opinion varies as to whether the behavior of steel structures can be predicted from impact tests involving very high strain rates, which seldom correspond to actual service conditions. Consequently, notched slow-bend tests have been proposed for investigating brittle fracture of steel structures. In such tests, specimens are geometrically similar to the standard Charpy V-notch specimen and may range

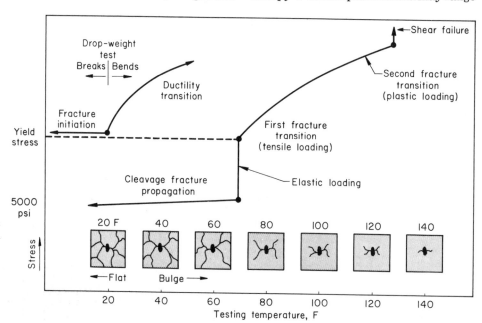

Fig. 24. Sketches of plates tested at various temperatures by the explosion-bulge method, and their relation to type of fracture in tests on the same material by drop-weight testing and by tension testing (W. S. Pellini)

in size from ⅜ in. square by 2 in. long to 9 in. square by 6 ft long. The notch radius is kept constant for each series of specimens. Specimens are bent in a tension-testing machine at very low strain rates with the notch in tension. Load and deflection measurements are recorded. The load-carrying ability (strength) of the material can be calculated from the breaking load. The deflection serves as a measure of relative ductility.

This test has been used primarily for testing at room temperature. Brittle or ductile behavior depends on the size of the specimen; small pieces bend, larger bars of the same material break.

The Lehigh bend test, another slow-bend test, is more widely used. It may be applied to specimens containing a longitudinal weld bead or with no weld deposit. The Lehigh test specimen (Fig. 25) is 3 in. wide by 12 in. long by ½ to ¾ in. thick and is notched across its entire width. The notch may be a standard V-notch or a less severe notch (1 mm radius and 0.080 in. deep). The specimen is bent slowly until failure occurs, at which time contraction in width just below the notch, percentage of fibrous fracture, and bend angle at maximum load are measured. Ductility transition temperature is usually defined as that point at which a lateral contraction of 1% is obtained by plotting lateral contraction against temperature. As in the Charpy specimen, the fracture appearance transition is defined as a temperature corresponding to 50% shear fracture.

The Robertson test utilizes a large rectangular specimen, usually 12 in. wide. This test measures the temperature at which a brittle crack, initiated by impact, stops in a plate under uniform stress with a superimposed temperature gradient. The specimen has a knob through which a hole is drilled and a jeweler's saw cut is made. The cut acts as a crack initiator. A tensile load is applied, as shown in Fig. 26(a), while a stress gradient is established on the specimen by use of a liquid-nitrogen cup on one side and a strip heater on the opposite side. Impact force is then imposed on the knob.

Tests of this general type using a temperature gradient were carried out in the laboratory of the Standard Oil Development Co. However, the specimens were longer than the typical Robertson specimen, to prevent stress-wave reflection due to impact, and contained a wire cut to obtain a sharper initial crack. Results of tests using this type of specimen as well as another modification that eliminated the Robertson knob were difficult to evaluate, because there was some doubt as to the stress level existing at the time the crack stopped. In view of this doubt, it was concluded that "go, no-go" tests at constant temperature and stress were subject to fewer uncertainties. This

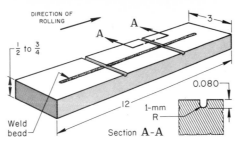

Fig. 25. Notched slow-bend test specimen with longitudinal weld bead (Lehigh test specimen)

led to the development of the Esso (Feely) test, which is described next.

The Esso test (Feely) specimen is also made from a slab of steel with end connections suitable for stressing in a tension-testing machine, as shown in Fig. 26(b). Length of the specimen in the direction of applied tension varies from 3 to 6 ft; width, from 16 in. to 6 ft. Saw cuts are made at the middle of each side, with a subsequent cut on one side using a fine wire and grinding compound. The specimen is then loaded as a simple beam to create a stress in the outer fiber of the wire-cut side by imposing a transverse load on the opposite side. The area in the vicinity of the saw cuts is then cooled by liquid nitrogen.

When the temperature of this area is about that of the liquid nitrogen, a wedge is driven into the saw cut in which the wire cut has been made, by impact from a small slug shot at high velocity from a power gun. This induces a fine crack at the base of the wire cut that acts as a severe stress concentrator. The saw cut on the opposite side from the wire cut serves merely to improve the distribution of stress.

The specimen, now in the precracked stage, is loaded axially with an insulated box around the central portion. Dry nitrogen cooled in a coil immersed in liquid nitrogen is injected into the box on both sides of the specimen. When the desired temperature is reached (as indicated by thermocouple) a predetermined tensile

load is applied to the specimen and the power gun is again used to drive a wedge into the previously prepared crack. If failure does not occur, the stress is raised and the specimen is subjected to impact at successively higher stress levels until brittle fracture occurs.

Below a certain critical temperature, reproducible results are obtained for the stress level at which failure will occur. This is true regardless of whether the specimen is subjected to a number of impacts at progressively increasing stress or whether the breaking stress is applied at the first impact. This situation does not exist at higher temperatures, and more specimens must be used to determine the lowest stress at which a specimen will fail from the first impact.

The Navy tear-test (Kahn) specimen is flame cut from a full plate and is machined in the manner shown in Fig. 26(c). Actually, only the edge opposite the notch is a machined surface. The specimen is supported at the pinholes on pins that are mounted on shackles. In this test, a series of specimens are subjected to slow tensile loading at various temperatures. Measurements are made of the maximum load, the energy input required to initiate fracture and the input required to complete fracture. Transition temperature is the temperature corresponding to 50% shear fracture or the point of abrupt energy change at which tearing begins after initial fracture.

Correlations. Although slow-bend-test specimens are used to measure notch toughness or transition temperature, they differ markedly in severity of notch, strain rate and size. The correlation of test results obtained with various specimens is poor, since the same property of the steel may not be measured in each test. Energy measurements derived with one type of specimen should not be compared with ductility measurements derived with a second specimen or with the fracture appearance of a third. When seeking a correlation among different test methods, appearance of the fracture has

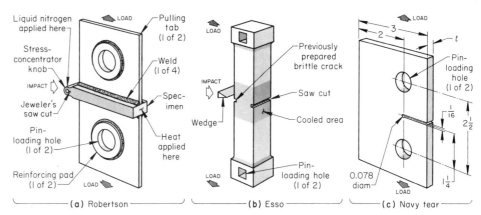

Fig. 26. Robertson specimen (left) and the Esso, or Feely, specimen (center) used for evaluating brittle behavior of steels. The Navy tear-test, or Kahn, specimen (right) utilizes full plate thickness, t.

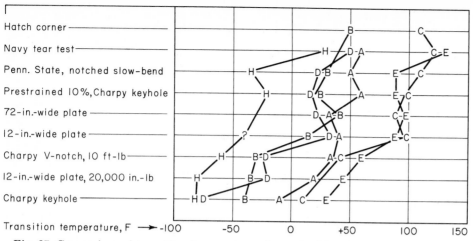

Transition temperature, F ⟶   -100   -50   0   +50   100   150

Fig. 27. Comparison of transition temperatures determined by nine different methods on six steels. Letter designations correspond to the steel compositions similarly identified in the table that accompanies Fig. 21.

proved to be the best criterion. Nevertheless, notch toughness of two steels should be compared only if the same type of specimen and criteria are used. Test results are relative rather than absolute.

Comparisons of energy-temperature curves obtained by Charpy keyhole and Charpy V-notch tests of the same 12 steels were shown in Fig. 21. Transition temperatures determined by nine different methods on six steels are plotted in Fig. 27. Included in Fig. 27 are transition temperatures determined by several special tests that are not described in this Appendix. For details of these tests, see Ref 20.

APPENDIX 2

Fracture-Toughness Testing and Evaluation

This Appendix describes details of, and gives references to, a variety of tests for determination of fracture toughness — both in plane-strain situations and in situations to which plane-strain fracture toughness is not applicable.

Plane-Strain Fracture-Toughness Test. Currently, several approaches are being taken to develop procedures for evaluating toughness in more-ductile metals. For materials having generally high strength and low toughness, the plane-strain toughness parameter, K_{Ic}, is the one most commonly determined. ASTM E399-72 defines K_{Ic} as the material-toughness property measured in terms of the stress-intensity factor, K_I, by a specified procedure. The procedure is designed to determine the stress intensity at which unstable crack propagation begins. According to this ASTM standard, K_I is "a measure of the stress-field intensity near the tip of an ideal crack in a linear-elastic medium when deformed so that the crack faces are displaced apart, normal to the crack plane (opening mode or mode I deformation)", as illustrated

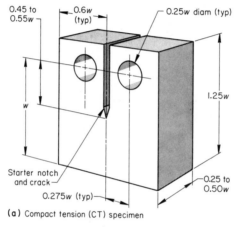

(a) Compact tension (CT) specimen

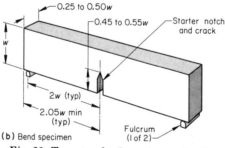

(b) Bend specimen

Fig. 28. Two standard specimens for determination of plane-strain fracture toughness (ASTM E399-72)

in Fig. 7. Currently, there are no standard procedures for measurement of fracture toughness with deformation modes II (shear perpendicular to the crack tip with plane-strain or plane-stress conditions) or III (shear parallel to the crack tip with anti-plane-strain conditions). For K_{Ic} measurements, ASTM E399-72 describes procedures using specimens like those shown in Fig. 28. The crack-tip plastic region is small compared to crack length and to specimen dimensions in the constraint direction. From a record of load versus crack opening and from previously determined relations of crack configuration to stress intensity, plane-strain fracture toughness can be mea-

sured accurately provided that all the criteria for a valid test are met.

Using the same type of relation that permits calculation of a K_{Ic} value from load required to initiate extension of a given crack, it is possible to calculate the load that would initiate extension of a crack of a different configuration or to calculate the maximum size of crack that could be present without inducing fracture in a part under a certain load. From such calculations, it is possible to determine how rigorous inspection must be if all cracks that might lead to fracture are to be detected.

Numerous other specimen designs for the determination of K_I values have been proposed, and K_{Ic} values derived from them have been reported in the literature. In the advanced, seven-volume treatise "Fracture" (Ref 22), which provides detailed discussion of the theoretical background of fracture processes, the chapter by Srawley (Ref 23) discusses single-edge-crack, double-edge-crack and center-crack rectangular specimens, and circumferentially cracked cylindrical specimens, all loaded in tension. There is interest in developing a specimen in which a surface crack will grow with an elliptical contour, propagating both along the surface and into the material.

For tougher, more ductile steels, specimens large enough to ensure loading under plane-strain conditions often are larger than the structures to be built. Consequently, other toughness tests and procedures are in use. One such test applicable to high-strength sheet metals is described in ASTM E338-68. Specimens such as those shown in Fig. 29 are used to determine the tensile strength of a sharply notched or precracked specimen, which then can be compared with the

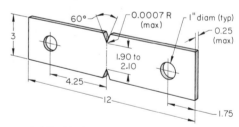

(a) Machined sharp edge-notch (EN) specimen

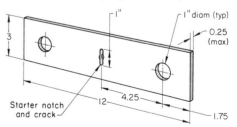

(b) Fatigue center-crack (CC) specimen

Fig. 29. Two standard specimens for determination of sharp-notch tensile strength. Alternative specimens are 8 in. long, with notches 2.25 in. from the loading holes. (ASTM E338-68)

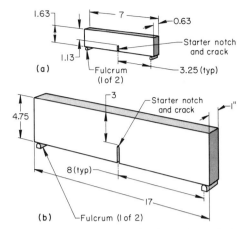

1.63
7
0.63
1.13
(a)
Starter notch and crack
Fulcrum (I of 2)
3.25 (typ)

3
Starter notch and crack
4.75
I"
8 (typ)
17
(b)
Fulcrum (I of 2)

In the specimens, a crack with a sharp tip is produced by making a brittle electron-beam weld or by pressing with a knife edge. With either method for providing the crack tip, and with either size of specimen, maximum constraint conditions are attained.

Fig. 30. Two sizes of the standard specimen for the NRL-standardized dynamic tear (DT) test

tensile strength of an unnotched (or uncracked) specimen. Other tests are designed to allow approximation of K_{Ic} values of tough metals that crack with plastic zones too large for valid measure-ment by the methods in ASTM E399-72. The use of specimens of K_{Ic} configuration but smaller than required for valid K_{Ic} tests may be possible if tested by loading at high speeds, thus generating K_{Id} values (where d designates "dynamic"). For large specimens or very high speeds, such testing involves advanced research techniques. For many steels of technical interest, however, Charpy-type specimens can be used effectively with the root of the V-notch extended by fatigue cracking. As is discussed below, testing of pre-cracked Charpy specimens can yield values that are strongly related to K_{Ic} values.

Dynamic Tear Test. Many metals and alloys, especially at lower strength levels, are too tough and too ductile to fracture under plane-strain conditions in the sizes normally used in structures. In an effort to obtain reliable values of fracture toughness of ductile metals and alloys, the Naval Research Laboratory introduced the dynamic tear (DT) test. This test is intended to evaluate metals and alloys over a wider range of fracture toughness than can other fracture-toughness tests. Correlation of DT toughness and K_{Ic} toughness has been published by Pellini (Ref 24).

The standard DT-test specimen, two sizes of which are illustrated in Fig. 30, is similar to the Charpy specimen but has greater depth and has a proportionately deeper notch, which is sharpened by a pressed knife edge. The DT-test specimen is broken by impact opposite the notch in a manner similar to the Charpy specimen and the energy not absorbed is measured by the swing of the pendulum, if this type of machine is used, or by deformation of lead or aluminum plates if a drop-weight machine is used. (For details of the DT test, see the Proposed Method for ⅝-In. (16-Mm) Dynamic Tear Testing of Metallic Materials, in the Related Material section of Part 10 of the 1975 Annual Book of ASTM Standards, and also Ref 25.)

The DT test is a 1964 modification of the NRL drop-weight tear test (DWTT), which originally had a deep, sharp crack introduced by an electron-beam weld, rather than a notch. A different modification of the DWTT was introduced in 1963 by Battelle Memorial Institute. The Battelle DWTT, which is described in ASTM E436-74, uses a shallow notch pressed by a sharp chisel edge, rather than a deep crack or notch. In the Battelle DWTT, only the fracture appear-

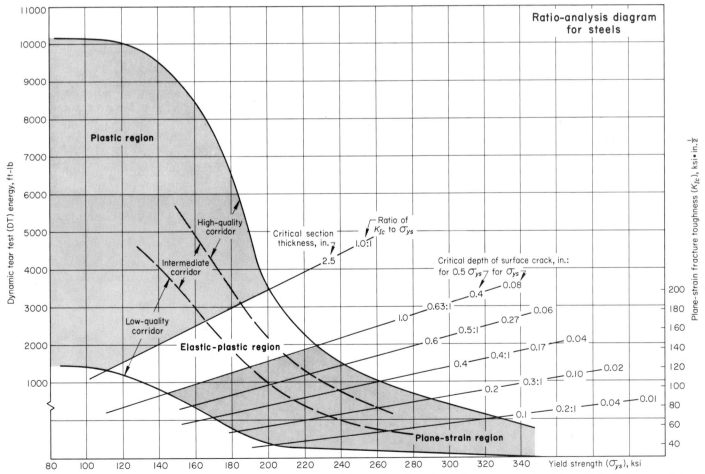

Fig. 31. Ratio-analysis diagram (RAD) for steels, as prepared for trade-off analyses for components 1.0 in. thick. Data were determined using specimens 0.5 to 3.0 in. thick. The upper limit of the high-quality corridor is based on the 1970 technological limit. (Taken from Ref 26)

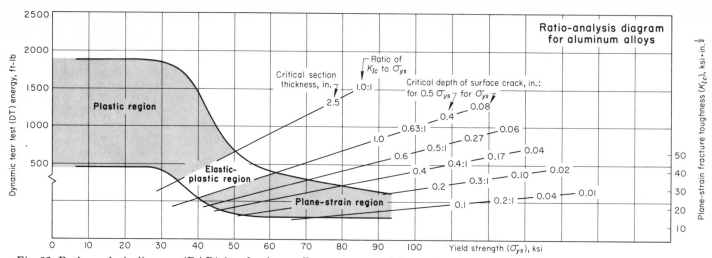

Fig. 32. Ratio-analysis diagram (RAD) for aluminum alloys, as prepared for trade-off analyses for components 1.0 in. thick. Data were determined using specimens 1.0 to 4.0 in. thick. The upper limit of the band of toughness values is based on the 1970 technological limit. (Taken from Ref 26)

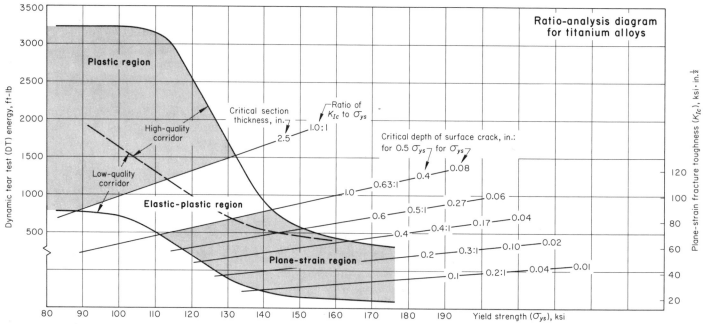

Fig. 33. Ratio-analysis diagram (RAD) for titanium alloys, as prepared for trade-off analyses for components 1.0 in. thick. Data were determined using specimens 1.0 to 4.0 in. thick. The upper limit of the high-quality corridor is based on the 1970 technological limit. (Taken from Ref 26)

ance is recorded, whereas in the DT test, the energy to fracture the specimen is recorded.

Ratio-Analysis Diagram. From consideration of fracture-mechanics and plastic-flow properties, and from numerous measurements, a ratio-analysis diagram (RAD) can be constructed to represent many of the conditions relating to material selection for fracture control. Pellini has discussed the conception and development of this tool (Ref 26). Simplified versions of ratio-analysis diagrams for steels, aluminum alloys and titanium alloys originally presented in Ref 26 are given here in Fig. 31, 32 and 33. On the ordinate scales are values of DT energy and values of K_{Ic} that correspond to the DT values. The K_{Ic} scale is extended to the point corresponding to a 1-to-1 ratio

of K_{Ic} to σ_{ys} (yield strength) for the best alloy of those to be considered. Sloping lines representing various ratios of K_{Ic} to σ_{ys} are drawn. By the equations of fracture mechanics, these ratios can be related to the critical flaw (crack) depth expected to initiate fracture in a plate of a particular thickness. Each sloping line is applicable to a certain critical thickness. Such a line can be constructed by plotting values of toughness versus yield strength for each alloy being considered for a design. If the thickness in the design is less than the critical thickness denoted by the sloping line, crack tips in the part will not be stressed under plane-strain conditions and either elastic-plastic or gross-yielding behavior can be expected. If design thickness is greater than critical thickness, the part can sus-

tain even greater crack-tip stress intensity before crack extension will begin.

Because the modulus of elasticity is implicit in the relations between K_{Ic} and crack size, different diagrams are required for steel, aluminum alloys, and titanium alloys. Furthermore, at a given yield strength, different alloys have different fracture-toughness levels. Consequently, the diagrams may be divided into quality corridors based on test results for alloys with high, intermediate and low toughness. With a ratio-analysis diagram (RAD), it is then possible to guide the selection of alloys and working yield strengths so as to place the metal in either the ductile regime or the fracture-mechanics regime, as may be appropriate for the cost or risk involved. Results obtained in dynamic tear tests extend fracture analysis beyond the linear-elastic fracture-mechanics range.

Crack-Opening-Displacement Test. A procedure that has been utilized, particularly in Great Britain, for fracture control of materials too tough for rigorous plane-strain testing is the crack-opening-displacement (COD) test. Although this test was designed to measure crack-tip displacement as the load on the test piece is increased, it is so difficult to make actual measurements of this displacement that measurements of surface-crack openings in specimens resembling plane-strain bend specimens have had to suffice. For COD specimens, size requirements are not so rigorous as for K_{Ic} specimens, and sometimes, for beam specimens, the angle of bending is measured rather than the crack opening. Many aspects of this test are described in Ref 27 and 28.

J-Integral Fracture Criterion. Interest in the integral designated J, which was proposed by Rice (Ref 29), stems from its potential for determining plane-strain fracture toughness, K_{Ic}, from elastic-plastic or fully plastic laboratory specimens that are too small to meet the full-constraint criteria stipulated in ASTM E399-73T. The J-integral parameter represents an extension of G, the linear-elastic fracture-mechanics strain-energy-release parameter, to include nonlinear load-displacement response; thus, J is a criterion for the initiation of crack extension. Application of J-integral fracture analysis as an alternative to, and an extension of, K_{Ic} evaluation has been demonstrated by several investigators (Ref 30 and 31). The work of Landes and Begley (Ref 32) with rotor and pressure-vessel steels represents the primary experimental validation of the J-integral parameter. They reported that J is independent of specimen configuration and that the critical value of J for crack extension (J_{Ic}) as measured on small, fully plastic specimens $\frac{1}{2}$ to 2 in. thick agrees with the value of G_{Ic} as determined from K_{Ic} testing of plates 8 and 12 in. thick.

J-integral fracture analysis on titanium alloy Ti-6Al-4V, utilizing four different specimen types, has demonstrated that the value of J associated with a given amount of crack extension is independent of specimen thickness and initial crack length (Ref 33). For the various criteria for initiation of crack extension that were examined in this investigation, the resultant J_{Ic} values were in good agreement with a valid K_{Ic} value obtained for the same alloy.

A related approach for obtaining lower-bound (minimum-expectance) K_{Ic} values for steels that must be tested at temperatures at which valid K_{Ic} values cannot be obtained is the equivalent-energy method, originally described by Witt at Oak Ridge. Buchalet and Mager

(Ref 34) concluded that by utilizing this method as proposed by Witt, lower-bound fracture-toughness data can be obtained with small, compact specimens.

Instrumented Impact Test. A recent modification of the Charpy test (and other impact tests), the instrumented impact test utilizes a strain-gaged tup that strikes the specimen so that a record is obtained of load and energy versus time, which correlates with deflection. From the record of load versus deflection, it is possible to determine the elastic portion of the stress-strain curve, the onset of crack extension, the energy for crack initiation, and the energy for crack propagation (Ref 7). With use of the instrumented impact test on precracked specimens, values of K_{Id} (where d signifies "dynamic") may be obtained under the same restrictions and in a similar manner as valid K_{Ic} values, reportedly at much less specimen-preparation cost (Ref 8).

R-Curve Analysis. In testing tougher materials, in which plane-strain conditions do not develop at the crack tip for specimen thicknesses of interest, or in testing product forms that are limited in thickness, such as sheet materials, fracture-toughness properties can be evaluated by means of fracture-extension-resistance, or R-curve, analysis, in which crack-growth resistance, R, per unit of crack extension, Δa, is determined (Ref 35). The crack-growth resistance may be expressed in terms of either the strain-energy-release rate, G or R_p, or the fracture-mechanics stress-intensity factor, K. Investigations at the Naval Research Laboratory have shown that R-curve analysis can be used to characterize metals of all fracture states — plane-strain, elastic-plastic, and plastic (Ref 36) — and that dynamic-tear-test R-curve characterizations can be directly translated to design criteria by correlation with results of larger-scale tests that model generic types of configurations and loadings. These investigations also have shown that the energy to fracture a dynamic-tear-test specimen is related to specimen dimensions and crack extension by the following equation:

$$E = R_p (\Delta a)^2 B^{\frac{1}{2}} \qquad \text{(Eq 5)}$$

where E is the dynamic-tear-test energy, Δa is the crack extension, B is the specimen thickness, and R_p is a constant that for any given material is related to the R-curve slope and is a measure of the inherent resistance of the material to crack extension (Ref 36). This ductile-fracture equation applies equally well for steels at temperatures corresponding to upper-shelf (100% ductile) fracture conditions and for aluminum alloys, but is not applicable for titanium alloys because of temperature-transition effects. The use of the R_p parameter in association with the

ratio-analysis diagram (RAD) permits an independent analysis of metallurgical and mechanical aspects of the fracture properties of materials for a wide range of section sizes.

Another approach to the determination of R-curves has been taken by McCabe and Heyer (Ref 37), who express the R-curve as a plot of stress-intensity factor, K, versus crack length, a, utilizing a modified wedge-opening-loading (WOL) or compact-tension (CT) fracture-toughness specimen. This approach is directed primarily toward higher-strength sheet materials.

References

1. D. E. Driscoll, Reproducibility of Charpy Impact Test, p 70-75 in "Symposium on Impact Testing", ASTM STP 176, American Society for Testing and Materials, 1956

2. J. E. Srawley and J. B. Esgar, "Investigation of Hydrotest Failure of Thiokol Chemical Corporation 260-Inch-Diameter SL-1 Motor Case", NASA TM X-1194, National Aeronautics and Space Administration, Washington, Jan 1966, 105 pages

3. C. F. Tiffany and J. N. Masters, Applied Fracture Mechanics, p 249-277 in "Fracture Toughness Testing and Its Applications", ASTM STP 381, American Society for Testing and Materials, 1965

4. J. G. Kaufman, Progress In Fracture Testing of Metallic Materials, p 3-21 in "Review of Developments in Plane Strain Fracture Toughness Testing", ASTM STP 463, American Society for Testing and Materials, 1970

5. E. A. Steigerwald, Crack Toughness Measurements of High-Strength Steels, p 102-123 in "Review of Developments in Plane Strain Fracture Toughness Testing", ASTM STP 463, American Society for Testing and Materials, 1970

6. W. F. Brown, Jr., and J. E. Srawley, Commentary on Present Practice, p 216-248 in "Review of Developments in Plane Strain Fracture Toughness Testing", ASTM STP 463, American Society for Testing and Materials, 1970

7. C. E. Turner, Measurement of Fracture Toughness by Instrumented Impact Test, p 93-114 in "Impact Testing of Metals", ASTM STP 466, American Society for Testing and Materials, 1970

8. R. A. Wullaert, R. D. Ireland and A. S. Tetelman, Use of the Precracked Charpy Specimen in Fracture Toughness Testing, p 255-282 in "Fracture Prevention and Control", American Society for Metals, Metals Park, Ohio, 1974

9. A. H. Priest and M. J. May, Effect of Loading Rate on the Fracture Toughness of Several High-Strength Steels, p 16-23 in "Fracture Toughness of High-Strength Materials: Theory and Practice", ISI Publication 120, 1970

10. S. Venzi, A. H. Priest and M. J. May, Influence of Inertial Load in Instrumented Impact Tests, p 165-180 in "Impact Testing of Metals", ASTM STP 466, American Society for Testing and Materials, 1970

11. C. Vishnevsky and E. A. Steigerwald, Plane Strain Fracture Toughness of Some Cryogenic Materials at Room and Subzero Temperatures, p 3-25 in "Fracture Toughness Testing at Cryogenic Temperatures", ASTM STP 496, American Society for Testing and Materials, 1971

12. J. C. Bjeletich and T. M. Morton, Fracture Mechanics Technology for Optimum Pressure Vessel Design, p 439-460 in "Progress in Flaw Growth and Fracture Toughness Testing", ASTM STP 536, American Society for Testing and Materials, 1973

13. W. G. Clark, Jr., and E. T. Wessel, Application of Fracture Mechanics Technology to

Medium-Strength Steels, p 160-190 in "Review of Developments in Plane Strain Fracture Toughness Testing", ASTM STP 463, American Society for Testing and Materials, 1970

14. E. J. Imhof and J. M. Barsom, Fatigue and Corrosion-Fatigue Crack Growth of 4340 Steel at Various Yield Strengths, p 182-205 in "Progress in Flaw Growth and Fracture Toughness Testing", ASTM STP 536, American Society for Testing and Materials, 1973

15. B. F. Brown, A New Stress-Corrosion Cracking Test for High-Strength Alloys, *Mater Res Std,* Vol 6, No. 3 Mar 1966, p 129-133

16. R. T. Ault, G. M. Waid and R. B. Bertolo, Development of an Improved Ultra-High-Strength Steel for Forged Aircraft Components, AFML-TR-71-27, Air Force Materials Laboratory, Wright-Patterson Air Force Base, Ohio, Feb. 1971

17. R. P. Wei, S. R. Novak and D. P. Williams, Some Important Considerations in the Development of Stress Corrosion Cracking Test Methods, *Mater Res Std,* Sept 1972, p 25-30

18. B. F. Brown, Stress-Corrosion Cracking: A Perspective View of the Problem, NRL Report 7130, U. S. Naval Research Laboratory, Washington, June 1970

19. "Damage Tolerant Design Handbook", MCIC-HB-01, Metals and Ceramics Information Center, Battelle, Columbus, Ohio, Dec 1972, 419 pages; also, Supplement to the Damage Tolerant Design Handbook, MCIC-HB-01 Supplement, Dec 1973, 700+ pages

20. A. Boodberg, H. E. Davis, E. R. Parker and G. E. Troxell, Causes of Cleavage Fracture in Ship Plate — Tests of Wide Notched Plates, *Welding J,* Apr 1948, p 186s-199s

21. E. R. Parker, "Brittle Behavior of Engineering Structures", John Wiley & Sons, 1957

22. H. Liebowitz (Ed.), "Fracture", Vol I to VII, Academic Press, New York, 1968-1972

23. J. E. Srawley, Plane Strain Fracture Toughness, p 45-68 in "Fracture", Vol IV, H. Liebowitz (Ed.), Academic Press, New York, 1969

24. W. S. Pellini, Evolution of Principles for Fracture-Safe Design of Steel Structures, NRL Report 6957, U. S. Naval Research Laboratory, Washington, Sept 1969

25. E. A. Lange, P. P. Puzak and L. A. Cooley, Standard Method for the ⅝" Dynamic Tear Test, NRL Report 7159, U. S. Naval Research Laboratory, Washington, July 1970

26. W. S. Pellini, Criteria for Fracture Control Plans, NRL Report 7406, U. S. Naval Research Laboratory, Washington, May 1970

27. M. O. Dobson (Ed.), "Practical Fracture Mechanics for Structural Steel", Chapman & Hall, 1969

28. A. A. Wells, Fracture Control: Past, Present and Future, *Exp Mechanics,* Oct 1973, p 401-410

29. J. R. Rice, A Path Independent Integral and the Approximate Analysis of Strain Concentration by Notches and Cracks, *J Appl Mech,* Vol 35, No. 3, Sept 1968, p 379-386

30. "Fracture Toughness", ASTM STP 514, American Society for Testing and Materials, 1972

31. "Progress in Flaw Growth and Fracture Toughness Testing", ASTM STP 536, American Society for Testing and Materials, 1973

32. J. D. Landes and J. A. Begley, Effect of Specimen Geometry on J_{Ic}, p 24-39 in "Fracture Toughness", ASTM STP 514, American Society for Testing and Materials, 1972

33. G. R. Yoder and C. A. Griffis, J Integral and the Initiation of Crack Extension in a Titanium Alloy, NRL Report 7662, U. S. Naval Research Laboratory, Washington, Feb 1974

34. C. Buchalet and T. R. Mager, Experimental Verification of Lower Bound K_{Ic} Values Utilizing the Equivalent Energy Concept, p 281-296 in "Progress in Flaw Growth and Fracture Toughness Testing", ASTM STP 536, American Society for Testing and Materials, 1973

35. "Fracture Toughness Evaluation by R Curve Methods", ASTM STP 527, American Society for Testing and Materials, 1973

36. R. Judy, Jr., and R. Goode, R-Curve Characterization and Analysis of Fractures in High-Strength Structural Metals, *Metals Eng Quart,* Vol 13, No. 4, Nov 1973, p 27-34

37. D. E. McCabe and R. H. Heyer, R-Curve Determination Using a Crack-Line-Wedge-Loaded (CLWL) Specimen, p 17-35 in "Fracture Toughness Evaluation by R-Curve Methods", ASTM STP 527, American Society for Testing and Materials, 1973

Ductile-to-Brittle Fracture Transition

*By the ASM Committee on Analysis of Ductile and Brittle Fractures**

MANY METALS can exhibit both ductile and brittle fracture behavior; under certain conditions of stress state, temperature and strain rate they fracture in a largely brittle manner, whereas under other conditions fractures may be wholly ductile. Mechanical conditions that cause a tough metal to fracture in a brittle manner are discussed in the article on Ductile and Brittle Fractures, which begins on page 61 in this volume. In the present article, the factors that determine whether a metal or alloy will be tough or fragile are presented.

Certain metals are tough at high temperatures but fragile at low temperatures. These metals are said to undergo a ductile-to-brittle transition in fracture behavior. If a component made of one of these metals is used at or below the temperature at which it becomes fragile, the component may fail unexpectedly in service. Thus it can be important to the analysis of broken components to know whether the metal was tough at the service temperature. The methods by which toughness is measured are presented in the article on Toughness and Fracture Mechanics, which begins on page 30 in this volume. The application of these

methods to the evaluation of ductile-to-brittle fracture transition is described and illustrated in the present article.

Effect of Temperature on Transition

Generally, curves that represent the decrease in ductility of metals with decreasing temperature are of two types: class I and class II transition curves. In

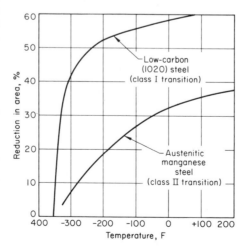

Fig. 1. Effect of temperature on the ductile-to-brittle transition of low-carbon steel (class I transition) and austenitic manganese steel (class II transition)

class I transition there is an abrupt decrease in ductility (and toughness) over a relatively narrow range of temperature (see Fig. 1); many carbon and low-alloy steels exhibit class I transition. A somewhat arbitrarily defined temperature in the transition range is called the ductile-to-brittle-fracture transition temperature, or T_c. Above T_c the fracture is predominantly by microvoid coalescence; below T_c the fracture is predominantly by cleavage. Because brittleness is seldom desirable, it is usually necessary to prevent brittle behavior by keeping T_c below the expected service temperature.

In class II transition there is a gradual loss of ductility (and toughness) over a wide range of temperature, as shown by the curve for austenitic manganese steel in Fig. 1. Class II transition is not considered undesirable in most engineering applications; nevertheless, the loss of ductility and toughness at very low temperatures still may be great enough to have an adverse effect on performance.

The ductile-to-brittle fracture transition can be assessed theoretically by means of the Griffith-Irwin criterion, which predicts the stress at which rapid fracture will occur (Ref 1). It is generally agreed that the major cause of brittle fracture is inability of the metal to resist

*See page 30 for committee list.

crack propagation through relaxation of stress at the crack tip by local plastic flow. If time is not sufficient to allow for stress relaxation, the crack will spread rapidly, which will lead to a brittle fracture. Because the rate of stress relaxation decreases with decreasing temperature, it follows that brittle fracture can be promoted at low temperatures, which is consistent with experimental observation. The dislocation model for ductile-to-brittle fracture transition developed by Heslop and Petch (Ref 2) predicts that the Peierls-Nabarro lattice-friction stress increases with decreasing temperature, thus increasing the likelihood of cleavage fracture.

The value of the critical plane-strain stress-intensity factor, K_{Ic}, for a metal or alloy reflects the ease of crack propagation in that metal or alloy — the lower the value of K_{Ic}, the more brittle the fracture behavior. In certain metals and alloys, such as carbon and low-alloy steels, K_{Ic} decreases with decreasing temperature. It is not surprising, therefore, that the rate of crack propagation in these same metals and alloys increases with decreasing temperature. This is demonstrated in Fig. 2, which shows the effects of temperature on fracture-surface appearance for a low-carbon steel. At 42 and 27 C (107 and 80 F), the fracture surface has a shear pattern with a "fibrous" appearance, whereas at 16 and −3 C (60 and 27 F), the fracture surface has a chevron pattern with a "granular" or "crystalline" appearance. Crack velocities were about 440 ft per second at 42 and 27 C (107 and 80 F), 1425 ft per second at 16 C (60 F), and 1665 ft per second at −3 C (27 F).

Determination of Transition Temperature

Several tests and methods are used to determine the ductile-to-brittle-fracture transition temperature, T_c. With some tests and materials, T_c can be defined readily to within ±5 F; however, different test methods usually yield different values of T_c for the same material. Because the values of T_c determined by standard Charpy V-notch impact testing correlate well with the temperatures at which many brittle fractures have occurred in service, this test is the most widely used. This test, as well as the other standard notched-bar impact tests — Charpy U-notch, Charpy keyhole, Izod and Schnadt — are described in Appendix 1 of the article on Toughness and Fracture Mechanics (see page 37).

Other tests that have been used to determine T_c include the drop-weight test, the explosion-bulge test, and the notched slow-bend test (which are described on page 38), and the dynamic tear test (described on page 41). Conventional ten-

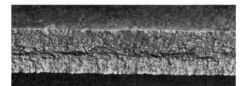

Tested at 42 C (107 F)   1.25×

Tested at 27 C (80 F)   1.16×

Tested at 16 C (60 F)   0.92×

Tested at −3 C (+27 F)   0.96×

These light fractographs show fracture surfaces of four sections cut from a single length of low-carbon steel pipe, which were burst by hydraulic pressure at the temperatures indicated. The steel had a yield strength of 60 ksi.

Fracture mechanism varied with testing temperature, being 100% shear at 42 and 27 C (107 and 80 F), brittle with 15% shear lip at 16 C (60 F), and brittle with minute shear lip at −3 C (+27 F). Chevron patterns on the two brittle-fracture surfaces indicate that the direction of crack propagation was right to left.

Fig. 2. Transition in fracture-surface appearance with changes in testing temperature (Ref 3)

sion testing also can be used to determine T_c; in this method, transition temperature is determined from measurements of elongation and reduction in area.

Energy Transition. The Charpy notched-bar impact tests are especially effective in the determination of T_c for plain carbon and low-alloy steels. Figure 3(a) shows that, in a plot of energy absorbed during fracture versus testing temperature, there is a sharp drop in absorbed energy as the testing temperature decreases through a narrow range; this drop is called the energy transition and identifies T_c. As shown in Fig. 3(a), in this series of tests on low-carbon steel plate the drop in energy for the Charpy keyhole specimens was steeper and more sharply defined than for the Charpy V-notch specimens; thus, the value of T_c for keyhole specimens was more precise. However, the value of T_c for keyhole specimens was lower than the tempera-

tures at which brittle fractures occurred in service and lower than T_c for V-notch specimens. On the other hand, T_c for V-notch specimens correlated well with the temperatures of service failures of components made of this steel.

The wide range of temperature over which V-notch transition occurs (see Fig. 3) emphasizes the need for a standard criterion for selecting the point on the curve to be defined as T_c. One criterion is the average-energy criterion (the temperature corresponding to the median between the maximum energy, or upper-shelf energy, and the minimum energy, or lower-shelf energy). In many instances, the temperature at which the transition curve crosses an arbitrary value of absorbed energy (such as 15 or 30 ft-lb) is chosen. An alternative criterion is the average-temperature criterion (the median temperature of the transition range).

Fracture Transition. Another method of determining T_c is to examine the appearance of the fracture surfaces in notched-bar impact-test specimens. The fracture-appearance method is based on the concept that shear (fibrous) fracture occurs above the transition-temperature range whereas cleavage (crystalline) fracture occurs below the range. This concept appears to be appropriate, at least for body-centered-cubic iron-base alloys. In the transition-temperature range, fracture is initiated at the root of the notch by fibrous tearing. A short distance from the notch, the fracture mechanism changes to cleavage, which produces radial marks in the central portion of the specimen. As the crack front progresses across the specimen, the crack-propagation rate is retarded and fracture reverts to the stable fibrous mode. Final fracture occurs at the sides and back of the specimen by shear-lip formation. Thus a "picture frame" of shear (fibrous) fracture surrounds a radial zone of cleavage (crystalline) fracture, as illustrated in Fig. 3(b).

The relative amount of the total shear area (fibrous zones plus shear lips) in a given fracture surface can be measured using the empirical methods established in ASTM A370. Figure 4 shows the percentage of shear fracture in a series of Charpy V-notch impact tests of 4340 steel at different temperatures. The results of such measurements may be plotted against testing temperature as either: (a) ascending percentage of shear (fibrous) fracture (see Fig. 3b) or of fibrosity; or (b) descending percentage of cleavage (crystalline) fracture.

The fracture-appearance transition temperature (FATT) is the temperature at which the fracture exhibits a specified percentage of shear. (ASTM A370 uses the abbreviation FATT$_n$, where n equals the specified percentage of shear frac-

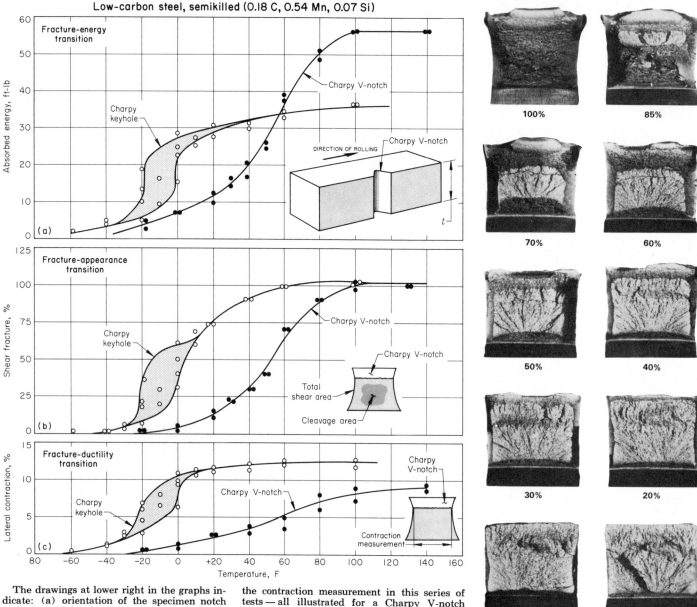

Low-carbon steel, semikilled (0.18 C, 0.54 Mn, 0.07 Si)

Fig. 3. Characteristics of the transition-temperature range of Charpy V-notch and Charpy keyhole tests of low-carbon steel plate, as determined by (a) fracture energy, (b) fracture appearance, and (c) fracture ductility (Redrawn from Ref 4)

The drawings at lower right in the graphs indicate: (a) orientation of the specimen notch with plate thickness, t, and direction of rolling; (b) location of the total shear area and cleavage area on the fracture surface; and (c) location of the contraction measurement in this series of tests — all illustrated for a Charpy V-notch specimen. Percentage of shear fracture and lateral contraction were based on the original dimensions of the specimen.

Fig. 4. Series of fractographs of Charpy V-notch specimens of 4340 steel tested at different temperatures, showing the change in appearance and estimated percentage of shear fracture (Army Materials and Mechanics Research Center, Watertown Arsenal)

ture.) The percentage of shear most often used to determine fracture-appearance transition temperature is 50%, but 0%, 30% and 100% also have been used. The highest temperature at which any cleavage appears is called the propagation-transition temperature.

Ductility Transition. A third method of determining T_c is to measure the change in width of the impact-test specimens, which is an indication of fracture ductility. Lateral contraction is measured at the root of the notch (see Fig. 3c), or lateral expansion is measured on the side opposite the notch. The change in contraction or expansion with temperature is called ductility transition. The ductility-transition temperature is the tempera-ture corresponding to a specified amount of contraction or expansion, such as 1% contraction or 15 mils of expansion.

Plane-Strain Fracture-Toughness Transition. Experiments with carbon, low-alloy and maraging steels, such as those reported in Ref 5, have shown a general correlation between the Charpy V-notch impact energy and the critical plane-strain stress-intensity factor, K_{Ic}; both values are expected to be high in tough materials. Therefore, K_{Ic} can be used to determine T_c. By plotting K_{Ic} against increasing test temperature, a sharp increase in K_{Ic} will be observed over a narrow temperature range, which identifies a value of T_c close to that determined by Charpy V-notch impact testing.

Nil-Ductility Transition. One of the tests mentioned earlier that is used to determine the temperature of ductile-to-brittle transition is the drop-weight test. This is a "go, no-go" test in which the specimen will either break or fail to break, and was specifically designed to determine a transition temperature called the nil-ductility transition temperature (NDT temperature).

The method of determination of the nil-ductility transition temperature is established in ASTM E208, which defines this temperature as the maximum temperature at which a standard drop-

Table 1. Recommended Toughness Tests for Five Engineering Objectives, as Affected by Range of Material Strength(a) (Ref 7)

| | Type of toughness test for materials of: | | |
Engineering objective	Low strength (b) $\sigma_y < E/300$	Medium strength (b) $E/300 < \sigma_y < E/150$	High strength (b) $E/150 < \sigma_y$
Choosing materials on a comparative basis	NDT: Charpy V-notch (appearance); DWTT (appearance); notched tensile (thin sheet)	Charpy V-notch (appearance and energy); DWTT (appearance); notched tensile (thin sheet)	K_{Ic} or K_c
Establishing design data: (a) Safe working stress at given temperature and thickness	K_{Ic} or K_c	K_{Ic} or K_c	K_{Ic} or K_c
(b) Safe working temperature at given levels of applied stress	NDT (for steel); DWTT (appearance)	Charpy V-notch (appearance); DWTT (appearance); K_{Ic} or K_c	.....
Determining whether there is a high probability of catastrophic failure from service conditions	Charpy V-notch (appearance); notched tensile (very thin sheet)	Charpy V-notch (appearance); DWTT (energy); notched tensile (very thin sheet)	DWTT (energy); K_{Ic} or K_c
Quality control test by maker of materials	NDT: Charpy V-notch (energy); notched tensile (thin sheet)	Charpy V-notch (energy); DWTT (appearance); notched tensile (thin sheet)	DWTT (appearance); K_{Ic} or K_c
Analysis of service failures	Visual analysis; NDT (for steel); Charpy V-notch (appearance and energy); K_c (at low temperature or in thin sheet)	Visual analysis; DWTT (appearance); Charpy V-notch (appearance and energy); K_c (at low temperature or in thin sheet)	Visual analysis; K_{Ic} or K_c

NOTE. σ_y = yield strength; E = modulus of elasticity; NDT = nil-ductility transition; DWTT = drop-weight tear test; K_{Ic} = plane-strain fracture toughness; K_c = plane-stress fracture toughness.

(a) For fracture in the absence of cyclic loading or reactive environment. (b) Potential modes of brittle fracture: For low-strength materials — cleavage (in all materials except face-centered-cubic metals) and shear rupture (in thin sheets). Medium-strength materials — cleavage (in all materials except in face-centered-cubic metals), normal rupture (at low temperature) and shear rupture (in thin sheets). High-strength materials — normal rupture, and shear rupture (in thin sheets).

weight-test specimen breaks in this test. The nil-ductility transition temperature also has been defined as "that temperature above which cleavage fracture can be initiated only after appreciable plastic flow at the base of the notch, and below which cleavage will be initiated with little evidence of notch ductility" (Ref 6). Using this latter definition, a nil-ductility transition temperature can be determined from results of other toughness tests, such as the dynamic tear test.

Fracture Transition, Elastic. When specimens with small cracks or flaws are tested by conventional impact loading, the nil-ductility transition temperature is an adequate measure of the temperature at which the metal becomes brittle. However, for specimens with large cracks or flaws, especially when tested by rapid dynamic loading (such as by explosion), the fracture transition, elastic (FTE) temperature is a better measure of the temperature for onset of brittle behavior. As determined in an explosion-bulge test (described on page 38), the FTE temperature is the highest temperature at which a crack will propagate into the elastically loaded region at the edges of the test plate. The temperature at which fracture will not propagate from the starter crack into the plastically deformed region in the center of the test plate is known as the fracture transition, plastic (FTP) temperature.

Selection of tests and methods for determination of the ductile-to-brittle fracture transition should be made on the basis of their correlation with the behavior of parts in service. It has been found that this correlation depends on the strength range of the material and the engineering objective. Tetelman and McEvily (Ref 7) have evaluated the usefulness of the various tests and methods for different engineering objectives, and their recommendations for the selection of the proper test or method are summarized in Table 1.

Effect of Metallurgical Factors on Transition

Several metallurgical phenomena affect the ductile-to-brittle fracture transition of metals and alloys. These phenomena are associated with the crystal structure, microstructure, chemical composition and other characteristics of the specific metal or alloy.

Crystal Structure and Deformation Mode

As mentioned previously, the ductile-to-brittle fracture transition of a number of carbon and low-alloy steels is associated with a change in the fracture mode from shear to cleavage. This phenomenon does not occur in all iron-base alloys, but rather is restricted to a limited number

of iron-base alloys with body-centered-cubic crystal structures. Other engineering alloys, including most face-centered-cubic alloys, may not show clear changes in fracture mode with changes in temperature. Even some body-centered-cubic iron-base alloys, such as low-carbon martensitic steels with substantial amounts of alloying elements, exhibit shear fracture at subzero temperatures. For example, 18Ni-5Mo-9Co maraging steel may exhibit shear fracture at temperatures as low as −196 C (−322 F). At these low temperatures, cleavage and quasicleavage fracture occurs in this and similar maraging steels (and some hexagonal, close-packed alloys) only under impact loading.

Body-centered-cubic iron-base alloys are known to slip on the {110}, {112} and {123} planes, all in the close-packed ⟨110⟩ directions — a total of 48 possible slip systems. (For further information on the slip systems in iron-base alloys, see the article "Plastic Deformation Structures in Iron and Steel", which begins on page 218 in Volume 8 of this Handbook.) Experimental evidence indicates that extensive cross slipping prevents the occurrence of cleavage fracture. However, the ability of body-centered-cubic iron-base alloys to cross slip is greatly reduced with decreasing temperatures, and this is believed to be responsible for cleavage fracture and the loss in toughness below T_c.

Because low temperatures inhibit cross slip in body-centered-cubic iron-base alloys, it has been suggested that twinning is the major mechanism of deformation in those iron-base alloys that exhibit shear fracture at low temperatures and that twinning is blocked in those alloys exhibiting cleavage.

Low stacking-fault energy generally promotes cross slip in body-centered-cubic crystals. Although the addition of substantial amounts of alloying elements to iron is believed to lower the stacking-fault energy, this process currently has not been proven responsible for the shear-fracture behavior at −196 C (−322 F) of the 18Ni-5Mo-9Co maraging steel mentioned above.

Face-Centered-Cubic Iron-Base Alloys. The ease with which cross slip occurs, even at low temperatures, is believed to be primarily responsible for the ductile behavior of austenitic steel, as well as copper, aluminum and many other face-centered-cubic metals and alloys. However, stacking faults in face-centered-cubic crystals inhibit cross slip (opposite to the effect in body-centered-cubic crystals); thus, the presence of

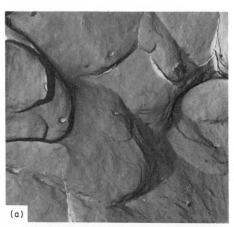

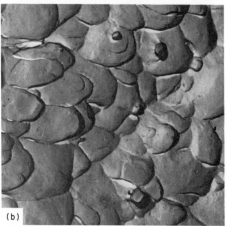

Fig. 5. TEM fractographs, at 5000×, of flat, center portions of fracture surfaces in type 304 stainless steel, showing the reduction in size of dimples when temperature at fracture is reduced from (a) room temperature to (b) −196 C (−322 F) (Ref 8)

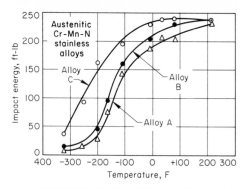

Fig. 6. Transition-temperature ranges of three austenitic Cr-Mn-N experimental alloys, as measured on longitudinal Charpy V-notch specimens (Ref 9)

Alloy	Composition, %				
	C	Mn	Cr	Ni	N
A	0.09	14.70	18.40	0.22	0.54
B	0.12	14.90	17.80	0.14	0.38
C	0.12	14.95	18.43	3.95	0.38

large numbers of stacking faults can seriously reduce macroscopic ductility.

Type 304 stainless steel exhibits a gradual decrease of impact energy with decreasing temperature, which is typical of face-centered-cubic alloys; an accurate determination of T_c for these alloys is difficult. With decreasing temperature, although the impact-fracture mode does not change from shear to cleavage, the dimples produced on the fracture surface are smaller (see Fig. 5).

In contrast to type 304 stainless steel, austenitic Cr-Mn-N stainless alloys containing 15% manganese show an abrupt decrease in impact energy over a narrow range of decreasing temperature (see Fig. 6). This embrittlement is believed to take place because the high alloy content reduces stacking-fault energy, which increases the incidence of stacking-fault generation. It has been suggested that low-temperature deformation of austenitic Cr-Mn-N stainless alloys is associated with the profuse generation of stacking faults (Ref 9).

Part Size

Large structures are more susceptible to brittle fracture than small structures. As is described under "Effect of section thickness on initial crack extension", on page 89 in the appendix to the article on Ductile and Brittle Fractures, thick sections give rise to plane-strain conditions and have lower ductility and fracture toughness than thin sections made from identical material.

Variation in fracture behavior also can result from differences in metallurgical structure between thin and thick stock of a given material. For example, the transition temperature of hot rolled low-carbon steel varies with plate thickness, as shown in Fig. 7. In these tests, the specimen size was constant, yet T_c still

increased with increasing plate thickness. The reduction of fracture toughness with increasing plate thickness is not limited to low-carbon steel, but apparently applies to all metals. Because of the characteristics of normal commercial processing, the metallurgical structure of thick stock is different from that of thin stock, resulting in inherently lower toughness for the thicker stock. More importantly, the probability that a given part will contain a crack or a flaw of critical size (or greater) increases with increasing stock thickness. The lower inherent toughness of thick stock and the higher probability that thick stock contains a large crack or flaw, combined with the plane-strain conditions inherent in thick members, is the reason that large structures are more susceptible to brittle fracture than small structures.

It should be noted that, because of the small size of Charpy specimens, Charpy data, as used in Fig. 7, may underestimate the brittleness of a large part. A more realistic estimate may be made by conducting a drop-weight test or a dynamic tear test (these tests are briefly described on pages 38 and 41, respectively).

Grain Size

For ferritic low-carbon and medium-carbon steels and many other body-

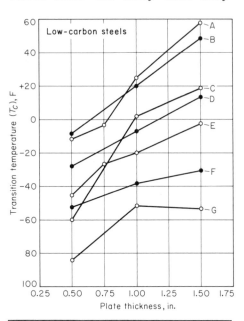

Steel	Composition, %	
	C	Mn
A (semikilled)	0.23	0.45
B (aluminum killed)	0.23	0.45
C (silicon-aluminum killed) ..	0.16	0.45
D (silicon killed)	0.23	0.45
E (semikilled)	0.16	0.75
F (semikilled)	0.16	0.95
G (silicon-aluminum killed) ..	0.16	0.75

Fig. 7. Effect of plate thickness on the ductile-to-brittle transition temperature of plates of seven low-carbon steels, as determined by Charpy keyhole impact tests (Ref 10)

centered-cubic iron-base alloys, the ductile-to-brittle-fracture transition temperature, T_c, is found to decrease with decreasing grain diameter, d. A typical example of the effect of ferrite grain size on T_c is shown in Fig. 8, which shows the results obtained from a 0.15% C steel. Also shown in Fig. 8 is the accompanying increase of the lower yield stress at T_c with decreasing d. The linear relationship of T_c versus $d^{-\frac{1}{2}}$ may be explained by the Hall-Petch-Heslop equation (Ref 2):

$$\sigma_y = \sigma_0 + kd^{-\frac{1}{2}} \qquad (Eq 1)$$

where σ_y is the lower yield strength, k is a material constant, and σ_0 is the lattice friction stress, which for body-centered-cubic metals consists of a temperature-dependent portion (denoted by the symbol $\sigma_0{}^+$) and a temperature-independent portion (denoted by the symbol $\sigma_0{}^*$). The temperature-dependent portion is related to the absolute temperature, T, in the manner shown in the equation:

$$ln\ \sigma_0{}^+ \propto -\beta T \qquad (Eq 2)$$

where β is a material constant. By solving Eq 1 and 2 for σ_y (at T_c) we find:

$$T_c \propto ln\ d^{-\frac{1}{2}} \qquad (Eq 3)$$

or in its simplified form:

$$T_c \propto d^{-\frac{1}{2}} \qquad (Eq 3a)$$

Qualitatively, the embrittling effect of large grains in ferritic steel may be explained by stress concentration at the ends of slip bands and at grain boundaries. The larger the grains, the longer will be the slip bands and greater the stress concentration. Severe stress concentration will induce nucleation of microcracks, which in turn may cause early and catastrophic fracture. This explanation, however, does not provide a direct and satisfactory explanation for the linear relationship between $d^{-\frac{1}{2}}$ and transition temperature, as shown in Fig. 8.

The grain size of a carbon or low-alloy steel workpiece is mainly a function of the melting and deoxidation practice, hot working practice, and final heat treatment used. For example, in hot rolled products, excessively high finishing temperatures and slow cooling after rolling may result in coarse grain size. The grain size of as-hot-rolled steel may be large enough to cause the transition temperature to be above room temperature. Therefore, when toughness is required in an application, such as the support arm described in the following example, normalizing is recommended to lower the transition temperature by refining the ferrite grain size and pearlite spacing. Normalizing also minimizes the variation in transition temperature from heat to heat and plate to plate.

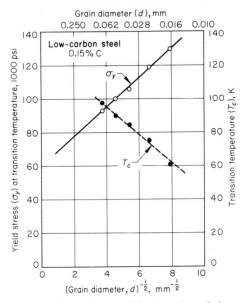

Fig. 8. Dependence of the ductile-to-brittle transition temperature (T_c), and the lower yield stress (σ_y) at T_c, on the average grain diameter, d, of ferrite in a low-carbon (0.15% C) steel (Ref 11)

Example 1. Brittle Fracture of an ASTM A572 Steel Support Arm for a Front-End Loader, Because Transition Temperature of the Steel Was Above 93 C (200 F)

A support arm on a front-end loader failed in a brittle manner while lifting a load. The arm had a cross section of 2 by 8 in. Material used for the arm was hot rolled ASTM A572, grade 42 (type 1), steel, which exhibited poor impact properties in the as-rolled condition and had a ductile-to-brittle transition temperature that was greater than 93 C (200 F). This transition temperature was much too high for the application.

It was recommended that a modified ASTM A572, grade 42 (0.15% C max), type 1 or type 2, steel be used. (Type 1, which

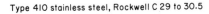

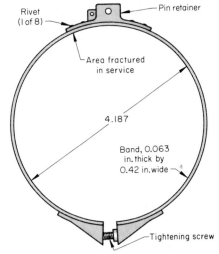

Fig. 9. Type 410 stainless steel clamp-strap assembly that broke in service because of brittleness due to coarse grain size (Example 2)

contains columbium, might be needed to meet strength requirements.) The steel should be specified to be killed, fine-grained, and normalized, with Charpy V-notch impact-energy values of 15 ft-lb at −46 C (−50 F) in the longitudinal direction and 15 ft-lb at −29 C (−20 F) in the transverse direction.

When steel is heated, small austenite grains form at temperatures above Ac₁. Grain size continually increases with time at temperature, and higher temperatures result in faster grain growth. The strength, ductility and toughness of coarse-grained metals are impaired not only by the large grain size, but also by grain-boundary precipitation. Generally, when a metal has been overheated and incipient melting has not occurred, reheat treating at proper time and temperature will restore desirable small-grained structure and satisfactory properties.

In the following example, coarse grain size, with its attendant reduction in strength, ductility and toughness, was responsible for the brittle fracture of a clamp strap; excessively high temperature during austenitizing caused the large grain size.

Example 2. Brittle Fracture of a Type 410 Stainless Steel Clamp-Strap Assembly Because of Coarse Grain Size Due to Improper Austenitizing Temperature (Fig. 9)

The clamp-strap assembly shown in Fig. 9, which was used for securing the caging mechanism on a star-tracking telescope, fractured while being installed. In installation, the clamp ends were separated manually to 4.187 in. so as to fit over the telescope. The clamp strap was specified to be type 410 stainless steel — austenitized at 955 to 1010 C (1750 to 1850 F), oil quenched, and tempered at 565 C (1050 F) for 2 hr to achieve a hardness of Rockwell C 30 to 35.

Investigation. Visual examination showed that the strap had fractured transversely across two rivet holes closest to one edge of the pin retainer (see Fig. 9) in a completely brittle manner.

Microscopic examination of a section transverse to the fracture showed the fracture to be predominantly transgranular with some grain-boundary separation. The grain size was determined to be as large as ASTM No. 2 to 3. This coarse grain size indicated that the material was at an excessively high temperature during austenitizing.

The hardness of the failed strap was found to be Rockwell C 29 to 30.5 (specified hardness was Rockwell C 30 to 35), and spectrographic analysis confirmed that the material was type 410 stainless steel.

For comparison, similar information was determined for a clamp that had not failed. This clamp had a hardness of Rockwell C 27.5 to 28 and a structure that consisted of tempered martensite. The grain size observed was predominantly ASTM No. 7. Spectrographic analysis showed that the material was type 410 stainless steel.

Slow-bend tests were performed on full-width specimens cut from the failed strap and the unfailed strap at locations remote from the rivets. Cracking occurred with an audible click in the specimen from the broken strap at a bend angle of approximately 20°. Fracture occurred by transgranular cleavage with a slight amount of grain-boundary separation. The specimen from the unfailed strap was bent through an angle of approximately 180° with no cracking and only slight orange peel on the outside of the bend.

Additional full-width specimens were removed from both straps for reheat treatment. The specimen from the broken strap was austenitized at 970 C (1775 F), which was within the specified range of 955 to 1010 C (1750 to 1850 F), oil quenched and tempered at 565 C (1050 F) for 2 hr. The specimen from the unfailed ductile strap was austenitized at an excessively high temperature of 1055 C (1935 F), oil quenched, and also tempered at 565 C (1050 F) for 2 hr. Slow-bend tests and metallographic examination were performed on both specimens. The specimen from the failed strap exhibited restored bend ductility and a refined grain size of ASTM No. 5 to 6. The specimen from the unfailed strap, originally a ductile material, fractured by cleavage and exhibited a coarsened grain size of ASTM No. 4.

Conclusions. Transgranular cleavage (brittle) fracture occurred across rivet holes in the clamp strap closest to one edge of the pin retainer. Coarse grain size (ASTM No. 2 to 3) was responsible for the brittle fracture. Excessively high temperature during austenitizing caused the large grain size.

The fact that the hardness of the strap that failed was lower than the specified hardness of Rockwell C 30 to 35 had no effect on the failure. The actual hardness of Rockwell C 29 to 30.5 was considered sufficient for satisfactory performance of a properly treated strap, and the hardness of the strap that did not fail was even lower.

Recommendation. The strap should be heat treated as specified to maintain the required ductility and grain size.

Thermomechanical treatments for control of decomposition of austenite have made possible the successful production of a much-refined grain structure in a number of steels, including maraging steels. The strength and toughness of these steels are strongly dependent on the size of the substructure, whether it is in the form of martensite, bainite or massive ferrite. Figure 10 shows the logarithmic variation of T_c with grain diameter, d, for pure iron and for five ferritic or martensitic Fe-Mn alloys with different structures and manganese contents. Both the ferritic and the martensitic Fe-Mn alloys maintain a logarithmic relation of T_c to d that satisfies Eq 3.

Not all engineering alloys will follow a well-behaved linear relation of T_c to $d^{-\frac{1}{2}}$ or $\ln d^{-\frac{1}{2}}$. Thornley and Wronski (Ref 13) carried out tensile tests on specimens of molybdenum rod that were subjected to various heat treatments. The tests showed that T_c can be unaffected, lowered or raised by coarsening the grain size. The value of T_c, however, is directly

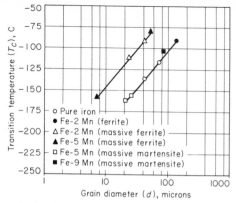

Grain diameter, d, was taken as the average grain-boundary intercept length for ferrite and massive ferrite grains and the average martensite-packet intercept length for massive martensite. T_c was determined by Charpy V-notch impact energy.

Fig. 10. Variation of the ductile-to-brittle transition temperature, T_c, *with grain diameter,* d, *for pure iron and five Fe-Mn alloys (Ref 12)*

influenced by the annealing temperature, which, in the region of 650 to 870 C (about 1200 to 1600 F), affects the size and distribution of precipitate particles. The results are discussed in terms of Cottrell's theory relating the change in T_c to the grain diameter (Ref 14), which is essentially the same as the Hall-Petch-Heslop theory.

Cappelli and Molaroni (Ref 15) determined the effect of carbon, nickel and aluminum contents, and austenite grain size, on the nil-ductility transition temperature, as determined in the drop-weight test, of fine-grained C-Mn and C-Mn-Ni steels designed for use at temperatures as low as −60 C (−77 F). The nil-ductility transition temperature was raised by 12 to 15 C (22 to 28 F) by an increase of 0.1% carbon; lowered by 15 C (28 F) by an increase of 1% nickel; lowered by 2.5 C (4 F) by an increase of

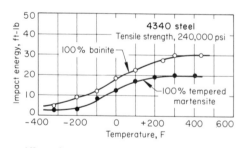

All specimens were austenitized for 30 min at 843 C (1550 F) in neutral salt. 100% bainite was produced by isothermal transformation for 1 hr at 315 C (600 F) in agitated salt. 100% tempered martensite was produced by quenching in agitated oil at 49 to 57 C (120 to 135 F) and tempering at 315 C (600 F). All specimens had the same tensile strength.

Fig. 11. Comparison of Charpy V-notch impact energies, at various test temperatures, for specimens of 4340 steel with structures of 100% bainite and 100% tempered martensite (Ref 17)

0.01% aluminum; and lowered by 18 C (32 F) by a reduction of 10 microns in austenite-grain diameter.

Composition and Microstructure

Both alloying and impurity elements are contained in most commercial metals. These elements — sometimes even when present in minute proportions — exert a strong influence on the resultant microstructure. This, in turn, affects the ductile-to-brittle fracture transition as discussed below.

Microstructural Constituents in Steel. At a given strength level, the transition temperature of a steel is determined by its microstructure (Ref 16). For example, of the major microstructural constituents found in steels, ferrite displays the highest transition temperature, followed by pearlite, upper bainite, and finally lower bainite and tempered martensite. The transition temperature of each of these constituents varies with the temperature at which the constituent formed and, where applicable, the temperature at which the steel was tempered. In practice, the cooling or quenching rate and the time-temperature transformation characteristics of a steel (including its conventional hardenability) determine the resulting microstructure or mixture of microstructures. The transformation characteristics, in turn, are controlled by the alloy composition, austenitizing temperature and austenite grain size.

Generally, treatments that produce microstructures with inferior room-temperature fracture toughness also raise T_c. Precipitated second-phase particles are detrimental to fracture toughness, especially if located at grain boundaries. However, a spheroidization treatment can improve fracture toughness by reducing strength and eliminating ferrite plates, which are paths of easy cleavage fracture in pearlite. Steels also can lose toughness because of various embrittlement phenomena, which are discussed in the section on Embrittlement Failures of Steel Parts, on page 78 in the article on Ductile and Brittle Fractures.

Isothermally transformed lower bainite has superior fracture toughness, and a slightly lower transition temperature, than tempered martensite of the same strength (see Fig. 11). However, mixed structures, which result from incomplete bainitic treatments causing partial transformation to martensite, have lower fracture toughness and much higher transition temperature than either 100% tempered martensite or 100% lower bainite. Thus, it is important that bainitic treatments be carried to completion to avoid the adverse effects of mixed structure.

Finally, the presence of austenite inhibits the fast propagation of cleavage fracture in some ferritic and martensitic steels. For example, the presence of retained austenite in martensitic maraging steel significantly improves fracture toughness. The means by which fracture toughness is improved is not fully understood, but it is thought to occur as follows (Ref 18):

1 When large quantities (on the order of 50% or more) of retained austenite are present, the austenite undergoes a strain-induced transformation to martensite in the plastic region ahead of the crack tip. This consumes energy, thereby raising the total energy required for the fracture process.

2 When austenite is retained as a lamellar phase (in lesser quantities than for strain-induced transformation), the retained-austenite lamellae block the growth of secondary cracks in the martensite matrix just ahead of the main crack front.

For further discussion concerning the effect of austenite-to-martensite transformation on fracture toughness, see the section of this article headed "Allotropic Transformation and Microstructure", which begins on the next page.

Alloying Elements in Steel. Although toughness and transition temperature of steel vary mainly with variations in microstructure, the presence of certain alloying elements can alter the toughness and transition temperature of steel with a given microstructure. The effects of most elements are highly dependent on steel type. However, single-element effects are difficult to assess by comparing the toughness of commercial steels, because differences in strengthening mechanism and in composition among various steels can cause these effects to be inconsistent.

Sulfur and phosphorus impurities are undesirable with respect to both toughness and transition temperature. Excessive carbon content is detrimental; consequently, for maximum toughness, carbon should be limited to the minimum level needed to achieve the desired strength. A practical way of attaining toughness is to use a boron-containing grade of steel with a lower carbon content. As shown in Fig. 12, 10B21 steel has greater toughness than 1038 steel at all strength levels. However, the benefit of boron is applicable only to quenched-and-tempered steels; boron reduces the toughness of steel that is used as-rolled, as-annealed or as-normalized.

Manganese levels above those required for hardenability and sulfide formation may be detrimental, particularly in martensitic steels with carbon contents in excess of 0.30 to 0.35%. In amounts greater than those normally required for deoxidation and grain refinement, aluminum appears to raise T_c and to lower toughness slightly.

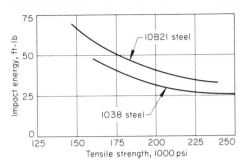

Fig. 12. Variation of room-temperature Charpy V-notch impact energy with tensile strength for 10B21 and 1038 steels with martensitic structures

Vishnevsky and Steigerwald evaluated effects of individual alloying elements on the notch-bend fracture toughness of a 0.35C-3Ni-Cr-Mo-V martensitic steel having a room-temperature yield strength of approximately 160,000 to 180,000 psi (Ref 19). Carbon, manganese, silicon, chromium and molybdenum raised the notch-bend fracture-toughness transition temperature, generally raised the work-hardening exponent, and reduced the toughness. On the other hand, nickel lowered the transition temperature and improved toughness at the lower testing temperatures.

Generally, with respect to both toughness and transition temperature, nickel is beneficial to steel with less than about 0.40% C (see Fig. 13). At carbon contents above 0.40%, nickel additions in excess of about 1.5% are not effective.

Vanadium improves toughness of low-alloy steels, primarily by acting as a grain refiner. In alloy steels to which carbide formers such as chromium and molybdenum are added to enhance hardenability, the presence of these elements has relatively little effect on toughness. On the other hand, in types of steel to which chromium and molybdenum are added as secondary-hardening agents (for example, many of the highly alloyed tool steels), the presence of chromium and molybdenum can impair toughness.

The specific effects of carbide formers vary widely with steel type and microstructure, as do the effects of other alloying elements. Generally, it is more fruitful to achieve a desired level of toughness at low temperatures by varying the strength level or microstructure of a given steel. However, in certain critical applications where a combination of ultrahigh strength and high toughness is needed, it may be necessary to establish the effect of certain alloying elements on toughness, and to control composition for optimum properties.

In the following example, a change in material and processing — from rephosphorized and resulfurized steel to a quenched-and-tempered alloy steel with significantly greater toughness — eliminated brittle fractures in check-valve poppets. The original material had been selected on the basis of its good machinability, but it was necessary for check-valve poppets made of this material to be carburized in order to develop the speci-

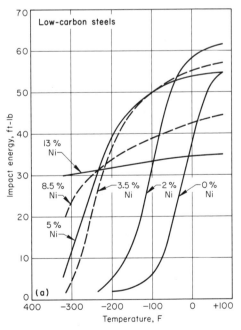

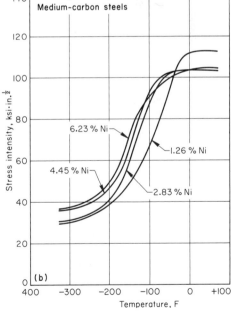

(a) Charpy keyhole impact energy versus test temperature for pearlitic low-carbon steels containing various amounts of nickel; these steels contained 0.10% carbon except for those with 0% and 2% nickel, which contained 0.20% and

0.15% carbon, respectively (Ref 20). (b) Notch-bend fracture toughness versus test temperature for martensitic 0.35C-Cr-Mo-V gun steels containing various amounts of nickel and having yield strengths of 160 to 180 ksi (Ref 21).

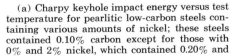

Fig. 13. Effects of nickel content on transition behavior of (a) normalized low-carbon steels and (b) quenched-and-tempered medium-carbon steels

fied surface hardness — which, acting in combination with the high content of inclusions inherent in the material, resulted in extreme brittleness.

Example 3. Brittle Fracture of a Rephosphorized, Resulfurized Steel Check-Valve Poppet Across Nonmetallic Inclusions (Fig. 14)

The poppet shown in Fig. 14(a) was used in a check valve to control fluid flow. The maximum operating pressure was 3500 psi.

Specifications required that the part be made of 1213 or 1215 rephosphorized and resulfurized steel for good machinability. The poppet was specified to be case hardened to Rockwell C 55 to 60, with a case depth of 0.025 to 0.035 in.; the hardness of the mating valve seat was Rockwell C 40.

After about two weeks in service, the poppet broke. Fracture occurred through the two 0.313-in.-diam holes at the narrowest section of the poppet (see Fig. 14a). The valve continued to operate after it broke, which resulted in extensive loss of metal between the holes. Other poppets reportedly made of the same material by the same manufacturing procedures withstood laboratory test-stand runs of 1000 hr at 3500 psi. The failed poppet and a poppet that had withstood a 1000-hr test were submitted to the laboratory for metallurgical evaluation on a production-stoppage basis.

Chemical analysis of the metal in the failed poppet indicated that it was made of 1213 or 1215 steel. However, the part that withstood the 1000-hr test contained 0.68% Mn, 0.005% P, 0.048% S, and 0.01% Si, indicating that the material was a low-carbon steel with 0.05% max sulfur.

Metallurgical Examination. Surface hardness measurements were taken at 12 places along the length of each poppet. Hardness of the failed poppet ranged from Rockwell C 61 to 65, with an average of Rockwell C 63. The unfailed poppet had a hardness range of Rockwell C 57 to 62, with an average of Rockwell C 59.5.

Both of the parts were sectioned longitudinally for microscopic examination. Figure 14(b) is a micrograph of the failed poppet, which shows cracks extending across nonmetallic inclusions in the rephosphorized, resulfurized 1215 steel. The unfailed poppet had a much cleaner microstructure and exhibited no evidence of incipient cracking. Figure 14(c) is a macrograph of a longitudinal section through the unfailed poppet and shows the carburized case extending to the center of the cross section. The failed part was in a similar condition.

Hardness surveys were taken across the transition section between the two diameters of the poppet body on both failed and unfailed parts. The hardness values were as shown in the following tabulation:

Location	Rockwell C hardness	
	Failed part	Unfailed part
Outer surface	63.5	59.5
Center of section . .	29-30	50-51
Inner surface	65.5	56

Several poppets were taken from stock and inspected by magnetic-particle and liquid-penetrant methods. None of the parts inspected had crack indications.

Conclusions. The check-valve poppet failed by brittle fracture. Surface hardness was excessive — Rockwell C 61 to 65 instead of the specified Rockwell C 55 to 60. Cracking occurred across nonmetallic inclusions.

The inclusions inherent in rephosphorized and resulfurized steel resulted in low resistance to brittle fracture, especially at the specified hardness levels.

Corrective Measures. The valve was redesigned as shown in Fig. 14(d). The material was changed to 4140 steel, hardened and tempered to Rockwell C 50 to 55. The improved design and the change in material eliminated failures of this type of poppet.

Interstitial Atoms. By increasing the quantities of interstitial atoms (such as carbon, oxygen, hydrogen and nitrogen) in both ordered and disordered ferrous alloys, the ductility is generally decreased and T_c is raised. In nonferrous alloys, oxygen is known to embrittle refractory metals (molybdenum, tungsten, rhenium, columbium and tantalum), and oxygen and nitrogen are known to embrittle titanium and zirconium.

Allotropic Transformation and Microstructure

The discovery that austenitic manganese steel loses all ductility at very low temperatures led to development of the concept that the transformation of austenite to martensite is associated with the loss of ductility. This concept was extended to explain the brittle fracture of other steels — for example, high-carbon tool steel and high speed tool steel, in which retained austenite is present. In recent years, it has been recognized that many high-manganese steels in which the austenite is stable also experience an abrupt drop in impact energy and ductility over a relatively narrow range of temperature. In the few instances where austenite-to-martensite transformation is induced by deformation, the amount of martensite present is at best very small.

In a study of a series of austenitic Cr-Mn-N alloys, Schaller and Zackay (Ref 22) found that the presence of interstitial nitrogen is also important in affecting the ductile-to-brittle fracture transition. This led to further development of the theory that the loss of ductility is related to number of interstitial atoms, strain rate, and degree of transformation to martensite induced by deformation. This theory is basically different from that proposed by Defilippi et al (Ref 9), which attributes the loss in ductility of these steels to the formation of stacking faults.

The transformation of metastable austenite to martensite may lead to an enhancement in ductility and fracture toughness. This enhancement has been reported for type 301 stainless steel (Ref 23), high-strength steels of the TRIP

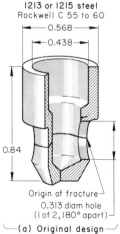
1213 or 1215 steel
Rockwell C 55 to 60

0.568
0.438
0.84

Origin of fracture
0.313 diam hole
(1 of 2, 180° apart)
(a) Original design

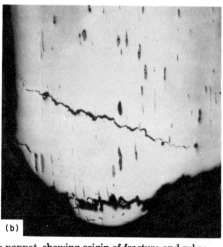
(b)

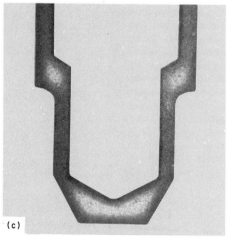
(c)

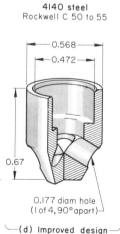
4140 steel
Rockwell C 50 to 55

0.568
0.472
0.67

0.177 diam hole
(1 of 4, 90° apart)
(d) Improved design

(a) Original design of the poppet, showing origin of fracture and subsequent complete fracture between two opposing holes in the narrowest section of the poppet. (b) Micrograph, at a magnification of 80×, of an unetched longitudinal section taken through the failed poppet, showing cracks extending across nonmetallic inclusions. (c) Macrograph, at a magnification of 4×, of a 5%-nital-etched longitudinal section taken through a poppet that did not fail, showing the carburized case extending to the center of the cross section. (d) Improved design of the poppet.

Fig. 14. Check-valve poppet, used to control fluid flow, that was redesigned to eliminate breakage in service caused by the presence of nonmetallic inclusions in the rephosphorized, resulfurized steel (Example 3)

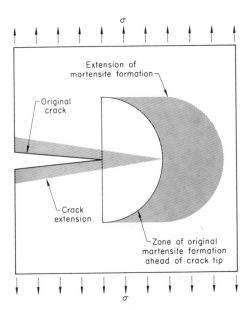

Fig. 15. Schematic diagram illustrating crack extension in metastable austenitic steel under stress, σ, with simultaneous formation of martensite in a zone ahead of the crack tip (Ref 28)

(transformation-induced plasticity) type (Ref 24 to 26) and some similar alloys (Ref 17 and 27) in which the austenite is relatively unstable and will transform to martensite under a plastic strain. Some workers (Ref 23 and 27) have shown that austenite-to-martensite transformation will give rise to localized strain hardening in the zone affected by the transformation and, in tensile tests, will cause a delay of necking by lengthening the time in which uniform thinning of the gage section takes place. The net effect is to enhance the ductility. Antolovich et al (Ref 17, 26 and 28) proposed that the basis for the enhanced ductility rests on the absorption of energy by the austenite-to-martensite transformation; this energy otherwise would be available for furtherance of crack propagation. The schematic diagram in Fig. 15 shows the zone ahead of a crack tip where austenite-to-martensite transformation is expected to take place. The larger the zone, the greater is the amount of energy absorbed by the transformation and thus the more effective is the enhancement of fracture toughness and ductility. Enhancement in fracture toughness can be determined by plotting values of K_{Ic} versus testing temperature, as in Fig. 16. In Fig. 16 there are two distinct groups of data — those in the low-temperature range from −200 C to +20 C (−328 to +68 F) and those in the high-temperature range of 100 C (212 F) and above. A gap exists between the values of K_{Ic} extrapolated from the two groups, and is defined as $\Delta K_{Ic}^{A \rightarrow M}$, which represents the net increase of the K_{Ic} value at any given temperature when martensitic transformation is induced during the fracture.

Although transformation is influenced by the testing temperature and the metastability of the austenite, other factors — including the stress and strain parameters, the strain rate, and the interactions between these parameters — also may influence the transformation. Thus, it may be difficult to predict quantitatively the enhancement in ductility and fracture toughness for a given alloy. Qualitatively, however, Gerberich et al (Ref 29) have established that the interlacing of two different fracture mechanisms — namely, cleavage in the martensite followed by dimpled rupture in the untransformed austenite — is probably the most important single factor contributing to the enhanced ductility and fracture toughness for TRIP and similar steels.

Jones et al (Ref 30) studied the use of an allotropic phase change to enhance the ductility of Fe-Ta alloys. The fracture behavior of two-phase Fe-Ta alloys was converted from brittle to ductile by use of ferrite-to-austenite transformation. Continuous grain-boundary Laves-phase networks present in these alloys after age hardening were spheroidized by a simple thermal treatment utilizing ferrite-austenite-ferrite transformation. The fracture characteristics of age-hardened specimens were converted from brittle to ductile, with a marked increase in elongation and reduction in area. On the other hand, Holzmann and Man (Ref 31) have described experimental studies showing that in a 0.06C-0.27Mn steel, heat treated to produce various grain sizes, the thickness of the grain-boundary cementite film has no apparent effect on the transition temperature and that the critical fracture stress for different cementite

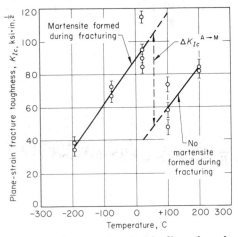

The gap between the straight lines through the two groups of data, $\Delta K_{Ic}^{A \rightarrow M}$, represents the net increase in K_{Ic} at a given temperature due to stress-induced transformation of austenite to martensite.

Fig. 16. Variation of plane-strain fracture toughness, K_{Ic}, with testing temperature for a high-carbon TRIP (transformation-induced plasticity) steel that was deformed approximately 75% at 460 C (860 F) (Ref 26)

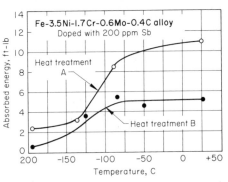

Heat treatment A: austenitize 4 hr at 1250 C (2280 F), oil quench to room temperature, temper 2 hr at 650 C (1202 F), water quench to room temperature, and age 1000 hr at 480 C (896 F).

Heat treatment B: austenitize 4 hr at 1250 C (2280 F), furnace cool to 900 C (1652 F) and hold 24 hr, oil quench to room temperature, temper 2 hr at 650 C (1202 F), water quench to room temperature, and age 1000 hr at 480 C (896 F).

Fig. 17. Effect of heat treatment on energy absorbed at various test temperatures. Tests were made on notched-bar toughness specimens of a Ni-Cr-Mo-C iron-base alloy doped with antimony. (Ref 32)

thicknesses is the same. Thus, the embrittling effect depends to a considerable extent on the nature of the second-phase precipitates.

In many nonferrous alloys (for example, aluminum alloy 7075 and titanium alloys Ti-8Mn and Ti-8Al-1Mo-1V), embrittlement resulting from second-phase precipitation at the grain boundaries causes a change in the fracture mode from transgranular to intergranular. The phenomenon is similar and somewhat related to the 500 F ("350 C") embrittlement that occurs in many martensitic steels. There are numerous occasions where grain-boundary precipitation has caused fracture of an alloy to be intergranular without necessarily altering the value of T_c for the alloy. Figure 17, which shows the curves of absorbed energy versus testing temperature for impact specimens of a Ni-Cr-Mo-C iron-base alloy with two different austenitizing heat treatments, illustrates one such instance. The impact energies at all testing temperatures for the specimens with the direct quench from 1250 C (2280 F) followed by a temper are seen to be consistently higher than the impact energies for the specimens that were originally furnace cooled to 900 C (1650 F), then quenched. However, there is no noticeable change of T_c.

Anisotropy

Metals acquire a preferred orientation, or directionality, as a result of crystallographic texturing and mechanical fibering during working. Results of toughness tests and other mechanical tests of worked metals are affected by the orientation of the specimen taken from a part. Anisotropy, therefore, is an important consideration in design, fabrication and failure analysis of rolled, extruded and forged parts.

The effect of specimen orientation on the notch toughness of an as-rolled low-carbon steel plate is shown in Fig. 18. Specimens parallel to the rolling direction (orientations L-S and L-T) show higher impact energies throughout the ductile-to-brittle transition-temperature range than do specimens perpendicular to the rolling direction (orientation T-L). Therefore, when a part is to be cut from plate, it may be advisable to specify the orientation of the part relative to the rolling direction.

The rolling schedule during fabrication of the plate affects anisotropy. For example, if the steel had been cross rolled so that it received about the same amount of hot reduction in both directions, the curves for orientations L-T and T-L would nearly coincide.

Regardless of the amount of cross rolling, specimens that are notched parallel to the plate surface (orientation L-S) absorb greater amounts of energy than those notched at right angles to the plate surface (orientation L-T). However, the temperature range over which transition occurs (and also the shear-fracture transition temperature) is the same regardless of notch or specimen orientation. Also, the maximum spread in energy absorption due to orientation occurs at the high-energy portion of the curves. At low energy levels, the curves nearly coincide. For data on the effect of specimen direction on notch toughness of low-carbon and medium-carbon alloy steels, see pages 229 to 231 in Volume 1 of this 8th Edition of METALS HANDBOOK.

Effect of Strain Rate on Toughness

It is generally established that increasing strain rate has an adverse effect on fracture toughness of iron and of ferritic and pearlitic steels. In pearlitic steel, fracture is strongly dependent on the spacing between the pearlite lamellae; an increase in the rate of strain is known to promote the formation of microcracks, which leads to a lowering of fracture toughness and K_{Ic}. On the other hand, increasing strain rate is also known to raise the yield strength of iron and low-carbon steel. Figures 19 and 20 show the increase of lower yield stress as a function of grain diameter, d, at three different strain rates for pure iron and for a 0.2% C steel, respectively. Note that for each level of the strain rate, the increase in yield stress obeys the Hall-Petch-Heslop relationship, similar to that shown in Fig. 8. In other words, both decreasing grain size and increasing

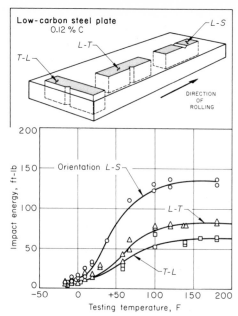

Fig. 18. Effect of specimen orientation on Charpy V-notch impact energy of as-rolled low-carbon (0.12% C) steel plate (Ref 33)

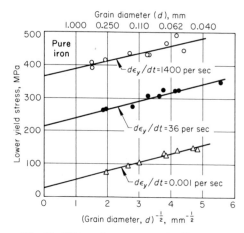

Fig. 19. Effect of average grain diameter, d, on the lower yield stress of pure iron tested at three values of $d\epsilon_y/dt$, which is the mean strain rate during yielding (Ref 34)

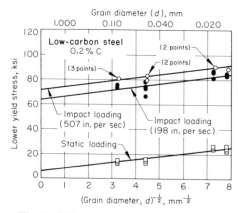

Fig. 20. Effect of average grain diameter, d, on the lower yield stress of low-carbon (0.2% C) steel tested at three loading rates (Ref 35)

strain rate will increase the yield stress of iron and low-carbon steel. Although decreasing grain size may also enhance fracture toughness, increasing strain rate will most likely lower it.

It is possible that strain rate interacts with other parameters. For instance, Hartbower (Ref 36) found that the fracture energy of D-6ac steel (nominal composition: 0.48% C, 0.2% Si, 1% Mo, 1.2% Cr, 0.5% Ni) is lower in a slow-bend test than in an impact test when tested at 149 to 315 C (300 to 600 F). The loss in fracture energy was attributed to a strain-aging effect, which the slow strain rate allowed to take place.

Studies of some alloys having face-centered-cubic and hexagonal, close-packed crystal structures indicate that higher strain rates increase both yield stress and ductility. These results are opposite to those reported for body-centered-cubic iron-base alloys. Apparently, strain rate affects fracture toughness differently for each of the three crystal structures because each structure deforms by a different mechanism.

Transition of Ferromagnetic Alloys

Fracture toughness of a number of ferromagnetic alloys is dependent on the crystallographic state of the alloys — that is, whether the alloys have an ordered or disordered lattice. Generally, an ordered alloy of the ferromagnetic type, such as Fe-49Co-2V or AlFe, is likely to fracture intergranularly. On the other hand, transgranular-cleavage fracture is obtained in disordered Fe-49Co-2V. Neither type of fracture, however, may be classified as ductile. Jordan and Stoloff (Ref 37) found that both the ordered and disordered alloys followed the Hall-Petch-Heslop relationship (Eq 1) of yield stress versus grain size at various temperatures, but that the ordered alloy showed a 550 C (1022 F) increase in T_c. They also found that for the ordered alloy, the predominant slip plane was {321} at low temperatures, {211} at intermediate temperatures, and {321} or possibly {110} at high temperatures. In contrast, wavy glide combined with slip on {321}, {211} and {110} planes was observed for the disordered alloy over a wide temperature range. The preference for a single slip plane at a given temperature was considered a possible cause for the low ductility observed in the ordered alloy.

Transition of Body-Centered-Cubic Refractory Metals

Body-centered-cubic refractory metals are characterized by the ductile metals columbium and tantalum, which typically exhibit transition temperatures below liquid-nitrogen temperature (−196 C or −321 F), and the more brittle metals molybdenum and tungsten, which have transition temperatures near room temperature and substantially above room temperature, respectively. This marked difference in ductility is attributed to differences in the mobility of screw dislocations in these metals. In columbium and tantalum, screw and edge dislocations have nearly equal mobilities at cryogenic temperatures. In contrast, screw dislocations have much lower mobility than edge dislocations in molybdenum and tungsten, which gives rise to brittle behavior. For tungsten, the temperature must be increased to 200 to 300 C (392 to 572 F) for screw-dislocation mobility to approach edge-dislocation mobility, with an accompanying transition to ductile behavior.

Columbium-base and tantalum-base alloys also exhibit transition temperatures below −196 C (−321 F). Alloys have been developed that utilize solid-solution or dispersed-phase strengthening for high-temperature service, yet maintain good fabricability, weldability and low-temperature ductility. Exceptions to this good ductility are columbium alloys containing 10 to 15 at. % tungsten, which have transition temperatures near room temperature. Columbium and tantalum and their alloys are extremely susceptible to interstitial-impurity embrittlement. Hydrogen present as an interstitial or as a hydride can raise the transition temperatures of these alloys to above room temperature. Oxygen and nitrogen have similar, but not quite as deleterious, effects on transition temperature (Ref 38).

Molybdenum alloys such as Mo-0.5Ti and Mo-TZM exhibit transition temperatures near room temperature whereas tungsten alloys such as W-2ThO₂, W-3Re and W-5Re have transition temperatures from 100 to 300 C (212 to 572 F). Molybdenum and tungsten and their alloys are not susceptible to hydrogen embrittlement; however, oxygen, nitrogen or carbon contamination, rough surface condition, high strain rate, and intermediate grain size can increase the transition temperatures of these metals (Ref 39). Transition temperatures near −196 C (−321 F) can be achieved in molybdenum and tungsten by alloying with approximately 30 at. % rhenium. However, because of the high cost of rhenium, these alloys have limited use.

Transition of Hexagonal, Close-Packed Metals

Deformation of titanium and some other hexagonal, close-packed metals and alloys by mechanical twinning is more prevalent with decreasing temperatures. The influence of testing tem-

perature on the fracture behavior of titanium and titanium alloys is shown in Fig. 21 for titanium and in Fig. 22 for five commercial titanium alloys. Unalloyed titanium containing 0.25% oxygen undergoes a ductile-to-brittle transition in the temperature range where second-order {112̄2} twinning within twins becomes prominent (see Fig. 21). There is experimental evidence linking the formation of microcracks by twin-matrix separation with the production of second-order twins, although it is not certain that the microcracks directly contribute to the loss of fracture toughness. The interstitial oxygen content of the material also significantly affects the fracture energy of the material. In addition, the crystallographic features of twinning planes, the interactions between a twinning plane and grain boundaries, and the interactions between two intersecting twins are important to the fracture of titanium, particularly at temperatures as low as −129 C (−200 F) and below.

The various commercial titanium alloys for which data are shown in Fig. 22 did not exhibit sharp transition temperatures. There was no observed change in the fracture mode (ductile dimpled rup-

ture), although the impact energy of the alloys decreased with decreasing testing temperature.

The ductile-to-brittle transition with decreasing temperature for a number of hexagonal, close-packed metals, including zinc, magnesium and beryllium, has been attributed to the change from easy secondary slip to obstruction of secondary slip in accordance with Taylor's multiple-glide operation (Ref 42 and 43). The fracture surface of magnesium at low temperatures, about −196 C (−321 F), is strongly aligned with the basal {0001} and the prismatic {101̄0} slip planes, but at higher temperatures (room temperature and above), dimpled rupture by microvoid coalescence is the predominant fracture mechanism. Utilizing the Hall-Petch-Heslop relationship (Eq 1), Armstrong (Ref 42) determined that the larger the values of the Taylor orientation factor, the yield stress, and the critical resolved shear stress for the primary slip operation, the higher is the transition temperature. This implies that with the obstruction of the primary slip operation, the yield stress will increase accompanied by an increase in T_c. The presence of inclusions may also influence the plas-

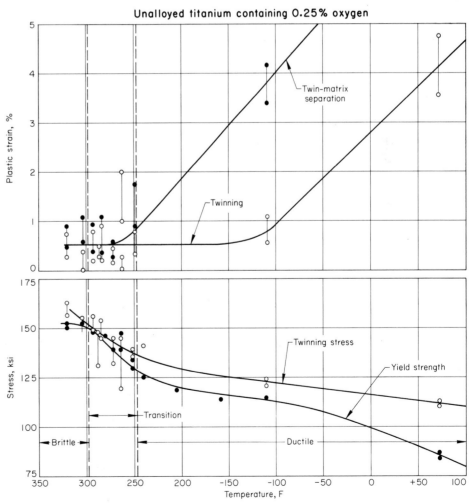

Fig. 21. Effect of temperature on yielding, twinning and twin-matrix separation in large-grained specimens of unalloyed titanium containing 0.25% oxygen (Ref 40)

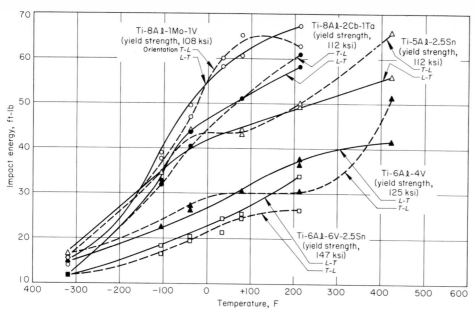

Fig. 22. Charpy V-notch impact energy versus testing temperature for specimens of five titanium alloys having two orientations (see Fig. 18 for orientation code) (Ref 41)

tic-flow pattern and fracture properties of some hexagonal, close-packed metals. For example, initiation of microvoids in some magnesium alloys (Ref 43) is due to the presence of zirconium hydride and thorium-zirconium-magnesium inclusions in the magnesium matrix.

References

1. G. R. Irwin, NRL Report 4763, U. S. Naval Research Laboratory, Washington, D. C., May 1956; see also G. R. Irwin, J. A. Kies and H. L. Smith, Fracture Strengths Relative to Onset and Arrest of Crack Propagation, *Proc ASTM,* Vol 58, 1958, p 640-660

2. J. Heslop and N. J. Petch, The Ductile-Brittle Transition in the Fracture of α-Fe: II, *Phil Mag,* Vol 3, 1958, p 1128; see also E. O. Hall, The Deformation and Aging of Mild Steel, *Proc Phys Soc (London),* Vol 64, Sec B, 1951, p 742-753

3. A. R. Duffy, G. M. McClure, R. J. Eiber and W. A. Maxey, Fracture Design Practices for Pressure Piping, p 200 in "Fracture", Vol V, H. Liebowitz (Ed.), Academic Press, New York, 1969

4. W. S. Pellini, Evaluation of the Significance of Charpy Tests, in "Symposium on Effect of Temperature on the Brittle Behavior of Metals with Particular Reference to Low Temperatures", STP 158, ASTM, 1954, p 222; see also W. S. Pellini, Evolution of Principles for Fracture-Safe Design of Steel Structures, NRL Report 6957, U. S. Naval Research Laboratory, Washington, D. C., Sept 1969, p 9

5. J. M. Barsom and S. T. Rolfe, Correlations Between K_{Ic} and Charpy V-Notch Test Results in the Transition-Temperature Range, in "Symposium on Impact Testing of Metals", STP 466, ASTM, p 281-302

6. M. Szczepanski, "The Brittleness of Steel", John Wiley & Sons, New York, 1963

7. A. S. Tetelman and A. J. McEvily, Jr., "Fracture of Structural Materials", John Wiley & Sons, New York, 1967, p 113

8. T. G. Heberling and G. E. Selby, Drop-Weight Tear Test — Effect of Variables on Test Results, in "Symposium on Impact Testing of Metals", STP 466, ASTM, 1970, p 224-240

9. J. D. Defilippi, K. G. Brickner and E. M. Gilbert, "Ductile-to-Brittle Transition in Austenitic Cr-Mn-N Stainless Steels", *Trans Met Soc AIME,* Vol 245, Oct 1969, p 2141-2148

10. M. E. Shank (Ed.), "Control of Steel Construction to Avoid Brittle Failure", Welding Research Council, New York, 1957, p 30

11. F. deKazinczy, W. A. Backofen and B. Kapadia, discussion in: N. J. Petch, The Ductile-Cleavage Transition in Alpha Iron, p 54-64 in "Fracture", B. L. Averbach, D. K. Felbeck, G. T. Hahn and D. A. Thomas (Ed.), The Technology Press of M.I.T., and John Wiley & Sons, New York, 1959

12. M. J. Roberts, Effect of Transformation Substructure on the Strength and Toughness of Fe-Mn Alloys, *Met Trans,* Vol 1, 1970, p 3291

13. J. C. Thornley and A. S. Wronski, The Relation Between the Ductile-Brittle Transition Temperature and Grain Size in Polycrystalline Molybdenum, *Scripta Met,* Vol 3, Dec 1969, p 935

14. A. H. Cottrell, Theoretical Aspects of Fracture, p 20-44 in "Fracture", B. L. Averbach, D. K. Felbeck, G. T. Hahn and D. A. Thomas (Ed.), John Wiley & Sons, New York, 1959

15. F. Cappelli and A. Molaroni, The Effect of Composition, Grain Size and Degree of Hot Reduction on the Transition Temperature of Steels for Low Temperature, *Met Ital,* Vol 61, June 1969, p 251 (in Italian)

16. K. J. Irvine, A Comparison of the Bainite Transformation With Other Strengthening Mechanisms in High-Strength Structural Steel, p 55-65 in "Symposium: Steel-Strengthening Mechanisms", Climax Molybdenum Co., May 1969

17. R. F. Hehemann, V. J. Luhan and A. R. Troiano, The Influence of Bainite on Mechanical Properties, *Trans ASM,* Vol 49, 1957, p 409-426

18. S. D. Antolovich, A. Saxena and G. R. Chanani, Increased Fracture Toughness in a 300 Grade Maraging Steel as a Result of Thermal Cycling, *Met Trans,* Vol 5, 1974, p 623

19. C. Vishnevsky and E. A. Steigerwald, Influence of Alloying Elements on the Low-Temperature Toughness of Martensitic High Strength Steels, *Trans ASM,* Vol 62, Feb 1969, p 305-317

20. Nickel Steels, Brochure NS-4, The International Nickel Company, Inc., New York

21. C. Vishnevsky and E. A. Steigerwald, Influence of Alloying Elements on the Toughness of Low-Alloy Martensitic High-Strength Steels, AMMRC CR-80-09(F), Army Materials and Mechanics Research Center, Watertown, Massachusetts, Nov 1968

22. F. W. Schaller and V. F. Zackay, Low Temperature Embrittlement of Austenitic Cr-

Mn-N-Fe Alloy, *Trans ASM,* Vol 51, 1959, p 609-628

23. J. P. Bressanelli and A. Moskowitz, Effect of Strain Rate, Temperature, and Composition of Tensile Properties of Metastable Austenitic Stainless Steels, *Trans ASM,* Vol 59, 1966, p 223

24. V. F. Zackay, E. R. Parker, D. Fahr and R. Busch, The Enhancement of Ductility in High-Strength Steels, *Trans ASM,* Vol 60, 1967, p 252

25. W. W. Gerberich, P. L. Hemmings, M. D. Merz and V. F. Zackay, Preliminary Toughness Result on TRIP Steel, *Trans ASM,* Vol 61, 1969, p 843

26. S. D. Antolovich and B. Singh, On the Toughness Increment Associated with the Austenite Phase Transformation in TRIP Steels, *Met Trans,* Vol 2, 1971, p 2135

27. D. V. Neff, T. E. Mitchell and A. R. Troiano, The Influence of Temperature, Transformation and Strain Rate on the Ductility Properties of Austenitic Stainless Steels, *Trans ASM,* Vol 62, 1969, p 858

28. S. D. Antolovich, Fracture Toughness and Strain-Induced Phase Transformation, *Trans AIME,* Vol 242, 1968, p 2371-2373

29. W. W. Gerberich, P. L. Hemmings and V. F. Zackay, Fracture and Fractography of Metastable Austenites, *Met Trans,* Vol 2, 1971, p 2243

30. R. H. Jones, E. R. Parker and V. F. Zackay, Use of an Allotropic Phase Change to Enhance Ductility in Fe-Ta Alloys, p 829-838 in "Electron Microscopy and Structure of Materials", University of California Press, 1972

31. M. Holzmann and J. Man, Influence of Grain-Boundary Cementite Thickness on the Brittleness Transition Temperature and the Critical Fracture Stress of Low-Carbon Steel, *J Iron and Steel Inst,* Vol 209, Oct 1971, p 836

32. B. J. Schulz and J. C. McMahon, Jr., Fracture of Alloy Steels by Intergranular Microvoid Coalescence as Influenced by Composition and Heat Treatment, *Met Trans,* Vol 4, 1973, p 2485-2489

33. P. P. Puzak, E. W. Eschbacher, W. S. Pellini, Initiation and Propagation of Brittle Fracture in Structural Steels, *Welding Res Supp,* Dec 1952, p 569-s

34. J. Harding, The Effect of Grain Size and Strain Rate on the Lower Yield Stress of Pure Iron at 288°K, *Acta Met,* Vol 17, 1969, p 954

35. J. D. Campbell and J. Harding, "The Effect of Grain Size, Rate of Strain and Neutron Irradiation on the Tensile Strength of α-iron, Response of Metals to High Velocity Deformation", Interscience, 1960, p 66

36. C. E. Hartbower, Materials Sensitive to Slow Rates of Straining, in STP 466, ASTM, 1970, p 281

37. K. R. Jordan and N. S. Stoloff, Plastic Deformation and Fracture in FeCo-2 pct V, *Trans AIME,* Vol 245, Sept 1969, p 2027-2034

38. W. D. Wilkinson, Properties of Refractory Metals, ASM-USAEC monograph, Gordon and Breach Science Publishers, 1969

39. J. R. Stephens, A Review of the Deformation Behavior of Tungsten at Temperatures Less Than 0.2 the Melting Point (K), *Reviews on the Deformation Behavior of Materials,* Vol 1, No. 1, 1974, Tel-Aviv, Israel

40. M. F. Amateau, E. A. Steigerwald, The Relationship Between Plastic Deformation and Fracture in Alpha Titanium, AFML-TR-66-263, June 1966, Air Force Materials Laboratory, Wright-Patterson Air Force Base, Ohio

41. R. W. Huber and R. J. Goode, Fracture Toughness Tests for Titanium Alloy Plate and Forgings, NRL Report 6228, Apr 21, 1965, U. S. Naval Research Laboratory, Washington, D. C.

42. R. W. Armstrong, Theory of the Tensile Ductile-Brittle Behavior of Polycrystalline HCP Materials, with Application to Beryllium, *Acta Met,* Vol 16, 1968, p 347-355

43. C. D. Calhoun and N. S. Stoloff, Effects of Particles on Fracture Processes in Magnesium Alloys, *Met Trans,* Vol 1, 1970, p 997-1006

FAILURES FROM VARIOUS MECHANISMS AND RELATED ENVIRONMENTAL FACTORS

CONTENTS

Identification of Types of Failures

ANALYSIS of a failure of a metal structure or part usually requires identification of the type of failure. Failure can occur by one or more of several mechanisms, including surface damage such as corrosion or wear, elastic or plastic distortion, and fracture. The individual articles that follow in this section discuss these various types of failure. For example, surface damage by corrosion is discussed in the articles on Corrosion Failures and on Elevated-Temperature Failures. Wear is discussed in three articles — those on Wear Failures, on Fretting Failures, and on Liquid-Erosion Failures. Elastic and plastic distortion is dealt with in the article on Distortion Failures, and time-dependent plastic distortion (creep) is dealt with in the article on Elevated-Temperature Failures.

Because there are several types of failure by fracture, including those affected by chemical or thermal environment, the various methods of describing and classifying fractures are discussed in the present article.

Classification of Fractures

Many elements of fracture have been used to describe and categorize the types of fractures encountered in the laboratory and in service. These elements include loading conditions, rate of crack growth, and macroscopic and microscopic appearance of fracture surfaces.

Failure analysts often find it useful to classify fractures on a macroscopic scale

as ductile fractures, brittle fractures, fatigue fractures, and fractures resulting from the combined effects of stress and environment. The last group includes stress-corrosion cracking and liquid-metal embrittlement (which are discussed in the article on Stress-Corrosion Cracking), interstitial embrittlement (discussed in the article on Hydrogen-Damage Failures), corrosion fatigue (see article on Corrosion-Fatigue Failures), and stress rupture (see article on Elevated-Temperature Failures). Fractures by combined or mixed mechanisms frequently occur.

Loading Conditions. A fracture that has resulted from loading being increased at a low or moderate rate to the breaking point of the material often is called an *overload fracture;* when the load is increased at a high rate, the resulting fracture often is called an *impact fracture. Stress-rupture fracture* is produced by sustained application of a fairly steady load. *Fatigue fracture* is produced by repeated or cyclic application of load. The direction of loading is described by terms such as tension, compression, bending, torsion, direct shear, and contact. Additional terms are used to describe directions of fatigue loads; these terms are discussed in the article on Fatigue Failures, which begins on page 95 in this volume.

Crack-Growth Rate. Cracks that lead to ductile fracture grow at a low rate — generally, less than 20 ft per second. This "slow" cracking (which is known as

stable crack growth) proceeds only while external loading is applied.

Unstable crack growth can proceed at a rate as high as several thousand feet per second. This "fast" cracking can proceed under internal elastic stressing, without the need for a continuing externally applied load, and can lead to catastrophic brittle failure of a structure. The rate of crack growth may diminish significantly with increasing temperature so that, at some temperatures, fracture may proceed by a mixture of plastic deformation and brittle cracking, or may occur as ductile fracture.

In addition to being affected by temperature, crack-growth rate is affected also by the chemical composition, crystal structure, microstructure and grain size of the alloy, the size of the part, the direction of loading, the strain rate, and the chemical environment. The effects of these various factors are discussed in the individual articles that follow in this section of this volume.

Macroscopic Examination. The macroscopic appearance of a fracture surface is described in terms of light reflection (bright or gray) and in terms of texture (smooth or rough, crystalline or silky, granular or fibrous). The use of the terms brittle and ductile to describe macroscopic strain that occurs prior to final separation, and the terms *flat-face* and *shear-face* to describe the macroscopic direction of fracture, are discussed below. The terms that describe macroscopic modes of fracture, which are gross (or net-section) yielding, plane stress, plane strain, and mixed mode, are described on pages 87 and 88 in the Appendix to the article on Ductile and Brittle Fractures.

Microscopic Examination. The microscopic appearance of a fracture surface is described in terms of the microscopic features that are present. For example, a dimpled rupture exhibits mainly dimples and a cleavage fracture exhibits mainly cleavage facets. A fracture that exhibits separated-grain facets (see Fig. 6) sometimes is called a "rock candy" fracture. (When the grain size is large, a "rock candy" fracture also can be observed macroscopically.)

Microscopic mechanisms of fracture include grain-boundary separation, microvoid coalescence, cleavage and fatigue. The microscopic path followed by any fracture in a metal can be used to classify the fracture as either transgranular (by microvoid coalescence, cleavage or fatigue) or intergranular (by grain-boundary separation with or without microvoid coalescence).

There are two crystallographic modes by which materials can fracture: they can cleave or they can shear. In close-packed crystals (face-centered cubic and hexagonal, close-packed), shear (slip) may occur on the same crystallographic planes as cleavage; in body-centered-cubic crystals such as iron, shear and cleavage occur on different planes.

Ductile Fractures

Ductile fractures are characterized by tearing of metal accompanied by appreciable gross plastic deformation and expenditure of considerable energy. Ductile tensile fractures in most materials have a gray, fibrous appearance and are classified on a macroscopic scale as either flat-face (square) or shear-face (slant) fractures.

Flat-face tensile fractures in ductile materials are produced under plane-strain conditions (that is, in thick sections), with necking, and typically occur normal (perpendicular) to the direction of loading, with some shear lip being formed at the junction of the fracture surface and the part surface (Fig. 1). The ratio of the area of the flat-face region to the area of shear lip usually becomes greater as the section thickness is increased.

Microscopic examination of flat-face tensile fractures in ductile materials at magnifications of about 100 diameters and greater will reveal equiaxed dimples, formed by microvoid coalescence, in the flat-face region (Fig. 2).

Shear-face tensile fractures in ductile materials are produced under plane-stress conditions (that is, in thin sections or near free surfaces), with or without necking, and typically occur at angles of about 45° to the surface of the part. Figure 3 shows an alloy steel bolt that fractured in a ductile manner because of overloading caused by the fatigue fracture of another portion of the assembly. The angle of the full-slant fracture surface (approximately 45°) and the fine, gray, silky appearance of the fracture are both characteristic of shear-face tensile fractures in ductile materials. Necking is faintly visible in the threaded area near the fracture surface.

Microscopic examination of shear-face tensile fractures (and the shear lips of flat-face tensile fractures) in ductile materials at magnifications of about 100 diameters and greater will reveal elongated dimples with their long axes in the direction of the shear force (Fig. 4). The elongated dimples produced by tensile shearing point in opposite directions on mating fracture surfaces. Elongated dimples are produced also by tensile tearing, but such dimples point in the same direction on mating fracture surfaces — which distinguishes them from shear dimples (see Fig. 45 on page 91 in the Appendix to the article on Ductile and Brittle Fractures, in this volume).

Fig. 3. Shear-face tensile fracture in an alloy steel bolt that broke by overload when another portion of the assembly fractured by fatigue. (Light fractograph; actual size)

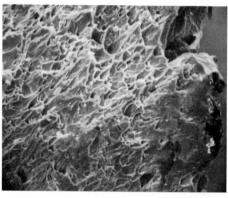

The free edge of the shear-lip zone is the vertical margin at the right. The dimples are elongated, and their rounded ends point in the same direction. The mating surface of this shear-lip zone would show similar elongated, parallel dimples, but the rounded ends of the dimples would point in a direction opposite to that shown in this fractograph.

Fig. 4. Shear dimples in the shear-lip zone of a Charpy impact fracture in hot rolled 1040 steel. (SEM fractograph; 400×)

Brittle Fractures

Brittle fractures are characterized by rapid crack propagation with less expenditure of energy than with ductile fractures and without appreciable gross plastic deformation. Brittle tensile fractures have a bright, granular appearance, are of the flat-face type, and are produced under plane-strain conditions with little or no necking. They are typified by an almost featureless fracture surface that is generally normal (perpendicular) to the direction of loading. A chevron pattern may be present on the fracture surface, pointing toward the origin of the crack. Figure 5 shows a fragment of a titanium alloy pressure vessel that failed catastrophically by brittle tensile fracture under a service load. It was found that electric engraving of a serial number on the vessel had created small cracks, which initiated the fracture. Note that the fracture surface, which is nearly perpendicular to the surfaces of the vessel, exhibits a well-developed chevron pattern.

Microscopic examination of brittle fractures will reveal intergranular or

(a)   (b)

(a) A view of a portion of the fracture surface. (b) A profile view of the fracture. The flat-face region is clearly visible across the center of the fracture; above and below it are shear lips, which are at a 45° slant to the flat-face region.

Fig. 1. Flat-face tensile fracture in an aluminum alloy plate pulled to rupture in a universal testing machine. (Light fractographs; 2×)

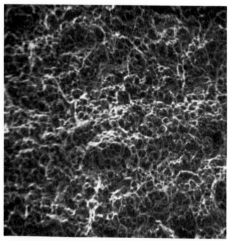

Fig. 2. Equiaxed dimples on the flat-face fracture surface of a 1020 steel specimen broken in tension. Note large dimples that contain smaller dimples. (SEM fractograph; 100×)

Fracture was initiated by small cracks created by electric engraving of a serial number on the vessel. Note that the fracture is flat-faced and exhibits a well-developed chevron pattern pointing to the left, toward the fracture origin (not visible).

Fig. 5. Brittle tensile fracture in a titanium alloy pressure vessel that broke in a catastrophic manner under a service load. (Light fractograph; ¾×)

Fig. 6. Intergranular brittle fracture in 4340 steel (with a tensile strength of 260 to 280 ksi), showing facets that are the surfaces of equiaxed grains that have separated without microvoid coalescence; a "rock candy" fracture surface. (TEM fractograph of a plastic-carbon replica; magnification, 1700×)

transgranular facets. Intergranular facets are grain surfaces that have been exposed by crack propagation along grain boundaries (Fig. 6). The transgranular facets observed on brittle fractures are produced by cleavage along numerous parallel crystallographic planes, thus creating a terraced fracture surface. The individual levels of the terraced surface are separated by cleavage steps that are formed by fracture of the thin ligaments joining the cleavage-crack segments. As the transgranular crack propagates, the crack segments join together on fewer and fewer planes. As a result, the cleavage steps converge in the direction of local crack propagation to form a river pattern (see Fig. 7).

Fatigue Fractures

Fatigue fractures result from cyclic loading, and appear brittle on a macroscopic scale. They are characterized by incremental propagation of cracks until the cross section has been reduced to where it can no longer support the maximum applied load, and fast fracture ensues. Frequently, the progress of a service-induced fatigue crack is indicated by a series of macroscopic crescents, or "beach marks", progressing from the origin of the crack. Figure 8 illustrates a fatigue fracture in an alloy steel lift pin from a large crane. An improper heat treatment resulted in insufficient fatigue strength in this part, and repeated loading caused a fatigue crack to propagate across the section. Note that crack propagation proceeded from both the top and

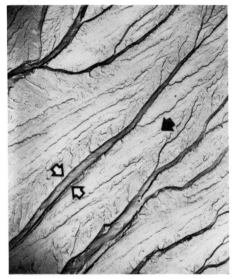

The white arrows point to a cleavage step; the black arrow shows the direction of crack propagation. (TEM fractograph of a plastic-carbon replica; 4900×)

Fig. 7. River patterns on the surface of a brittle transgranular fracture in an Alnico alloy specimen

The pin had insufficient fatigue strength because of improper heat treatment. Two fatigue zones are evident (at top and at bottom), each containing a set of beach marks. Final fracture was by ductile shear, in the horizontal band near the midsection of the pin.

Fig. 8. Fatigue fracture in an alloy steel lift pin from a large crane. (Light fractograph; actual size)

the bottom of the pin, as shown by the two sets of beach marks, with final fracture occurring by ductile shear on a band near the midsection of the pin.

Figure 9 shows the surface of a fatigue fracture in a forged steel trailer towbar that broke after a comparatively low number of load cycles. Examination revealed the towbar to be made of coarse-grained pearlitic steel with a heavily decarburized outer surface. The decarburized surface had greatly reduced tensile strength, and caused fracture to initiate under cyclic tensile stress. The area of final fracture is relatively large because the coarse-grained pearlitic microstructure had poor resistance to impact loading in the presence of the fatigue crack.

In the fatigue fracture shown in Fig. 9, the fracture surface consists of three distinct zones — a fairly smooth, multiple-origin fatigue zone containing "ratchet marks", a low-cycle, rougher fatigue zone, and a single-cycle final-fracture zone. The last zone may be described as brittle because it is perpendicular to the principal tensile stress and shows no visible plastic deformation. This is an example of the type of fracture in which the fatigue-cracking mechanism accounts for only a small portion of the entire fracture surface. In highly notch-sensitive materials, the fatigue crack that initiates final, fast fracture may be so small as to be nearly invisible to the unaided eye.

Microscopic examination of fatigue fractures often reveals characteristic striations. Each striation is the result of a single cycle of loading; however, a recognizable striation is not necessarily produced by each cycle. Striations formed by high-cycle fatigue in aluminum alloy 6061-T6 are shown in Fig. 10.

Three zones can be seen: at bottom are several crack origins on slightly different planes, forming "ratchet marks"; the cracks from these origins combined to form a single crack front, which progressed through the next, rougher zone (at bracket A) by low-cycle fatigue; the large, brittle zone at top was formed during final fracture by a single load cycle.

Fig. 9. Surface of a fatigue fracture in a forged steel trailer towbar that broke after a comparatively low number of load cycles. (Light fractograph; actual size)

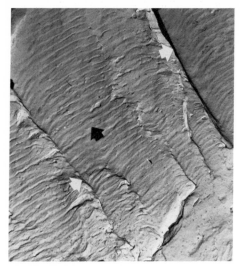

The striations are closely spaced and propagate on flat plateaus joined by shear steps (at white arrows). Black arrow indicates direction of crack propagation. (TEM fractograph of a plastic-carbon replica; 4900×)

Fig. 10. High-cycle fatigue striations in a fracture surface of aluminum alloy 6061-T6

Environmentally Affected Fractures

Figures 11 and 12 show two fractures caused by the combined effects of stress and corrosive environment. Figure 11 shows a "C-ring" specimen that was cut from aluminum alloy 7039-T6 plate. The specimen fractured by stress-corrosion cracking under applied tensile stress while immersed in a salt solution. Note that at the low magnification of ¾× neither the ring surface nor the fracture surface exhibits evidence of appreciable corrosive attack. The flat-face fracture surface, with no visible evidence of plastic deformation, is typical of stress-corrosion fractures.

Figure 12 shows the fracture surfaces of two aluminum alloy 2024-T4 plates that failed by liquid-metal embrittlement. The plates were inoculated with liquid mercury and then loaded to fracture in tension. The plates broke at a stress well below the nominal yield strength. Rapid fracture occurred under these conditions, producing a fracture surface consisting of a flat, mercury-damaged region surrounded by a shear region. The extent of the mercury-damaged region always depends on the amount of mercury available at the site of inoculation, but the surrounding fracture surface may be either ductile or brittle, depending on the notch sensitivity of the attacked metal. In Fig. 12, the mercury-damaged region is clearly delineated on the fracture surface. The inoculation region is on the left side of the plate areas shown. Near the inoculation region, the aluminum alloy is reduced to a mass of grain fragments.

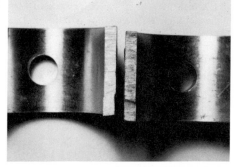

Fracture occurred under applied tensile stress during immersion in a salt solution. No appreciable evidence of corrosive attack is visible on the ring surface or on the fracture surface. (Light fractograph; ¾×)

Fig. 11. Stress-corrosion-cracking fracture in a "C-ring" specimen cut from an aluminum alloy 7039-T6 plate

Figures 13 and 14 illustrate the multiple cracking that is typical of corrosion fatigue. Note that the parallel cracks in Fig. 14 are filled with corrosion product. The fracture surface of a steel rail head that broke by fatigue at a subsurface hydrogen-induced flake is shown in Fig. 15. Flake formation in steel is one of the types of damage that can result from exposure to hydrogen. Subsurface initiation is common in fractures of this type.

Determination of Fracture Type

Several analytical procedures are available for distinguishing among the various types of fracture. For example, the presence or absence of plastic macro-deformation can be determined with the unaided eye, or by use of a steel scale, a machinist's micrometer, or a machinist's or measuring microscope. Differences in some dimensional attribute of parts (such as width or thickness) at and well

The corrosion-fatigue cracks are adjacent to a weld joining the superheater tube to a stainless steel tube (at left). At this junction, the temperature normally encountered is approximately 595 to 620 C (1100 to 1150 F). The fatigue stress was caused by the tube vibrations inherent in normal operation of the boiler.

Fig. 13. Circumferential corrosion-fatigue cracks in a low-alloy steel superheater tube (at right). About ⅞×

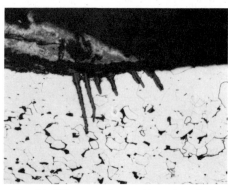

Fig. 14. Micrograph, at 100×, of a nital-etched section through a plain carbon steel boiler tube, showing parallel corrosion fatigue cracks in the initial stages of development. Note the gray corrosion product that fills the cracks. The fatigue stress was caused by tube vibration.

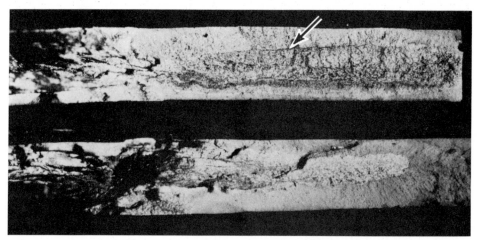

Fracture occurred rapidly at a stress well below the nominal yield strength of the plates. Visible on each fracture surface is a flat, mercury-damaged region (see arrow in upper fracture) surrounded by a shear region. The region nearest the wetting (at left) consists of a dark mass of grain fragments. (Light fractograph; 1⅔×)

Fig. 12. Liquid-metal-embrittlement fractures in two aluminum alloy 2024-T4 plates that were wetted with liquid mercury and then loaded to fracture in tension

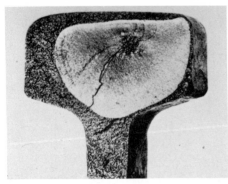

Fig. 15. A transverse fracture in a 1075 steel railroad rail. Fracture nucleus (small dark area near top of railhead) is a hydrogen-induced flake (or "fisheye"), which initiated a fatigue crack (large light zone surrounding the nucleus).

away from the fracture can serve to define macrodeformation after assurance that both points of measurement had the same dimension before fracture.

Fracture-surface matching is also used to determine the presence or absence of plastic deformation. It is very important, however, to resist the temptation to fit the matching fracture surfaces together, because this almost always destroys (smears) microscopic features. The fracture surfaces should never actually touch during fracture-surface matching.

Macroscopic and microscopic examination of a fracture may reveal features that will help in distinguishing fatigue and environmentally affected fractures from the fractures discussed in detail in

the article on Ductile and Brittle Fractures. Features that indicate the fracture may be the result of fatigue include beach marks (see Fig. 8), multiple crack origins (see Fig. 9), striations (see Fig. 10), and smooth, rubbed regions. Fatigue striations, however, are the only reliable indicators, because the remaining three are found also in other types of fractures. For example, beach marks sometimes are observed on stress-corrosion fractures. It also should be noted that the absence of any or all of these features is not evidence that the fracture was not by fatigue.

If corrosion pits or corrosion products are found only on the slow-growth portions of a fracture surface, the environment probably was sufficiently corrosive to affect the fracture mechanism. However, if evidence of corrosion is found on both the slow-growth and fast-growth portions, some corrosion took place subsequent to fracture and the environment may or may not have influenced fracture.

Like ductile and brittle fractures, stress-corrosion cracking can follow either transgranular or intergranular paths. Therefore, fracture path alone is not a reliable indicator of whether or not a corrosive environment has affected the fracture mechanism. Stress-corrosion cracks, however, are distinguished by pronounced secondary branching from the main fracture, and by secondary cracks located adjacent to the main fracture but not connected to it.

A microscopic feature that often is found on the facets of intergranular frac-

Fracture shown was produced in a specimen of 4315 steel by stress-corrosion cracking in a 3½% NaCl solution. (TEM fractograph of a plastic-carbon replica; 2680X)

Fig. 16. Transgranular-cleavage fracture showing hairline indications (fine tear ridges) at A, together with tongues at B, shallow dimples at C, and secondary cracks at D

tures caused by stress-corrosion cracking or hydrogen embrittlement is the fine tear ridge called a "hairline indication" (see features at A on the fracture surface in Fig. 16). However, it should be noted that, as with features of fatigue fractures, the absence of any or all of these features (corrosion pits, corrosion products, secondary cracks, crack branching and hairline indications) is not conclusive evidence that the fracture was not influenced by a corrosive environment.

Ductile and Brittle Fractures

By the ASM Committee on Analysis of Ductile and Brittle Fractures*

DUCTILE AND BRITTLE are terms that describe the amount of macroscopic strain that occurs prior to final separation of a specimen or part as it breaks. Fractures that do not exhibit significant ductility (elongation or reduction in area) are considered to be brittle, regardless of whether or not there is microscopic evidence of plasticity on the fracture surface. Fractures are not always exclusively ductile or brittle; often a fracture surface will exhibit both a ductile region and a brittle region. This article discusses factors that determine whether a fracture (or a fracture region) will be ductile or brittle, types of fracture initiators, causes of ductile and brittle fractures, and analysis of failures due to ductile or brittle fracture.

*See page 30 for committee list.

Classification of Fractures

Fractures in fragile materials occur in a brittle manner, whereas fractures in tough materials are usually ductile. A part made of a tough material, however, can sometimes fracture in a brittle manner, if that part (or a component of that part) contains a large enough flaw, or if there is sufficient elastic and plastic constraint.

As determined macroscopically, the occurrence of ductile or brittle behavior depends on the degree of localization of plastic flow. Consequently, the extent of plastic flow that occurs prior to fracture is strongly influenced by the stress state, which is defined by part thickness and the absence or presence of cracks (flaws) or other stress raisers. These effects are discussed in the Ap-

pendix to this article (see page 87), and in the article on Toughness and Fracture Mechanics, which begins on page 30.

Microscopic Classification. All fractures that occur in engineering metals can be grouped into one or more of the following general classifications, on the dual basis of the microscopic fracture path and the microscopic mechanism of fracture:

Transgranular fracture, by:
    Microvoid coalescence
    Cleavage
    Quasicleavage (combination of cleavage and microvoid coalescence)
    Fatigue
Intergranular fracture, by:
    Grain-boundary separation, with or without microvoid coalescence.

Fatigue-induced fractures are described in the article on Fatigue Failures,

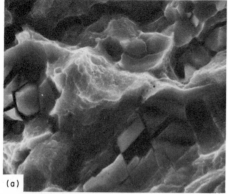

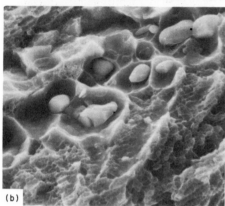

Fractographs are of an aluminum alloy 7075-T6 specimen containing a large concentration of relatively large second-phase particles. In both fracture-surface areas shown, fine dimples are visible in regions where there are no particles. Fracture of the particles visible in (a) was by cleavage. Considerable plastic deformation occurred in the material around the particles visible in (b).

Fig. 1. SEM fractographs, at 1000×, of two areas of the surface of a macroscopically brittle fracture caused by mixed mechanisms

which begins on page 95, and the article on Corrosion-Fatigue Failures, which begins on page 240, rather than in the present article. Fractures in each of the other classifications are described in the Appendix to this article (see page 87).

For an extensive presentation of the microscopic features of fracture surfaces, and a description of fractographic techniques utilizing light microscopy, and transmission and scanning electron microscopy, the reader is referred to Volume 9 of this Handbook.

The types of fracture dealt with in this article are those for which corrosive environment is not a major factor. For discussion of fractures due to stress-corrosion cracking, liquid-metal embrittlement, and hydrogen damage, see the articles that begin, respectively, on pages 205, 228 and 230 in this volume.

Fracture by Mixed Mechanisms. A fracture surface that exhibits intermingled features of two or more mechanisms of fracture in a given area is generally labeled a "mixed-mode" fracture. This is not to be confused with a fracture sur-

Fracture was initiated by a surface scratch, which can be located at lower edge of surface by tracing radial marks to their point of convergence. Fracture surface is that of an A2 tool steel die body, heat treated to Rockwell C 54 to 56, that broke on being loaded to 125,000 psi for a second time.

Fig. 2. Fracture surface exhibiting radial marks that converge at fracture origin

face having features that suggest successive operation of different fracture mechanisms as cracking proceeds across a section. In the latter instance, the individual fracture mechanisms can be analyzed sequentially and therefore require no special discussion.

The occurrence of fracture by mixed mechanisms often indicates (a) that the usual factors that determine the operative mechanism (such as state of stress, loading history, microstructure and environment) favor both mechanisms, and (b) that the fracture mechanism in adjacent microscopic or submicroscopic regions is determined by factors such as grain orientation or microstructure. For instance, in an alloy where second-phase particles are present, two effects are to be anticipated. First, because most of the second-phase particles are considerably harder and stronger than the matrix, their presence will undoubtedly contribute to the over-all strength of the alloy. Second, the fracture mechanism operating in the region where these hard particles are located may be different

from that operating in the regions where the particles are not located.

An example of the effects of hard second-phase particles may be seen in Fig. 1, which shows SEM fractographs of two areas in an aluminum alloy 7075-T6 specimen that broke in a macroscopically brittle manner. In both fractographs, fine dimples are visible in the regions where there are no particles, whereas in the regions where there are relatively large second-phase particles, the operative fracture mechanism was different. In Fig. 1(a), the fracture of the particles clearly was by cleavage; in Fig. 1(b), it is evident that considerable plastic deformation occurred in the material around the second-phase particles. Both fractographs, therefore, show mixed-mode fracture.

Transition From Ductile to Brittle Fracture

Some parts made of normally ductile metals fracture in a brittle manner without warning — that is, they undergo a ductile-to-brittle transition in fracture behavior. Unexpected brittle fracture often is attributed to low temperatures in service, but such fractures also can be induced by high strain rates, especially in thick sections containing sharp notches.

Characteristically, there are two aspects to be considered in the ductile-to-brittle fracture transition of metals. The first arises from conditions of constraint in the part, which may be treated by an analysis of the macroscopic fracture modes, as discussed in the Appendix to this article (see page 87). The second arises from the more specific metallurgical phenomena associated with the crystal structure, microstructure, composition and other characteristics of the metal. The effects of temperature and strain rate on these phenomena that bring about a change in the fracture toughness of the metal are discussed in detail in

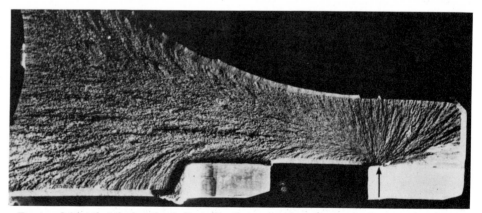

Fracture initiated at the location indicated by the arrow, where the corner of a snap-ring slot was specified to have a zero minimum radius. Fracture surface is that of a forging of AMS 6434 (vanadium-modified 4335) steel that was heat treated to a yield strength of 190,000 psi.

Fig. 3. Fracture surface exhibiting a chevron pattern (at left) pointing toward fracture origin, at a sharp corner

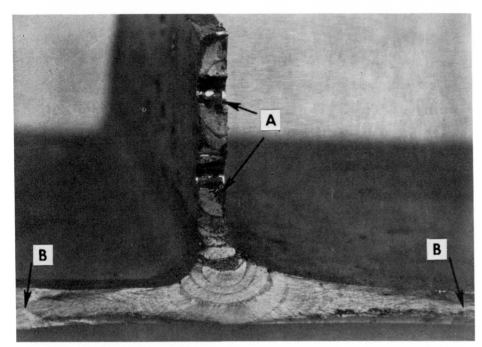

Cracking initiated at two rivet holes (arrows A) on the web of a structural-support beam of aluminum alloy 7075-T6, propagated slowly by fatigue to points B on the flange, then changed to unstable crack growth (rapid fracture). Light fractograph; about ¾×.

Fig. 4. Facture surface exhibiting crack-arrest lines (beach marks) that are characteristic of stable (slow) crack growth

the article on Ductile-to-Brittle Fracture Transition, which begins on page 44 in this volume.

Fracture Origins

Visual examination followed by low-power optical examination are often the first steps in determining the cause of fracture of a metal part. Oblique illumination frequently will reveal lines radiating from a point on the fracture surface (see Fig. 2). These lines, which are usually called radial marks or shear ledges, result from the intersection and connection of fractures propagating at different levels. Thus, by following these lines back to the point of convergence, the fracture-initiation site can be identified. In the radial zone of fractures in a part that has a width appreciably greater than the thickness, the radial marks will form a chevron, or herringbone, pattern pointing toward the origin of the fracture (see Fig. 3).

Radial marks on a fracture surface are indicative of unstable crack growth. During unstable crack growth, the crack front propagates at a relatively high velocity (which under some conditions may approach the speed of sound in the material).

Stable Crack Growth. It is not unusual, on tracing the fracture to its origin, to observe evidence of slow crack propagation that preceded unstable crack growth. This slow propagation, known as stable crack growth, can be identified by the presence of concentric rings surrounding the initiation site; these are crack-arrest lines and are sometimes referred to as beach, clamshell or conchoidal marks. Beach marks are most often associated with fatigue cracking, although they also are found on fractures caused by environmentally assisted fracture mechanisms (especially corrosion fatigue and stress-corrosion cracking).

A typical example of fatigue beach marks is presented in Fig. 4, which shows the fracture surface of a structural-support beam of aluminum alloy 7075-T6 that broke in a laboratory test under cyclic loading. It can be seen that fracture initiated independently at two origins, each of which is located at a rivet hole. The subsequent slow growth of fatigue cracks can be identified by the crack-arrest lines. The advancing cracks propagated first in the vertical direction — either up or down, depending on their relative location. After reaching the flange section in the lower part of the beam, the cracks propagated horizontally until a substantial portion of the cross section of the beam was fractured and the beam could no longer support the load. At that point, crack growth became unstable, which led to final separation by rapid fracture.

Figure 5 shows a fracture produced by stable crack growth, under an increasing load, in a hydrostatic proof test of a second-stage A-1 Polaris rocket-motor case. The case had been gas tungsten-arc welded from AMS 6434 (modified 4335) steel. The fracture origin shows evidence of a pre-existing small weld crack on the inside of the motor case. The next portion of the crack formed during the proof test and apparently was assisted by corrosion from inadequately inhibited hydrostatic-test fluid. Beyond the crack-arrest line, the crack extended further, slowly, but was less obviously aided by corrosion. Where the rough part of the fracture begins, crack growth became unstable and the fracture propagated rapidly in a brittle manner. In addition to having been hydrostatically tested with inadequately inhibited fluid, the rocket-motor case had been tempered in the temper-embrittlement range for AMS 6434 steel. When tempering and fluid inhibitor were corrected, no further failures occurred in rocket-motor cases of this design.

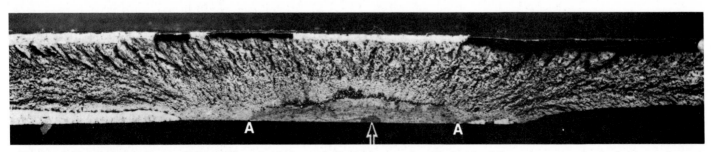

Fracture initiated at a small pre-existing weld crack (dark area indicated by arrow) on the inside of the motor case and extended to crack-arrest line (between A's) during hydrostatic testing, apparently assisted by corrosion. Next extension was slow (light area beyond crack-arrest line), which was followed by unstable, rapid fracture (rough region of radial marks formed by brittle fracture). The black areas and white areas at the plate surfaces are shear lips, which were the final regions to fracture.

Fig. 5. Light fractograph, at 3×, of a fracture surface of a second-stage A-1 Polaris rocket-motor case that was gas tungsten-arc welded from AMS 6434 (vanadium-modified 4335) steel

Notch Effects

The presence of discontinuities in a structural member subjected to load greatly influences the state of stress, and the fracture behavior, of the member. These discontinuities are often fracture origins. Discontinuities caused by abrupt changes in direction of a free surface are called notches. Intentional notches are inherent in many designs. Among the more common intentional notches are sharp fillets and corners (see Fig. 3), holes (see Fig. 4), threads, splines and keyways. Notches also can be produced accidentally by mechanical damage, such as from dents, gouges or scratches (see Fig. 2), or can be in the form of service-induced or pre-existing cracks (see Fig. 5).

Regardless of the source of the notch, the stress in a loaded member containing a notch abruptly increases at the root of the notch. For elastically loaded members, the magnitude of the increase of stress at the notch root is a function of the size, the contour, and, most of all, the sharpness of the notch. The increase in stress at the root of the notch is referred to as stress concentration, and the notch is referred to as a stress raiser or stress concentrator.

Stress Concentration. In one method of representing a stress field, lines are used to indicate the direction of principal stress. This method is illustrated in Fig. 6 for a circumferentially notched cylindrical specimen under axial tension. The nonuniform distribution of axial stress in the loaded specimen and the concentration of stress at the notch root is shown by the curve marked σ_A in Fig. 7. The major factor that determines stress concentration is the ratio of notch-root radius to notch diameter (the diameter of the specimen at the notch root). Under purely elastic stress conditions, stress concentration at the notch root becomes extremely high when the notch-root radius approaches zero. However, when the stress at the notch root exceeds the yield strength of the metal, plastic flow occurs. Plastic flow tends to blunt the notch, greatly reducing the stress concentration at the notch root.

Triaxial Stresses. In addition to having a stress-concentrating effect, the presence of a notch creates a stress state called triaxiality. Along the "walls" of a notch there is a relatively large mass of unstressed metal. When highly stressed metal at the root of a notch tries to contract laterally in response to axial strain produced by tensile stress, it is restrained by the adjacent unstressed metal. The result of this restraint is that lateral stresses are generated at the notch root. A triaxial stress state is attained when lateral stresses that are both parallel and perpendicular to the notch root exist in

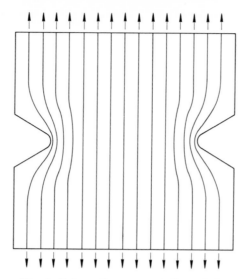

Fig. 6. Schematic representation of the stress field in a longitudinal section of a circumferentially notched cylindrical specimen subjected to axial tension. The vertical lines indicate directions of principal stress.

a plane perpendicular to the applied tensile stress. In a notched cylindrical specimen, triaxiality consists of axial, radial and circumferential stresses, whereas in a notched rectangular specimen, triaxiality consists of three mutually perpendicular stresses, one of which is in the through-thickness direction.

As shown in Fig. 7, the radial stress is zero at the free surface at the notch root, but rises to a high value in the interior of the cylinder before dropping to a lower value at the cylinder axis. The tangential stress is higher at the notch root than at the cylinder axis.

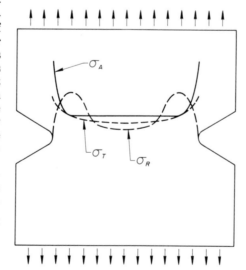

σ_A = axial stress; σ_R = radial stress; σ_T = tangential (circumferential) stress. Height above notch root of any point on curves indicates relative magnitude of stress at that radial position.

Fig. 7. Schematic illustration of the distribution of stresses in a circumferentially notched cylindrical specimen subjected to axial tension

In a thin rectangular member with a notch at one edge or with notches at opposite edges, there is no restraint in the through-thickness direction (parallel to the notch root), and no stress is generated in this direction. The stress state would then be biaxial.

Plastic Constraint. In the stress state shown in Fig. 7, the existence of lateral stresses increases the axial stress at which yielding occurs. This can be illustrated if it is assumed that yielding (plastic flow) takes place at a critical shear stress, τ_c.

For an unnotched cylinder under tension, the value of shear stress is given by:

$$\tau = \sigma_A/2 \qquad \text{(Eq 1)}$$

where σ_A is the axial stress. For a circumferentially notched cylinder under tension, the value is given by:

$$\tau = (\sigma_A - \sigma_R)/2 \qquad \text{(Eq 2)}$$

where σ_R is the radial stress. Because τ_c, the value of critical shear stress for yielding, is the same in both instances, it may be seen that the existence of radial stresses requires a higher value of σ_A to produce yielding.

The amount by which the presence of a notch increases the axial stress necessary to produce yielding can be expressed as a plastic-constraint factor. In contrast to stress-concentration factors for purely elastic-stress conditions, which can be extremely high, the plastic-constraint factor cannot exceed a value of about 3 (Ref 1).

Local Strain Rate. Besides the stress-concentration effect and the plastic-constraint effect, a notch produces a local increase in the strain rate in a member subjected to increasing load. While the member is still loaded elastically, the stress (and strain) increases more rapidly around the notch root than elsewhere because of the steep stress gradients there. When yielding occurs, plastic flow reduces the stress around the notch root and introduces plastic constraint. As a result, a high rate of plastic strain develops around the notch root.

Fracture Initiators

Notches of one kind or another may be found in almost any structure. Good design practice dictates that intentional notches be confined to regions of low nominal stress. Also, if notches cannot be avoided, good design practice restricts the stress concentration they produce to regions that are small compared to the over-all dimensions of the structural members. Regardless of whether the presence of a notch is intentional or accidental, when fracture occurs it almost always initiates at the notch.

Many structures made of ductile materials can fracture rapidly if notches are present. In the following example, fracture resulted from high stress concentrations caused by notches at critical points in the side rails of an aluminum alloy ladder.

Example 1. Ductile Fracture of an Aluminum Alloy 6063-T6 Side Rail in an All-Aluminum Ladder Because of Unnecessary Concentration of Stress (Fig. 8)

One of the legs of the lower section of an aluminum alloy extension ladder collapsed inward as the ladder was being used by a 180-lb man. The ladder was constructed of channel-shape side rails, 1.29-in.-diam, 15.2-in.-long rungs, and sleeves that anchored the rungs to the side rails, as shown in Fig. 8.

In assembly, a metal sleeve was placed over each end of the rungs and then into the holes punched in the side rails. The sleeves were upset, as shown in section B-B in Fig. 8, anchoring the rungs to the rail longitudinally and radially. The rungs were 1 ft apart in the ladder section that failed.

Investigation. The ladder broke transversely at the point where the lowest rung was anchored into the side rail, as shown in the side-rail and assembly details in Fig. 8. Failure, as determined visually, occurred by the right-hand rail bending inward under dynamic loading, followed by shear fracture that started at the edges of the lowest rung hole. When the ladder was moved, the crack propagated further, completely separating the leg from the ladder. Deformation in torsion also had occurred prior to the final fracture by bending.

Examination of the outer surface of the side rail revealed extensive deformation marks that were readily visible. These marks extended 1/8 in. or more from the fracture surface. Cracking had initiated from two of the eight semicircular notches that were located at 45° intervals around the circumference of the rung hole, as shown in the side-rail detail in Fig. 8. Light-microscope fractography did not reveal any indications of fatigue.

Chemical analysis and hardness tests indicated that the side-rail material was aluminum alloy 6063-T6.

Estimates of stress concentration were also made. The direction of applied bending stress is indicated at points P in the side-rail detail in Fig. 8. Assuming elastic behavior, the maximum tensile stress occurred at the edges of the rung hole, indicated by points A in the side-rail detail in Fig. 8. In a strip of material of finite width having a circular hole, the stress concentration at points A in Fig. 8 would be about 4.7 times the applied stress. The notches at points A approximately double the stress concentration; thus, the elastic-stress-concentration factor would be about 9.4. This means that the yield stress of the material at the root of the notches at points A would be exceeded when the applied bending moment exceeded 35 ft-lb. It was estimated that the static bending moment could have been as high as 225 ft-lb under certain circumstances when the ladder was used by a 180-lb man. Thus, the local stress at the notches could have reached 6 or 7 times the yield stress.

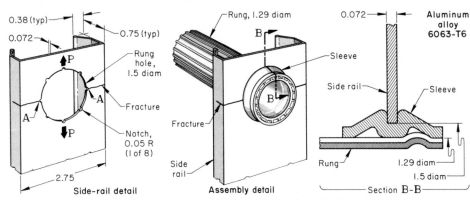

Fig. 8. *Aluminum alloy 6063-T6 side rail of an all-aluminum ladder that failed by ductile fracture at a rung hole, where stress was highly concentrated* (Example 1)

Conclusions. The side rail of the ladder failed by shear-face ductile fracture caused by overload in bending. Three features of the design unnecessarily concentrated applied stresses and promoted the failure:

1 The use of rung holes that were of relatively large diameter compared to the width of the section

2 The location of notches at the points of maximum bending stress

3 The use of a channel section rather than an I-beam. This resulted in maximum tension in the web where the rung holes were pierced. Also, channel sections tend to fail by combined torsion and flexure, and evidence of torsional deformation was noted in this failure.

Recommendations. Redesign of the side rails and/or the method of attachment of the rungs was recommended. Specific changes that would improve this design are:

1 Elimination of the notches at points A. This would reduce the stress concentration at the points of fracture by 50%.

2 Retain the notches on a 45° angular spacing, but rotate the notch pattern by 22.5°. This could be accomplished at little or no cost and would reduce the stress concentration by about 30%, with no other change in the properties of the ladder.

3 Use an I-beam section for the side rails, instead of the channel. This practice would place the web on the neutral axis of the beam, thereby reducing the bending stress at the rung holes to approximately 10% of the stress in a channel having the same over-all dimensions.

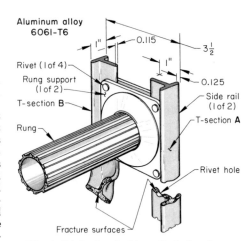

Fig. 9. *Right-hand side rail of aluminum alloy 6061-T6 that failed in an aluminum alloy extension ladder from ductile overload fracture* (Example 2)

Although notches of some sort are the initiators of almost all fractures, they may exist in stressed members that fractured from a cause other than the presence of the notches. When this happens, elimination of a severe notch that has initiated previous fractures will only mean that future fractures of the part will be initiated at one of the less severe notches remaining in the part.

In some instances, neither the initiator or even the fracture itself is the real cause of failure. This is illustrated in the example that follows, which describes fracture of three rails of an aluminum alloy ladder that was initiated by stress concentration near rivet holes but was caused by bending (distortion failure) of the fourth rail.

Example 2. Ductile Overload Fracture of an Extension Ladder Caused by Low Strength in Improperly Aged Aluminum Alloy 6061-T6 Extrusions (Fig. 9)

A two-section aluminum extension ladder, owned by the fire department of a large city, broke in service after having been used at the sites of several fires. Fire-department officials noticed that one of the structural members of the ladder section that broke had a pattern of cracks along its edges. The ladder was sent to a laboratory to determine the cause of failure.

The ladder was constructed of aluminum alloy extrusions and stampings that were riveted together at each rung location and at the ends of side rails. Each side rail consisted of two extruded T-sections (made from aluminum alloy 6061-T6) that were held in position by rivets through stamped rung supports, as shown in Fig. 9. An end cap, consisting of a curved T-section and two flat plates, was riveted to each end of the side rails (not shown in Fig. 9) in a manner quite similar to the rung supports. The rungs, which were hollow cylindrical extrusions with shallow longitudinal grooves along the outer surface, were spaced about 1 ft apart and were upset at each end to lock them into the rung supports.

Investigation. Both side rails in the lower section of the ladder, called the bed section, had broken immediately below the fifth rung from the top. Figure 9 illustrates the right-hand side rail in the area of the fracture and shows that the upper T-section (T-section

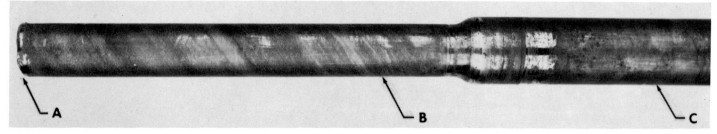

Fig. 10. Portion of an S7 tool steel axle shaft from a racing car that failed in service from ductile fracture in torsion (Example 3)

A, the one that faced away from the burning structure) fractured at a rivet holding the rung support in place.

An extensive amount of macroscopic plastic deformation was associated with the fracture in the lower T-section, indicated by B in Fig. 9, whereas the deformation in the upper T-section, indicated by A in Fig. 9, was more localized in the fracture region. T-section A also had kinked between the fifth and sixth rungs from the top of the bed section. The upper T-section of the left-hand side rail, not shown in Fig. 9 but designated here as T-section C, also had bent between the fifth and sixth rungs; this location roughly coincided with the location of the bottom end of the upper section (or fly) of the ladder at the moment of failure.

In the left-hand side rail, only T-section C had broken. The lower T-section, also not shown in Fig. 9 but designated here as T-section D, had bent almost at a right angle to its original position. This severe bend also occurred immediately below the fifth rung, at approximately the same location in relation to the rung as the fracture in T-section B in the right-hand side rail. All four T-sections had suffered other damage of a lesser degree, mostly caused by their being bent and/or twisted as the ladder collapsed.

The fracture surfaces were examined visually and by light stereomicroscopy. From the general fracture appearance and the degree of deformation, it was concluded that all fractures occurred by overload.

The composition of a sample taken from T-section B was found to be within the specified limits for aluminum alloy 6061. Microscopic examination did not disclose any significant differences in microstructure or grain size among the four T-sections.

Thickness measurements at various locations in undeformed areas indicated that among the four T-sections the flanges and stems were of equal thickness within 0.004 in. This is well within standard industry tolerances for aluminum extrusions in this size range.

The Rockwell B hardness of all four T-sections was measured at several widely spaced locations; ranges were as follows:

T-section	Hardness, R_B
A (upper, right side rail)	20 to 32
B (lower, right side rail)	48 to 51
C (upper, left side rail)	47 to 55
D (lower, left side rail)	19 to 25

These data indicated that T-sections B and C had been properly aged, since their hardnesses were in the lower end of the range for 6061-T6 (acceptable hardness, Rockwell B 47 to 72). On the other hand, T-sections A and D had hardnesses that were considerably lower than the acceptable

hardness for the T6 temper and were within the range for 6061-T4 (acceptable hardness, Rockwell B 19 to 45). This indicated that T-sections A and D had been naturally aged at room temperature after solution heat treatment.

The four T-sections were visually examined for edge cracking. The edges of both flanges and the edge of the stem of T-section A had numerous small cracks over a substantial length in the general area of the fracture. About 5 ft above the fracture, cracks were observed on both flanges but not on the stem, whereas cracks were present on only one flange about 5 ft below the fracture. T-section B exhibited edge cracks on both flanges in the general area of the fracture and on only one flange about 5 ft above the fracture. No cracks were found on the edge of the stem in T-section B or anywhere on T-sections C and D. Although one of the major fractures passed through an edge crack, it was concluded that the edge cracks, which were caused by too high a temperature in the workpiece or excessive speed in the extrusion process, had no causative relation to the failure.

The exact load on the ladder and the position of the load at the instant of failure were not reported. However, when this type of ladder is in use, the lower T-section in each side rail (T-section B or D) is generally stressed in tension, whereas the upper T-section (A or C) is generally stressed in compression. Because aluminum alloy 6061-T4 has about half the yield strength of 6061-T6, failure probably occurred because T-section D yielded locally under load. (T-section D was in the T4 temper and was stressed in tension.) After T-section D had yielded, the load distribution on the side rail changed in the region of the yielding, placing the stem portion of T-section C in tension (and perhaps also affecting the load distribution in the right-hand side rail to put the stem of T-section A in tension as well). T-section C became overloaded and bent, then fracture originated at the edge of the stem near a stress concentration at a rivet hole and propagated toward the flange. The rapid failure of the left-hand side rail caused the right-hand side rail to become overloaded and to fail by ductile fracture as the ladder collapsed.

Three regions of T-section A were examined and all were found to be soft. If T-section A had been softened by exposure to the heat of a fire, T-section B, which would have been closer to the fire, also would have been softened. However, examination of T-section B showed that it had not been softened.

Conclusions. The fire ladder broke because two of the four extruded aluminum alloy

T-sections (A and D) in the side rails had a low yield strength — they had been naturally aged after solution heat treatment, rather than artificially aged. Solution treatment could not have occurred as a result of exposure to the heat of a fire in prior usage because one T-section in each side rail had properties that were in agreement with published values for artificially aged aluminum alloy 6061.

Bending, caused by overload, was the mechanism of failure in one T-section; the three others then failed by ductile fracture, also caused by overload.

Edge cracking in two of the T-sections was the result of improper conditions during extrusion of the T-sections; however, this condition was not a primary cause of failure.

When there is considerable damage to the fracture surfaces, the evidence that would allow identification of the initiator of the fracture is often destroyed. However, in those instances where the initiator is not the real cause of failure, as in the ductile fracture of an axle shaft described in the following example, damage to the fracture surfaces need not inhibit the failure analysis.

Example 3. Ductile Fracture in Torsion of an S7 Tool Steel Axle Shaft From a Racing Car (Fig. 10)

An axle shaft fractured after several months of use in a racing car. The fractured axle, a portion of which is shown in Fig. 10, was made from a 1⅝-in.-diam bar of S7 tool steel (0.50% C, 3.25% Cr, 1.40% Mo). Specific information concerning the heat treatment performed on the axle shaft and the loads encountered in service was not available.

Investigation. Visual examination of the fracture surfaces, one of which is indicated by A in Fig. 10, did not provide any useful information, because the opposing fracture surfaces had rubbed together and were badly chafed and smeared. However, spiral marks (deformation bands) that indicated severe deformation in torsion were visible on the 0.73-in.-diam segment of the failed shaft (indicated by B in Fig. 10). Measurements of the 1-in.-diam teeth on the splined end (not shown in Fig. 10) of the 0.92-in.-diam section of the shaft (indicated at C in Fig. 10) revealed that this area also was deformed.

The material in the failed shaft was verified by x-ray spectroscopy to be S7 tool steel. Hardness tests before and after a liquid-nitrogen refrigeration treatment indicated that the shaft had not been heat treated, but only slightly hardened by cold working, and that there was no retained austenite in the microstructure. Microscopic examination revealed a structure of ferrite containing spheroidized carbides, which indicated that the material had been used in the spheroidized condition.

Conclusion. The shaft failed by ductile fracture in torsion because it had a torsion strength in the cold-worked condition of approximately 58,000 to 65,000 psi (estimated from Rockwell C hardness), which was too low for the application. The low strength resulted from failure to heat treat the component.

Recommendation. To avoid service failures in this type and size of axle shaft, it was recommended that S7 tool steel axle shafts be heat treated to a hardness of Rockwell C 38 to 43 (tensile strength of 180,000 to 200,000 psi and torsion strength of about 90,000 to 100,000 psi). This treatment would involve air cooling from an austenitizing temperature of 940 C (1725 F), followed by tempering at 620 to 650 C (1150 to 1200 F).

In addition to intentionally and accidentally produced notches, failures can be initiated by discontinuities in the metal that do not involve a free surface. These discontinuities include imperfections and abnormalities present in the as-received material, imperfections and irregularities introduced during fabrication and heat treatment, and defects and damage induced during service. Failures by brittle or ductile fracture resulting from the presence of these discontinuities and other deficiencies are discussed in the following sections.

Failures From Deficiencies in Material

Imperfections, abnormalities and other deficiencies can be introduced in material by primary fabrication processes, such as melting, deoxidation, grain refining, casting, teeming of ingots, hot or cold reduction and shaping, and thermal treatment. For example, a cast ingot or cast part may contain segregation, undesirable microstructure, inclusions, porosity, tears, cracks, or surface discontinuities. Most of the deficiencies present in castings and ingots are of minor importance and seldom lead to failure. However, some discontinuities, such as cracks, can have serious consequences. For an extensive discussion of failures caused by casting discontinuities, see the article on Failures of Iron and Steel Castings, which begins on page 315. Also, see the articles on Solidification Structures of Steel, Aluminum Alloy and Copper Alloy Ingots, pages 158 to 174 in Volume 8 of this Handbook.

Additional deficiencies can be introduced during conversion of an ingot to a billet or other wrought product. For instance, depending on the type of alloy, "speed" cracks can develop on an extru-

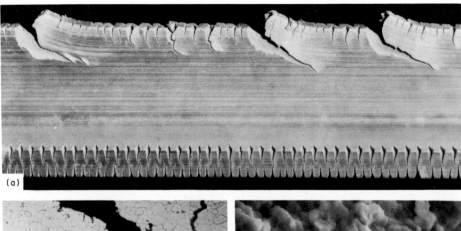
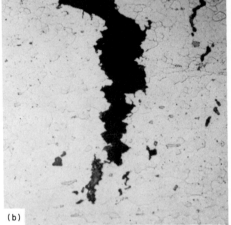

Fig. 11. (a) *An aluminum alloy 7004 extrusion with "speed" cracks on two edges; shown at actual size.* (b) *Micrograph of a section through a speed crack that propagated along grain boundaries when critical extrusion speed was exceeded; 350× (etched in Keller's reagent).* (c) *SEM micrograph, at 1250×, showing knobbly appearance of a speed-crack surface that is evidence of localized melting at grain boundaries.*

sion if the extrusion speed is above a critical level. An extreme example of this type of cracking is shown in Fig. 11(a). When the critical extrusion speed is exceeded, die friction raises the surface temperature to the point at which the grain boundaries can no longer withstand the longitudinal surface stresses produced during extrusion and transverse intergranular cracks result (see Fig. 11b). The knobbly surface of the crack (Fig. 11c) results from localized melting at the grain boundaries.

Laps, folds, seams, flakes, forging bursts, laminations in sheet and plate, and undesirable grain flow are some additional deficiencies that can be introduced by working processes. Sometimes, a subsequent forming operation will serve as an inspection for serious deficiencies, preventing the deficiencies from reaching the finished product. For example, cold heading of bar stock to produce a bolt head will open any seam that is present, making a large crack that is readily visible. For a discussion of material deficiencies caused during forging, see the article on Failures of Forgings, which begins on page 291. Failures caused by seams also are discussed in the article on Failures of Springs, which begins on page 487.

Failures From Improper Fabrication

Imperfections produced during forming, machining, joining, plating and other fabrication processes can lead to ductile or brittle fracture. Examples of some of these imperfections and resulting part failures are presented in this section.

Forming

Forming operations, such as cold heading, cold extrusion, stamping, drawing, bending and straightening, can produce severe imperfections if proper processing and material controls are not used. For example, during tightening of a nut onto a 7/16-20 clamp bolt of 1541 steel, a small percentage of the bolts fractured at the interface between the square shoulders and the round head at or below the required torque of 35 ft-lb. A typical fracture surface showed two distinct regions of fracture; one region had a dark fibrous appearance and the other had a light-gray fibrous appearance. The darkening on the one region was the result of oxidation during heat treatment; the light-gray region was the region of final fracture.

When other 1541 steel clamp bolts were examined by through-transmission

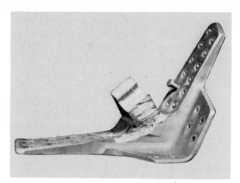

Fig. 12. Catapult-hook attachment fitting, forged from aluminum alloy 2014-T6, that cracked during straightening, and then fractured in service (Example 4)

ultrasonic inspection, some were found to have internal fractures of various sizes. Some of these fractures did not extend to the surface of the bolts and could not be detected by visual or liquid-penetrant methods. The internal fractures occurred during the trimming operation after the bolts were cold headed. The bolts were not stress relieved after cold heading and prior to trimming. It was found that the material used to make the defective bolts came from a high-manganese heat of 1541 steel; this, together with the lack of stress relief, led to internal fracturing during trimming. Fracturing of bolts was eliminated by adding a stress-relief heat treatment prior to trimming and by changing from 1541 to 4037 steel.

Forward cold extrusion can produce internal imperfections known as central bursts, or chevrons. Their occurrence is nearly always restricted to isolated lots of material and usually to only a small percentage of the pieces extruded in any particular production run. Some of the factors that can contribute to the formation of chevrons are (a) incorrect die angles; (b) either too great or too small a reduction in cross-sectional area; (c) incomplete annealing of slug material; (d) excessive work-hardenability of the

slug material; (e) presence of an excessive amount of seams and other imperfections in the slug material, (f) segregation in steel slug that results in hard martensitic particles in the center of the slug, which act as barriers to material flow; and (g) insufficient die lubrication.

Blanking. Burrs produced by blanking can sometimes lead to failure. For instance, examination of a spring washer of 17-7 PH stainless steel that fractured in a simulated-service test revealed that fracture originated from the burr side of the washer, which also was the tension side. By processing so that burrs are on the compression side of the washer, no additional fractures have been experienced.

Hot or cold forming operations such as drawing, bending and straightening can produce grain deformation, "orange peel", thinned corners, local regions of severe work hardening, and cracks. These effects, which may lead to failure, are discussed for cold formed parts in the article that begins on page 285 in this volume. In the example that follows, cracks that were produced during a straightening operation led to fracture of an aluminum alloy aircraft fitting.

Example 4. Fracture of an Aluminum Alloy 2014-T6 Catapult-Hook Attachment Fitting for Naval Aircraft (Fig. 12)

The forged aluminum alloy 2014-T6 catapult-hook attachment fitting shown in Fig. 12, which was from a naval aircraft, broke in service. The surface of the fitting had been anodized by the chromic acid process to protect it from corrosion.

Investigation. The fitting was analyzed spectrographically and found to be within the required composition limits for aluminum alloy 2014. Visual examination revealed a brown stain on the fracture surface. The stain was analyzed and found to be a residue of chromic acid, evidently from the anodizing treatment. Minute cracks were discovered on the inside surface of the bearing hole, and small areas of pitting corrosion were visible on the exterior surface of the fitting.

Microscopic examination revealed a small number of rosettes, suggestive of eutectic melting, in an otherwise normal structure. They did not appear to be associated with the cracks or to have contributed to failure.

Tensile-test coupons were cut from the fitting, and were found to have the following mechanical properties: tensile strength, 64,900 psi; yield strength, 58,900 psi; and elongation in 2 in., 11%. Minimum longitudinal properties of an aluminum alloy 2014-T6 die forging with a section thickness of 4 in. or less (which apply to this attachment fitting) are: tensile strength, 65,000 psi; yield strength, 55,000 psi; and elongation in 2 in., 7%.

Conclusions. The presence of chromic acid stain on the fracture surface proved that the forging had cracked prior to anodizing. This suggests that the crack initiated during straightening, either after machining or after heat treatment.

The structure and composition of the alloy appear to have been acceptable. Although the tensile and yield strengths were barely acceptable for aluminum alloy 2014-T6 die forgings of 4-in. thickness or less, this fact is not considered to have affected the failure, because the ductility was acceptable. The rosettes found in the microstructure are believed to have been nondamaging. Had they contributed to the failure, the ductility would have been very low.

Recommendations for avoiding a recurrence of this type of failure were:

1 The catapult-hook attachment fittings in stock should be inspected for cracks.
2 The manufacturing process should be revised to include a fluorescent-liquid-penetrant inspection prior to anodizing, because chromic acid destroys the penetrant. This inspection would reduce the possibility of cracked parts being used in service.

Machining

Parts often contain machining marks when completed. The location and severity of such marks are important in determining how much influence, if any, they have on fracture. Generally, stress raisers consisting of sharp depressions on the surface of a part are produced by machining. However, corners and edges resulting from missed machining or deburring operations are more serious stress raisers. For example, transverse cracking of the 8620 steel rock-drill cylinder shown in Fig. 13 occurred through the bottom after only 15% of its expected service life. The cylinder was saw cut through the top to expose the crack surface, revealing that the crack propagated progressively from a sharp edge at the junction of the annular exhaust groove and the lower exhaust port. Case and core hardness, case depth, composition, and microstructure were as specified. The design called for the sharp edge to be beveled; however, the operation was missed in fabrication and overlooked in final inspection.

Another type of stress concentrator that can be produced during machining is embedded tool chips in the surface of the workpiece. In one instance, during

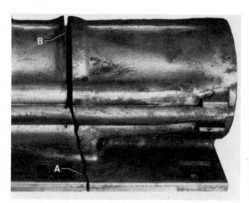 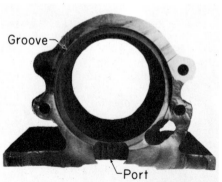

Fig. 13. Cylinder of a pneumatic-percussion rock drill that cracked transversely through the bottom (at A) from a sharp edge at junction of the annular exhaust groove and the bottom exhaust port. At B is the saw cut made to open the crack for examination; end view of saw-cut cylinder is shown at right. The cylinder, 6 in. in diameter and 19¼ in. long, was made from a casting of 8620 steel, then carburized to a case depth of 0.070 in. and hardened.

nondestructive testing of a stainless steel part by radiography, a high-density inclusion was detected. The inclusion was identified by scanning electron microscopy and spectrometry to be a chip from a tungsten carbide tool bit. If the part had not been thoroughly inspected, the chip may have caused the part to break.

Grinding. Many steel parts are designed to have smooth hard surfaces for resistance to wear in service. These parts include journals on shafts, piston pins, and bearing surfaces. Normally, these types of parts are machined, hardened by heat treatment, and ground to extremely close tolerances.

Cracks can result from grinding burns, or scorches, caused by localized frictional heating during grinding. Grinding burns vary in severity from a lightly tempered condition to fresh, untempered martensite. Sometimes, only a shallow layer, 0.0001 to 0.0003 in. deep, is affected, but heavy grinding produces much deeper burned layers. Heavy grinding causes localized heating sufficient to raise the surface temperature to the austenitizing temperature of 760 to 870 C (about 1400 to 1600 F). Subsequent rapid quenching by the grinding coolant results in brittle surface layers of untempered martensite. Also, if the surface contains residual compressive stresses (such as those developed during carburizing), heating the surface to its austenitizing temperature will relieve these beneficial compressive stresses.

Mild grinding burns consist of shallow layers that have only been tempered — maximum surface temperatures do not exceed Ac_1. In many respects, mild grinding burns resemble heat-affected zones in steel weldments. A similar shallow, tempered layer exists beneath the untempered layer of a severe grinding burn. These tempered layers, although less brittle than untempered layers, nevertheless are regions where material properties differ from those in the interior of the part. Tempering can induce changes of surface stresses or formation of cracks, or both. Because the heated area is localized, its ability to contract is restricted by surrounding harder and stronger martensitic regions that have not been heated (tempered) during grinding. The tempered regions subsequently contain residual tensile stress. If this residual tensile stress is great enough to exceed the strength of the tempered material, cracks form, as shown in the following two examples.

Example 5. Brittle Fracture of a Case-Hardened Latch Tip on an 8620 Steel Stop Arm Because of Low Impact Resistance and Grinding Burns (Fig. 14)

The latch tip on the main-clutch stop arm shown in Fig. 14(a) fractured during normal operation in a business machine. In operation, the latch tip was subjected to

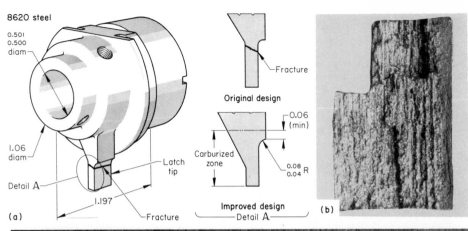

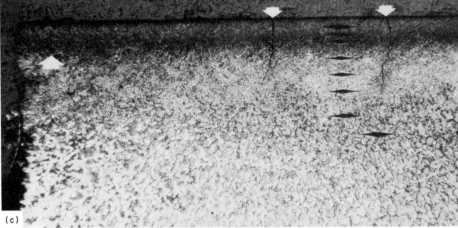

(a) View of stop arm showing location of fracture in latch tip, and detail showing original and improved designs of latch tip. (b) Fractograph, at 9×, of a typical fracture surface, showing brittle appearance; note fine-grained appearance of the hardened case (at right). (c) Micrograph of a section through a fractured latch tip that shows two of several small cracks (arrows at right) that extended through the hardened case to the core, and the burned layer on latch surface (dark band indicated by arrow at left) that resulted from grinding burns.

Fig. 14. Main-clutch stop arm of 8620 steel on which the case-hardened latch tip failed in service from brittle fracture because of low impact resistance and grinding burns
(Example 5)

intermittent impact loading. Three stop arms that failed in service were sent to the metallurgical laboratory to determine the cause of failure.

The stop arms were machined from 8620 steel. The latch tips were carburized and then induction hardened to a minimum surface hardness of Rockwell C 62.

Investigation. Examination of two stop arms indicated that fracture of the latch tip (see "Original design" view in detail A in Fig. 14a) occurred at the hardness-transition zone that was created by induction hardening of the carburized case on the tips. This transition zone, because of its inhomogeneous structure, decreased the overall strength of the parts. In addition to the transition zone, a sharp ground relief step at the location of failure contributed to low impact resistance of the arm. The hardness-transition zone usually coincided with, or was slightly outward (radially) from, the relief step.

The fracture surface, which is shown in Fig. 14(b), had a typical brittle appearance, with no necking or shear lips. The fracture surface had a fine-grained appearance in the hardened case (at right in Fig. 14b), but was somewhat coarser throughout the rest of the fracture.

Examination of an etched section through another fractured latch tip disclosed several small cracks that extended almost through the hardened case to the core; two of these cracks are indicated by arrows at right in Fig. 14(c). Fracture of the parts may have occurred through similar cracks. Also observed was a burned layer approximately 0.003 in. deep on the latch surface. This layer, indicated by arrow at left in Fig. 14(c), was caused by improper grinding and the cracks present in the part were apparently the result of this grinding. Hardness at a depth of 0.001 in. in this layer was Rockwell C 52 (a minimum of Rockwell C 55 was specified).

In an attempt to relocate the transition zone, and as a method of salvaging finished parts that had the transition zone coinciding with the relief step, several stop arms were induction hardened a second time. Erratic results obtained when samples were impact tested indicated that the parts were not usable.

Conclusions. The induction hardened stop arms failed by brittle fracture in the hardness-transition zone as the result of excessive impact loading.

The presence of several cracks through the hardened case near the region of fail-

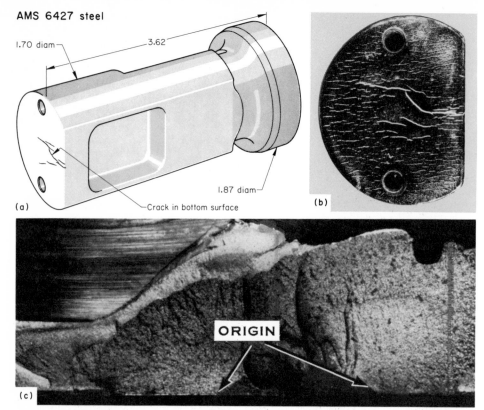

AMS 6427 steel

1.70 diam

3.62

1.87 diam

(a)

Crack in bottom surface

(b)

ORIGIN

(c)

(a) Attachment lug, showing site of cracking on the bottom surface. (b) Photograph, at 2×, of the bottom of the lug, showing a large number of small cracks in addition to the main crack enhanced by fluorescent magnetic parti-cles. (c) Fractograph, at 5×, of the surface of the main crack, showing origin at grinding crack. The area of crack origin appears dark because of the presence of corrosion products or of a lubricant residue.

Fig. 15. Aircraft-wing pylon-attachment lug of AMS 6427 steel that cracked in service because of overheating during grinding (Example 6)

ure on one of the latch tips indicated that fracture apparently occurred through a similar crack. A burned layer on the surface of the latch indicated that the cracks had been caused by improper grinding after hardening.

Corrective Measures. To strengthen the stop-arm latch tip, the size of the backing web that reinforced the tip was increased, as shown in the "Improved design" view in detail A in Fig. 14(a). Also the radius at the relief step was increased to 0.06 ± 0.02 in., proper grinding techniques were used, and the hardened zone was specified to ex-tend 0.06 in. (min) beyond the step.

No failures of parts made to those speci-fications have been reported.

Example 6. Brittle Fracture of an AMS 6427 Steel Pylon-Attachment Lug Because of Overheating During Grinding (Fig. 15)

An attachment lug for an aircraft-wing pylon, shown in Fig. 15(a), failed in service by cracking across its bottom surface. The lug had been forged of AMS 6427 steel, which is essentially equivalent to 4330 mod steel, and heat treated to a tensile strength of 220,000 to 240,000 psi. The bottom sur-face of the lug was ground to meet speci-fied dimensions, then this surface and the chamfered surface at the top of the lug were cadmium plated. The remainder of the lug was chromium plated. Finally, a coat of dry-film lubricant was applied to both top and bottom surfaces before installation in the aircraft.

Investigation. The failure consisted of a crack through the centerline of the lug on the bottom (cadmium-plated) surface (see Fig. 15a). This surface was inspected by the fluorescent-magnetic-particle method and, as shown in Fig. 15(b), a large number of small cracks were detected in addition to the main crack. The top surface was similarly inspected, and no indications of defects were found.

The depth of the main crack was not known initially, which made it difficult to expose the fracture surface accurately. The procedure finally adopted was to chill the lug in liquid nitrogen and then break it open. The crack surface was relatively clean, with only a few rust spots. The frac-ture appeared to have originated at the dark arc-shape area indicated at the bottom of Fig. 15(c). SEM fractographs showed that the surface at the crack origin was inter-granular, whereas away from the origin the surface was primarily intergranular but possessed ductile features characteristic of a delayed fracture mechanism, probably stress-corrosion cracking.

Longitudinal sections through the frac-ture area were examined microscopically; several small cracks that had been detected by fluorescent-magnetic-particle inspection were found to extend 1/64 in. to about 1/32 in. upward from the bottom face parallel to the main crack. A microhardness scan was made with a Knoop indenter and a 500-gram load. The values ranged from about Knoop 550 in the interior to Knoop 337 adjacent to the

bottom surface. It was evident that the bot-tom of the lug had undergone significant softening since being heat treated. A subsize tensile-test specimen cut from the failed lug showed, however, that tensile strength of the lug was within the specified range of 220,000 to 240,000 psi.

Conclusions. Cracks on the bottom surface and a microhardness gradient indicated that the bottom of the lug was overheated during grinding; the brittle, intergranular nature of the fracture surface at the origin was a typical indication of grinding cracks in martensitic steels. In service, the crack propagated farther into the lug by a delayed fracture mechanism, probably stress-cor-rosion cracking.

Corrective Measure. To avoid further fail-ures of these pylon-attachment lugs, the surface-grinding procedure was revised to minimize the probability of overheating and cracking the bottom surface of the lugs.

Hardened surfaces containing patches of retained austenite are exceedingly sensitive to grinding operations. If the heat or stress generated in grinding is sufficient to induce transformation of the retained austenite to fresh martensite (normally referred to as untempered mar-tensite), cracks may form in the surface or just below it. If cracks do not occur immediately, the newly transformed regions often crack or spall under the additional stresses encountered under load in service. Severe grinding also can develop grinding cracks in unhardened parts.

Grinding burns can be revealed by etching the ground surface in an aqueous solution of 5 to 10% nitric acid. A surface that contains grinding burns will exhibit a series of dark-gray streaks on a light-gray background. The streaks will follow the grinding direction, and the severity will vary from a few very small streaks to an almost completely dark-gray surface.

The effects of grinding of hardened steel parts is discussed further in the article on Failures of Dies, which begins on page 500 in this volume.

Electrical discharge machining (or EDM) is a technique for machining electrically conductive materials by the erosive action of spark discharge; the workpiece is the anode and the electrode is the cathode. Each spark erodes a small amount of metal. Electrical discharge machining has received considerable ap-plication in the machining of dies, be-cause the process is capable of machin-ing intricate cavities economically.

However, surfaces machined by the EDM technique exhibit some damage. The depth of this damage is related to the EDM procedures utilized. The rate of metal removal depends on the volume of the crater formed by each spark and the frequency of the sparking. The crater depth establishes the degree of surface roughness. The surface often has a "splattered" or a wavelike appearance due to the resolidification of molten droplets that were not removed by the spark action, and by the dielectric fluid that fills the gap between electrode and workpiece, during EDM processing.

Metallurgical examination indicates that surface heating is due to the melting action of the spark. The microstructure at the surface of electrical discharge machined dies often resembles the microstructure of welds; the surface frequently exhibits an as-solidified appearance. In highly alloyed die steels, the surface layer usually consists of fresh martensite, retained austenite and eutectic-type carbides. Below this "white layer", the steel has been gradiently heated and contains a range of microstructures, hardnesses and properties. Zones heated above the Ac_3 or the Ac_{cm} temperature of the steel usually contain fresh martensite and retained austenite. Below these zones, the steel has been heated into the two-phase region and may contain fresh martensite, annealed microstructures, and carbides, depending on the steel composition. Below this two-phase zone, the heat of the operation tempers the original microstructure, with the degree of tempering decreasing with depth until the base hardness is obtained.

The depth of the white layer and the gradiently tempered zones vary considerably, depending on the EDM procedures employed. In addition to the commonly observed surface condition discussed above, other surface abnormalities, such as carburization or decarburization, occasionally have been observed on electrical discharge machined surfaces. Cracks also are occasionally observed in these surface layers. Residual stresses also are created during cooling after EDM.

Electrical discharge machined surfaces frequently exhibit greater wear resistance than that normally achieved after conventional quenching and tempering. This is due to the high hardnesses associated with the white layer. The metal at an electrical discharge machined surface generally exhibits a lower endurance limit than obtained with the same steel after conventional processing. Hence, tools or dies that have been produced by EDM usually do not perform as well in situations where fatigue is involved. Lapping of the surface after the EDM operation will restore the original fatigue life. Electrical discharge machined surfaces should be removed if the tool or die is subjected to high tensile stresses, high impact loads, or cyclic stressing.

Problems associated with EDM can be avoided if the nature of these problems is understood and the proper steps are taken. Manufacturers of EDM equipment usually can recommend procedures for handling different types of tool steels. The safest procedure to follow is to:

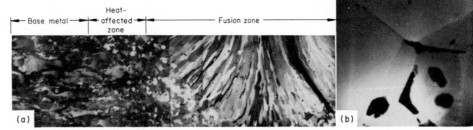

Fig. 16. *Structure of an electron beam weld in beryllium sheet that cracked because of hot shortness in the heat-affected zone. (a) Polarized-light macrograph, at 10×, of a section through the weld. (b) TEM micrograph, at 4300×, of a region in the heat-affected zone that exhibited grain-boundary melting; dark, irregular-shape particles are low-melting aluminum-rich precipitate. (Ref 2)*

1 Perform EDM operations on tool steels in the annealed condition only.
2 Stress relieve below the Ac_1 temperature of the steel.
3 Remove the electrical discharge machined surface by grinding or lapping.
4 Quench and temper, using the appropriate procedures.

If the part is in the hardened condition prior to EDM processing, it should be stress relieved (tempered) immediately after machining, using the highest temperature consistent with the desired hardness. Removal of the surface layer by grinding or lapping will help to prevent premature failure. This surface layer also may be removed by electro-chemical machining.

For additional information on electrical discharge machining, the reader is referred to the article on Failures of Dies, which begins on page 500 in this volume, and to the article on pages 227 to 233 in Volume 3.

Welding and Brazing

Welding and brazing techniques are often used for joining of metals. Occasionally, welded joints are the primary origins of failures. These failures often occur in a catastrophic manner. When failure occurs in a weldment, the failure analyst should make every effort to pinpoint as closely as possible the exact origin and mechanism of the failure.

Two micrographs of an electron beam weld in beryllium sheet can be seen in Fig. 16. This illustration clearly shows a typical transition from unaffected base metal having a microstructure of elongated grains, through the heat-affected zone of fully recrystallized grains, to the cast structure in the fusion zone consisting of large columnar grains. Initial visual examination of the weld showed large cracks, apparently in the center of the weld. However, a more detailed and thorough observation with an electron microscope revealed that these cracks actually originated in the adjacent heat-affected zone, where the heat input had produced grain-boundary precipitates (Ref 2). The precipitates, which were identified by microanalysis as an alu-

minum-rich phase, had melted during welding. This introduced a hot-shortness condition that combined with thermal stresses to produce cracks. These cracks subsequently propagated intergranularly along the large columnar grains of the fusion zone. Proper adjustment of weld settings minimized the heat-affected zone and eliminated the cracking problem, but this example illustrates the interrelationship of the entire weld microstructure.

Prime consideration to several factors, such as stress concentration, should be given early in the design of a weld. Often, welded and brazed joints are placed in a design configuration that introduces the possibility of notch-type stress concentrations. The failure analyst should be aware of the possibility of such stress-concentration effects whenever a weld is suspected as the origin of a component failure.

Weld Imperfections. One of the most common factors associated with weld failures is the introduction of weld imperfections, such as porosity, incomplete fusion, inclusions, arc strikes, and hard spots, which act as crack sources and initiation points and often provide ready paths for subsequent crack propagation in a brittle manner. A void caused by incomplete fusion is illustrated in Fig. 17, which shows a gas tungsten-arc weld between a nickel alloy and an alloy steel. Special care must be taken when welding with nickel alloy filler metal in order to avoid this problem of incomplete fusion. The primary factor is weld-joint design. Molten nickel alloy weld metal is sluggish and does not spread or flow as well as steel weld metal. Therefore, joint accessibility must be sufficient to allow proper control of the arc.

The other important factor in welding a nickel alloy is the welding procedure. The inherent lower penetration of nickel alloys requires smaller weld beads and strict guidance of the arc. An increase in amperage will not significantly increase the penetration, but instead will cause overheating and "puddling" of the molten weld metal with resultant loss of deoxidizers and "rolling" of the weld metal, leading to unsound welds. The

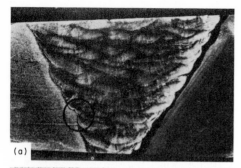

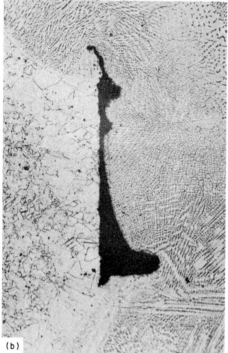

(a) Macrograph at 1½×; base metal at left is Incoloy 800 nickel alloy, that at right is 2.25Cr-1.0Mo alloy steel. Filler metal was ERNiCr-3, used with "cold" wire feed. (b) Micrograph, at 75×, of the area circled in (a), showing a void. Section shown in both views was etched in 2% nital.

Fig. 17. Section through an automatic gas tungsten-arc weld containing voids caused by incomplete fusion

void shown in Fig. 17, which was found by radiographic and ultrasonic inspection but could have led to failure in service, was caused by misguidance of the welding arc.

When the weld assembly is to be used in low-temperature service, the probability of weld imperfections leading to brittle fracture is increased, as shown in the following example.

Example 7. Low-Temperature Brittle Fracture in a Steel Tank Car Because of Weld Imperfections (Fig. 18)*

A railway tank car developed a fracture in the region of the sill and shell attachment during operation at −34 C (−30 F). On either side of the sill-support member, cracking initiated at the weld between a

*Adapted from a report prepared for this volume by Energy, Mines and Resources of Canada

Fig. 18. Brittle fracture that originated at a weld (arrow) between a frontal cover plate (bottom) and a side support plate (center), both of carbon steel, for a tank car. Chevron marks in both plates point to fracture origin. At top is a side plate. (Example 7)

¼-in.-thick frontal cover plate and a ⅝-in.-thick side support plate. The crack then propagated in a brittle manner upward through the side plate, through the welds attaching the side plate to the 1-in.-thick shell plate, and for several inches in the shell plate before terminating. The fracture surfaces displayed chevron marks pointing back to the weld (indicated by arrow in Fig. 18) between the frontal cover and side support plates at the point of fracture origin.

Investigation. Examination of the weld at the fracture origin revealed imperfections, including small root cracks, unfused regions, and small hard spots on the surfaces of the weld and adjacent plates. Micrographs and hardness values (up to Rockwell C 45) showed that the hard spots had been rapidly cooled, but why they formed was not ascertained. The presence of these hard spots indicated that the assembly had not been adequately stress relieved following structural modifications that involved welding in the region of the sill and shell attachment.

The shell plate met the chemical-composition requirements of ASTM A212, grade B, steel. Other plates involved were not positively identified but were generally classified as semikilled carbon steels.

The toughness properties of the shell and side support plates were measured and

were found to be inadequate for the service conditions in the presence of weld imperfections. Charpy V-notch testing gave a 15-ft-lb transition temperature of −7 to +5 C (+20 to +40 F) for the shell plate and −1 to +5 C (+30 to +40 F) for the side support plates. Drop-weight tests on the shell plate gave a nil-ductility temperature of 5 to 10 C (40 to 50 F).

Conclusions. The fracture was initiated by weld imperfections and propagated in a brittle manner as a result of service stresses acting on plate having inadequate toughness at the low temperatures encountered in service.

Recommendations. On the basis of fracture-toughness studies, it was suggested that the specifications for the steel plates be modified to include a toughness requirement; the Charpy V-notch requirement of 15 ft-lb at −46 C (−50 F), which is specified in ASTM A300 for ASTM A212, grade B, steel, should be adequate for this application. In addition, the welding and inspection practices should be improved to greatly reduce the incidence of weld imperfections.

It should be noted that, since the investigation discussed in Example 7 was completed, ASTM A212, grade B, steel has been superseded by ASTM A516, grade 70, steel, which has a low-temperature requirement of 15 ft-lb at −34 C (−30 F) as specified in ASTM A593. Because the temperature at which 15 ft-lb is required is significantly higher in ASTM A593 than it was in ASTM A300, it may be necessary to use a different grade of steel (such as the nickel-containing steel specified by ASTM A203, grade B), in order to obtain suitable toughness for applications in which critical low temperatures are involved, as with the tank car discussed in Example 7.

In another application where low temperatures were encountered in service, a 1033 steel angle, which formed part of a truss of a roof under construction, fractured in a brittle manner when the temperature dropped below freezing and the wind velocity was 30 to 40 mph. Chevron marks clearly pointed toward a segment of an intermittent edge weld that con-

Fig. 19. (a) Light fractograph, at about 1.4×, of a fracture surface of a high-carbon steel pry bar that broke in a brittle manner as the result of a welding-arc strike; arrow indicates fracture origin. (b) Micrograph, at 40×, of layer of brittle untempered martensite at the arc strike. (Example 8)

tained a large cavity and was the fracture origin (see fractographs 4828 to 4831 on page 386 in Volume 9 of this Handbook). Metallographic examination showed a crack that extended from the weld into the heat-affected zone, which contained hard, brittle martensite. If welding had not been done, or if preheating and postheating of the weld had been done, or if a lower-carbon steel had been used, failure probably could have been avoided.

Another instance of brittle fracture that resulted from a welding arc that produced a brittle martensitic region is presented in the next example.

Example 8. Brittle Fracture of a High-Carbon Steel Pry Bar Resulting From an Arc Strike (Fig. 19)

A pry bar, made from 1¼-in. hexagonal stock with one end flattened, broke in a brittle manner while being used to lift a heavy machine. A fracture surface of the bar is shown in Fig. 19(a). Although the actual service life of the tool was unknown, it had been in use for several years.

Investigation. Fracture occurred 12 in. from the flattened end and initiated at a defect that appeared to have developed from a welding-arc strike. The arc strike could have occurred when two identification letters were welded onto the surface farther along the bar, or could have occurred accidentally in service.

Microscopic examination of sections taken through the defect on the fracture surface and at one of the welded letters disclosed a layer of brittle untempered martensite at each location, having a hardness of about Rockwell C 65. The layer of martensite, which is shown in Fig. 19(b), was about 0.015 in. deep at the fracture surface and contained several cracks. The dark structure below the martensite was normal pearlite developed during normalizing. The surface hardness of the bar was Rockwell C 29.

In this plant, pry bars usually were made of 4140 steel; however, this pry bar was made of a high-carbon steel with a composition of: 0.80% C, 0.007% P, 0.018% S, 0.22% Mn, 0.18% Si, rem Fe.

Conclusions. Brittle fracture was caused by a microstructural defect resulting from an arc strike. The defect from which the crack propagated was a layer of untempered martensite that developed from very rapid heating and cooling, such as would occur from an arc strike. Cracks readily propagated from this hard, brittle area when the tool was highly stressed in bending.

Recommendations. Welding on or around high-carbon or alloy steels is bad practice, and workmen should be informed of the danger of inducing a fracture-prone microstructure in these materials. Tools that may be highly stressed, such as pry bars, should not have welded, electric-etched or metal-stamped identification marks, because these create notches from which fracture can initiate. The only safe method of identification is by painting.

The detrimental effect of a brittle microstructure caused by welding on a hardenable steel can be nullified by heat treatment;

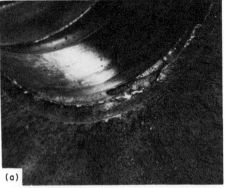

(a) Portion of a fracture surface of the die, shown at ⅓×. (b) Macrograph of a section transverse to the fracture, showing that the crack originated at the end of a weld deposit (light area) and progressed through the heat-affected zone into the darker-etching base metal; fracture-surface profile is at top left. (Shown at ⅔×; etched in hot 50% HCl.)

Fig. 20. Drop-hammer forging die that fractured catastrophically from progressive cracking that originated in the end fillet of the die cavity

however, it would not be common practice to heat treat a tool such as a pry bar because it would be unusual to suspect the existence of a localized microstructural defect.

Because weld imperfections are one of the most common factors associated with weld failures, it is good practice, whenever possible, to inspect joints by appropriate nondestructive methods to detect the imperfections. If a weld failure has been attributed to a weld imperfection, the cause of the imperfection must be ascertained and a solution provided. In this solution, the importance of metal and weld cleanness often is stressed. Unfortunately, overzealous joint preparation by an operator who is not aware of metallurgical considerations also has resulted in failures in weldments and brazements. Heavy, rough grinding of certain ferrous alloys is particularly damaging and introduces flaws that produce subsequent failure.

Postwelding operations, such as stress relieving, should not be overlooked as a possible source of problems associated with joint failures, especially in view of the large thermal stresses and residual stresses caused by welding some metal structures. The role of residual stresses in failures of welds is discussed in the section on Welding Stresses, on page 77 in this article.

Repair Welding and Brazing. Because of their relative ease and efficiency, welding and brazing are often used to provide quick repairs to critical metal components. However, without proper safe-

guards, these procedures can destroy the part they were intended to repair. For instance, a crack was found in the end fillet of the cavity of a drop-hammer forging die. Without metallurgical consultation having been obtained, the crack was dry ground and filled with high-nickel weld metal, the form was resunk, and the die was quickly and hastily placed back in production. After forging only 200 additional parts, the die suddenly fractured catastrophically (see Fig. 20a). Subsequent metallographic examination (Fig. 20b) revealed that progressive cracking originated in the interface between the low-hardness (Rockwell A 58), high-nickel weld deposit and the much harder die metal (Rockwell C 41). Once the cracking reached the more notch-sensitive die metal, it quickly propagated to the final, explosive fracture during the forging blow.

Other welding and brazing problems, such as hydrogen embrittlement, can cause brittle fracture. For further discussion of these problems, the reader is referred to the articles that begin on pages 333 and 369 in this volume.

Failures From Improper Thermal Treatment

Imperfections and abnormalities can be produced during any of the thermal treatments associated with hot or cold reduction or shaping, such as homogenization, preheating and annealing. Overheating and burning, both of which reduce strength and ductility, are two examples that are discussed in the article on Failures of Forgings, which begins on page 291. Case hardening of parts is another important source of imperfections and abnormalities that can lead to failure. For instance, fatigue cracks often initiate at the case-core interface (where the strength gradient is steep) in case-hardened parts subjected to cyclic bending or torsional loads.

Unless precautions are taken, case hardening may jeopardize toughness properties gained by proper material selection. For example, a sharp notch in a steel part requiring good toughness should not be carburized or nitrided. If case hardening of the part is necessary, the notched area should be masked off, or the case formed in this area should be removed by machining or grinding.

Final heat treatment and tempering to the required strength, ductility and toughness levels is another type of thermal treatment that can cause deficiencies that can lead to failure by brittle or ductile fracture. Quench cracks or embrittlement can occur during these various thermal treatments, as discussed below and in the section on Failures Resulting From Embrittlement, which begins on page 78 in this article.

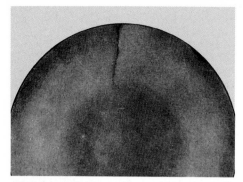

Extent of lighter-etching outer region indicates depth of martensitic transformation. Note that the crack is confined to the hardened region and extends in a nearly straight line toward the center of the bar.

Fig. 21. Quench crack in a round steel bar (nital etch; actual size)

Quench Cracking of Steel*

Quench cracks in steel result from stresses produced during the austenite-to-martensite transformation, which is accompanied by an increase in volume. As-quenched martensite is hard and exhibits almost no ductility.

When a component made of a fully hardenable alloy steel is quenched, martensite first forms at the outermost surfaces, which are first to reach the M_s temperature. The martensitic expansion "works" the softer austenite below and is almost unrestricted in its growth at the outer surfaces. As cooling progresses and the material near the center of the section reaches the M_s temperature, the expansion accompanying the newly formed martensite is restricted by the outer layers of martensite formed earlier. This results in internal stress that places the surface in tension. Cracking occurs when enough martensite has formed to set up an internal stress sufficient to exceed the tensile strength of the as-quenched martensite at the outer surfaces of the component.

Quench cracks have several characteristics that are easily recognized:

1 In general, the fracture runs from the surface toward the center of mass in a relatively straight line, as shown in Fig. 21; the crack also is likely to open or spread and may exhibit a shear lip at the extreme surface.
2 Because quench cracking occurs at relatively low temperatures, the crack will not exhibit any decarburization when examined macroscopically or microscopically (Fig. 22).
3 The fracture surfaces will exhibit a fine crystalline texture. When tempered after quenching, the fracture surfaces may be blackened by oxidation (see Fig. 25b). Microscopic examination of a quench crack tempered at higher tem-

*The contents of this section, excluding Example 9, were compiled mostly from pages 312 to 317 of "Republic Alloy Steels", Republic Steel Corp., 1968

peratures and under oxidizing conditions will disclose tempering scale (Fig. 23).

Factors Controlling Cracking. Any condition that concentrates the stresses encountered in quenching will promote the formation of quench cracks. Whenever possible, sharp changes in section, such as rectangular keyways or holes, should be avoided or plugged during quenching. The sharp change in section in the punch shown in Fig. 24 was eliminated by redesign so that the small T-shape section was machined and heat treated separately and then bolted to the larger portion of the punch.

Cold stamping marks used to identify parts have also been known to nucleate quench cracks. The distribution of mass and the lack of uniform or concentric

Fig. 22. Quench cracks in steel, which are characteristically free of decarburization (nital etch; 100×)

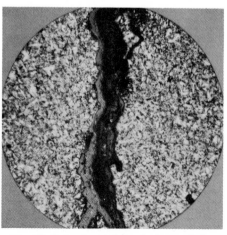

Fig. 23. Quench crack in steel containing tempering scale. Presence of the scale indicates that crack surfaces were exposed to oxidizing conditions in the tempering furnace. (Etched in 4% picral; 500×.)

Fig. 24. Large quench crack in an oil-hardening tool steel punch, which originated at fillet where there was a major change in cross section

cooling of the parts also influence the promotion of quench cracking.

Faster quenching mediums promote deeper hardening. The selection of a suitable quenching medium is often a significant factor in eliminating quench cracks. The quenchants most commonly used are caustic solutions, brine, water, oil and air; the fastest quench can be obtained in caustic solutions and the slowest in still air. Molten salts or metals with low melting points are also used for more complicated hardening treatments such as martempering and austempering.

The selection of heat treating schedules, quenching mediums, and tempering schedules is governed by the following factors:

1 The hardness and mechanical properties required for the part to give the best service life; these may determine a specific microstructure
2 The alloy steel selected for the part, which inherently determines the nature of the treatment to yield the desired properties
3 The design of the part in relation to hardening and processing after heat treatment
4 The equipment available in a specific shop to do the job
5 The production economics of the operations in relation to specific shop conditions.

Because the most important and universally accepted method of heat treating steel is quenching and tempering (which yields a product that differs materially from a normalized or annealed product), the basic factors considered in selecting a specific heat treating schedule and quenching medium to produce the required microstructure should be understood. Failure to obtain the desired properties will result in poor service life in most instances. Ideally, the quenching medium should be selected for its quenching rate; that is, the ability of the quench to effect a cooling rate sufficient to develop the desired microstructure. After quenching, it is important that the hardened piece be tempered as soon as possible to

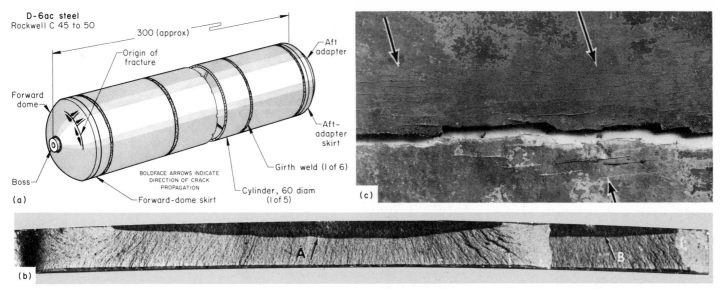

Fig. 25. (a) *D-6ac alloy steel rocket-motor case that failed from brittle fracture because of delayed quench cracks that originated in the forward dome and partly penetrated the wall of the case.* (b) *Fractograph, at about 3×, showing oxidized quench crack (at A) that was the primary origin of fracture, and adjacent quench crack (at B) that was a secondary origin.* (c) *Photograph of the fracture region, at about actual size, showing quench-crack patterns (at arrows) on both sides of the main fracture.* (Example 9)

relieve the internal stresses formed in quenching. A good rule of thumb is to draw the work from the quenching medium while it is still warm, about 65 to 93 C (150 to 200 F), and transfer to a tempering furnace. When oil-quenching, the part should be smoking lazily during transfer from the quench to the tempering furnace.

Delayed Cracking. A common misconception is that quench cracks can occur only while the work is in the quenching medium. Actually, quench cracks can occur an hour, a day, or a week after quenching if the work is allowed to stand after hardening without tempering, as illustrated in the example that follows.

Example 9. Brittle Fracture of a Rocket-Motor Case That Originated at Delayed Quench Cracks (Fig. 25)

The rocket-motor case shown in Fig. 25 failed during proof-pressure testing. Specifications required hydrostatic testing to a pressure of 838 psig, but the case burst at 443 psi.

Fabrication. The motor case was made of consumable-electrode vacuum-arc-remelted D-6ac alloy steel (0.47% C, 0.75% Mn, 0.22% Si, 1.05% Cr, 0.55% Ni, 1.00% Mo, 0.11% V, rem Fe).

The forward dome and aft adapter were made from machined forgings. The five cylinders were made by cold shear spinning of forged, machined and spheroidized preforms. The cylinders were annealed after spinning and before welding. All the components were joined by girth welds using the automatic gas tungsten-arc process. There were no longitudinal seams.

The rocket-motor case was 25 ft long and 5 ft in diameter, and had a stock thickness of 0.180 in. at the girth welds and 0.150 in. elsewhere.

After being assembled, the motor cases were heat treated as follows: preheat to 482 C (900 F); stabilize at 705 C (1300 F)

for 4 hr; austenitize at 899 C (1650 F) for ½ hr; furnace cool to 844 C (1550 F) and hold for ½ hr; quench in salt bath at 205 C (400 F) for 20 min; air cool to 52 C (125 F); wash in hot water; air dry; "snap temper" at 316 C (600 F) for 4 hr; air cool; final-temper at 552 C (1025 F) for 4 hr; air cool.

A 6-hr time interval occurred between the start of the quench, out of a gantry furnace, and the start of the 316 C (600 F) snap temper in an air-atmosphere pit furnace. The time was consumed in completing the modified marquench in 205 C (400 F) salt, cooling in air, rinsing to remove encrusted salt, and drying. For about 4½ of the 6 hr, the case was left standing on its aft end, drying and waiting for the pit furnace to be available.

The 316 C (600 F) snap temper was used to impart sufficient ductility to the motor case so that it could be fixtured with a series of adjustable spiders and shoes that rounded the casing to final dimensions. The 552 C (1025 F) temper served a dual purpose — it developed the required material properties and acted as a temper-straightening operation. Attempts to eliminate the 316 C (600 F) snap temper in favor of a 219 C (425 F) temper in the same salt bath used for quenching had been tried unsuccessfully on other parts. Although the 219 C (426 F) temper provided some ductility, it was not enough to prevent cracking during installation of the temper-straightening fixtures.

The final hardness of the rocket-motor case was Rockwell C 45 to 50. Temper scale was removed by light abrasive blasting.

Visual examination of the failed motor case revealed that brittle fracture originated in the elliptical portion of the forward dome and propagated circumferentially, then propagated radially into the immediately adjacent cylinder, as indicated in Fig. 25(a). The late stages of crack propagation were in macroscopic shear, a ductile-fracture mode.

The primary-fracture origin was identified from radial marks and was coincident with an oxidized prior crack (dark region

at arrow A in Fig. 25b) that had initiated at the outer surface of the dome and had partly penetrated the dome wall. Several secondary origins were identified at other pre-existing surface cracks, all of which contained oxide scale (see, for example, the dark region at arrow B in Fig. 25b). Close visual examination disclosed an extensive pattern of cracks with a maximum length of 1.5 in. and a maximum depth of 0.06 in. in the fractured dome. These cracks (at arrows in Fig. 25c) followed a chordal path about 36 in. long and 4 in. wide, passing within 12 in. of the boss on the dome.

Magnetic-particle inspection of the entire motor case revealed an extensive pattern of short circumferential cracks on the outer surface encircling the forward dome skirt and the first cylinder. Cracks were found in a pattern that extended about one-half the circumference of the aft-adapter skirt. There were no cracks in the remaining four cylinders.

Microhardness surveys were taken on specimens from the forward dome; one survey was adjacent and parallel to the fracture surface, and one was parallel to the outer surface. The first survey showed partial, but acceptable, decarburization of the outer surface, which occurred during austenitizing. The latter survey showed a uniform hardness and no decarburization of the fracture surface.

These data indicated that cracking occurred after the austenitizing stage of heat treatment, which would decarburize exposed surfaces. Thus, the pre-existing cracks occurred after austenitizing but before tempering.

Microscopic examination of polished sections from the dome, first cylinder, and aft adapter identified the scale in the cracks as temper scale, similar to that which would form on the casing surface during final tempering at 552 C (1025 F). This indicated that the cracks appeared before or during the final tempering phase of the heat treatment. A section was taken across one of the cracks in the motor case, and the specimen was given a sensitizing heat treatment to reveal prior-austenite grain boundaries. Carbide precipitation at prior-austenite boundaries was accomplished by heating the specimen to 455 C (850 F) and holding at that temperature for 5 hr. The specimen was prepared for microscopic examination and etched in ethereal picral (a mixture of picric acid in water, zephiran chloride solution and anhydrous ether, from which the ether layer is decanted for etching) until the prior-austenite boundaries became visible. Cracks in the etched specimen were intergranular, which is typical of cracks that occur in as-quenched steel. These results indicated that cracking had occurred while the steel was in the as-quenched condition, before the 316 C (600 F) snap temper.

X-ray-diffraction studies of material from the fractured dome showed a very low level of retained austenite (about 1%). Specimens from the dome that were heat treated in the laboratory to the as-quenched condition had about 3 to 5% retained austenite. This indicated that transformation of retained austenite had occurred during the extended delay between quenching and snap tempering.

Chemical analysis of the metal in the three components that cracked showed a carbon content of 0.47 to 0.50%, compared with 0.44 to 0.46% carbon in the components that did not crack. There was no correlation between cracking and the amount of other alloying elements in the material. Thus, cracking appeared to be related only to the carbon content of the material. Components with higher carbon contents were more susceptible to cracking than those with lower carbon contents.

Bend Tests. Specimens for slow-bend tests were machined from samples taken from the failed dome. Specimens for static-bend tests were machined from a forged ring of D-6ac steel containing 0.50% C and from a ring containing 0.42% C. The former were heat treated in the laboratory to simulate various stages of the production process, then tested. Results showed that only the as-quenched condition produced brittle cracking along prior-austenite grain boundaries. Static loading of as-quenched specimens to various stress levels produced delayed cracking that resembled the processing cracks in the casing in both high-carbon and low-carbon D-6ac steels.

The greater probability for delayed quench cracking in higher carbon material, demonstrated in the static-bend tests, correlated with observations of cracking in the three components in the failed case that had the highest carbon contents.

Conclusions. Brittle fracture of the rocket-motor case during hydrostatic testing originated at pre-existing cracks in the elliptical portion of the forward dome.

The patterns of pre-existing cracks along a chordal path in the dome and in circumferential bands in the first cylinder and aft adapter were the result of delayed quench cracking.

The most likely mechanism of delayed quench cracking was isothermal transformation of retained austenite to martensite under the influence of residual quenching stresses.

Corrective Measures. To reduce the probability of delayed quench cracking, the

Fig. 26. Quench cracks in steel, which are associated with coarse austenitic grain size. Note how the cracks and crack tributaries follow the coarse prior-austenite grain boundaries. (Etched in 4% picral and Vilella's reagent; 60×.)

quenching portion of the heat treating cycle was modified as follows: quench in a salt bath at 205 to 219 C (400 to 425 F) for 10 min; cool to 38 to 52 C (100 to 125 F) in air; as soon as the motor case reaches 38 to 52 C (100 to 125 F), return it to the salt bath and hold at 205 to 219 C (400 to 425 F) for 2 hr, then cool to room temperature.

Tempering in the salt pot used for quenching, immediately after quenching and before the case temperature dropped below 38 C (100 F), was entirely successful in eliminating the problem. No other instances of this type of failure were experienced.

Causes of Cracking. Some of the more common causes of quench cracks in steel are the following:

1 Overheating during austenitizing so that normally fine-grained steels are likely to coarsen. Coarse-grained steels are deeper hardening and are inherently more susceptible to quench cracking than fine-grained steels (Fig. 26).

2 Improper selection of quenching medium; for instance, the use of water, brine, or caustic solution when oil is the proper quenching medium for the specific part and type of steel.

3 Improper selection of steel.

4 Time delays between quenching and tempering.

5 Allowing temperature of component to drop too low before tempering. (Applicable mainly to hypereutectoid high-alloy and tool steels.)

6 Improper design of keyways, holes, sharp changes in section, and other stress raisers.

7 Improper entry of the part into the quenching medium with respect to its shape, which results in nonuniform or eccentric cooling.

Depending on the grade of steel, certain of the items listed above will be more important than others in determining whether a given component is likely to crack on quenching.

Although they may not quench crack, parts treated to high strength levels (high hardness) that contain localized high concentrations of residual stress

may fracture instantaneously in service if the residual-stress pattern is acting in the same direction as the applied load.

Failures From Improper Electroplating

One of the most serious problems that may be encountered during electroplating steel parts is the absorption of hydrogen, which can lead to the formation of flakes or to general embrittlement. Hydrogen may also develop during acid pickling, or during service (from such sources as hydrogen-bearing fluids and certain corrosion products). Hydrogen embrittlement is discussed in further detail later in this article, and in the article beginning on page 230 in this volume.

Arc striking is another problem that can occur during electroplating, although arc striking also can occur during electrocleaning, magnetic-particle inspection, and tests requiring electrical contact, as well as welding (see Example 8 on page 73). In the following example, arc striking during cadmium plating led to brittle fracture of 4140 steel retainers.

Example 10. Brittle Fracture of a Cadmium-Plated 4140 Steel Retaining Ring at a Hard Spot Caused by an Arc Strike (Fig. 27)

The retaining ring shown in Fig. 27 was used to hold components of a segmented fitting in place under a constant load. The ring was made of 4140 steel tubing and heat treated to Rockwell C 36 to 40, then cadmium plated. Several rings that broke after less than 30 days in service were examined to determine the cause of failure.

Investigation. Metallographic examination of a section adjacent to one fracture surface showed that the microstructure was tempered martensite and the inclusion content was low. The fracture was brittle in appearance and there were no shear lips.

Examination also revealed a pit or burned spot on the outer surface of the ring, as shown in section A-A in Fig. 27(a) and in Fig. 27(b). The pit appeared as a semicircular defect in the fracture surface at the outer edge of the ring (see Fig. 27c). The defect was approximately 0.007 in. deep and 0.020 in. in diameter and had a hardness of Rockwell C 58 to 60. The base metal adjacent to the defect had a hardness of Rockwell C 36 to 40. At higher magnifications, small cracks or fissures were evident within the defect.

Two unbroken rings were examined visually and found to have defects similar in appearance to those on the rings that fractured in service. These two rings were fractured for further examination. Each fracture surface contained a small hard spot similar to those on the rings that failed; however, a shear lip at the inside diameter indicated an inherently ductile material.

The difference in hardness, etching characteristics, and surface appearance of other parts of the ring indicated that the small hard spot was untempered martensite that formed as the result of an arc strike during the cadmium-plating operation. Arc-

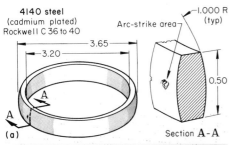

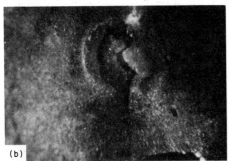

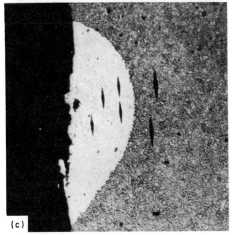

(a) View of retaining ring, and section showing location of arc strike. (b) Photograph of the retaining ring at 12×, showing pit or burned spot on the outer surface. (c) Micrograph showing the pit as a semicircular defect in the fracture surface at the outer edge of the ring (nital etch; 100×).

Fig. 27. Retaining ring of cadmium-plated 4140 steel that failed by brittle fracture at a hard spot caused by an arc strike during plating (Example 10)

ing at the point of contact between the ring and a finger on the plating rack or arcing between rings while on the rack caused local overheating above the critical temperature of 733 C (1350 F). This arcing occurred either as the ring entered the plating bath or when it was in the bath. The part was quenched by the bath, resulting in transformation to hard, brittle martensite at the locations of arcing.

Conclusion. The rings failed in brittle fracture as the result of an arc strike (or burn) on the surface of the ring. At the site of the arc strike, a small region of hard, brittle untempered martensite was formed. Fracture occurred readily when the ring was stressed.

It should also be noted that certain hard electrodeposits (especially hard chromium) frequently contain micro-cracks. These microcracks can be detrimental to parts that require good toughness. If plating is required for corrosion resistance, a soft metal such as zinc or cadmium is often preferred.

Failures From Residual Stresses

Residual stresses are stresses that exist in a part independent of external force or restraint. Nearly every manufacturing operation affects the residual-stress pattern in varying degrees. Cold heading, cold extruding, drawing, bending, straightening, machining, surface rolling, shot blasting, shot peening, and polishing all are mechanical processes that produce residual stresses by plastic deformation. Thermal processes that introduce residual stresses include hot rolling, welding, torch cutting, and heat treating (through thermal expansion and contraction or allotropic transformation) and carburizing and nitriding (through increase in case volume).

Heat treating processes that usually produce compressive residual stresses at the surfaces of parts are surface hardening, carburizing and nitriding. Some mechanical procedures (shot peening, surface rolling, cold drawing through a die, extruding and polishing) produce the same effect. Nearly all other manufacturing operations produce residual tensile stresses at the surfaces of parts. Grinding, improper heat treatment, straightening and welding generally produce the most severe residual tensile stresses.

Residual stresses can be of great help if the stress patterns are favorable. In general, residual stresses are beneficial when they are parallel to the direction of the applied load and of opposite sense — that is, a compressive residual stress and a tensile applied load or a tensile residual stress and a compressive applied load. The magnitude of residual stresses is important, particularly when service stresses are fluctuating in nature; residual tensile stresses raise the mean stress, thereby reducing fatigue life. Also, the residual-stress pattern may be altered by the applied stress — that is, localized yielding can occur when the sum of residual and service stresses exceeds the yield stress of the material. When the service stress is removed, the residual-stress pattern will be different from what it was before the service stress was applied.

Welding Stresses. Figure 28 shows a 56-in.-diam steel backup roll that catastrophically fractured during shipment. The backup roll had been salvaged from previous operations in a steel mill, and a 1-in.-thick overlay had been applied by submerged-arc welding to rebuild the surface. Ultrasonic inspection after welding indicated the weld to be perfectly sound. However, during shipping in a railroad car in winter, the shrinkage stresses caused by low temperatures in combination with residual welding stresses triggered the fracture. The excessive residual hoop stress after welding was due to an inadequate stress-relieving heat treatment. Thorough stress relief after welding would have prevented failure.

Heat Treating Stresses. Heat treating generally produces appreciable residual stresses. Although stresses resulting from proper heat treatment are generally favorable, many factors (such as material, case depth, and quench rate) influence the nature of the stresses produced. If processing of carburized parts having high core hardness or deep cases, or both, induces high residual tensile stresses at the surface, the results can be particularly damaging.

Stress Relieving. Residual stresses can be removed from most parts by the proper thermal treatment. The severity and type of the residual stresses determine the necessary thermal treatment required. Each part must be evaluated as a separate component, with consideration given to its function in service. An effective stress-relief treatment may require an optimum or compromise temperature, which relieves the detrimental stresses but keeps distortion and loss of strength to a minimum. For instance, a flange for a steering shaft was made from 1008 steel strip by stamping in a multiple-stage progressive die, stress relieving at 425 C (800 F) for 1 hr, and broaching of serrations in a center hole. Then the steering shaft was staked to the flange. The flanges fractured through the serrated-hole section on impact loading. The parts were found to have high residual tensile stress in this section after the 425 C (800 F) stress relief. The stress-relief tempera-

Fig. 28. Salvaged steel backup roll, 56 in. in diameter, that fractured during winter shipment because of shrinkage stresses from low temperatures plus residual stresses from submerged-arc welding of a 1-in.-thick surface overlay

ture was increased to 495 C (925 F), which removed the forming stresses and enabled the part to meet impact-test requirements.

Failures Resulting From Embrittlement

There are many forms of embrittlement of steel parts that can lead to brittle fracture. At least nine forms can occur during thermal treatment or elevated-temperature service. These forms of embrittlement (and the types of steel that some forms specifically affect) are:

Strain-age embrittlement (low-carbon steel)

Quench-age embrittlement (low-carbon steel)

Blue brittleness

Temper embrittlement (alloy steels)

500 F (also called "350 C") embrittlement (high-strength low-alloy steels)

400 to 500 C (752 to 932 F) embrittlement (ferritic stainless steels)

Sigma-phase embrittlement

Graphitization (carbon and low-alloy steels)

Embrittlement by intermetallic compounds (galvanized steel)

In addition, steels (and other metals and alloys) can be embrittled by environmental conditions. The four forms of environmental embrittlement are:

Neutron embrittlement
Hydrogen embrittlement
Stress-corrosion cracking
Liquid-metal embrittlement

The various forms of embrittlement in the two lists above are discussed in this section, but stress-corrosion cracking, liquid-metal embrittlement, and hydrogen embrittlement are discussed in much greater detail in the articles in this volume that begin, respectively, on pages 205, 228 and 230.

Strain-Age Embrittlement. If low-carbon steel is deformed, its hardness and strength will increase upon aging, with a resultant loss of ductility. Rimmed or capped sheet steels are particularly susceptible to strain-age embrittlement. These steels are temper rolled to suppress the yield point. The return of the yield point or the presence of Lüders strain in the stress-strain curve is evidence that strain-age embrittlement has occurred. The degree of embrittlement is a function of the aging temperature and the time at temperature. Room-temperature aging may require a few hours to a year. However, as the aging temperature is increased, the required time decreases, with embrittlement occurring in a matter of minutes at 204 C (400 F).

If Lüders bands are present on the surface of a formed part, the part is often rejected on the basis of appearance alone and is never used in service. In other instances, the lower ductility and the in-

creased strength accompanying strain aging reduces the formability of sheet metal and may lead to rupture on forming. During forming, the metal undergoes nonhomogeneous reduction. If the component is then subjected to some treatment involving heating, such as galvanizing, enameling or paint baking, the component may fracture in critically worked areas.

The susceptibility of box-annealed rimmed steel to strain-age embrittlement is a function mainly of the dissolved nitrogen content and is not generally affected by variations in mill practice. The susceptibility of box-annealed aluminum-killed sheet steel increases slightly as the carbides coarsen, although this type of steel is essentially nonaging.

Quench-Age Embrittlement. If low-carbon steels are rapidly cooled from temperatures slightly below the lower critical temperature (Ac_1) of the steel, the hardness of the steel increases, with a resultant loss of ductility upon aging at room temperature. As with strain aging, quench-age embrittlement is a function of time at the aging temperature until the maximum degree of embrittlement is reached. A period of several weeks at room temperature is required for maximum embrittlement.

A decrease in the quenching temperature decreases the extent of the embrittlement. Quenching from temperatures of 560 C (1040 F) and below does not produce quench-age embrittlement. Steels with carbon contents of 0.04 to 0.12% appear most susceptible to quench-age embrittlement; increasing the carbon content above 0.12% reduces the effect. Quench-age embrittlement results from (a) precipitation of solute carbon at existing dislocations, and (b) precipitation hardening because of differences in the solid solubility of carbon in ferrite at different temperatures. Quenching these steels produces a supersaturated solid solution of carbon in ferrite. Aging at room temperature therefore enables the excess carbon to precipitate out of solution.

Blue Brittleness. When plain carbon steels and some alloy steels are heated between 232 and 371 C (450 and 700 F), there is an increase in strength and a marked decrease in ductility and impact strength. This embrittling phenomenon is known as "blue brittleness", because it occurs in the blue-heat range. Blue brittleness is an accelerated form of strain-age embrittlement. The increase in strength and decrease in ductility are caused by precipitation hardening within the critical-temperature range. Deformation while the steel is heated in the blue-heat range results in even higher hardness and tensile strength after cooling to room temperature. If the strain rate is increased, the blue-brittle temperature range increases.

The use of steels that have been heated in the blue-brittleness range should be avoided, especially if the steels are subjected to impact loads, because the toughness of this material will be considerably less than optimum.

Temper Embrittlement. In certain alloy steels, temper embrittlement is caused by either (a) tempering within a critical-temperature range, or (b) slow cooling after tempering at higher temperatures. In critical-temperature tempering, embrittlement results irrespective of the cooling rate after tempering, although the degree of embrittlement will vary according to the holding time and the rate of cooling after tempering. Rapid cooling from the tempering temperature and short holding times minimize the embrittlement. In slow cooling, the degree of embrittlement depends on the cooling rate.

When temper embrittlement is evaluated on a time-temperature basis, the embrittlement exhibits a "C-curve" type of behavior. The rate of embrittlement, as well as the maximum temperature at which embrittlement can occur, varies with changes in the chemical composition. The critical temperature range for temper embrittlement is approximately 350 to 575 C (662 to 1067 F).

Although temper embrittlement is common in alloy steels, the more highly alloyed steels designed for through-hardenability and toughness are more susceptible than the lower-alloyed pearlitic steels. Plain carbon steels containing less than 0.6% Mn are not susceptible.

The degree of temper embrittlement increases as the amounts of antimony, phosphorus, tin and arsenic increase. These elements normally are present only in trace amounts in alloy steels, but even such amounts are sufficient to cause embrittlement. Chromium, manganese and silicon, and to a lesser extent nickel, enhance temper embrittlement in the presence of antimony, phosphorus, tin, and arsenic. Presence of small amounts of molybdenum and tungsten inhibit temper embrittlement, but larger amounts promote temper embrittlement. Lowering the carbon content helps to reduce the susceptibility to temper embrittlement; increasing the austenitic grain size increases susceptibility.

Temper embrittlement can occur with microstructures other than martensite. Temper embrittlement with bainitic microstructures is less severe than with martensitic microstructures and much less severe with pearlitic microstructures.

Temper embrittlement causes an increase in the ductile-to-brittle transition temperature. The mechanism of brittle fracture changes from cleavage in unembrittled steels to grain-boundary separation along prior-austenite grain boundaries in embrittled steels. Fortunately, temper embrittlement is reversible; that is, retempering at a temperature above the critical range followed by rapid cooling through this range will restore toughness. No significant change in hardness or strength is associated with temper embrittlement.

Temper embrittlement can be a critical problem during stress relieving of fabricated structures, because the slow cooling rates required to prevent distortion after stress relief also promote temper embrittlement. Consequently, for these applications, steels have been developed that have low susceptibility to temper embrittlement during stress relief.

500 F ("350 C") embrittlement of high-strength low-alloy steels occurs over a temperature range of approximately 400 to 700 F (205 to 370 C). It occurs mainly in steels that have been heat treated to a microstructure of tempered martensite; thus the more descriptive term tempered-martensite embrittlement is sometimes used. Steels with microstructures of tempered lower bainite also are susceptible to 500 F embrittlement, but steels with pearlitic microstructures and other bainitic steels are not.

500 F embrittlement is evaluated by measuring the effect of tempering temperature on room-temperature impact energy; this is in contrast to temper embrittlement, which is evaluated by measuring the effect of tempering temperature on the ductile-to-brittle transition temperature.

500 F embrittlement is believed to be caused by precipitation of cementite platelets at prior-austenite grain boundaries, which results in the formation of thin grain-boundary networks of ferrite. However, some investigators believe that the precipitation of grain-boundary cementite platelets as such is responsible for 500 F embrittlement.

Steels containing substantial amounts of chromium or manganese are highly susceptible to 500 F embrittlement. Aluminum contents above 0.04% reduce embrittlement, and additions of 0.1% Al usually eliminate the problem. Some degree of embrittlement has been observed when phosphorus, antimony, arsenic, tin, silicon, manganese or nitrogen additions were made to high-purity steels. Additions of nitrogen produced intergranular fractures, but the other embrittling agents did not. (Commercial grades of steel that are subjected to 500 F embrittlement treatments fracture intergranularly.)

Embrittlement in low-alloy steels heat treated to high strength levels can be minimized by:

1 Developing special steels with retarded martensite-tempering characteristics
2 Developing steels with faster rates of martensite tempering
3 Using steels capable of transformation to 100% bainite at the desired strength level and section size
4 Avoiding tempering in the region of susceptibility
5 Using the lowest possible carbon content consistent with the desired strength level.

400 to 500 C (752 to 932 F) Embrittlement. Fine-grained, high-chromium stainless steels normally possess good ductility. However, if they are held for long periods of time at temperatures in the range of 400 to 500 C (752 to 932 F), they will become harder, but embrittled. Embrittled high-chromium ferritic stainless steels contain two ferrites, one rich in iron and one rich in chromium.

Susceptibility to 400 to 500 C embrittlement increases with increasing chromium content, with the highest degree of embrittlement occurring with chromium contents greater than 19%. At least 15% chromium is necessary for embrittlement to occur. The effect of carbon content on embrittlement is minimal. High-chromium steels that contain at least 1% Ti are more susceptible to embrittlement than are similar steels with lower titanium contents. High-chromium steels that contain 2.4 to 4.15% Cb are more susceptible to embrittlement than are similar steels with lower columbium contents. 400 to 500 C embrittlement occurs more rapidly in steels with high levels of silicon.

The embrittlement caused by prolonged soaking within the 400 to 500 C (752 to 932 F) range can be removed by soaking at somewhat higher temperatures for several hours.

Sigma-Phase Embrittlement. The formation of sigma phase in ferritic and austenitic stainless steels during long periods of exposure to temperatures between approximately 560 to 980 C (1050 to 1800 F) results in considerable embrittlement after cooling to room temperature. Sigma phase can be formed by either (a) slow cooling from temperatures of 1088 to 1149 C (1900 to 2100 F); or (b) water quenching from 1088 to 1149 C (1900 to 2100 F) followed by heating at 560 to 980 C (1050 to 1800 F), with heating at 850 C (1562 F) producing the greatest effect. The embrittlement is most detrimental after the steel has cooled to temperatures below 260 C (500 F). At higher temperatures, stainless steels containing sigma phase usually can withstand normal design stresses. However, cooling to 260 C (500 F) or below results in essentially complete loss of toughness. Hence, maintenance of high-temperature components containing sigma phase must be performed with great care to prevent damage. Boiler tubes made from high-chromium ferritic stainless steels, such as type 446, have been known to shatter when dropped following removal after extended service life.

Sigma phase is an iron-chromium compound of approximately equal atomic proportions of iron and chromium. Sigma phase is extremely brittle and hard (hardness of Rockwell C 68.5, according to Ref 3).

Sigma phase can exist in pure iron-chromium alloys with chromium contents from 25 to 76%. Small amounts of silicon greatly increase the rate of sigma-phase formation (Ref 3) and extend the range of formation to lower chromium levels. Hence, sigma phase can be formed in iron-chromium-silicon alloys with much lower chromium contents. Additions of aluminum and molybdenum act in a manner similar to silicon (Ref 3), although aluminum is not as effective in promoting sigma-phase formation as molybdenum. Additions of small amounts of nickel and manganese also expand the range of sigma-phase formation, but larger amounts change the steel from ferritic to austenitic, which results in less susceptibility to sigma-phase formation. The addition of carbon to iron-chromium alloys decreases the susceptibility to sigma-phase formation.

Austenitic stainless steels, such as the 18Cr-8Ni types, can be balanced to prevent sigma-phase formation during stress relief or to improve the hot workability. Coarse grain sizes and high initial annealing temperatures retard sigma-phase formation while cold working promotes it. Sigma phase has been observed in many austenitic stainless steels. Sigma phase forms more rapidly in austenitic stainless steels that contain ferrite.

The presence of sigma phase greatly increases notch sensitivity. The hardness and tensile strengths are usually not significantly affected by the presence of sigma phase, but the impact strength is greatly affected. Sigma phase exerts a strengthening effect at high temperatures; however, the impact strength at high temperatures of an alloy containing sigma phase is lower than the impact strength at room temperature of an alloy without sigma phase. If resistance to impact loads at high temperatures is not required, the presence of sigma phase in high-temperature applications may be helpful. The high hardness of sigma phase improves the wear resistance, and some alloys have been designed to make use of this property.

Heat-resistant grades of cast stainless steels, depending on composition, may contain sigma phase. Sigma phase, in general, should be avoided in these steels, because it reduces creep resistance and promotes thermal fatigue. Sigma phase reduces the corrosion resistance of ferritic and austenitic stainless steels.

The presence of sigma phase can markedly reduce the ductility of austenitic stainless steel weldments. Usually, some ferrite is desirable in weldments

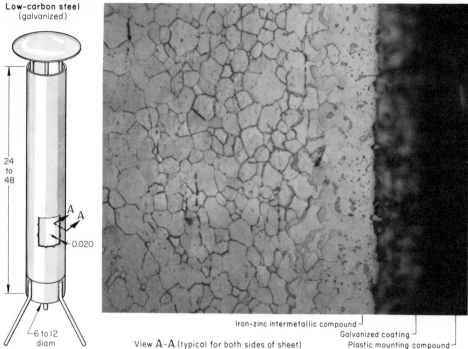

Low-carbon steel
(galvanized)

24
to
48

A
A
0.020

6 to 12
diam

Iron-zinc intermetallic compound
Galvanized coating
Plastic mounting compound

View A-A (typical for both sides of sheet)

Fig. 29. Orchard heater of galvanized low-carbon steel that broke in a brittle manner because of an iron-zinc intermetallic compound along the grain boundaries. View A-A is a micrograph of an etched section that shows the microstructure of the steel sheet at 400×. (Example 11)

of austenitic stainless steel for good ductility; however, if the ferrite transforms to sigma phase during subsequent weld passes, heat treatment, or service temperatures, the toughness of the weldment will be reduced.

Graphitization of carbon and carbon-molybdenum steel piping during service at elevated temperatures above 427 C (800 F) has caused numerous failures in steam power plants (Ref 4) and refineries (Ref 5). Graphite formation generally occurs in a narrow region in the heat-affected zone of a weld where the metal has been briefly heated above the lower critical temperature. The graphitization tendency of carbon and carbon-molybdenum steels is increased when the aluminum content exceeds about 0.025%. Carbon-molybdenum steels exhibit greater resistance to graphitization than carbon steels. Steels deoxidized with silicon may also be susceptible to graphitization. Deoxidation with titanium usually will produce good resistance to graphitization.

The degree of embrittlement depends on the distribution, size and shape of the graphite. The severity of graphitization is frequently evaluated by bend testing. If graphitization is detected in its early stages, the material can often be rehabilitated by normalizing and tempering just below the lower critical temperature. Steel that has undergone more severe graphitization cannot be salvaged in this manner; the defective region must be cut out and rewelded, or the section must be replaced. Steels used for these applica-

tions can be rendered less susceptible to graphitization by tempering just below the lower critical temperature.

Embrittlement of galvanized steel can result from long periods of exposure at elevated temperatures below the melting point of the zinc in the coating. In this type of embrittlement, zinc diffuses from the galvanized coating to grain boundaries in the steel, resulting in the formation of a brittle intergranular network of iron-zinc intermetallic compound. The presence of this compound can lead to brittle fracture, as in the example that follows.

Example 11. Brittle Fracture of Galvanized Steel Heater Shells Because of Embrittlement by Iron-Zinc Intermetallic Compounds (Fig. 29)

After only a short time in service, oil-fired or gas-fired orchard heaters, such as the one shown in Fig. 29, were easily broken, particularly by impact during handling and storage. Failure occurred in the portion of the heater shell that normally reached the highest temperature in service.

The orchard heaters were pipes, generally 6 to 12 in. in diameter and 24 to 48 in. long. When in use, fuel was burned inside a pipe, which served as a windguard and a heat sink, and heat was transferred to nearby trees by radiation and convection. The heaters were used only a few nights a year and were stored outdoors when not in use. To minimize both cost and deterioration from atmospheric corrosion, the heater shells were made of galvanized low-carbon steel sheet about 0.020 in. thick.

Investigation. Visual examination of a broken heater revealed that the area around

the fracture was not shiny like the rest of the pipe, but was gray in color. Metal from these areas was very brittle and easily broken.

Pieces of metal from the failure area were prepared for metallographic examination. A brittle and somewhat porous metallic layer about 0.001 in. thick was observed on both surfaces of the sheet. Next to this was an apparently single-phase region nearly 0.002 in. in thickness (see view A-A in Fig. 29). This phase also was present along the grain boundaries of the steel beneath this second layer and became progressively less observable nearer the center of the sheet. The region of observable penetration was about 0.003 in. thick, but this phase probably extended to the center of the sheets as a thin band that could not be resolved by optical microscopy.

Conclusions. Prolonged heating of the galvanized steel heater shells caused the zinc-rich surface to become alloyed with iron and reduce the number of layers. Also, heating caused zinc to diffuse along grain boundaries toward the center of the sheet. Zinc in the grain boundaries reacted with iron to form the brittle intergranular phase, which is visible in view A-A in Fig. 29.

The result was failure by brittle fracture at low impact loads during handling and storage.

Corrective Measure. Galvanized steel sheet was replaced by aluminized steel sheet for the combustion chamber. The increase in service life more than compensated for the more costly and difficult-to-fabricate aluminized sheet metal.

Neutron Embrittlement. Neutron irradiation of steel components in nuclear reactors usually results in a significant rise in the ductile-to-brittle transition temperature of the steel. The transition temperature, as determined by Charpy V-notch impact tests, may be raised substantially, depending on such factors as the neutron dose, neutron spectrum, irradiation temperature, and steel composition (Ref 6). The amount by which the transition temperature increases because of neutron irradiation is usually at least 17 C (30 F) but less than 195 C (350 F).

The increase in the ductile-to-brittle transition temperature, or in the nil-ductility transition temperature, has been determined for many steels used for these applications under various conditions of irradiation. High-strength steels, which have lower initial nil-ductility transition temperatures than low-strength steels, are generally less susceptible to radiation embrittlement. Steels with low initial nil-ductility transition temperatures, fine-grained microstructures and high dislocation densities generally offer greater resistance to neutron embrittlement (Ref 7). Neutron embrittlement renders the steel more susceptible to intergranular fracture.

Heat treatment practice greatly affects the susceptibility of a steel to neutron embrittlement. Steels with tempered-martensite microstructures are less susceptible than those with tempered-upper-bainite or ferritic microstructures. Vacuum degassing and control of residual elements help reduce susceptibility to neutron embrittlement (Ref 8).

Stainless steels, principally the austenitic types, are used as cladding materials for pressurized-water and boiling-water reactors. Irradiation of these steels also results in a significant decrease in ductility. The martensitic grades (annealed or heat treated), the ferritic grades, and the precipitation-hardenable grades of stainless steels also are susceptible to neutron embrittlement.

Hydrogen embrittlement has been a long-time problem. Quantitative knowledge regarding the influence of hydrogen on metals is difficult to obtain; however, from a qualitative standpoint, the effects of hydrogen have been well documented in the literature. Quantitative descriptions of the effects of hydrogen are hampered by the difficulty in obtaining representative samples and also the problems associated with obtaining accurate analytical data of gases present in very low parts-per-million quantities.

Absorption of hydrogen results in a general loss of ductility. Historically, hydrogen-embrittlement effects have been evaluated by reversed-bend tests, single-bend tests and fatigue tests. Reduction-in-area and elongation values determined by standard tensile tests also show the effect of hydrogen embrittlement. Impact tests generally are not a good method for detecting hydrogen embrittlement.

Hydrogen is an extremely mobile element in steel and other metals. Hydrogen can come from many sources, such as water vapor, pickling and electrolysis. Hydrogen dissolves in steel to form an interstitial solid solution. The solubility of hydrogen increases as the temperature increases, with solubility increasing greatly at the melting point of the alloy. The greater the amount of hydrogen dissolved in the molten steel, the greater the possibility of unsoundness (porosity, flakes or cooling cracks) in the solid steel. Hydrogen is more soluble in austenite than in ferrite (either alpha or delta ferrite) and flakes are rarely observed in austenitic steels.

The influence of alloying elements on the solubility of hydrogen in steel is not well documented. Increasing concentrations of carbon and aluminum apparently decrease the solubility of hydrogen in steel, whereas additions of manganese and nickel apparently increase its solubility. Hydrogen may be present in steel either in atomic or molecular form. In the atomic form, hydrogen is present interstitially; in the molecular form, hydrogen is present in microcracks and may be present at dislocations.

The degree of hydrogen embrittlement is highly dependent on the strength level of steel: resistance to hydrogen embrittlement decreases as the strength level is increased. Two forms of hydrogen embrittlement — slow-strain-rate embrittlement and static fatigue (the latter is also referred to as hydrogen-induced delayed cracking) — are both particularly damaging to high-strength low-alloy martensitic steels.

The effects of hydrogen embrittlement decrease as the strain rate increases. These effects are most pronounced at intermediate service temperatures, and disappear at high and low temperatures. Because the solubility of hydrogen is greater at high temperatures than at low temperatures, the concentration of hydrogen can exceed solubility limits at room temperatures on rapid cooling from high temperatures, such as after forging and heat treatment. Any excess hydrogen present, therefore, must diffuse to the surface of the steel or form discontinuities in the interior of the part. Pockets of hydrogen in these discontinuities may develop enough pressure to form hairline cracks or shatter the steel.

Hydrogen embrittlement appears to affect all steel microstructures. The chemical composition of the steel appears to exert a strong effect on the ability of the material to recover from hydrogen embrittlement at room temperature, and the microstructure also has some influence on this ability.

Hydrogen embrittlement of steel may occur during pickling to remove scale and rust. The rate of hydrogen pickup depends on the type and concentration of acid, temperature of the solution, pickling time, and the presence and concentration of inhibitors. Strongly ionized acids, such as hydrochloric, sulfuric and hydrofluoric, cause severe embrittlement. Nitric acid apparently causes little embrittlement even though it is an oxidizing acid. Inhibitors generally help to reduce hydrogen embrittlement. Embrittlement will diminish if the steel is allowed to age at room temperature or is baked at a somewhat higher temperature.

Hydrogen embrittlement of steel may occur during electroplating. The coating itself may become embrittled if hydrogen becomes trapped in the coating during plating. Embrittled coatings frequently develop blisters; ruptures of the plating may result if sufficient hydrogen pressure develops in a blister.

Hydrogen embrittlement of steel also may occur during arc welding, as discussed in the article that begins on page 230 in this volume.

In addition to steel and other iron-base alloys, several nonferrous metals and alloys, including hexagonal, close-packed titanium and zirconium alloys and body-centered-cubic refractory alloys, are subject to hydrogen damage. For a more complete discussion of hydrogen embrittlement and other hydrogen damage in metals, see the article that begins on page 230 in this volume.

Stress-corrosion cracking is a mechanical-environmental failure process in which mechanical stress and chemical attack combine to initiate and propagate fracture in a metal part. Stress-corrosion cracking is produced by the synergistic action of sustained tensile stress and a specific corrosive environment; this action causes failure to occur more rapidly than it would if the separate effects of the stress and the corrosive environment were simply added together.

Failure by stress-corrosion cracking frequently is caused by simultaneous exposure to a seemingly mild chemical environment and to a tensile stress well below the yield strength of the metal. Under such conditions, fine cracks can penetrate deeply into the part while the surface exhibits only insignificant amounts of corrosion. Hence, there may be no macroscopic indications of an impending failure. Stress-corrosion cracking is discussed in detail in the article that begins on page 205 in this volume.

Liquid-metal embrittlement can cause cracking and fracture in stressed parts of many metals. Not all combinations of solid and liquid metals produce embrittlement. For example, aluminum is embrittled by liquid gallium, sodium and tin, and steel is embrittled by liquid cadmium and lithium. (Liquid-metal embrittlement of steel also has been reported to be caused by liquid copper, brass, aluminum bronze, antimony and tellurium.) Both aluminum and steel are embrittled by liquid indium, zinc and mercury; fractures in aluminum alloy plates that were embrittled by contact with liquid mercury may be seen in Fig. 12 on page 60 in the article on Identification of Types of Failures, in this volume.

The melting temperature and chemical reactivity of a liquid metal are not deciding factors as to whether it will cause embrittlement or not. Instead, most instances of embrittlement are accompanied by low intersolubilities and absence of intermetallic-compound formation. There are exceptions, however. For instance, zinc has considerable solid solubility in iron and the two metals form an intermetallic compound at the melting temperature of zinc.

Liquid-metal embrittlement requires effective wetting to establish a true interface between the liquid and the solid metal; the interfacial area need not be large. Cracking resulting from liquid-metal embrittlement most frequently is intergranular, although a portion of the cracking may be transgranular. The velocity of crack propagation depends primarily on the manner of stress application. The supply of liquid metal to the advancing crack front governs the extent to which the crack will propagate. The level of applied stress above the threshold value also affects the extent of cracking.

Upon exposure to a liquid metal, cracking is instantaneous at high levels of static or dynamic stress, whereas at low stresses delayed fracture is common. Liquid-metal embrittlement can be obtained by loading in simple tension, bending or torsion. Liquid-metal embrittlement has not been observed with compressive loading. If a specimen loaded in simple tension is embrittled by a liquid metal, it will break transverse to the loading axis.

A liquid metal contacting a metal component may limit (a) the total ductility prior to fracture, or (b) the stress at fracture if the fracture occurs before yielding. Low-carbon steel embrittled by liquid lithium at 200 C (392 F), for instance, will fracture after only 2 to 3% elongation.

The grain size of single-phase materials exerts a marked influence on the fracture stress during liquid-metal embrittlement. Coarser grain sizes result in lower fracture strengths. The presence of notches also reduces wetted fracture strength. Generally, a steel heat treated to high strength and hardness is more severely embrittled than the same steel heat treated to lower strength and hardness.

For a more extensive discussion of cracking and fracture caused by liquid-metal embrittlement, see the article that begins on page 228 in this volume.

Failures Resulting From Damage in Service

Damage that occurs during service can cause a variety of ductile or brittle fractures in metal components. Ductile or brittle fracture is the process by which final separation occurs in parts that have been cracked in service by other mechanisms such as fatigue, stress-corrosion cracking and liquid-metal embrittlement. Ductile or brittle fracture also may result from temperature effects such as (a) sigma-phase embrittlement, (b) loss of hardness in heat treated or strain-hardened alloys, and (c) service at temperatures below the ductile-to-brittle fracture-transition temperature.

Service-induced imperfections — for example, shallow fatigue cracks, thermal checks (such as are found in gun barrels), and scratches — may lead to ductile fracture by reducing the cross-sectional area and by acting as stress concentrators, or may lead to brittle fracture if the critical flaw size is exceeded.

Brittle fracture is likely to result when one or more factors (rate of loading, low

(a) Ultraviolet-light photograph of the muzzle end of the cannon tube, at actual size, showing a pair of fluorescent-magnetic-particle crack indications (at arrows) on the bore surface. (b) Fractograph, at 2×, of radial marks on fracture surface that originate at a 1-mm-deep fatigue crack, the length of which is indicated by bracket at O.

Fig. 30. Large alloy steel cannon tube that broke during firing at low temperature by catastrophic brittle fracture that originated at a shallow fatigue crack

temperature, or presence of a notch) exceeds the level anticipated. Application of fracture-mechanics design concepts makes it possible to fabricate components from high-strength materials, assuming that available nondestructive-testing techniques can detect flaws slightly smaller than critical size. Periodic in-service nondestructive inspection may be necessary to ensure that flaws have not grown to critical size during service.

An example of brittle fracture that originated at a shallow fatigue crack is

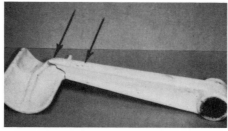

The brake pedal, cast from aluminum alloy 356-T6, was used on a heavy tracked vehicle. The region between the arrows was twisted out of shape by overload before fracture occurred (at left arrow).

Fig. 31. Brake pedal that failed by ductile overload fracture because of inadequate cross-sectional area

shown in Fig. 30. A pair of fluorescent-magnetic-particle crack indications at the muzzle end of a large alloy steel cannon tube is shown in Fig. 30(a). These cracks formed after only a few rounds of ammunition had been fired. When another round was fired, at low temperature, brittle fracture occurred and the tube broke into more than a hundred pieces. When all the pieces were reassembled, chevron patterns on the fracture surfaces pointed to the fracture origin. Figure 30(b) shows the origin of fracture, near the muzzle end of the tube, at the location of the crack indications shown in Fig. 30(a). A shallow (1 mm deep) fatigue crack can be seen at the tube surface in the center of radial marks on the fracture. Subsequent mechanical testing of the alloy steel revealed it to have low impact toughness, unsuitable for low-temperature service even when the largest crack was only 1 mm deep. This finding resulted in new material-toughness requirements and a redesign of the tube section to provide increased resistance to fatigue cracking. Nondestructive-testing techniques were developed to permit measurement of flaw depth as well as to simply locate the flaw, as had been done with the magnetic-particle inspection. These changes proved adequate, and there were no subsequent failures.

Overloading of structures is a common cause of ductile or brittle fracture. If a structure that meets all specifications fractures in a completely ductile manner, overloading is the probable cause. Underdesign (inadequate cross-sectional area) was the cause of the ductile overload fracture of the aluminum alloy brake pedal shown in Fig. 31. Overload fractures resulting from underdesign, however, need not be completely ductile, as described in the example that follows.

Example 12. Ductile-and-Brittle Overload Fracture of a Low-Carbon, Low-Alloy Steel Ordnance Bolt (Fig. 32)*

A bolt that was one of two used to hold an adapter-block, gun-barrel and breech-ring assembly of an experimental cannon broke during firing of the fifteenth round. The bolt, 1⅞ in. in diameter and 12 in. long, was threaded for 4 in. of its length with 12–UN3A threads having a minor diameter of 1.773 in. The bolt was made of a low-carbon, low-alloy steel (0.3% C, 0.8% Mn, 0.02% P, 0.02% S, 0.55% Si, 1.65% Cr, 0.4% Mo), heated to 830 to 857 C (1525 to 1575 F), oil quenched, and tempered at 316 to 427 C (600 to 800 F) to give a hardness of Rockwell C 46 to 49. This heat treatment produced fine tempered martensite and a yield strength of about 200,000 psi.

Investigation. The estimated tensile stresses on the bolt in service were 80,000 psi axial from the firing load plus 20,000 psi

*Adapted from a report prepared for this volume by W. Wallace, Research Officer, National Research Council of Canada

(a) Fractograph, at 1.2×, of the fracture surface, showing two fracture zones (indicated by A and B). (b) Micrograph, at 80×, showing secondary cracking at a sharp fillet in a thread root. (c) Micrograph, at 300×, showing secondary cracking through tempered martensite at center of the thread root. (d) TEM fractograph, at 3660×, showing shear dimples in zone A. (e) TEM fractograph, at 3000×, showing quasicleavage facets in zone B. (f) TEM fractograph, at 3000×, showing three separated-grain surfaces among quasicleavage facets in zone B.

Fig. 32. Low-carbon, low-alloy steel ordnance bolt that broke through the threads because of overload during firing of an experimental cannon (Example 12)

from pre-tensioning. The maximum shear stress on the thread was estimated to be 23,000 psi. The major stresses were essentially impact, the time to reach peak gun pressure being 4 millisec with a further 4-millisec dwell at 80% of peak load.

Failure of the bolt occurred by transverse (plane-strain) cracking that originated in the thread approximately 1 in. from the shank (see Fig. 32a). At failure, the bolt showed both shear of the thread and necking at the bolt end of the thread. Secondary cracking to a maximum depth of 0.08 in. was found to be nucleated at a sharp fillet at the root of the thread (see Fig. 32b) and also at the center of the thread root (see Fig. 32c).

The fracture surface was found to contain two discrete zones, indicated by A and B in Fig. 32(a). The circumferential zone A penetrated to a depth of about 0.08 to 0.12 in. from the thread root and showed shear dimples (Fig. 32d), which are characteristic of ductile overload fracture. Zone B showed features that are characteristic of quasicleavage (see Fig. 32e), which is often associated with brittle fracture in quenched-and-tempered steels. Isolated areas resembling intergranular fracture were also found, as indicated by the separated-grain surfaces shown in Fig. 32(f). Intergranular

fracture is sometimes associated with tempered-martensite (500 F or "350 C") embrittlement in low-alloy steels, but no other indications of embrittlement associated with prior-austenite grain boundaries were found.

Conclusions and Recommendations. The macroscopic evidence of necking, together with the dimpled fracture zone, suggested that the basic problem was one of underdesign — that is, inadequate load-carrying capacity and insufficient consideration of stress concentration at the threads. Because 95% of the fracture surface consisted of quasicleavage, the notch sensitivity of the steel in this heat treated condition was too great for this application. The heat treatment used reflects the demand for high yield strength, which would be at a maximum for this treatment. However, the notched-bar impact strength (as indicated by Izod values), and probably the fracture toughness as well, would be at a minimum. Tempering to a lower hardness would improve notch sensitivity but would lower the yield strength; therefore, it was recommended that more than two bolts be used to hold the assembly.

Improper operation is another cause of overloading that can lead to ductile or

brittle fracture. For instance, a splined shaft, part of a spur gear made of 8620 steel, broke in two during testing of a heavy vehicle. Because the gear train, of which the broken gear was a part, was used only to apply the parking brake, this part was not expected to receive a high level of stress in service. Figure 33(a) shows the fracture surface, which is a fine, fibrous surface with no visible evidence of fatigue. Analysis of the part showed that it met specified composition, mechanical properties, and dimensions. Figure 33(b) shows the spline surface at the edge of the fracture, showing 45° cracks leading off the fracture surface, and severe distortion of the spline area. Figure 33(c) shows an area similar to that in Fig. 33(b), but illuminated to show the severe indentation on the side of a spline tooth. Figure 33(d), which is a section through a spline tooth, perpendicular to the fracture surface, shows severe grain distortion. This clear evidence of overloading, plus the fact that the material conformed to specification, led to the conclusion that the parking brake had been used to try to stop the

(a) Fracture surface, at actual size, showing a fine, fibrous appearance. (b) Photograph, at 10×, of the spline surface at the edge of fracture (at left), showing cracks and severe distortion. (c) Photograph, at 10×, of another area of the spline surface, illuminated to show severe indentation (at arrow) on the side of a spline tooth. (d) Micrograph of a section through a spline tooth; severe grain distortion is evident at left. (Etched in nital; 250×.)

Fig. 33. Splined shaft of 8620 steel that broke during testing of a heavy vehicle

heavy vehicle while it was still in motion — a use for which the parking brake was not designed.

A different type of improper operation led to the ductile fracture described in the example that follows.

Example 13. Ductile Fracture of Steel Wire Rope Because of Mishandling

Steel wire hoisting rope that supported a "spreader bar" used to carry coils of steel rods and wire in a sulfuric acid cleaning (pickling) line in a mill broke when lifting a partly loaded spreader bar, allowing one end of the bar to drop about 6 ft. At the time of the failure, two four-rope hoists about 10 ft apart were being used with an overhead traveling crane and two hoist drums to convey a load of rods or wire from tank to tank in the cleaning line.

Fabrication. The wire rope was specified to be ½-in.-diam extra pliable hoisting rope, right regular lay, blue-center steel, nominally 6x37. It consisted of six strands, each containing 35 steel wires, around a lubricant-saturated central core of polypropylene fiber.

The individual wires were made from high-carbon steel; a processing sequence of cold drawing, patenting, and final heavy cold reduction was used to obtain the required tensile strength and toughness. The wires were stranded in helical layers around a center wire, in a counterclockwise direction, as indicated below:

Layer	Number of wires	Nominal diam, in.
Outside	14	0.028
Interstitial	7	0.0135
Intermediate	7	0.033
First	6	0.020
Center wire	1	0.020

The six 35-wire strands, each about ⁵⁄₃₂ in. in diameter, were laid helically around the polypropylene core in a clockwise direction to make the ½-in.-diam right-regular-lay rope.

Breaking strength of the wire rope was specified as 20,400 lb minimum. Tensile strength of the individual wires was 250,000 to 296,000 psi.

Service Conditions. The conditions under which the wire rope was used in service permitted a maximum load of about 3000 lb on the rope, assuming uniform load distribution.

Standard practice limited the maximum load per rope to 20% of its minimum static breaking strength (a load of 4080 lb for this rope), to allow for the effects of dynamic loading, possible unevenness of loading, and deterioration that might not readily be detected by visual inspection.

The static load on each wire rope at the instant before the failure was approximately 1800 lb, based on an assumed uniform distribution of the weight of the partly loaded spreader bar among all of the hoist ropes.

The atmosphere in which the rope was used contained fumes from pickling tanks that contained 8 to 12% by weight sulfuric acid at a temperature of about 70 to 80 C (160 to 180 F). The relative humidity was usually very high, frequently reaching 95 to 100%. The rope was lubricated regularly at weekly intervals, or more frequently if needed.

Investigation. Because of the exceptionally severe corrosive environment, it was suspected that corrosion could have caused the failure, and so the rope was first examined visually for evidence of corrosion. No significant corrosive attack was found, and the rope appeared to be well lubricated throughout its cross section along its entire length.

The steel strands near the break and for a considerable distance in both directions showed little external or internal wear, and there was no crushing or gouging in this region. However, localized chafing and compression marks were found at a point on the wire rope about 12 ft from the break, corresponding to the location of an equalizer sheave on the spreader bar.

The ends of the broken wires were examined at a magnification of 30 diameters, using a stereoscopic microscope. Most of the broken ends of the individual wires showed the necking-down (cup-and-cone) type of rupture that is characteristic of ductile fracture in tensile overload. Irregular and jagged secondary shear fracture also was observed on some of the ruptured wires.

Chemical analysis of several samples of wire from the rope gave an average content of 0.88% carbon and 0.46% manganese, which is normal for this material, and a low content of incidental elements. Breaking strength of an apparently undamaged portion of the failed rope was 23,750 lb — well above the specified minimum of 20,400 lb.

Conclusions. The wire rope failed in tension under a sudden overload that was

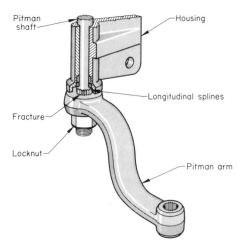

Fig. 34. Automobile steering assembly in which the pitman shaft, of 6118H steel, broke by ductile fracture under torsional impact loading (Example 14)

caused by binding of the rope at an equalizer sheave while the spreader bar was being lifted. The rope apparently became slack and kinked or tangled in the sheave assembly as a result of rapid manipulation of the crane hoist mechanism by the operator. As a result, one of the ropes on the hoist was suddenly subjected to the approximately 7200-lb weight previously distributed among the four ropes, or about 1¾ times the normal maximum working load per rope. The rope then broke because of the sudden and nonuniform application of load on some of the six strands of the kinked or tangled rope, with the strands failing in succession under excessive dynamic loading.

The wire rope met specifications, had ample strength for normal service in this application, and was in good condition. Corrosion was not a factor in the failure of the rope, which had been protected by regular lubrication.

Examination of the equalizer-sheave assembly showed that binding of the rope should not occur as long as reasonable care was exercised by the crane operator. No defects or malfunctions were found in the equipment.

Recommendations. Close adherence to proper operating procedures and the scheduling of more frequent inspection of the rope for kinks or sharp bends would eliminate failure.

Occasionally, it is difficult to determine whether overloading that resulted from an accident caused a ductile or brittle fracture, or whether the fracture caused the accident. Laboratory tests on components that are similar or identical to one that has broken in service are sometimes useful in pinpointing the causes of such fractures, as in the next example.

Example 14. Ductile Fracture of a 6118H Steel Pitman Shaft in a Steering Mechanism Because of Torsional Impact Loading (Fig. 34)

A driver in a relatively new automobile lost control and collided with a pole. The driver claimed that the steering had failed, causing the accident. The broken 6118H steel pitman shaft from the steering mechanism of the damaged car was examined to determine whether or not failure of this part did in fact cause the accident.

Investigation. Visual examination disclosed that the pitman shaft had broken alongside the pitman arm as shown in Fig. 34, leaving a relatively smooth fracture surface that was roughly transverse to the shaft axis. Longitudinal splines that were used to prevent rotation of the pitman arm on the shaft were deformed above the fracture plane. This indicated that deformation under a torsional load had preceded or accompanied fracture.

SEM fractography was used to examine the fracture surface for fatigue striations, which would indicate fracture and loss of steering prior to the accident, as claimed by the driver; no striations were found. A laboratory test, in which an identical shaft was subjected to heavy torsional impact, produced a fracture with an appearance that

Fig. 35. Cylinder sleeve for a rock drill that broke by progressively cracking from two sides when operated while rods were loose. The 3.6-in.-ID, 0.45-in.-wall sleeve was made of 94B17 steel, and carburized and hardened to Rockwell C 58 to 63 at the surface.

was similar in almost all respects to that of the fracture in the failed shaft.

Conclusion. It was concluded, primarily on the basis of the laboratory test, that the shaft broke under torsional impact — a result of the accident, rather than the cause.

Loosening of threaded fasteners may expose parts to excessively high or unbalanced loads, which in turn may result in impact or overload fracture. Figure 35 shows the brittle fracture that occurred by progressive cracking (caused by incremental crack propagation on successive applications of overload, rather than by fatigue) in a 94B17 steel cylinder sleeve for a pneumatic-percussion rock drill when the nuts on the side rods became loose. This cylinder sleeve extended into both the cylinder and chuck end to maintain alignment. The entire assembly was held together by two side rods, which passed through holes in the side-rod ears of the backhead, cylinder, cylinder sleeve, and chuck end. Tension in side rods of the type used in this assembly must be checked and adjusted on a regular basis to take up any slack caused by fretting wear on the threads or loosening because of vibration. If this is not done, one or both of the side rods can become loose, allowing the chuck end to move and cock with respect to the cylinder. The fracture shown in Fig. 35 occurred during drilling while both side rods were loose. Progressive cracking started in line with both side rods, indicating complete reverse bending of that portion of the sleeve inside the chuck end. When only one side rod is loose, the result is the same, but cracking progresses only from the side where the rod is loose, the opposite side going into compression as the sleeve is cocked.

Lack of proper lubrication has led to progressive cracking by brittle fracture in rock-drill components. Figure 36(a) shows a splined piston hammer for a rock drill that broke transversely through the

splines. Breakage was caused by progressive cracking that originated at scoring cracks on the sides of the hammer splines (Fig. 36b and c). Although Fig. 36(c) shows progressive cracking from both sides of a spline, some splines cracked only from one side. This is typical of failures encountered in drills that incorporate self-generated or integral rotation, when there is a brief interruption of lubricant or the oil that is used has inadequate film strength. In either event, loss of the separating lubricant film allows metal-to-metal contact between the splines, which are quench hardened in brine, and the splined nut of class D phosphor bronze, through which the

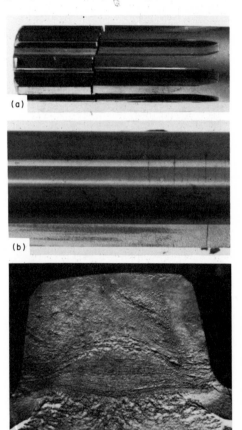

(a)

(b)

(c)

(a) Splined end of the hammer, showing the fracture. The hammer, 2.375 in. in diameter, was made of 1.10% C tool steel with controlled hardenability. (b) Close-up view of the splines on another hammer, showing well-developed scoring cracks. (c) Fracture surface of a hammer spline, at 5×, showing the progressive nature of the cracking, which originated from both sides of the spline.

Fig. 36. Splined piston hammer for a rock drill, which broke in a brittle manner from progressive cracking on the sides of the splines

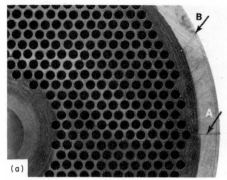

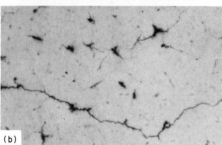

(a) Part of plate surface, at about actual size. At A is the major crack that progressed from the edge to the center of the plate; at B are grinding-burn marks introduced during resharpening. (b) Micrograph, at 320×, of the plate surface, etched in nital, showing numerous randomly oriented cracks.

Fig. 37. Meat-grinder chopper plate, of D2 tool steel, that failed in service from brittle cracking (Example 15)

hammer operates. Frictional heating of the steel surface is sufficient to heat a thin layer above the critical temperature. The austenitized material is rapidly quenched by the cold underlying material as soon as motion stops, forming brittle white martensite. By either mechanical impact or thermal fatigue, scoring cracks are produced in the brittle layer, forming lines of stress concentration normal to the direction of motion. Because the cracks are transverse, they are acted on by subsequent thermal cycling and by longitudinal and flexural shock waves generated by impact of the hammer against the shank end of the drilling string. The life of a scored hammer is usually quite brief once the cracks are formed, regardless of whether it is a new hammer or one that has been operating for several thousand hours.

The fact that lack of proper lubrication is the cause of a failure by brittle fracture is not always as obvious as in the failure of the splined hammer described above. In the example that follows, a meat-grinder plate overheated during idling due to lack of the lubrication normally supplied by the meat being ground.

Example 15. Brittle Cracking of a D2 Tool Steel Meat-Grinder Plate Because of Overheating in Service (Fig. 37)

The fine-hole chopper plate from a meat grinder, a portion of which is shown in Fig. 37(a), cracked in service. The plate was

6 in. in diameter, ¾ in. thick, had ⅛-in.-diam holes and was made of D2 tool steel heat treated to a hardness of Rockwell C 59 to 63.

Investigation. Visual examination of the chopper plate revealed a major crack (at A in Fig. 37a) that progressed from the outer edge toward the center of the plate, then most of the way around the plate. The surface of the plate was discolored, which indicated the metal had been heated to a temperature of approximately 288 C (550 F). Wear marks on the surface of the plate suggested that it had been subjected to unlubricated wear such as would result if the grinder was allowed to run with the plate rubbing against the knife with no meat being fed into the grinder.

The surfaces of the plate were etched with nital, which caused parallel marks typical of grinding burns to become visible on both sides of the plate. These marks (at B in Fig 37a) differed substantially from the marks commonly produced by the manufacturer's sharpening process and appeared to have occurred during resharpening of the chopper plate on a planer-type surface grinder. Probable causes of the grinding burn were either insufficient coolant flow during resharpening, feed rate too high, or improper grinding wheel.

Numerous randomly oriented surface cracks were observed on the plate, as shown in Fig. 37(b). These cracks could have been the result of high stresses produced when cold meat quenched the plate after it had been heated by unlubricated contact with the knives.

Conclusions. The plate failed in brittle fracture because of high stresses produced when cold meat quenched the plate after it had been heated by unlubricated contact with the knives. Both surface cracks and through cracks were caused by these high stresses.

The surface of the plate also was damaged by grinding burns resulting from improper resharpening practices.

Recommendations. The meat grinder should not be operated without meat being fed through the machine or other means provided for lubrication at the contact surface of the knives and chopper plate. The machine should be adjusted so that the proper pressure is exerted between the plate and knife.

Resharpening techniques should be revised to avoid the grinding burns observed on this type of chopper plate.

Modification of a machine may introduce an unexpected factor that affects the life of a component in the machine with a long history of excellent service. For example, in older models of a rock drill, rotation of the drill string and bit was transmitted by a ratchet-and-pawl mechanism to index a rifle bar and turn the piston hammer. The rotation of the hammer was then transmitted to a chuck driver, a chuck, and hence to the drill string. A new design provided direct gear drive to the chuck driver, eliminating the pawls, rifle bar, and a bronze nut in the head of the hammer. Because the hammer was no longer a member in the

torque linkage, a bronze nut in the chuck driver also was eliminated. Rotation of the hammer was considered beneficial to produce even wear, and steel splines were provided in the chuck driver to turn the otherwise free-floating hammer. The splines on both the hammer and the chuck driver were case hardened (Rockwell C 63 and 60, respectively), and a continuous flow of lubricant was provided so the unit pressures to turn the hammer were negligible. Wear on these splines was not considered possible.

Although it was entirely unexpected, this new hammer failed by extreme wear on both sides of the splines (Fig. 38), which developed in less than 10% of the predicted life. At one point, the splines had worn to a thin edge and fracture resulted. Chipping of this edge undoubtedly provided the stress-concentrating notch, which developed into transverse fracture. The broken surfaces had been chipped and battered by continued operation.

The only possible reason for such rapid wear was severe pressure on the splines, but the source of this pressure was not immediately apparent. Deduction, confirmed by strain-gage measurements, indicated interruption of continuous rotation of the bit as it penetrated rock during each impact. Because the chuck driver continued to turn, torsional energy was stored in the drill rods and released as a shock wave when the bit was withdrawn from the rock. The pressure on the splines then became a rapid series of impacts on both sides, rather than the smooth, light sliding operation that had been assumed. Correction of this condition was effected by a reduction of the

Fig. 38. Broken 1.10% C tool steel piston hammer (left) and carburized-and-hardened 94B17 steel chuck driver (right) for a rock drill. Extreme wear shown on the case-hardened hammer splines led to fracture and damage to both parts caused by operation after the hammer broke.

play between splines and a return to the use of the bronze nut in the chuck driver.

References

1. E. Orowan, Fracture and Strength of Solids, *Rept Progr Phys,* The Institute of Physics (London), Vol 12, 1948-49, p 185

2. F. J. Fraikor, G. K. Hicken and V. K. Grotsky, Precipitation in EB Welded Beryllium Ingot Sheet, *Welding Research* (Supplement to Welding Journal), May 1973, p 204s-211s

3. A. J. Lena, Sigma Phase — A Review, *Metal Prog*, July 1954, p 86-90, Aug 1954, p 94-99, and Sept 1954, p 122-128

4. J. B. Nuchols and J. R. McGuffey, Graphitization Failures in Piping, *Mech Eng,* Vol 81, May 1959, p 43-45

5. J. G. Wilson, Graphitization of Steel in Petroleum Refining Equipment, Welding Research Council Bulletin No. 32, Jan 1957

6. H. Thielsch, "Defects and Failures in Pressure Vessels and Piping", Reinhold Publishing Co., New York, 1965, p 184

7. L. E. Steels, J. R. Hawthorne and R. J. Gray, Jr., Neutron Irradiation Embrittlement of Several Higher Strength Steels, STP 426, ASTM, 1967, p 346-370

8. J. R. Hawthorne and L. E. Steels, Metallurgical Variables as Possible Factors Controlling Irradiation Response of Structural Steels, STP 426, ASTM, 1967, p 534-572

Selected References

A. J. Birkle, R. P. Wei and G. E. Pellissier, Analysis of Plane Strain Fracture in a Series of 0.45C-Ni-Cr-Mo Steels with Different Sulfur Contents, *Trans ASM,* Vol 59, 1966, p 981

P. J. Grobner, The 885F (475C) Embrittlement of Ferritic Stainless Steels, *Met Trans,* Vol 4, 1973, p 251

Y. H. Liu, Correlation of Microstructures with Toughness, *Trans ASM,* Vol 62, 1969, p 55

W. Rostoker, J. M. McCaughey and H. Markus, "Embrittlement by Liquid Metals", Reinhold Publishing Corp., New York, 1960

M. Szczepanski, "The Brittleness of Steel", John Wiley & Sons, New York, 1963

APPENDIX

CHARACTERISTICS OF DUCTILE AND BRITTLE FRACTURES

Macroscopically, a fracture is considered to be ductile or brittle depending on the amount of plastic deformation that can be seen in the fracture region. Microscopically, it is the degree of plasticity found on the fracture surface that enables determination of whether the material was tough or fragile. These macroscopic and microscopic features of fractures are described in this Appendix.

Macroscopic Fracture Features

As determined macroscopically, fragile materials (that is, those materials that exhibit little or no microscopic plasticity on the fracture surface) always fail in a brittle manner. However, the occurrence of brittle fracture in tough materials (those materials that do exhibit microscopic plasticity on the fracture surface) depends on the thickness of the specimen or structural member and the presence of cracks (flaws) or other severe stress raisers.

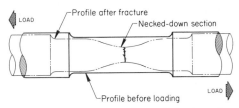

Solid profile indicates shape of specimen before loading. Phantom profile indicates shape of specimen after fracture; note the necked-down section resulting from plastic deformation.

Fig. 39. Schematic representation of fracture caused by gross yielding in a smooth (unnotched) cylindrical specimen loaded in pure tension

The following sections discuss several modes of fracture in tough materials, ranging from the fully plastic mode exhibited by smooth specimens to the brittle mode exhibited by thick specimens containing notches and cracks.

Fully Plastic Fracture of Smooth Specimens

A smooth (unnotched) cylindrical specimen subjected to axial-tension load is shown schematically in Fig. 39. As the load is increased, first the yield stress is reached in the entire test section of the specimen; then the maximum load-carrying capacity is attained at the same time that necking (reduction in cross section) begins in the central portion of the specimen. Most of the necking occurs across a plane perpendicular to the axis of the specimen. Using the mathematical theory of plasticity (Ref 1), it can be shown that the plane of maximum necking, which contains unrestrained plastic flow in the direction of the axis of the specimen, also is a plane of fracture instability; this theory is in accord with experimental evidence. Fracture occurs in this plane in a fully plastic manner. Because the nominal stress at the time of fracture is greater than the yield stress, this mode of fracture is often said to be the result of gross (net-section) yielding.

Effect of Constraint. The mode of fracture in a homogeneous material is related to the degree of constraint. For a uniaxially loaded specimen, the degree of constraint is dependent on thickness or shape of the specimen. In thin, smooth (unnotched) sheets, fully plastic fracture occurs on planes inclined to the direction of the load (and to the surfaces of the sheet). After the yield stress is reached in the entire specimen, unrestrained plastic flow, necking and fracture instability become localized in thin deformation bands called Lüders bands or stretcher strains.

In regions at and near the surface of a smooth cylindrical specimen, axial and tangential stresses can be supported, but the material cannot support a radial stress and maintain equilibrium. However, interior regions of the specimen

near the centerline are constrained so that axial, tangential and radial stresses can be supported. When the constraint is sufficient, the maximum stress lies in a plane perpendicular to the direction of the applied load. It should be noted that although the directions of the fracture surfaces in smooth cylindrical specimens and in thin sheet differ, the fractures in both instances do not occur until the net-section stresses are well above the yield stress.

Effect of Type of Loading. Although uniaxial-tension loading is the most commonly encountered type of loading that leads to fracture of smooth specimens, there are several other primary types of loading, such as pure compression, torsion and direct shear, and a large variety of mixed types of loading. In those instances of compression loading where buckling does not occur, the curve of load versus strain is similar to that obtained from tension loading. The mechanisms of elastic and localized plastic deformation appear to be very similar for tension and compression, except that the localized plastic deformation that takes place during yielding in compression results in an increase in cross section. As with tension, fracture in compression takes place by a combination of shear along planes oriented 45° to the direction of the applied load and rupture perpendicular to the direction of loading. In practice, compression fractures are very sensitive to the axiality of loading and small misalignments of loading direction with respect to specimen axis result in progressive formation of planes of fracture instability.

Other types of loading, such as bending, do not produce uniformly stressed sections. Bending fractures in smooth specimens usually consist of flat-face regions (perpendicular to the direction of principal normal stress) and shear-face regions (at 45° to the direction of principal normal stress) that occur for the same reasons of material constraint as in axially loaded specimens.

Plane Strain and Plane Stress

Plane strain and plane stress are fracture-mechanics terms that indicate the relationship of a plane of fracture instability to the stress state. Plane strain describes a situation in which the plane of fracture instability is perpendicular to the direction of principal normal stress. Plane stress describes a situation in which the plane of fracture instability is inclined 45° to the direction of principal normal stress. In a structural member or specimen containing a notch, flaw or crack, plane-strain conditions prevail when there is no strain in the direction parallel to the crack front; plane-stress conditions prevail when

Fig. 40. Fractograph, at 4×, of a "cup-and-cone" fracture surface on a circumferentially notched cylindrical specimen of 4340 steel that broke in tension

there is no stress in the direction parallel to the crack front.

A fracture is brittle if a crack grows rapidly under plane-strain conditions and where, except at the crack tip, no plastic deformation can be detected macroscopically. In this mode of fracture, the maximum net-section stress ordinarily is well below the uniaxial yield stress. By contrast, fracture under plane-stress conditions is considered to be ductile, as general yielding can easily be observed as the crack propagates at a stress near or above the yield stress.

Most fracture surfaces will exhibit a finite plastically deformed region just ahead of the crack tip. The term "elastic-plastic" is used to denote this condition, because the plastically deformed region (plastic zone) is surrounded by a much larger mass of elastically deformed material. How small this region is and what happens in this region are critical to the fracture process. If, for example, the size of this region is rather small compared to the crack size and specimen dimensions, the stresses and strains at locations quite close to the crack tip are essentially unaffected by the presence of the plastic zone. In such situations, the Griffith criterion for fracture in a purely elastic material (Ref 2) can be modified by adding

Fig. 41. Fractograph, at 4×, of a flat-face fracture surface on a cylindrical specimen of 4340 steel that broke in tension under plane-strain conditions induced by a shallow circumferential notch

a small correction factor (Ref 3). By contrast, if the size of the plastic zone is very large, the stresses and strains throughout the specimen cannot be computed from elastic theory alone and advanced concepts of elastic-plastic fracture mechanics must be used (Ref 4 and 5).

Critical Crack Size. The concept of a critical size of crack (or flaw), its growth under certain stress and strain conditions, and the mathematical treatment within the framework of linear-elastic fracture mechanics, are discussed in the article on Toughness and Fracture Mechanics, which begins on page 30 in this volume. On the basis of these concepts, it should be possible to predict when a brittle or a ductile fracture will occur. However, in practice, it is not possible to predict when failure will occur, primarily because of a lack of understanding of how flaws in materials actually behave, and because of inadequate definition of actual service stresses.

Crack Extension. The basic equation of crack extension, which is defined on page 32, is:

$$K_c{}^2 = EG_c$$

Figures 5 and 6 on pages 32 and 33 show variation of K_c with section thickness; the value of K_c drops as section thickness is increased, and at some critical section thickness (which is different for each material and heat treated condition), the value of K_c levels out to a minimum, and crack propagation is governed by plane-strain conditions. For isotropic materials, K_c is defined as the critical stress-intensity factor (plane-stress fracture toughness) and K_{Ic} as the critical plane-strain stress-intensity factor (plane-strain fracture toughness). The basic equation for plane-strain crack extension is:

$$K_{Ic}{}^2 = EG_c/(1 - \nu^2)$$

where ν is Poisson's ratio. The term $(COD)_c$, the critical crack-opening displacement, can be used to help establish the criteria for plane-strain conditions. This term is defined as:

$$(COD)_c = l \times \epsilon_f$$

where l and ϵ_f are the critical distance ahead of the crack tip and the corresponding strain, respectively. When the critical value is reached, the crack will grow rapidly and the fracture is said to have become "unstable". (Detailed information regarding the treatment of fracture instability following finite crack extension is given in Ref 3, 6 and 7.)

Critical crack-opening displacement $(COD)_c$, which is an extension of linear-elastic fracture mechanics, is used to evaluate toughness of those materials and thicknesses that have too large a

plastic zone ahead of the crack front for the Griffith-Irwin criterion to be effective. $(COD)_c$ is used mainly to evaluate low-strength and medium-strength structural steels of thicknesses, and at temperatures, that most aptly apply to welded, structural applications. Critical values of $(COD)_c$ depend on thickness, on strain rate, and on degree of triaxiality (as affected mainly by thickness and localized conditions in the material).

Mixed-Mode Fracture. Purely plane-strain or plane-stress conditions are seldom found in engineering structures; instead, fracture usually occurs by a mixed mode, usually with plane-strain conditions in the central, or constrained, region and plane-stress conditions at the free surfaces.

Figure 40 shows a cylindrical specimen that fractured in tension. In this fracture, there is a substantial amount of shear lip, which is inclined approximately 45° to the central flat-face region, thus producing a typical "cup-and-cone" fracture surface. Here, the shear (plane-stress) region and the flat-face (plane-strain) region each account for approximately 50% of the cross-sectional area.

Figure 41 shows a fracture surface on a cylindrical specimen that broke in tension under almost entirely plane-strain conditions. Except for a shallow machined notch at the outermost rim, flat-face fracture covers almost the entire cross section.

Amount of Plastic Flow and Energy Absorption. The presence of plane-strain conditions precludes a large amount of plastic flow. In smooth specimens, plane-strain fracture occurs at the maximum load with no localized yielding (necking). In notched or cracked (flawed) specimens, crack propagation occurs with a minimum of localized yielding, sometimes at a stress as low as 30% of the net-section yield strength.

The presence of plane-stress conditions, which usually promote a ductile, shear fracture, requires a larger amount of energy for crack propagation than does the presence of plane-strain conditions.

Fracture Initiation. With specimens or parts that contain stress raisers such as notches or cracks, it is important to differentiate between the onset of fracture and general fracture instability (rupture). Particularly for thin specimens, initial localized fracture at the crack tip and subsequent finite crack extension may be followed by fracture arrest rather than rupture, and an appreciable increase of load beyond the load at which initial crack extension occurred may be required for the specimen to separate. This is in contrast to the fully plastic fracture of smooth specimens discussed above where the onset of cracking corresponds to the maximum load-carrying capacity. For many engineering applications, however, the onset of crack extension can be assumed to correspond to the useful design load. Thus, the following discussion is limited to initial crack extension as influenced by the specimen thickness.

Effect of section thickness on initial crack extension can be described by considering a tensile specimen with a pre-existing crack. The critical value of externally applied stress, σ_c, which corresponds to rupture of the specimen, depends strongly on the specimen thickness, t. For a given initial crack length, a_0, the variation of σ_c with t is as shown in Fig. 42(a). This curve was obtained for aluminum alloy sheet, but qualitatively the same behavior also is found for various steels (Ref 8). For very thin specimens, such as those in the foil-thickness range, σ_c initially increases with increasing t until a maximum is reached; then it decreases, asymptotically approaching a minimum value. More common practice is to show the variation with thickness of K_c, which is proportional to $\sigma_c(a_0)^{\frac{1}{2}}$; such curves also follow the trend exhibited in Fig. 42(a). Two examples of the variation of K_c with thickness are presented in Fig. 5 on page 32 and Fig. 6 on page 33, in the article "Toughness and Fracture Mechanics".

Associated with the change of critical stress for fracture is a change in the orientation of the fracture surface (see Fig. 42b). In thin sheets (thicknesses corresponding to the ascending portion of the curve of σ_c versus t), the fractures are of the slant (shear-face) type, with the fracture surfaces at an angle of 45° to the sheet surface. At thicknesses beyond the maximum in the curve of σ_c versus t, a portion of the fracture surface at mid-thickness becomes normal (perpendicular) to the sheet surface; the result is the formation of a square (flat-face) fracture with slanting shear lips. The greater the thickness, the larger the flat-face portion and the smaller the slant fraction.

The macroscopic mode of fracture is generally believed to be determined by the stress state just ahead of the crack tip. Thick specimens usually develop plane-strain conditions, at least through the major portion of the specimen thickness. Thin specimens usually develop plane-stress conditions. The difference between the two stress states just ahead of the crack tip is shown in Fig. 43(a). Figure 43(b) shows that orientation of the plane of maximum shear stress, τ_{max}, where plastic deformation by shear can be expected to occur, depends on the stress state. Necking that occurs in plane-stress conditions is similar to the necking that follows formation of Lüders bands, which was discussed previously in connection with fully plastic fracture of thin, smooth sheets. The plane of the crack that forms under each stress condition is

shown in Fig. 43(c). In the crack plane, plastic deformation generally occurs in thin wedges ahead of the crack tip. Because of the lack of elastic constraint, the maximum normal stress cannot exceed the uniaxial yield stress, and the stress state is biaxial. By contrast, under plane-strain conditions slip planes form a hinge-type plastic deformation zone, as shown at far right in Fig. 43(b). Here, plastic deformation is greatest in extent directly above and below the crack plane. Also, in contrast to the situation in thin sheets, the stress state is essentially tri-axial. As the result of plastic constraint in the direction of the thickness, the normal stress that can develop may be as much as 2.7 times the nominal yield stress, and there is an attendant loss of ductility and fracture toughness.

Plane-stress and plane-strain conditions represent the maximum and minimum values of fracture toughness. Most of the plate thicknesses used in engineering applications fracture by a mixed mode, as shown for two specimens in Fig. 42(b). In thick plates, plane-stress conditions are approached at the surface and plane-strain conditions occur in the interior. Actual fracture toughness would be between the fracture-toughness values for pure plane stress (K_c max) and pure plane strain (K_{Ic}).

Effect of Ductility on Fracture Mode. There are many metallurgical factors that can alter macroscopic ductility (and thereby the macroscopic fracture mode) of a uniaxially loaded homogeneous metal. Two examples of these factors are (a) microstructure, which can alter the macroscopic ductility by altering the microscopic mechanism of fracture, and (b) anisotropy, which can result in a change in macroscopic fracture mode by a change in direction of principal stress.

The effect of anisotropy is illustrated in Fig. 44, which shows longitudinal and transverse tensile fractures in specimens from a high-strength, low-ductility steel forging. In the longitudinal specimen shown in Fig. 44(a), the axis is parallel to the forging flow lines; fracture originated at the center of the part, propagated radially outward and formed a thin shear lip at the outermost rim. In contrast, the mode of fracture shown in the transverse specimen in Fig. 44(b) was entirely different. Here, planes of weakness (caused by segregates along the flow lines) are coplanar with the fracture plane and essentially no plastic deformation accompanied fracture. As a result, the fracture mode is predominantly plane-strain. In this type of situation, the origin of fracture typically coincides with a small stress raiser, like an inclusion or a void.

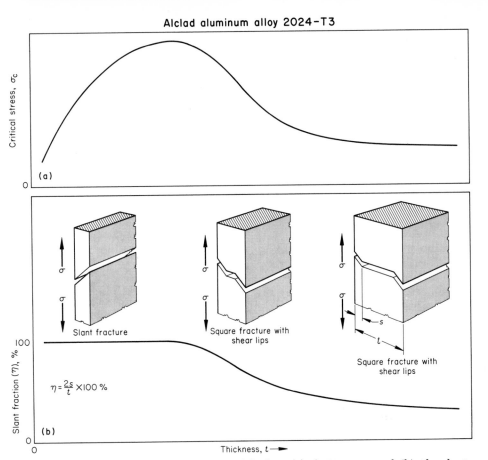

Fig. 42. Effect of section thickness, t, on (a) the critical stress, σ_c, and (b) the slant fraction, η, of fractures in tensile specimens of alclad aluminum alloy 2024-T3 sheet that contained precracks of equal length (Ref 8)

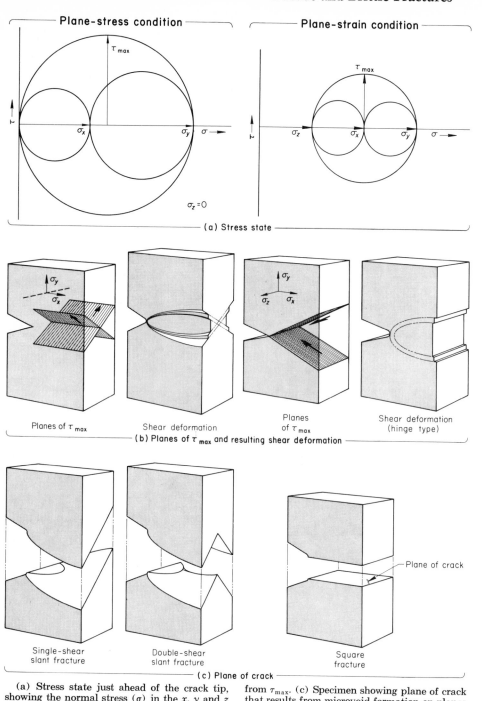

(a) Stress state just ahead of the crack tip, showing the normal stress (σ) in the x, y and z directions and the resulting maximum shear stress (τ_{max}). (b) Specimens showing the plane of τ_{max} and the shear deformation resulting from τ_{max}. (c) Specimen showing plane of crack that results from microvoid formation on planes of most extensive slip and from subsequent crack growth in plane of largest microvoids and maximum microvoid concentration.

Fig. 43. Schematic representation of plane-stress (no lateral constraint) and plane-strain (appreciable lateral constraint) stress states, and the shear deformation and crack planes that result from the two stress states in rectangular specimens subjected to tension loading (Redrawn from Ref 8)

Microscopic Fracture Features

All fractures are transgranular, intergranular, or a mixture of the two. Transgranular fracture follows crystallographic planes, whereas intergranular fracture follows boundaries between adjacent crystals. The following sections describe the microscopic features found on fracture surfaces of both tough and fragile materials.

Transgranular Fracture by Microvoid Coalescence

The majority of overload fractures that occur in the common alloys, regardless of loading rate, temperature, and part shape and size, are caused by microvoid coalescence. Microvoid coalescence is evidence of plasticity, and indicates that separation occurred by means of plastic deformation, regardless of

whether the fracture is macroscopically brittle. Features on the surfaces of these types of fractures consist mainly of small cupules, which are the result of growth and coalescence of minute neighboring voids (microvoids) that form and grow until the material between the voids in the fracture plane necks down and ruptures. (Each cupule is one-half of a microvoid through which fracture has occurred.)

Microvoids are usually nucleated at grain boundaries, subgrain boundaries, second-phase particles, cleavage planes that are favorably oriented with respect to the direction of principal stress, regions of dislocation pileup, or any other site where there may be a strain discontinuity. As strain increases, microvoids grow, coalesce, and eventually form a continuous fracture surface consisting of the small cupules. The cupules are more usually called "dimples", and the predominant appearance of a fracture caused by microvoid coalescence is commonly called "dimpled rupture".

(a) Longitudinal specimen (tensile strength, 180,000 psi; yield strength, 150,000 psi; elongation, 10%); (b) transverse specimen (tensile strength, 170,000 psi; yield strength, 145,000 psi; elongation, 6%). Steel contained 1.0% C, 2% Mn, 2% Si. Fracture surfaces shown at 8X.

Fig. 44. Surfaces of longitudinal and transverse tensile fractures in specimens from a high-strength, low-ductility steel forging

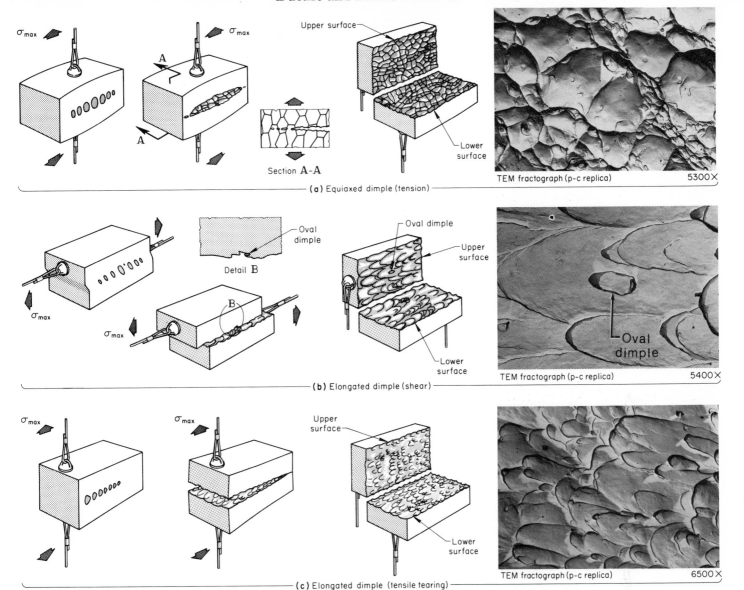

Fractographs (of plastic-carbon replicas) show shapes of dimples formed. (a) In tension, equiaxed dimples are formed on both fracture surfaces. (b) In shear, elongated dimples point in opposite directions on mating fracture surfaces. (c) In tensile tearing, elongated dimples point toward fracture origin on mating fracture surfaces.

Fig. 45. Influence of direction of principal normal stress, σ_{max}, on the shape of dimples formed by microvoid coalescence

Dimple Shapes. Often, the shape of the dimples in a fracture surface can be used to determine the direction of local crack propagation. The three basic modes of coalescence, as originally classified by Beachem (Ref 9), are illustrated in Fig. 45(a), (b) and (c). These modes — tension, shear and tensile tearing — differ only in the manner in which the material immediately surrounding the individual microvoids is plastically strained. The stress systems responsible for the plastic strains consist of the principal normal stress, σ_{max}, the directions of which are indicated in Fig. 45, and the two minor normal stresses that are perpendicular to each other and to the principal normal stress. Under local conditions of uniaxial tension loading (Fig. 45a), the two minor stresses are approximately the same magnitude, as in the necked region of a cylindrical tensile specimen, with negligible

stresses acting to shear the bulk material above the fracture plane with respect to the bulk material below the fracture plane. The other characteristic of the stress system in Fig. 45(a) is that the magnitude of σ_{max} is uniform over the cross section under consideration. As a result of this stress system, fracture under local conditions of uniaxial tensile loading usually results in the formation of equiaxed dimples.

Under conditions of shear loading (Fig. 45b), the bulk material above the fracture plane shears relative to the bulk material below the fracture plane, as in the slant fracture of material at the free surfaces of tensile specimens. According to Beachem (Ref 10), practically all slant fractures (oblique, "shear" surfaces) formed during tensile separation are created by shear rupture, not by pure shear. Shear-rupture surfaces may be

identified by elongated or parabolically shaped dimples that point in the direction of shear on mating fracture surfaces. Because the relative shear directions are opposite on the two sides of the fracture plane, the dimples point in opposite directions on mating fracture surfaces.

The shape of shear-rupture dimples depends on the ratio of normal strain to shear strain during the growth and coalescence of microvoids; a high ratio gives short, almost equiaxed dimples and a low ratio yields long or ensiform dimples. Occasionally, oval dimples are observed on the flat portions of elongated shear dimples. An oval dimple is thought to occur as a result of the intersection of a small subsurface microvoid with the surface of an already existing microvoid.

Under conditions of tensile tearing (Fig. 45c), the stress system is very similar to that in Fig. 45(a), differing only in

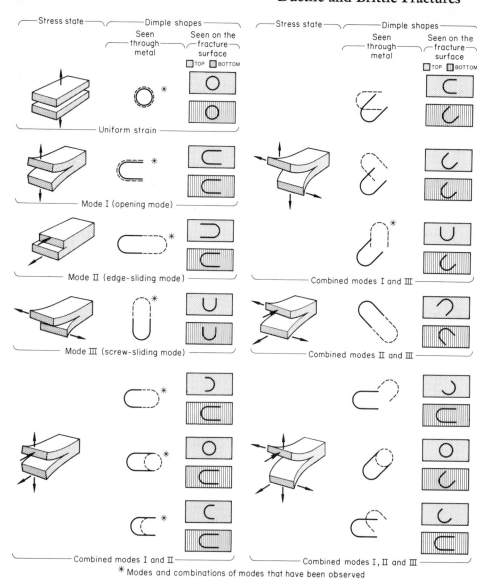

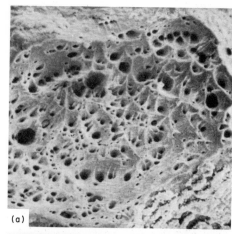

(a)

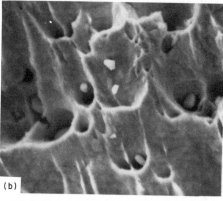

(b)

(a) SEM fractograph, at 750×, which shows that the fracture was ductile and of the "cup-and-cone" type. Note the equiaxed dimples in the central, or cup region. (b) Central region, at 2250×, in SEM fractograph taken at a tilt of 40° from the incident electron beam. Oxide particles are visible in the bottoms of some of the dimples.

Fig. 47. Fracture surface of a 0.006-in.-diam wire of copper 110 (electrolytic tough pitch copper) that broke in tension after approximately 40% elongation

Fig. 46. Fourteen probable combinations of mating dimple shapes, resulting from different stress states that caused metal at the crack tip to deform by various modes (Ref 11)

that the magnitude of σ_{max} is not uniform over the entire cross section. This is the type of stress system found at the root of a notch or crack, be it at an internal (submerged) opening or at the surface of the specimen. The resulting plastic flow is greatest at the tip of the crack. This produces elongated dimples that point toward the fracture origin on mating fracture surfaces.

The shape of dimples produced by tensile tearing depends largely on the ratio of plastic strain at the tip of the crack to the plastic strain in the material ahead of the crack, with a high ratio giving short, almost equiaxed dimples and a low ratio yielding long dimples.

In addition to the three basic types of dimples (tension, shear and tensile tearing), Beachem (Ref 11) has shown that there may be as many as five additional types, and as many as 14 ways of forming dimples, depending on the stress state near the crack tip (see Fig. 46).

Microvoid Initiation. Inclusions and hard second-phase particles are generally believed to be principally responsible for the initiation of microvoids. Even when they are present in a relatively small quantity, such as oxide inclusions in copper 110 (electrolytic tough pitch copper), these particles often play a direct role in the initiation of dimples.

Figure 47(a) is an SEM fractograph of 0.006-in.-diam wire of copper 110 that was fractured in tension after approximately 40% elongation. The fracture is a ductile fracture of the "cup-and-cone" type and is typified by the presence of equiaxed dimples in the central, or cup, region of the fracture surface. Oxide particles are faintly visible in the bottoms of some of the dimples. When this same fracture is viewed at a higher magnification and at a favorable tilting angle (see SEM fractograph in Fig. 47b), the role played by these particles in initiating the dimples is clearly visible.

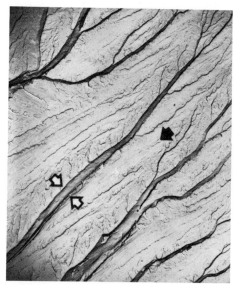

Fig. 48. River patterns on a fracture surface of an Alnico alloy specimen. A cleavage step is indicated by white arrows; black arrow shows direction of crack propagation. (TEM fractograph of a plastic-carbon replica; 4900×)

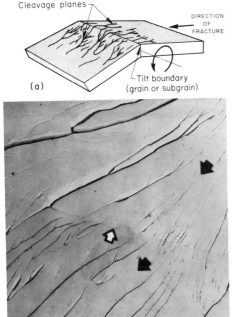

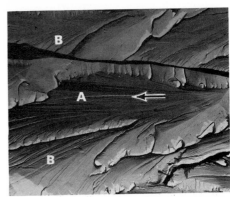

Fig. 51. Feather marks (at A) on a surface of a cleavage fracture in unalloyed tungsten. Features at B's resemble very fine river patterns, rather than feather marks. Arrow shows fracture direction. (TEM fractograph of a plastic-carbon replica; 5500×)

(a) Fracture model showing fracture direction, cleavage planes, and low-angle tilt boundary. (b) TEM fractograph (p-c replica), at 4900×, of a low-angle tilt boundary in a fracture surface of columbium alloy B-66 (5% Mo, 5% V, 1% Zr). Black arrows show fracture direction; white arrow shows a tilt boundary.

Fig. 49. Effect of low-angle grain or subgrain tilt boundary on cleavage-crack propagation

Transgranular Fracture by Cleavage

Cleavage is a fracture mechanism that generally takes place along well-defined crystallographic planes within a crystal (grain). Investigation with the scanning electron microscope, using an electron-channeling technique, has shown that the amount of plastic strain on the "cleaved" surface may be large or small but is highly localized in a layer within a few thousand Angstroms of the "cleaved" surface.

Ideally, a cleavage fracture in a single crystal has perfectly matching fracture surfaces and is completely flat and featureless. In polycrystalline specimens, however, the grains are generally randomly oriented with respect to one another. A cleavage fracture propagating through one grain will probably have to change direction as it crosses a grain boundary, a twin boundary or a subgrain boundary. In addition, most engineering metals have precipitates, inclusions or other discontinuities that further complicate the fracture path, so that true featureless cleavage is difficult to obtain even within a single grain. The change of orientation between grains and the imperfections within a grain usually pro-

duce unique marks on the fracture surface that are readily associated with cleavage.

Cleavage Steps. One of the principal features of cleavage fracture is a surface mark called a cleavage step (see Fig. 48). This feature is usually observed within a grain, and is a step between cleavage-crack segments on parallel cleavage planes in the grain. As the cleavage-crack segments progress through a grain, they grow in width and approach each other. The resultant steps observed between cleavage planes are fractures of the thin ligaments joining the cleavage-crack segments. The cleavage steps converge in the direction of local crack propagation to form a pattern called a "river pattern".

When a progressing cleavage crack has to change direction as it crosses a misoriented adjacent grain or subgrain, fracture features change. For example, if the adjacent grains or subgrains are only slightly misoriented (as in a low-angle tilt boundary), the cleavage steps are continuous across the boundary (see Fig. 49). If an adjacent grain or subgrain is axially misoriented relative to the local fracture direction, the boundary of that grain is a twist boundary. New cleavage

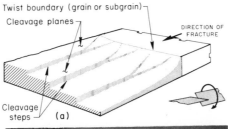

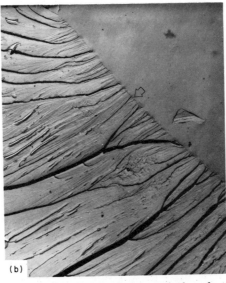

(a) Fracture model showing a twist boundary and the new cleavage steps that develop as the propagating crack crosses a twist boundary. (b) TEM fractograph (p-c replica), at 4900×, showing cleavage steps that initiated at a twist boundary (open arrow) on a fracture surface of columbium alloy B-66 (5% Mo, 5% V, 1% Zr). Solid black arrow indicates fracture direction.

Fig. 50. Effect of grain or subgrain twist boundary on cleavage decoration

steps will form when the propagating crack crosses the twist boundary (Fig. 50).

Another distinct cleavage-fracture feature is called "feather marks" (Fig. 51). Feather marks, which consist of cleavage steps, have an appearance similar to chevron patterns in that they usually point back in the direction of local crack origin.

If a cleavage crack initiates at only one point along the grain boundary, it has to fan out into the rest of the grain from this one point to grow. This produces cleavage surfaces that are separated by cleavage steps, which radiate from the crack origin. The resulting overall appearance is called a "fan".

Transgranular Fracture by Quasicleavage

"Quasicleavage" is a less well-understood type of fracture that shows characteristics of cleavage, yet exhibits some plastic deformation. Quasicleavage typically occurs in quenched and tempered steels that contain fine dispersions of carbide particles in a martensite matrix, and where features characteristic of two fracture mechanisms may be distinguished. In many of these steels, fracture surfaces produced at temperatures considerably above the ductile-to-brittle transition temperature consist of dimples, while those created at temperatures considerably below the transition range are mainly composed of flat facets and other features that resemble cleavage. At temperatures within and near the transition-temperature range, various percentages of both dimples and flat facets are found.

The origin of a quasicleavage fracture of a grain is frequently contained within the grain, whereas with true cleavage, the initiation point is invariably at the edge of each grain. According to Beachem *et al* (Ref 12), quasicleavage fracture is believed to initiate as a cleavage step, which

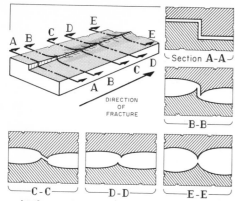

At the top left is the lower surface of a fracture, showing a step at the lower left and a ridge at the upper right. At right and at bottom are sections through the fractured member, showing profiles of both the upper and the lower fracture surfaces.

Fig. 52. Fracture model showing a cleavage step blending in with a tear ridge in a quasicleavage fracture surface

then becomes a tear ridge as the fracture proceeds. This is illustrated schematically in Fig. 52.

Three of the characteristics of true crystalline cleavage have been found in quasicleavage fracture of several quenched and low-temperature tempered steels, such as 4340 steel, type 410 stainless steel, and H11 tool steel (Ref 10). However, a characteristic of cleavage — that is, maintaining one or a few crack fronts as the crack passes from grain to grain — is usually absent in quasicleavage. In dry, overload fracture of these steels, fracture usually progresses by the formation of thousands of small secondary cracks in the material ahead of the main crack front and by the growth of these cracks to unite with one another or with the main crack. This feature of quasicleavage is shown in type 410 stainless steel in Fig. 53, where the arrows indicate submerged crack-initiation sites. This behavior is referred to by Beachem (Ref 10) as "satellite nucleation" of cracks. Its occurrence is dependent on the test temperature, with lower temperature causing lower ductility of the material between the quasicleavage facets and therefore favoring the continuing propagation of cracks on a few existing fronts, as is characteristic of true cleavage.

Intergranular Fracture

Intergranular fracture occurs by grain-boundary separation, with or without microvoid coalescence. Most intergranular fractures have appearances that make them easily distinguishable from other types of fractures. However, intergranular fractures that appear similar to each other may have resulted from different causes. Among the causes of intergranular fracture are the presence of grain-boundary phases that are weak or brittle,

and environmental or mechanical factors, such as stress corrosion, hydrogen damage, heat damage, and triaxial stress states.

In some instances, intergranular fractures exhibit dimples resulting from microvoid coalescence within a thin layer of metal at the grain interfaces. High-strength aluminum alloys frequently fracture by grain-boundary separation with microvoid coalescence (Fig. 54). It has been suggested that the fracture progresses along alloy-depleted zones in the grain boundaries, which are soft in comparison to the matrix. This is a brittle fracture in the macroscopic sense and a plastic fracture in the microscopic sense. Many intergranular fractures, such as those caused by hydrogen embrittlement, stress corrosion, brittle grain-boundary phases, quench cracking, and grinding cracks, show little or no evidence of dimples and they have a "rock candy" appearance. (See Fig. 6 on page 59 in the article on Identification of Types of Failures.)

References Cited in This Appendix

1. T. Y. Thomas, Plastic Flow and Fracture in Solids, Vol 2 in "Mathematics in Science and Engineering", Richard Bellman (Ed.), Academic Press, New York, 1961, p 184-263

2. A. A. Griffith, *Phil Trans Roy Soc London,* Vol 221A, 1920, p 163-198

3. F. A. McClintock and G. R. Irwin, Plastic Aspects of Fracture Mechanics, p 84-113 in "Fracture Toughness Testing and Its Applications", STP 381, ASTM, 1965

4. J. R. Rice, Mathematical Analysis in the Mechanics of Fracture, p 191-311 in "Fracture", Vol II, H. Liebowitz (Ed.), Academic Press, New York, 1968

5. F. A. McClintock, Plastic Aspects of Fracture, p 47-225 in "Fracture", Vol III, H. Liebowitz (Ed.), Academic Press, New York, 1971

6. G. R. Irwin and P. C. Paris, Fundamental Aspects of Crack Growth and Fracture, p 1-46 in "Fracture", Vol III, H. Liebowitz (Ed.), Academic Press, New York, 1971

7. Fracture Toughness Evaluation by R Curve Methods, STP 527, ASTM, 1973

8. D. Broek, The Effect of the Sheet Thickness on the Fracture of Cracked Sheets, NLR-TR.M.2160, National Aerospace Laboratory, Amsterdam, Jan 1966

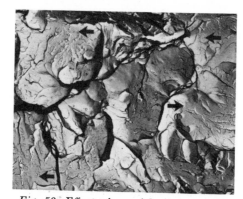

Fig. 53. Effect of quasicleavage on the fracture-surface appearance of type 410 stainless steel. Arrows indicate submerged crack-initiation sites. (TEM fractograph of a plastic-carbon replica; 4000×) (Ref 10)

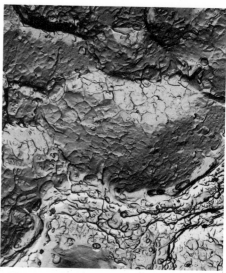

Fig. 54. Grain-boundary fracture in aluminum alloy 7075-T6, showing very shallow dimples that resulted from microvoid coalescence on the grain surfaces (TEM fractograph of a plastic-carbon replica; 6500×)

9. C. D. Beachem, An Electron Fractographic Study of the Influence of Plastic Strain Conditions upon Ductile Rupture Processes in Metals, *Trans ASM,* Vol 56, 1963, p 318-326

10. C. D. Beachem, Microscopic Fracture Processes, p 243-349 in "Fracture", Vol I, H. Liebowitz (Ed.), Academic Press, New York, 1968

11. C. D. Beachem, The Effects of Crack Tip Plastic Flow Directions Upon Microscopic Dimple Shapes, *Met Trans A,* Feb 1975, p 377-383

12. C. D. Beachem, B. F. Brown and A. J. Edwards, Characterizing Fractures by Electron Fractography, Part XII, Illustrated Glossary, Section I, Quasicleavage, NRL Memo Report 1432, Naval Research Laboratory, June 1963

Selected References

G. T. Hahn and A. R. Rosenfield, Elastic-Plastic Fracture Mechanics, AFML-TR-67-143, Report (AD829-191), Oct 1972

W. S. Pellini and R. W. Judy, Jr., Significance of Fracture Extension Resistance (R-Curve) Factors in Fracture-Safe Design for Non-Frangible Metals, NRL Report 7187, Naval Research Laboratory, Washington, D. C., 1970

J. N. Robinson and A. S. Tetelman, The Critical Crack-Tip Opening Displacement and Microscopic and Macroscopic Fracture Criteria For Metals, UCLA Eng. Report 7360, Los Angeles, Aug 1973

B. V. Whiteson, A. Phillips and V. Kerlins, "Techniques of Metals Research", Chapter 14, Vol II, Part 1, Interscience, 1968

W. S. Pellini and P. P. Puzak, Fracture Analysis Diagram Procedures for the Fracture-Safe Engineering Design of Steel Structures, NRL Rept 5920, U. S. Naval Research Laboratory, Washington, D. C., 1963

"Control of Steel Construction to Avoid Brittle Failure", M. E. Shank (Ed.), American Welding Society, New York, 1957

W. T. Mathews, The Role of Impact Testing in Characterizing the Toughness of Materials, in "Symposium on Impact Testing of Metals", STP 466, ASTM, 1970, p 3-20

N. J. Petch, Metallographic Aspects of Fracture, p 351 in "Fracture", Vol I, H. Liebowitz (Ed.), Academic Press, 1968

E. A. Steigerwald, Crack Toughness Measurements of High-Strength Steels, in "Review of Development in Plane Strain Fracture Toughness Testing, STP 463, ASTM, 1970, p 102

Fatigue Failures

*By the ASM Committee on Analysis of Fatigue Failures**

FATIGUE is the progressive localized permanent structural change that occurs in a material subjected to repeated or fluctuating strains at stresses having a maximum value less than the tensile strength of the material. Fatigue may culminate in cracks or fracture after a sufficient number of fluctuations.

Fatigue fractures are caused by the simultaneous action of cyclic stress, tensile stress and plastic strain. If any one of these three is not present, fatigue cracking will not initiate and propagate. The cyclic stress starts the crack; the tensile stress produces crack growth (propagation). Although compressive stress will not cause fatigue, compression loads may do so.

In early literature, fatigue fractures were attributed to "crystallization", because of their crystalline fracture appearance. But metals are crystalline solids, and therefore the use of the term crystallization in connection with fatigue is confusing and should be avoided.

The process of fatigue may be considered as consisting of three stages:

1 Initial fatigue damage leading to crack initiation
2 Crack propagation until the remaining uncracked cross section of a part becomes too weak to carry the loads imposed
3 Final, sudden fracture of the remaining cross section.

Prediction of Fatigue Life

In practice, prediction of the fatigue life of a material is complicated because, except for a few relatively brittle materials, the fatigue life of a material is very sensitive to small changes in loading conditions, local stresses and local characteristics of the material. Because it is difficult to account for these minor changes in either the dynamic stress-prediction techniques or in fatigue-failure criteria, there is a large uncertainty inherent in analytical predictions of fatigue life. Thus, the designer also is required to rely on experience with similar parts and eventually on qualification testing of prototypes or production parts. Although laboratory fatigue tests performed on small specimens are not sufficient for precisely establishing the fatigue life of a part, it is useful to examine these data because laboratory tests (a) are the major source of fatigue-failure criteria, (b) isolate the loading variables involved in fatigue, (c) are useful in rating materials in terms of their relative resistance to fatigue, and (d) can be used to establish the relative importance of such items as fabrication method, surface finish, heat treatment, assembly technique and environment on the fatigue life.

In general, fatigue life can be expected to depend on the following:

1 Type of loading (uniaxial, bending, torsional)
2 Shape of loading curve
3 Frequency of load cycling
4 Loading pattern (periodic loading at constant or variable amplitude, programed loading or random loading)
5 Magnitude of stresses
6 Part size
7 Fabrication method and surface roughness
8 Operating temperature
9 Operating atmosphere.

Traditionally, fatigue life has been expressed as the total number of stress cycles required for a fatigue crack to be initiated and then to grow large enough to produce catastrophic failure (separation of the specimen into two pieces). In this article, fatigue data are expressed in terms of total life.

Fatigue data also can be expressed in terms of crack-growth rate. In the past, it was commonly assumed that total fatigue life consisted mainly of crack initiation (stage I of fatigue-crack development), and that the time required for a minute fatigue crack to grow and produce failure was a minor portion of the total life. However, as better methods for detection of cracks became available, it was discovered that cracks develop early in the fatigue life of the material and grow continuously until catastrophic failure occurs. This discovery has led to the use of crack-growth rates for prediction of fatigue life, as discussed on page 34 in the article on Toughness and Fracture Mechanics.

Concepts Related to Fatigue

Most laboratory fatigue testing is done either with uniform axial loading or in uniform bending, thus producing only tensile and compressive stresses. The stress is usually cycled either between a maximum and a minimum tensile stress or between a maximum tensile stress and a maximum compressive stress. The latter is considered a negative tensile stress, is given an algebraic minus sign, and therefore is called the minimum stress.

Stress Ratio. The algebraic ratio of two specified stress values in a stress cycle is called the stress ratio. Two commonly used stress ratios are: the ratio, A, of the alternating stress amplitude to the mean stress ($A = S_a/S_m$); and the ratio, R, of the minimum stress to the maximum stress ($R = S_{min}/S_{max}$). If the stresses are fully reversed, the stress ratio R becomes -1; if the stresses are partially reversed, R becomes a negative number less than 1. If the stress is cycled between a maximum stress and no load, the stress ratio R becomes zero. If the stress is cycled between two tensile stresses, the stress ratio R becomes a positive number less than 1. A stress ratio R of 1 would mean no variation in stress, and the test would become a sustained-load creep test rather than a fatigue test.

Applied Stresses. Three descriptions of the applied stress are sometimes given. The mean stress, S_m, is the algebraic average of the maximum and minimum stresses in one cycle, $S_m = (S_{max} + S_{min})/2$. In the completely reversed test,

*JAMES L. MCCALL, *Chairman*, Manager, Materials Characterization Section, Battelle – Columbus Laboratories; SHAFFIQ AHMED, Chairman and Professor, Dept. of Metallurgical Engineering, Youngstown State University; BANI R. BANERJEE, Assistant Director of Research, Research and Development Center, Ingersoll Rand Co.

BRUCE P. BARDES, Chief Metallurgist, Bimba Manufacturing Co.; H. EDWARD FAIRMAN, Senior Metallurgical Engineer, Advanced Technology Div., Sundstrand Corp.; HENRY O. FUCHS, Professor, Design Div., Mechanical Engineering Dept., Stanford University; F. L. JAMIESON, Supervising Metallurgist, Metallurgical Laboratory, Steel Co. of Canada; JAMES S. LAUB, Senior Engineer, Research Div., Carrier Corp.;

JEROME MOGUL, Director, Materials Engineering, Curtiss-Wright Corp.; MARION RUSSO, Group Engineer, Metallurgical Laboratory, McDonnell-Douglas Corp.; RAY SHAHANI, Supervisor, Design Engineering, Marion Power Shovel Co., Inc.; JOHN P. SHEEHAN, Vice President, Packer Engineering Associates.

WHITNEY SNYDER, Manager, Quality Laboratory, Kenosha Plant, American Motors Corp.; WILLIAM J. TEAFORD, Senior Engineer, Applied Mechanics, Product Engineering Dept., John Deere Waterloo Tractor Works; FREDERICK R. WAGNER, Associate Professor, Dept. of Mechanical Engineering, University of Utah; PHILIP D. HARVEY, *Secretary*, Senior Editor, Metals Handbook.

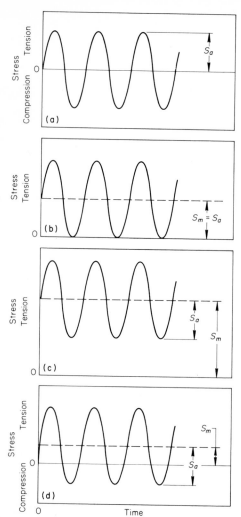

(a) Alternating stress in which $S_m = 0$ and $R = -1$. (b) Pulsating tensile stress in which $S_m = S_a$, the minimum stress is zero, and $R = 0$. (c) Fluctuating tensile stress in which both the minimum and maximum stresses are tensile stresses (for the instance shown, $R = \frac{1}{3}$).
(d) Fluctuating tensile-to-compressive stress in which the minimum stress is a compressive stress and the maximum stress is a tensile stress (for the instance shown, $R = -\frac{1}{3}$).

Fig. 1. Types of fatigue-test stress

the mean stress is zero. The range of stress, S_r, is the algebraic difference between the maximum and minimum stresses in one cycle, $S_r = S_{max} - S_{min}$. The stress amplitude, S_a, is one-half the range of stress, $S_a = S_r/2 = (S_{max} - S_{min})/2$.

During a fatigue test the stress cycle is usually maintained constant, so that the applied stress conditions can be written $S_m \pm S_a$, where S_m is the static or mean stress, and S_a is the alternating stress, equal to half the stress range. The positive sign is used to denote a tensile stress; and the negative sign, a compressive stress. Some of the possible combinations of S_m and S_a are illustrated in Fig. 1. When $S_m = 0$ (Fig. 1a), the maximum tensile stress is equal to the maximum compressive stress; this is called an alternating stress, or a completely reversed

stress. When $S_m = S_a$ (Fig. 1b), the minimum stress of the cycle is zero; this is called a pulsating or repeated tensile (or compressive) stress. Any other combination is known as a fluctuating stress, which may be a fluctuating tensile stress (Fig. 1c) or a fluctuating compressive stress, or may fluctuate between a tensile and a compressive value (Fig. 1d).

S-N Curves. The results of fatigue tests are usually plotted as maximum stress or stress amplitude to number of cycles, N, to fracture using a logarithmic scale for the number of cycles. Stress is plotted on either a linear or a logarithmic scale. The resulting curve of data points is called an *S-N* curve. Three typical *S-N* curves are shown in Fig. 2. The two curves for 2340 steel are typical for steels — a fairly straight slanting portion at low cycles straightening into a horizontal line at higher cycles, with a sharp transition between the two.

An *S-N* curve usually represents the median life for a given stress — the life that half the specimens attain or surpass and half fail to attain. Scatter of fatigue lives can cover a very wide range.

Fatigue Limit and Fatigue Strength. The horizontal portion of an *S-N* curve represents the maximum stress that the metal can withstand for an infinitely large number of cycles with 50% probability of failure and is called the fatigue (endurance) limit, S_f. Most nonferrous metals do not exhibit a fatigue limit. Instead, their *S-N* curves continue to drop at a slow rate at high numbers of cycles, such as is shown by the curve for aluminum alloy 7075-T6 in Fig. 2. For these metals, instead of reporting the fatigue limit, it is necessary to report the fatigue strength, which is the stress to which the metal can be subjected for a specified number of cycles. There is no standard number of cycles, so it is necessary that

each table of fatigue strengths specify the number of cycles for which the strengths are reported. Sometimes, the fatigue strength of nonferrous metals at 100 million (10^8) or 500 million (5×10^8) cycles is erroneously called the fatigue limit.

Stress-Concentration Factor. Stress is concentrated in a metal by structural discontinuities, such as notches, holes or scratches, which act as stress raisers. The stress-concentration factor, K_t, is the ratio of the greatest stress in the region of the notch (or other stress concentrators) to the corresponding nominal stress. For determination of K_t, the greatest stress in the region of the notch is calculated from the theory of elasticity, or equivalent values are derived experimentally. An experimental stress-concentration factor is a ratio of stress in a notched specimen to the stress in a smooth (unnotched) specimen.

Fatigue Notch Factor. The fatigue notch factor, K_f, is the ratio of the fatigue strength of a smooth (unnotched) specimen to the fatigue strength of a notched specimen at the same number of cycles. The fatigue notch factor will vary with the position on the *S-N* curve and with the mean shear stress. At high stress levels and short cycles, the factor is usually less than at lower stress levels and longer cycles.

Fatigue notch sensitivity, q, for a material is determined by comparing the fatigue notch factor, K_f, and the stress-concentration factor, K_t, for a specimen of a given size containing a stress concentrator of a given shape and size. A common definition of fatigue notch sensitivity is $q = (K_f - 1)/(K_t - 1)$, in which q may vary between zero (where $K_f = 1$) and 1 (where $K_f = K_t$). This value may be stated as a percentage. As the fatigue notch factor varies with the position of the *S-N* curve, so will the notch sensitivity. Most metals are fully notch sensitive at low stresses and long cycles. If they are not, it may be that the fatigue strengths for the smooth (unnotched) specimens are lower than they could be, because of surface imperfections. Most metals are not fully notch sensitive at high stresses and low cycles, because at high stresses the actual peak stress at the base of the notch is partly in the plastic-strain region and therefore is lower than the theoretical peak elastic stress used in the calculation of the theoretical stress-concentration factor.

Stages of Fracture From Fatigue

The fracture surface that results from fatigue failure has a characteristic appearance that can be divided into three zones or progressive stages of fracture.

Stage I is the initiation of cracks and their propagation by slip-plane fracture,

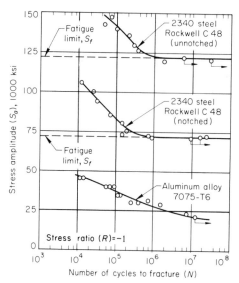

Fig. 2. Typical S-N *curves for constant amplitude, and sinusoidal loading*

Fig. 3. Transition from stage I to stage II of a fatigue fracture in a coarse-grained specimen of aluminum alloy 2024-T3

extending inward from the surface at approximately 45° to the stress axis. A stage I fracture never extends over more than about two to five grains around the origin. In each grain the fracture surface is along a well-defined crystallographic plane, which should not be confused with a cleavage plane although it has the same brittle appearance. There are usually no fatigue striations associated with a stage I fracture surface. In some instances (depending on the material, environment and stress level), a stage I fracture may not be discernible.

Stage II. The transition from stage I to stage II fatigue fracture is the change of orientation of the main fracture plane in each grain from one or two shear planes to many parallel plateaus separated by longitudinal ridges. The plateaus are usually normal to the direction of maximum tensile stress.

A transition from stage I to stage II in a coarse-grained specimen of aluminum alloy 2024-T3 is shown in Fig. 3. The presence of inclusions rich in iron and silicon did not affect the fracture path markedly. The inclusions, which were fractured, ranged from 5 to 25 microns in diameter. In Fig. 3 the stage II area shows a large number of approximately parallel fatigue patches containing very fine fatigue striations that are not resolved at the magnification used. Fine striations are typical in stage II, but frequently are seen only under high magnification.

Stage III occurs during the last stress cycle when the cross section is unable to sustain the applied load. The final fracture, which is the result of a single overload, can be brittle or ductile, or a combination of the two.

Fracture Characteristics Revealed by Macroscopy

Examination of fatigue-fracture surfaces usually begins visually or by low-magnification light microscope. Macro-

scopic examination of fracture surfaces employs relatively simple techniques; it can often be done at the failure site, requires little or no preparation of the specimen, requires minimal and relatively simple equipment, and does not destroy the specimen or alter the fracture surfaces. Macroscopic examination is particularly useful in correlating fracture-surface characteristics with part size and shape, and with loading conditions. The crack origin can best be found by first viewing the fracture surface at low magnifications (25 to 100 diameters).

Beach Marks. The most characteristic feature usually found on fatigue-fracture surfaces is beach marks, which are centered around a common point that corresponds to the fatigue-crack origin. Also called clamshell, conchoidal and arrest marks, beach marks are perhaps the most important characteristic feature in identifying fatigue failures. Beach marks can occur as a result of changes in loading or frequency or by oxidation of the fracture surface during periods of crack arrest from intermittent service of the part or component.

Examples of fatigue-fracture surfaces containing beach marks are shown in Fig. 4. The fracture surface shown in Fig. 4(a) is that of an aluminum alloy 7075-T6 plate that was fractured in a laboratory by spectrum-load fatigue testing. The beach marks were produced by changes in crack growth as a result of variations in applied load levels. The final-fracture region (stage III) covers about 40% of the fracture surface. Figure 4(b) shows the surface of a fatigue fracture in a 4130 steel shaft that failed in service; this surface exhibits beach marks produced by oxidation of the fracture when the shaft was idle. The beach marks shown in Fig. 4(c) were produced by a combination of variations in loading and periods of rest normally experienced by an automotive crankshaft — in this instance, a ductile iron crankshaft. Fracture originated at a notch in the root of a weld. The final-fracture area was very small and contained shear lips, indicating that plane-stress conditions prevailed as the crack neared the surface.

Many fatigue fractures produced under conditions of uninterrupted crack growth and without load variations do not exhibit beach marks. The fracture surface of a specimen tested in a laboratory where the load was repeated at the same intensity and without interruption through final fracture is shown in Fig. 5. The fracture surface produced by fatigue contains no beach marks.

Final-Fracture Zone. The final-fracture zone of a fatigue-fracture surface often is fibrous, resembling the fracture surfaces of impact or fracture-toughness test specimens of the same material. The size of the final-fracture zone depends on the

(a)

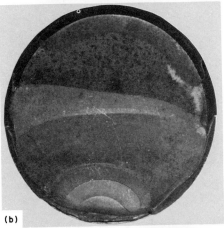

(b)

(c)

Fig. 4. Beach marks in the fatigue region on fracture surfaces of three different metals. See text for discussion.

Fig. 5. Fracture surface on a laboratory fatigue-test specimen made of titanium alloy Ti-6Al-6V-2Sn. Fatigue zone (A) contains no beach marks because load was not varied during the test.

magnitude of the loads, and its shape depends on the shape, size and direction of loading of the fractured part. In tough materials, with thick or round sections, the final-fracture zone will consist of a fracture by two distinct modes: (a) tensile fracture (plane-strain mode) extending from the fatigue zone and in the same plane, and (b) shear fracture (plane-stress mode) at 45° to the surface of the part bordering the tensile fracture. These two modes are illustrated in the surface of a fatigue fracture through a thick section shown in Fig. 6. In Fig. 6, two features in the final-fracture zone that aid in determining the origin of fracture are: (a) fatigue usually originates at the surface, and therefore the fatigue origin is not included in the shear-lip fracture; and (b) the presence of characteristic chevron marks in the tensile fracture that point back to the origin of fracture.

In thin sheet-metal pieces having sufficient toughness, final fracture occurs somewhat differently. As the crack propagates from the fatigue zone, the fracture plane rotates around an axis in the direction of crack propagation until it forms an angle of about 45° with the loading direction and the surface of the sheet. The fracture plane, inclined 45° to the load direction, can occur on either a single-shear or a double-shear plane, as illustrated in Fig. 7.

Fracture Characteristics Revealed by Microscopy

Examination of fatigue fractures by light microscopy is often difficult because the height of features on the fracture surface may exceed the depth of field of the microscope, especially at high magnifications. Metallographic examinations of cross sections through suspected fatigue fractures typically show that the crack path was transgranular. A cross section through a crack that has not grown enough to cause separation of the component is often useful in showing deficiencies in design or manufacture, or in showing the result of unanticipated service conditions.

Striations. In the electron-microscope examination of fatigue-fracture surfaces, the most prominent features found are patches of finely spaced parallel marks, called fatigue striations. The fatigue striations are oriented perpendicular to the microscopic direction of crack propagation and, with uniform loading, generally increase in spacing as they progress from the origin of fatigue. Each striation is the result of a single cycle of stress (but every stress cycle does not necessarily produce a striation), and striation spacing is strongly dependent on the level of applied loading. The clarity of the striations depends on the ductility of the material. Striations are more visible at stress levels higher than the fatigue limit; also, they are more readily visible in ductile materials. Thus, patches of fatigue striations in high-strength steel are less visible than in an aluminum alloy. Also, the striations are more visible at high stress levels than they are near the fatigue limit.

Fig. 6. Surface of a fatigue fracture in a 4330V steel part. Chevron marks point to origin of fatigue in lower left corner. Shear rupture along the periphery is indicated by arrows.

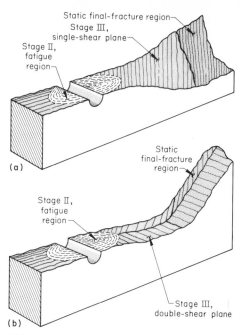

Fig. 7. Single-shear and double-shear fracture planes that are 45° to the direction of loading

At high rates of crack growth (10^{-4} in. per cycle or more), the striations become wavy, and develop a rough front. A large plastic zone exists in front of the crack, which may cause extensive secondary cracking. Each secondary crack propagates as a fatigue crack, creating a network of secondary striations. The local crack direction may differ markedly from the over-all direction of crack propagation because of the many changes in direction of the local fracture path.

In steels, fatigue striations that are formed at ordinary crack-growth rates are not always as well-defined as they are in aluminum alloys. The striations that are formed in aluminum alloys at very low crack-growth rates (less than 5×10^{-6} in. per cycle) are difficult to resolve and often cannot be distinguished from the network of slip lines and slip bands associated with plastic deformation at and near the crack front as it propagates through the section.

Fatigue Cracking

Fatigue cracking normally results from cyclic stresses that are well below the static yield strength of the material. (In low-cycle fatigue, however, or if the material has an appreciable work-hardening rate, the stresses also may be above the static yield strength.) Generally, a fatigue crack is initiated in a highly stressed region of a component subjected to cyclic stresses of sufficient magnitude. The crack propagates under the applied stress through the material until complete fracture results. On the microscopic scale, the most important feature of the fatigue process is the nucleation of one or more cracks under the influence of reversed stresses that exceed the flow stress, followed by the development of cracks at persistent slip bands or at grain boundaries. Subsequently, fatigue cracks propagate by a series of opening and closing motions at the tip of the crack that produce, within the grains, striations that are parallel to the crack front.

Crack Initiation

Fatigue cracks form at the point or points of maximum local stress and minimum local strength. The local stress pattern is determined by the shape of the part (including local features such as surface and metallurgical imperfections that concentrate macroscopic stress) and by the type and magnitude of the loading. Strength is determined by the material itself, including all discontinuities, anisotropies and inhomogeneities present. Local surface imperfections such as scratches, mars, burrs and other fabrication flaws are the most obvious flaws at which fatigue cracks start. Surface and subsurface material discontinuities in critical locations also will influence crack initiation. Inclusions of foreign material, hard precipitated particles, and crystal discontinuities such as grain boundaries and twin boundaries are examples of microscopic stress concentrators in the material matrix. On the submicroscopic scale, the dislocation density, lattice defects, and the orientation of cross-slip planes control the formation of (a) persistent slip bands, (b) intrusions and extrusions and (c) dislocation cells — the ultimate nucleation mechanisms.

In the roots of small fatigue-crack notches, the local stress state is triaxial (plane strain). This reduces the local apparent ductility of the material and helps control the orientation of the crack as long as the crack is small. On a microscopic level, the fracture surface at the origin consists of the crystallographic planes in individual grains that are most favorably oriented for slip.

Crack Nucleation. A variety of crystallographic features have been observed to nucleate fatigue cracks. In pure metals, tubular holes that develop in persistent slip bands, extrusion-intrusion pairs at free surfaces (see micrograph 3353 on page 216 in Volume 8 of this Handbook), and twin boundaries are common sites for crack initiation. Cracking also initiates at grain boundaries in polycrystalline materials, even in the absence of inherent grain-boundary weakness; at high strain rates, this seems to be the preferred site for crack nucleation. Nucleation at a grain boundary appears to be purely a geometrical effect, whereas nucleation at a twin boundary is associated with active slip on crystallographic planes immediately adjacent and parallel to the twin boundary. The

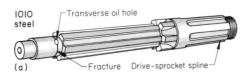

(a)

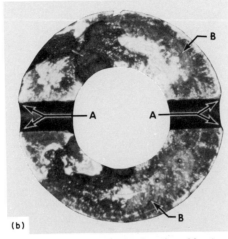

(b)

(a) View of shaft, showing location of fracture. Shaft was made of carburized and hardened 1010 steel (case hardness, Rockwell C 40; core, Rockwell B 85). (b) A fracture surface of the shaft, at 4×, showing crack-initiation sites at A's, and curved crack-arrest marks at B's that indicate slower crack propagation in the soft core than in the hardened case.

Fig. 8. Case-hardened motorcycle-transmission shaft that fractured in service from high-cycle fatigue

foregoing processes also occur in alloys and heterogeneous materials. However, alloying and commercial production practices introduce segregation, inclusions, second-phase particles and other features that disturb the structure, and these have a dominant effect on the crack-nucleation process. In general, alloying that (a) enhances cross slip, (b) enhances twinning, or (c) increases the rate of work hardening will stimulate crack nucleation. On the other hand, alloying usually raises the flow stress of a metal, thus at least partly offsetting the potentially detrimental effect on fatigue-crack nucleation.

Relation to Environment. In observing locations of crack nucleation, the possibility of environment-related mechanisms (including pitting corrosion, stress-corrosion cracking and other effects of a hostile environment) must be considered. For instance, a great number of fatigue failures in otherwise lightly loaded structures originate in fretted areas. In any structure having joints with some relative motion, fretting provides a possible locus for initiating failure. Environmental effects are discussed in more detail in the article on Corrosion-Fatigue Failures, which begins on page 240.

Crack Propagation

Once a fatigue crack has been nucleated, its rate and direction of growth are controlled by localized stresses and by the structure of the material at the tip of the crack.

Initial Propagation. Stage I of crack propagation occurs perpendicular to the maximum tensile stress. On a microscopic level, the local directions of propagation are controlled to some extent by crystallographic planes and may form on or be parallel to slip bands in grains near the surface. In interior grains, cleavage cracks often form at the intersection of slip bands with grain boundaries. In high-strength materials containing spheroidal second-phase particles, secondary crack nucleation ahead of the main crack front (slipless fatigue) occurs around such particles. In slipless fatigue, cracks form along lattice planes that are unfavorably located with respect to the maximum tensile stress.

Crack Enlargement. After a crack has nucleated and propagated to a finite size, it becomes a macroscopic stress raiser and can be more influential than any stress raiser that is already in the part. At this point, the crack tip will take over control of the fracture direction. Subsequently, the orientation of the crack surface will depend on the stress field at the crack tip and in many instances will follow a series of void coalescences in advance of the crack front.

On the macroscopic scale, early crack extension occurs under plane-strain conditions. This gives a typical fine-grained, flat-faced surface that, when produced under random loading or sequences of high and low stress amplitudes, exhibits characteristic beach marks.

Crack-propagation variations in anisotropic or inhomogeneous materials occasionally produce difficult-to-interpret beach marks. Figure 8(a) shows a case-hardened steel transmission shaft, with a transverse oil hole, that fractured after extended service in a racing motorcycle. Fracture initiated in the hardened case at the outer-circumference corners of the transverse hole (at A's in Fig. 8b) and progressed around the shaft in both directions. During periods of low operating stress, there was no crack progress, resulting in crack-arrest marks (at B's in Fig. 8b). During cycles of high stress, crack progress was reinitiated. The crack front in the soft core was curved backwards against the propagation direction, indicating greater ductility, lower notch sensitivity and lower stress over much of the rotation cycle in the core material than in the hardened case. The back curvature of the crack front may also have been the result of the severe stress-concentration effect of the cracked case.

In highly anisotropic materials, such as spring wire, a fatigue-fracture surface may exhibit regions where the crack propagated in typical fatigue and other regions where it propagated preferentially in another mode along planes of weakness (see the article on Failures of Springs, which begins on page 487).

Final Propagation. After a crack has grown to the size where it significantly changes the load-carrying capacity of the part, a change in the direction of crack growth usually follows. Fractures in sheet metal exhibit a shear lip at approximately 45° to the initial flat-face fracture. In cylindrical parts, although the fracture may in general still appear planar if the level of operating stress is low, the surface appearance becomes more fibrous and shows greater ductility (larger size of plastic zone at the crack front), indicating a change from crack extension to final, fast fracture. As a general rule, low-stress, high-cycle fatigue produces flat-face (plane-strain) fractures. The fracture surface appears fine grained and lightly polished near the crack-nucleation site, where the stress intensification is least. The surface becomes progressively rougher and more fibrous as the crack grows and the intensity of stress increases. On high-stress, low-cycle fatigue surfaces, found in certain areas of all complete fatigue fractures, the surface is fibrous, rough and more typical of plane-stress loading conditions, where the general fracture direction is at 45° to the main tensile load.

Effect of Type of Loading and Part Shape

Nucleation and growth of a fatigue crack and the features on the fracture surface are all strongly affected by the shape of the part and the type and magnitude of loading exerted on the part in service, as well as metallurgical and environmental factors.

In a beam of simple uniform cross section subjected to fluctuating or alternating stresses, fracture analysis is relatively simple and the appearance of fracture surfaces in test specimens is predictable.

Unidirectional Bending. A beam with a uniform cross section subjected to pure, fluctuating, unidirectional bending has a bending moment that is uniform along the length of the beam, and the tensile fiber stress is likewise uniform along the length of the beam. Therefore, a fatigue crack may be initiated at any point along the beam; in fact, several fatigue cracks may have been active before one of them became large enough to cause the final fracture.

A related form of loading is cantilever loading, in which the bending moment and therefore the tensile fiber stress vary along the length of the beam. Fracture will initiate at the point of highest stress, adjacent to the rigid mounting. Because of the shear-stress component characteristic of cantilever loading, the direction of the maximum tensile stress makes a small angle with the axis of the beam. Consequently, a fatigue crack usually

4150 steel
Rockwell C 27 to 34

View A-A

The shaft, of 4150 steel, was used in a piston-type pump. View A-A shows beach marks over a large area of a fracture surface; oval region near bottom center is the final-fracture area.

Fig. 9. Pump shaft that fractured in service from reversed-bending and torsional fatigue (Example 1)

will propagate into that portion of the beam within the fixed mounting.

Alternating Bending. If the loading of a beam is alternating instead of fluctuating, fatigue cracks may be initiated on both sides of the beam. In pure bending, the cracks on opposite sides of the beam are not necessarily in the same plane; final fracture may therefore occur at some angle other than 90° to the axis of the beam. If the same load is applied to the beam in both directions, the two fatigue cracks should be symmetrical. The size of the final-fracture zone is indicative of the relative loading of the beam. There is one significant difference between the appearance of the fatigue cracks formed under fluctuating load and those formed under alternating load. With an alternating load each crack is opened in one half-cycle and closed and pressed together during the other half-cycle, which rubs and polishes the high points on opposite sides of the fatigue crack. Under fluctuating load the rubbing is less pronounced. Consequently, beach marks are usually more observable after alternating loading than after fluctuating loading.

Rotational Bending. A machine component that is commonly subjected to a bending load is a rotating round shaft. A unique feature of rotational-bending loading is that during one revolution of

the shaft both maximum and minimum loading are exerted around the entire circumference of the shaft in the region of maximum bending moment. Because the loading is axially symmetrical, a fatigue crack can be initiated at any point, or at several points, around the periphery of the shaft. Multiple cracks do not necessarily occur in the same plane, and are separated from each other by ridges, called ratchet marks. The presence of multiple cracks normally indicates a relatively high applied load and rotational bending. Under low or moderate overloads, a rotating shaft may fail as a result of a single fatigue crack. When the shaft is always rotated in the same direction, the crack usually advances asymmetrically — that is, the apparent center of the area of beach marks shifts in a direction opposite to that of shaft rotation (see second row from the bottom in Fig. 12). Asymmetric fatigue-crack growth is indicative of rotational bending and the direction of rotation. Under periodically reversing rotating-bending loads, fatigue cracks grow symmetrically (see Fig. 9 and 12). Even without reversing the direction of rotation, a rotating-bending fatigue crack may advance symmetrically. See also Fig. 5, page 377, and related text, in the article on Failures of Shafts, in this volume.

The following example describes the failure of a shaft from reversed bending and rotational loading to a stress not much greater than the fatigue limit (a low overstress) but with a high stress concentration.

Example 1. Bending-Fatigue Fracture of a 4150 Steel Pump Shaft Because of High Stress Concentration but Low Overstress (Fig. 9)

Shafts used in piston-type pumps failed after the pumps had been intermittently used for about 12 months. Reports showed that four of 200 shafts in service failed. Two shafts were examined; one of them is shown in Fig. 9. Material specified for the shafts was 4150 steel, heat treated to a hardness of Rockwell C 27 to 34 and a minimum tensile strength of 129,000 psi. The pumps operated at a speed of 1585 rpm, pressure of 2000 psi, temperature of 57 C (135 F), and a capacity of 10.5 cu in. per revolution.

Investigation. Visual and macroscopic examination of the fracture surfaces of the two shafts disclosed beach marks over a large part of each surface. The appearance of the fracture surfaces suggested fatigue resulting from reversed bending and rotational loading with a high stress concentration but a low overstress. In one shaft the final-fracture area was oval and encircled with a gray area (shown in view A-A in Fig. 9), and consisted of 10 to 15% of the cross-sectional area. The other shaft exhibited a final-fracture area of similar shape but near the center of the shaft.

Metallographic examination of a section through a shaft revealed light and dark bands. The dark bands (alloy-rich areas)

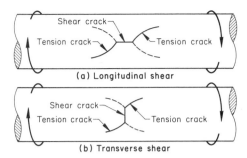

Fig. 10. Schematic representation of the way in which torsional fatigue cracks in a shaft may begin in longitudinal shear or transverse shear. Dashed lines indicate other cracks that can appear when torsional stresses are reversed.

had a hardness of Rockwell C 44.5 to 45.5; the light bands (alloy-lean areas), Rockwell C 29 to 30. Surface hardness of the shafts from end to end ranged from Rockwell C 29 to 33; surface hardness in the fracture area was about Rockwell C 30.

Conclusions. The shafts failed in reversed-bending and torsional fatigue that resulted from high stress concentration at a low overstress.

Corrective Measure. The shaft diameter in the failure area was increased from 1 in. to 1.125 in. for subsequent shafts, which reduced the nominal stresses by about 25% and was expected to provide a safe operating condition.

Torsional Loading. Under torsional loading of a shaft, the maximum local tensile stresses are at 45° to the axis of the shaft. Under a fluctuating torsional load, fatigue cracks may develop normal to the tensile stresses. Under alternating (reversed) torsional loading ($S_m = 0$, $R = -1$), two sets of fatigue cracks, perpendicular to each other, may develop. Torsional fatigue cracks can begin in longitudinal shear (Fig. 10a) or transverse shear (Fig. 10b); the relatively equal length of the cracks in each pair in Fig. 10 indicates that the equal and opposite stresses have occurred during loading. At later stages of fatigue-crack growth, one crack of a pair usually grows much faster than the other and eventually causes rupture of the shaft. Beams that are subjected to fluctuating torsion ($S_m < S_a$, $R > 0$) will typically show fatigue cracks in only one direction; the presence of perpendicular fatigue cracks in a component subjected to fluctuating

torsion probably is an indication of the presence of torsional vibration.

Axial Loading. In each of the previously discussed types of loading there are stress gradients within the beam; stresses are greatest at the surface of the beam, which increases the normal likelihood for fatigue cracks to initiate at the surface. In pure axial loading of a simple, uniform beam, however, the stress is constant across the cross section of the beam, and a fatigue crack may initiate at a discontinuity within the member rather than at the surface. The appearance of fatigue cracks caused by fluctuating tensile loads is often similar to that described for bending loads. The stress states within beams subjected to the two types of loading are similar, although purely axial loading is rarely found in service.

Loading of flat components differs from that of long, somewhat cylindrical components. In flat components, biaxial tension is more common and torsion less common. Under conditions of biaxial tension, fatigue life depends on the maximum shear stress rather than the principal tensile stresses. Thus, fatigue failure may not occur when the loading conditions result in low shear stresses but high tensile stresses.

In sheet or plate materials, the fatigue-crack front may extend under plane-strain conditions to give a wholly flat-face fracture (see Fig. 11a). Fatigue fractures in very thin sheet subjected to high stress intensities may shift from flat face (plane-strain conditions) to shear face (plane-stress conditions), as shown in Fig. 11(b).

Effect of Overstress and Stress Concentration

The magnitude of the nominal stress on a cyclically loaded component is often measured by the amount of overstress — that is, the amount by which the nominal stress exceeds the fatigue limit or the long-life fatigue strength of the material used in the component. The number of load cycles that a component under low overstress can endure is high; thus, the term high-cycle fatigue is often applied. Increasing the magnitude of the nominal stress has the following effects:

(*a*) initiation of multiple cracks is more likely; (*b*) striation spacing is increased; and (*c*) the region of final fast fracture is increased in size.

With very high overstress, low-cycle-fatigue fractures are produced. The arbitrary but commonly accepted dividing line between high-cycle and low-cycle fatigue is considered to be about 100,000 (10^5) cycles. In practice this distinction is made by determining whether the dominant component of the strain imposed during cyclic loading is elastic (high cycle) or plastic (low cycle), which in turn depends on the properties of the metal as well as the magnitude of the nominal stress. In extreme conditions, the dividing line between high-cycle and low-cycle fatigue may be even less than 100 cycles.

Stress Concentrations. Notches, grooves, holes, fillets, threads, keyways and splines are common design features. All such sectional discontinuities increase the local stress level above that estimated on the basis of minimum cross-sectional area. In addition to the reduction of fatigue strength or fatigue life, increasing the severity of stress concentration has the following effects on fatigue-crack features: (*a*) initiation of multiple cracks is more likely; (*b*) beach marks usually become convex toward the point of crack origin; (*c*) under rotational loading the beach marks may completely surround the final-fracture zone; and (*d*) combined stress states may be introduced, thereby influencing the direction of crack growth.

Figure 12 schematically shows how magnitude of nominal stress, severity of stress concentration, and type of loading affect the appearance of fatigue-fracture surfaces of components with round, square and rectangular cross sections, and those of thick plates. The chart in Fig. 12 is intended for use only as a guide. Deviations from this chart will be found for various material, test and service conditions. Figure 12 is based on the following principles:

1 As local stress increases in regions of potential crack initiation, so does the number of active crack nuclei or initiation sites. Therefore, at high overstress or in the presence of a severe stress con-

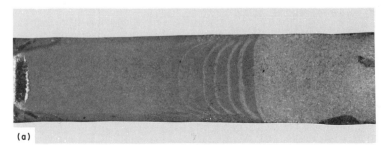

Fig. 11. Fatigue-fracture zones in aluminum alloy 7075-T6 plates. (a) Fatigue crack that grew as a flat-face fracture with a shallow convex crack front. (b) Change in orientation of fatigue fracture from plane strain (at A) to plane stress (at B).

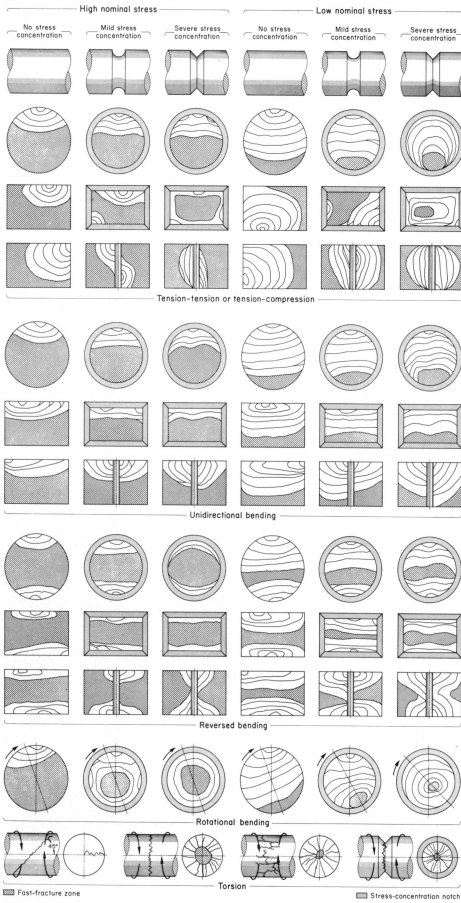

Fig. 12. Schematic representation of marks on surfaces of fatigue fractures produced in smooth and notched components with round, square and rectangular cross sections, and in thick plates, under various loading conditions at high and low nominal stress

centration, multiple crack origins will be seen. In most instances the cracks from these origins will eventually unite to form a single crack front. Before the single crack front is formed, the individual microcracks will be separated by small, vertical ledges, called ratchet marks. Alternatively, at just above the fatigue limit, or minimum stress for fracture, a single origin will occur and the entire fracture will emanate from that point.

2   In the absence of stress concentrations at the surface, cracks propagate more rapidly near the center of a section than at the surface. This occurs because deformation constraints cause the stresses to be triaxial and more severe away from the surface. However, when there is a stress-concentrating notch at the surface (such as a thread with a sharp root), the stress near this notch may be more severe than it is farther below the surface. Under conditions of severe notching, W-shape crack fronts will sometimes be observed.

3   For a given material, the size of the region of catastrophic fracture (or final, fast fracture) relative to the size of the region of subcritical crack propagation will increase as nominal stress increases. Under an overload that is slightly more than adequate to cause fracture, the region of final, fast fracture will be relatively small; under a much higher applied stress, this region will be relatively large.

4   In a fracture caused by rotating bending, the final-fracture region will often be rotated, or offset, toward the origin in a direction opposite to the direction of rotation. Also, all other conditions being the same, the region of final fracture will move toward the center of the section as the nominal stress increases.

5   Fracture initiation usually occurs at or near the surface, because in most engineering situations such as in bending or when stress concentrations are present, the surface is subjected to the greatest stress. Subsurface origins have been observed in tension-tension or tension-compression fatigue, or in Hertzian-stress situations such as rolling-contact fatigue of bearings and gear teeth, if there is a large inclusion or imperfection below the surface in the interior of the specimen or part, but this is unusual. Crack initiation at corners or at the ends of drilled holes may result from the presence of burrs remaining at these locations after machining.

Effect of Frequency of Loading

Exclusive of environmental effects, there are no distinguishing surface features of a fatigue fracture produced at high frequency that differentiate it from other types of fatigue fractures during either visual or light-microscope examination. At best, when examined with a light microscope, a fracture surface created at a high frequency will have a brittle appearance, showing mostly a platelike structure throughout the fatigue zone. Beach marks may or may not be present, depending on whether crack growth was steady or intermittent or if load variations occurred. The fracture surface shown in Fig. 13(a) was produced by subjecting a 0.020-in.-thick panel of aluminum alloy 7075-T6 to high-frequency (200 Hz) vibration with superimposed loading at lower frequency (1 Hz). Figure 13(b) shows the characteristic platelike structure and well-defined striations that were created as a result of the superimposed low-frequency loads. Examination of the fracture surface with a scanning electron microscope revealed finely spaced (5 to 6 micro-in.) striations attributable to crack growth resulting from the stresses induced during high-frequency vibration (Fig. 13c). The narrowly spaced striations are expected at high-frequency loading because in each cycle the length of time at peak loading is very short, and the increment of crack growth per cycle is correspondingly small.

Effect of Stress on Fatigue Strength

Fatigue cracks generally form preferentially at the surface, because the level of stress generally is higher at the surface. Experimental results indicate that fatigue can occur under high vacuum and at low temperature, suggesting that the primary mechanism of fatigue does not involve corrosive attack or thermal activation, although both may contribute to final failure.

Mean Stress. A series of fatigue tests can be conducted at various mean stresses and the results plotted as a series of S-N curves. For design purposes, it is more useful to know how the mean stress affects the permissible alternating stress amplitude for a given life (number of cycles). This usually is accomplished by plotting the allowable stress amplitude for a specific number of cycles as a function of the associated mean stress. At zero mean stress, the allowable stress amplitude is the effective fatigue limit for a specified number of cycles. As the mean stress increases, the permissible amplitudes steadily decrease until at a mean stress equal to the ultimate tensile strength of the material, the permissible amplitude is zero.

The two straight lines and the curve shown in Fig. 14 represent the three most widely used empirical relations. The straight line joining the alternating fatigue strength to the tensile strength is the modified Goodman law. Goodman's original law, which is no longer used, included the assumption that the alternating fatigue limit was equal to one-third of the tensile strength; this has since been modified to the relation shown in Fig. 14, using the alternating fatigue strength determined experimentally. Gerber found

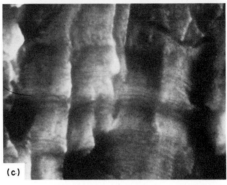

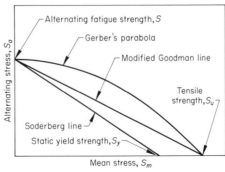

(a) and (b) Light fractographs of part of the fracture surface at 20× and 800×, respectively; (b) shows platelike structure with striations created by low-frequency loading. (c) SEM fractograph of part of the fracture surface, at 5000×, showing fine striations between coarse ones.

Fig. 13. Fatigue-fracture surface of an aluminum alloy 7075-T6 panel, 0.020 in. thick, produced by high-frequency vibrations with superimposed loadings at lower frequency

Fig. 14. Effect of mean stress on the alternating stress amplitude, as shown by the modified Goodman line, Gerber's parabola, and Soderberg line. See text.

that the early experiments of Wöhler fitted closely to a parabolic relation, and this is known as Gerber's parabola (curve in Fig. 14). The third relation, known as Soderberg's law, is given in Fig. 14 by the straight line from the alternating fatigue

strength to the static yield strength. For many purposes it is essential that the static yield strength not be exceeded, and this relation is intended to fulfill the conditions that neither fatigue failure nor yielding occurs. The relations may be written mathematically as:

Modified Goodman law:
$$S_a = S[1 - (S_m/S_u)]$$
Gerber's law: $S_a = S[1 - (S_m/S_u)^2]$
Soderberg's law: $S_a = S[1 - (S_m/S_y)]$

where S_a is the alternating stress associated with a mean stress S_m, S is the alternating fatigue strength, S_u is the tensile strength; and S_y is the yield strength.

An understanding of the Goodman, or constant-life, diagram has resulted in many varied and useful treatments for improving fatigue life. According to a constant-life diagram, an example of which is shown in Fig. 41 on page 120, increased tension decreases the fatigue life and increased compression increases it. Because most cracks originate at the surface of the part, placing the surface under compressive stress should be beneficial. Recognition of this has resulted in development of such surface treatments as nitriding, carburizing, shot peening, surface rolling and overstressing. When these treatments are properly applied, the surface is in a state of residual compression. However, if not properly applied, they can have a detrimental effect on fatigue life.

Stress Amplitude. Because stress amplitude will vary widely under actual loading conditions, it is necessary to predict fatigue life under various stress amplitudes. The most widely used method of estimating fatigue under complex loading is provided by the linear-damage law. This is a hypothesis first suggested by Palmgren and restated by Miner, and is sometimes known as Miner's law (Ref 1). The assumption is made that the application of n_i cycles at a stress amplitude S_i, for which the average number of cycles to failure is N_i, causes an amount of fatigue damage that is measured by the cumulative cycle ratio n_i/N_i, and that failure will occur when $\Sigma(n_i/N_i) = 1$.

This method is not applicable in all cases, and numerous alternative theories of cumulative linear damage have been suggested (Ref 2). Some considerations of redistribution of stresses have been clarified, but there is as yet no approach that seems satisfactory in all situations.

The effect of varying the stress amplitude (linear damage) may be evaluated experimentally by means of a test in which a given number of stress cycles are applied to a test piece at one stress amplitude and the test is continued to fracture at a different amplitude. Alternatively, the stress may be changed from one stress amplitude to another at regular intervals; such tests are known as block, or interval, tests. These tests do not simulate service conditions, but may serve a useful purpose for assessing the linear-damage law and indicating its limitations. Results of tests by several investigators have shown that initial overstressing reduces both the fatigue limit and the subsequent fatigue life at stresses above the fatigue limit. The results also show that a slight overstress does not markedly reduce the fatigue limit, even if continued for a large proportion of the normal life of a material. However, this is not true for a high overstress.

Residual Stress. Fatigue fractures generally propagate from the surface. Processing operations, such as grinding, polishing and machining, that work harden or increase residual stress on the surface can influence the fatigue strength, although there is no generalized formulation that will predict the extent of improved fatigue strength that can be derived from work hardening and residual stress. Compressive residual surface stresses generally increase the fatigue strength, but tensile residual surface stresses do not. There may be a gradual decrease in residual stress if the cyclic stresses cause some plastic deformation. Compressive residual surface stress provides greater improvement in the fatigue strength of harder materials (like alloy spring steel), and in softer materials (like low-carbon steel) work hardening effectively improves fatigue strength. This is because the harder material can sustain a high level of residual elastic surface stress, and the tensile strength (and thus the fatigue limit) of the softer material is improved by work hardening.

In a notched high-strength steel, the beneficial effect of prestretching and the detrimental effect of precompression are much greater than in a plain carbon steel because of the type of residual stress present at the notch. A compressive residual stress introduced during quenching from a tempering temperature will increase the fatigue strength, particularly in notched specimens.

In general, residual stresses are introduced by (a) misfit of structural parts; (b) a change in the specific volume of a metal accompanying phase changes; (c) a change in shape following plastic deformation; or (d) thermal stresses resulting from rapid temperature changes such as occur in quenching.

The influence of residual stress on fatigue strength is, in principle, similar to that of an externally applied static stress. A static compressive surface stress increases the fatigue strength and static tensile surface stress reduces it.

Complex Stresses. The criteria of static failure have been applied to fatigue failure. If S_1, S_2 and S_3 are the amplitudes of the principal alternating stresses where $S_1 \geq S_2 \geq S_3$, and if S is the alternating uniaxial fatigue strength, then the following criteria apply:

1 Maximum principal-stress criterion $S_1 = S$
2 Maximum shear-stress criterion $S_1 - S_3 = S$
3 Shear-strain energy $(S_1 - S_2)^2 + (S_2 - S_3)^2 + (S_3 - S_1)^2 = S^2$
4 Maximum principal-strain criterion $S_1 - \mu(S_2 + S_3) = S$, where μ is Poisson's ratio.

Because fatigue cracks usually propagate from the surface, where one of the principal stresses is zero, only biaxial stresses need be considered. When the two principal stresses are of the same algebraic sign, the criteria of maximum principal stress and maximum shear stress give the same relationship. If the principal stresses are of opposite algebraic sign, then all criteria give a different relationship. It is often convenient to determine the suitability of the various criteria by comparing the fatigue strength in torsion t and bending b. No single criterion adequately describes the general behavior of the stresses; for ductile materials, the closest correlation with the experimental results of (t/b) is provided by the shear-strain-energy criterion (Ref 3).

Frequency. The frequency range of 500 to 10,000 cycles per minute is generally employed in a fatigue test. In this range the fatigue strength of most materials, based on a given number of cycles to fracture, is little affected by frequency. In general, there is a slight decrease in fatigue strength with decrease in frequency, because the fatigue limit may be related to the amount of plastic deformation that occurs during the stress cycle. For instance, at high frequency, there is less relaxation time during each stress cycle for deformation to occur, which results in less damage. For steel, the fatigue limit is not affected between 200 and 5000 cycles per minute. However, at high frequencies up to 100,000 cycles per minute, steels that are 100% ferritic show marked increase in fatigue strength. In nonferrous metals, the fatigue strength increases continuously with increase in frequency; in plain carbon steel, the fatigue strength reaches a maximum value, then decreases with an increase in frequency.

Effect of Stress Concentrations on Fatigue Strength

Fatigue cracks usually start at some region of stress concentration resulting from the presence of surface discontinuities (stress raisers), such as a step or shoulder, a screw thread, an oil hole or a bolthole, or a surface flaw. The stress-concentration factor, K_t, of the discontinuity is a measure of intensity of stress that occurs. (See the section on Concepts Related to Fatigue, on page 95 in this article.) In some situations, values of K_t can be calculated using the theory of elasticity or can be measured using photoelastic plastic models. Many of these values are reported in standard references (Ref 4 to 7).

The mathematical theory of elasticity is based on an ideal isotropic material free of any internal discontinuity, a strictly accurate profile, and an increase in stress concentration due solely to the presence of the surface discontinuity. In actual parts, the stress intensification is affected not only by the surface discontinuity but also, to an undetermined extent, by the size of the part, by local readjustments of stress because of plastic yielding, by surface roughness, and by the heterogeneous structure of the material itself, including anisotropy and inherent internal discontinuities. Therefore, the deleterious effect of a stress raiser on a part usually is determined experimentally and expressed in terms of a fatigue notch factor, K_f. This is the ratio of the fatigue strength without stress concentration to fatigue strength with stress concentration. In general, experimentally determined values of K_f are somewhat less than the values of K_t calculated for the same specimens.

Under static loading conditions a stress raiser has little or no effect in the majority of situations, provided that the material is ductile. If the stress locally exceeds the yield strength of the material, plastic deformation occurs and there is a redistribution of stress. Provided the amount of plastic deformation is not excessive, no adverse effect need be anticipated. But if the part is subjected to fluctuating or alternating stresses, then, if a fatigue crack nucleates at a stress below the yield strength of the material, stress redistribution by plastic yielding will not occur and the full effect of the stress raiser will occur.

Stress concentrations affect the fatigue behavior of different materials differently. For instance, relatively brittle materials such as quenched-and-tempered steels are more susceptible to the effects of stress raisers than are ductile materials such as normalized or annealed steels; also, cast irons, containing innumerable internal stress raisers, show little further adverse effects from externally introduced stress raisers.

Distribution of Stress. To visualize the distribution of stress at a change in section size or shape, it is helpful to consider the part in terms of electricity flowing through a conductor of similar cross section. In diagrammatic form, stress flow can be represented as a series of parallel lines, the stress being inversely proportional to the distance between the lines; that is, the lines bunch together in regions of high stress. The flow of stress associated with several of the stress raisers typically found in parts in service is shown in Fig. 15.

Progressive increases in stress with decreasing fillet radii are shown in Fig. 15(a), (b) and (c), and the relative magnitude and distribution of stress resulting from uniform loading of these parts is indicated in Fig. 15(d), (e) and (f).

Stress caused by the presence of an integral collar of considerable width is shown in Fig. 15(g); Fig. 15(h) shows the decrease in stress concentration that accompanies a decrease in collar width. Stress conditions are very similar when collars or similar parts are pressed or shrunk into position. The stress flow at the junction of a bolt head and a shank is as represented in Fig. 15(j).

A single notch introduces a considerably greater stress-concentration effect than does a continuous thread: the reason for this is clear when the stress flow is considered. The stress-concentration effect of a single sharp notch is as shown in Fig. 15(k). The stress concentration at the right of the arrow in Fig. 15(m) is very similar to that in the narrow collar in Fig. 15(h), because of the mutual relief afforded by adjacent threads. To the left of the arrow, however, the last thread is relieved from one side only and in consequence there is a considerable stress concentration, similar to that of the single notch in Fig. 15(k). This is why bolts so frequently fracture through the last full thread.

The effect of a groove or gouge on stress concentration (Fig. 15n) is less severe than that of a sharp notch. A series of grooves will have an effect similar to that shown in Fig. 15(m).

In the following example, a sharp corner in a milled slot was the point of stress concentration and the site of fracture initiation.

Example 2. Fatigue Fracture of a Cast Stainless Steel Lever That Was Initiated by Stress Concentration at a Sharp Corner (Fig. 16)

A main fuel control was returned to the factory for examination after service on a test aircraft engine that had experienced high vibrations. There were no apparent problems with the fuel control, but it was removed for examination to ensure that no problems had developed as a result of the vibrations. When the fuel control was disassembled, the lever shown in Fig. 16(a) was found to be cracked.

The lever was cast from AMS 5350 (type 410) stainless steel, through-hardened to Rockwell C 26 to 32, and passivated.

Investigation. There were no corrosion products or stains on the lever; however, a slight bluish cast, probably caused during chemical etching of the part number, was found on the slotted arm. The general condition of several holes and surfaces of the lever was good, although the sides of the rec-

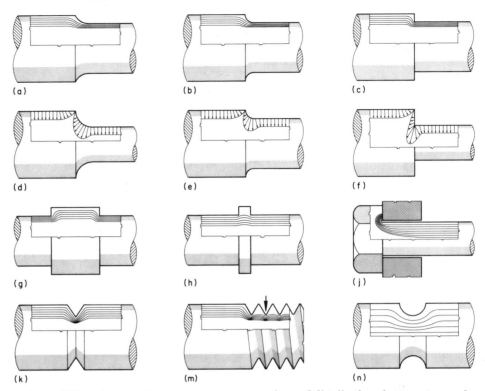

Fig. 15. Effect of stress raisers on stress concentration and distribution of stress at several changes of form in components. See text for discussion.

tangular slot in the base were abraded from rubbing against the mating part. The sides of the elongated hole in the slotted arm were polished by motion of the mating member. There was negligible wear in the round hole and in the elongated holes where fracture occurred.

The crack initiated at the sharp corner of the milled slot and propagated across to the outer wall, as shown in detail A in Fig. 16. The surfaces of the part at the crack were slightly offset, indicating some plastic deformation. This deformation could have occurred after the failure and during disassembly of the lever from the fuel control.

To examine the fracture surface, the sections were spread apart about 30°, resulting in a slight tearing in one corner of the section surrounding the elongated hole. Bending of the part was easily done, indicating that the general ductility of the part was satisfactory. The bent section was sub-

sequently broken off and another crack was observed in the casting; however, it was remote from and unrelated to the fracture under investigation. The lever had been magnetic-particle inspected during manufacture, and the crack was of a size that should have been detected.

The fracture surface under investigation (see Fig. 16b) had beach marks initiating at the sharp corner along the milled slot. Changes in frequency or amplitude of vibration caused different rates of propagation, resulting in a change in pattern. Motion of the part after failure occurred caused some obliteration of the fracture characteristics.

Conclusions. The lever failed in fatigue as a result of excessive vibration of the fuel control on the test engine. Cracking initiated in a sharp corner of a milled slot.

Corrective Measure. Conditions on the test stand were more severe than those that the engine was expected to survive in service

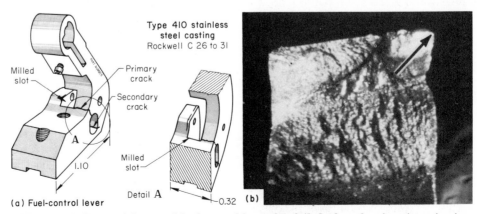

Fig. 16. (a) Cast stainless steel fuel-control lever that failed when the aircraft engine in which it was mounted experienced excessive vibration. (b) View of a fracture surface; arrow indicates region of fracture origin. (Example 2)

Aluminum alloy 7075-T73
Rockwell B 85.5

25.5

4.94

10.200

Primary-fracture surface

Fracture

Lug (1 of 2)

A

Lubrication hole

Lubrication hole

1.750-in.-diam bushing, 0.090-in. wall

1"

3.62 diam

Secondary fracture

(a) Original design   Improved design

Detail A

(b)

Fig. 17. (a) Landing-gear torque-arm assembly of aluminum alloy 7075-T73 that was redesigned to eliminate fatigue fracture at a lubrication hole. (b) Fracture surface, at about 2×, showing fatigue beach marks. (Example 3)

without major damage and were solely responsible for failure of the lever. If any corrective measure at all were necessary on the part, it would be to specify a large radius in the corner where cracking originated. This would reduce the stress-concentration factor significantly, thus minimizing the susceptibility of the lever to fatigue.

In the following example, failure occurred at a lubrication hole located at a region of high stress concentration.

Example 3. Fatigue Fracture of an Aluminum Alloy 7075-T73 Landing-Gear Torque Arm That Originated at a Lubrication Hole in the Lug (Fig. 17)

The torque-arm assembly for an aircraft nose landing gear, shown in Fig. 17(a), failed after 22,779 simulated flights. The part, made from an aluminum alloy 7075-T73 forging, had an expected life of 100,000 simulated flights.

Two cadmium-plated flanged bushings, made of copper alloy 630 (aluminum bronze), were press-fitted into each bored hole in the lug. A space between the bushings provided an annular groove for a lubricant. A lubrication hole extended from the outer surface to the bore of the lug, as shown in the "Original design" view in detail A in Fig. 17.

Investigation. Initial study of the fracture surfaces indicated that the primary fracture initiated from multiple origins on both sides of the lubrication hole, as shown at arrows in Fig. 17(b). Beach marks on the fracture surface indicate that cracking was initiated and propagated by fatigue until an overload stage was reached.

A fracture on the opposite side of the lug, shown as "Secondary fracture" in detail A in Fig. 17, appeared to be typical for a static overload failure.

A section was taken normal to the fracture surface and in the region contacted by the bushing flange, and prepared for metallographic examination. Results showed small fatigue-type cracks in the hole adjacent to the origin of primary fracture. There were no indications of inclusions or discontinuities in the plane of the section that could contribute to the initiation of lug fracture.

Hardness of the material at the face of the lug adjacent to the fracture surface was Rockwell B 85.5. Electrical conductivity of the material was 39% IACS, typical for aluminum alloy 7075.

Conclusions. The arm failed in fatigue cracking that initiated on each side of the lubrication hole. No material defects were found at the failure origin.

Corrective Measures. The location of the lubrication hole was changed as shown in the "Improved design" view in detail A in Fig. 17. The faces of the lug were shot peened for added resistance to fatigue failure. Also, the forging material was changed to aluminum alloy 7175-T736 for its higher mechanical properties.

Keyways in components frequently act as stress raisers. When the stress is predominantly torsional, fatigue cracks usually start in the fillets of the keyway, which is to be expected from the disturbance of the stress flow caused by the presence of the keyway. The transition of torsional stress as it reaches a keyway is shown by comparison of shaded zones A and B in Fig. 18. The distribution of torsional stress in regions away from the keyway (zone A) is smooth and wedge-shaped (stress is zero at center and maximum at the surface of the shaft). In regions near the keyway (zone B) the stress distribution is distorted by the stresses caused by contact between the key and keyway, resulting in maximum torsional stress below the surface. When the end of a keyway is formed with a sharp step, a further concentration of stress occurs, especially in the presence of bending stresses, and cracking very often begins at this point. This further stress concentration can be reduced considerably by using a sled-runner type of keyway, in which the transition at the end of the keyway is gradual.

Reduction of Stresses. The detrimental effect of stress concentrations can be reduced or eliminated by the use of induced stresses. These stresses may be introduced by plastic deformation of the surface, such as in cold working and shot peening, by phase transformation, such as in case hardening, or by proof loading with a load high enough to cause local plastic flow in the notch but low enough to avoid general yielding.

Extreme or incorrect cold working may have adverse effects under fatigue conditions, because it may give rise to minute cracks in the surface of the material or at least make the surface prone to such cracks. If the correct amount of cold working is applied, however, improvement in the fatigue strength is appreciable. For instance, a screw thread produced by rolling is more resistant to fatigue failure than one that has been cut. Surface rolling and shot peening, especially of springs, are other examples of the successful application of cold working. Apart from the increase in fatigue strength of the surface of the material arising from work hardening, the stress distribution is modified considerably. Figure 19(a) shows the stress distribution in a specimen notched by machining and then subjected to a tensile load $L = 1$. This load just starts to produce yielding at the root of the notch, which has a stress-concentration factor of 3.0. Figure 19(b) shows the same specimen loaded to $L = 1.5$, which produces yielding to a greater depth. The result of decreasing the load to $L = 1$ is shown in Fig. 19(c). The beneficial effect of the overload is indicated by the reduction of peak stress. The residual-stress distribution after removal of the external load ($L = 0$) is shown in Fig. 19(d). The stress distribution produced in a specimen in which the notches have been shot peened is shown in Fig. 19(e). The stress in the shot-peened specimen after application of load is shown in Fig. 19(f). If the amount of cold working is so adjusted that the residual compressive stress in the part effectively reduces the applied peak tensile stress below the fatigue limit of the material, fatigue failure will not occur. It is difficult in practice,

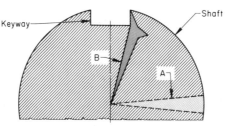

Keyway

Shaft

B

A

Fig. 18. Comparison of the distribution of torsional stresses in a shaft at and away from a keyway. See text.

however, to ensure the correct amount of cold working. Cold working intended to improve the endurance of a part should be chosen with appropriate consideration of the affected stress system. Residual compressive surface stresses improve fatigue strength only under conditions involving bending and torsional stresses. Where the stress is purely tensile (though infrequent in real-life engineering applications), the fatigue strength may be reduced, because the compressive stress at the surface is balanced by a region of tensile stress just below the surface. In tensile loading, the stress is uniformly distributed across the section and is augmented by the residual tensile stress, and failure is likely to take place by cracking just beneath the surface.

Other methods of reducing the effect of stress concentration are to raise the fatigue strength of the material in the region of high stress and to produce compressive residual stresses by flame hardening, carburizing, or nitriding. If performed correctly, any of the three processes is beneficial in raising the fatigue strength, but the extent of the treated region needs to be carefully chosen; otherwise, failure is likely to occur at one of the junctions between the treated and untreated regions.

Influence of Design on Fatigue Strength

Mechanical and structural design encompasses two categories: configuration, and material properties. Selection of material is often influenced by requirements other than fatigue characteristics, such

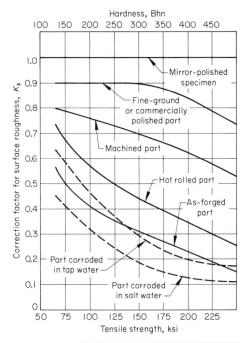

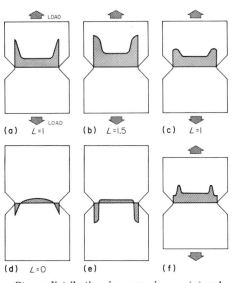

Stress distribution in a specimen: (a) subjected to a load $L = 1$; (b) subjected to a load $L = 1.5$; (c) after the load was decreased to $L = 1$; (d) after removal of the external load (residual stresses); (e) after being shot peened; and (f) subjected to a load after shot peening.

Fig. 19. Stress distribution produced in a notched specimen under various conditions

Factor	Type of load		
	Bending	Torsion	Axial
K_l	1.0	0.58	0.9(a)
K_d, where:			
$d \leq 0.4$ in.	1.0	1.0	1.0
0.4 in. $< d \leq 2$ in. .	0.9	0.9	1.0
K_s	—From chart above—		

(a) A lower value (0.6 to 0.85) may be used to account for known or suspected undetermined bending because of load eccentricity.

Fig. 20. Correction factors for surface roughness (K_s), type of loading (K_l), and part diameter (K_d), for fatigue life of steel parts. See text for application.

as resistance to corrosion or to elevated temperatures. Regardless of the controlling property, the material used in a part designed for fatigue resistance must possess an acceptable combination of many properties. Not all designs necessarily require a value for all possible properties, and data may not be available for all specific materials, conditions and forms.

Simple rules for fatigue-resistance design cannot be stated because of the diversity in function, loads, stresses, materials and environments. However, a number of useful practices can be defined that, when applied with good engineering judgment, can be expected to result in a significant reduction in the probability of fatigue failure.

Correction Factors for Test Data. The available fatigue data normally are for a specific type of loading, specimen size and surface roughness. For instance, the Moore rotating-beam fatigue-test machine uses a 0.3-in.-diam specimen that is free of any stress concentrations because of specimen shape, is polished to a mirror finish and is subjected to completely reversed bending stresses. Juvinall (Ref 8) suggests that the fatigue-life data used in design calculations be cor-

rected by multiplying the number of cycles (life), N_i', determined in a fatigue test by three factors that account for the variation in the type of loading, part diameter and surface roughness. Thus the design life $N_i = K_l K_d K_s N_i'$, where K_l is the correction factor for the type of loading, K_d for the part diameter, and K_s for the surface roughness.

Values of the three factors for correcting standard Moore fatigue-test data on steel are given in Fig. 20.

Interference at Line of Contact. Two design guides that can minimize interference at the line of contact between mating parts are: (a) provide generous fillets and radii, and (b) design parts for minimum mismatch at installation for lowest residual and preload tensile strains. In some instances, generous fillet radii can cause interference if the corner radii on the mating parts are too small. Therefore, a large corner radius would result in minimum mismatch at installation.

In the following example, the sharp edge of a part was in contact with a fillet radius on the mating part. Galling and rubbing of the fillet resulted in tearing, and cracking initiated at the tear.

Example 4. Fatigue Fracture of a D-6ac Steel Structural Member at the Line of Contact With Another Member (Fig. 21)

Fatigue testing of a structure had been in operation several months when a postlike member ruptured. Fracture occurred in the fillet of the post that contacted the edge of a carry-through box bolted to the member, as shown in Fig. 21. At failure, the part was receiving the second set of loads up to 103.6% of design load.

The post was made of D-6ac steel and heat treated to a tensile strength of 220,000 to 240,000 psi.

Investigation. The edge of the carry-through box along the line of contact with the post was permanently deformed and galled by rubbing, and adjacent contact points on the post were polished. The line of fracture in the post coincided with the top edge of the rubbed and galled area on the box. A fillet on the riblike surface of the post in the stressed area was tangent to the forward lower surface edge of the box. Rubbing and galling occurred across the entire width of the fillet where it was in contact with the edge of the box, as shown in section A-A in Fig. 21. Also seen was light fretting surrounding many of the boltholes and at several other high spots on the faying surfaces.

Microscopic examination of the fracture surface indicated that the origin of the crack was between 0.05 and 0.10 in. from the edge of the post. Also, several beach marks on the fracture surface indicated that various static and dynamic loads had been applied to the structure prior to final fracture. Chevron marks on the fracture surface showed that the crack propagated toward the bolthole and that the last area to fail was between the bolthole and the back edge of

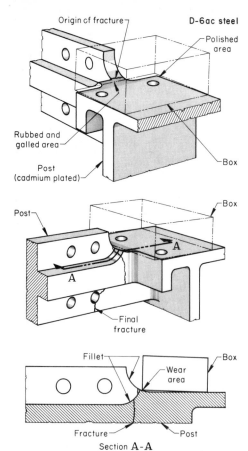

Fig. 21. Structural member (post) of D-6ac steel that failed from fatigue cracking initiated by rubbing and galling from a mating carry-through box that was bolted to the post (Example 4)

the post. Inspection of the edge of the fracture surface revealed numerous indications of small secondary cracks.

Metallographic examination of sections through the fracture surface revealed evidence of cold work and secondary cracking in the rubbed and galled area. The grain size and microstructure were satisfactory, and no evidence of decarburization or oxidation was found on the surfaces. The post had apparently been shot peened and cadmium plated.

Electron fractography confirmed that cracking had initiated at a region of tearing, and that the cracks had propagated by fatigue. Some intergranular features observed near the origins were associated with the tearing.

Standard-size, round tensile specimens were cut from the thick sections of the post on each side of the fracture and prepared. The axis of each specimen was parallel to the long dimension of the post. The mechanical properties of all specimens exceeded the minimum values specified for the post.

Conclusions. Fatigue was the primary cause of failure. A fillet on the post created an area of interference with the edge of the carry-through box bolted to the post. Rubbing of the faying surfaces worked the interference area on the post until small tears developed. These small tears became stress-concentration points that nucleated fatigue cracks that ultimately resulted in fracture.

Recommendations. The edge of the box in the area of contact with the post should be rounded to assure a tangency fit.

Joint Design. The importance of the effect of joint design on fatigue behavior cannot be overemphasized. The conventional approach to designing a multi-member structure for fatigue resistance is to consider the members as first in importance, and the joints as inevitable complications.

Of equal importance is the shape of the parts within the joint, because the shape may transform the external loading to a different mode, causing possible stress concentrations.

In the following example, improper fit between a wheel and an axle caused movement during operation. The point of maximum stress shifted, causing the axle to fracture.

Example 5. Fatigue Fracture of a Forged 4150 Steel Drive Axle in an Overhead Crane Caused by Shifting of the Crane Wheel (Fig. 22)

A stepped drive axle used in a high-speed electric overhead crane broke after 15 months of service. The axle, shown in Fig. 22(a), was made from a hardened and tempered resulfurized 4150 steel forging. The overhead crane was rated at 7½ tons and handled about 220 lifts per day, each lift averaging four to six tons.

Investigation. Fracture occurred approximately 2 in. from the driven end of the large-diameter keywayed section on the stepped axle and approximately 1½ in. from one end of the keyway where the crane wheel was keyed to the axle, as shown in Fig. 22(a). There were visual indications that the crane wheel had moved during operation to a position approximately ½ in. farther away from the driven end of the axle. The interference fit between the wheel and the shaft was insufficient to prevent radial and axial movement during operation. The axial movement of the crane wheel allowed the torsional moment to be displaced toward the location of the maximum bending moment, increasing the total effective stress. The edges of the portion of the keyway in the broken axle were battered and misshapen (see Fig. 22c), apparently from repeated impact against the key during the latter stages of failure.

Visual examination of the fracture surface revealed three fracture regions as shown in Fig. 22(c): a region of bending fatigue (at A); a region of combined bending and torsional fatigue (at B); and a region of final, fast fracture (at C). The dark, convex bending-fatigue region accounted for less than 5% of the fracture surface. The greater part of the fracture surface, more than 80%, was the region of combined bending and torsional fatigue — the flat, relatively featureless area at B in Fig. 22(c) that covers the upper half of the fracture surface and looks progressively less smooth as it approaches the rough final-fracture region (at C) adjacent to the bending-fatigue region (at A).

Beach marks in the bending-fatigue region indicated that cracking started at the surface approximately at the center of the bending-fatigue region. Cracking in the region of combined bending and torsional fatigue had multiple origins at the surface. Several of the origins can be seen immediately to the left of the bending-fatigue region (A) in Fig. 22(c). Final fracture was by mixed ductile and brittle fracture, as indicated by a chevron pattern that followed a generally elliptical contour in the final-fracture region (C).

The hardness of the axle varied from 305 Bhn near the surface to 277 Bhn at the center. This was within the specified hardness range of 269 to 331 Bhn.

Macroscopic and microscopic examination revealed indications of slight porosity near the center of the axle, but this had no causative relationship to the fracture. The microstructure was acicular tempered mar-

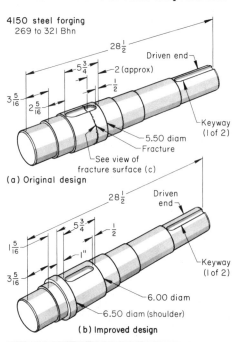

(a) Original design showing location of fracture. (b) Improved axle design that utilized a narrow shoulder at stress area to prevent shifting. (c) Fracture surface showing regions of bending fatigue (at A), combined bending and torsional fatigue (at B), and final, fast fracture (at C).

Fig. 22. Drive axle of 4150 steel for an overhead-crane wheel that fractured from fatigue in service because of insufficient interference fit between the wheel and the axle (Example 5)

tensite with moderately numerous elongated manganese sulfide inclusions.

The chemical composition was within the normal range for 4150 steel except for manganese, which was slightly above the high limit for 4150 steel, and sulfur, which was intentionally added to improve machinability of the hardened and tempered material.

Conclusions. Cracking initiated in bending fatigue at a location approximately opposite the keyway. This was followed by torsional-fatigue cracking from multiple origins, and final fracture by mixed ductile and brittle fracture.

Axial shift in position of the crane wheel during operation, because of insufficient interference fit, was the major cause of fatigue cracking. This shift significantly increased the bending stresses on the shaft.

Corrective Measures. The axle was redesigned as shown in Fig. 22(b). The critical diameter was increased from 5.50 in. to 6 in., and a narrow shoulder was added to keep the drive wheel from shifting during operation. Metallurgical changes were not considered necessary, because the metallurgical condition did not appear to be a factor in this failure.

Welded Joints. The fatigue strength of good as-welded joints depends on the stress state in the load path through the weldment, the stress-concentration factor at the toe of the weld, the condition of the material in the heat-affected zone, and the presence or absence of inclusions and other defects in the weld. Fatigue strength, at a reasonable life, of as-welded joints in carbon and low-alloy steels is independent of the steel used.

The fatigue strength of as-welded joints can be increased by cold working, because this inhibits the growth of cracks. Stress relieving after welding does not have much effect on the repeated tension-fatigue strength, but, because of the lower maximum tensile stress in the loading cycle, it can increase zero-mean-load values.

In the following example, a joint was redesigned so that the weld was away from the region of maximum stress.

Example 6. Fatigue Cracking of a Stainless Steel Elbow Assembly at a Welded Joint in a High-Stress Region (Fig. 23)

The welded elbow assembly shown in Fig. 23 was part of a hydraulic-pump pressure line for a jet aircraft. The other end of the tube was attached to a flexible metal hose, which provided no support and offered no resistance to vibration. The components of the elbow were made of type 321 stainless steel and were joined with ER347 stainless steel filler metal by gas tungsten-arc welding.

The line was leaking hydraulic fluid at the nut end of the elbow, and the assembly was returned to the manufacturer to determine the cause of failure.

Investigation. Visual examination of the elbow assembly revealed a crack in the fillet weld that joined the tube to the shoulder fitting. In assembly, the tube was inserted

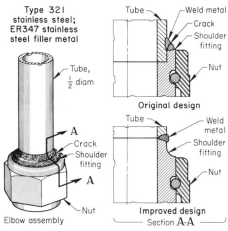

Fig. 23. Welded stainless steel elbow assembly that, as originally designed, cracked at the root of the weld under cyclic loading. The improved design moved the weld out of the high-stress area. (Example 6)

into a counterbore in the shoulder fitting, as shown in the "Original design" view in section A-A in Fig. 23, then welded by the gas tungsten-arc process.

The fitting was separated from the tubing so that the surfaces of the cracked area could be examined. Stains on the fracture surface indicated that fatigue cracks had initiated at the root of the weld, at a notch inherent in the design of the joint. Cracking in the weld metal had progressed partway around the joint, thus producing a leakage path through which pressurized hydraulic fluid had escaped.

Conclusion. Failure was by fatigue cracking initiated at a notch at the root of the

weld, and was propagated by cyclic loading of the tubing as the result of vibration and inadequate support of the hose assembly.

Corrective Measures. The joint design was changed from a cylindrical lap joint (tube inserted into a counterbore) to a square-groove butt joint, as shown in the "Improved design" view in section A-A in Fig. 23. The new joint design provided a more flexible joint by eliminating the notch and by moving the weld out of the high-stress area.

An additional support was provided for the hose assembly to minimize vibration at the elbow.

In the following example a steel liner for a bellows-type expansion joint had three design features that could promote fatigue failure: (a) the liner was made of thin material and cantilevered in a dynamic system subject to vibration; (b) the circumferential weld joining the liner to the expansion joint was at the point of maximum stress; and (c) the weldment was of dissimilar metals, thus presenting a problem in selection of a filler metal and welding procedure that would reduce dilution of the weld metal and base metal.

Example 7. Fatigue Fracture of Welded Type 321 Stainless Steel Liners for a Bellows-Type Expansion Joint Because of Faulty Design (Fig. 24)

The liners for bellows-type expansion joints in a duct assembly (Fig. 24a) failed in service. The duct assembly, used in a low-pressure nitrogen-gas system, consisted of two expansion joints (bellows) connected by a 12¾-in.-OD pipe, of ASTM A106, grade B, steel. Elbows, of ASTM A234, grade B,

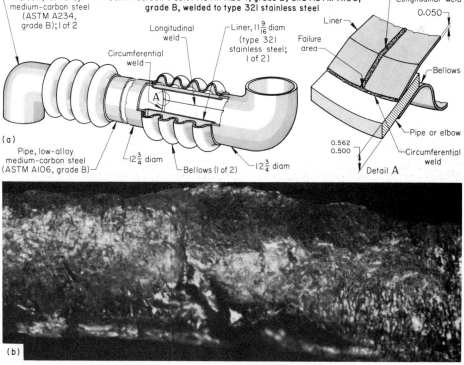

Fig. 24. (a) Duct assembly of medium-carbon steels in which welded bellows liners of type 321 stainless steel fractured in fatigue. (b) Light fractograph at 30×, showing fracture origin, at top edge, and fatigue striations, at bottom right. (Example 7)

steel, 180° to each other, were attached to each end of the assembly. A liner with an outside diameter of 11⁹⁄₁₆ in. was welded inside each expansion joint. The liners were 0.050 in. thick and made of type 321 stainless steel. The upstream end of one liner was welded to an elbow, and the upstream end of the other liner was welded to the pipe; this allowed the downstream ends of the liners to remain free and permitted the components to move with expansion and contraction of the bellows.

Investigation. In field inspection, portions of the two failed liners were found downstream in the duct assembly. These were removed and sent to the laboratory for failure analysis. Many of the fracture surfaces had undergone extreme deformation, making the exact fracture interpretation extremely difficult. However, portions of the fracture surfaces were undamaged and the origin of failure and characteristic fracture pattern could be seen.

Laboratory inspection showed that the origin of failure in the portion of the fracture surface studied was in an area where two welds intersected — the longitudinal or seam weld forming the liner and the circumferential weld attaching the liner to the pipe or elbow. A fractograph of the fracture surface at the weld intersection indicating the fracture origin and fatigue striations is shown in Fig. 24(b).

Metallographic examination of a cross section containing the longitudinal weld revealed that the microstructure of the weld area contained no irregularities. Metallurgical evaluation of the cross section in the transverse plane of the fractured piece containing the intersection of the longitudinal and circumferential welds exhibited extreme banding within the microstructure. The banding was the result of chromium and nickel dilution in one area and the enrichment of the same elements in areas adjacent to that area. In addition, the intersection of the two welds contained cracks similar in appearance to those normally formed when variations in thermal expansion and contraction are encountered when welding dissimilar metals.

A microhardness traverse across the weld area revealed a base-metal average hardness of Rockwell B 89. The hardness of the heat-affected zone on both sides of the weld was Rockwell B 87, and the weld metal had a hardness of Rockwell B 93 to 98.5.

Conclusions. The liners failed in fatigue that was initiated at the intersection of the longitudinal weld forming the liner and the circumferential weld that joined the liner to the bellows assembly.

Because the liners were welded at one end and the other end was free, the components moved with expansion and contraction of the joints, and were subjected to vibrational stresses imposed by the transfer of nitrogen gas. The stresses, created by cyclic loading, were concentrated mainly at the metallurgical notches formed at the interface of the weld metal and base metal. Differences in composition caused a variation in strength at the critical region of high residual stresses. Vibrational stresses were concentrated at the circumferential interface between weld metal and base metal, and at the intersection of the circumferential and longitudinal welds. The origin of the failure

was at the intersection of the two welds — the region containing the most severe stress raisers.

The design allowed the two liners to be cantilevered in a dynamic system subjected to both thermal stresses and vibrations from gaseous flow.

Corrective Measure. The thickness of the liners was increased from 0.050 in. to 0.075 in., which successfully damped some of the stress-producing vibrations.

Effect of Material Conditions on Fatigue Strength

In fatigue fracture, localized plastic deformation is responsible for crack propagation. The microstructure of the material can influence this crack growth by inhibiting or modifying the plastic-deformation process. Sometimes, the nature of the cracking process is changed from ductile to brittle. Transition of the cracking process from one involving plastic deformation to another involving cleavage is largely determined by the microstructure of the material.

Grain Size

Under high cyclic strain (low-cycle fatigue), the fatigue life of many metals is independent of grain size. In contrast, under low cyclic strain (high-cycle fatigue), the fatigue life of many metals is increased when grain size is reduced. However, the effect of grain size on high-cycle-fatigue properties is difficult to assess, because these properties may be altered by the same treatments that alter grain size.

In some alloys, an improvement in resistance to high-cycle fatigue brought about by a decrease in grain size may be partly offset by a deleterious effect on another property. For example, a decrease in grain size is thought to raise the smooth-bar fatigue limit in some steels; however, small grain size increases notch sensitivity in these steels, and thus the net result may constitute no improvement in resistance to notched-bar fatigue. As another example, fine grain size in high-temperature alloys (which may be subjected to both fatigue and creep) may result in high fatigue life but low stress-rupture life at normal service temperatures, and thus an intermediate grain size may afford the longest service life.

Alloying

The influence of chemical composition on fatigue strength is approximately proportional to its influence on tensile strength. The fatigue limit of plain carbon steel increases with carbon content. Molybdenum, chromium and nickel have a similar effect.

The fatigue limit of high-strength steel with tensile strength in the range of 200,000 psi can be increased by the addition of copper. Although the phosphorus content of steel is generally kept at a

minimum to prevent brittleness, steels with high phosphorus contents have greater fatigue strength. A sulfur content of 0.01% has no effect on fatigue limit. Austenitic steels containing nickel and chromium have a high fatigue limit, together with low notch sensitivity and high resistance to corrosion fatigue.

The fatigue strengths of titanium alloys are higher than those of steel. Some titanium alloys maintain considerable strength up to 500 C (932 F) and have high resistance to corrosion fatigue. Even though titanium alloys are particularly susceptible to hydrogen embrittlement, the presence of hydrogen does not affect fatigue properties.

Solid-Solution Strengthening. Aluminum alloys that are solid-solution strengthened show an increase in fatigue strength to about the same degree as the corresponding increase in tensile strength.

If the strength of magnesium alloys is increased by solute addition, the fatigue strength is also increased in proportion to the increase in tensile strength.

Second phases that often are present in metallurgical systems affect crack propagation on the basis of three factors: (a) the lattice strain caused by the presence of the second phase; (b) the stress concentration determined by size, shape and distribution of the second phase; and (c) the nature of the bond between the second phase and the matrix.

Second phases have a marked influence on the mechanism and kinetics of crack nucleation and propagation because they can accelerate or inhibit crack-propagation rate under various circumstances. For example, investigations on aluminum alloys containing a large number of particles of precipitated, intermetallic second phase showed that the particles acted as stress raisers from which fatigue cracks nucleated.

The grain boundaries of age-hardened alloys generally are free of precipitate particles and, as a consequence, are relatively soft. Hence, stress relaxation takes place along the boundaries, resulting in localized stress concentration, and crack nucleation, at grain-boundary triple points.

The instability of coherent precipitate particles is considered to be the most important factor responsible for low fatigue life of high-strength aluminum alloys. Experimental results indicate that reversion takes place during the early stages of cyclic loading. Reversion under cyclic straining involves the passage of dislocations back-and-forth through the precipitate particles, which disintegrates the particles to subcritical size. The solute then goes back into solution or is distributed along the dislocation network, thereby softening the slip bands and bringing about crack nucleation.

Work Hardening

Work-hardened Cu-Al alloys (75 wt % Al) do not soften under cyclic stresses. This results in lower rates of crack propagation in work-hardened alloys, thereby indicating a small amount of deformation at the crack tip during fatigue. Experimental results on annealed and cold worked alpha brass suggest that a work-hardened alloy is harder at the crack tip than an annealed alloy.

In alloys that are not strengthened by heat treatment (some copper alloys, aluminum alloys, and stainless steels), fatigue strength can be increased by cold working. However, no improvement in fatigue strength is obtained by cold working of age-hardenable alloys. Alloys that are hardened by transformation processes (such as martensitic steels) exhibit a lesser degree of improvement by cold working than the nonhardenable alloys.

Heat Treatment

Fatigue strength generally is increased by any heat treatment that increases tensile strength. In steels, a tempered-martensite structure has the best fatigue properties. The lower fatigue resistance of mixed structures is generally the result of metallurgical notches such as are formed by coarse pearlite, free ferrite, retained austenite, and carbide segregation.

In copper alloys, particularly in copper-zinc and copper-tin alloys, the fatigue strength can be improved by solution heat treatment. The fatigue strength of age-hardenable aluminum alloys also can be raised by solution heat treatment; however, subsequent aging, which occurs at room temperature in some alloys, has no further beneficial effect and may even decrease fatigue strength.

Effect of Discontinuities on Fatigue Strength

Discontinuities within a metal, either at the surface or subsurface, can adversely affect fatigue strength. These discontinuities may arise from melting practices or primary or secondary working of the material, or may be a characteristic of a particular alloy system.

Surface Discontinuities

All wrought metal is subjected to thermal-mechanical processing that shapes the metal by plastic deformation, generally by rolling, hammering, squeezing or drawing. The movement of metal during these processes, whether performed at room temperature or at elevated temperatures, makes them common sources of surface discontinuities, such as laps, seams and cold shuts. Oxides, slivers or chips of the base material or foreign material can be embedded into the surface by rolling or forging.

These surface imperfections produce a notch of unknown severity that acts as a stress raiser under load and adversely affects fatigue strength and also may serve as a site for crack initiation during fabrication or in service.

Laps and seams are surface discontinuities that are caused by folding over of metal without fusion. They are usually filled with scale and, on steel components, are enclosed by a layer of decarburized metal.

In the next example, a forging defect extended to the surface of a connecting-rod cap. The surfaces of the defect were oxidized during heat treatment or by heating during forging, and thus did not weld (join) during forging.

Example 8. Fatigue Fracture of a 15B41 Steel Connecting-Rod Cap That Initiated at an Open Forging Defect (Fig. 25)

A connecting-rod cap (Fig. 25a) from a truck engine fractured after 40,500 miles of service. The cap was made from a 15B41 steel forging and hardened to Rockwell C 29 to 35. There were no known unusual operating conditions that would have caused fracture.

Investigation. In the laboratory, visual examination of the fracture surface disclosed an open forging defect across one of the outer corners of the cap. The defect extended approximately 3/8 in. along the top surface and 5/8 in. along the side of the cap. The fracture surface exhibited beach marks typical of fatigue, as shown in view A-A in Fig. 25. The surface of the defect was stained, indicating that oxidation occurred either in heat treatment or in heating during forging. Deep etching of the fracture surface revealed grain flow normal for this type of forging, but no visible defects.

Metallographic examination of a section through the fracture surface showed that the microstructure was an acceptable tempered martensite. However, oxide inclusions were present at the fracture surface (Fig. 25b).

Conclusion. Fatigue fracture initiated at a corner of the cap from a forging defect that extended to the surface. Fatigue cracking was propagated by cyclic loading inherent to the part.

Recommendation. Failure of the caps could have been minimized by more careful fluorescent magnetic-particle inspection of the forged surfaces before machining and before putting the part into service:

Burning is the result of heating a metal to a temperature so close to its melting point as to cause permanent damage to the metal by intergranular oxidation or incipient melting. Burned steel usually contains both oxide films and voids or cracks at grain boundaries that act as nuclei for fatigue cracking. Burning most often occurs in forging, either during preheating or during the forging operation itself. The fatigue fracture of the forged steel rocker arm shown in Fig. 26 was initiated at a coarse, intergranular area of burned metal (indicated by arrows) incurred during forging.

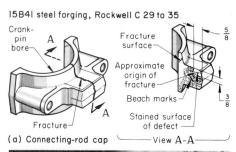

15B41 steel forging, Rockwell C 29 to 35

(a) Connecting-rod cap — View A-A

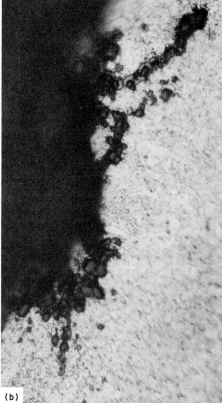

(b)

Fig. 25. (a) Forged 15B41 steel connecting-rod cap that fractured from fatigue; cracking originated at an open forging defect. (b) Micrograph at 400× of a section through the fracture surface, showing oxide inclusions. (Example 8)

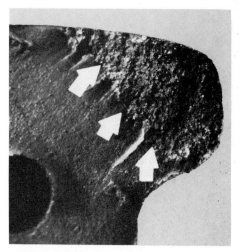

Fig. 26. Fracture surface of a forged steel rocker arm showing fatigue (at arrows) nucleating from a coarse, intergranular surface typical of burning

Subsurface Discontinuities

Subsurface and core discontinuities originate in the as-cast ingot. Voids in cast materials from gas porosity, shrinkage porosity, and improper metal fill are common. In ingots that are subsequently hot and cold reduced, the portion dominated by voids is removed and discarded. The remaining internal voids normally weld shut from the temperature and pressure used to reduce the ingot, which results in a continuous, homogeneous product. When the surfaces of the voids are oxidized or otherwise contaminated, the opposing surfaces do not weld together and the defect is retained in the wrought product.

Gas Porosity or Shrinkage Porosity. Gas porosity or gas holes are rounded cavities (spherical, flattened, elongated or partially collapsed) that are caused by the generation or accumulation of gas bubbles in the molten metal as it solidifies. Shrinkage cavities result from varying rates of contraction while the metal is changing from the molten to the solid state. Shrinkage porosity is mainly characterized by jagged holes or spongy areas lined with dendrites. The fatigue strength of cast alloys is only slightly reduced by the presence of shrinkage or gas porosity, but is much reduced when the porosity extends to the surface, regardless of severity, because of the notch effect.

Inclusions. The presence of nonmetallic inclusions at or close to the surface is detrimental, because the inclusions act as stress raisers and form points for initiation of fatigue cracks. The larger the number of discontinuities, the greater the possibility of fatigue failure. However, there does seem to be a limit to the number of inclusions that could cause fatigue. If discontinuities like graphite flakes in cast iron or sulfide inclusions in free-cutting steels are very numerous, mutual stress relief occurs, on the principle of a single groove versus a continuous thread, and the material tends to become less prone to fatigue.

Inclusions in ferrous alloys are usually oxides, sulfides and silicates. Many inclusions, however, are of a more complex intermediate composition. Every commercial metal has its own characteristic inclusions. In cast metals, the shape of the inclusions is about the same in all polished sections; in wrought metals, the shape depends on the orientation of the polished surface. Deformation in mechanical working causes inclusions to plastically deform to elongated shapes and to appear in longitudinal sections as stringers or streaks, although in transverse section the shape is globular or flat. Hard, refractory and very small inclusions, like alumina inclusions in steel, are not deformed by mechanical work.

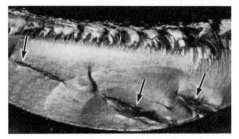

Fig. 27. Fracture surface of a hardened steel connecting rod, showing large inclusions (at arrows) from which fatigue cracking initiated

Fig. 28. Fracture surface of a hardened steel valve spring that failed in torsional fatigue. Arrow shows fracture origin, at a subsurface nonmetallic inclusion.

Fig. 29. Fracture surface of a carburized and hardened steel roller. As a result of banded alloy segregation, circumferential fatigue fracture initiated at a subsurface origin near the case-core interface, indicated by the arrow.

Fatigue properties of high-strength alloys are degraded by inclusions, with a more marked effect being apparent on the transverse fatigue properties of wrought alloys than on the longitudinal properties. In general, however, the effect of inclusions depends on the size and shape of the inclusions, on their resistance to deformation and their orientation relative to the stress, and on the tensile strength of the alloy. Soft steels, for instance, are much less affected by inclusions than are hard steels.

The fracture surface of a hardened steel connecting rod is shown in Fig. 27; large inclusions that intersect the surface are indicated by arrows. Loads on this rod were transverse to the forging grain flow. Inclusions, like most discontinuities, are most damaging when they intersect the surface; however, subsurface inclusions also can be responsible for premature fatigue failure, when the stress level at the inclusions is high enough to initiate a crack. Figure 28 shows the surface of a torsional-fatigue fracture that initiated at a large, subsurface nonmetallic inclusion in a hardened steel valve spring. Fatigue fracture originating at large, coarse, subsurface sulfide inclusions in a 1040 steel crankshaft is described in Example 13 on page 392 in the article on Failures of Shafts.

Internal bursts in rolled and forged metals result from the use of equipment that has insufficient capacity to work the metal throughout its cross section. If the working force is not sufficient, the outer layers of the metal will be deformed more than the inside metal, sometimes causing wholly internal, intergranular fissures that can act as stress concentrators, from which fatigue cracking may propagate under tensile, bending or torsional loading.

Alloy Segregation

Distribution of alloying elements in industrial alloys is not always uniform. Localized deviations from the average composition originate from specific conditions during solidification of the alloys. Hot working and soaking tend to equalize the compositional differences, but sometimes these differences persist into the wrought product. Inhomogeneous distribution of alloying elements in heat treated alloys is particularly objectionable, because it may lead to the formation of thermal cracks caused by uneven contraction or expansion in heating and cooling.

Banding. When segregation in an alloy occurs in layers or bands, the alloy is said to have a banded structure. Banding can lead to discontinuities that in turn can cause premature fatigue failure. Figure 29 shows the fatigue fracture of a carburized and hardened steel roller. Banded alloy segregation in the metal used for the rollers resulted in heavy, banded retained austenite, particularly in the carburized case, after heat treatment. When the roller was subjected to service loads, the delayed transformation of the retained austenite to martensite caused microcracks near the interface of the case and core. These internal microcracks nucleated a fatigue fracture that progressed around the circumference of the roller, following the interface between case and core.

Flakes are internal fissures in ferrous metals, attributed to stresses produced by localized transformation and decreased solubility of hydrogen during cooling after hot working.

For alloy steels, flakes often are associated with (a) high hydrogen content in the steel; (b) chemical-element segregation, producing regions of high alloy content; and (c) rapid cooling from the hot working temperature.

Effect of Heat Treatment on Fatigue Strength

Most metals and alloys utilized in highly stressed components undergo some form of heat treating to improve properties.

Heat treatment always involves controlled heating and cooling operations. Imperfections may arise during heat treatment as a result of improper temperatures or furnace atmospheres, improper or uneven rates of heat application or heat removal, and improper preparation of surfaces or shapes prior to heat treatment. The fatigue resistance of a component may be increased if the surface layer is made more fatigue resistant. This can be done by case carburizing, by nitriding or by carbonitriding, provided the treatment is carried out properly so as to avoid gross structural discontinuities such as carbide networks (carburizing), excessive white layer (nitriding), unsatisfactory carbon or nitrogen gradient (carbonitriding), or quenching cracks.

In the following example, failure to follow specified procedures for heat treating resulted in a brittle structure that fractured under torsional loading.

Example 9. Fatigue Fracture of an 8617 Steel Pilot-Valve Bushing Because of Improper Heat Treatment (Fig. 30)

The pilot-valve bushing shown in Fig. 30 fractured after only a few hours of service. In operation, the bushing was subjected to torsional stresses with possible slight bending stresses. A slight misalignment occurred in the assembly before fracture.

The bushing was made of 8617 steel and case hardened to a depth of 0.005 to 0.015 in. by carbonitriding. Specifications required that the part be carbonitrided, cooled, re-hardened by quenching from 790 C (about 1450 F), and then tempered at about 175 C (about 350 F). This heat treating procedure would produce a part having a tough, fine-grained structure.

Investigation. The mating pieces of the bushing showed that no gross deformation occurred during fracture. A small area on the fracture surface of the larger portion of the fractured bushing had been ground flat, etched and tested for hardness. A spot of red rust on the fracture surface adjacent to the cross hole near the cracks appeared to be the result of the etching. Except for the rust in the etched area, no corrosion products were present, and general wear on the spline teeth was negligible.

Only one spline tooth showed any ductility associated with the fracture. This tooth was apparently in the area of final fracture. Metallographic examination of the fracture surface revealed a smooth pattern and beach marks that indicated propagation of the

crack in fatigue. Several cracks started at the hole in the spline, as shown in Fig. 30, but it was impossible to determine which crack started first.

Microstructural examination revealed an unsatisfactory carbonitrided case structure resulting from improper heat teatment, and many fine nonmetallic stringer inclusions in the core material.

Conclusions. The bushing fractured in fatigue because of a highly stressed case-hardened surface of unsatisfactory microstructure and subsurface nonmetallic inclusions. Cracks were initiated at the highly stressed surface and propagated across the section as a result of cyclic loading. The precise cause of the unsatisfactory microstructure of the carbonitrided case could not be determined, but it was apparent that heat treating specifications had not been closely followed.

Recommendations. It was recommended that inspection procedures be modified to avoid the use of steel containing nonmetallic stringer inclusions and that specifications for carbonitriding, hardening and tempering be rigorously observed.

Overheating. In the heat treatment of metals, high temperatures generally cause large grains to develop; depending on the metal and application, large grains may have undesirable attributes. In most metals, large grains will generally reduce fatigue strength. The properties of coarse-grained metals are impaired by the size of the grains and also by changes that occur at the grain boundaries, such as the precipitation of solid impurities, which may form weak, continuous grain-boundary films. Damage from overheating is especially evident in high-carbon steels, in which all the harmful effects of coarse grains on properties are combined with an increased probability of cracking during quenching from the hardening temperature.

Eutectic Melting. In aluminum and other age-hardenable alloys, solution

heat treatment improves mechanical properties by developing the maximum practical concentration of the hardening constituents in solid solution. The solubilities of these constituents increase markedly with temperature, especially just below the eutectic melting temperature. Consequently, the most favorable temperature for effecting maximum solution is very near that at which melting occurs. Melting in age-hardenable alloys produces an intergranular network of nonductile eutectic product and intra-granular circular spots ("rosettes"), both of which reduce ductility and fatigue strength. Similar effects of melting have been observed in high-temperature alloys such as the Stellites, and in high speed tool steels.

Quench cracks are a frequent cause of failure in hardened steel parts. The origin of quench cracks in steel is attributed to sudden volume changes that occur in hardening. The transformation of austenite into martensite is always accompanied by expansion, which, under unfavorable conditions, may result in cracking. Conditions that promote the formation of quench cracks are a quenching medium that is too severe, sharp edges and rough finishes, and hardening temperatures that are too high. Sometimes the cracks do not appear immediately but are delayed and take time to become visible. Delayed quench cracks are the result of additional transformation of retained austenite in the steel. In highly alloyed steels, delayed cracking can be avoided by tempering immediately following quenching.

Quench cracks are always intergranular. If a quench crack is open to the surface during tempering, the walls of the crack may be covered with scale and also may be decarburized.

Decarburization is a loss of carbon from the surface of a ferrous alloy as a result of heating in a medium that reacts with carbon. Unless special precautions are taken, the risk of losing carbon from the surface of steel is always present in any heating to high temperatures in an oxidizing atmosphere. A marked reduction in fatigue strength is noted in steels with decarburized surfaces. The effect of decarburization is much greater on high-tensile-strength steels than on steels with low tensile strength.

Influence of Manufacturing Practices on Fatigue Strength

Manufacturing practices influence fatigue strength by (a) affecting the intrinsic fatigue strength of the material near the surface, (b) introducing or removing residual stresses in the surface layers, and (c) introducing or removing irregularities in the surface that act as stress raisers.

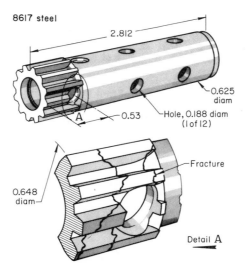

Fig. 30. Carbonitrided 8617 steel pilot-valve bushing that fractured in fatigue because of improper heat treatment (Example 9)

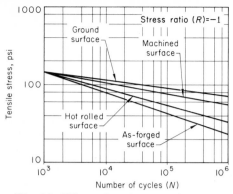

Fig. 31. Effect of surface roughness on the fatigue strength of a steel specimen with a tensile strength of 166,000 psi

Machining. Most components subjected to fatigue conditions have been machined. Heavy cuts and residual tool marks from rough machining can promote fatigue failure in a component.

Surface irregularities produced by rough machining act as stress raisers. However, a series of parallel grooves, such as results from turning operations, is less severe in its effect than an isolated groove, because parallel grooves provide mutual stress relief. Rough machining also damages the metal to an appreciable depth. A machining tool shears off metal, rather than cutting it, with the result that the surface is torn and also work hardened to an extent that depends largely on the depth of cut, the type and shape of the tool, and characteristics of the metal. Components intended to withstand fatigue conditions should be finished with a fine cut or preferably ground, and the direction of the final cut or grind should be parallel to that of the principal tensile load whenever practical.

The effect of surface roughness on fatigue strength is shown in Fig. 31. Several surface finishes are compared, such as a smooth ground surface, a rougher machined surface, and as-forged and hot rolled surfaces resulting from hot working.

Most mechanically finished metal parts have a shallow surface layer in residual compression. Apart from the effect it has on surface roughness, the final finishing process will be beneficial to fatigue life when it increases the depth and intensity of the compressively stressed layer and detrimental when it decreases or removes the layer. Processes such as electrolytic polishing and chemical and electrochemical machining, which remove metal without plastic deformation, may reduce fatigue properties. Electrical discharge machining can be detrimental to fatigue properties without proper control and subsequent processing because of surface and subsurface microstructural changes. Improperly controlled grinding can have similar effects on fatigue properties.

Occasionally, during machining of a component, a tool may scratch or groove the surface. If the part is highly stressed in service, the result can be a premature fatigue fracture nucleating at the tool mark.

Tool marks on springs that were the initiation points for fatigue fractures are discussed in Examples 5 and 6, on pages 490 and 491 in the article on Failures of Springs.

Stress raisers frequently occur at a change in section, such as the shoulder between two shaft sections of different diameters. Rough-machining marks, and steps resulting from improper blending of fillets with shaft surfaces, frequently serve as initiation sites for fatigue cracks. A shaft failure resulting from the presence of machining marks at a fillet between two diameters is described in Example 14 on page 467 in the article on Failures of Lifting Equipment.

Small fillet radii and rough-machining marks at the root of the splines on the shaft described in the following example acted as stress concentrators and contributed to fatigue fracture of the shaft.

Example 10. Fatigue Fracture of a 1040 Steel Splined Shaft Because of Machining Marks and Sharp Fillets (Fig. 32)

The splined shaft shown in Fig. 32 was from a front-end loader used in a salt-handling area. The shaft broke after having been in service approximately two weeks while operating at temperatures near zero degrees Fahrenheit. During summer months, similar shafts had a service life of five to eight months.

The shaft was made of 1040 steel, and heat treated to a hardness of Rockwell C 44 to 46 and a tensile strength of approximately 210,000 psi.

Investigation. Visual examination of the splines disclosed heavy chatter marks at

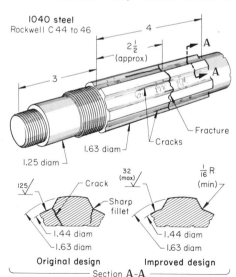

Fig. 32. Drive shaft that fractured from fatigue in the spline area because of sharp fillets and machining marks at spline roots (Example 10)

the root of the spline, with burrs and tears at the fillet area. Surface finish at the root of the splines was 125 micro-in.

Examination of the fracture surface showed that fatigue cracks propagated through about 75% of the shaft before final fracture occurred in a brittle manner. There were indications that fatigue cracks initiated in sharp fillets at the root of the splines.

Conclusions. The shaft failed in fatigue as the result of stress concentrations in the sharp fillets and rough surfaces at the root of the splines.

Failure occurred sooner in cold weather than in hot weather because the ductile-to-brittle transition temperature of the 1040 steel shaft was too high.

Corrective Measures. Premature cold-weather failures of these shafts were prevented by the following changes in design and material:

1 The fillet radius was increased to 1/16 in. (min), and the surface finish in the spline area was changed to 32 micro-in. (max).
2 The material for the shafts was changed to a low-nickel alloy steel with a nominal composition of 0.42% C, 0.78% Mn, 0.025% max P, 0.025% max S, 0.26% Si, 0.87% Cr, 2.08% Ni, 0.28% Mo and 0.25% V. The ductile-to-brittle transition temperature of this steel was approximately −73 C (−100 F).
3 The new shafts were heat treated to a hardness of Rockwell C 28 to 32 before machining, and used in the as-machined condition.

Drilling. The fatigue strength of components can be reduced merely by the presence of a drilled hole; it is further reduced by failure to remove burrs, incurred during drilling, from the hole edges. Fractures originating at drilled holes are common in complex parts containing internal, intersecting machined passages because of the difficulty and expense of providing adequate break-edge radii at such locations. A fatigue fracture originating at the sharp edges at the intersection of a surface groove and a cross hole in a hardened steel pin is described in Example 15 on page 467 in the article on Failures of Lifting Equipment.

Grinding. Proper grinding practice produces a smooth surface that is essentially free of induced residual stresses or sites for the nucleation of fatigue cracks. However, abusive grinding — particularly in steels heat treated to high hardness — is a common cause of reduced fatigue strength and failure, resulting from severe induced tensile stresses or intense localized heating, or both. Intense localized heating results in overtempering, formation of untempered martensite, burning, or formation of tight, shallow surface cracks usually referred to as grinding cracks.

Straightening. Components may be unintentionally plastically deformed during manufacture, during shipping or in service without cracking. These parts can be straightened manually, by heating, in presses or in roll straighteners. The initial deformation and subsequent work-

(a) Fracture surface showing brittle appearance, and final-fracture areas (at A's) at leading and trailing edges. (b) Crack-initiation region, at 12.5×, showing brittle appearance of fracture surface. (c) Electron fractograph, at 2300×, showing crack-progression bands in the fatigue zone.

Fig. 33. Aluminum alloy propeller blade that fractured in fatigue after being deformed in service and then cold straightened (Example 11)

ing operations can introduce residual stresses or stress raisers. Nicks, scratches or locally work-hardened surfaces are potential stress raisers.

Aircraft propeller blades frequently are damaged by deformation in minor ground accidents and repaired by cold straightening, either manually or in a press. The straightening operations are restricted to bends of less than a specified angle, varying with the location along the blade. Fracture of a propeller blade that had been cold straightened is described in the next example.

Example 11. Fatigue Fracture of a Cold-Straightened Aluminum Alloy Propeller Blade (Fig. 33)

An aluminum alloy propeller blade that had been cold straightened to correct deformation incurred in service fractured soon after being returned to service. A fracture surface of the blade is shown in Fig. 33(a).

Investigation. Examination of the fracture surface revealed that crack initiation occurred at the camber surface (top surface in Fig. 33a) in an area containing numerous surface pits. The macroscopic appearance of the surface was of brittle fracture (see Fig. 33b); however, crack-progression bands and fine, poorly resolved fatigue striations were visible in replica electron micrographs, as shown in Fig. 33(c). A small amount of ductile-overload fracture was found at the leading and trailing edges of the blade (at A's in Fig. 33a), suggesting that low stress levels were involved in high-cycle fatigue-crack propagation. No evi-

dence was found of a prior crack resulting from the initial deformation or the straightening operation.

A stress analysis using an x-ray method did not detect any residual stress in the camber surface of the propeller blade adjacent to the fracture. However, a spanwise tensile stress of approximately 7400 psi was indicated in the same surface of the unfailed mating blade at the location of the initial bend.

Conclusions. The residual stress may have originated with the straightening operation, and the apparent absence of stress in the fractured blade was the result of relaxation through fracture. Because no prior crack damage could be attributed to the initial deformation or to straightening, the rapid fracture may have been induced by residual stresses contributing to the normal spectrum of cyclic stresses. Also, the presence of surface pits acting as stress raisers would compound this problem. The origin of the pits was not known.

Corrective Measures. Stress-relief annealing after cold straightening, plus refinishing of the surface, reduced fracturing of propeller blades that were cold-straightened to correct deformation experienced in service.

Surface Compression. The beneficial effects of compressive residual stresses can be obtained by coining (such as around holes), surface rolling or shot peening. These processes often produce visible marks on the surface, such as burnished areas and peening dimples. The presence or absence of such marks is not a conclusive indication of the magnitude of stresses produced by these processes.

Residual stresses can be evaluated using x-ray diffraction techniques. However, because the stresses will be dissipated in the immediate vicinity of the fracture, stresses should be checked at a location somewhat removed from the fracture.

Fractures can result if a critical area is improperly worked. In the following example, shot peening was used before nickel sulfamate plating to minimize the effect of plating on the fatigue strength of the part. Incomplete shot peening of a fillet resulted in initiation of a fatigue crack.

Example 12. Fatigue Fracture of a Spindle for a Helicopter Blade Because of Incomplete Shot Peening Prior to Plating (Fig. 34)

The spindle of a helicopter-rotor blade (Fig. 34a) fractured after 7383 hr of flight service, causing the aircraft to crash. These spindles were overhauled and inspected at intervals of 1200 hr or less. Between the sixth overhaul and the failure, 464 flight hours had been accumulated.

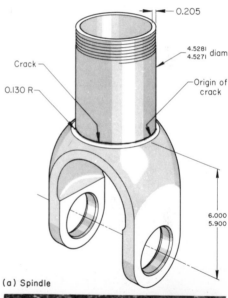

(a) Spindle

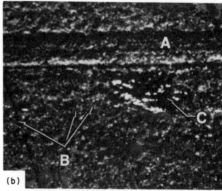

(b)

(a) Spindle, showing fracture region (at fillet between shank and fork). (b) Longitudinal score mark (A) and circumferential scratches (B) on shank that had been peened over. A galled area (C) is also visible.

Fig. 34. Helicopter-blade spindle that fractured in fatigue because it was incompletely shot peened before being plated (Example 12)

At every overhaul, the spindles were fluorescent-magnetic-particle inspected, and the surface was carefully examined for evidence of wear. If a spindle showed wear, it was reworked by grinding the shank to 0.004 in. under the finished diameter. The spindle was then shot peened with S170 shot to an Almen intensity of 0.010 to 0.012 A. Following shot peening, the shank was nickel sulfamate plated to 0.002 in. over the finished diameter, ground to finished size, and cadmium plated.

The spindle that failed had been overhauled six times and reworked twice.

Investigation. After the crash, four of the five rotor blades were found in the main impact area. The fifth blade was about $\frac{1}{4}$ mile away. The broken spindle was with this blade. The spindle had broken in the shank adjacent to the shoulder at the inboard end of the shank. Visual examination of the fracture surface revealed that a fatigue crack had propagated through approximately 72% of the shank cross section before final fracture.

Examination with a stereomicroscope showed the fatigue origin to be near the line where the cylindrical shank met the 0.130-in.-radius fillet at the junction of the shank and fork of the spindle. Hardness of metal near the crack origin was, in some spots, as low as Rockwell C 28. The specified hardness was Rockwell C 34 to 38. A banded microstructure was found near the low-hardness areas; it had interfered with the desired response to heat treatment.

On the surface near the fillet at the junction of the shank and fork, faint grinding marks and circumferential grooves could be seen. These marks and grooves would have been peened over and covered with peening dimples if peening had been done properly. Unlike the fillet area, the cylindrical portion of the shank exhibited the typical dimpled surface of peened parts (see Fig. 34b).

Life tests conducted after the accident with 30 spindles, new and used, peened and unpeened, showed that two spindles that had not been shot peened broke after 10% and 20% of the mean life of peened spindles.

Conclusions. The spindle failed in fatigue that originated near the junction of the shank and fork. The nonuniformity of the shot peened effect on the shank and fillet portions of the spindle resulted from a minimum of attention being afforded the fillet during peening. The fracture was of the low-stress high-cycle type, initiated by stresses well below the gross yield strength and propagated by thousands of load cycles.

Plating on metal surfaces can be detrimental to fatigue strength of the plated parts. Carbon and low-alloy steels, particularly steels of high hardness, are susceptible to hydrogen damage due to absorption of hydrogen during the plating cycle and the associated acid or alkaline cleaning cycles. A soft plating material, such as cadmium, may inhibit the escape of hydrogen from the steel and lead to hydrogen damage. However, the harmful effects of cadmium plating can be significantly minimized by following recommended procedures, which include plating at high current densities (6 to 8 amp per square decimeter) followed by baking at about 190 C (375 F) for 8 to 24 hr. A daily procedure for ensuring that the plating bath will give low hydrogen pickup is highly desirable. Apparatus for such a procedure is available in the form of the Lawrence Hydrogen Detection Gauge, an electronic-electrochemical instrument that measures the relative amount of hydrogen generated during electroplating.

Hard plating materials, such as chromium, usually are in a state of tensile stress after they have been deposited on the base metal. Cracks develop in the plating material, act as stress raisers and produce cracking in the base metal. Crack growth in the base metal can be prevented by introducing a compressive residual stress such as that produced by shot peening. Government specifications QQ-C-320 and MIL-G-26074A specify shot peening the part surface before plating with chromium or electroless nickel for all steel parts designed for long life under fatigue loading. Other recommended procedures for chromium plating of steel are given in ASTM B177. Several effective procedures for decreasing the residual tensile stress imposed by electroless nickel plating also have been developed, including the addition of saccharin and other organic compounds containing sulfur to the plating bath (see "Electroless Nickel Plating – A Review", *Metal Finishing*, Jan 1975, pages 38-44).

Cleaning is sometimes necessary for the removal of oil, grease or other contaminants from the surface of a workpiece. For production work, vapor degreasing or a dip into a solvent or a simple chemical cleaning solution may be employed. Many alkaline solutions that will remove grease and oil from aluminum are not satisfactory for most

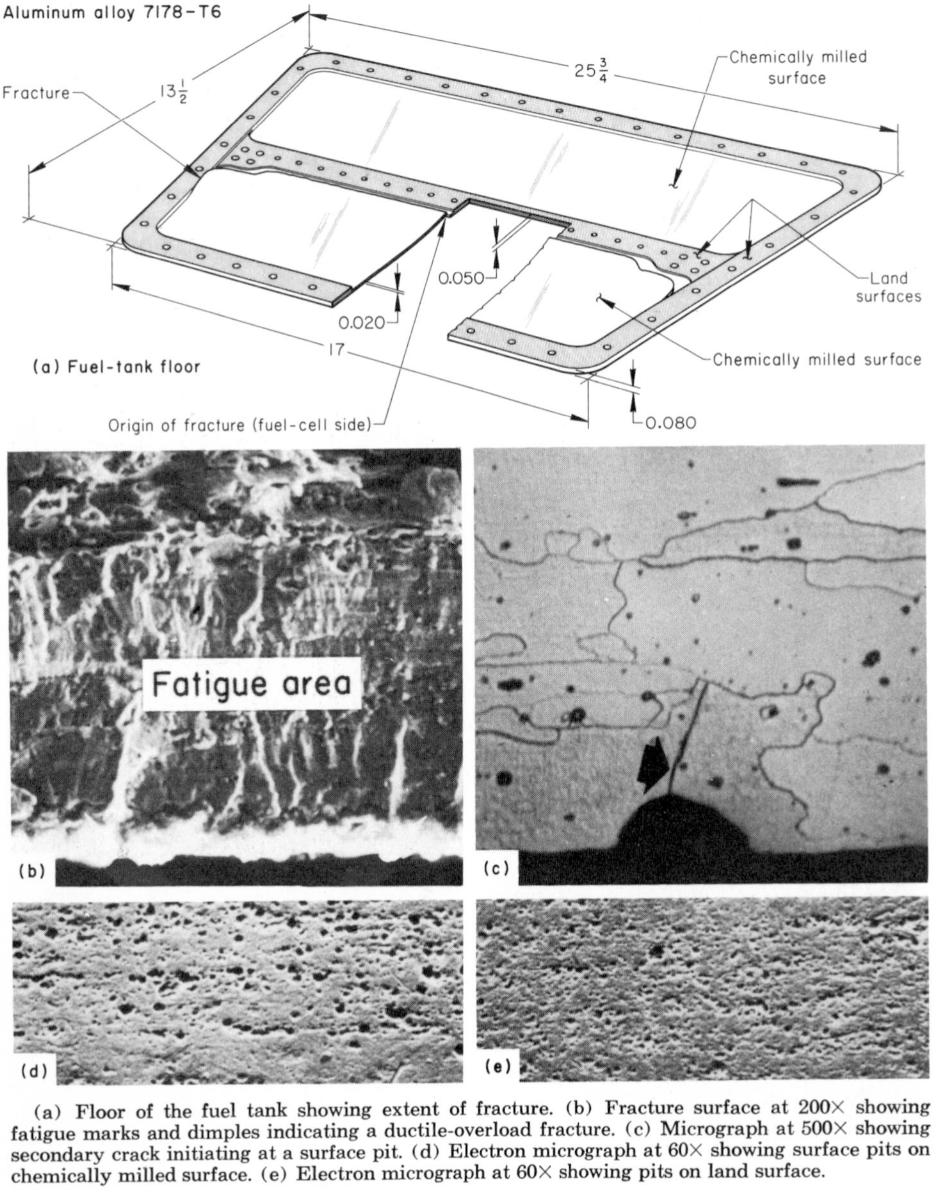

(a) Floor of the fuel tank showing extent of fracture. (b) Fracture surface at 200× showing fatigue marks and dimples indicating a ductile-overload fracture. (c) Micrograph at 500× showing secondary crack initiating at a surface pit. (d) Electron micrograph at 60× showing surface pits on chemically milled surface. (e) Electron micrograph at 60× showing pits on land surface.

Fig. 35. Aluminum alloy 7178-T6 floor of an aircraft fuel tank that failed by fatigue because of alkaline cleaning of the metal prior to painting (Example 13)

cleaning purposes, because they attack the surface. However, alkaline solutions that are suitably inhibited to eliminate the corrosive action can be used successfully. The cleaning treatment should be followed by a thorough rinsing in clean water and then drying.

In the following example, an aluminum alloy aircraft fuel-tank floor was pitted by an alkaline solution used to clean the floor before chemical milling and before painting after chemical milling. The pits acted as stress raisers from which fatigue cracks propagated.

Example 13. Fatigue Fracture of Aluminum Alloy 7178-T6 Aircraft Fuel-Tank Floors Because of Attack by an Alkaline Cleaner (Fig. 35)

The floors of the fuel tanks in two aircraft failed almost identically after 1076 and 1323 hr of service, respectively. The floors had been fabricated from aluminum alloy 7178-T6 sheet, with portions of the sheet chemically milled to reduce thickness as a saving in weight. Failure in both tanks occurred in the rear chemically milled section of the floor (see Fig. 35a).

The reduced sections were about 0.020 in. thick and were blended into the surrounding lands with a radius of about 0.035 in.; land thickness at the central surface was about 0.050 in., and at the edge about 0.080 in.

An alkaline etch-type cleaner was used for cleaning the panels before chemical milling and also before painting.

Visual Inspection. The fractures began near the center of the floor close to the radius between the chemically milled bay and the central land surface. Figure 35(a) shows the extent of fracture in the fuel-tank floor. The fractures followed the radius in both directions across the floor and then propagated toward the rear along both sides.

Examination of the fracture surface at low-power magnification revealed small, bright beach marks in the central 8 in. of the fracture. The beach marks initiated on the inside (fuel-cell side, which was opposite the chemically milled surface) edges of the fractures, indicating that failure was caused by fatigue cracks propagating through the thickness of the floor. The fatigue characteristics of both fractures were restricted to the central 8-in. section, with the remaining portions of the fracture surfaces showing features that are characteristic of overload fractures. No physical damage to the floors that could have caused the failures was found in the vicinity of the fractures.

Metallurgical Investigation. Fractographs taken with a scanning electron microscope confirmed that the beach marks observed at low-power magnification contained the parallel striations characteristic of fatigue. Beyond the fatigue zones the surface had the dimpled features typical of ductile-overload failure (Fig. 35b).

The microstructure of the metal in the fracture region was normal for aluminum alloy 7178-T6. The fracture profile had no unusual features, but a number of pits were on the inside surface of the floor. (The chemically milled surface was the outer surface of the floor.) Examination at 500 diameters revealed that many of the pits con-

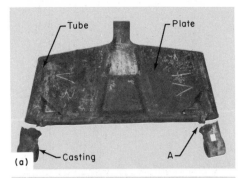

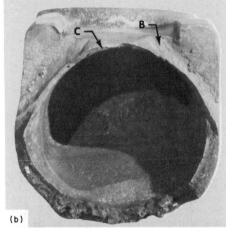

(a) Drawbar showing components, and fracture in the right cast connection at A; connection at left failed by brittle fracture. (b) Fracture surface of right cast connection, showing fatigue region at B and fracture origin in weld at C. (c) TEM fractograph at 20,000× showing fatigue striations at region B in fracture surface. (d) TEM fractograph at 6000× showing corrosion products (black dots) at region C.

Fig. 36. Highway tractor-trailer steel drawbar that fractured by fatigue at the cast connection at right because of a weld defect (Example 14)

tained secondary fatigue cracks, as shown in Fig. 35(c). The electron-microscope study also established that the cracks in the fatigue areas of the fracture surface initiated from corrosion pits. Secondary fatigue cracks originating in pits on the chemically milled surface, and parallel to the fracture surface, were also observed.

A section of each floor was stripped of all coatings to reveal the degree and severity of pitting on the chemically milled surfaces and on the land surfaces, which were not chemically milled. Light-microscope examination of the stripped sections revealed extensive pitting on both sides of the floors, including the chemically milled radii, which were mechanically machined after chemical milling. The pitted surface of a chemically milled area is shown in Fig. 35(d). The land surface, shown in Fig. 35(e), which had not been chemically milled, had more but slightly smaller pits.

Previous experience indicated that the alkaline etch-type cleaner used for cleaning the panels before chemical milling and before painting can cause pitting in aluminum alloys.

Chemical analyses, measurements of electrical conductivity, and hardness tests all indicated that the aluminum alloy used for the fuel-tank floors conformed to the specifications for 7178-T6.

Conclusions. The floors failed by fatigue cracking that initiated near the center of the fuel-tank floor and ultimately propagated as rapid ductile-overload fractures. The fatigue cracks originated in pits on the fuel-cell side (surface opposite the chemically milled areas) of the tank floors. Adjacent land surfaces were similarly pitted but, having appreciably thicker walls, were not subjected to so high a stress. The pits were attributed to attack caused by the alkaline-etch cleaning process used to prepare the surface for painting.

Corrective Measures. To avoid further fatigue failures from pitting, instructions were issued for critical monitoring of the alkaline-etch cleaning to avoid the formation of pits. Careful inspection following alkaline-etch cleaning was scheduled before release of the floor panels for painting.

Welding practices can have an effect on the fatigue strength of a metal at and below the surface. Surface defects resulting from poor welding practices provide stress raisers at which bending-fatigue and torsional-fatigue cracks can originate. Craters, underbead cracks, and arc strikes are typical surface defects. Subsurface defects, such as flux inclusions, incomplete fusion, and inadequate joint penetration, can originate cracking in parts loaded in tension, bending and torsion.

In the following example, a poor-quality weld on a drawbar for a highway truck-trailer was the origin of fatigue cracking.

Example 14. Fatigue Fracture of a Highway Tractor-Trailer Steel Drawbar That Initiated at a Weld Defect (Fig. 36)

A drawbar connecting the two tank-type trailers of a highway gasoline rig broke while the rig was on an exit ramp of an interstate highway causing the tractor, semitrailer and full trailer to overturn.

The driver's description of the way in which the rig behaved during the accident, together with physical evidence at the scene, suggested that the full trailer pulled to the right and overturned the rig.

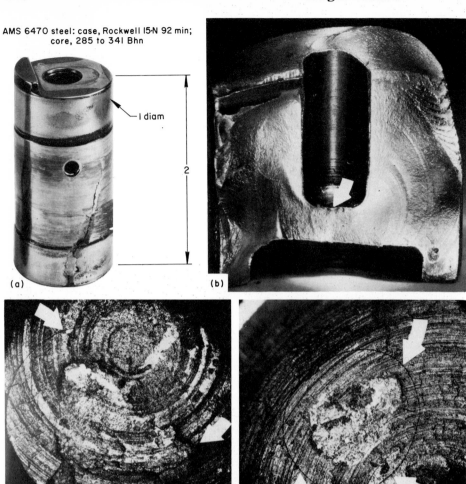

AMS 6470 steel: case, Rockwell I5-N 92 min;
core, 285 to 341 Bhn

(a) Knuckle pin, showing crack. (b) Fracture surface, at 2.8×, showing origin of fracture at arrow, and beach marks. (c) Macrograph at about 20× of bottom of oil hole in fractured pin, showing circular crack around the arc burn, indicated by arrow at top left and arrow at right.

Arrow at bottom left indicates fatigue fracture that nucleated from the circular crack. (d) Macrograph, at about 20×, of the bottom of an oil hole in an unused pin, showing circular crack (at arrows) around an arc burn that was made during magnetic-particle inspection.

Fig. 37. Knuckle pin, made of AMS 6470 nitriding steel, that failed in service by fatigue cracking that originated at an arc burn that had been made at the bottom of a longitudinal oil hole during magnetic-particle inspection (Example 15)

Magnetic-Particle Inspection. Localized regions of untempered martensite can be produced by arc burns that result when the probe used in magnetic-particle inspection touches the surface of the workpiece. Fatigue cracking of the pin described in the following example occurred in an area contacted by a conductor (probe) used during magnetic-particle inspection.

Example 15. Fatigue Fracture of AMS 6470 Steel Knuckle Pins Because of Arc Burn During Magnetic-Particle Inspection (Fig. 37)

Within about one month, several knuckle pins, similar to the one shown in Fig. 37(a), cracked in service. The pins, used in engines, failed over a range of 218 to 463 hr in operation.

Specifications for the pins required that they be made of AMS 6470 steel (a nitriding steel containing 1.6% Cr, 0.35% Mo, 1.15% Al, 0.38 to 0.43% C, rem Fe) and have a case hardness of Rockwell 15-N 92 min, a case depth of 0.017 to 0.022 in., and a core hardness of 285 to 341 Bhn.

Five knuckle pins, all from the same production lot and averaging 295 hr in service, were selected for failure analysis.

Investigation. Visual examination of the fracture surfaces revealed beach marks typical of fatigue cracks that had nucleated at the base of the longitudinal oil hole, as shown in Fig. 37(b). Examination showed that the fractures had been nucleated by circular cracks that apparently existed on the pins prior to their installation in the engine. Enlarged views of the bottom of the oil hole in a fractured pin and in an unused pin are shown in Fig. 37(c) and (d), respectively. The circular crack in the fractured pin (arrows at top left and center right in Fig. 37c) nucleated the fatigue fracture. A similar circular crack was found at the base of the oil hole in an unused pin, as indicated by the arrows in Fig. 37(d).

Micrographs of sections through the cracked areas of both unused and failed knuckle pins revealed a remelt zone and an area of untempered martensite within the region circumscribed by the cracks shown in Fig. 37(c) and (d). These findings indicated that a severe local application of heat, sufficient to cause partial melting of metal, had occurred. Such local areas of overheating, or burning, are attributable to electric-arc burning. The thermal stresses accompanying the burning caused the circular cracks that nucleated fracture.

A section was taken through the cracked areas in an unused pin for metallographic study. The cracks were about 0.017 in. deep, and the thermal transformation area was about 0.030 in. deep.

Tests showed that the failed knuckle pins were satisfactory with respect to case and core hardness, case depth, microstructure and inclusion content.

A check of the inspection procedures disclosed that the pins had been magnetic-particle inspected by inserting a probe into the longitudinal hole. Therefore, it was assumed that arc burning occurred during magnetic-particle inspection as a result of electric arcing between the probe and the

Investigation. The drawbar was a weldment of steel plates, tubes and castings. As shown in Fig. 36(a), the left and right cast connections to the full trailer broke in an area where welds joined the connections to the welded tube and plate.

The fracture surface on the right side of the drawbar (A in Fig. 36a) is shown in Fig. 36(b). The upper half of the fracture is through a weld, and the lower half is through the casting. No conclusive evidence of the fracture mechanism was discernible by light fractography. However, a TEM fractograph at 20,000 diameters (Fig. 36c) revealed fatigue striations in the region at arrow B in Fig. 36(b). Corrosion products on the fracture surface at the region at arrow C in Fig. 36(b), which are seen as black dots in Fig. 36(d), indicated that this area was most probably the site of fracture origin and that it had cracked before the accident happened.

The casting on the right side of the drawbar contained large voids and a significant amount of porosity, as shown in the lower portion of Fig. 36(b). Electron fractography established that the cast connection on the left side failed by brittle fracture.

Metallographic examination showed that both castings and the tubing had microstructures consisting of pearlite in a ferrite matrix. These microstructures were considered suitable for the application. However, weld quality was poor in the casting-to-tube joint, with evidence of incomplete fusion and inadequate penetration into the base metal.

Conclusions. The drawbar fractured in fatigue, which originated in the weld joining the cast connector to the right side of the drawbar assembly. The crack initiated in a region of poor weld quality. A contributing factor to fracture of both connectors was the presence of voids and porosity in the castings.

Corrective Measures. The welding procedures were revised, and receiving inspection of the connection castings was instituted.

knuckle-pin material. Cracking at the bottom of the oil hole by the central-conductor magnetic-particle inspection method was done in the laboratory, thus confirming that cracking can occur during magnetic-particle inspection of the pin.

Although arc burning does not always cause cracking, the thermal transformation of metal that accompanies arc burning can cause a severe metallurgical notch.

Conclusions. The knuckle pins failed by fatigue fracture nucleated from small circular cracks at the base of the longitudinal oil hole. The circular cracks were the result of arc burning, attributable to improper technique in magnetic-particle inspection.

Thermal transformation of the metal, which accompanies arc burning, causes a stress concentration that may lead to fatigue failure, even though cracking resulting from overheating or burning does not occur.

Recommendations. The conductor should be insulated to prevent arc burning at the base of the longitudinal oil hole. A boroscope or metal monitor may be used to inspect the hole for evidence of arc burning from magnetic-particle inspection.

In the following example, incomplete demagnetization of a coupling after magnetic-particle inspection caused metal chips to accumulate in gear teeth, resulting in fatigue fracture.

Example 16. Fatigue Fracture of a Cr-Mo Steel Integral Coupling and Gear Because of Steel Chips Trapped in Magnetized Gear Teeth (Fig. 38)

Figure 38 shows an integral coupling and gear, used on a turbine-driven main boiler-feed pump, that was removed from service after one year of operation because of excessive vibration.

Oil lines to the coupling were reportedly not operating shortly after the coupling was installed. Also, chips in the oil were reported on previous inspections of the coupling, but their nature was unknown.

Investigation. Visual examination revealed that the hub of the coupling was cracked and teeth on the coupling gear were severely damaged, and that a paste of gritty material was pressed into the gear teeth. Severe wear and broken teeth were also observed. A crack was found that apparently started in the keyway and continued circumferentially around the coupling (details A and B in Fig. 38).

Spectrographic analysis of the coupling material revealed it was made of a chromium-molybdenum steel, similar in analysis to 4130 steel. The gritty material in the gear teeth was found to be of the same composition as the metal in the coupling.

Surface hardness of the gear teeth was Rockwell C 56 to 58, and core hardness was Rockwell C 27 to 30; both hardness ranges were satisfactory for the work metal and the application. Metallographic examination revealed a desirable microstructure with no unusual features.

A section of the coupling containing gear teeth and part of the keyway was removed to permit examination of the fracture surface. Beach marks and evidence of cold work that are typical of fatigue failure were found on the surface.

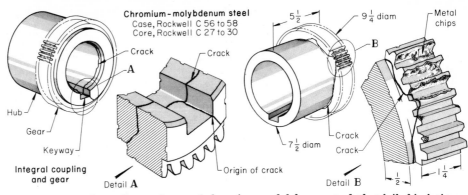

Fig. 38. Integral coupling and gear, of chromium-molybdenum steel, that failed in fatigue because part was magnetized and retained metal chips at tooth roots (Example 16)

When the cut was made on the coupling, chips remained in the cut and were difficult to remove, indicating a strong magnetic field in the part. A gauss-meter probe was inserted into the cut and a reading of 2000 gauss was obtained, which is a high residual flux density for steel (for comparison, magnetic steels have a flux density of about 9000 gauss). A field test around the boiler-feed pump indicated virtually no electrical forces that could induce magnetism in the gears. Therefore, the gear must have been magnetized before being put into service.

A logical source of magnetism in the gear teeth would be magnetic-particle inspection of the gear before it was put into service. Normally, workpieces are demagnetized after magnetic-particle inspection. However, in this instance, the coupling may have been only partly demagnetized or overlooked completely.

Conclusions. Failure of the coupling was by fatigue, as evidenced by the beach marks and signs of cold work. Incomplete demagnetization of the coupling following magnetic-particle inspection caused retention of metal chips in the roots of the teeth. These chips contributed to cyclic loading.

Improper lubrication caused gear teeth to overheat and spall, producing chips that eventually overstressed the gear, causing failure. Because the oil-circulation system was not operating properly, metal chips were not removed from the coupling.

Recommendations. To prevent damage to the replacement coupling, it should be checked for residual magnetism, and demagnetized if any is present. The lubricating oil should be changed or filtered to remove any debris from previous damage to the gears. The oil-circulation system should be put in operating condition.

Identification Marking. Excessive stresses may be introduced into components by identification marks (manufacturing date or lot number, steel heat number, size or part number). The location and method of making the marks can be important. They should not be in areas of high tensile, bending or torsional stresses.

Raised numerals or letters are preferable to those that are indented, and hot forging methods are recommended over cold forging, stamping or coining. For marks that are made on machined surfaces, the use of a marking ink is gen-

erally preferable to using an electric etching pencil or vibrating mechanical engraver, but either of the latter two is less abusive than using a cold steel stamp. However, using steel stamps for numbers in a nonstressed area may be preferable to some other type of identification mark in a more highly stressed region. Characters with straight-line portions have the greatest tendency to cause cracks, although characters with rounded contours also can cause cracking. If steel stamps must be used, low-stress stamps (stamps with the sharp edges removed from the characters) or dull stamps will cause the least trouble, particularly if light impressions are made. The stamping should be located in known low-stress areas — a practice that was not followed in the next example.

Example 17. Fatigue Fracture of Steel Wheels for a Coke-Oven Car That Was Initiated at Stamped Numerals (Fig. 39)

The double-flange trailer wheel shown in Fig. 39 had been in service on a coke-oven pusher car for about five years when it broke. Specifications called for rolled steel track wheels in conformity with ASTM A186 (since reclassified as A504), with no grade indicated.

Investigation. Chemical analysis showed the metal in the wheel to be medium-carbon steel within the ranges given in ASTM A186. Hardness of the tread was 302 Bhn, and of the web 255 Bhn.

Visual examination of the broken wheel revealed that cracking had extended circumferentially around the web before complete failure occurred (see Fig. 39a). The cracks ran parallel with the base of the lower row of numbers stamped with heavy indentation on the web section (see Fig. 39b). The ASTM specification states that the marks identifying the wheels must be stamped on the back face of the rim not less than 1/8 in. from the inner edge of the rim.

The fracture surface had an appearance typical of fatigue failure. However, the beach marks usually associated with this type of crack had been mostly removed by the constant rubbing of the fracture faces. The stamp marks from which the cracks initiated (indicated by arrows in Fig. 39c) were approximately 1/8 in. deep.

Microscopic examination showed the metal in the web, rim and tread to be in the

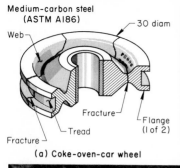

(a) Car wheel showing position of stamp marks and fractures in the rim and web. (b) Stamp marks showing heavy impression, and fracture extending along the base of the lower row of numbers. (c) Notches (at arrows) created from the heavily indented stamp marks, and from which cracks initiated, along the top at the fracture surface.

Fig. 39. Double-flange trailer wheel of ASTM A186 steel, for a coke-oven pusher car, that failed in fatigue cracking initiated at heavily indented and improperly placed stamp marks (Example 17)

normalized condition. Cleanness and soundness of the steel were satisfactory for the application.

Conclusions. Fatigue failure of the wheel was the result of heavy stamp marks that acted as stress raisers in the weaker web section. Because this was a double-flange wheel, considerable side thrust was applied to the wheel, causing stress concentration at the web.

Recommendation. The ASTM specification A504 regarding location of stamped identification numbers should be followed.

For additional discussions on the effect identification marks have on part failures, the reader is referred to Example 8 on page 73 in the article on Ductile and Brittle Fractures, and to page 387 in the article on Failures of Shafts.

Fatigue Failure at Elevated Temperatures

Failure by fatigue usually can occur at any temperature below the melting point of a metal and still maintain the characteristic features of fatigue fractures, usually with little deformation, over the whole temperature range. At high temperatures, however, both the fatigue strength and the static strength of metals generally decrease as the operational temperature increases. Typical *S-N* curves for reversed-bending-fatigue tests conducted on a structural metal alloy at various temperatures are shown in Fig. 40. The fatigue limit clearly is lower at the higher temperatures. Mechanical-property data on most alloys at high temperatures also show that, as at room temperature, the fatigue strength is closely

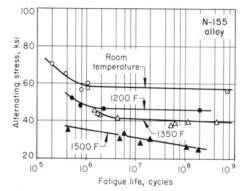

Fig. 40. Fatigue life of a specimen of N-155 alloy when subjected to various temperatures and reversed-bending stress

related to the tensile strength, unless the temperature is high enough for the fatigue strength to be affected by creep phenomena. Data from tests in which the load is completely reversed during each cycle usually can be interpreted as being uncomplicated by creep. Under actual service conditions, however, this is rarely the case.

At high temperatures, the application of a constant load to a metal component produces continuous deformation or creep, which will eventually lead to fracture if the load is maintained for a sufficient length of time. The stress-rupture strength is defined as the stress that a metal can withstand for a given time, at a given temperature, without breaking. With increases in temperature, stress-rupture strength decreases rapidly, to values that may be considerably lower than fatigue strength. Therefore, the primary requirement of a metal that is to be

subjected to high temperatures is that it have adequate stress-rupture strength. Many alloys that possess good creep resistance are also resistant to fatigue; however, the condition of an alloy that will provide maximum stress-rupture strength is not necessarily the condition that provides maximum fatigue strength. In practice, it is necessary to design against failure by fatigue and against excessive distortion or fracture by creep, just as it is necessary to take into account combined tensile and fatigue loads at room temperature.

At room temperature, and except at very high frequencies, the frequency at which cyclic loads are applied has little effect on the fatigue strength of most metals. This effect, however, becomes much greater as the temperature increases and creep becomes more of a factor. At high temperatures, the fatigue strength seems to depend on the total time the stress is applied rather than solely on the number of cycles. This behavior occurs because of continuous deformation under load at high temperatures. Under fluctuating stress, the cyclic frequency affects both the fatigue life and the amount of creep. This is shown in Fig. 41, a typical constant-life diagram, which illustrates the temperature behavior of S-816 alloy tested under a fluctuating axial load. At room temperature, the curves converge at the tensile strength, plotted along the mean-stress axis. At high temperature, the curves terminate at the stress-rupture strength — which, being a time-dependent property, results in termination at a series of end points along the mean-stress axis.

Fractures resulting from fluctuating stresses at high temperatures may be similar in appearance to fatigue fractures or stress-rupture fractures, or a mixture of the two, depending on the relative magnitudes of the mean and alternating stresses. Figure 42 shows a high-temperature fatigue fracture in a jet-engine turbine blade; alternating stresses were primarily responsible for this fracture, and static stresses played a minor role. A fatigue fracture through

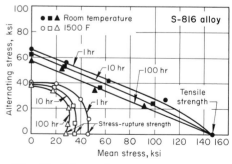

Fig. 41. Effect of temperature on the fatigue life of S-816 alloy tested under a fluctuating axial load at a frequency of 216,000 cycles per hour

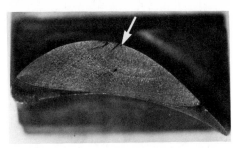

Fig. 42. Surface of a high-temperature fatigue fracture in a nickel alloy jet-engine turbine blade. Fatigue pattern nucleating on the convex side of the airfoil is indicated by the arrow.

Fig. 43. Fracture surface of a steel turbine disk for a jet engine that failed from fatigue. Fracture was nucleated by stress-rupture cracks in tenons, indicated by arrows. High mean stress was a major factor in this high-temperature failure.

the tenons of a turbine disk is shown in Fig. 43. In this fracture, mean stresses played a major role, with fatigue being nucleated by stress-rupture cracking. Generally, the amount of deformation in the region of high-temperature fatigue fractures decreases as the ratio of alternating stress to mean stress increases.

An important requirement for fatigue resistance at high temperatures is that the component have resistance to oxidation and other forms of high-temperature corrosion. Fatigue strength at high temperature can be seriously reduced by surface attack from fuel ash containing vanadium pentoxide, from leaded fuels, and from other contaminants. In general, however, materials are less notch sensitive at high temperatures than at room temperature.

Extended operation at high temperatures may result in metallurgical changes in the alloy structure, which may also play a role in reducing fatigue strength. Generally, however, short-duration exposure to high temperatures, which does not result in metallurgical changes such as recrystallization, tempering, phase changes, precipitation, melting or diffusion, will not have a serious effect on fatigue life upon return to normal operating temperatures.

The following example describes a fatigue failure in which several high-tem-

perature phenomena contributed to the sensitivity of a stainless steel gas-turbine inlet line to cracking under normal, fluctuating service stresses.

Example 18. Intergranular Fatigue Cracking of a Type 321 Stainless Steel Expansion Joint Because of Grain-Boundary Embrittlement (Fig. 44)

A type 321 stainless steel bellows expansion joint on a 6¾-in.-OD inlet line in a gas-turbine test facility cracked during operation. Cracking occurred in welded joints and in unwelded portions of the bellows.

As Fig. 44 shows, the line consisted of two bellows and a pipe. The bellows were of type 321 stainless steel, 0.093-in. wall thickness; the pipe was type 347 stainless steel pipe, 6.065-in. ID, and 0.340-in. nominal wall thickness. The bellows were made by forming the convolution halves from stainless steel sheet, then welding the convolutions together as shown in detail B in Fig. 44.

The line carried high-purity nitrogen gas at 150 psia with a flow rate of 12 to 18 lb per second. During the line's 800-hr operation, the nitrogen gas became contaminated because oil and oil vapor leaked into the system. The nominal gas temperature was 650 C (about 1200 F), although on occasion the maximum inlet temperature to the turbine exceeded 675 C (about 1250 F).

Before the line was put in service, 47 open-cycle tests were carried out on the piping. In the tests, the piping was pressurized with air at 40 to 45 psi and subjected to temperatures of 620 to 650 C (about 1150 to 1200 F), for an approximate total exposure time of 100 hr at temperature. Closed-cycle operation with high-purity nitrogen gas started approximately 13 months after the piping was initially installed and then failed after about 23 months. After field repairs, the piping operated about six weeks, when a second failure occurred. There were 130 thermal cycles;

the average time to reach temperature was 1.5 hr, the average cooling time was 1.2 hr. A new line was installed, and samples of the cracked line were sent to a laboratory for failure analysis.

Visual examination indicated that the bellows unit nearest the turbine contained the most cracking; therefore, only this bellows section was selected for analysis. The bellows were split in half, the reflector sleeve was removed, and the bellows was vapor blasted and liquid-penetrant inspected to reveal all visible cracking.

The most severe crack occurred in the welded joint between the first and second convolutions from the downstream end of the bellows. The crack appeared to initiate along the surface of the inner wall opposite the external weld, then propagated toward the outer surface of the convolution.

No cracks were observed in the welded joint between the second and third convolutions. Cracks were found in the welded joints on each side of the bellows where it was joined to the pipe. A stainless steel strap had been field welded around the top of the first two downstream convolutions to repair the area where leakage occurred.

Heavy deposits of carbon were found on the inner walls of the convolutions and on the back side of the reflector sleeve. The reflector sleeve was intended to prevent contaminants from reaching the inner walls of the convolutions and to streamline gas flow across the convolutions.

Chemical analyses were made of the piping and of samples from welds 1 and 2 (see Fig. 44). Although some minor deviations from normal composition were found (particularly involving molybdenum, columbium and titanium contents), these deviations did not affect material properties.

Microhardness measurements were taken on three sections of pipe and on two weld samples. Hardness readings taken within the carburized zone at the inner surface of the pipe wall averaged Rockwell C 36, near the center of the wall Rockwell B 90, and at

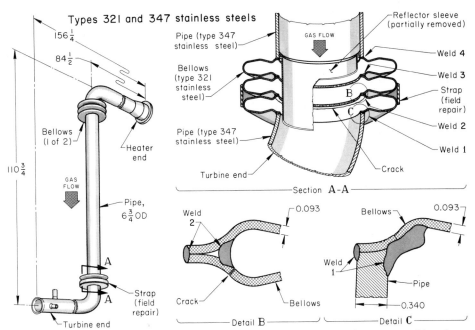

Fig. 44. Stainless steel pipeline for carrying hot nitrogen gas from heater to turbine that failed in the bellows section because of grain-boundary embrittlement (Example 18)

the outer surface Rockwell B 95. The hardness gradient was believed to be the result of oxygen penetration from the outer surface, which was exposed to air, and carbon diffusion from a carburized zone on the inner surface.

The weld samples showed slightly higher hardness values than normally occur in type 321 stainless steel, which was attributed to the presence of a hard grain-boundary precipitate. Hardnesses of the weld metal and adjacent base metal ranged from Rockwell B 95 to 99.

Metallographic examination showed the piping to be sound, although thin carburized layers occurred on the inner surfaces. Carburization appeared to have been caused by a buildup of carbon, deposited during service through breakdown of an oil contaminant in the nitrogen gas. This condition was observed in all of the piping.

The microstructure was normal for annealed type 347 stainless steel. Large particles, probably columbium carbides (CbC) and complex carbonitrides (CbC,N), were randomly dispersed through the structure. These particles were believed to have been present in the as-received material. Fine carbide precipitates noted in the pipe structures were not detrimental, because they showed no preference for the grain boundaries but were well dispersed throughout the austenite grains.

The weld metal appeared to be of good quality and did not indicate the presence of inclusions or show many signs of overheating. No excessive grain growth occurred near the interface between weld metal and base metal. Intergranular carbide precipitation was found in both the weld metal and the heat-affected zone of the base metal of weld 3. This was attributed to local overheating during the welding process that had vaporized most of the titanium stabilizer. Carbides then formed with subsequent heating within the sensitizing-temperature range. Extensive intergranular cracking and intergranular oxidation were found in weld 1. Carbonaceous material was found in unusually large crevices at the head of the cracks.

Intergranular cracking was found in the heat-affected zone in all four of the welded joints in the bellows. At normal operating temperatures for this gas-inlet line, intergranular fatigue failure in austenitic stainless steels usually occurs only in the presence of grain-boundary embrittlement. This type of embrittlement is usually the result of nitriding, intergranular oxidation, carbide precipitation, or the formation of sigma phase or chi phase.

There was no metallographic evidence to indicate that nitriding had occurred. Intergranular oxidation was present, but because failure did not occur until long after air testing was concluded, its presence was not considered to be the mechanism causing the embrittlement, even though it undoubtedly weakened the bellows.

A light-colored precipitate occurred in small amounts in all of the welded joints of the bellows convolutions and was suspected of containing either complex carbides or sigma phase. The sample from weld 3 was etched with Vilella's reagent, specifically to reveal carbides and sigma phase, then polished lightly to remove the etchant and re-

etched with Murakami's reagent, which reveals only carbides. The two etching operations revealed that significant quantities of both complex carbides and sigma phase were present.

The grain-boundary precipitate was identified as consisting largely of a continuous network of sigma phase. The amount of sigma phase formed was small; however, because sigma was found in a continuous network, the amount of sigma formed was considered sufficient to cause the grain boundaries to be highly embrittled. Because the roots of the convolutions were points of maximum flexure, and because of the loss of plasticity resulting from sigma embrittlement, the structure could not withstand the fluctuating thermal and mechanical stresses encountered during service.

Cracking occurred in the weld heat-affected zones, as well as the roots of the convolutions that were areas of maximum flexure. These areas were highly strained, which would accelerate carbon penetration in the cracked areas, and would account for carburization at these points, even though carburization was not found in other areas of the samples examined.

Intergranular cracking occurred at the welded joints of the convolutions and originated at the root of crevices. The crevices were caused by surface oxidation during open-cycle testing and acted as open stress raisers. Open-cycle testing also caused stress oxidation within the convolution roots, which accounted for the intergranular oxygen penetration found in the cracks on all of the welded joints examined. In general, intergranular oxygen penetration increases with increasing time and temperature at any given stress above a specific minimum stress.

Conclusions. Failure of the bellows occurred by intergranular fatigue cracking along a continuous grain-boundary network of sigma phase, which had precipitated under normal operating conditions. Fatigue cracks originated at crevices caused by surface oxidation during open-cycle testing prior to normal service.

Secondary degrading effects on the piping and bellows included grain-boundary carbide precipitation, intergranular oxidation on the outside surface, and carburization of the inside surface. Quality of the piping and of the welds had no bearing on the cause of failure.

Recommendations. Type 321 stainless steel is satisfactory for the bellows convolutions, provided that open-cycle testing does not result in surface oxidation and crevices. However, type 347 stainless steel would be better, because it has greater stability during welding, even though, like type 321, it is susceptible to sigma-phase formation. Inconel 600 would be an even better choice for the bellows because of its improved stress-oxidation properties and because it is not susceptible to sigma-phase formation.

Welds in a type 321 bellows should be stress relieved by solution treatment at 950 to 980 C (about 1750 to 1800 F) prior to open-cycle testing. Reheating at 870 to 900 C (about 1600 to 1650 F) for 1 to 2 hr after annealing would precipitate the greater part of the dissolved carbon as titanium carbide,

thus at least partially stabilizing the type 321 stainless steel bellows and welds.

Prevention of oil leakage into the system would minimize carburization of the piping and bellows.

For a more extensive discussion of elevated-temperature failures, see the article beginning on page 249.

Thermal Fatigue

Thermal-fatigue failure is the result of temperature cycling, as opposed to fatigue at high temperatures caused by strain cycling. Two conditions necessary for thermal fatigue are some form of mechanical constraint and a temperature change. Thermal expansion or contraction caused by a temperature change acting against a constraint causes thermal stress. Constraint may be external (for example, constraint imposed by rigid mountings for pipes), or it may be internal, in which case it is set up by a temperature gradient within the part. In thick sections, temperature gradients are likely to occur both along and through the material, giving rise to highly triaxial stresses and reducing material ductility, even though the uniaxial ductility often increases with increasing temperature. Reduction in the ductility of the material gives rise to fractures that have a brittle appearance, often with many cleavage-like facets in evidence.

Identifying features of low-cycle thermal-fatigue failures are: (a) multiple initiation sites that join randomly by edge sliding to form the main crack, (b) transverse fractures, (c) an oxide wedge filling the crack, and (d) transgranular fracture. Cracks having similar characteristics but distinguished by intergranular fracture, are caused by stress-rupture phenomena (long periods at elevated temperature under high static tensile load). The primary failure mechanism involved in stress rupture is grain-boundary sliding. In thermal-fatigue cracks, slip processes and cleavage operate much as they do in failure at normal temperature, but often the evidence is destroyed by oxide formation, flame polishing and melting processes.

True thermal fatigue occurs in such components as internal-combustion engines, where thick-section cast materials are used, and in appliances or heat exchangers, where thin wrought material is used. In cast materials, uniform sections, mild strain gradients, and short-flake graphite are desirable design features. On oil-fired and gas-fired furnace heat exchangers, the thermal cycle is important, because it controls temperature gradients, and in thin sections, external constraints are of minor importance.

Under certain circumstances, thermal-fatigue and stress-rupture failures blend into each other. Thermal fatigue is the basic mechanism in failures that occur because of numerous, short heating and cooling cycles. Stress rupture becomes an important consideration as the cycle times increase, and hence is primarily a long-term rate process. Most thermal-fatigue fractures are of the low-cycle, high-strain type; the fracture surfaces are rough and faceted at or near the initiation sites, and more fibrous and with shear lips at 45° angles in the final-fracture area.

For additional discussion of thermal fatigue, see page 252 in the article on Elevated-Temperature Failures.

Contact Fatigue

Elements that roll, or roll and slide, against each other under high contact pressure are subject to the development of surface pits or spalls after many repetitions of load. Pitting is a manifestation of metal fatigue from imposed cyclic contact stresses. Factors that govern pitting fatigue are the contact stress, the material properties and metallurgy, and the physical and chemical characteristics of the contacting surfaces, including the oil film lubricating the surfaces.

The magnitude and distribution of stresses at and below the surface of contact have been described by Hertz (Ref 9) and others (Ref 10 to 14). The significant stress in rolling-contact fatigue is the maximum alternating shear stress that undergoes a reversal in direction during rolling. In pure rolling, this shear stress occurs on a plane slightly below the surface and can lead to initiation of fatigue cracks in the subsurface material. As these cracks propagate under the repeated loads, they reach the surface and produce small pits.

When sliding is imposed on rolling, the tangential forces and thermal gradient caused by friction alter the magnitude and distribution of stresses in and below the contact area. The alternating shear stress is increased in magnitude and is moved nearer to the surface by sliding forces. Thus, initiation of contact-fatigue cracks in gear teeth, which are subjected to significant amounts of sliding adjacent to the pitch line, is found to be in the surface material. These cracks propagate at a shallow angle to the surface, and pits result when the cracks are connected to the surface by secondary cracks. If pitting is severe, the bending strength of the tooth may be decreased to the point where fracturing can occur.

Surface-Pitting Fatigue. Test specimens of carburized steel examined during and after contact-fatigue testing disclose the mechanism of surface pitting. A surface pit having a shell-like appearance with the apex of the "V" of the pit pointing in the direction of rotation is shown in Fig. 45(a).

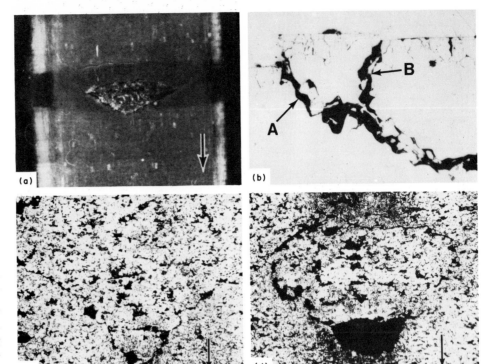

(a) Macrograph, at 4×, showing shell-like surface pit. (b) Micrograph, at about 380×, of a section through the surface fatigue crack. Crack A initiated at the surface and propagated from left to right. Crack B, a large subsidiary crack, is almost normal to the surface. Note small subsidiary cracks, and grain-boundary oxide network. (c) Micrograph, at about 55×, of the surface of the specimen, showing apex of pit (at bottom) encircled by the crack. (d) Micrograph, at about 55×, showing apex of the pit spalled away and crack encircling a larger area.

Fig. 45. Specimen of carburized steel showing surface-origin pitting that resulted from contact-fatigue testing. Arrows denote direction of rotation.

A crack begins at the surface and propagates at an acute angle to the surface in the same direction that the loading wheel rolls over the surface opposite to the direction of rotation. The crack and resulting pit are confined to the outer portion of the carburized case. Several stages of pitting development are shown in Fig. 45(b). At the apex a small volume of metal has been released and is ready to spall off. The small subsidiary cracks shown in Fig. 45(b) will eventually join and release a much larger volume of metal. This progression of failure, viewed on the surface of the specimen, appears as shown in Fig. 45(c) and (d). The apex of the pit is encircled by a crack in Fig. 45(c), while in Fig. 45(d), the apex has spalled away and the crack has encircled a larger area. Figure 45(b), (c) and (d) illustrate the sequence of events leading to surface pitting, which is considered to be the typical mode of failure when sliding and rolling are present between contacting surfaces.

The specimen shown in Fig. 45(a) has a single pit but no evidence of other surface damage in the contact path. This is typical of specimens tested at high contact stresses and run for relatively small numbers of cycles (less than 10^7) before developing the failure pit. On the other hand, specimens tested at lower contact stresses and run for many more cycles (greater than 2×10^8) develop scores of small pits that result in a severely worn contact path.

Small pits begin the same way as the large pit in Fig. 45(a); however, the fatigue crack seems to lack the driving force to penetrate very far below the surface but, rather, quickly returns to the surface and results in a small and shallow pit. The continuing passage of the loading roller over these small pits tends to obliterate their characteristic V shape.

Subsurface Cracking. Another form of contact-fatigue failure initiates in the subsurface but results in severe pitting or spalling on the surface. In pure rolling, or where subsurface stress concentrations arise because of rolling and sliding, cracking originates below the contact surfaces, frequently originating at an inclusion, and propagates parallel to the surface. In the early stages, subsidiary cracks may appear on the surface; ultimately, large areas spall away as the main subsurface crack spreads. In case-hardened parts, when insufficient case depth and/or core hardness exists, the cracking frequently occurs at the case-core interface, causing severe spalling (called subcase fatigue).

For more discussion of contact fatigue, see pages 425 to 430 in the article on Rolling-Element Bearings, and page 151 in the article on Wear Failures.

Corrosion Fatigue

Corrosion fatigue is associated with alternating or fluctuating stresses that occur in a corrosive environment and cause accelerated crack initiation and propagation at a location where neither the environment nor the stress acting alone would be sufficient to produce a crack. Fatigue cracking in a corrosive environment is identified by the presence of numerous small cracks adjacent to the fracture, and of compacted corrosion product on the fracture surface, which may damage and obscure fine surface detail of the fracture.

The corrosive environment usually introduces stress raisers on the surface. The irregular surface that results is detrimental to the fatigue properties of the part in a mechanical or geometric sense. For parts susceptible to embrittlement by hydrogen, or for parts that are exposed to a fairly continuous corrosive environment with intermittent applications of loading, the cracking mechanism may be somewhat more complex.

An important feature of corrosion fatigue is that the stress range required to cause fracture diminishes progressively as time and number of stress cycles increase. It is, therefore, impractical and uneconomic to attempt solely to design against corrosion fatigue. Although different alloys show differing performance under a given corrosion-fatigue environment, it is customary to protect the surface to achieve adequate performance at low cost.

For more extensive information on corrosion fatigue, see the article beginning on page 240 in this volume.

Inspection Schedules and Techniques

The occurrence of fatigue failures can be reduced by maintaining routine inspection schedules that include nondestructive testing.

If a crack or discontinuity is found in a vital component that could fail and cause serious damage, the component should be replaced or repaired as soon as possible. Where failure is not so critical, the part containing a discontinuity can be inspected at regular intervals until it is considered that the component is near its failure point before it is replaced. Critical components that are exchanged in assemblies during routine maintenance should be inspected to ensure that the removed part is usable as a spare.

Records of failures should be kept so that recurring instances of failures on certain components can be noted. Components that repeatedly fail indicate that perhaps a different design and/or material should be utilized. Where it may be unreasonable to change the design or

material, examination of the records should give a rough life expectancy. Knowing this, the part can be replaced before failure results. However, most preventive-maintenance systems assume that all parts are exactly the same, which is not necessarily true; therefore, such systems should be used only to give some rough guidelines and should be supplemented by nondestructive inspection.

Visual inspection can sometimes reveal fatigue cracks. The cracks are frequently located at obvious points of stress concentration, such as section changes, sharp fillets, last thread in threaded components, toe of welds, and keyways. These stress concentrations may be the result of design-fabrication defects or accidental notches. Once fatigue cracks become visible to the naked eye, they usually propagate at a rate such that the remaining life will be only a small percentage of the total life of the part.

Nondestructive Testing. Liquid-penetrant inspection, electromagnetic inspection, and magnetic-particle inspection (of ferrous metals) are reliable methods for detection of surface cracks and discontinuities. However, fatigue strength, or number of load applications required to produce fatigue failure, usually cannot be predicted from test indications.

Ultrasonic inspection and radiography are mainly used for internal examination. For crack detection, ultrasonics is much more reliable than radiography. It is not unusual to monitor fatigue cracks by ultrasonics until crack growth is considered to have reached a critical size.

Stresscoating, strain gages, photoelastic coatings and x-ray diffraction generally are not used for fractured parts, but rather for unfailed mating or similar parts to study the residual stresses in a part or the induced stresses imparted by specific loadings. The results of these tests can be used to analyze the stresses in parts that failed by fatigue. More information on nondestructive testing is presented in the article on General Practice in Failure Analysis, which begins on page 10 in this volume.

Determination of Fatigue Damage and Life

Fatigue causes over 80% of the operating failures of machine elements, and in many of these the stress cycles may be very complex with occasional high peaks — for example, the gust loading of aircraft wings. For satisfactory correlation with service behavior, full-size or large-scale specimens must be tested under conditions as close as possible to those existing in service. This method often is completely uneconomical, but it does provide valuable data. A less costly testing procedure is by simplified labora-

tory tests. By using the fatigue information obtained from the testing of standard specimens, or models, and applying the proper correction factors for configuration, surface finish, environment and various other parameters, an approximation of the lifetime of the component can be determined. (For an example of test-data correction factors, see Fig. 20 and discussion, on page 107 in this article.) It should be emphasized, however, that this is just an approximation, and without full-scale tests such as those mentioned previously, this information could be almost useless.

For improving production designs, the target load/life test method of evaluating the design of a part has been used by automotive, farm-equipment, construction-equipment, and aircraft companies. In this method, numerous failures from actual operating machines are observed. From these observations, conclusions can be drawn as to the type of loading that causes the failures. A fatigue test is then set up to apply the appropriate loading. After obtaining failures during the test, certain adjustments can be made in the magnitude and method of applying the loads until the same type of failure is developed in the test as those experienced by the operating machines.

Target lives for the parts in the fatigue test can be established, based on the time to failure on the machines in service, the time to failure in the fatigue tests, and the desired life in service. For example, if a certain part fails in one-fourth the desired life of the machine, and during the fatigue tests these same parts fail in 25,000 cycles, one would not consider any revised parts satisfactory unless they exceeded 100,000 cycles without failing. Once the appropriate loading and number of cycles are established for a part on a production machine, the same test can be used to ensure that similar parts on new machines will be satisfactory.

One application on which this method has been used is the rear axles of automobiles, where maximum tractive torque is applied to the rear axle for 100,000 cycles. If the axle gears withstand this loading, they are considered satisfactory for customer usage. The advantages of this procedure are that it makes use of the experience gained from many machines already in use, and that it is rather rapid. Its disadvantage is that sufficient machines must be placed in customers' hands to develop the failed parts for study and evaluation of test methods.

The differences in the operating conditions, environment, fatigue properties of the parts, and processing methods between the production design and new design must be small to produce accurate results. Therefore, this technique is used mostly when there is ample experience, as in improving parts that have a history of failure in service or in evaluating machines that are similar to existing production models.

References

1. M. A. Miner, Cumulative Damage in Fatigue, *Trans ASME*, Vol 67, 1945, p A159
2. H. J. Grover, Fatigue of Aircraft Structures, NAVAIR 01-1A-13, Naval Air Systems Command, U. S. Department of the Navy, 1966
3. P. G. Forrest, "Fatigue of Metals", Pergamon, 1962, p 113
4. R. E. Peterson, "Stress Concentration Design Factors", Wiley, 1974
5. H. Neuber, Theory of Notch Stresses: Principles for Exact Calculation of Strength With Reference to Structural Form and Material, Springer Pub., 1958, AEC-Tr-4547; available through NTIS, U.S. Dept. of Commerce
6. R. J. Roark, "Formulas for Stress and Strain", 4th Ed., McGraw-Hill, 1965
7. T. Topper, R. Wetzel and J. Morrow, Neuber's Rule Applied to Fatigue of Notched Specimens, *J Mater*, Vol 4, No. 1, Mar 1969
8. R. C. Juvinall, "Engineering Considerations of Stress, Strain and Strength", McGraw-Hill, 1967
9. H. R. Hertz, Miscellaneous Papers, Macmillan & Co., London, 1896
10. J. O. Smith and C. K. Liu, Stresses Due to Tangential and Normal Loads on Elastic Solids With Application to Some Contact Stress Problems, *J Appl Mech*, Vol 20, No. 2, June 1953
11. R. E. Denning and S. L. Rice, Surface Fatigue Research With the Geared Roller Test Machine, SAE Paper 620 B, Society of Automotive Engineers, New York, 1963
12. G. J. Moyar and J. D. Morrow, Surface Failure of Bearings and Other Rolling Elements, University of Illinois, Engineering Experiment Station Bulletin No. 468, 1964
13. W. E. Littman and R. L. Widner, Propagation of Contact Fatigue From Surface and Subsurface Origins, ASME Paper No. 63-WA/CF-2
14. J. P. Sheehan and M. A. Howes, The Role of Surface Finish in Pitting Fatigue of Carburized Steel, SAE Paper 730580, Society of Automotive Engineers, New York, 1973

Selected References

C. Laird and D. J. Duquette, Mechanisms of Fatigue Crack Nucleation, in "Corrosion Fatigue: Chemistry, Mechanics and Microstructure", NACE, Houston, 1972
A. F. Madayag, "Metal Fatigue: Theory and Design", Wiley, New York, 1969
C. C. Osgood, "Fatigue Design", Wiley-Interscience, New York, 1970
G. Sines and J. L. Waisman, "Metal Fatigue", McGraw-Hill, New York, 1959
"Structural Fatigue in Aircraft", STP 404, American Society for Testing and Materials, Philadelphia, 1966
"Fatigue at High Temperature", STP 459, American Society for Testing and Materials, Philadelphia, 1969
"Damage Tolerance in Aircraft Structures", STP 486, American Society for Testing and Materials, Philadelphia, 1971
"Metal Fatigue Damage — Mechanism, Detection, Avoidance and Repair", STP 495, American Society for Testing and Materials, Philadelphia, 1971

Distortion Failures

By the ASM Committee on Analysis of Ductile and Brittle Fractures*

DISTORTION FAILURE occurs when a structure or component is deformed so that it (*a*) no longer can support the load it was intended to carry, (*b*) is incapable of performing its intended function, or (*c*) interferes with the operation of another component. Distortion failures can be either plastic or elastic, and may or may not be accompanied by fracture. There are two main types of distortion: *size distortion,* which refers to a change in volume (growth or shrinkage); and *shape distortion* (bending or warping), which refers to a change in geometrical form (Ref 1).

Distortion failures ordinarily are considered to be self-evident — for example, damage of a car body in a collision or bending of a nail being driven into hard wood. However, failure analysts often are faced with more subtle situations. For example, the immediate cause of distortion (bending) of an automobile-engine valve stem is contact of the valve head with the piston, but a failure analyst must go beyond this immediate cause in order to recommend proper corrective measures. The valve may have stuck open because of faulty lubrication; the valve spring may have broken because corrosion had weakened it; the spring may have had insufficient strength and taken a set, allowing the valve to drop into the path of the piston; or the engine may have been over-revved many times, causing coil clash and subsequent fatigue fracture of the spring. Without careful

*See page 30 for committee list.

consideration of all the evidence, a failure analyst may miss the true cause of a distortion failure.

In this article, several common aspects of failure by distortion are discussed, and suitable examples of distortion failures are presented for illustration.

Overloading

Every structure has a load limit beyond which it is considered unsafe or unreliable. Applied loads that exceed this limit are known as overloads and sometimes result in distortion or fracture of one or more structural members. Estimation of load limits is one of the most important aspects of design and is commonly computed by one of two methods — classical design or limit analysis.

Classical Design. The conservative, classical method of design assumes that failure occurs whenever the stress at any point in a structure exceeds the yield strength of the material. Except for members that are loaded in pure tension, the fact that yielding occurs at some point in a structure has little influence on the ability of the structure to support the load. However, yielding has long been considered a prelude to structural collapse or fracture, and therefore a reasonable basis for limiting applied loads.

Classical design keeps allowable stresses entirely within the elastic region and is used routinely in the design of parts. Generally, allowable stresses for static service are set at one-half the yield strength for ductile materials and one-

sixth for brittle materials, although other fractions may be more suitable for specific applications. The reason for using such low fractions of yield strength is to allow for such factors as possible errors in computational assumptions, accidental overload, introduction of residual stress during processing, temperature effects, variations in material quality including imperfections, degradation as from corrosion, and inadvertent local increases in applied stress resulting from notch effects.

Classical design also is used for setting allowable stresses in other applications — for example, where fracture can occur by fatigue or stress rupture. In these instances, fatigue strength or stress-rupture strength is substituted for yield strength as a point of reference.

Limit Analysis. The upper limit in design is defined as the load at which a structure will break or collapse under a single application of force. This load can be calculated by a method known as limit analysis (Ref 2 and 3). With limit analysis, it is unnecessary to estimate stress distributions, which makes stress analysis much simpler by this method than by classical design. However, limit analysis is based on the concept of tolerance to yielding in the most highly stressed regions of the structure and therefore cannot be used in designing for resistance to fatigue or elastic buckling, or in designing flaw-tolerant structures.

Limit analysis assumes an idealized material — one that behaves elastically up to a certain yield strength and then

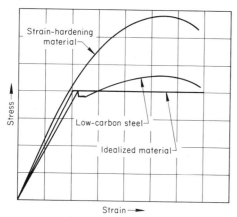

Fig. 1. Schematic comparison of the conventional stress-strain behavior of a low-carbon steel, a strain-hardening material, and the idealized material assumed in limit analysis, all having the same yield strength

does not work harden but undergoes an indefinite amount of plastic deformation with no change in stress. The inherent safety of a structure is more realistically estimated by limit analysis in those instances when the structure will tolerate some plastic deformation before it collapses. Because low-carbon steel, one of the most common materials used in structural members, behaves somewhat like the idealized material, limit analysis is very useful to designers, especially in the analysis of statically indeterminate structures.

Figure 1 illustrates the relative stress-strain behavior of a low-carbon steel, a strain-hardening material and an idealized material — all with the same yield strength (the upper yield point for the low-carbon steel, and the stress at 0.2% offset for the strain-hardening material). Load limits for parts made of materials that strain harden significantly when stressed in the plastic region can be estimated by limit analysis, as can those for parts made of other materials whose stress-strain behavior differs from that of the idealized material. In these situations, the designer bases his design calculations on an assumed strength that actually may lie well within the plastic region for the material.

Safety Factors. In both classical design and limit analysis, yielding is assumed to be the criterion for calculating safe loads on statically loaded structures. For a given applied load, the two methods differ in that the safety factor (the ratio of the theoretical capacity of a structural member to the maximum allowable load) generally is higher when calculated by limit analysis. For example, classical design limits the capacity of a rectangular beam to the bending moment that will produce tensile yielding in the regions farthest from the neutral axis; limit analysis predicts that complete collapse will occur at a

bending moment 1.5 times the limiting bending moment determined by classical design. It is important that a designer be able to relate the actual behavior of a structure to its assumed behavior, because, for a given applied load and safety factor, a structure designed by limit analysis usually will have thinner sections than a structure designed by classical methods.

Safety factors are important design considerations, because they allow for factors that cannot be computed in advance. Overload failure can occur either when the applied stress is increased above the design value or when the material strength is degraded. If either situation is a characteristic of the fabricated structure, the design must be changed to allow for these factors more realistically. In the following example, aluminum alloy extension ladders collapsed because the safety factor of the I-beam-shape side rails was too low to allow for accidental overload.

Example 1. Collapse of Aluminum Alloy 6063-T6 Extension Ladders by Overloading of Side Rails (Fig. 2)

Several aluminum alloy extension ladders of the same size and type collapsed in service in the same manner; the extruded aluminum alloy 6063-T6 side rails buckled, but the rungs and hardware remained firmly in place. The ladders had a maximum extended length of 21 ft, and the recommended maximum angle of inclination to the vertical was 15°.

Investigation. Visual examination disclosed that the side-rail extrusions, which had the I-beam shape shown in Fig. 2(a), had failed by plastic buckling, with only slight surface cracking in the most severely deformed areas. There were no visible

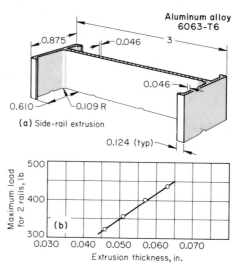

Fig. 2. (a) Aluminum alloy 6063-T6 extension-ladder side-rail extrusion that failed by plastic deformation and subsequent buckling. (b) Relation of maximum applied load to the section thickness of the flanges and web of the side-rail extrusion. (Example 1)

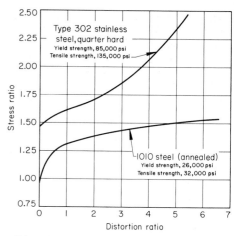

Distortion ratio is permanent deflection, measured at a distance from the support ten times the beam thickness, divided by beam thickness. Stress ratio is maximum stress, calculated from applied load and original beam dimensions, divided by yield strength.

Fig. 3. Relation of distortion ratio to stress ratio for two steel cantilever beams of rectangular cross section

defects in materials or workmanship, and all dimensions of the side rails were within specified tolerances.

Hardness tests using a portable hardness tester, metallographic examination, and tensile tests of specimens from the buckled side rails were conducted. All results agreed with the typical properties reported for aluminum alloy 6063-T6 extrusions.

Stress analysis of the design of the ladder, using actual dimensions, indicated that the side-rail extrusions had been designed with a thickness that would provide a safety factor of 1.2 at ideal loading conditions (15° max inclination) and that use of the ladders under other conditions could subject the side rails to stresses beyond the yield strength of the material. Once yielding occurred, buckling would continue until the ladder collapsed.

The stress analysis was extended to include an evaluation of the relation of maximum applied load to section thickness with the ladder at its maximum extension of 21 ft and at an inclination of 15°. This relation is shown in Fig. 2(b).

Conclusion. The side rails of the ladders buckled when subjected to loads that produced stresses beyond the yield strength of the alloy. Failure was by plastic deformation, with only slight tearing in the most severely deformed regions.

Corrective Measure. The flange and web of the side-rail extrusion were increased in thickness from 0.046 in. to 0.057 in. This increased the safety factor from 1.2 to 1.56. After this change, no further failures were reported to have occurred.

Amount of Distortion. When designing structures using limit analysis, designers do not always consider the amount of distortion that will be encountered. A rough illustration of the distortion that resulted from overloading of small cantilever beams is given in Fig. 3. Known loads were applied to rectangular-section beams of low-carbon steel and of stainless steel, and the permanent deflection at the loading point was measured. Maximum fiber stresses were calculated from the applied load and original specimen dimensions.

This type of test provides a simplistic but useful concept of distortion by showing how much distortion occurs at strains beyond the yield point. As shown in Fig. 3, the beam made of low-carbon steel, which strain hardens only slightly, exhibited nil distortion when the calculated maximum fiber stress was equal to the yield strength (at a stress ratio of 1.00). However, this beam collapsed at a load equivalent to a fiber stress just above the tensile strength, shown in Fig. 3 where the lower curve became essentially horizontal. This collapse load agrees with the limit-analysis collapse load of 1.5 times the load at yield. The beam made of stainless steel, which strain hardens at a rather high rate, showed no distortion at fiber stresses up to 1.47 times the yield strength. When the calculated stress equaled the tensile strength (at a stress ratio of 1.59), distortion was 0.7 times the beam thickness, and the beam supported a calculated stress of 1.5 times the tensile strength without collapse.

When loads increase gradually, distortion is gradual and design can be based on knowledge of the amount of distortion that can be tolerated. Thus simple bench tests of full-size or scaled-down models often can be used in estimating the loads required to produce various amounts of distortion.

When rapid or impulse loads are applied (as in impact, shock loading or vibration), the amount of distortion that can occur without fracture is considerably less predictable. For most structural materials, measured values of strength are higher under impulse loading, and values of ductility are lower, than the values measured under static loading. (Tensile and yield strengths as much as 20% higher than the slow-tension-test values have been measured under very high rates of loading.) In addition, the variation, or scatter, among replicate tests of mechanical properties is greater when strain rates are high than it is when strain rates are low. The amount of distortion that can occur at high rates of loading is difficult to analyze or predict, because (a) the crystallographic processes that are involved in deformation and fracture are influenced by strain rate and temperature, (b) impulse loading creates an adiabatic condition that causes a local increase in temperature, and (c) impulse loading involves the propagation of high-velocity stress waves through the structure.

Effect of Temperature. Distortion failures caused by overload can occur at any temperature at which the flow strength of the material is less than the fracture

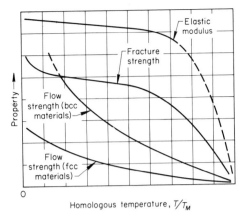

Fig. 4. Schematic diagram of the temperature dependence of elastic, plastic and fracture behavior of polycrystalline materials that do not exhibit a solid-state transformation. T is the instantaneous absolute temperature and T_M is the absolute melting temperature of the material.

strength. In this discussion, flow strength is defined as the average true stress required to produce detectable plastic deformation caused by a relatively slow, continuously increasing application of load; fracture strength is the average true stress at fracture caused by a relatively slow, continuously increasing application of load. The flow strength and fracture strength of a material are temperature dependent, as is the elastic modulus (Young's modulus, bulk modulus or shear modulus). Figure 4 illustrates this temperature dependence schematically for polycrystalline materials that do not undergo a solid-state transformation. Two flow strengths are shown — one for a material that does not have a ductile-to-brittle transition in fracture behavior, such as metal with a face-centered-cubic (fcc) crystal structure, and one for a body-centered-cubic (bcc) material that exhibits a ductile-to-brittle transition.

As shown in Fig. 4, the flow strength, fracture strength and elastic modulus of a material generally decrease as temperature increases. If a structure can carry a certain load at 20 C (70 F), it can carry the same load without deforming at lower temperatures. (Sometimes, stressed members made of materials having a ductile-to-brittle fracture transition will fracture spontaneously if the temperature is lowered to a value below the transition temperature. For a more detailed discussion of this phenomenon, the reader is referred to the article on Ductile-to-Brittle Fracture Transition, which begins on page 44 in this volume.) If the temperature is increased so that the flow strength becomes lower than the applied stress, a structure may deform spontaneously with no increase in load. A change in temperature also may cause an elastic-distortion failure because of a change in modulus, as might occur in a

control device whose accuracy depends on a predictable elastic deflection of a control element or a sensing element. For most structural materials, the curve defining the temperature dependence of elastic and plastic properties is relatively flat at temperatures near 20 C (70 F).

In face-centered-cubic materials, and in body-centered-cubic materials at temperatures above the transition temperature, distortion (gross yielding) always accompanies overload fracture in a section that does not contain a severe stress raiser. In addition, gross yielding is one of the criteria that determine whether fracture in a section containing a stress raiser is a ductile-overload (plane-stress) fracture. Localized distortion also accompanies brittle crack extension in ductile materials (plane-strain fracture). In inherently brittle materials, where the fracture stress is less than the flow stress, no gross or localized distortion accompanies fracture. For a more detailed discussion of distortion that accompanies fracture, see the Appendix to the article on Ductile and Brittle Fractures, which begins on page 87.

At temperatures higher than about $T_M/2$ (one-half the absolute melting temperature), phenomena such as creep may cause distortion failure. Creep is a relatively long-time phenomenon and can be distinguished from overload distortion by relating the length of time at temperature to the amount of distortion, as discussed in the article that begins on page 249 in this volume.

Changes in operating temperature can affect the properties of a structure in other ways. For example, if a martensitic steel is tempered at a given temperature and then encounters a higher temperature in service, yield strength and tensile strength will decrease because of overtempering. Long-time exposure to moderately elevated temperatures may cause overaging in a precipitation-hardening alloy, with a concurrent loss in strength. The volume change accompanying the transformation of retained austenite in a martensitic steel on exposure to cryogenic temperatures may cause a distortion failure (dimensional growth or warpage) in a close-tolerance assembly such as a precision bearing. When the temperature is changed, different coefficients of thermal expansion for different materials in a heterogeneous structure can cause interference between structural members (or can produce permanent distortion because of thermally induced stresses if the members are joined together). A failure analyst must understand the effect of temperature on properties of the specific materials involved when analyzing failures that have occurred at temperatures that are substantially above or below the design or fabrication temperature.

Incorrect Specifications

Large errors in specification of material or processing for a part can lead to distortion failures. These errors often are the result of faulty or incomplete information being available to the designer. In such instances, the designer has to make assumptions concerning the conditions of service. In the next example, a high operating temperature was not properly considered when the specification for a wire spring was written, although this error was not the primary cause of failure.

Example 2. Distortion Failure of a Steel Automotive Valve Spring Caused by the Combined Effects of Improper Microstructure and High Operating Temperature (Fig. 5)

The engine of an imported car lost power and compression and emitted an uneven exhaust sound after many thousand miles of operation. When the engine was dismantled, it was found that the outer spring on one of the exhaust valves was too short to function properly. The short steel spring, and an outer spring taken from another cylinder in the same engine (both shown in Fig. 5), were examined in the laboratory to determine why one had distorted and the other had not.

Investigation. The failed outer spring (at left in Fig. 5) had decreased in length to about the same free length as that of its companion inner spring. Most of the distortion had occurred in the first active coil (toward the top in Fig. 5), and a surface residue of baked-on oil present on this end of the spring indicated that a temperature of 175 to 205 C (350 to 400 F) had been reached. Temperatures lower than 120 C (250 F) usually do not cause relaxation (or set) in high-carbon steel springs.

The load required to compress each outer spring to a length of 1 in. was measured. The distorted spring needed only 67 lb, whereas the longer spring needed 90 lb. The distorted spring had suffered 25% set, which was the immediate cause of the engine malfunction.

The microstructure of both springs was primarily heavily cold drawn fine pearlite, but the microstructure of the distorted spring contained small amounts of proeutectoid ferrite. Although the composition of the spring alloy was unknown, the microstructure indicated that the material was patented and cold drawn high-carbon steel wire. (For representative structures, see micrographs 347, 357 and 358 in Volume 7 of this Handbook.) The distorted spring had a hardness of Rockwell C 43 and the longer spring had a hardness of Rockwell C 46, as determined on precisely calibrated equipment. Both hardness and microstructure indicated that the material in the deformed spring had 10% lower yield strength than material in the undeformed spring. The estimates of yield strength were considered valid because of two factors: (a) the accuracy of the hardness testing, and (b) characteristically consistent ratios of yield strength to tensile strength for the grades of steel commonly used in spring wire.

Fig. 5. Valve springs made from patented and drawn high-carbon steel wire. Distorted outer spring, at left, exhibited about 25% set because of proeutectoid ferrite in the microstructure and high operating temperature. Outer spring at right is satisfactory. (Example 2)

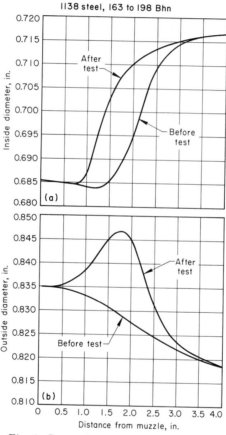

Fig. 6. Comparison of longitudinal profiles of (a) inside diameter, and (b) outside diameter, of an 1138 steel shotgun barrel before and after a test in which 1000 rounds of a new type of ammunition were fired (Example 3)

Conclusions. The engine malfunctioned because one of the exhaust-valve springs had taken a 25% set in service. Relaxation in the spring material occurred because of the combined effect of improper microstructure (proeutectoid ferrite) plus a relatively high operating temperature.

The undeformed spring exhibited little or no set because the tensile strength and corresponding yield strength of the material (estimated from hardness measurements)

were about 10% higher than those of the material in the deformed spring.

Recommendations. A higher yield strength and a higher ratio of yield strength to tensile strength can be achieved in steel springs by using quenched-and-tempered steel instead of patented and cold drawn steel. An alternative would be to use a more expensive chromium-vanadium alloy steel instead of plain carbon steel; the chromium-vanadium steel should be quenched and tempered.

Regardless of material or processing specifications, if springs are stressed close to the yield point of the material, close control of material and processing plus stringent inspection are needed to ensure satisfactory performance.

Sometimes service conditions are changed, invalidating certain assumptions that were made when the part was originally designed. Such changes include (a) an increase in operating temperature to one at which the material no longer has the required strength; (b) an increase in the load rating of an associated component, which the user may interpret as an increase in the allowable load on the structure as a whole; or (c) an arbitrary increase in applied load by the user on the assumption that the component has a high enough safety factor to accommodate the added load.

In the following example, the conditions of service for a shotgun were changed, making the specification for the material used in the barrel incorrect.

Example 3. Bulging of an 1138 Steel Shotgun Barrel Caused by a Change From Lead Shot to Iron Shot (Fig. 6)

A standard commercial shotgun barrel deformed during a test that was made with a new type of ammunition. Use of the new ammunition, which contained soft iron shot with a hardness of about 72 Bhn, was intended to reduce toxicity; the old ammunition had contained traditional lead shot with a hardness of 30 to 40 Bhn.

Investigation. The shotgun barrel, made from seamless 1138 steel tubing, was of uniform inside diameter from the breech to a point 3 in. from the muzzle; at this point, the inside diameter began to decrease (see the curve marked "Before test" in Fig. 6a). This taper, or integral choke, which is intended to concentrate the shot pattern, ended about 1½ in. from the muzzle, and the final portion of the barrel had a relatively uniform inside diameter.

After a test in which 1000 rounds of ammunition containing soft iron shot were fired, the shotgun barrel had a longitudinal profile of inside diameter as shown in the curve marked "After test" in Fig. 6(a). Comparison of this curve with the profile before the test shows that the effect of firing soft iron shot was to deform the gun barrel so that the choke taper was shifted toward the muzzle. After the test, there was a bulge on the outside surface of the barrel, shown in comparison to the longitudinal profile of the outside diameter before the test in Fig. 6(b). Deformation of the barrel had been detected after the first 100 rounds of iron-shot ammunition had been fired, and

Chart labels (Fig. 6):
1138 steel, 163 to 198 Bhn
Inside diameter, in.
0.720 / 0.715 / 0.710 / 0.705 / 0.700 / 0.695 / 0.690 / 0.685 / 0.680
After test / Before test / (a)
Outside diameter, in.
0.850 / 0.845 / 0.840 / 0.835 / 0.830 / 0.825 / 0.820 / 0.815 / 0.810
After test / Before test / (b)
Distance from muzzle, in.
0   0.5   1.0   1.5   2.0   2.5   3.0   3.5   4.0

the bulge grew progressively larger as the test continued.

Apparently, the bore of the failed barrel was not concentric with the outside surface, because the wall thickness at a given distance from the breech varied widely among different points around the circumference. For example, at a distance of 0.2 in. from the muzzle, the wall thickness varied from 0.051 in. to 0.080 in.

The microstructure of the barrel material was a mixture of ferrite and coarse pearlite. The alloy had a hardness of 163 to 198 Bhn (converted from Vickers hardness measurements).

Based on previous tests, in which the hoop stress in shotgun barrels had been measured when lead-shot ammunition was fired, the safety factor had been estimated at 2.0. In this instance, it was concluded that wall-thickness variations had reduced the safety factor to about 1.3 for lead-shot ammunition. Previous tests also had shown that lead shot was deformed extensively by impact with the bore in the choke zone of this type of gun barrel.

Analysis. The major stresses in the choke zone are produced by impact of shot pellets against the bore. When lead shot is used, the lead absorbs a considerable amount of the impact energy as it deforms. Soft iron shot, on the other hand, is much harder than lead and does not deform significantly. More of the impact energy is absorbed by the barrel when iron shot is used, producing higher stresses.

In this instance, had the gun barrel been of more uniform wall thickness around its circumference, it might not have deformed. However, it was believed that conversion to iron-shot ammunition would increase stresses in the barrel enough to warrant an increase in the strength of this type of barrel.

Conclusions. The shotgun barrel deformed because a change to iron-shot ammunition increased stresses in the choke zone of the barrel. Bulging was enhanced by a lack of uniformity in wall thickness.

Recommendations. Three alternative solutions to this problem were proposed, all involving changes in specifications:

1 The barrel could be made of steel with a higher yield strength.
2 The barrel could be made with a greater and more uniform wall thickness.
3 An alternative nontoxic metal shot with a hardness of about 30 to 40 Bhn could be developed for use in the ammunition.

Failure to Meet Specifications

Parts sometimes do not perform to expectations because the material or processing does not conform to requirements, leaving the part with insufficient strength. For instance, a part can be damaged by decarburization, as discussed below for a spiral power spring.

Figure 7 shows two spiral power springs that were designed to counterbalance a textile-machine beam. The spring at left in Fig. 7 was satisfactory and took a normal set when loaded to solid deflection in a presetting operation. The spring at right in Fig. 7, after having been intentionally overstressed in the same manner

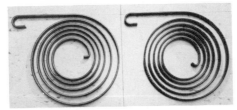

Fig. 7. Two spiral power springs from a textile machine. Spring at left is an acceptable part, whereas spring at right took an excessive set (the inner end of the spiral is 30° out of position) because of insufficient yield strength and a decarburized surface layer.

as the satisfactory spring, exhibited 15% less reaction force than was required at 180° angular deflection because it had taken a set that was 30° in excess of the normal set.

The material in the satisfactory spring had a hardness of Rockwell C 45, whereas the material in the spring that failed had a hardness of Rockwell C 41.5. This represents about a 10% disparity in tensile and yield strengths between the two springs. The spring that failed had a 0.003-in.-thick surface layer of partial decarburization that further weakened the region of the cross section where maximum stresses are developed in the spring under load. The decarburized layer, which had a lower yield strength than the bulk of the material, yielded excessively during presetting and thus the spring did not attain its specified shape in the free state following this operation.

Another material deficiency that can lead to deformation failure is variability in response to heat treatment among parts in a given production lot. Certain alloys, particularly hardenable low-alloy steels and some precipitation-hardening alloys, can vary in their response to a specified heat treatment because of slight compositional variations from lot to lot or within a given lot. This can result in some parts having too low a strength for the application even though they were properly heat treated according to specification.

Remedies for variability in response to heat treatment usually involve changes in the heat treating process, ranging in complexity from (a) tailor-

Fig. 8. Two hardened-and-tempered 1070 steel hold-down clamps. The clamp at top was acceptable. The clamp at bottom was slack quenched because of faulty loading practice (stacking), and failed by distortion (flattening) because of the resultant mixed microstructure.

ing the heat treating conditions for each lot or sublot to (b) making a small adjustment in the heat treatment specification. Experiments on each lot or sublot almost always are needed to establish parameters when heat treating conditions are tailored.

An adjustment in heat treating conditions was successful in avoiding variation in properties among sublots of heat treated 17-7 PH stainless steel Belleville washers. Two of these washers — one of which was from an acceptable sublot and the other from a deficient sublot — were subjected to examination. The washer from the acceptable sublot had developed the required hardness upon solution heat treating at 955 C (1750 F) followed by refrigeration at −75 C (−100 F) and aging. The other washer was soft after an identical heat treatment and yielded under load (flattened). The microstructure of the acceptable washer was a mixture of austenite and martensite, whereas the structure of the washer that flattened consisted almost entirely of austenite.

Previous experience with 17-7 PH stainless steel indicated that some alloy segregation was not unusual and that relatively minor variations in composition could affect response to heat treatment, perhaps by depressing the range of martensite-transformation temperatures to a variable degree. As noted in Ref 4, the solution treating temperature has a marked effect on the M_s temperature in the precipitation-hardening stainless steels that are austenitic as solution annealed and martensitic as aged (17-7 PH, AM-350, AM-355 and PH 15-7 Mo). Consequently, although it never was clearly established whether temperature variations inside the solution treating furnace or minor variations in composition were responsible for the observed variability in properties of the 17-7 PH Belleville washers, all sublots attained the required strength when the solution treating temperature was lowered to 870 C (1600 F).

Faulty Heat Treatment. Mistakes made in heat treating hardenable alloys are among the most common causes of premature failure. Temperatures that are either too high or too low can result in the development of inadequate or undesirable mechanical properties. Quenching a steel part too fast can crack it; quenching too slowly can fail to produce the required strength or toughness. If parts are shielded from a heating or cooling medium, they can respond poorly to heat treatment, as discussed below.

Two hold-down clamps, both from the same lot, are shown in Fig. 8. Both clamps were bowed to the same degree after fabrication, as intended, but the clamp at bottom flattened when it was installed. A small percentage of the clamps, all of which were made from hardened-and-tempered 1070 steel, deformed when a bolt was inserted through the hole and tightened. The clamp at top in Fig. 8 was acceptable, with a microstructure of tempered martensite and a hardness of Rockwell C 46; the clamp at bottom, which deformed, had a mixed structure of ferrite, coarse pearlite and tempered martensite, and a hardness of only Rockwell C 28.

An analysis of the heat treating process revealed that the parts were stacked so that occasional groupings were slack quenched as a result of shielding; this promoted the formation of softer upper-transformation products. When the loading practice was changed to ensure more uniform quenching (so that transformation to 100% martensite was accomplished on all parts), the problem was solved.

Proper control of temperature and time in a heat treating furnace is essential to the processing of many hardenable alloys. In the following example, poor control of furnace conditions caused a slat track on a military aircraft to have different properties in different regions.

Example 4. Bending of a 4140 Steel Aircraft-Wing Slat Track (Fig. 9)

A curved member called a slat track (see Fig. 9), which supported the extendable portion of the leading edge of the wing on a military aircraft, failed by bending at one end after very short service. It was estimated that the slat track, fabricated from heat treated 4140 steel, had undergone only one high-load cycle.

Investigation. Hardness measurements were taken at various points along the length of the track. The end that bent (at right in Fig. 9) had a hardness of Rockwell C 30, compared with a hardness of Rockwell C 41 for the remainder of the part.

Metallographic examination of specimens from both ends of the slat track revealed that the microstructure of the end that bent contained a large number of ferrite islands in a matrix of tempered martensite. The microstructure of the opposite end contained no ferrite.

Conclusions. Bending had occurred in a portion of the slat track because service stresses had exceeded the strength of the material in a region of mixed martensite and ferrite. It was determined that the most likely cause of the mixed structure was nonuniform austenitization during heat treatment. The end that bent never became fully austenitic, because the furnace temperature

4140 steel

Region of failure

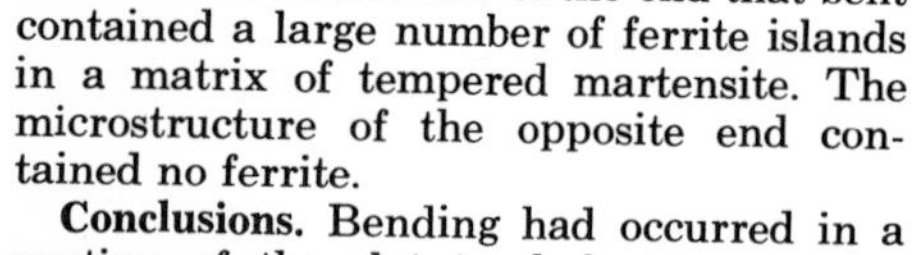

Fig. 9. A 4140 steel slat track from a military aircraft wing that bent because one end did not become fully austenitic during heat treatment, producing a low-strength structure of ferrite and tempered martensite (Example 4)

was locally too low or because the soaking time was too short, or both.

It was decided that material or design changes were not warranted, considering the nature of the failure and the probable cause of the mixed microstructure in one end of the slat track.

Corrective Measures. Steps were taken to improve control of temperature of parts during austenitization.

Another instance in which faulty heat treatment resulted in failure by deformation is described in Example 2 on page 65 in the article on Ductile and Brittle Fractures, in this volume. In that example, an aluminum alloy 6061 extension ladder fractured in service. The material in two of the four extrusions that were used to fabricate the side rails of the ladder was naturally aged, rather than being artificially aged as had been specified. One of the two naturally aged members, which had yield strength about one-half the required value, yielded under load, causing the ladder to collapse; fracture of the other three extrusions occurred as the ladder collapsed.

Warping during heat treatment or during stress-relief annealing also is a common type of distortion failure. Warping is the result of nonuniform residual stress or thermal or transformational stress that is introduced during heating or cooling. When residual stress causes distortion, the amount of distortion is proportional to the magnitude of the residual stress. When distortion is caused by thermal or transformational stress, the extent of the distortion is greater for parts that have complex configuration or large differences in section thickness and for faster heating or cooling rates.

Most warping is the result of plastic deformation that occurred in some region of the part at elevated temperature or during a change in temperature. Dimensional changes accompanying stress relief are the result of readjustments involving both elastic and plastic strain. Distortion that occurs during other types of heat treatment involves mainly plastic strain and generally results in high levels of residual stress in the warped part. The magnitude and distribution of residual stresses, and whether they are tensile or compressive, are determined by the composition, shape, size and heat treating conditions of a given part.

Warping most often is severe in heat treatments that involve quenching. In hardenable steels, the principal cause of warping on quenching is nonuniform rates of transformation. The effect of transformational stresses may be intensified if a nonuniform composition exists; this nonuniformity may be the result of segregation, or it may be the result of processing, as in a carburized part. Such inhomogeneities may produce a variation in transformation temperature at

locations that are geometrically equivalent and that cool at the same rate. Nonuniform transformational stresses that result from inhomogeneity also can occur during tempering.

Warping often can be minimized by modifying the heat treating conditions. For example, slow heating and cooling rates are less likely to cause warping, because local variances in temperature and in rates of temperature change are minimized. Preheating prior to austenitizing often is used as a means of minimizing warping of some tool steels and heavy sections, because preheating reduces the temperature gradient between the surface and the interior of the part. Induction hardening and nitriding have been used to minimize warping when surface hardness is of primary importance to the performance of a part.

In heat treatments requiring rapid cooling or quenching, excessive warping usually can be reduced by changing the quenching conditions. In many instances, the orientation of a part as it enters the quenchant will influence the amount of distortion that occurs. Quenching in special fixtures, or "quench presses", is widely used in certain industries to minimize distortion by providing different controlled cooling rates at different locations in a given part. Martempering also has been used to minimize distortion, because in this process transformation rates are equalized throughout the part.

Faulty Case Hardening. Carburizing, which both increases the surface hardness of a part and provides resistance to wear and indentation, can, if improperly controlled, produce a case that has too low or too high a carbon content. With too low a carbon content, the surface may not be hard enough to withstand normal service loads. This condition may be accompanied by shallow case depth, which aggravates the problem. With an excessively high carbon content, which generally is the result of an excessively high carbon potential or improper diffusion during the carburizing cycle, excessive amounts of retained austenite may be present in the carburized zone after heat treatment, depending on the composition of the steel. Retained austenite reduces the resistance of the surface layer to deformation (indentation) and, under certain conditions, may transform to martensite in service. When transformation in service occurs, the resulting untempered martensite may crack and thus promote early failure by surface fatigue, or a distortion failure in a close-fitting assembly may occur because of the volume change that accompanies transformation. The example that follows describes a distortion failure that occurred as the result of just such a volume change.

Example 5. Seizing of a Spool-Type Hydraulic Valve Caused by Transformation of Retained Austenite in a Carburized Case (Fig. 10)

Occasional failures were experienced in spool-type valves used in a hydraulic system. When a valve would fail, the close-fitting rotary valve would seize, causing loss of flow control of the hydraulic oil. The rotating spool in the valve was made of 8620 steel and was gas carburized. The cylinder in which the spool fitted was made of 1117 steel, also gas carburized.

Investigation. Low-magnification visual examination of the spool and cylinder from a failed valve revealed some burnishing, apparently the result of contact between the spool and the inside cylinder wall. Measurement of the surface profile of the spool showed no evidence of wear or galling. When this profile was compared with that of a spool from a valve that operated satisfactorily, no significant difference was found.

Metallographic sections were made of the cylinder from the failed valve and from the one that operated satisfactorily. The microstructure of the carburized case on the cylinder from the satisfactory valve was well-defined martensite interspersed with some austenite (white-etching areas in Fig. 10a). On the other hand, the microstructure of the case from the failed valve contained a much greater amount of retained austenite, especially near the surface (see Fig. 10b). In addition, some patches of untempered martensite were found close to the surface upon overetching the section of the failed valve cylinder.

Microhardness traverses of the two sections revealed that, in general, the hardness of the case from the failed part was about 100 Knoop points lower than the case hardness of the unfailed part. At the surface, the case hardness of the failed part was 300 Knoop points lower.

Conclusions. Momentary sliding contact between the spool and the cylinder wall (probably during valve opening) caused unstable retained austenite in the failed cylinder to transform to martensite. The increase in volume resulted in sufficient size distortion (growth) to cause interference between the cylinder and the spool, seizing and loss of flow control.

The failed parts had been carburized in a process where the carbon potential was too high, which resulted in a microstructure having excessive retained austenite after heat treatment.

Corrective Measure. The composition of the carburizing atmosphere was modified to yield carburized parts that did not retain significant amounts of austenite when they were heat treated. After this change was made, occasional valve failure by seizing ceased. (Further information on carburizing can be found in the series of articles beginning on page 93 in Volume 2 of this Handbook.)

In nitrided parts, distortion failures that are caused by improper processing most often involve insufficient core hardness. Failure occurs by case crushing, because the substrate does not have enough strength to support the thin nitride case. Low core hardness is more likely in steels

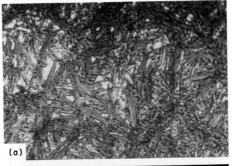

(a)

(b)

The cylinder of the valve that operated satisfactorily (a) had little retained austenite in the case, whereas the cylinder of the seized valve (b) had much retained austenite that transformed to martensite in service, resulting in size distortion (growth).

Fig. 10. Microstructure at 500× of cross sections through the carburized 1117 steel cylinders from two spool-type hydraulic valves (Example 5)

that are not specifically intended for nitriding, and usually is the result of: (a) improper heat treatment prior to nitriding, as in Example 6 in this article; or (b) tempering at too low a temperature, so that overtempering occurs during nitriding. Proper material selection and process control are discussed on pages 146 to 163 in Volume 2 of this Handbook.

Faulty Repairs. Products often are repaired to correct deficiencies that are found in new parts during quality-control inspections or in used parts after they have deteriorated in service. Repair welding and brazing generally are recognized as potential sources of unwanted alterations of the properties of heat treatable alloys. Parts can be made softer or more brittle by careless repair, depending on the alloy and the conditions under which the repair was made.

Substitution of a part, particularly a fastener, whose properties do not match the properties of the part it replaces can lead to failure of the substitute part, failure of another part, or both, as in the following instance.

A carrying handle of complex configuration was secured to a heavy, portable device by means of a ring clamp at one end of the handle and a special 1/4-20 hardened bolt through a small flange at the other end. For some unknown reason, the special slotted hexagonal-head bolt was replaced by a standard commercial

hexagonal-head cap screw whose hardness was Rockwell B 93 instead of the specified hardness of Rockwell C 28.

The commercial cap screw was distorted in service as illustrated in Fig. 11(a), causing the handle to become loose at one end. This in turn caused eccentric and excessive loading on the small flange of the handle with the result that the flange bent and then broke. Figure 11(b) shows the broken flange; the bright area next to the hole is where the loose flange chafed against the distorted bolt and is an indication of the eccentric load distribution on the flange. A fastener of the correct hardness and length is shown in Fig. 11(c) for comparison with the distorted commercial cap screw.

Analyzing Distortion Failures

Distortion failures often are considered to be relatively simple phenomena, easy to analyze because deformation can occur only when the applied stress exceeds the flow strength of the material. On the contrary, distortion is not always the result of simple overload or use of an improperly processed part. As often as not, analysis of a distortion failure must be exceptionally thorough and rigorous in order to determine the cause of failure and, more importantly, to specify proper corrective action. The analyst must consider factors that may not have been anticipated in design of the part, such as material substitutions or process changes during manufacture, and misuse, abuse, or occurrence of complex stress fields in service.

A seemingly innocent substitution of material resulted in distortion of small volute springs made of cold worked, spring-temper Inconel. Normally the material was purchased as cold flattened wire, but one lot of springs was formed

(a)

(b)

(c)

Fig. 11. (a) Distorted commercial cap screw that was used as a replacement for a hardened bolt. (b) Carrying-handle flange that broke because the cap screw bent. (c) Correct replacement part.

from cold rolled and slit strip because flattened wire could not be obtained in time to meet the delivery schedule. After a presetting operation, the strip springs were consistently out of tolerance; they had taken an excessive set. The Inconel strip had a hardness of 360 dph, compared to 390 dph for the wire that normally was used. This represents a difference of about 10% in strength, and accounts for the observed distortion. Had this problem gone undetected during manufacture, it might well have resulted in distortion failures in service.

Analytical Procedure. The article that begins on page 10 in this volume gives a general procedure that can be followed for any failure analysis. That article also gives helpful hints concerning methods of analysis and precautions that will increase the validity of the analysis. The ten steps in the list that follows are adapted from the general procedure and are suggested specifically for analysis of a distortion failure:

1 Define the effect of the failure on the structure or assembly, and define the desired results of corrective action.
2 Obtain all available design and service information.
3 Examine the distorted part, making a record of observations, including a sketch or a photograph of the distorted part and a notation of all pertinent measurements of dimensions. It usually is helpful to enter these measurements, which should be made with at least the same precision as in a quality-control inspection, alongside the design dimensions on a blueprint of the part.
4 Perform laboratory tests as necessary to confirm the composition, structure and other chemical or metallurgical characteristics of the distorted part.
5 Trace the failed part through all manufacturing processes to discover whether process deviations occurred during production.
6 Compare the actual conditions of service with design assumptions.
7 Compare the actual material properties with design specifications.
8 Determine whether any differences found in step 6 or 7 fully account for the distortion observed in the failed structure. If the differences do not fully account for the observed distortion, the information obtained in step 2 or 4 is incorrect or incomplete.
9 Prepare alternative courses of action to correct the variant factors that caused the observed distortion, and select the course that seems most likely to produce the desired result, which was defined in step 1.
10 Test the selected course of corrective action, to verify its effectiveness. Evaluate side effects of the corrective action, such as its effects on cost or on ease of implementation.

The next example contains all the elements of a thorough analysis of a failure that resulted from multiple causes, and

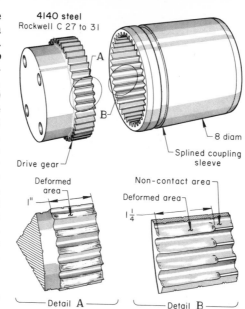

4140 steel
Rockwell C 27 to 31

A

B

Drive gear

8 diam

Splined coupling sleeve

Deformed area
1"
Non-contact area
Deformed area
1 1/4

Detail A

Detail B

Fig. 12. Gas nitrided 4140 steel drive-gear assembly in which gear teeth deformed because of faulty design and low core hardness. Details A and B show deformed areas on drive-gear teeth and mating internal splines (Example 6)

includes recommendations of two essential and two optional courses of action to correct the deficiencies.

Example 6. Deformation of a Gas Nitrided Drive-Gear Assembly, Caused by Faulty Gear-Tooth Design and Low Core Hardness (Fig. 12)

Slipping of components in the left-side final drive train of a tracked military vehicle was detected after the vehicle had been driven 8500 miles in combined highway and rough-terrain service. No abnormal service conditions were recorded in the history of the vehicle. The slipping was traced to the mating surfaces of the final drive gear and the adjacent splined coupling sleeve (see Fig. 12).

Failure analysis was conducted to determine the cause of the malfunction and to recommend corrective measures that would prevent similar failures in other vehicles.

Material and Fabrication. Specifications required the gear and coupling to be made from 4140 steel bar oil quenched and tempered to a hardness of 265 to 290 Bhn (equivalent to Rockwell C 27 to 31), and the finish-machined parts to be single-stage gas nitrided to produce a total case depth of 0.020 in. and a minimum surface hardness equivalent to Rockwell C 58.

Visual Examination. Low-magnification examination of the drive gear and coupling showed that the teeth of the gear and the mating contact surfaces of the internal splines on the coupling were almost completely worn away. The spline surfaces had been damaged mainly by severe indentation and plastic deformation. No spalling, cracking or other indications of fatigue damage were visible on the splines, nor was there any indication that abrasive wear had been the mechanism of failure.

Metal on the drive side of the gear teeth had been plastically deformed and subse-

quently removed (see details A and B in Fig. 12). The damaged areas on the splines were wider (axial dimension) than the gear teeth, indicating that there had been excessive lateral play between the components.

Examination of the surfaces of the internal splines that contacted a gear on the opposite end of the coupling (not illustrated) revealed a much smaller amount of deterioration than on the failed end. For instance, the machined flats on the crests of the splines showed no damage, the follower sides of the splines had very shallow, almost imperceptible wear areas that were only about 0.004 in. wide, and the drive side of each spline had a gently radiused, concave area of damage approximately 1/4 in. by 1 in. and 0.005 in. deep at its center. However, the amount of damage on the drive side of these splines was considered to be excessive for only 8500 miles of service.

Conformance to Material Specifications. Spectrographic analysis of the two components confirmed that composition was within the range specified for 4140 steel.

Core hardness was in the required range of Rockwell C 27 to 31 (264 to 294 Bhn). Total case depth, as determined by the microscopic method on polished specimens etched in 2% nital, was satisfactory. Surface hardness, as measured using a Knoop indenter, was equivalent to Rockwell C 50, substantially lower than the required value of Rockwell C 58.

Microstructure of the cases and cores of the two components was examined at 500 diameters on polished sections etched in 2% nital. There was a white layer (nitrogen-rich iron nitride, Fe_2N) about 0.001 in. thick on the surfaces of the gear teeth and the splines, and grain-boundary networks of iron nitride were present to a slight degree near the surface. The microstructure of the core consisted mainly of tempered martensite, but contained large amounts of blocky ferrite.

Gear and Spline Configuration. Measurements of the gear teeth and splines in areas showing little damage established that the parts as manufactured had been in conformance with the engineering drawings. The splines were straight axially and convex radially. However, the gear teeth that failed were convex in both directions in the vicinity of the pitch line. This design, which was intended to facilitate alignment and adjustment, provided extremely small contact areas between tooth and spline surfaces and hence very heavy localized loading.

The gear that engaged the other end of the internally splined coupling (not shown in Fig. 12) was designed to provide larger contact areas with the splines in the vicinity of the pitch line, providing lighter and more uniform local loading.

Conclusions. The premature failure occurred by "case crushing" as a result of several factors, which are listed below in order of importance:

1 Design that produced excessively high localized stresses at the pitch line of the mating components
2 Specification of a core hardness (Rockwell C 27 to 31) too low to provide adequate support for a 0.020-in.-thick case or permit attainment of the specified surface hardness of Rockwell C 58 after nitriding; actual surface hardness was Rockwell C 50

3 The presence of large amounts of blocky ferrite in the core (a microstructure conducive to case crushing) as a result of faulty heat treatment prior to nitriding

4 The presence of a nitride white layer about 0.001 in. thick at the surface and of nitride networks in the case.

Recommendations. Measures to correct the first two deficiencies listed above were recommended as the most important steps in obtaining adequate drive-train performance.

First, the excessively high local stresses at the pitch line should be reduced to an acceptable level by modifying the gear-tooth contour in the vicinity of the pitch line to provide a wider and longer initial contact area than in the original design. Second, a core hardness of Rockwell C 35 to 40 should be specified, to provide adequate support for the case and to permit attainment of the specified surface hardness of Rockwell C 58. Closer control of heat treating, which would be necessary to consistently produce the recommended higher core hardness, would also eliminate the presence of blocky ferrite in the core.

For maximum service life, consideration should also be given to controlling single-stage gas nitriding to minimize the thickness of the white layer and the extent of nitride networks in the case or using double-stage gas nitriding to provide a diffused nitride layer, and specifying final lapping or honing to remove the white layer.

Note that in the preceding example, continued use of nitrided 4140 steel in a critical application appeared to hinge on the ability of the processor to control the composition and response to heat treatment of the alloy. In other situations, it may be necessary to specify a steel such as AMS 6470 for guaranteed results in nitriding, or a steel such as AMS 6382 for more consistent response to heat treatment. Information on the gas nitriding process is presented on pages 149 to 163 in Volume 2 of this Handbook. A comparison of the microstructures resulting from single-stage and double-stage gas nitriding can be found on pages 66 and 67 in Volume 7.

Special Types of Distortion Failure

Analysis of distortion failures can be particularly difficult when there is no apparent permanent deformation of the part or when complex stress fields are involved. In this section, three types of distortion failure are discussed, which may provide useful insights into the problems of analyzing unusual mechanisms of distortion.

Elastic Distortion. A distortion failure does not necessarily involve yielding under a single application of load. Most parts deflect elastically under load. If, for example, a part ordinarily made of a high-modulus alloy is made of a low-modulus alloy, it will deflect more under a given load than if it were made of the high-modulus alloy. If this greater amount of deflection places the part in the path of another part in an assembly, it could be said to have failed by elastic distortion. As mentioned earlier, a change in the modulus of a material because of a change in temperature can cause an elastic-distortion failure. Elastic buckling of a long, slender column is another type of distortion failure in which the yield strength of the material is not exceeded (unless the structure collapses).

Ratcheting. Cyclic strain accumulation, or ratcheting, requires that a part be stressed by steady-state loading, either uniaxial or multiaxial, and that a cyclically varying strain in a direction other than the direction of principal stress be superimposed on the part. In ratcheting, an oscillating load or a cyclic variation of temperature strains the material beyond the yield point on alternate sides of a single member, or on alternate members of a structure, during each half-cycle. With succeeding cycles, plastic strain accumulates, with the result that one or more of the over-all dimensions of the member or the structure change relatively uniformly along the direction of steady-state stress. Deformation produced by a cyclic variation in load is known as isothermal ratcheting (even though a temperature change may occur simultaneously with the load variation). Progressive growth due to plastic strain incurred during a change in temperature is called thermal ratcheting. Ratcheting may ultimately result in ductile fracture or in failure by low-cycle fatigue.

As an illustration of isothermal ratcheting, consider a hollow cylinder that is stressed elastically in tension along its longitudinal axis. If a cyclic torsional load of sufficient magnitude to cause plastic straining is superimposed on the longitudinal load, the cylinder can increase in length by as much as 20% before local instabilities disrupt uniform strain accumulation (Ref 5 and 6).

At elevated temperatures, ratcheting must be distinguished from creep or stress relaxation. Ratcheting is solely a strain-dependent phenomenon, whereas creep and stress relaxation are time-dependent phenomena. Exposure to elevated temperature for an extended length of time is necessary for creep or stress relaxation to occur, but extensive deformation by ratcheting can occur in short periods of time — sometimes only minutes. Ratcheting can appear to be time dependent when the cyclic strains are imposed at regular intervals. However, the factor that distinguishes ratcheting is the occurrence of plastic strain during *both* halves of the cyclic variation.

In general, the proper corrective action for failures by ratcheting involves (*a*) changing the design of the part or the conditions of service to reduce the magnitude of the service stresses, or (*b*) specifying a material with a higher yield strength for the application.

Inelastic Cyclic Buckling. Some materials exhibit cyclic strain softening — a continuous decrease of elastic limit or tangent modulus that occurs with imposition of alternating stresses whose magnitude lies between the proportional limit and the yield strength. Columns made from materials that exhibit this behavior can fail by lateral displacement at the midspan (buckling) under stresses much lower than those predicted by classical design.

Table 1 presents the results of a test in which cylindrical specimens of cold worked 1020 steel, resembling tensile specimens with threaded ends, were stressed by alternating tensile and compressive loads of equal magnitude (Ref 7). Buckling occurred at 60% to 90% of the number of cycles to failure at stresses below the 0.2%-offset yield strength but above the proportional limit of the material, corresponding to the inelastic portion of the stress-strain curve. When an aluminum alloy was tested in the same manner, buckling did not occur in the range of stresses between the proportional limit and the 0.2%-offset yield strength. Aluminum alloys are among those that do not exhibit cyclic strain softening.

Table 1. Summary of Data on Inelastic Cyclic Buckling of Cylindrical Specimens of Cold Worked 1020 Steel(a) (Ref 7)

Peak stress, ksi	Stress cycles At buckling	Stress cycles At failure	Failure mode
87 to 94	$\frac{1}{4}$	$\frac{1}{4}$	(b)
80	14	20	(b)
71	130	143	(b)
64	380	691	(c)
61	1900	2377	(c)
58	. . .	4730	(d)

(a) Tensile strength of the steel, 100 ksi; yield strength, 90 ksi; proportional limit, 50 ksi. (b) Buckling, with or without fracture. (c) Buckling, followed by buckling-induced fracture. (d) Low-cycle fatigue fracture.

References

1. B. S. Lement, "Distortion in Tool Steels", American Society for Metals, Metals Park, Ohio, 1959

2. J. W. Jones, Limit Analysis, *Machine Design*, Vol 45 (No. 23), Sept 20, 1973, p 146-151

3. D. Goldner, Plastic Bending in Tubular Beams, *Machine Design*, Vol 45 (No. 24), Oct 4, 1973, p 152-155

4. A. J. Lena, Precipitation Reactions in Iron-Base Alloys, p 244-327 in "Precipitation From Solid Solution", American Society for Metals, Metals Park, Ohio, 1959

5. D. Burgreen, Review of Thermal Ratcheting, "Fatigue at Elevated Temperatures", STP 520, ASTM, 1973, p 535-551

6. K. D. Shimmin, Cyclic Strain Accumulation Under Complex Multiaxial Loading, RTD-TDR-63-4120, Dec 1963

7. C. R. Preschmann and R. I. Stephens, Inelastic Cyclic Buckling, *Experimental Mechanics*, Vol 12 (No. 9), Sept 1972, p 426-428

Wear Failures

By the ASM Committee on Analysis of Wear Failures*

WEAR is a surface phenomenon that occurs by displacement and detachment of material. Because wear usually implies a progressive loss of weight and alteration of dimensions over a period of time, wear problems generally differ from those entailing outright breakage. Although worn parts may break, it is more likely for a worn part to be removed from service because it no longer can perform satisfactorily or because the quality of its performance is marginal. Although the replacement of a broken part is seldom questionable, the replacement of a worn part may be, particularly in the absence of established standards.

All mechanical components that undergo sliding or rolling contact are subject to some degree of wear. Typical of such components are bearings, gears, seals, guides, piston rings, splines, brakes and clutches. Wear of these components may range from mild, polishing-type attrition to rapid and severe removal of material with accompanying surface roughening. Whether or not wear constitutes failure of a component depends on whether the wear deleteriously affects the ability of the component to function. For example, even mild, polishing-type wear of a close-fitting spool in a hydraulic valve may cause excessive leakage and thus constitute failure, even though the surface of the spool is smooth and apparently undamaged. On the other hand, a hammer in a rock crusher, for example, can continue to function satisfactorily in spite of severe denting, gouging and the removal of as much as several inches of surface metal.

Lubrication implies the intentional use of a substance that reduces friction between contacting surfaces. Lubrication is a mitigating factor in wear, and thus lubricated and nonlubricated wear, although they are not wear mechanisms, are differentiated in this article. In general, nonlubricated wear is associated with those types of applications in which the use of a lubricant either is not feasible or is not possible.

Types of Wear

Wear, according to a dictionary definition, is deterioration due to use. Gradual deterioration often is implied and the effects are mostly surface phenomena, but these restrictions should not be rigorously applied in failure analysis. Neither should the assumption that wear is entirely mechanical be accepted, because chemical corrosion may combine with other wear factors.

Wear failures may be gradual, rapid or, occasionally, catastrophically sudden. Sudden fracture is not accepted universally as an aspect of wear, but it must be considered in analysis of wear failure if for no other reason than that the more wear-resistant materials are often quite brittle and fracture-prone. Failures can occur over a wide range of temperatures and stresses. Stress is almost always involved with wear and thus is a primary consideration in failure analysis; unfortunately, often only qualitative evaluation of stress is possible.

For many years, there was considerable disagreement regarding the types or forms of wear and the primary cause of each type of wear. The terminology of wear was unsettled, and basic definitions were not standardized. None of these problems has been completely resolved, but areas of general agreement continue to emerge. It is now widely accepted that there are five primary types of wear — adhesive wear, abrasive wear, erosive wear, corrosive wear, and surface-fatigue wear. In addition, there are other types of wear which, although not regarded as primary, are afforded separate status. These include erosion-corrosion, fretting, and cavitation erosion.

In general, wear may be defined as damage to a solid surface caused by the removal or displacement of material by the mechanical action of a contacting solid, liquid or gas. Wear is usually detrimental, but in mild form (such as "breaking in"), wear may be beneficial. When a failure is caused predominantly by one type of wear, analysis may be relatively simple. However, many wear failures result from a combination of types or modes of wear. In addition, as wear progresses there may be a change in the predominant wear mode. Under these conditions, analysis is more complex.

Adhesive wear, also known as scoring, galling, seizing and scuffing, occurs when two metallic surfaces slide against each other under pressure. Microscopic projections or asperities bond at the sliding interface under very high local pressure. Subsequently, the sliding forces fracture the bonds, tearing metal from one surface and transferring it to the other. This results in the formation of minute cavities on one surface and minute projections on the other — which, in turn, can lead to further damage. The process may also result in the formation of loose wear particles, and these may contribute to abrasive wear.

Abrasive wear is displacement of material from a surface by contact with hard projections on a mating surface, or with hard particles, that are moving relative to the wearing surface. When hard particles are involved, they may be trapped between two sliding surfaces and abrade one or both of them, or they may be embedded in either of the surfaces and abrade the opposing surface. Abrasive wear may occur in the dry state or in the presence of a liquid. In the next example, abrasive wear was caused by silt carried by water pumped from a river.

Example 1. Failure of a Hard-Faced Stainless Steel Pump Sleeve Because of Abrasive Wear by River-Water Silt (Fig. 1)

Whenever river water is used in a manufacturing process, the presence of abrasive silt in the water can be expected to result in wear problems. A typical wear problem was encountered in a brine plant when river water was pumped into the plant by a battery of vertical pumps, each operating at 3600 rpm and at a discharge pressure of 120 psi. The pumps were lubricated by means of controlled leakage. The 1½-in.-OD pump sleeves were made of an austenit-

*Howard S. Avery, *Chairman*, Consulting Engineer, Abex Corp.; Wayne L. Amber, Metallurgical Engineer, Energy Control Div., Bendix Corp.; Kenneth G. Budinski, Materials Engineering Laboratory, Eastman Kodak Co.; A. J. Cienkus, Engineering Research, International Harvester Co.

John Dodd, Manager, Technical Development, Abrasion-Resistant Alloys, Climax Molybdenum Co.; H. A. Fabert, Jr., Technical Director, Amsco Div., Abex Corp.; W. A. Glaeser, Lubrication Mechanics Section, Battelle-Columbus Laboratories; D. William Hall, Scientific Research Staff, Ford Motor Co.; Telfer E. Norman, Consulting Engi-

neer; Thoni V. Philip, Supervisor – Tool and Alloy Research, Research and Development Center, Carpenter Technology Corp.; B. W. Roberts, Manager, Materials Technology, Steam Turbine Div., Westinghouse Electric Corp.; L. W. Sarver, Research and Development Div., Babcock & Wilcox Co.

R. C. Tucker, Jr., Manager, Materials Development, Linde Div., Union Carbide Corp.; David Wallace, Senior Technical Manager, Metallic Materials, Black and Decker Manufacturing Co.; Paul M. Unterweiser, *Secretary*, Senior Editor, Metals Handbook, American Society for Metals.

Sleeve at left, coated with a fused nickel-base hard facing alloy, shows severe abrasive wear by river-water silt after 3387 hr of service. Sleeve at right, coated with plasma-deposited chromium oxide, shows little evidence of wear after 5190 hr of service.

Fig. 1. Hard-faced austenitic stainless steel pump sleeves used to pump river water to a brine plant (Example 1)

ic stainless steel and were hard faced with a fused, nickel-base hard facing alloy (hardness: approximately Rockwell C 58, or 653 dph). Packing for the pumps consisted of a braided Teflon-asbestos material.

After several weeks of operation, the pumps began to leak and to spray water over the platforms on which they were mounted at the edge of the river. In addition to decreasing pumping efficiency, the leaks resulted in the formation of ice on the platforms in cold weather, thus creating a safety hazard. The leaks were caused by excessive sleeve wear that resulted from the presence of fine, abrasive silt in the river water. The silt, which contained hard particles of silica, could not be filtered out of the inlet water effectively. A severely worn sleeve that was removed from a pump after only 3387 hr of service is shown at left in Fig. 1. Maximum depth of wear on this sleeve was about 1/16 in.

Corrective Action. To prevent excessive sleeve wear, the nickel-base hard facing alloy coating on the sleeves was replaced with a plasma-deposited chromium oxide coating with a hardness of about 1300 dph. The coating was ground and lapped to a thickness of 0.004 to 0.005 in. and a surface finish of 6 to 8 micro-in. Wear resistance in service was extremely favorable, as shown by the sleeve at right in Fig. 1, which was removed from a pump after 5190 hr of service.

Erosive wear is abrasive wear involving loss of surface material by contact with a fluid that contains particles. Relative motion between the surface and the fluid is essential to this process, and the force on the particles that actually inflict the damage is applied kinetically. Although erosive wear most often involves solid particles, one type — *liquid-impingement erosion* — is caused by liquid droplets carried in a rapidly moving stream of gas. Erosion in which the relative motion of solid particles is nearly parallel to the eroded surface is called *abrasive erosion,* whereas erosion in which the relative motion of particles is nearly normal to the eroded surface is called *impingement erosion.*

Corrosive wear is a type of abrasive wear in which chemical or electrochemical reaction with the environment significantly contributes to the wear rate. In some instances, chemical reaction takes place first and is followed by the removal of corrosion products by mechanical action (abrasion). However, mechanical action may precede chemical action and result in the formation of very small particles of debris, which subsequently react with the environment. Chemical reaction, even when mild, and mechanical action may be mutually enhancing, as in the following example.

Example 2. Wear Failure of a Stainless Steel Drive-Roller Sleeve Under Mildly Corrosive Conditions (Fig. 2)

The drive-roller sleeve shown in Fig. 2 was used at an end of a belt conveyor for anthracite coal and associated rock mined with the coal. The sleeve, which was made of type 440A stainless steel and hardened and tempered to Rockwell C 57, was partly submerged in water during its seven months of service. Failure resulted predominantly from abrasive wear under mildly corrosive conditions. The service life of the type 440A sleeve was far longer than that of austenitic stainless steel sleeves, which lasted only six to nine weeks. However, further improvement was obtained with a type 440C sleeve heat treated to a hardness of Rockwell C 60. This sleeve exhibited only negligible wear after six months of service.

Erosion-corrosion is a type of wear in which there is relative movement between a surface and a corrosive fluid (which also may carry abrasive particles), the wear rate being directly related to the rate of relative movement. When abrasive particles are present, material removal is effected mainly by contact with the particles (erosive wear).

A special form of erosion-corrosion called *cavitation erosion* can occur on a surface in contact with a liquid that does not contain particulate matter. In cavitation erosion, the repeated formation and collapse of vapor bubbles at the surface imposes large repetitive contact stresses that can cause pitting or

spalling. (Damage by cavitation erosion strongly resembles that by liquid-impingement erosion, as discussed in the article that begins on page 160.)

Another special form of erosion-corrosion, *fretting* (sometimes known as wear oxidation, friction oxidation, or chafing), occurs between two contacting surfaces subjected to repeated, small-amplitude relative sliding, such as from vibration, in the presence of oxygen. The damage may appear as pits or grooves, with surrounding corrosion products (oxides), on one or both surfaces. Fretting is a complex process and often involves a combination of corrosive, adhesive and abrasive wear. As a result of vibration, surface-fatigue wear also may be involved in fretting.

The following example describes erosion-corrosion of an aluminum alloy tube brought about by an antifreeze fluid suspected of being corrosive to aluminum.

Example 3. Failure of an Aluminum Alloy Heat-Exchanger Tube by Erosion-Corrosion (Fig. 3)

One of the tubes in an aluminum alloy 3003-O heat exchanger used to cool transmission oil in a heavy off-the-road vehicle developed a leak after 1459 hr of operation. At the time the failure occurred, the heat-exchanger tubes contained a permanent-type antifreeze and water. Although the tube that failed was not returned to the laboratory for examination, sufficient evidence was obtained from examination of adjacent tubes in the heat exchanger to establish the cause of failure.

Macroscopic examination of the inside surface of an adjacent tube revealed a pronounced pattern of erosion-corrosion in the inlet area, as shown in Fig. 3(a) and (b). The pattern was most pronounced at the inlet; away from the inlet the pattern became less severe and disappeared entirely at about 2 in. from the inlet. Virtually no evidence of erosion-corrosion was found at the outlet; however, a mild condition of corrosion pitting was observed, as shown in Fig. 3(c).

A longitudinal cross section through an eroded area was prepared for metallographic examination. As shown in Fig. 3(d), the pattern revealed indicates that the cause of failure was erosion-corrosion. This form of attack is associated with turbulent aerated fluids. If the fluids are corrosive or contain particulate debris, attack is more aggressive. Although the antifreeze fluid in

Fig. 2. Worn type 440A stainless steel drive-roller sleeve that was used in a belt conveyor under mildly corrosive conditions (Example 2)

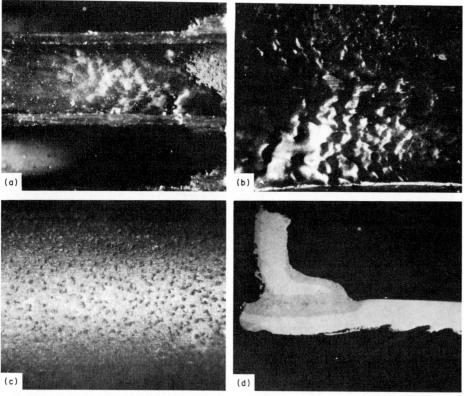

Fig. 3. Four specimens from an aluminum alloy 3003-O heat-exchanger tube, showing:
(a) and (b) a pronounced pattern of erosion-corrosion; (c) a mild condition of corrosion
pitting found near the tube outlet; and (d) a pattern of erosion-corrosion on a longitudinal cross section prepared for metallographic examination (Example 3)

the heat exchanger was not available for examination, it was suspected of being corrosive to aluminum.

Surface fatigue is a special type of surface damage whereby particles of metal are detached from a surface under high cyclic contact stresses, causing pitting or spalling. For more detailed discussion of this type of damage, see the section on Evaluation of Surface-Fatigue Pitting, pages 151-152 in this article; the section on Contact Fatigue, page 123 in the article on Fatigue Failures; and the section on Failure by Rolling-Contact Fatigue, pages 425-430 in the article on Failures of Rolling-Element Bearings.

The next example describes spalling of a layer of chromium plating on tool steel that was caused by surface fatigue and resulted in failure of a tool.

Example 4. Spalling Failure of a Notching Tool Resulting From Surface Fatigue of Chromium Plating (Fig. 4)

A notching tool used to notch polystyrene sheet 0.020 to 0.040 in. thick failed after a short period of service, when chromium plating spalled from the shaft of the tool. The tool, which is shown in Fig. 4, consisted of a shaft with a notched end that was machined from S7 tool steel and hardened and tempered to Rockwell C 45, and a linear ball bushing that rode on the shaft. To prevent shaft wear, a layer of hard chromium plating 0.002 in. thick was deposited on the bearing surface of the shaft.

In normal operation, the notched end of the shaft was driven downward upon the polystyrene sheet, beneath which was located a tool steel cutting die. The shaft, or punch, was cam actuated and operated at a speed of about 50 strokes per minute for 8 to 24 hr per day. When the shaft was sub-

mitted for failure analysis, it was determined that spalling of the hard chromium plating had been caused by the Hertzian contact stresses imposed by the rolling balls in the linear ball bushing. This failure illustrates that plated coatings, hard or soft, should not be used to resist wear by rolling elements, because the mechanical bond of the coating to the substrate often is insufficient to resist surface fatigue and consequent spalling.

Corrective Action. An improved shaft was made from S7 tool steel selectively carburized to a depth of 0.050 in. on the bearing surface only; the notched end was not carburized, but was hardened and tempered to Rockwell C 56. This provided both a shock-resistant notching tool and a very hard, wear-resistant bearing surface that could resist spalling under the Hertzian contact stresses of the balls in the ball bushing. After 2½ years of service, the improved shaft showed no evidence of wear.

Role of Friction in Wear

Friction between two contacting surfaces is caused by the same contact conditions that are basic to the wear process. Friction and wear both begin at localized contact points. It is at these concentrated contacts that high stresses cause fracture, shearing or flow; minute fragments may be separated from the surface to become wear debris. The process is complex and can follow one or more of several mechanisms, depending on the forces between the contacting surfaces and on the composition and properties of the surface and the surrounding environment, including the effect of any particulate matter in the environment.

Surface Features. When a solid cube is placed on a flat surface, one face of the cube appears to be in intimate contact with the flat surface. However, real surfaces have a certain amount of roughness and waviness; thus, the actual area of contact between the cube face and the flat surface (true-contact area) is the sum of a very large number of minute areas where high points on opposing surfaces contact one another. Individual areas of true contact are about 10^{-3} to 10^{-5} in. in diameter and are randomly distributed over the apparent-contact area.

The surface roughness and waviness of manufactured parts have distinctive geometrical patterns characteristic of the process that produced the parts. The surface of a turned shaft is made up of ridges and furrows; the surface of a ground ball-bearing raceway consists of shallow, parallel, U-shape troughs with thin ridges between them; the surface of a gold-plated electrical contact normally is a distribution of small convex surfaces, resembling a mass of close-packed bubbles. The size and configuration of these fine-scale surface features determine the actual conditions of contact between opposing surfaces, and what occurs at these

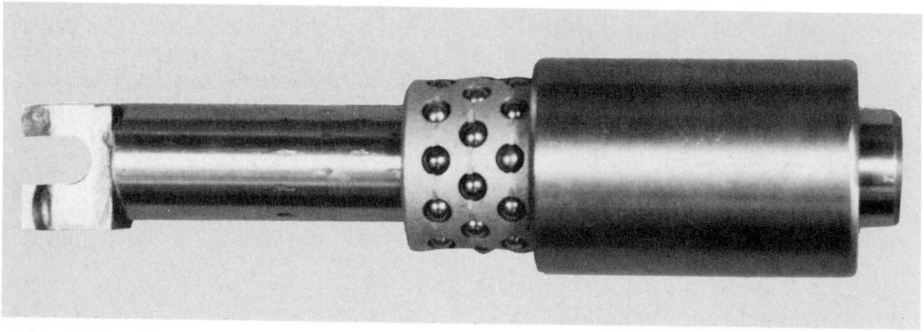

Fig. 4. Notching tool that failed in service when a layer of hard chromium plating spalled
from the S7 tool steel shaft (Example 4)

points of contact has a significant influence on friction and wear.

Microscopic stress conditions at points of contact can be described most simply by the analogy of a smooth sphere supported by a smooth planar surface. The resulting stress at the point of tangency is sufficiently high to cause elastic deformation of both the sphere and the flat surface, and the minute contact area spreads out until the stress is reduced to slightly below the elastic limit. Upon application of an external load in a direction perpendicular to the planar surface, the area of contact will increase roughly in proportion to the increase in load taken to the two-thirds power. As load is increased, the elastic limit of the planar surface (which is related to hardness) eventually is exceeded. When the elastic limit is exceeded, a permanent dent in the surface occurs. (This is comparable to what occurs in a hardness test, in which the penetrator is harder than the surface being tested.)

Because deformation of true-contact areas under load is similar to deformation of the area under the penetrator in a hardness test, penetration hardness is a material property that provides an approximate measure of resistance to wear. Under similar contact conditions, harder materials generally exhibit greater wear resistance than softer materials.

Frictional Force. When one solid body slides over another, high spots on the opposing surfaces contact one another and either (*a*) deform under localized contact stress or (*b*) bond together and then shear apart. Frictional force is a measure of resistance to tangential motion, and is the sum of the forces required to shear the bonded high spots and deform the unbonded ones. As sliding progresses, a steady frictional force is maintained by formation and shearing of many tiny bonds between the surfaces.

It has long been known that for many material systems the frictional force between two contacting surfaces is proportional to normal load and is independent of the apparent-contact area. According to modern friction theory, the true-contact area increases proportionally with load, and frictional force is proportional to load and to true-contact area. If frictional force is proportional to the sum of the areas of the microscopic junctions being sheared (true-contact area), the following simple relation results:

$$F = SA \qquad \text{(Eq 1)}$$

where F is frictional force, in pounds; S is shear strength of the weaker of the two constituents of the junction, in pounds per square inch; and A is true contact area, in square inches.

The adhesion theory of friction assumes that adhesion occurs at contact junctions and that frictional force equals the sum of the forces required to shear those junctions. The true-contact area is inversely proportional to the hardness of the softer material and proportional to the normal load:

$$A = W/p \qquad \text{(Eq 2)}$$

where A is true-contact area, in square millimeters; W is normal load (or contact force), in kilograms; and p is indentation hardness (often determined in a Vickers test), in kilograms per square millimeter. Equation 2 can be combined with Eq 1 to give:

$$F = SW/p, \text{ or } F/W = S/p \qquad \text{(Eq 3)}$$

where $S/p = \mu$, the coefficient of friction. Figure 5 shows the relationship between W, the normal load, and F, the frictional force, on a body sliding across a stationary horizontal surface.

It may be noted from the equation for calculating the coefficient of friction, $\mu = S/p$, that the coefficient is lowest when the hardness of the softer member of the contacting pair is high relative to its shear strength. Because the usual treatments that increase the hardness of a metal or alloy also increase its shear strength, a high ratio of hardness to shear strength is seldom found in a single metal or alloy. A high ratio can be achieved, however, by using a composite material. In wear-resistant electrical contacts, for example, a low coefficient of friction has been achieved by plating a hard substrate with a very thin layer of gold.

The equation $\mu = S/p$ is useful in the analysis of friction phenomena. However, the factor S (shear strength) is difficult to measure for real contacting surfaces, and thus wide variations in coefficient of friction are observed for any given material combination.

Surface Conditions. On real surfaces, the factor S (shear strength) in the equation for the coefficient of friction probably represents a complex parameter not only associated with the yield properties of the weaker member of a sliding pair, but also dependent on the condition of the surfaces in contact. If a bonded junction is weak and shearing takes place at the bond and not through subsurface ma-

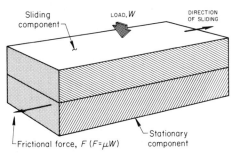

Fig. 5. Schematic representation of relation between normal load and frictional force on an object sliding across a stationary horizontal surface

terial, the condition of the surface has a decided effect on the friction level and may contribute to boundary lubrication. There are many ways of weakening the junction. In fact, a "natural" surface is so contaminated with adsorbed gases and solids that contact in air generally inhibits bonding of contacting asperities. Problems encountered with sliding surfaces in space missions have demonstrated the effect of truly clean surfaces kept clean in a gasless environment. Under these conditions where naturally occurring oxides and adsorbed films have been removed by heat or ion bombardment, metal surfaces bond together. In such an environment, where conventional lubricants would evaporate, low-shear-strength, low-vapor-pressure solids, such as metal sulfides, selenides and tellurides, have been applied as bonded coatings to reduce friction.

Even a few molecular layers of an organic material on a metal surface can account for a large-percentage decrease in its coefficient of friction. Published friction-coefficient values therefore are often highly questionable because of the effect of surface films.

Naturally occurring metal oxides generally reduce adhesion forces of surfaces. Some oxides are better "lubricants" than others. For instance, the friction produced by hardened steel sliding against hardened steel can have a threefold variation as the partial pressure of oxygen on the surface is varied. The lower oxides of iron (Fe_3O_4 or FeO) exist at low partial pressures of oxygen and have better lubricating properties than Fe_2O_3, the iron oxide normally found in air.

It is possible to encounter high friction in sliding contact when a combination of high speed and heavy load is encountered. This combination produces frictional heating, softening of surface layers and breakthrough of "protective" oxide films, bringing clean, active metal surfaces into contact. This process is the basis for friction welding, which can be used to join metals of different chemical compositions.

Surface Roughness and Crystal Structure. Other factors that have been found to be influential in controlling frictional forces include surface roughness and crystal structure. Generally, friction is highest when a surface is very rough and when interlocking of jagged high points occurs, or when the contacting surfaces are very smooth, allowing surface tension of fluid films or molecular attraction between the surfaces to become significant.

Studies of sliding friction using single-crystal materials in high vacuum have shown that materials with hexagonal, close-packed crystal structures exhibit lower friction than materials with body-centered-cubic, face-centered-cubic, or

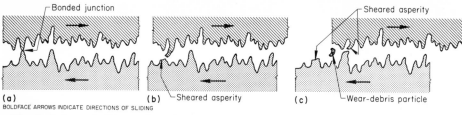

Fig. 6. Schematic illustration of one process by which a particle of wear debris is detached during adhesive wear. As the surfaces slide across one another, a bonded junction (a) is torn from one asperity (b), then is sheared off by impact with a larger, adjacent asperity to form the particle of wear debris (c).

tetragonal crystal structures. It also has been found that the coefficient of friction varies significantly depending on the crystallographic direction of sliding. Sliding in the close-packed direction in any crystal system produces the lowest friction. However, regardless of crystallographic direction, the coefficient of friction is high for clean surfaces of crystals; consequently, there are few applications in which the crystallographic direction of sliding is important.

Graphite is an outstanding solid lubricant that has very low friction, apparently because of its hexagonal crystal structure and easy slip in close-packed $\langle 0001 \rangle$ directions. However, the low friction of graphite actually is a consequence of adsorbed water vapor on exposed basal planes. Without adsorbed water vapor, the friction of graphite is high.

Mechanism of Adhesive Wear

True adhesive wear is most often found under nonlubricated or dry-contact conditions and when both contacting surfaces are metallic. Adhesive wear does occur in lubricated contact, but on a much reduced scale compared to nonlubricated contact.

A simple mathematical model for adhesive wear has been developed and modified by several researchers. It is based on the assumption that wear occurs by shearing of the true-contact area between two contacting surfaces and that the true-contact area is a function of the contact yield stress of the surface of the softer material (the mean contact yield stress is about three times the tensile yield stress). Thus, the lower the yield point the larger the true-contact area for a given load, and the greater the wear. Furthermore, because each asperity contact during motion of the surfaces has a statistical probability of producing a wear particle, wear is proportional to the total sliding distance. (Figure 6 is a schematic representation of a sequence of events by which a particle of wear debris can be produced in adhesive wear.) A simple equation has been derived on the basis of these assumptions:

$$V = KlW/p \qquad \text{(Eq 4)}$$

where V is volume loss, in cu mm; K is wear coefficient; l is sliding distance, in mm; W is normal load, in kg; and p is indentation hardness, in kg per sq mm.

It has been verified experimentally that wear is proportional to load and distance of sliding, and inversely proportional to the hardness of the softer material. The principle that wear is proportional to load holds so long as the wear occurs by a single mechanism. Increasing the load to the point where the mechanism of surface damage changes can be accompanied by a change in wear rate of one order of magnitude. The wear coefficient, K, has been interpreted as a measure of the probability that each asperity contact will produce a wear particle. The wear coefficients determined experimentally for various pairs of materials cover a wide range of values (several orders of magnitude), but for each pair there is a specific value. Representative values of K for the end of a cylinder

sliding against the flat surface of a ring at 1.8 meters per second under a 400-gram load are given for various combinations of cylinder and ring materials in Table 1.

The wear coefficient is derived from experiments in which a stationary specimen with a small surface area rubs against a moving specimen with a large surface area. Wear of the small stationary specimen is measured as loss in weight or volume, and K is derived from Eq 4. Wear rate of this specimen generally is high, because its contact area is in constant contact and does not have a chance to cool and oxidize as readily as the larger moving surface.

For most practical applications, volume or weight loss is converted to a linear value representing penetration or decrease in length. Therefore, the sizes and configurations of contacting bodies are important to consider when relating Eq 4 to component design. For instance, in analyzing a worn brush in an electric motor, it may be necessary to compare the actual wear (decrease in length) to the design wear rate, determined from laboratory tests of the brush material. In a worn journal bearing, the increase in diameter (resulting in an increase in bearing clearance) may need to be related to a predicted wear rate, which would have established the design life of the bearing. The volume loss predicted by Eq 4 does not depend on area. However, because the attribute having design importance is a linear dimension, the same volume loss represents a large linear decrease when the contact area is small and a small linear decrease when the contact area is large.

Abrasive Wear*

Abrasive wear occurs when hard particles, such as rocks, sand or fragments of certain hard metals, slide or roll under pressure across a surface. This action cuts grooves across the surface much like those produced by a cutting tool.

Abrasive wear is of considerable importance to the service life of any part moving in relation to an abrasive. Tools in contact with the ground, such as plows, cultivators, scraper blades, and bulldozer blades, are designed to operate in abrasives. Machines for processing ores, such as crushers, and for grinding of natural minerals, such as ball mills, also are subjected to abrasive wear. For many other types of machinery components, contact with abrasives is not a normal circumstance but may occur inadvertently.

*The contents of this section are based largely on material presented on pages 1 through 4 of SAE Information Report HSJ-965, "Abrasive Wear", Society of Automotive Engineers, Warrendale, Pa., Aug 1966.

Table 1. Wear Coefficients for Various Combinations of Materials Under Conditions of Dry Sliding(a)

| Sliding combination | | Wear coefficient (K) | Hardness of softer member, 10^6 g/cm² |
Cylinder material	Ring material		
Low-carbon steel	Low-carbon steel	7.0×10^{-3}	18.6
60-40 brass	Hardened steel	6.0×10^{-4}	9.5
Teflon	Hardened steel	2.5×10^{-5}	0.5
Bakelite	Hardened steel	7.5×10^{-6}	2.5
Beryllium copper	Hardened steel	3.7×10^{-5}	21.0
Tool steel	Hardened steel	1.3×10^{-4}	85.0
Stellite	Hardened steel	5.5×10^{-5}	69.0
Tungsten carbide	Low-carbon steel	4.0×10^{-6}	18.6
Tungsten carbide	Tungsten carbide	1.0×10^{-6}	130.0

(a) Wear coefficients given are for the end of a cylinder sliding against the flat surface of a ring at 1.8 meters per second under a 400-gram load.

Types of Abrasive Wear. Abrasive wear may be defined as the removal of material from a surface by mechanical action of abrasive (hard) particles in contact with the surface. As noted in Ref 1, the types of abrasive wear may be classified generally as (a) gouging abrasion, (b) high-stress grinding abrasion, and (c) low-stress scratching abrasion or erosion.

Gouging Abrasion. The result of this type of abrasive wear is the removal of large particles from a metal surface. Worn surfaces show heavy gouges.

High-Stress Grinding Abrasion. This type of abrasive wear occurs on the surfaces of components used for progressive fragmentation of abrasive particles. The wear is believed to be caused by concentrated compressive stress at the point of abrasive contact and to result from plastic flowing and fatiguing of ductile constituents and cracking of hard constituents of the metal surface. The use of the term "high-stress" in this classification is intended to imply that the crushing strength of the abrasive is exceeded.

Low-Stress Scratching Abrasion or Erosion. The result of this type of abrasive wear is scratching of the metal surface, and the scratches are usually minute. The stress imposed on the abrasive particle does not exceed the crushing strength of the abrasive.

The action of a hard particle on a surface under the influence of a force oblique to the surface generally is referred to as abrasive wear. The interaction between the particle (of high crushing strength) and the surface is very much like the interaction between a cutting tool and a workpiece in machining. With a ductile material, a particle similar to a continuous machining chip is removed from the surface by each cutting abrasive particle. With a brittle material, many particles are removed during a single encounter with an abrasive particle. The parameters that are important in metal cutting should be important also in abrasive wear. However, in contrast to most metal-cutting operations, it is difficult to precisely define the configuration of the cutting faces of abrasive particles because of their random shape.

Mechanisms of Abrasive Wear. Abrasive wear differs from adhesive wear (Ref 2, 3 and 4), which occurs between two surfaces. In adhesive wear, the contacting asperities on adjacent surfaces bond together, and the resulting interaction can lead to the removal of material from the surfaces. In abrasive wear, material is removed from the surfaces by the cutting action of abrasive particles. The hardness of the abrasive particle must exceed that of the abraded surface in order for cutting to occur. When the crushing strength of the abrasive is exceeded, the method of material removal may be somewhat different from a simple cutting action.

The force component that is normal to the surface and that acts on the hard particle causes penetration of the surface by the particle. The force component that is parallel to the surface causes relative tangential motion to occur between the particle and the surface. This results in shearing, plowing or chipping of the surface, which produces grooves. For ductile surfaces and hard particles with sharp-edged faces, shearing occurs and metal is removed in a form resembling a continuous machining chip. Particles with smooth-edged or rounded faces tend to merely plow a ductile surface. During plowing, the surface material is pushed transversely to the direction of the particle motion to form a groove. Most of the displaced material piles up along the groove edges rather than being removed from the surface.

The severity of abrasive wear for a given material and abrasive will vary markedly, depending on the magnitude of the acting forces. When the forces are low, the wear rate per abrasive particle is also low. This mechanism is sometimes referred to as scratching (low-stress abrasion) when either fixed or loose particles are involved. In shop terminology, this type of abrasion is referred to as polishing. It is called erosion when flowing loose particles attack a single surface. During erosion, the over-all wear rate can be high if the flow rate of the abrasive particles is high. When the magnitude of the acting forces is higher, the wear rate per abrasive particle will also be higher, and the mechanism is referred to as gouging when either fixed particles or loose particles are involved.

When loose particles are present between two sliding surfaces (entrapped loose particles), this type of abrasion is referred to as lapping in shop terminology. This three-body, loose-particle wear removes less material per encounter than two-body, fixed-particle wear because the loose particles tend to roll without cutting about 90% of the time (Ref 5). If the stress applied to the abrasive is so high as to exceed its crushing strength, then this type of abrasion is referred to as grinding abrasion. Here the abrasive is being ground up and was initially of a small size. This high-stress grinding abrasion should not be confused with machine-shop grinding, which is classified as gouging abrasion.

When crushing of the abrasive occurs, as in grinding abrasion, the mechanism of material removal may be somewhat different from the simple cutting mechanism. The abrasive may have little opportunity to roll or cut before crushing occurs, and the major effect on the abraded surface would then be due to the concentrated compressive stress at the point of abrasive contact. The surface of a ductile material will be displaced plastically by the abrasive in the manner of an indentation-hardness impression.

With many closely spaced impressions, the displaced material may flow back and forth, to fail eventually by fatigue. There is also the possibility of some cutting action by the rupturing abrasive, with the cutting force being supplied by the elastic energy stored in the compressed abrasive particle. On the surface of a hard material, little plastic displacement will occur. Wear in this situation may occur as a result of brittle cracking (chipping) of the surface material. There is also the possibility of subsurface cracking due to fatigue under repeated stressing, as occurs in the spalling of ball-bearing raceways.

Analytical Approaches. All types of abrasive wear involve basically the same mechanism, except perhaps when the abrasive particle is crushed. Penetration and subsequent grooving of the surface by the abrasive particle occur. When the abrasive is crushed, grooving of the surface may not occur; however, penetration of the surface does occur. The appearance of the wear fragments and the wear surface will vary depending on the ductility of the surface material and on the configuration of the particle.

The means by which force is applied to the abrasive particle can be divided into two categories: (a) the direct mechanical application of force by the surfaces when entrapped loose particles are involved, or by the abrasive bond and the surface when fixed abrasive particles are involved; and (b) the kinetic application of force resulting from the kinetic energy of a flowing abrasive particle as it encounters a surface.

The first category of force application is experienced in gouging abrasion, grinding abrasion and scratching abrasion. The second category is experienced in erosion abrasion, and pertains to the handling of abrasives in pneumatic or liquid systems, sand blasting, or dust erosion of compressor blades in gas turbines. The second category of force application is probably not as common as the first. However, it will be considered here, because a fair amount of analytical work has been carried out for this category. There is a distinctly different analytical expression for abrasive wear for each category of force application.

Theory of Abrasive Wear With Direct Mechanical Application of Force to Abrasive Particles. There have been several investigations of abrasive wear involving direct mechanical application of force to the abrasive particles (Ref 5 to 12). There is general agreement that simplified theory results in the following differential expression for volume rate of wear per unit length of sliding, q:

$$q = dQ/dl, \text{ or } q \propto W/p \qquad \text{(Eq 5)}$$

where Q is volume swept out by abrasive, l is sliding distance, W is load, and p

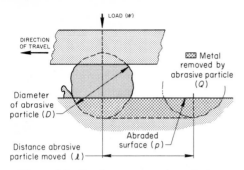

Fig. 7. Idealized representation of abrasive wear resulting from mechanical application of force to an abrasive particle

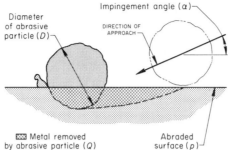

Fig. 8. Idealized representation of abrasive wear resulting from kinetic application of force to an abrasive particle

is hardness of abraded surface. If q_t is the time rate of wear, then $q_t = qv$, where v is velocity of sliding. Figure 7 is an idealized representation of this type of wear.

Equation 5 assumes that the abrasive particles are harder than the surface being abraded and that the abrasive particle is rigid (not crushed). Equation 5 is valid for abrasive-particle size, D, greater than 70 microns. (For D less than 70 microns, q also depends on D; the relationship between q and D is different, however, because with fixed particles clogging occurs and with loose particles the wear fragments are about the same size as the abrasive particles.) The ratio of abrasive particles that cut to those that do not cut, and particle shape, are important.

Equation 5 applies to annealed metals. The wear resistance $(1/q)$ of hardened steels is a function of their elastic limit, as well as of their hardness. However, in this instance, the wear resistance varies as low fractional powers of these parameters. Fatigue of the surface may also be of importance. For brittle materials, higher wear rates can occur because of the possibility of the formation of wear fragments having a total volume greater than the volume swept through by the abrasive particle (Ref 5 and 8). However, brittle materials do generally follow the relationship of Eq 5 even though higher wear rates are encountered (Ref 13).

The presence of water vapor in the atmosphere, or the presence of a lubricating fluid on the abraded surface, can increase the wear rate, apparently by flushing wear debris from the system and thereby increasing the effectiveness of the abrading action. Rabinowicz (Ref 14) discusses this effect, together with some of the other limitations of Eq 5 mentioned above.

Equation 5 is not necessarily valid for grinding abrasion — that is, when small abrasive particles are being crushed. A theoretical expression for the wear rate in grinding abrasion is not presently available. Grinding abrasion is common in ball and rod milling.

In ball milling, the abrasive is caught between adjacent balls or between ball and liner, and the ball weight crushes the hard particles (Ref 1). Although impact may occur in ball mills, it is not the important crushing force (Ref 1). Grinding can be produced without impact. In fact, the most efficient ball mills are those that only roll and tumble the balls. Because the abrasive may have little opportunity to cut before it is crushed, the abraded surfaces are subjected merely to repetitive concentrated compressive stress over a period of time. The abraded surface therefore is subjected to attack similar to that resulting from sand blasting with the blast directed perpendicular to the surface. This is substantiated by the fact that there seems to be a correlation between results of sand-blasting wear tests and results of ball-mill wear tests.

Bitter (Ref 15 and 16) indicates that no cutting wear should occur during sand blasting at a 90° impingement angle and that frequent repetition of elastic impact should not cause wear, apart from possible fatigue damage. If, however, during collision, the elastic limit is exceeded, plastic deformation occurs at the point of maximum stress; the repeated collisions of a large number of particles will form a plastically deformed surface layer. The resulting deformation hardening increases the elastic limit, and, upon further plastic deformation, this limit will eventually become equal to the maximum strength of the material. The material has then become relatively hard and brittle and can no longer be plastically deformed. If, subsequently, upon increasing the load, the elastic limit of the material is exceeded, the surface is destroyed and fragments of it are removed. Therefore, an initially ductile material will wear in a manner similar to abrasive wear of brittle materials. Bitter refers to this type of wear as "deformation wear". Equation 7, further on in this section, gives the expression for volume worn by this mechanism in brittle materials. Equation 7 and Bitter's work apply to impact between the abrasive and the surface; however, ball milling in-

volves no impact. Therefore, Eq 7 does not apply to grinding abrasion, but it seems feasible that the fundamental abrasion mechanism for this type of wear could very well be a "deformation wear" mechanism. This would be a good starting point in developing a theory for grinding abrasion.

Theory of Abrasive Wear With Kinetic Application of Force to Abrasive Particles (Erosion). In abrasive wear in which kinetic force is applied to the abrasive particle (erosion), the kinetic energy of the particle is dissipated on a ductile surface in plastic work, which causes indentation or shearing of the surface. When particles merely indent the surface, layerlike exfoliations are extruded from the surface (Ref 17). However, when shearing takes place, material is gouged out of the surface. On brittle materials, the kinetic energy of the particle is dissipated in crack propagation, which causes chipping of the surface.

The volume, Q, removed from a ductile surface due to a mass, m, of angular abrasive particles having a velocity, v, is given by Eq 6 (Ref 18, 19 and 20):

$$Q \approx mv^2/8p \times f(\alpha) \qquad \text{(Eq 6)}$$

where v is velocity of particle approach; p is hardness of abraded surface; and $f(\alpha)$ is $(\sin 2\alpha - 3\sin^2\alpha)$ for $\alpha \leq 18.5°$, and is $\cos^2\alpha/3$ for $\alpha \geq 18.5°$ (α is angle of particle impingement, measured relative to the abraded surface).

If m is expressed as the mass impinging on a surface per unit of time, thereby establishing a time rate, Q becomes q_t — that is, the time rate of wear. Figure 8 is an idealized representation of this type of wear. A more recent treatment for this type of wear takes into account the elastic properties of the abrasive particles and the abraded surface (Ref 15).

The volume, Q, removed from a brittle surface under similar impact conditions, but not necessarily restricted to angular particles, is given by Eq 7 (Ref 16):

$$Q \propto \frac{m(v\sin\alpha - K)^2}{e} \qquad \text{(Eq 7)}$$

where K is velocity of impact at which the elastic limit is just reached, and e is energy needed to remove one unit volume of material from the surface. Values for K and e in Eq 7 are:

$$K \propto P_e^{5/2}(1/D)^{1/2}[(1-\mu_1)/E_1 + (1-\mu_2)/E_2]^2 \qquad \text{(Eq 7a)}$$
$$e \propto P_e^2/E_2 \qquad \text{(Eq 7b)}$$

where P_e is elastic limit, μ is Poisson's ratio, E is modulus of elasticity, D is size of abrasive particles, and subscripts 1 and 2 refer to the particle and the surface, respectively.

Equation 7 assumes that the particle penetrates into the surface to a depth

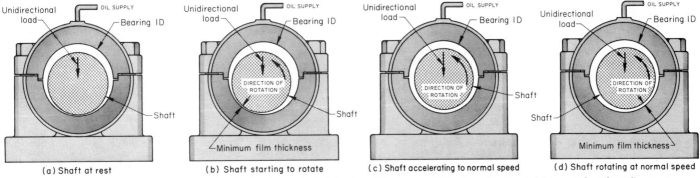

Fig. 9. Step-by-step development of a hydrodynamic lubricating film in a unidirectionally loaded journal bearing. See text.

only a fraction of its own diameter. For sharp-edged particles, the resulting K value will be smaller. At high velocities, large fragments may be broken from the surface, resulting in a lower value of e.

Equation 6 predicts reasonably well the trends for silicon carbide abrasives on 1020 steel and for silica dust on 1050 steel. However, it underestimates Q at high α angles (Ref 18, 19 and 20); this error has been found to be due to the lack of accounting for the elastic properties of the abrasive particles and the abraded surface (Ref 15). The erosion of glass by steel shot is in good agreement with Eq 7 (Ref 16). These expressions do not take into account fatiguing of the surface, which may be of importance.

Lubricated Wear

One important means of reducing wear is lubrication. Lubrication not only reduces power consumption needed to overcome friction but also protects rolling and sliding contact surfaces from excessive wear. Even with lubrication, however, wear still occurs.

On lubricated surfaces, the wear process is mild and generates fine debris of a particle size as small as one or two microns. Abrasive wear predominates under lubricated conditions. Electron-microscope examination of worn surfaces from lubricated assemblies usually reveals a multitude of fine scratches oriented in the direction of relative motion. The fine debris that is generated by abrasion becomes suspended in the oil or grease. In devices using circulating-oil lubrication, advantage has been taken of the fact that wear debris can be analyzed by spectroscopy, and that deterioration of the device by wear can be diagnosed from these results. This technique is used to monitor the condition of vital components in aircraft and locomotive engines.

Modes of Lubrication

There are several basic modes of lubrication. In all modes, contact surfaces are separated by a lubricating medium, which may be a solid, a semisolid or a pressurized liquid or gaseous film. *Hy-drodynamic lubrication* is a system in which the shape and relative motion of the sliding surfaces cause the formation of a fluid film having sufficient pressure to separate the surfaces. *Hydrostatic lubrication* is a system in which the lubricant is supplied under sufficient external pressure to separate the opposing surfaces by a fluid film. *Elastohydro-dynamic lubrication* is a system in which the friction and film thickness between the two bodies in relative motion are determined by the elastic properties of the bodies, in combination with the viscous properties of the lubricant at the prevailing pressure, temperature and rate of shear. *Dry-film (solid-film) lubrication* is a system in which a coating of solid lubricant separates the opposing surfaces and the lubricant itself wears away. *Boundary lubrication* and *thin-film lubrication* are two modes in which friction and wear are affected by properties of the contacting surfaces as well as by properties of the lubricant. In boundary lubrication, each surface is covered by a chemically bonded fluid or semisolid film, which may or may not serve to separate opposing surfaces, and viscosity of the lubricant is not a factor affecting friction and wear. In thin-film lubrication, the lubricant usually is not bonded to the surfaces, it does separate opposing surfaces, and lubricant viscosity affects friction and wear.

Mechanical devices often operate under several lubrication modes simultaneously or alternately. For instance, when a hydrodynamic journal bearing starts turning from rest, it operates under boundary lubrication and then thin-film lubrication for a short time until it lifts up on a stable, thick oil film and the solid surfaces separate. During the initial boundary-lubricated conditions, wear occurs. The process is reversed when rotation is slowed or stopped. On the other hand, gears experience both elastohydrodynamic and boundary lubrication at the same time. For example, during meshing of one tooth of a spur gear with a tooth of a mating gear, initial contact is sliding contact, which results in wear and scuffing at the tips and roots of the teeth. Contact along the pitch line, however, is essentially rolling contact, and elastohydrodynamic conditions prevail. Pitchline damage takes the form of pitting or spalling and is similar to rolling-contact fatigue found in ball and roller bearings.

Hydrodynamic Lubrication. The step-by-step development of a hydrodynamic fluid film is illustrated in Fig. 9 for a full journal bearing under unidirectional loading. In Fig. 9(a), the machine is at rest. The oil supply is shut off, and most of the oil has leaked from the normally full clearance space (greatly exaggerated in the illustration). The remaining film on the bearing and journal surfaces is extremely thin, and there is probably some metal-to-metal contact between asperities on the mating surfaces at the bottom where the journal surface rests on the bearing.

In Fig. 9(b), the machine has been started and the shaft has begun to rotate. The oil supply has been turned on, and oil has filled the clearance space. At the start, friction is momentarily high, and the shaft tends to climb up the side of the bearing in a direction opposite to the direction of rotation. As it does so, it rolls onto a thicker oil film, friction is reduced, and the tendency to climb is balanced by a tendency to slip back on the thicker oil film.

As the journal gains speed (see Fig. 9c), oil is drawn into the wedge-shaped clearance space at the lower left. A fluid pressure is developed in this region of the film, which pushes the journal to the right and lifts it.

Finally, at full speed, the journal is supported on a thick film and assumes the position shown in Fig. 9(d) — on the opposite side of the bearing from the position at start-up (compare with Fig. 9b). The converging wedge-shaped oil film has moved to a position under the journal, and the point of nearest approach of the journal and bearing (that is, the point of minimum film thickness) is slightly to the right of a vertical line through the center of the bearing.

Fluid dynamics can be used to define and predict load capacity, friction and heat generation in a fluid film when hydrodynamic lubrication, hydrostatic lubrication, or elastohydrodynamic lubrication prevails. The viscosity of the lubricant is important in determining operating characteristics and whether or not wear can be anticipated. The pressure generated in the liquid-lubricant film by the shearing process supports the load and keeps the solid surfaces separated. As the load increases, film temperature increases, shear rate decreases, film thickness diminishes, and the solid surfaces approach each other. When the thickness of the lubricant film approaches the dimensions of surface roughness, asperity contact begins and evidence of wear can be detected. For hydrodynamic conditions, the film thickness, t, or closest approach of the bearing surfaces, depends on this relationship:

$$t \approx \left(\frac{\mu v}{W}\right)^{1/2} \qquad \text{(Eq 8)}$$

where μ is bulk viscosity of the lubricant at bearing temperature, v is sliding velocity, and W is bearing load. A journal bearing operating under hydrodynamic conditions is somewhat self-regulating. That is, with an established thick lubricating film, an increase in velocity will increase the shear rate of the oil film, and the resulting increase in energy input will increase the oil-film temperature, resulting in a decrease in viscosity. In turn, the decrease in viscosity will diminish the effect of the velocity increase on film thickness. In addition, when the correct bearing materials are selected, a wear-in process will decrease the peaks of the surface asperities and allow operation on a thinner and thinner film without metal-to-metal contact and wear as the bearing continues to operate. Many sliding surfaces in machinery do not benefit from this seemingly self-regulating, infinite-life lubrication system. Because of misalignment, vibration, limited lubricant supply, and repeated start-stop operation, many bearings continually operate in the boundary regime where asperity contact and wear occur.

Hydrostatic lubrication, often used in high-speed precision bearings, is similar to the thick-film stage of hydrodynamic lubrication in that opposing surfaces slide on a relatively thick film of lubricant. However, in hydrostatic lubrication, the film is maintained by fluid pressure from an external source and by a fixed or controlled rate of leakage from between the surfaces. Because most hydrostatic bearings are designed to have fluid-pressure peaks equally spaced around the bearing surface, the shaft is positioned more nearly in the center of the bearing than in hydrodynamic lubrication, and film thickness is about the same for any two points around the bearing. One of the main advantages of hydrostatic lubrication over hydrodynamic lubrication is that, with hydrostatic lubrication, the shaft is supported

by a full oil film at any speed. Thus thin-film and boundary lubrication on start-up and shutdown, with the attendant increased friction and wear, are avoided. In addition, thick-film lubrication can be maintained with low-viscosity lubricants that in a hydrodynamic bearing would not be able to develop enough film pressure to support the shaft load.

Elastohydrodynamic Lubrication. Under elastohydrodynamic rolling-contact conditions, typical of ball and roller bearings, minimum lubricant-film thickness, $t_{\min}$, follows approximately the relationship expressed in:

$$t_{\min.} \approx (\mu\alpha)^{0.7}(N^{0.7}/W^{0.09}) \qquad \text{(Eq 9)}$$

where μ is bulk viscosity of lubricant at bearing temperature, α is coefficient of viscosity increase with pressure, N is rotational speed, and W is bearing load.

Under rolling-contact conditions, film thickness is not as sensitive to load as it is to rotational speed. An increase in load produces an increase in elastic deflection in the contact area and distributes the contact pressure over a larger area. Because rolling contact involves initial line, or point, contact, very large localized contact stress results, necessitating the use of high-yield-strength bearing materials (heat treated bearing steels). The extremely thin lubricant films involved (as small as ten millionths of an inch) also require very smooth surface finishes to ensure true elastohydrodynamic lubrication. Nevertheless, wear does occur in ball and roller bearings.

Rolling-contact wear can be very insidious, progressing with an improvement in surface finish and with no loss in sphericity, but with sufficient loss of material to cause loss of vital preload, such as can occur in miniature precision bearings. Spalling or pitting is another, more dramatic type of "wear" that can occur in rolling-contact applications. This is a self-aggravating type of surface damage that causes performance of rolling-element bearings to become increasingly rough and that ultimately may result in fracture of rolling elements. In recent studies of the role of lubrication in determining life of ball and roller bearings, it has been found that the ratio of minimum film thickness to combined surface roughness of two opposing surfaces provides a fairly good indicator of useful life. The greater the incidence of asperity contact through the lubricant film, the sooner the onset of spalling.

Boundary lubrication occurs in a large number of mechanical devices, because the conditions required for full-film lubrication (or even thin-film lubrication) using a fluid substance often cannot be attained without utilizing a complex and expensive lubrication system. For instance, a grease-lubricated bearing sub-

jected to intermittent oscillating motion under heavy load operates almost exclusively under boundary lubrication. Under these conditions, high points or asperities on surfaces come into contact, but bonding is prevented by very thin, soft, solid films. These films shear easily and prevent metal removal or heavy scoring of the surfaces.

Boundary films have a wide variety of forms and compositions. Experiments have shown that a single monolayer of stearic acid will lubricate and prevent asperity adhesion. Under practical operating conditions, however, the boundary films active in machinery are complex reaction products of the lubricant, the atmosphere, and the constituents in the bearing surface. Although full-film conditions of lubrication do not exist, with the addition of lubricant the wear rate of contacting surfaces can be reduced to as little as 5% of the rate for nonlubricated wear.

Surface temperature probably has the greatest influence on the effectiveness of boundary lubrication. Frictional energy produces heat on sliding surfaces. With boundary lubrication, generally there is not sufficient lubricant flow to carry away the heat, compared with hydrodynamic lubrication, which is quite effective in removing frictional heat. There are several possible consequences of frictional heating during boundary lubrication. Under extreme-pressure (EP) lubrication, chemical additives in the lubricant react with metal surfaces to form soft, solid reaction products, which presumably are the agents that prevent metal adhesion and surface damage. Heat increases the reaction rate so that at asperity contacts, where the local "flash" surface temperatures are highest, the reaction rate is greatest and a solid lubricant is provided in the spots where the potential for adhesion is greatest. Thus, by chemical attack modified by the localized surface temperature, the occurrence of severe wear is prevented by substitution of mild corrosion.

Effect on Surface Features

The features on a surface that has been worn under lubricated conditions are different from those found on a surface that has undergone nonlubricated wear. Examination of sliding surfaces by high-magnification electron microscopy reveals that, when a lubricant is present, wear occurs by deformation of the highest surface asperities rather than by galling and tearing, which predominate with nonlubricated wear. For example, when a ground surface is subjected to mild lubricated wear, the microscopic surface ridges resulting from the abrasive action of hard particles in the grinding wheel come into contact with the opposing surface and flatten out. The highest ridges come into contact first and are subjected to large contact stresses, which cause plastic flow. When the tops of the ridges deform, they often develop thin tongues of extruded metal that subsequently break off, forming very fine particles of wear debris. In this way, the surface is gradually leveled or smoothed out as more and more ridges come into contact.

On polished or lapped surfaces, lubricated wear produces an extremely fine pattern of microscratches that often are invisible except by electron microscopy. Examination of these microscratches reveals that they are caused by plastic deformation and not by plowing or micromachining. The deformation appears to be the result of contact by hard asperities in the mating surface, or by fine debris. Each scratch usually is a shallow trough with a flat bottom and steep sides. The ridges produced by this scratching process are worn, which produces fine debris much in the same way as wear debris is generated from ground surfaces.

For additional information on lubricated wear, including examples of lubricated wear in service, the reader is referred to the following articles in this volume: Failures of Sliding Bearings (page 397), Failures of Rolling-Element Bearings (page 416), Failures of Mechanical Face Seals (page 437), and Failures of Gears (page 507).

Lubricants

Almost any surface film can act as a lubricant, preventing cold welding of asperities on opposing surfaces or allowing opposing surfaces to slide across one another at a lower frictional force than would prevail if the film were not present. Lubricants may be either liquid or solid. (On some occasions, gas films may act as lubricants.) One of the functions of a lubricant is to carry away heat generated by two surfaces sliding under contact pressure. Liquid lubricants can dissipate heat better than solid or semifluid lubricants, but in all types the shear properties of the lubricant are critical to its performance.

Properties of Lubricants. Liquid lubricants maintain separation of opposing surfaces by pressure within the film, which opposes the contact force. This pressure may be generated within the film, usually as a result of the shape of the opposing surfaces, or the liquid may be forced between the opposing surfaces by pressure from an external source. Regardless of the means of creating pressure within the film, the opposing surfaces slide on a pad of liquid. Friction and wear are directly influenced by the thickness and shear properties (viscosity) of the liquid. Where appropriate, the use of a high-viscosity lubricant usually re-

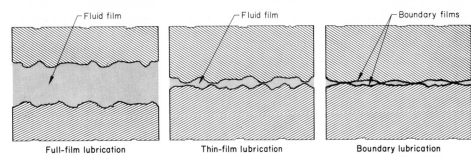

Full-film lubrication   Thin-film lubrication   Boundary lubrication

Fig. 10. Schematic illustration of the relation of surface roughness to film thickness under conditions of full-film, thin-film and boundary lubrication

sults in a relatively thick film and a low wear rate. However, high sliding speeds cannot be accommodated by a viscous film, because excessive heat generated within the film causes it to become less viscous and to chemically decompose.

Full-film (thick-film) lubrication, such as occurs under hydrostatic or hydrodynamic conditions, effectively separates asperities on opposing surfaces, whereas thin-film and boundary lubrication allow asperity contact. The differences among these three conditions of liquid lubrication are illustrated schematically in Fig. 10.

Some special types of boundary lubricants, most notably the extreme-pressure (EP) lubricants, react with a metallic surface, often at high temperatures, to produce a monomolecular film on the surface. This very thin film "contaminates" the mating surfaces and prevents metal-to-metal contact or adhesion. Extreme-pressure lubricants often contain extremely reactive constituents that re-form the film instantly if it is scraped off one of the surfaces. Film formation of this type is, in effect, corrosion; when it is uncontrolled, or when the film is repeatedly scraped off and re-formed, deterioration of the surface can result.

Solid-film lubricants must be adherent to be effective; otherwise, they allow metal-to-metal contact or introduce unwanted particles that roll and slide within the joint. When they can be kept within the joint, graphite and molybdenum disulfide make good lubricants because they shear easily in certain

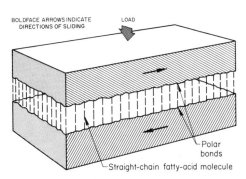

BOLDFACE ARROWS INDICATE DIRECTIONS OF SLIDING   LOAD

Polar bonds

Straight-chain fatty-acid molecule

Fig. 11. Schematic illustration of the polar bonding and orientation of straight-chain fatty-acid molecules in a boundary lubricant between sliding surfaces

crystallographic directions. Hard, adherent oxide films, such as Fe_3O_4 on steel or anodized Al_2O_3 on aluminum, withstand wear because they resist penetration and do not bond with most mating surfaces.

Lubricating oils are relatively free-flowing organic substances that are used to lower the coefficient of friction in mechanical devices. They are available in a broad range of viscosities, and many are blended or contain additives to make them suitable for specific uses. In general, lubricating substances that are fluid at 20 C (68 F) are termed oils; lubricating substances that are solid or semifluid at 20 C are termed greases or fats.

Oils are derived from petroleum (*mineral oils*) or from plants or animals (*fixed oils*). Mineral oils are classified according to source (type of crude), refining process (distillate or residual), and commercial use. The commercial mineral-oil-base products consist mainly of saturated hydrocarbons (even though naphthene-base crudes are predominantly unsaturated) in the form of chain or ring molecules that are chemically inactive and do not have polar heads. These commercial products may or may not contain waxes, volatile compounds, fixed oils, and special-purpose additives. Fixed oils and fats differ from mineral oils in that they (a) consist of an alcohol radical and a fatty-acid radical, (b) can be reacted with an alkali (sodium hydroxide or potassium hydroxide, for example) to from glycerin and soap. (c) cannot be distilled without decomposing, and (d) contain 9 to 12.5% oxygen. All fixed oils are insoluble in water and, except for castor oil, are insoluble in alcohol at room temperature.

Fixed oils generally are considered to have greater "oiliness" than mineral oils. Oiliness is a term that describes the relative ability of any lubricant to act as a boundary lubricant. Electron-diffraction experiments have shown that molecules of the effective lubricating agent — a long-chain fatty acid of high molecular weight, such as stearic acid or oleic acid — are attached to a metallic surface by polar bonding and stand up much like individual strands in a pile carpet, as illustrated in Fig. 11. This results in a

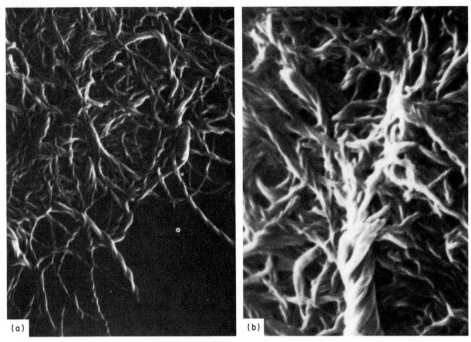

Fig. 12. Scanning electron micrographs showing the fibrous appearance of soap particles in a lithium-base grease at magnifications of (a) *15,000× and* (b) *24,000×*

surface layer with high adhesion, high resistance to contact stress, and low resistance to lateral shear along the surface.

Lubricating grease, as defined by ASTM, is a solid to semifluid product consisting of a dispersion of a thickening agent in a liquid lubricant. In more practical terms, most greases are stabilized mixtures of mineral oil and metallic soap. The soap is usually a calcium, sodium or lithium compound and is present in the form of fibers (see Fig. 12) whose size and configuration are characteristic of the metallic radical in the soap compound.

Solid lubricants, which are solids with lubricating properties, can be maintained between two moving surfaces to reduce friction and wear. Numerous solid inorganic and organic compounds, as well as certain metals and composite materials, may be classified as solid lubricants. Molybdenum disulfide, graphite and polytetrafluoroethylene (TFE) are the solid lubricants most commonly used. Several hundred different compounds and mixtures have been described as potential solid lubricants.

Solid lubricants have been used as thin films, structural sections of bearing assemblies, reinforced laminates, and inserts. Figure 13 shows three bearing designs utilizing different means for solid lubrication: a rolling-element bearing having films of solid lubricant bonded to the surfaces of the raceways and the retainer (Fig. 13a), a plain spherical bearing having a liner of resin-bonded TFE fibers between the spherical inner ring and the outer ring (Fig. 13b), and a journal bearing having a spring-loaded solid insert of molybdenum disulfide in the housing to maintain a supply of lubricant to the shaft (Fig. 13c).

Although solid lubricants may be applied to achieve design simplification or weight reduction, they usually are adopted because of their good stability (a) at elevated temperatures, (b) in chemically active environments, and (c) when exposed to nuclear radiation.

Solid lubricants also provide certain advantages in high-vacuum, aerospace or cryogenic applications, where liquids would evaporate or congeal.

Lubricant Failures Leading to Wear

In devices that depend on lubricants to combat friction and avoid deterioration by wear, failure of the lubricant can be disastrous. Most lubricant failures occur by (a) chemical decomposition, (b) contamination, (c) changes in properties caused by excessive heat, or (d) outright loss from, or inadequate flow of a pressurized fluid into, lubricated areas. Lubricating oils and greases can fail by any one of the foregoing processes alone. However, in most situations, chemical decomposition, contamination and temperature are all involved and are interrelated. For example, when oil is heated in the presence of air, oxidation occurs. Oxidation increases the viscosity and organic-acid concentration of mineral oils, with the result that varnish and lacquer deposits may form on hot metal surfaces. Under severe conditions, the deposits may be converted to hard, carbonaceous substances. Fixed oils absorb oxygen more readily than do mineral oils, and some may dry, thicken, and form elastic solids. Certain fixed oils (castor, olive, sperm and lard oils) oxidize more slowly than others. These fixed oils are more widely used in blended oils because of their nondrying characteristics. Temperature affects oxidation rates; in mineral and blended oils, for example, the rate doubles with each 10 C (18 F) rise in temperature. Oxidation rates also are higher when the oil is agitated or foams, or when catalysts such as copper or acids are present.

In general, solid-film lubricants fail by mechanical removal of microscopically thin layers. Wear debris, which consists primarily of lubricant particles, is generated by the sliding action of a sharp edge against the bonded film on a contact surface. The sharp edge shears a layer of the film (and sometimes the entire film) from the substrate. Contact between a rolling element and a sharp ridge can chip the film, which often initiates more extensive failure. This process eventually results in a lack of dynamic stability (as would result from excessive clearance in a bearing) or in galling and seizing of metallic contact surfaces.

Many bonded solid lubricants derive their adhesion from binders, which are incorporated into the film in quantities up to about 20% by volume. Metals, oxides, silicates, or other ceramics are the most common binders. When wear debris contains binder particles, it abrades the remaining film more rapidly than when it consists solely of particles of the lubricating substance.

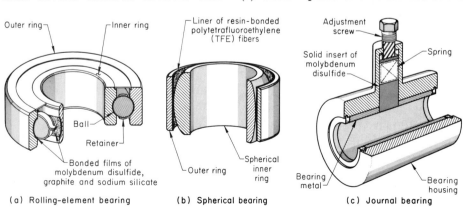

Fig. 13. Bearing designs using three different types of solid lubrication

Pressurized lubricating systems involving circulation of fluid lubricant are susceptible to certain types of failure that affect the ability of the system to provide the required flow rate or pressure at the point of lubricant injection. Decomposition of wax-containing mineral oils or contamination of oil with certain chemical substances can cause formation of sludge, which may clog flow passages, resulting in loss of flow or pressure, or both. Severe agitation of the oil sometimes results in entrapment of air in the form of tiny bubbles (foaming). The presence of water, many additives, and particulate foreign matter (debris) in oils increases the likelihood of their forming stable foams. Foaming causes pump-inlet starvation, loss of circulation, and sponginess in control systems, and can cause an oil reservoir to overflow because of the volumetric increase resulting from air entrapment. Increases in viscosity caused by oil decomposition (oxidation, for example) or by excessive cooling of the oil fed to the pump can cause reduced flow of the circulating oil and starvation of bearing surfaces. A decrease in viscosity because of excessively high operating temperatures can cause a reduction in film thickness in a hydrostatic or hydrodynamic bearing, resulting in increased wear or seizure.

Contamination of the lubricant with water or reactive chemical substances can lead to lubricant decomposition or corrosion of contact surfaces, or both. Contamination with abrasive substances or debris can cause abrasive wear, especially when the size of the contaminant particles is about the same as the thickness of the lubricating film.

In internal-combustion engines, water, halide acids, sulfur acids, and products of partial combustion of fuel hydrocarbons are picked up by the lubricating oil. These contaminants can cause a wide variety of undesirable chemical reactions with oil and metallic surfaces, resulting in the formation of varnish deposits, sludges or viscous emulsions in the oil, or in corrosive wear of engine components.

Because of their chemical nature, fixed oils are particularly susceptible to chemical alteration by alkalis. Alkalis cause saponification (formation of soap) by direct chemical reaction with the fatty acids in fixed oils. This reaction alters the nature of the lubricant and, consequently, its lubricating properties.

Viscosity of mineral oils, fixed oils, and greases is affected by both temperature and pressure. An increase in pressure causes an increase in viscosity, although the effect is generally not significant except at very high pressures. Conversely, any change in temperature has a very significant effect on viscosity. Decreasing the temperature of mineral oil from 100 C (212 F) to 0 C (32 F) can

increase viscosity by 100 times or more, making the oil much less free-flowing. The viscosity of fixed oils is affected to a lesser degree by temperature; for example, the viscosity of lard oil is increased by only about 30 times when the temperature is decreased from 100 C (212 F) to 0 C (32 F).

Greases that are solid or semisolid at room temperature gradually soften with increasing temperature and can become fluid and free-flowing at operating temperatures from 95 to 205 C (200 to 400 F), depending on the type of grease. Every grease has a "dropping point", defined as the temperature at which the first drop of liquid grease falls in a standard test. This temperature is the lower boundary of the melting range of the grease.

Oils containing substantial quantities of volatile compounds may lose these components by evaporation when operating temperatures are too high. This process not only alters the viscosity, but also upsets the chemical nature of the oil, thus changing other properties. In some instances, volatilization can take place within the lubricating film — for example, when frictional heat is ineffectively removed by the circulating fluid. Bubble formation within the film reduces the load-carrying capacity of the film, leading to adhesive or abrasive wear or, in severe cases, cavitation-erosion of opposing surfaces.

Transition Temperature. When boundary lubrication is provided by soft, metallic soaps (iron stearate, for example), a rise in surface temperature can result in a marked increase in the coefficient of friction and a sudden change in wear rate from mild to severe. The temperature at which this change occurs (transition temperature) is the point at which the soap desorbs from the metal surface and no longer provides a bonded, continuous surface film. Transition temperatures generally are within the range of 120 to 205 C (250 to 400 F), depending on the lubricant and the chemical composition of the metal substrate. Extreme-pressure (EP) lubricants function by reaction with the metal surface rather than by adsorption of components in the lubricant, and often are used as substitutes for soap-type boundary lubricants when operating temperatures exceed the transition temperature.

Prevention of Lubricant Failures

Often, lubricant failure can be traced to the selection of an inappropriate lubricant. Petroleum lubricating oils are available in a wide variety of formulations, with an equally wide variety of special properties. When these properties cannot be obtained by conventional refining techniques, or are obtainable only at a very high cost by refining, they are imparted to the lubricant by additives.

Oil additives may serve to improve one or more of the properties of the base oil, to impart to it entirely new performance characteristics, or to reduce the rate at which undesirable changes in the oil take place during service. Some of the more common additives include:

1 **Viscosity-Index Improvers.** These substances decrease the effect that temperature has on viscosity, making the oil more viscous at high temperature than it would be without the additive.
2 **Pour-Point Depressants.** These substances make a wax-containing oil less viscous at low temperatures by inhibiting the growth and coalescence of wax crystals suspended in the oil.
3 **Defoamants.** These additives promote the coalescence of tiny entrapped air bubbles into larger bubbles, which can rise to the surface and collapse.
4 **Wetting Agents and Emulsifiers.** These additives enable the oil either to displace water from metal surfaces or to absorb the water as a stable emulsion, thus promoting oil-film formation on a metal surface.
5 **Oxidation Inhibitors.** These combat oxidation of the oil itself either by interrupting the chain of chemical reactions leading to deterioration or by deactivating catalytic metallic surfaces.
6 **Detergents and Dispersants.** Widely used in lubricants for internal-combustion engines, these additives combat the formation of sludge and varnish.
7 **Corrosion Inhibitors.** Additives in this classification are used to reduce or prevent corrosion of lubricated surfaces by contaminants in the oil such as oxygen, water, acids and combustion products.
8 **Lubrication-Property Improvers.** This category includes a variety of additives that are intended to reduce friction (especially under boundary lubrication), speed up a "wearing in" process, enhance film strength, or provide lubrication under high contact pressures.

Mechanical Design. Certain types of lubricant failure can be prevented by changes in the design of the device itself or in the design of the lubricating system. Starvation of a bearing caused by inadequate lubricant flow or by clogging of oil passages sometimes can be corrected by increasing the size of the passages. Often, an increase or decrease in clearance between sliding surfaces will enable the lubricant to function more effectively. Shields, covers and seals sometimes can be used to prevent lubricant contamination from external sources. In other instances, filtration or absorption devices can be incorporated into the system to remove unwanted contaminants.

Nonlubricated Wear

Metal adhesion and cold welding characterize the process of wear in the absence of a lubricant. The conditions of nonlubricated wear are difficult to define because, in most practical situations, there is some kind of "lubricant" on any sliding or rolling surfaces. In addition to the naturally occurring oxide on most metals, the atmosphere and its industrial contaminants provide a wide variety of adsorbing organic and inorganic molecules. These surface contaminants protect contacting surfaces in much the same way as boundary lubricants do, in that they prevent intimate contact between chemically active metal surfaces. Only when metal surfaces are kept in an ultrahigh-vacuum environment and are cleaned by an electron beam or an electric arc are they truly "nonlubricated". Under these conditions, cold welding of the surfaces can take place immediately upon contact.

Contaminating films on metal surfaces can be penetrated under high contact stresses, resulting in cold welding of asperity contacts. If the asperity junction is stronger than the weaker of the two metals in contact, sliding motion will cause subsurface shear of the junction and a particle larger than the junction will be torn out of the surface. It is also possible that the junction will not shear off but will grow by subsurface shear until a critical size is reached and the heavily worked junction breaks off. This process is known as "prow formation" and is found most often under point-contact conditions involving a hard metal sliding on a soft metal.

Analyzing Wear Failures

There are three sources of evidence that will lead to an accurate analysis of a wear failure: the worn surface, the operating environment and the wear debris.

Surface damage can range from polishing or burnishing to removal of a relatively large volume of material. Examination of the worn surface can provide much information — for example, the amount of material removed, the type of damage (scratching, gouging, plowing, adhesion, pitting, corrosion, spalling or simple penetration), the existence and character of surface films, whether certain constituents are being attacked preferentially, the direction of relative motion between a worn surface and abrading particles, or whether abrading particles have become embedded in the surface.

Environmental conditions have such a profound effect on the mechanism and rate of metal removal that detailed knowledge of these conditions should always be sought. For instance, a limestone crusher sustained erratic wear, with greater wear occurring when rock from one side of a quarry was processed. The rock from that side looked the same as rock from the rest of the quarry, but

geological analysis revealed that it contained the silicified remains of a coral reef with sponges that were much harder and more abrasive than the surrounding limestone.

Wear environments may be corrosive, may have been altered during service (such as by breakdown of a lubricant), may provide inadequate lubrication, or may differ from the assumed environment on which the original material selection was made.

Wear debris, whether found between worn surfaces, embedded in a surface, suspended in the lubricant, or beside the worn part, can provide clues to the wear mechanism. A wear particle that consists of a metallic center with an oxide covering is probably a particle that was detached from the worn surface by abrasive or adhesive wear and subsequently was oxidized by exposure to the environment. On the other hand, a small wear particle that consists solely of oxide may be the result of corrosion on the worn surface with subsequent mechanical removal of the corrosion product.

Procedure for Wear Analysis. Generally, the steps entailed in analyzing a wear failure are as follows:

1 Identify the actual materials in the worn part, environment, abrasive, wear debris, and lubricant.
2 Identify the mechanism, or combination of mechanisms, of wear: adhesive, abrasive, corrosive, surface fatigue, or erosive.
3 Define the surface configuration of both the worn surface and the original surface.
4 Define the relative motions in the system, including direction and velocity.
5 Define the force or pressure between mating surfaces or between the worn surface and the wear environment on both the macroscopic and microscopic scales.
6 Define the wear rate.
7 Define the coefficient of friction.
8 Define the effectiveness and type of lubricant: oil, grease, surface film, naturally occurring oxide layer, adsorbed film, or other.
9 Establish whether the observed wear is normal or abnormal for the particular application.
10 Devise a solution, if required.

Solutions to Wear Problems. Wear may be combated by either of two methods: (*a*) altering the conditions of service to provide a less destructive environment, or (*b*) selecting a more wear-resistant material for the worn component. Generally, the latter method is easier and less expensive, and thus changing to a different material is more frequently chosen as a course of action in avoiding wear problems. The selection of materials for wear resistance is discussed in detail in several articles in Volume 1 of this Handbook.

Laboratory Examination of Worn Parts

Analysis of a wear failure depends to a large degree on knowledge of the service conditions under which the wear occurred. However, as with other failures, proper analysis of a wear failure depends on consideration of many factors and on careful examination, both macroscopic and microscopic.

Wear failures generally are the result of relatively long-time exposure, yet certain information obtained at the time the failure is discovered can be useful in establishing cause. For example, analysis of samples of the environment (especially the lubricant), or of sludge from the lubricating system or from a used oil filter, can reveal the nature and amount of wear debris or abrasive in the system.

Physical Measurement. Examination of a worn part generally begins with visual observation and measurement of dimensions, which usually involves the use of micrometers, calipers and standard or special gages. Observations of the amount and character of surface damage often must be made on a microscopic scale. An optical comparator, toolmaker's microscope, recording profilometer or other fine-scale measuring equipment may be required for adequately assessing the amount of damage that has occurred.

Weighing of a worn component or assembly and comparison of its weight with that of an unused part can help define the amount of material lost, as in abrasive wear, or the amount of material transferred to an opposing surface, as in adhesive wear. Weight-loss estimates also can help to define relative wear rates for two opposing surfaces that may be made of different materials or that may have been worn by different mechanisms.

Screening of abrasives or wear debris to determine the particle sizes, and weight percentage of particles of each size, is often helpful. The combination of determination of particle size with chemical analysis of the various screenings can provide useful information — for instance, when one component in an abrasive mixture is the primary cause of wear, or when wear debris and an abrasive coexist in the wear environment. The combination of screening with microscopy often can reveal such details as progressive alteration of the size and shape of abrasive particles with time, as might occur in a ball mill.

Physical measurements can define the amount and location of wear damage, but they can seldom provide enough information to establish either the mechanism or the cause of the damage.

Microscopy is used to study features of the worn surface, including the configuration, distribution and direction of scratches or gouges, and indications of the preferential removal of specific constituents of the microstructure. Abrasive particles or wear debris can be viewed under the microscope to study their shape and the configuration of their edges (sharp or rounded), and to establish whether or not they have fractured during the wear process.

Examination of the worn surface by light microscopy at magnifications up to about 100 diameters usually is required to detect uneven or abnormal wear patterns and to reveal the direction of relative movement between the worn surface and the opposing surface or abrasive. Sometimes, higher magnifications are required, and either transmission electron microscopy (TEM) or scanning electron microscopy (SEM) may be necessary to study areas of slight wear.

Direct observation at magnifications greater than about 50 diameters is difficult when the part does not fit in the stage of a metallurgical microscope. Sectioning to remove a portion of the worn surface for direct observation precludes repair and reuse of the part. Replication, which is required for TEM studies, also can be used for light-microscope or SEM observations of worn surfaces of large parts. Replication using plastic films or harder cast materials offers the additional advantage that a reproduction of the surface can be obtained at a remote site and carried back to the laboratory for detailed study. Hard replicas can be used for physical measurements such as with a profilometer.

Metallography. Examination of the microstructure of a worn part can reveal such information as whether the initial microstructure was proper or improper, the existence of a localized phase transformation, the existence of a cold worked surface layer, the presence of an adherent surface film or, as in the following example, the presence of embedded abrasive particles.

Example 5. Scoring Damage Caused by Chipping of Chromium Plating on a 4340 Steel Cylinder (Fig. 14)

Several large chromium-plated 4340 steel cylinders were removed from service because of deep longitudinal score marks in the plating. One of the damaged cylinders, and a mating cast aluminum alloy B750-T5 (now B850-T5) bearing adapter that also exhibited deep longitudinal score marks, were submitted for examination. In service, the bearing adapter slid along the surface of the cylinder. Scoring on the cylinder and on the bearing adapter are shown, respectively, in Fig. 14(a) and (b).

The grooves or score marks on the cylinder were about 10 in. long and were in a band with a width of about $\frac{1}{12}$ the circumference of the cylinder. The deeper grooves had completely penetrated the chromium plating, exposing the base steel. The score marks on the aluminum alloy adapter also

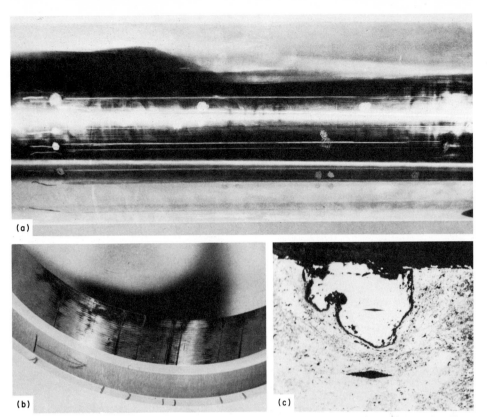

Fig. 14. Scoring damage caused by chipping of chromium plating on a 4340 steel cylinder: (a) scoring on the cylinder; (b) scoring on a mating cast aluminum alloy B750-T5 (now B850-T5) bearing adapter; and (c) view at 100× of a cross section through a deep score mark in the aluminum alloy adapter, revealing an embedded large particle of chromium (Example 5)

were in a $\frac{1}{12}$-circumference band, but they were deeper than those on the cylinder and were filled with shiny particles. In addition, the adapter showed evidence of heavy, localized burnishing in the general area in which scoring occurred.

Investigation. The hardness and adherence of the chromium plating on the cylinder were checked with a steel file and a vibratory etching tool and were found to be satisfactory. No lifting or peeling of the plate was noted in the areas tested.

Microscopic examination of a cross section through one of the deep score marks in the aluminum alloy adapter revealed a large particle of chromium embedded in the groove, as shown in Fig. 14(c). A hardness test performed on the particle indicated a hardness of 850 Knoop (Rockwell C 66); the hardness of the aluminum alloy adjacent to the particle was 186 Knoop (Rockwell B 86).

Conclusion. It was concluded that high, localized loads on the cylinder had resulted in chipping of the chromium plating, particles of which became embedded in the aluminum alloy adapter. The sliding action of the adapter with embedded hard particles resulted in scoring of both the cylinder and the adapter. If only the cylinder had been available for examination, it might have been concluded that the scoring had been caused by entrapped sand or debris from an external source.

For valid failure analysis, techniques such as taper sectioning sometimes are needed to allow metallographic observations or microhardness measurements of

very thin surface layers. It is almost always necessary to use special materials that support the edge of a specimen in a metallographic mount (for example, nickel plating on the specimen or powdered glass in the mounting material), and to polish the mounted specimen with care so that the edge is not rounded.

Etchants, in addition to preparing a specimen for the examination of microstructure, can be used also to reveal characteristics of the worn surface. Two examples of features that can be revealed by etching a worn surface are phase transformations caused by localized adhesion to an opposing surface and the results of overheating caused by excessive friction, such as the "white layer" (untempered martensite) that sometimes develops on steel or cast iron under conditions of heavy sliding contact. (White layer has been detected on scuffed cylinder liners from diesel engines.) Etching a worn surface also can help in detecting the selective removal of specific constituents of the microstructure. The worn surface should be examined under the microscope and photographed before it is etched, because some topographical features may be easier to observe on the unetched surface.

Macroscopic and microscopic hardness testing can provide an indication of the resistance of a material to abrasive wear.

Because harder materials are likely to cut or scratch softer materials, comparative hardness of two sliding surfaces may be important. Microhardness measurements on martensitic steels may indicate that frictional heat has overtempered the steel and, when used in conjunction with a tempering curve (a plot of hardness versus tempering temperature), can allow a rough estimate of surface temperature. Hardness measurements also can indicate whether or not a worn part was heat treated correctly.

X-ray and electron diffraction analyses can disclose the structure of a crystalline solid. These techniques are particularly valuable for analyzing abrasives, wear debris or surface films, because they can identify compounds, not merely elements. Microstructural features such as retained austenite cannot always be seen in microscopic examination of an etched specimen; quantitative diffraction analysis can reveal the relative amounts of such unresolved constituents in the microstructure.

Chemical and Geological Analysis. One or more of the various techniques of chemical analysis — wet analysis, spectroscopy, colorimetry, x-ray fluorescence, atomic absorption, or electron-beam microprobe analysis — usually is needed for properly analyzing wear failure. The actual compositions of the worn material, the wear debris, the abrasive and the surface film must be known in order to devise solutions to most wear problems. An analysis of the lubricant can establish whether the proper base stock and additives were present. Chemical analysis may be needed to establish or confirm the wear mechanism. The example that follows describes an instance in which galling, or adhesive wear caused by solid-phase welding between sliding surfaces, was verified by electron-beam microprobe analysis.

Example 6. Galling Wear on a Carburized 4720 Steel Inner Cone of a Roller-Bearing Assembly (Fig. 15)

When a roller-bearing assembly was removed from an aircraft for inspection after a short period of service, several areas of apparent galling were noticed around the inside surface of the inner cone of the bearing. These areas were roughly circular spots of built-up metal, such as the spot shown in Fig. 15. The bearing had not seized, and there was no evidence of heat discoloration in the galled areas.

The inner cone, made of modified 4720 steel and carburized for wear resistance, rode on a 17-4 PH stainless steel spacer. Consequently, it was desirable to determine whether the galled spots contained any stainless steel from the spacer. Other items for investigation were the nature of the bond between the galled spot and the inner cone and any evidence of overtempering or rehardening resulting from localized overheating.

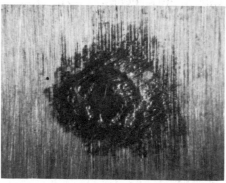

Fig. 15. Evidence of galling, or adhesive wear, on the inside surface of a carburized 4720 steel inner cone of a roller-bearing assembly. Galling was confirmed by use of electron-beam microprobe analysis. (Example 6)

Investigation. Electron-beam microprobe analysis on a cross section through the largest galled spot verified the composition of the spot as 17-4 PH stainless steel. Microscopic examination revealed that the built-up metal was welded to the cone. Microhardness readings on the unaffected carburized case and on the case beneath the galled area indicated that the heat generated by galling had resulted in localized tempering of the case under the galled spot.

Conclusion. It was concluded that galling had been caused by a combination of local overload and abnormal vibration of mating parts of the roller-bearing assembly.

The geological study of soils or similar abrasive mixtures of minerals is mandatory in analyzing wear of tillage tools, earthmoving equipment, and ore-handling devices. The abrasive characteristics of sandy soils are different from those of coarse, rocky soils, clay or fine silt. Particle hardness and shape (jagged or rounded) are important. The degree of compaction determines the amount of pressure that forces abrasive soil particles against a surface that is being dragged through the mixture. In addition, moisture content is important, because it determines, in part, the lubricity and cohesiveness of the mixture. Many ores, slags and similar bulk materials are extremely abrasive to equipment for handling and moving materials; geological analysis can define the abrasive character of these aggregates.

Importance of Service History in Failure Analysis

One of the early steps in wear-failure analysis is the identification of the type of wear, or if more than one type can be recognized, evaluation of the relative importance of each type as quantitatively as possible. This identification of the type or types of wear requires a detailed description of the service conditions based on close observation and on adequate experience. A casual and su-

perficial description of service conditions is not likely to be of much value.

More often than not, descriptions of service conditions are incomplete, thus imposing a serious handicap on the failure analyst, especially if he is working in a laboratory remote from the service site. For instance, assume that an analyst must study the problem of a badly seized engine cylinder — obviously an instance of adhesive metal-to-metal wear (or lubricated wear, because use of a suitable engine oil is implied). Furthermore, assume that during an oil change the system had been flushed with a solvent such as kerosine to rinse out the old oil and had been inadvertently left filled with solvent instead of new oil. Also assume that a slow leak, resulting in loss of the solvent, was not detected during the operating period immediately preceding seizure. The analyst probably would receive the damaged parts (cylinder block and pistons) after they had been removed from the engine, cleaned and packed. If evidence of the substitute "lubricant" could not be clearly established, determination of the cause of failure would be extremely difficult or perhaps impossible.

Similarly, incomplete descriptions of service conditions can be misleading in analysis of abrasive wear. For example, in describing the source of abrasion that produces wear of mining and ore-handling equipment, generalized references to the ore, such as "copper ore", are not uncommon. Such descriptions are too vague to be meaningful; the mineral being extracted usually has little effect on the abrasiveness of the mixture, whereas the bulk rock, or gangue, is the principal source of abrasive particles. Unless the gangue minerals are studied both qualitatively and quantitatively, a valid assessment of wear, whether normal or abnormal, is not possible.

In analysis of conventional lubricated wear, detailed description of the lubricant is essential and often must be supplemented by data regarding pressures applied to mating surfaces, operating temperatures and surface conditions. When corrosion is a factor in lubricated wear, it may be difficult to determine the temperature, degree of aeration, hydrogen-ion concentration, and velocity of the lubricant, and the composition and concentration of the corrodent in the lubricant. Other complications that make the analysis more difficult include the presence of substances that inhibit or accelerate corrosion.

Effect of Material Properties on Wear

Various means of identifying the compositions of the worn part, wear debris, surface film, abrasive and wear environment are discussed in the section on Laboratory Examination of Worn Parts, in this article (see page 146). Failure analysis can be valid only when the properties of each component in a system and the effect of these properties on the wear process are fully understood.

Adhesive wear is likely to be severe when similar metals rub with little or no lubrication. Metallic particles will be torn from one or both surfaces. Under light contact loads, the particles will be very fine and, if air is present, probably will react completely with oxygen to form oxide wear debris. Under heavy loads, the particles will be somewhat larger and the wear debris will be mainly metallic, even when air is present. If the metals are dissimilar, they are more likely to be mutually insoluble (nonbondable), and thus less susceptible to adhesive wear. This is the principle of materials used in sliding bearings; they are deliberately chosen to be insoluble in the mating material. However, complete insolubility is rare, and thus satisfactory performance usually depends on a third factor, such as a lubricant or surface film.

Rubbing of a metal against a nonmetal such as a plastic sometimes causes reactions similar to metal-to-metal adhesive wear. Particles of the plastic may adhere to the metal and become torn away, eventually resulting in destruction of the plastic component. Plastics have poor thermal conductivity, and cannot readily dissipate heat at a junction. For this reason, thin films of certain plastics (such as nylon or Teflon) superimposed on a metal base often are better than thicker layers of plastic alone, because the metal substrate acts as a heat sink to keep the plastic cool.

Abrasive wear can occur on sliding surfaces that operate in a contaminated environment, as often occurs with journal bearings. Dirt particles may enter the thin space between the journal and the bearing surface and become partly embedded in the soft bearing metal. The resulting projections can cut the journal like many tiny tool bits. Consequently, an important property of any bearing material is its capacity to embed foreign particles deeply enough to avoid damage to the shaft.

Agricultural and earthmoving machines utilize carefully shaped tools intended to be pulled through a mass of particles. Materials that perform well under certain soil conditions may perform poorly in a different type of soil, or even in the same soil under different conditions of moisture, compaction or speed.

Because rubbing generates frictional heat, materials with high hot strength and high hardness are more resistant to both abrasive and adhesive wear than are materials with lower hot strength and

Fig. 16. Worn yarn eyelet made of hardened and tempered 1095 steel. Service life was improved by changing eyelet material to M2 high speed tool steel, which contains spheroidal carbides in a matrix of martensite.

lower hardness. This is a major reason for the success of high speed tool steels and cemented carbides in cutting tools. Smoothly polished tungsten carbide sliding across a hardened steel surface under high load provides a low-wear system. Adhesive wear cannot occur, because the two materials are mutually insoluble; abrasive wear is minimal, because the

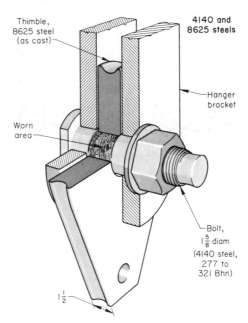

Fig. 17. Bolt-and-thimble assembly used for connection of wire rope to a crane hanger bracket, showing worn area of bolt (Example 7)

tungsten carbide has no projections to penetrate and cut into the mating steel.

Coatings with temperature-resistant properties provide excellent resistance to severe abrasive wear in agricultural tillage tools and earthmoving equipment when rock-free soil is involved. However, when rocky soils are involved, the susceptibility of such coatings to brittle fracture makes their usage unwise.

Effect of Microstructure

The microstructural heterogeneity of a wear surface influences the wear process, because constituents such as carbides, inclusions, intermetallic compounds and dispersed phases have properties different from those of the matrix. Hard microconstituents such as carbides can make a metal extremely resistant to abrasive wear if they are closely spaced in a relatively hard matrix. For instance, the yarn eyelet shown in Fig. 16, which was made of 1095 steel and hardened and tempered to Rockwell C 60 and which was used in a textile machine to guide highly abrasive synthetic yarn, was severely worn in service. The yarn, which was drawn through the eyelet at high speed, changed direction at the exit of the eyelet, riding on the inside corner at the exit. Eyelet life was increased significantly when the eyelet material was changed to heat treated M2 high speed tool steel, which usually exhibits a microstructure of closely spaced spheroidal carbides in a matrix of ferrite (annealed structure) or tempered martensite (hardened structure). Micrographs 967 and 968 on page 120 in Volume 7 of this Handbook illustrate these two microstructures.

Matrix hardness is important to wear resistance. If hard microconstituents are widely dispersed in a matrix that is not hard enough to have good wear resistance of its own, the matrix may wear away rapidly, leaving the hard particles projecting from the surface, where they can cut into a mating surface. For this reason, under dry sliding conditions, fine pearlite exhibits considerably better wear resistance than does coarse pearlite or a mixture of ferrite and pearlite.

In the following example, a wire rope was attached to a crane hanger bracket using a hardened bolt and a cast steel thimble. The difference in hardness levels of the bolt and the thimble resulted in excessive wear of the bolt surfaces.

Example 7. Wear Failure of a 4140 Steel Thimble Bolt Because of Low Hardness (Fig. 17)

Figure 17 shows a bolt and a thimble used to connect a wire rope to a crane hanger bracket. The bolt, which attached the thimble to the hanger bracket, was worn excessively. Two worn bolts, one new bolt and a new thimble were examined.

Specifications required the bolts to be made of 4140 steel heat treated to a hardness of 277 to 321 Bhn. Thimbles were to be made of cast 8625 steel, but no heat treatment or hardness were specified.

Investigation. Transverse sections were taken through the worn areas of the used bolts and the corresponding area of the new bolt. The thimble was not sectioned, but hardness readings were taken on the outer surface adjacent to the top of the hole that normally wears under service conditions. Hardness values for the bolt sections and the thimble were as follows:

	Hardness, Bhn		
Sample	Wear surface	Opposite surface	Center
Used bolt	327	324	331
Used bolt	319	327	340
New bolt	454	...	376
Thimble	253	231	...

Hardness of the used bolts was within or only slightly above the specified range; the hardness of the new bolt was well above the range. As noted earlier, no hardness was specified for the thimble.

Microstructure of the bolts was tempered martensite. The microstructures of the two used bolts were similar in appearance; however, the microstructure of the new bolt appeared slightly different because it had been tempered at a lower temperature than the used bolts.

The thimble showed a bainitic microstructure typical of as-cast steel rather than of heat treated steel.

Discussion. Mating of the hard bolt surface with the soft thimble surface was conducive to wear of both surfaces. The wearability of the bolt-thimble arrangement could be improved only by equalizing and increasing the hardness of the mating surfaces. Although the bolt was heat treated, the specified hardness of 277 to 321 Bhn did not produce a surface hardness that yielded good wearability.

Case hardening of the bolt and thimble hole to equal hardness values would produce the best wearing characteristics. However, loading of case-hardened bolts could cause the case to spall or fracture from the base metal; also, case hardening the bolt would not improve its impact strength. Both wearability and impact properties of the bolt would be improved by tempering after through hardening.

Conclusion. Wearing of the bolt surfaces was accentuated because the bolt surfaces and the mating thimble surfaces were of different hardnesses. the hardnesses of both surfaces were too low to give good wear characteristics.

Corrective Measures. The bolts were through hardened and tempered to the hardness range of 375 to 430 Bhn. The thimbles were heat treated to a similar microstructure and the same hardness range as those of the bolt.

Molybdenum disulfide was liberally applied during the initial installation of the bolts. A maintenance lubrication program was not suggested, but galling could be reduced by periodic application of a solid lubricant.

No further failures were reported after these measures were incorporated.

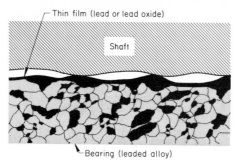

Fig. 18. Schematic illustration of how free lead in a bearing alloy provides boundary lubrication

The abrasion resistance of carbide-containing steels with a hardness greater than about 0.6 times the hardness of a contacting abrasive is significantly greater than the abrasion resistance of softer carbide-containing steels. In the softer steels, carbides have little effect on abrasion resistance — probably because the matrix does not provide the necessary support for the dispersed phase. In hypereutectoid steels, maximum hardness is not necessarily optimum for wear resistance. A grain-boundary network of carbides, which may be encountered in many hypereutectoid steels, causes brittle behavior and can result in chipping of the wear surface. Therefore, hypereutectoid steels must be processed so that the carbides are redistributed as a dispersed phase; this usually does not produce maximum hardness.

Austenitic manganese steel is an extremely tough nonmagnetic alloy in which the usual hardening transformation has been suppressed by a combination of high carbon and manganese contents and rapid cooling from a high temperature. Manganese steel exceeds even the austenitic stainless steels in ability to work harden and probably has no equal in this respect. This property makes the alloy exceptionally resistant to wear accompanied by heavy impact, such as in ore-crushing and earthmoving equipment and in railway frogs and crossings.

It is sometimes believed that unless manganese steel has been work hardened, it has poor resistance against wear. This is not a valid generalization. The misunderstanding has probably developed because, where much impact and attendant work hardening are present, 12% Mn steel is so clearly superior to other metals that its performance is attributed to the surface hardening. However, controlled abrasion tests have indicated that there are circumstances where the abrasion resistance of austenitic manganese steel is modified little by work hardening, and others where it will outwear harder pearlitic white cast irons without work hardening.

As with other steels, quenching suppresses austenite transformation, with the difference that the critical cooling velocity is quite low below Ar′. (Grain-boundary carbide precipitation between Ae_{cm} and Ar′ is the primary cause of impaired properties associated with slow cooling.) Isothermal transformation between 500 F and the upper Ae_1 temperature will develop acicular or pearlite structures, which appear slowly and require very long times for attainment of equilibrium. As with mixed structures in other steels, the mechanical properties of partially transformed austenite are poor — particularly when carbides or other brittle constituents form in large flat plates parallel to crystallographic planes. The mechanical properties are low also when pearlite, which seems to nucleate most readily at grain boundaries, develops in sufficient quantity to form an envelope around each grain. These structures account for the low ductility and reduced strength of austenitic manganese steel after reheating.

Tin bronzes are used widely in plain bearings that operate under boundary lubrication, because they will not gall a steel shaft if the lubricant film breaks down. Tin in bronze also strengthens adsorption bonds of the active agent in many boundary lubricants. However, a tin content exceeding 12% can form a hard $Cu_{31}Sn_8$ intermetallic phase that will scratch a steel shaft.

Lead, which is used in bearing bronzes in amounts up to 10%, exists as a separate phase and, under dry sliding conditions, will smear out over the surface, as shown schematically in Fig. 18, to act as a boundary lubricant — either as metallic lead or as lead oxide. Lead in bearing bronzes can reduce the coefficient of friction in dry sliding against steel by as much as 50%. Lead also can enhance lubrication by influencing the chemical processes that produce semisolid films on the bearing surface in an oil-lubricated system.

Cast irons generally have good wear resistance. Although little is known about the specific roles of the various constituents, particularly graphite, it is generally agreed that abrasion-resistant gray irons should have a microstructure consisting of free graphite in a fine pearlitic matrix with little or no free ferrite. White cast irons can be very resistant to abrasion if the composition is controlled to produce a microstructure of carbides (Fe_3C or Cr_7C_3) in martensite with a small amount of retained austenite for toughness. Martensitic abrasion-resistant cast irons typically contain chromium, in amounts up to 35%. Low-chromium martensitic irons are alloyed with 4 to 5% nickel for maximum hardness; larger amounts promote austenite retention. Sometimes, small amounts of molybdenum or copper are added to enhance hardenability in thick sections.

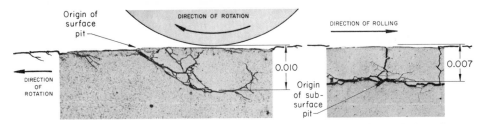

Fig. 19. Micrographs of incipient pitting caused by surface fatigue. The relation of surface-pit origin and shape to direction of rolling is shown in the micrograph at left. Cracking parallel and perpendicular to the surface is shown in the micrograph at right, with creation of a subsurface pit illustrated schematically.

Combined Wear Mechanisms

More than one mechanism can be responsible for the wear observed on a particular part. For example, an agricultural tool used in an acidic soil can undergo simultaneous abrasive, corrosive and erosive wear. Analysis of wear involving combined mechanisms is very difficult and demands rigorous attention to every detail.

Interaction between wear mechanisms can complicate analysis. For example, in erosion-corrosion, the rate of deterioration by corrosive action can increase by one order of magnitude or more when erosion also occurs. Many corrosion-resistant alloys, such as stainless steels, are relatively stable in a corrosive medium, because they form a thin, tightly adherent surface film that inhibits further corrosion. If the film is removed by abrasive or erosive action, corrosion can proceed on the newly exposed metal surface. Chemical action may reestablish the film, but if erosion removes it as fast as it forms, stability in the corroding medium no longer can exist.

Selection of material for wear applications often is based on arbitrary screening tests involving an artificial wear environment. Differences between this artificial environment and the actual conditions of service cannot be overlooked in a failure analysis, and, if screening tests are to be used as the basis for corrective action, they should duplicate as closely as possible the actual mechanism or mechanisms of wear in service.

Surface Configuration

Because wear is a surface phenomenon, the original surface configuration of the components in contact influences wear by influencing resistance to relative motion. In bearings, for example, mechanical wear will increase with an increase in surface roughness or out-of-roundness — factors that increase resistance to rolling or sliding. Cutting tools will wear abnormally if their cutting edges are not sharp or if their cutting angles and clearance angles are incorrect for the application.

Changes in surface configuration that occur during the wear process affect subsequent stages of wear. The process of "wearing in", which involves progressive reduction in surface roughness by adhesive or abrasive wear of opposing surfaces, generally is followed by a period of relatively little wear. The initial smoothing-out of asperities, particularly in lubricated systems that operate under boundary lubrication, reduces the microscopic hills and valleys on the surface to a height about the same as the thickness of the lubricant film. The surfaces then ride on each other with no interference

between peaks on the opposing surfaces, and wear essentially ceases.

In other instances, particularly if the initial surfaces are somewhat rougher or if boundary lubrication is ineffective, adhesive wear may result in progressive surface roughening and eventual failure. If this process releases wear debris into the joint, and if this debris has a particle size that exceeds the thickness of the lubricating film, combined adhesive and abrasive wear between the opposing surfaces and the wear debris can result in rapid deterioration.

Direction of Relative Motion. When only unidirectional sliding is involved, scratches or gouges produced on the worn surface are aligned with the direction of relative motion. In a sleeve bearing, for example, the scratches should run circumferentially on the inner surface of the bearing and on the mating shaft. Scratches resulting from wear that are oriented in other directions indicate such factors as misalignment, vibration or looseness. These factors can contribute to the severity of the wear.

In devices that undergo combined rolling and sliding, knowledge of the relative velocities and directions of rolling and sliding is necessary for definition of the wear mechanism. The direction of rolling is defined as the direction in which the point of contact moves; the direction of rolling is always opposite to the direction of rotation of a rolling element. On a given surface, a condition

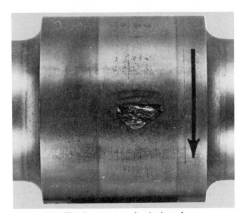

Fig. 20. Early stage of pitting from surface origins, showing arrowhead shape of pitted area with the apex pointing in the direction of rotation (black arrow)

of positive sliding exists if the direction of sliding is the same as the direction of rolling. Negative sliding occurs on the mating surface, where the directions of rolling and sliding are opposite to each other. Most surface-fatigue failures originate in regions of negative sliding, because the shear stresses there are usually more severe than in regions of positive sliding. Negative sliding occurs on the dedenda of gear teeth, on the cam follower riding on a cam and, in other devices, on the part that has the lower surface velocity in a rolling-sliding system.

Evaluation of Surface-Fatigue Pitting

In a rolling or rolling-sliding system, the location of maximum shear stress, which may be at or slightly below the surface, determines where a surface-fatigue pit will originate. When the maximum shear stress is at the surface, pit origins also will be at the surface, as shown at left in Fig. 19, and a single crack can produce a pit. However, when the maximum shear stress is subsurface, cracks must propagate beneath the surface and radiate up to the surface, joining with adjacent cracks to form a pit. This process is shown at right in Fig. 19.

Pitting from a surface origin generally can be distinguished by initial crack propagation along a relatively shallow acute angle and usually will have an exit angle more nearly perpendicular to the surface (see view at left in Fig. 19). The pitted area, at least in the early stages, is shaped like an arrowhead, with the apex pointing in the direction of rotation (opposite to the direction of rolling), as illustrated in Fig. 20. In later stages of pitting from surface origins, the shape of the pitted area may become more irregular.

Pitting from subsurface origins can be distinguished by crack propagation both parallel and perpendicular to the surface (see view at right in Fig. 19). The shape of the pitted area is mainly irregular, sometimes with surface crazing along the edges. In many instances, operation of the device after subsurface pitting has occurred alters the original straight-sided, flat-bottomed pit by abrasive wear or deformation of the edges of the pitted area, making it difficult to identify the mechanism.

In devices where maximum contact stresses are subsurface, nonmetallic inclusions and similar metallurgical notches increase the likelihood of pitting. Elimination of these microstructural features — such as by replacing air-melted steel with vacuum-melted or vacuum-degassed steel — should provide increased service life. If vacuum treatment of the steel does not increase life, it is likely that mechanisms other than subsurface pitting are responsible for the failure.

Shear Stress. When only sliding is involved, as in sleeve bearings, the maximum shear stress occurs at the surface of each component; each surface drags the other surface along with it. Frictional heat is high at the interface unless the surfaces are smooth and well lubricated. However, when only rolling is involved, as in roller bearings, the maximum shear stresses in all rolling elements are slightly below the surface. Frictional heat is low unless high stresses or high speeds cause elastic deformation and sliding.

When both sliding and rolling are involved — such as the sliding and rolling motion of gear teeth (except at the pitch line, where rolling alone occurs), cams and cam followers — wear conditions are intermediate between those encountered with sliding alone or rolling alone. The location of maximum shear stress varies from surface to subsurface depending on the degree of sliding and on the lubricant, both of which affect the coefficient of friction. It is believed that the maximum shear stress will be at the surface when the coefficient of friction is greater than about 0.10.

Maximum shear stress is important because it causes fatigue. If shear stress exceeds shear strength at any location for several cycles, fatigue cracks ordinarily will be initiated. With succeeding applications of load, the fatigue cracks may propagate, eventually releasing relatively large fragments from the surface and leaving cavities or pits. The pits, in turn, enlarge rapidly and ultimately can result in the complete destruction of both surfaces, especially when the fragments resulting from surface fatigue (wear debris) remain trapped between contact surfaces and abrade them.

Contact Stress. Stresses produced by the loads that force components into close contact can be considered on both the macroscopic and the microscopic scales. Apparent contact stress (macroscopic stress) is calculated using the applied load and the apparent contact area; in reality, macroscopic stress is only a rough estimate of the stress at areas of true contact. Stresses on the microscopic

scale are always higher than this estimate, because the load actually is carried on the true-contact area.

Peak stresses are usually well into the plastic range when asperities from opposing surfaces meet. Under favorable conditions, only plastic deformation of the asperities takes place. This increases the true-contact area by increasing the total number of microscopic areas that have the same height and are in contact with similar areas on the opposing surface. Microscopic stresses are reduced in proportion to the number of new asperity contacts that are produced by this action, until an equilibrium is reached wherein stresses at contacting asperities do not exceed the yield strength, and plastic deformation of projections ceases. This process is the means by which opposing surfaces "wear in" and is desirable in many machinery components. When conditions are less favorable, the wearing-in process may never cease and progressive deterioration will continue until the part is worn out or until another, more devastating mechanism of wear takes over.

Under sliding alone, wear is a function of macroscopic stress and surface roughness and occurs by adhesion, scratching or gouging. Such wear can be reduced by increasing the strength of the surfaces or by making the surfaces smoother, or both, or by improving the system of lubrication.

Under combined rolling and sliding, the contact stress necessary to cause surface-fatigue failure (which is the predominant failure mechanism in the absence of an abrasive) increases rapidly as the proportion of rolling increases. At about 65% rolling and 35% sliding, hardened steels commonly pit at 20 to 30 million stress cycles when the calculated contact stress is about 350,000 psi. When rolling alone is involved, the calculated contact stress must be 600,000 to 650,000 psi to cause pitting in the same number of stress cycles.

Effect of Contact Stress on Abrasive Wear

High repetitive contact forces between a surface and an abrasive lead to plastic deformation and fracture. High-stress battering occurs, for example, on rock-crushing tools and power-shovel teeth. Austenitic manganese steel often is used in these applications, because it work hardens under severe pounding and thereby resists wear. Low-stress abrasive wear will not work harden this steel; consequently, the service life of parts made from austenitic manganese steel is not always satisfactory under conditions of low-stress abrasive wear.

When abrasive particles strike a surface at an acute angle or slide along the

surface under a sufficient contact force, they plow furrows in the surface. In both instances, the surface eventually is eroded, which is one form of abrasive wear. But when particles strike the surface at an angle that is roughly perpendicular to the surface, they rebound without producing severe damage. Nevertheless, in time, enough small fragments may be broken away from the surface to constitute severe impingement erosion. High velocities of abrasive particles, either trapped between sliding surfaces or in an impinging stream of fluid, cause a large number of particles to contact the surface at a high stress; hence, more metal is removed at high velocities than at low velocities.

Coefficient of Friction

As defined earlier, the coefficient of friction indicates relative resistance to sliding. It is not measured directly, but is determined from Eq 3, using measurements of the frictional force and contact force. The coefficient of friction is influenced by the contacting materials, surface finish, and any lubricant or film between contact surfaces, but is independent of load, speed, shape and apparent-contact area.

When no abrasive or wear debris is present, high coefficients of friction result from simultaneous shearing of many tiny bonded contacts, such as when similar metals free of surface contamination are rubbed together in vacuum. Low coefficients of friction occur when mating surfaces glide across each other with little or no bonding at asperities, such as when shearing takes place entirely within a lubricant film of low viscosity. Intermediate coefficients of friction generally imply some adhesion between mating surfaces.

The presence of an abrasive or of wear debris in the junction increases the coefficient of friction mainly because particles contact the surfaces and effectively increase the shear strength of the junction. Even if particulate matter acted only to interfere with viscous flow within the lubricant film, this would amount to an increase in the coefficient of friction for the junction. Only when the lubricant film is relatively thick, and particulate matter is extremely small and widely dispersed, will abrasives or wear debris have little measurable effect on the coefficient of friction.

Environmental Effects

Service environment influences wear mainly by affecting (a) chemical reactions at the wear surface and (b) the chemical and physical stability of materials in the wear system.

Environmental effects can be subtle. Even relatively obscure variations, such as differences in atmospheric humidity, have been found to have large effects on friction and wear.

Chemical reactions of surfaces with the environment are involved in corrosive wear and erosion-corrosion. Often, some controlled corrosion is desired, as when extreme-pressure lubricants are used. However, if the corrosive additives in an extreme-pressure lubricant are overactive, the contacting surfaces can be damaged by excessive corrosion. It is important to understand the chemical reactions that can occur in the system under study, and the inhibiting or enhancing effects that specific environmental constituents can have on these reactions.

Temperature affects the chemical, physical and mechanical properties of materials. The bulk temperature of a mechanical device or system controls chemical-reaction rates in the environment or at surfaces, solubility of elements or compounds in the environment (or, at very high temperatures, the solubility of phases in a heterogeneous microstructure), and physical and mechanical properties of contacting materials or environment. Variations in temperature (such as those that can occur at surfaces because of frictional heat, or during start-up and shutdown) can cause different effects to prevail in different parts of the system or to prevail at different times. For example, bulk temperature may indicate that the materials in contact surfaces are stable; however, overheating caused by excessive friction can produce localized microstructural changes, which can alter the wear resistance of the surface material.

Wear Rates

Wear rates are most commonly evaluated when the objective of the failure analysis is to improve the service life of parts that ordinarily fail by wear. Wear testing may be required for evaluation of whether or not the observed wear rate is normal for the application.

Wear tests generally are less accurate and less reliable than tests of other engineering properties of materials or components. Because there is no universal wear test, wear rates are evaluated by many different procedures, each one designed to evaluate a specific type or mechanism of wear. A wear test is not a good engineering evaluation unless it is:

1 Reliable — that is, capable of producing wear of a certain material in a predictable and statistically significant manner
2 Able to rank materials — that is, able to achieve statistically significant differences in wear rates among different types of materials
3 Valid — that is, capable of accurately predicting the service performance of a given material.

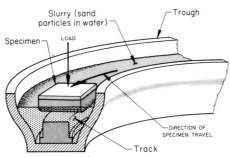

Fig. 21. Schematic illustration of a wet-sand abrasion test. This is a well-validated wear test simulating high-stress grinding abrasion.

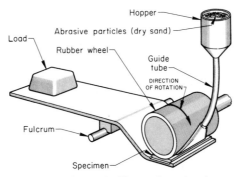

Fig. 22. Schematic illustration of a dry-sand erosion test used for evaluating resistance to low-stress scratching abrasion

Wear rates can be assessed by either service testing or laboratory testing in a controlled or artificial environment. Few service tests can meet the necessary criteria of reliability and ranking ability; thus, field tests seldom justify confidence. However, laboratory tests usually are conducted under artificial conditions that differ significantly from actual service conditions and thus may be of questionable validity.

Laboratory wear tests most often are conducted using an abrasive. They cannot be considered as more than preliminary screening evaluations, and can be misleading when used for material selection, unless they accurately simulate:

1 Hardness and particle size of the specific abrasive in the environment that controls wear in service (generally this is the hardest substance in an abrasive mixture)
2 Forces causing contact between the abrasive particles and the wear surface (contact pressure)
3 Relative motion (both speed and direction) between the abrasive and the wear surface.

Two abrasive-wear tests — one simulating high-stress grinding abrasion and the other simulating low-stress scratching abrasion — are known to be reliable, able to rank materials, and valid. These two tests are illustrated schematically in Fig. 21 and 22. Because some of the material properties that appear to provide good resistance to abrasive wear also seem to provide good resistance to adhe-

sive wear, abrasive-wear tests sometimes are used to rank materials for adhesive-wear applications. Nevertheless, such tests never truly simulate adhesive or corrosive wear and thus should not be used as the sole criterion for evaluating resistance to these types of wear.

Service testing represents the ultimate evaluation of wear resistance. Unfortunately, most service situations are subject to great variability of one or more conditions. Thus it may be impossible to find a single material that is best for a given wear application.

References

1. H. S. Avery, The Measurement of Wear Resistance, *Wear*, Vol 4 (No. 6), Nov-Dec 1961, p 427
2. R. Holm and E. Holm, "Electric Contacts, Theory and Application", 4th edition, Springer-Verlag, New York, 1967
3. J. T. Burwell and C. D. Strang, *J Appl Phys*, Vol 23, 1952, p 18
4. J. F. Archard, *J Appl Phys*, Vol 24, 1953, p 981
5. E. Rabinowicz, L. A. Dunn and P. G. Russell, A Study of Abrasive Wear Under Three-Body Conditions, *Wear*, Vol 4 (No. 5), Sept-Oct 1961, p 345
6. E. Rabinowicz, L. A. Dunn and P. G. Russell, The Abrasive Wear Resistance of Some Bearing Steels, *Lubrication Eng*, Vol 17 (No. 12), Dec 1961, p 587
7. T. O. Mulhearn and L. E. Samuels, The Abrasion of Metals: A Model of the Process, *Wear*, Vol 5 (No. 6), Nov-Dec 1962, p 478
8. J. Goddard and H. Wilman, A Theory of Friction and Wear During the Abrasion of Metals, *Wear*, Vol 5 (No. 2), Mar-Apr 1962, p 114
9. M. M. Khruschov, Resistance of Metals to Wear by Abrasion, as Related to Hardness, *Proc Conf Lubrication Wear, London*, 1957
10. B. W. E. Avient, J. Goddard and H. Wilman, An Experimental Study of Friction and Wear During Abrasion of Metals, *Proc Roy Soc (London), Ser A*, Vol 258, 1960, p 159
11. A. J. Sedriks and T. O. Mulhearn, Mechanics of Cutting and Rubbing in Simulated Abrasive Processes, *Wear*, Vol 6 (No. 6), Nov-Dec 1963, p 457
12. M. F. Stroud and H. Wilman, The Proportion of the Groove Volume Removed as Wear in Abrasion of Metals, *Brit J Appl Phys*, Vol 13 (No. 4), Apr 1962, p 173
13. J. N. King and H. Wilman, The Friction and Wear Properties, During Abrasion, of Compressed Graphite-Powder Compacts and Commercial Graphitised Carbons, *Wear*, Vol 5 (No. 3), May-June 1962, p 213
14. E. Rabinowicz, "Friction and Wear of Materials", J. Wiley and Sons, Inc., New York, 1965, p 167-186
15. J. G. A. Bitter, A Study of Erosion Phenomena – Part II, *Wear*, Vol 6 (No. 3), May-June 1963, p 169
16. J. G. A. Bitter, A Study of Erosion Phenomena – Part I, *Wear*, Vol 6 (No. 1), Jan-Feb 1963, p 5
17. T. Liu and R. J. Benzing, European Research on Lubrication, Part I – Impact Wear, *Lubrication Eng*, Vol 19 (No. 7), July 1963, p 297
18. I. Finnie, Erosion of Surfaces by Solid Particles, *Wear*, Vol 3 (No. 1), Jan-Feb 1960, p 87
19. I. Finnie, Erosion by Solid Particles in a Fluid Stream, ASTM Special Technical Publication No. 307, 1962, p 70
20. C. D. Wood and P. W. Espenschade, Mechanisms of Dust Erosion, Society of Automotive Engineers Paper presented at Summer Meeting, Chicago, June 9, 1964

Fretting Failures

By F. Eric Krueger, B.A.Sc., P.E.*

FRETTING is a wear phenomenon that occurs between two mating surfaces; it is adhesive in nature, and vibration is its essential causative factor. Usually, fretting is accompanied by corrosion. In general, fretting occurs between two tight-fitting surfaces that are subjected to a cyclic, relative motion of extremely small amplitude.

Fretting is also referred to as fretting corrosion, false brinelling, friction oxidation, chafing fatigue, molecular attrition and wear oxidation.

Fretting Characteristics

The difference between fretting and ordinary wear is that fretting generally occurs at contacting surfaces that are intended to be fixed in relation to each other, but that actually undergo minute alternating relative motion, called "slip", that is usually produced by vibration. There are exceptions, however, such as contact between balls and raceways in bearings, and between mating surfaces in oscillating bearings and flexible couplings. Fretting further differs from ordinary wear in that the bulk of the debris produced is retained at the site of fretting. In ferrous materials, the fretting process creates a mass of reddish oxide particles. Fretting also occurs in non-oxidizing materials, such as gold, platinum, and cupric oxide.

Common sites for fretting are in joints that are bolted, keyed, pinned, press fitted, and riveted; in oscillating bearings, splines, couplings, clutches, spindles and seals; in press fits on shafts; and in universal joints, baseplates, shackles and prosthetic devices. One problem with fretting is that it may initiate fatigue cracks — which, in shafts and other highly stressed components, often result in fatigue fracture. Localized wear and removal of material by fretting usually are not sufficient to cause serious problems, although material removal as deep as $1/16$ in. has been observed.

Fundamentals of Fretting

Although certain aspects of the mechanism of fretting are still not thoroughly understood, the fretting process is generally divided into the following three stages: (a) initial adhesion, (b) oscillation accompanied by the generation of

*Forensic Engineer, Centre of Forensic Sciences, Ontario Ministry of the Solicitor General, Toronto, Ontario, Canada

oxidized debris, and (c) fatigue and wear in the region of contact.

Initial Adhesion. Measurements of electrical resistance have established that intimate intermetallic contact occurs during the very early stages of fretting. Adhesion between fretting surfaces is developed by the formation of bonded junctions between asperities of the mating surfaces. For relatively high amplitudes of fretting motion, adhesion points may be created and destroyed several times over the amplitude. Fretting has occurred at amplitudes as small as 1 micro-in. (10^{-6} in.). However, if the relative motion is small enough to be absorbed by elastic deformation at the asperities of the surfaces, no fretting damage is produced. The coefficients of adhesion produced by fretting between a face-centered-cubic nonferrous alloy and a body-centered-cubic low-carbon steel are lower than if either of these materials fretted on themselves, presumably because of the differences in their crystal structures.

Initially, an oxide film, angstroms thick, which forms on the surfaces, prevents metallic contact. For the metals to adhere, the oxide film must first be disrupted to permit metal-to-metal contact. If the fretting couple is of identical material, deformation of the material underlying the oxide film will occur at both surfaces equally, and the oxide films on both surfaces will be disrupted. If the fretting couple consists of dissimilar metals, the softer metal will deform the greatest amount, so that the oxide film on the softer metal will be disrupted but that on the harder metal will stay intact. Hard metals of the same crystal structure generally produce adhesion coefficients of low values, whereas soft metals produce adhesion coefficients of high values. To a lesser degree, the hardness of the oxide appears also to play a role in producing adhesion coefficients. However, the relative hardness of the underlying metal is the prime factor. In steels, more efficient disruption of the oxide film occurs, and greater intermetallic contact is produced, as the hardness of the contacting dissimilar metal increases.

Generation of Debris. Disagreement exists among researchers as to whether the metal is oxidized before or after it is removed from the surface. Possibly both occur, with the relative contribution of each being controlled by the conditions of fretting. The major component of the debris produced by low-carbon steel or

iron when fretted in air is ferric oxide (α-Fe_2O_3), which is reddish-brown in color and highly abrasive. Ferric oxide occurs naturally as hematite and is used as a polishing agent in the form of a fine reddish-brown powder, which is commonly referred to as jeweler's rouge. Small amounts of metallic iron also are included in the debris. The color of the debris changes from black (the color of Fe_3O_4) to reddish-brown as the generated debris moves from the center of fretting toward peripheral areas where oxygen is more readily available. The color gradations are a function of both time and distance. If there is a high ambient humidity, hydrated ferric oxide (α-$Fe_2O_3 \cdot H_2O$), which is a form of rust, can be produced. Apparently, in the fretting process virgin material is removed from the surface, deformed, and finally oxidized spontaneously because of the increased chemical activity of the metal particles.

The debris formed by many nonferrous metals is largely unoxidized and is larger in particle size than that from ferrous metals. On the other hand, in hard materials such as tool steel and chromium, the initial wear particles are very small, with much oxide present. If fretting occurs in a protective or inert atmosphere, little debris is produced, although surface damage can be extensive.

There is evidence that local temperature rises under loads and at sliding speeds similar to those at which fretting occurs, and that consequently oxidation is accelerated by a local temperature increase during fretting wear. The variations of relative slip amplitude and frictional force show a hysteresis loop in one cycle, indicating the amount of energy lost in the fretting area. Calculations based on experimental data show that of the energy released in fretting vibration only one part in ten million to one billion parts, depending on the combination of materials, is consumed in wear by breaking bonds, with the remainder being dissipated as heat.

If one of the metals in a fretting couple is soft, hard oxide fragments may become embedded in the softer metal and thus reduce the wear rate. Therefore, the oxides formed in fretting can reduce the wear rate if they adhere to the surfaces or increase the wear rate if they remain loose. In gray irons, a pronounced increase in wear occurs when the size of the debris particle is smaller than the distance between the graphite flakes.

When fretted surfaces are examined in a microscope, an oxide usually is found embedded in the surfaces to such an extent that there is no longer a clearly defined boundary between the oxide and the metal but rather a gradual transition region consisting of intimately mixed metal and oxides. However, the mechanism by which damage is inflicted on the metallic surfaces appears to be more than one of abrasion. Fretting damage has been found in metals that were harder than their generated oxides. Thus, it appears that fretting damage is a surface-disintegration phenomenon that is promoted by the relative motion at the surfaces in contact.

Fatigue and Wear. Fretted regions are highly sensitive to fatigue cracking. Under fretting conditions fatigue cracks are initiated at very low stresses, well below the fatigue limit of nonfretted specimens. The initiation of fatigue cracks in fretted regions depends mainly on the state of stress in the surface and particularly on the stresses superimposed on the cyclic stress. The direction of growth of the fatigue cracks is associated with the direction of contact stresses and takes place in a direction perpendicular to the maximum principal stress in the fretting area. For this reason, fatigue strength that is based on crack initiation decreases linearly with increasing contact pressure.

A phenomenon peculiar to fretting is that some of the fatigue cracks produced do not propagate. The nonpropagation of such fatigue cracks is because the effect of contact stress extends only to a very shallow depth below the fretted surface. This surface fatigue produces local pitting or flaking, which is characteristic of fretting. Favorable compressive residual stresses retard or completely halt crack propagation, but they do not prevent crack initiation. Prevention of crack propagation in components that carry considerable stresses, such as axles or shafts, is vitally important, because the usual mode of failure of such components is fatigue initiated by fretting.

Recognition of Fretting

Fretting of ferrous metals in air produces a characteristic reddish-brown debris of ferric oxide which, when mixed with oil or grease, produces a debris that is often called "blood", "cocoa" or "red mud" debris. In components that are lubricated so that ordinary corrosion is not likely to occur, presence of the reddish-brown debris is indicative of fretting. If a component is not lubricated, the presence of oxide powder may not necessarily signify fretting but rather wear. However, wear usually is caused by lack of lubrication and can be entirely prevented by use of a proper lubricant. True

fretting, on the other hand, cannot be remedied completely by lubrication.

Analysis of the oxide can determine if the compound is ferric oxide (α-Fe_2O_3; hematite) or hydrated ferric oxide (α-$Fe_2O_3 \cdot H_2O$; goethite). These two compounds can be distinguished by x-ray diffraction, because their patterns are different, or by chemical analysis.

If fretting is present, macroscopic examination of the affected surface can be done after the corrosion has been scrubbed off with a paste of alumina and hexane, for example. The examination will reveal very reflective areas, as well as depressions and pits containing black patches of Fe_3O_4, which is produced when the oxygen supply is limited. If only ordinary corrosion is present, microscopic examination will show small but well-defined corrosion pits that have produced rust rosettes consisting of the voluminous hydrated iron oxide.

Prevention of Fretting

Components that are prone to fretting can be divided into two groups:

Group I. Components in which the fretting surfaces were never intended to undergo relative motion, which include shrink and press fits, and bolted, pinned and riveted surfaces.

Group II. Components in which the fretting surfaces are intended to undergo relative motion intermittently or continuously, such as rolling-contact or oscillating bearings, and seals on shafts.

Measures that will prevent or alleviate fretting are (a) elimination or reduction of vibration, (b) elimination of slip, (c) lubrication, (d) surface separation, and (e) induction of residual stresses.

Elimination or Reduction of Vibration. The ideal remedy for fretting is to eliminate vibration, which is the cause of slip between the fretting surfaces. This will minimize fretting of all types, because relative cyclic motion between the surfaces is the essential ingredient in any type of fretting. Although it sometimes is possible to change a design to reduce vibration sufficiently to stop slip, more often than not, vibration cannot be eliminated in practice.

Elimination of slip generally is effective only for components in group I. In these components, slip can be eliminated by increasing the load or increasing friction.

Increasing the load may be accomplished by simply tightening bolted connections or by increasing the closeness of a fit. However, if increasing the load does not prevent slip, the damage caused by fretting will be increased.

Increasing friction can be accomplished by applying a surface coating, such as nickel oxide, which is effective in stopping fretting of turbine blades. Cop-

per or lead plating of grit-blasted steel parts also is effective.

Lubrication. The slip at very small amplitudes that is usually involved in fretting produces an excellent cleaning effect and does not permit relubrication of the contact area. For this reason, fretting cannot be entirely prevented by lubrication. However, fretting damage can be greatly reduced or delayed by effective lubrication.

It has not been clearly established whether a lubricant is effective because of its ability to prevent access of oxygen to the surface, or because of its ability to separate the surfaces. Liquid lubricants cannot entirely separate the surfaces, but they can separate the surfaces to an extent that will significantly reduce the number of surface asperities in contact and therefore reduce the number of bonded junctions. Thus, for maximum effectiveness, the lubricant should have easy access to the surfaces. The effectiveness of fluid or semifluid lubricants, therefore, usually is applicable only to components in group II.

In the effective use of oils or greases, if practicable, the contacting surfaces should have a surface finish with microscopic grooves or valleys to permit the lubricant to penetrate as fully as possible to the areas of real contact. Oils should have the lowest practical viscosity to allow capillary flow in the grooved surface. Oils and greases also should contain suitable wear and oxidation inhibitors, such as phenyl-α-naphthylamine. Greases can be effective, provided they are sufficiently feedable or provided the amplitude of slip is great enough to permit relubrication of the fretted surfaces. Frequent disassembling, cleaning and relubrication of the surfaces protected by lubrication also is effective in controlling the effects of fretting.

Nonliquid lubricants may be effective for components in groups I and II. Solid lubricants of the surface-conversion type, such as sulfides and chlorides, are effective by themselves or in conjunction with liquid lubricants. Solid lubricants should be bonded to the surface to provide effective lubrication. In tests, molybdenum disulfide (MoS_2) when powdered onto steel surfaces protected the interface for 10^5 cycles, but when bonded to the surfaces, it protected for 10^7 cycles. Lead and indium films, which shear easily, also are effective. Phosphate coatings protect against fretting, and provide a base that improves adhesion of bonded laminar and other solid lubricants. Low shear strength but high elastic-strain limit is desirable in solid lubricants. Laminar lubricants, such as molybdenum disulfide or graphite, have been found very effective.

Lubrication delays but does not prevent fretting. Even with bonded solid lubricants, fretting is delayed only until the lubricant film is worn through.

Surface Separation. Complete separation of surfaces by inserting a material of high elastic-strain limit, such as rubber or a polymeric material, will prevent fretting, provided the inserted material can elastically absorb the vibrational amplitude. A film of bonded gum rubber can elastically absorb vibrations of 0.002 in. in amplitude.

Induction of Residual Stresses. Fatigue-crack propagation initiated by fretting, particularly in press-fitted assemblies, can be prevented by inducing residual compressive stresses on the surfaces. This can be accomplished by quenching below the phase-transformation temperature, or by surface rolling, shot peening, or glass-bead peening. Case hardening and nitriding also are effective in improving fatigue strength. These methods are effective not so much by reducing fretting but rather by improving fatigue strength.

Fretting in Wire Ropes

Relative movement between strands in wire rope occurs when the rope is under tension and flexed. When the flexing is repetitive, this relative movement can lead to fretting corrosion and subsequent fretting fatigue. When fretting occurs between the wires of a locked-coil type of wire rope, which is of a very compact construction, corrosion debris will force the wires apart, producing swelling of the rope, preventing sliding of the individual wires, and causing rigidity at the corroded location.

Choice of a suitable lubricant during manufacture of wire rope will prevent subsequent fretting in service. The viscosity of the lubricant must be such that it will flow readily to potential fretting sites without at the same time leaking from the rope. See also the section on Steel Wire Rope on page 457 in the article on Failures of Lifting Equipment, in this volume.

Fretting on Sliding Shafts

Fretting of shafts and bearing surfaces usually occurs as the result of one or more of the following:

1 Minute oscillatory motion between the two components
2 Bearing loads on a limited-contact area
3 Adhesion of asperities and transfer of metal between the components
4 Surface deterioration by abrasion.

Minute oscillatory motion usually creates a cloudiness following a circumferential line, in some instances several lines, on the shaft surface where the surface has been in contact with the bearing. Occasionally, the condition appears as a series of elliptical-shaped blemishes that

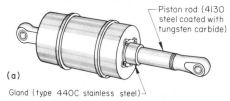

4130 steel coated with tungsten carbide; and type 440C stainless steel

Piston rod (4130 steel coated with tungsten carbide)

(a)

Gland (type 440C stainless steel)

(b)

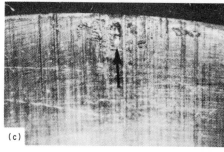

(c)

(a) Over-all view of the cylinder. Coating on piston rod contained about 15% cobalt as a carrier and binder. (b) Photograph, at 4×, of the piston rod, showing a longitudinal gouge, and deterioration of coating at midstroke (neutral) position. (c) Photograph, at 8×, of the surface of the type 440C stainless steel gland, showing particles of adhering metal (at arrow), impressions of metal chips, and scratches.

Fig. 1. Hydraulic cylinder that failed by fretting of the tungsten-carbide-coated 4130 steel piston rod (Example 1)

develop centrally located cavities as the fretting progresses. Blemishes that do not encircle the shaft indicate that bearing loads are absorbed by a limited-contact area.

Bearing Loads. Strictly static loads applied perpendicular to the bearing surfaces do not cause wear; however, in conjunction with a minute oscillating motion they are conducive to fretting corrosion.

Adhesion of Asperities. Wear begins in a bearing when the tips of the surface asperities are fragmented and oxidized to form hard oxide particles, which promote further abrasion. If mating surfaces approach to within angstroms of each other, bonding (cold welding) may result from pressure, however slight. Asperities are believed to bond and shear during wear, but this process is not necessarily undesirable as long as the bonds shear. However, when an asperity bond becomes stronger than the supporting metals, fracture occurs in the weaker base metal, and metal transfers to the opposite face of the bearing. These adhering particles build up and finally cause galling or scoring.

Rod-and-gland bearings of hydraulic actuators, under normal operating conditions, are not considered a major wear

problem. Where actuators are operated with long or full-stroke cycles, the bearing involves simple sliding friction; however, rapid, short-stroke cycling can cause an unexpected deterioration of the rod and gland bearing surfaces. In Example 1 in this article, a hydraulic cylinder malfunctioned and leaked fluid when the tungsten-carbide-coated piston rod galled after fretting caused transfer of tungsten carbide particles to the gland.

Abrasion. In nonlubricated bearings, when the constituents of both the shaft and the bearing have nearly equivalent hardnesses, they are mutually abraded and locally heated. A similar action would occur when a lubricant fails. Because of its hardness, the wear resistance of sintered tungsten carbide is very good, and shafts and bearings of this material can be operated with very-low-viscosity lubricants or mist-lubrication systems. The bearing cannot be run dry or stripped of lubricant without incurring severe damage.

Examples of Fretting Failures

The effects of fretting on components are described in the following examples. Illustrations that accompany the examples show various types of fretted surfaces that are produced under different conditions.

Example 1. Fretting of a Tungsten-Carbide-Coated Steel Piston Rod Because Cobalt Binder in Coating Became Bonded to a Stainless Steel Gland (Fig. 1)

The hydraulic cylinder shown in Fig. 1 (a) was used as a precision positioning device whose neutral position was approximately midstroke. Short-stroke, quivering vibration occurred at this point. Malfunction was indicated, and a leak developed in the actuator gland during a controls-system check.

The piston rod, specified to be 4130 steel heat treated to a hardness of Rockwell C 32 to 35, was flame-spray coated with tungsten carbide. The coating contained about 15% cobalt, which acted as a carrier and binder for the particles of tungsten carbide. Material for the gland was type 440C stainless steel, heat treated to a hardness of Rockwell C 57 min.

A metallurgical investigation was conducted to determine the quality of the metals involved and the possible cause of failure.

Investigation. When the cylinder was disassembled, the piston rod was found to have a deep longitudinal gouge on one line over the span of full travel (see Fig. 1b). Pitting on a circumferential line was noted at the midstroke, or neutral, position.

Cracks were found in the gouge; their appearance indicated that the rod was galled when moving away from the neutral position. The absence of plowed metal at the ends of the gouge was attributed to the hardness of the constituents.

Metallographic sections of the piston rod revealed that the bond was good at the interface between the steel rod and the coating.

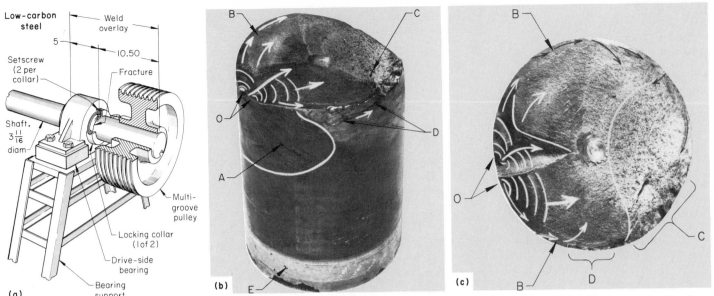

Fig. 2. (a) Schematic showing a low-carbon steel shaft for a cooling fan that failed in fatigue. (b) and (c) Fractographs showing mechanisms of fracture: A, fretting region at which fatigue cracks, indicated by O, originated; B, circumferential cracks; C, final-fracture region; D, region in which setscrew slipped; and E, weld overlay used to rebuild worn area on shaft. (Example 2)

The gouging action had deformed the substrate, but the coating was not separated from the rod. At a few locations, the coating was cracked and delaminated at several thickness levels.

The surface of the gland exhibited numerous scratches and adherent particles and chips of coating, as shown in Fig. 1(c). The chips were impressed into the surface, as evidenced by the sharp outline of the cavities and the absence of plowed metal. Fluoroscopic analysis of the chips disclosed primarily tungsten and cobalt, which were constituents of the coating, plus a trace of chromium, which most likely came from the type 440C stainless steel gland.

Examination also revealed diametrically opposed elliptical-shaped areas of burnishing at opposite ends of the gland — a condition indicating that the bearing loads were absorbed by a limited area. Electron microscopy confirmed that oscillatory motion had occurred in these areas.

The hardness of the gland was Rockwell C 55.5. The hardness of the piston rod was within the specified range of Rockwell C 32 to 35 and the tungsten carbide coating was within the specified range of 900 to 1250 dph (50-gram load).

Discussion. Normally, extremely hard metals abrade during fretting or wear, but in this instance particles of the tungsten carbide–cobalt coating bonded to the gland surface (see Fig. 1c). Because carbides and metals are mutually insoluble (nonweldable), and thus not likely to adhere to each other, the cobalt binder apparently bonded to the stainless steel gland, carrying the carbides with it. These strong bonds caused deformation of the 4130 steel substrate before the coating failed and was transferred to the gland.

Cobalt is a poor material to place in bearing contact with ferrous alloys, because cobalt and iron are mutually soluble, and therefore are likely to gall. With the cobalt forming strong bonds with the stainless steel at points of asperity contact during the fretting action at the neutral position, the

oscillatory motions were translated into fatigue loads on the coating, resulting in localized delamination. When the piston rod was moved, the transferred particles of carbide gouged the rod. Gouging resulted in the observed leak and malfunction of the hydraulic cylinder.

Conclusions. Fretting coupled with mutual solubility of the coating binder (cobalt) with the gland material (stainless steel) were the primary causes for the initial deterioration of the piston-rod coating.

Corrective Measures. Several coatings were tried on the gland to prevent or minimize fretting damage. Among these coatings were electrodeposited silver, silver-rhenium, and two commercial brands of Teflon cloth. The Teflon cloth provided the optimum solution to the problem.

Example 2. Fatigue Failure of a Low-Carbon Steel Fan Shaft, Which Originated at a Fretting Area That Contained Residual Welding Stresses (Fig. 2)

The shaft shown in Fig. 2(a) was the main shaft of a V-belt-driven cooling fan. The shaft fractured at the outer edge of the drive bearing. Sections of the shaft containing the fracture surfaces were removed for examination. The shaft was $3\frac{11}{16}$ in. in diameter at the fracture area and was made of low-carbon steel shafting, turned, ground and polished. Fan speed was 819 rpm.

Shaft History. Approximately $2\frac{1}{2}$ months before the shaft broke, the drive-side bearing failed, possibly from improper lubrication, scoring the shaft to such an extent that it was difficult to remove the bearing from the shaft after the drive pulley had been removed. The portion of the shaft supported by the bearing had been machined to $3\frac{9}{16}$ in. in diameter, resurfaced by welding, and then remachined to the required $3\frac{11}{16}$-in. diameter. The shaft was reinstalled in the fan, which ran satisfactorily until the fracture discussed here occurred.

Investigation. Visual examination of that portion of the shaft surrounded by the drive-side bearing disclosed light and dark

areas (see Fig. 2b), which indicated that the shaft did not seat completely in the bearing. There were indications of slight movement between the shaft and the bearing inner race, resulting in fretting corrosion (area A in Fig. 2b). The fretted area was black and brown in color and had increased in size and depth as small crevices joined to form larger and deeper crevices. The fretting debris had a brown rust color. The origins of two fatigue cracks, shown at O in Fig. 2(b) and (c), were at the confluence of several of the largest valleys or ragged crevices produced by fretting corrosion.

Further examination of the fracture surface disclosed typical fatigue striations emanating from the two origins and circumferential cracks that had developed around the shaft where the outboard lip of the bearing race was fretting on the shaft. The circumferential cracks, at B in Fig. 2(b) and (c), appeared to have progressed almost completely around the shaft, to the depth of the weld overlay (E in Fig. 2b) long before the final break (C in Fig. 2b and c).

The single-sided convex cracks that were progressing through the body of the shaft eventually joined with the circumferential cracks. When the shaft had cracked about two-thirds of the way across, the remaining one-third was unable to support the load. According to marks on the larger of the two pieces of shaft, the drive-pulley end wobbled for 8 to 10 revolutions before the shaft twisted completely off and fell to the floor. Two setscrews in the bearing collar slipped around the shaft, smearing and plowing metal for about 1 in. around the shaft (D in Fig. 2b and c).

The weld repair on the shaft appeared to be satisfactory; however, the weld overlay contained microscopic voids, fissures and pits, some of which were observed visually on the two pieces of shaft. Records did not indicate that the shaft had been stress relieved after welding.

Residual welding stresses could have acted in conjunction with the fretting corrosion, microscopic voids and fissures in the

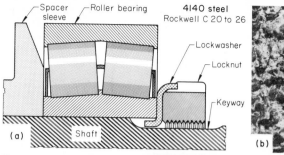

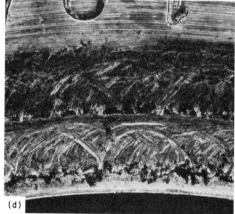

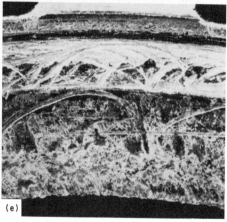

(a) Shaft and bearing assembly. (b) Failed region of shaft, at 2×, showing disturbed metal and partly closed keyway. (c) Shaft side of bearing inner ring, at 3×, showing pitting similar to fretting damage. (d) Bearing side of spacer sleeve, at 4.5×, showing disturbed metal. (e) Bearing side of lockwasher, at 4.5×, showing disturbed metal.

Fig. 3. Freon-compressor shaft of 4140 steel that failed by fretting corrosion in the bearing area (Example 3)

weld deposits, and the reverse bending of the rotating load imposed by the drive belts to cause initiation of fatigue cracks.

Conclusions. The shaft failed in fatigue as the result of reversed-bending stresses imposed by the drive belt as the shaft rotated. This caused an area of stress concentration to progress around the shaft at the point where the shaft was supported by the bearing during operation.

The fatigue cracks originated in an area of severe fretting, possibly compounded by microscopic fissures and pits in the weld overlay that was used to rebuild the scored shaft. Residual welding stress also may have contributed to fatigue failure.

The drive-side bearing was not available for examination, and so no definite reason for its failure could be established. However,

most bearings fail from material breakdown or overheating that results from lubrication breakdown. The antifriction bearing used for this installation could not have been overloaded, because its load rating exceeded the actual load conditions.

Recommendations. The shaft should be made of a high-strength low-alloy steel, with the bearing surfaces properly ground and press fitted into the bearing inner race. The drive-side bearing surface could be shot peened to add beneficial compressive stresses.

The tension on the V-belt drive should be carefully adjusted and vibration in the fan system minimized.

All repair welds on such shafts should be stress relieved to decrease the possibility of shaft failure.

Example 3. Fretting of a Freon-Compressor Shaft of 4140 Steel Because of a Loose Bearing (Fig. 3)

The shaft-and-bearing assembly (see Fig. 3a) in a freon compressor was subjected to severe pounding and vibration after six years of service. After about one year of service, the compressor had been shut down to replace a bearing seal. One month before the shaft failed, a second seal failure occurred, requiring the collar, spacer sleeve, seal, roller bearing, and lockwasher to be replaced.

The shaft was made of 4140 steel, heat treated to a hardness of Rockwell C 20 to 26. The seal, bearing and lockwasher were commercial components. Although the specifications did not call for hard facing of the bearing surface on the shaft, maintenance-department personnel thought the shaft had been hard faced.

The shaft, spacer sleeve, roller bearing and lockwasher were sent to the laboratory for examination.

Visual examination of the compressor shaft disclosed quantities of disturbed metal and partial closing of the keyway at the surface where it was contacted by a roller bearing, as shown in Fig. 3(b). The failed surface contained a groove approximately 0.040 in. deep and was coated with a black corrosion deposit. The spacer sleeve, roller bearing and lockwasher also were coated with the black deposit.

Deposits collected from the failed area and from the spacer sleeve, roller bearing, and lockwasher were identified by x-ray diffraction as ferric oxide (α-Fe_2O_3) with minor constituents of metallic iron and copper. Discoloration of the deposit was caused by the grease lubricant and mishandling during disassembly.

Spectrochemical analysis of scrapings taken from an affected area and an unaffected area of the bearing surface on the shaft and from areas adjacent to and away from the bearing surface of the shaft indicated that all surfaces were fabricated from 4140 steel. These findings discounted the theory that the bearing surface had been hard faced.

Readings taken along the shaft showed that the hardness of the area beneath the bearing was Rockwell C 24, while the area beneath the sleeve had a hardness of Rockwell B 90 (approximately Rockwell C 10). This suggests that the area of the shaft beneath the bearing had been heat treated. The hardness of the inner bearing race was Rockwell C 54.

Microscopic examination of the shaft side of the inner bearing race showed pitting similar to that associated with fretting corrosion (see Fig. 3c). Examination of the surfaces of the spacer sleeve and of the lockwasher that contacted the roller bearing disclosed disturbed metal, indicating there had been movement between the sleeve and the bearing and between the bearing and the lockwasher (see Fig. 3d and e). The direction of the disturbed metal on the sleeve and the lockwasher showed that movement was both radial and circumferential.

The peened appearance of the metal that partly covered the keyway indicated movement between the shaft and the inner bearing race. The inner bearing race could not move radially, because it was backed by the

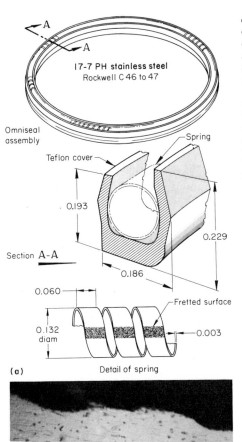

Fig. 4. (a) Omniseal assembly in which a 17-7 PH stainless steel spring in a Teflon cover failed by fretting. (b) Micrograph of a section taken through the fretted area. (Example 4)

rollers, outer race, and compressor shell, which were in good condition after the failure. Therefore, the shaft must have moved radially during failure. Because the lockwasher and spacer sleeve were attached to the shaft and moved with it, the circular scratches on the contacting surfaces of the bearing and the sleeve, and those of the bearing and the lockwasher, indicate radial motion of the shaft. The scratches on the sleeve and lockwasher were approximately 0.080 in. long, which was equal to the loss in diameter of the shaft at the failed area.

Conclusions. Shaft failure was initiated by fretting between the bearing race and the bearing surface on the shaft because of improper bearing installation. Once clearance was established between the bearing and the shaft, the shaft began pounding on the inner bearing race, causing final failure of the shaft surface.

Recommendations. Proper fitting of the shaft and bearing race is essential in preventing movement of the bearing on the shaft. Also, the lockwasher and locknut must be properly installed.

Example 4. Fretting Failure of a Stainless Steel Spring in a Teflon Cover (Fig. 4)

The omniseal assembly shown in Fig. 4(a) served as a hydraulic seal around the cylinder liners in a diesel-engine block. The assembly, consisting of a 17-7 PH stainless steel spring and a Teflon cover, sealed the

coolant from the oil in the crankcase. The open side of the cover was exposed to the coolant side of the engine. The spring failed after about six months of service and was sent to the laboratory to determine the cause of failure.

Investigation. Visual examination revealed wear in three general areas at various locations around the inside surface of the Teflon cover. Corresponding areas on the spring showed discoloration or evidence of fretting. These areas were at the points of contact between the cover and the spring, as shown in section A-A and "Detail of spring" in Fig. 4(a). Fracturing of the spring occurred almost entirely at the sites of fretting and discoloration.

A micrograph of a section through the fretted area (see Fig. 4b) showed no general evidence of corrosion or other mechanical damage. Also, evidence of stress corrosion was not present.

Hardness tests revealed that the failed spring and an unused spring both had a hardness of Rockwell C 46 to 47; the unused spring had a tensile strength of 206,000 psi. On the inner surface of the Teflon cover was a mixture of oil, water and fine black particles, typically found in a diesel-engine crankcase, as well as small flakes of metal.

Conclusion. Failure of the spring was caused by fretting that occurred at the points of contact between the spring and cover. The small black particles of residue on the inner surface of the cover promoted fretting corrosion. Vibration of the diesel engine imparted high-frequency – low-amplitude motion to the spring, thus causing fretting between the contacting surfaces of the spring and the cover.

Corrective Measures. The fluids (coolant and oil) were filtered to remove the fine black particles. Also, the seal was reversed in the engine so that the open side of the cover was exposed to the oil in the crankcase. With these changes, failures were greatly reduced and the seals operated successfully for at least 200,000 miles.

Example 5. Fretting Failure of a Zircaloy-2 Fuel-Element Tube Because of Contact With Jagged Metal (Fig. 5)

Water used for cooling fuel elements in a nuclear power reactor showed signs of being contaminated with fissionable material approximately five weeks after new elements had been installed, indicating leakage in one of the elements. A fuel element is shown in Fig. 5. The elements were removed from the reactor and examined in the discharge basin with a borescope and closed-circuit television to determine which elements had failed. This examination showed that the inner surface of one of the outer fuel pieces was leaking (see detail A in Fig. 5). The inner and outer fuel pieces were separated from each other, and the failed portion was given further metallographic examination.

Construction of Fuel Element. The fuel element was constructed of two thick-wall uranium pipes, one inside the other and both covered by Zircaloy-2 tubes, as shown in Fig. 5. There were passages for cooling water through the center of the inner fuel piece, through the annulus between the inner and outer fuel pieces and through the

annulus between the outer fuel piece and the inner wall of the horizontal process tube that contained the fuel elements. Several fuel elements were end-to-end in each process tube. Concentricity of the fuel pieces in the process tube was ensured by leaf-type spacer springs welded to the outer surfaces of both the inner and the outer fuel pieces. On the outer fuel piece, low-carbon steel shoes were attached to the leaf-type springs. These shoes minimized galling of the process tubes while the reactor was being recharged with new fuel elements.

Investigation. Visual examination of the inner surface of the outer fuel piece in the initial area of water penetration showed the surface of one of the Zircaloy-2 tubes to be abraded in one area with a small hole through the wall. This area had the appearance of a broad shallow pit.

Examination of the autoradiographs of the fuel element taken during manufacture showed that the pit was not present at the time of manufacture. Because the damaged area was on the inner surface of the fuel element, mechanical damage was not considered to be the cause.

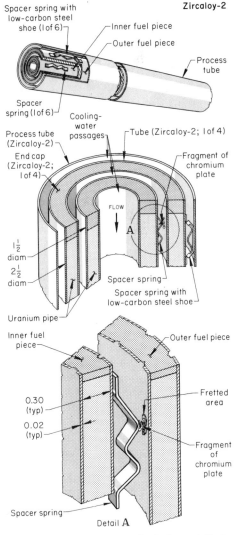

Fig. 5. Nuclear-reactor fuel element that failed by fretting because a jagged fragment of chromium plate caught on a spacer spring and oscillated against a Zircaloy-2 wall of the element (Example 5)

Because the damaged surface was near the bearing area of the spacer springs on the inner fuel piece, the springs on the inner fuel piece were carefully examined. Still clinging to one spring was a small piece of metal, approximately 3/8 in. long, 1/16 in. wide, and 0.002 in. thick, shaped like an elongated Z with jagged edges. Neutron-activation analysis showed the metal to be chromium. From appearance, it was a fragment of chromium plate, probably from a valve seat, that had been loosened by galling and had been carried along by the cooling water until, by chance, it caught on the spring. Flow of the water had caused the chromium fragment to oscillate rapidly. One end of the fragment apparently rubbed against the inner wall of the Zircaloy-2 tube and caused fretting until the wall was thinned and penetrated in one spot. Hot water in contact with the underlying uranium resulted in a voluminous corrosion product, which caused the thinned region to bend upward, thus enlarging the hole.

Galvanic corrosion of the Zircaloy-2 tube also may have occurred near the chromium fragment. However, galvanic corrosion was minimal, because small pieces of Zircaloy-2 caused fretting failures in other tubes.

Conclusion. Failure of the Zircaloy-2 tube was the result of fretting caused by the rapid oscillation of a jagged piece of chromium plate against the fuel-piece wall.

Corrective Measure. The cooling water was filtered as it entered the process tube, which eliminated failures of this type.

Fretting failures that occurred later in the nuclear-reactor fuel element discussed in the preceding example resulted when shavings of Zircaloy-2 were removed from the inside of the process tubes when fuel elements were charged into them or when others were being discharged. The details of these failures were similar to the one involving the fragment of chromium plate in the preceding example. The corrective action taken was to reduce the velocity of the ram that inserted the fuel elements into, or removed them from, the process tube. A reverse flow of rinsing water through the process tube removed any shavings.

In this same nuclear power reactor, another type of fretting failure sometimes occurred if the inner fuel piece did not fit tightly in the outer fuel piece. The vibration resulting from the high rate of cooling-water flow caused fretting of the inner surface of the outer fuel piece. To correct this, the springs were adjusted to ensure a tight fit.

Selected References

I-Ming Feng and B. C. Rightmire, The Mechanism of Fretting, *Lubrication Eng*, June 1953, p 134

R. T. Allsop, Fretting Corrosion of Metals, *Metallurgia*, Aug 1959, p 39

C. Nishimatsu and L. Gurland, Experimental Survey of the Deformation of the Hard-Ductile Two-Phase Alloy System WC-Co, *Trans Am Soc Metals*, Vol 52, 1960, p 469-484

B. Bethune and R. B. Waterhouse, Adhesion of Metal Surfaces Under Fretting Conditions: I — Like Metals in Contact, *Wear*, Oct 1968, Vol 12, No. 4, p 289-296

B. Bethune and R. B. Waterhouse, Adhesion of Metal Surfaces Under Fretting Conditions: II — Unlike Metals in Contact, *Wear*, Nov 1968, Vol 12, No. 5, p 369-374

P. L. Hurricks, The Mechanism of Fretting: A Review, *Wear*, June 1970, Vol 15, No. 6, p 389-409

W. D. Milestone and J. T. Janeczko, Friction Between Steel Surfaces During Fretting, *Wear*, July 1971, Vol 18, No. 1, p 29-40

R. G. Bayer, Understanding the Fundamentals of Wear, *Machine Design*, Dec 28, 1974, Vol 44, No. 31, p 73-76

D. Godfrey, Fretting Corrosion of Steel — How to Recognize and Stop It, *Lubrication Eng*, Feb 1973, Vol 29, No. 2, p 43-44

G. L. Goss and D. W. Hoeppner, Characterization of Fretting Fatigue Damage by SEM (Scanning Electron Microscope) Analysis, *Wear*, Apr 1973, Vol 34, No. 1, p 77-95

R. B. Waterhouse and D. E. Taylor, Fretting Fatigue in Steel Ropes, *Lubrication Eng*, Apr 1971, Vol 27, No. 4, p 123-127

R. E. Battilana, Fretting Corrosion Under Mechanical Seals, *Chem Eng*, Mar 8, 1971, Vol 78, No. 6, p 130, 132

J. B. Christian and B. D. McConnell, The Analysis of Mechanical Variables Influencing Fretting Corrosion in Grease Lubricated Bearings, ASLE Preprint No. 71AM 1B-1, Amer. Soc. of Lubrication Engrs., 1971

H. H. Mabie, N. S. Eiss, C. J. Hurst and G. C. Hite, The Vibration and Fretting Corrosion of Instrument Ball Bearings, ASLE Preprint No. 71LC-7, Amer. Soc. of Lubrication Engrs., 1971

Liquid-Erosion Failures

By FREDERICK G. HAMMITT and FRANK J. HEYMANN*

EROSION of a solid surface can take place in a liquid medium even without the presence of solid, abrasive particles in that medium. One mechanism of liquid erosion involves the formation and subsequent collapse of bubbles within the liquid, which is known as cavitation. The process by which material is removed from a surface is called cavitation erosion, and the resulting damage is cavitation damage. When liquid droplets collide with a solid surface at high speed, a form of liquid erosion called liquid-impingement erosion occurs.

Cavitation damage has been observed on ship propellers and hydrofoils, on dams, spillways, gates, tunnels and other hydraulic structures, and in hydraulic pumps and turbines. High-speed flow of

liquid in these devices causes local hydrodynamic pressures to vary widely and rapidly. In mechanical devices, severe restrictions in fluid passages have produced cavitation damage downstream of orifices and in valves, seals, bearings, heat-exchanger tubes, and venturis. Cavitation erosion also has damaged water-cooled diesel-engine cylinder liners.

Liquid-impingement erosion has been observed on many components exposed to high-velocity steam containing moisture droplets, such as blades in the low-pressure end of large steam turbines. A form of liquid-impingement erosion, rain erosion, frequently damages aerodynamic surfaces of aircraft and missiles when they fly through rainstorms at high subsonic or supersonic speeds. Liquid-impingement and cavitation erosion are of concern in nuclear-power systems, which operate at lower steam quality than conventional steam systems, and in systems using liquid metals as the working fluid, where the high density and corrosiveness of the liquid metal can promote rapid erosion of components.

Liquid erosion involves the progressive removal of material from a surface by repeated impulse loading at microscopically small areas. Liquid dynamics is of major importance in producing damage, although corrosion also plays a role in the damage process, at least with certain fluid-material combinations. The process of liquid erosion is less well understood than most other failure processes. It is difficult to define the hydrodynamic conditions that produce erosion and to define the metallurgical processes by which particles are detached from the surface. Evidently, both cavitation and liquid impingement exert similar hydrodynamic forces on a solid surface. In any event, the appearance of damaged surfaces and the relative resistance of materials to damage are similar for both liquid-impingement and cavitation erosion.

Cavitation

When the local pressure in a liquid is reduced without a change in temperature, eventually a condition is reached

*Dr. Hammitt is Professor-in-Charge, Cavitation and Multiphase Flow Laboratory, Mechanical Engineering Dept., University of Michigan. Mr. Heymann is Senior Engineer, Technology Development Dept., Steam Turbine Div., Westinghouse Electric Corp.

The two examples in this article are based on reports from contributors other than the authors.

where gas-filled bubbles (or cavities) nucleate and grow within the body of liquid. The gas in the bubbles may be vapor or molecules of a substance that formerly was dissolved in the liquid. If a bubble is formed by vaporization, bubble growth will occur rapidly, but if gas dissolution is required for bubble formation, growth will occur more slowly. Growth of gas-filled bubbles (as opposed to vapor-filled bubbles) depends on the diffusion of dissolved gas to the cavity or on the rate of gas expansion due to pressure reduction. If cavities formed in a low-pressure region pass subsequently into a region of higher pressure, their growth will be reversed and they will collapse and disappear as the vapor condenses or the gas is redissolved in the liquid. A vapor-filled cavity will implode, collapsing very rapidly (perhaps in as short a time as a few milliseconds), whereas a gas-filled cavity will collapse more slowly — both being the exact or nearly exact reverse of the bubble-growth process. (A thorough treatment of the liquid dynamics involved in bubble growth and collapse is given in Ref 1.)

Insofar as damage to materials is concerned, it is the collapse of cavities (bubbles) that produces the damage. The exact mechanism by which cavity collapse transmits severe localized forces to a surface is not fully understood. However, it most likely involves either shock waves that are produced by the collapse and immediate re-formation of a cavity, which is known as rebound (see Fig. 1), or impingement of a microjet of liquid through the collapsing cavity onto the surface being damaged as a result of nonsymmetrical cavity collapse (see Fig. 2). Both rebound and nonsymmetrical collapse with formation of a microjet have been observed experimentally, and partly computed analytically (Ref 1).

Collapse pressures were first estimated by Lord Rayleigh in 1917, and since have been estimated by many others using modifications of Rayleigh's theory. Rayleigh found that, for an empty cavity collapsing with spherical symmetry in an incompressible inviscid fluid, the velocity of the collapsing cavity wall and the pressure at the instant of complete collapse were infinitely large. Later analyses, most of them based on the assumption of adiabatic compression of gas in a collapsing cavity in a compressible fluid, predicted collapse pressures in the range of 300 to 2200 atm. Although even the more recent analyses predict wall velocities approaching infinity for a spherical empty cavity at the instant of complete collapse, the presence of gas within the cavity results in wall velocities that rise to a very high value just prior to complete collapse, then fall rapidly to zero at the instant of collapse.

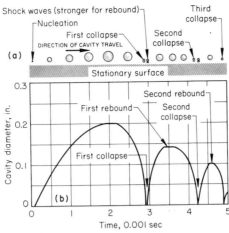

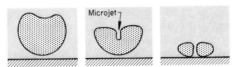

Fig. 1. (a) *Schematic representation of successive stages of growth, collapse and rebound of a single traveling cavity.* (b) *Graph of cavity diameter as a function of time for the cavity in* (a). (Based on data from Ref 2)

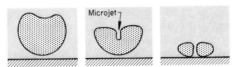

Fig. 2. Schematic representation of successive stages of nonsymmetrical cavity collapse with microjet impingement against a metallic surface

Actual collapses near a surface do not preserve spherical symmetry very far into the collapse; thus the Rayleigh model is largely voided. Actual collapses form microjets of liquid (Fig. 2), which probably attain velocities ranging from 100 to 500 meters per second. Thus the actual damaging process may be quite similar to that of liquid impingement.

An important aspect of the collapse of a gas-filled cavity is that, for the gas to significantly retard collapse and thereby reduce the amount of resulting damage, it must be capable of storing much of the thermodynamic work involved in collapsing the cavity. Usually, where cavitation occurs in a liquid of low vapor pressure and low concentration of dissolved gas, the contents of a cavity are incapable of absorbing any significant amount of the work. Thus, almost all of the energy of collapse will be used to compress the surrounding liquid. Only when the vapor pressure is high compared to the ambient pressure, or when dissolved-gas content is extremely high, do the contents of a collapsing cavity have a significant retarding effect on cavity collapse and the damage that results from it.

Liquid-Impingement Erosion

The high-velocity impact of a drop of liquid against a solid surface produces two effects that result in damage to the surface: (a) high pressure, which is generated at the point of impact; and

(b) liquid flow along the surface at high speed radially from the point of impact, which occurs as the initial pressure pulse subsides. Although there is not as yet any fully accepted theory for the pressure distribution in a solid upon impact with a spherical drop of liquid, a qualitative understanding is being developed through both analytical and experimental studies. There is ample evidence that the maximum pressure is developed not at the central point of impact but in a ring around it, and that the maximum pressure is close to twice the theoretical pressure for a "flat" impact. The theoretical pressure for a "flat" impact of a flat-ended body of water on a flat, rigid surface is 160,000 psi when the impact velocity is 1500 ft per second. Microscopic observation of damage caused by single impacts has revealed an annular zone of deformation, and sometimes tearing or cracking, which has been attributed to outward-flowing liquid with high superimposed pressures.

In liquid impingement, each collision between a drop of liquid and a surface is capable of producing damage. On the other hand, it has been estimated that the collapse of only one in 30,000 cavitation bubbles results in visible surface damage (p 335 in Ref 1).

Liquid-impingement erosion is believed to occur by the processes illustrated in Fig. 3. Upon impact, the impact pressure can produce circumferential cracks in the area of impact (Fig. 3a), depending on the properties of the surface material and the energy of impact. (For very ductile materials, the initial damage may be in the form of shallow craters surrounded by a circular ridge of deformed metal.) Following impact, the liquid flows away radially at high velocity. When the spreading liquid hits a nearby surface asperity, the force of this impact stresses the asperity at its base and may produce a crack (Fig. 3b). Subsequent impacts by other drops may widen the crack, or detach the asperity entirely, as shown in Fig. 3(c). Direct hits on existing cracks, pits or other deep depressions can produce accelerated damage by a microjet-impingement mechanism, as illustrated in Fig. 3(d). Eventually, the pits and secondary cracks intersect, and larger pieces of the surface become detached.

Characteristics of Erosion Damage

Materials may be damaged by deformation, ductile fracture, brittle fracture, or fatigue. Corrosion was once thought to play an essential role in cavitation erosion, but recent experiments (most notably, tests of plastics in water and of aluminum in toluene) strongly indicate that damage can occur even with the complete lack of corrosion. This does

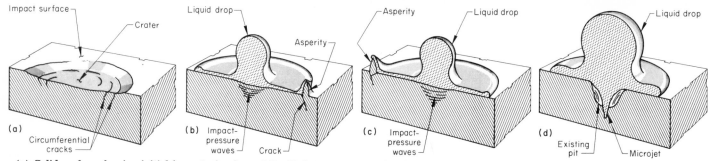

(a) Solid surface showing initial impact of a drop of liquid that produces circumferential cracks in the area of impact, or produces shallow craters in very ductile materials. (b) High-velocity radial flow of liquid away from the impact area is arrested by a nearby surface asperity, which cracks at its base; (c) subsequent impact by another drop of liquid breaks the asperity. (d) Direct hit on a deep pit results in accelerated damage, because shock waves bouncing off the sides of the pit cause the formation of a high-energy microjet within the pit.

Fig. 3. Processes by which a material is damaged by liquid-impingement erosion

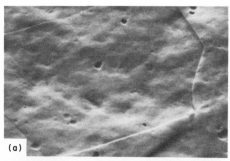

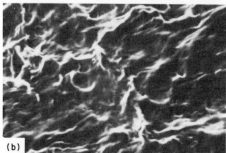

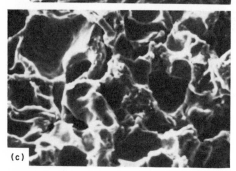

(a) Shallow craters that formed on the surface after exposure for 5 sec. (b) More widespread and deeper attack after exposure for 10 min. (c) Fracture of ridges between deep pits after exposure for 2 hr.

Fig. 4. Scanning electron micrographs of a surface of polycrystalline nickel damaged by exposure to intense cavitation in a vibratory test at 20 kHz (Ref 3)

not mean that corrosion does not influence damage in situations where corrosion is known to occur, but rather that corrosion is not a necessary factor in producing damage.

In ductile materials, liquid erosion often occurs by the formation of micro-scopically small craters under the impact of cavitation shock waves, drop impingement, or microjet impingement, as is shown in Fig. 4(a) for polycrystalline nickel exposed to intense cavitation in a standard vibratory cavitation test for 5 sec at 20 kHz. Longer exposure times result in more widespread damage and a deepening of previously formed shallow pits, as shown in Fig. 4(b), and eventually in fracture of extruded ridges between adjacent pits, as shown in Fig. 4(c). Metallographic examination and x-ray diffraction studies have shown plastic deformation — in the form of both slip and mechanical twinning — to occur in a layer about 30 to 300 microns below the surface during the initial stages of damage. This layer remains fairly constant in thickness throughout the subsequent stages of material removal. Apparently, material is lost by ductile fracture of asperities in early stages of the erosion process, with fracture of work-hardened surface material and of ridges between erosion pits predominating in later stages. Brittle materials are eroded mainly by fracture and chipping of microscopic particles from the surface.

There is convincing experimental evidence that some erosion damage is the result of single events. Pits that are observed on erosion-test specimens after short exposure times often are essentially unchanged after much longer exposure times. However, fatigue striations are occasionally found on a damaged surface, so fatigue cannot be dismissed as a possible damage mechanism. Figure 5 illustrates damage on a stainless steel pump component; erosion occurred in cavitating mercury. In Fig. 5, large individual craters are scattered over a background of typical small-scale pitting. Regions of fatigue also were found on this component.

Erosion Rates. The rate of cavitation or liquid-impingement erosion, commonly measured as weight or volume loss per unit of time, sometimes follows one of the patterns shown in Fig. 6. Erosion damage of most materials is not observ-

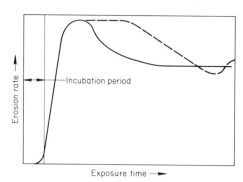

Fig. 5. Pitted surface of a stainless steel pump component that was damaged by exposure to cavitating mercury

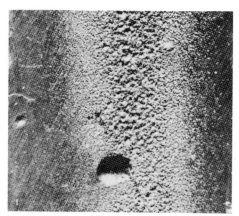

Fig. 6. Schematic representation of typical variation of liquid-erosion rate with exposure time. See text for discussion.

able as a weight loss until after an incubation period. The erosion rate rises rapidly to a maximum, which may persist for some time as shown in the dashed curve in Fig. 6, then usually decreases to a lower value, which either may remain relatively steady or may fluctuate in a completely unpredictable manner. The length of the incubation period, the maximum damage rate and the shape of subsequent portions of the erosion-rate curve depend on the intensity of cavitation or liquid impingement, the properties of the material, and (to a minor extent) the original surface condition. At low hydrodynamic intensities, the chemical activities of the material and environment also may influence the rate of damage.

The incubation period appears to coincide with the time needed to develop the subsurface work-hardened layer mentioned previously. During this time, only random surface pitting occurs with a very slight loss of microscopically small particles from widely separated locations on the surface. As detectable weight loss begins, the characteristics of the surface change, with fracture, deep pitting and fatigue becoming more evident. The exact mechanisms vary with the properties of the material and the hydrodynamic intensity. Reduction of the damage rate appears to occur when the surface has become so rough that the intensity of individual impacts is reduced by the presence of liquid trapped between deformation ridges, or by the ridges themselves. Advanced stages of liquid erosion produce a characteristic honeycomblike damaged surface, and variations in the erosion rate may occur because of gross changes in part contour.

Effect of Flow Velocity. Several investigators have attempted to correlate the rate of erosion with flow properties of the fluid stream (for cavitation), and impact velocity of drops (for liquid impingement). Although the results have not been adequately explained by any theory proposed to date, the maximum rate of volume loss per unit of area (sometimes expressed as mean-depth-of-penetration rate, or MDPR) usually varies with an exponential function of the relative velocity between surface and fluid.

In cavitation erosion, six is the exponent most commonly found, but exponents as high as ten and as low as two have been found for the dependence of MDPR on relative velocity. The value of the exponent in a given instance undoubtedly is affected by such factors as cavitation intensity, fluid pressure, type of cavitation, and specimen configuration. Nevertheless, a strong dependence of damage rate on flow velocity of the fluid stream is indicated.

In liquid-impingement erosion, the rate of volume loss usually varies with the fifth or sixth power of relative velocity. However, exponents as high as eight to ten have been determined for rain-erosion tests of some nonmetallic materials. Regardless of whether damage occurs by cavitation erosion or liquid impingement, the life of a component in a given erosive situation can be profoundly affected by small changes in relative velocity between the component and the eroding fluid.

Damage Resistance of Metals

The resistance of specific metals or other materials to liquid erosion, which is commonly evaluated by ASTM G32 (Standard Method for Vibratory Cavitation Erosion Test), does not depend on any one property, although many attempts have been made to correlate erosion damage with different intrinsic properties. Various properties such as hardness, true stress at fracture, strain energy to fracture, corrosion-fatigue strength, work-hardening rate, and "ultimate resilience" (one-half the square of ultimate strength, divided by the modulus of elasticity) appear to be good measures of resistance to erosion damage for certain metals or limited classes of alloys. Most such correlations break down, however, when attempts are made to extend them to a wide variety of alloys, or to both metallic and nonmetallic materials. Even elaborate correlations often err by as much as 300%, and for untested materials may predict erosion rates that are in error by an order of magnitude or more from the actual rate determined by subsequent testing. Brinell hardness appears to be as good a correlating factor as any; its usefulness is enhanced by its widespread use as a measure of material strength. For many alloys, MDPR varies inversely with Bhn^n, where the exponent n has a value between 2 and 3 (usually, 2.5).

Part of the uncertainty involved in developing meaningful correlations is due to the uncertain definition of exposure conditions that produce damage in various laboratory-test mechanisms. Even more influential is the fact that different mechanisms of metal removal appear to exist, depending on the intensity of the cavitation or impingement and the relative importance of corrosion. Intense hydrodynamic conditions seem to favor single-event processes, but conditions that produce impacts of a lesser magnitude are more conducive to fatigue, or to corrosion enhanced by the mechanical removal of protective films of corrosion products.

Effect of Hardness. Hardness usually is a good index of erosion resistance when the same alloy or very similar alloys are considered at different hardness levels. Yet erosion resistance of different types of alloys at the same hardness level may vary by as much as an order of magnitude or more.

In some instances, work hardening can increase erosion resistance, especially under mild erosive conditions. However, for long exposure times, or for intense exposure conditions, erosion resistance may be reduced, probably because work hardening by the eroding medium is a prelude to loss of material by fatigue or fracture. Surface treatments such as shot peening generally are not very effective, because they duplicate the processes that occur during the incubation period.

Thermal treatments, especially those that increase toughness as well as hardness, usually improve erosion resistance. Generally, a ductile and work-hardenable metal of a given hardness will resist erosion better than a brittle metal of the same hardness.

Both laboratory experiments and service experience universally confirm that the Stellites, a family of cobalt-chromium-tungsten alloys, are the most resistant to liquid erosion of all the structural alloys. Although the erosion resistance of Stellite alloys is approached by that of some high-strength ausformed or maraging steels, and may be equaled by that of some very hard tool steels, the Stellites achieve outstanding erosion resistance with lower hardness and greater resistance to corrosion and stress-corrosion cracking than either high-strength steel or tool steel. In relation to their hardness, titanium alloys and the Inconel nickel-base alloys exhibit above average erosion resistance.

Effect of Microstructure. Small grain size and fine dispersions of hard second-phase particles both enhance erosion resistance. These characteristics, particularly the latter, appear to give the Stellites and some tool steels their superior erosion resistance.

A recent investigation found evidence that cavitation impacts induced a transformation in crystal structure from face-centered-cubic to hexagonal close-packed in cobalt-base Stellites (Ref 4). It has not been established in what way, if any, this transformation affects erosion resistance.

Ranking for erosion resistance in a given situation is made difficult by the complications of defining both the fluid conditions that result in damage and the metal properties that influence erosion resistance. This is true for laboratory tests as well as for field evaluations. Even as late as 1960, attempts to rank materials for cavitation resistance were able to make only a qualitative comparison, because results from different sources varied widely in cavitation conditions and amount of damage for the same material.

A ranking system that is at least semiquantitative has been developed (Ref 5). In this system, the value of a "normalized erosion resistance", defined as the maximum rate of volume loss of a reference material divided by the maximum rate of volume loss for the material being evaluated, is computed. This allows comparison of materials that have been tested under different sets of conditions, provided that the reference material has been tested under each of the different sets of conditions. Figure 7 is a summary of normalized erosion resistance for a wide variety of alloys tested at different conditions, using 18Cr-8Ni austenitic stainless steel with a hardness of 170 dph as the reference material. Figure 7 shows

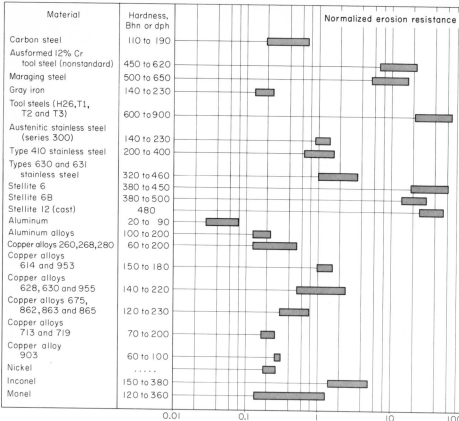

Material	Hardness, Bhn or dph	Normalized erosion resistance
Carbon steel	110 to 190	
Ausformed 12% Cr tool steel (nonstandard)	450 to 620	
Maraging steel	500 to 650	
Gray iron	140 to 230	
Tool steels (H26, T1, T2 and T3)	600 to 900	
Austenitic stainless steel (series 300)	140 to 230	
Type 410 stainless steel	200 to 400	
Types 630 and 631 stainless steel	320 to 460	
Stellite 6	380 to 450	
Stellite 6B	380 to 500	
Stellite 12 (cast)	480	
Aluminum	20 to 90	
Aluminum alloys	100 to 200	
Copper alloys 260,268,280	60 to 200	
Copper alloys 614 and 953	150 to 180	
Copper alloys 628, 630 and 955	140 to 220	
Copper alloys 675, 862, 863 and 865	120 to 230	
Copper alloys 713 and 719	70 to 200	
Copper alloy 903	60 to 100	
Nickel	. . . .	
Inconel	150 to 380	
Monel	120 to 360	

0.01   0.1   1   10   100

Normalized erosion resistance relative to 18Cr-8Ni austenitic stainless steel at 170 dph

Fig. 7. Classification of 22 alloys or alloy groups according to their normalized erosion resistance relative to 18Cr-8Ni austenitic stainless steel having a hardness of 170 dph

that the most resistant alloys (tool steels, Stellite alloys, and maraging steel) have greater erosion resistance than the reference material, by an order of magnitude or more, and the range of normalized erosion resistance spans almost four orders of magnitude. This range is far greater than any range of intrinsic material properties.

Effect of Corrosion

Liquid erosion is known to occur in the absence of any direct evidence of corrosion, yet corrosion can markedly influence the erosion process. At one time, liquid erosion was thought to be exclusively a corrosion-enhanced process. According to the corrosion theory, collapsing cavitation bubbles cause the mechanical removal of protective surface films. The newly exposed metal surface immediately begins to corrode, forming another film. Repeated removal and reformation of the film of corrosion products produces the characteristic pitting attack. Although largely rejected as the basic mechanism of liquid erosion, the erosion-corrosion process described above can drastically accelerate erosive attack, particularly at low hydrodynamic intensities in aggressive environments. At very high hydrodynamic intensities, corrosion rarely is a significant factor, even in aggressive environments.

Because corrosion was once thought basic to liquid erosion, several investigators experimented with cathodic protection as a means of reducing erosive damage. They found that cathodic protection did reduce damage. However, it now appears that damage was reduced only when the applied current density was sufficient to generate a layer of hydrogen bubbles on the tested surface. Thus damage may have been reduced primarily because the layer of hydrogen bubbles cushioned the surface against the hydro-

Fig. 8. Leading edge of a series 400 stainless steel impeller for a boiler feed pump, exhibiting deep local damage caused by cavitation erosion (Ref 1)

dynamic forces of bubble collapse, rather than because the cathodic current provided galvanic protection. Of course, cathodic protection will reduce total weight loss when corrosion is a significant factor in producing damage. Even so, recent experiments have shown that damage is reduced when an anodic current of sufficient density to evolve gas at the tested surface is applied.

Analysis of Liquid-Erosion Failures

Erosion damage typically appears as a pitted or honeycomblike region, as shown in Fig. 8 on a stainless steel impeller blade from a boiler feed pump. In some instances, erosion damage results in an appreciable loss of metal — for example, the propellers of high-speed ocean liners have sustained sufficient loss of metal in a single crossing of the Atlantic Ocean to require replacement.

In hydraulic components, the damaged area almost always will not be associated with the region of lowest static pressure. If low static pressure is the cause of cavitation, damage will be downstream of the low-pressure region in a location where vapor pockets cannot be sustained and bubbles implode. It is a common misconception that cavitation damage can occur only in low-pressure regions. Cavitation damage often occurs in relatively high-pressure regions; this is particularly true if sufficiently high flow velocity also occurs. A complete determination of the local cavitation parameter for the flow, K_f, and an estimation of the probable value of the local parameter for incipient cavitation, K_i, can be very valuable in establishing whether cavitation is responsible for observed damage. (The calculation of these parameters is discussed in Chapters 7 and 11 of Ref 1.) Regardless of other environmental effects, the existence of either drop impingement or hydraulic conditions conducive to cavitation should be positively ascertained before the damage is ascribed to liquid erosion.

In the following example, considerable amounts of air drawn into the suction side of a water pump induced cavitation that damaged the impeller of the water pump, although several other pumps operating under similar conditions remained undamaged. This erratic occurrence of cavitation damage is typical of many hydraulic machines; for example, condensate pumps in steam power plants often are designed to cavitate continuously as a means of controlling the discharge pressure, yet excessive erosion of pump components is not often encountered. However, improper design or construction of pump-inlet passages can cause excessive cavitation, which may result in damage to pump impellers.

Example 1. Failure of a Bronze Pump Impeller by Cavitation Damage Because of Excessive Air in the System (Fig. 9)

Figure 9(a) shows the impeller from one of two water pumps that were taken out of service because the output of the pumps was greatly reduced. Both impellers showed considerable material loss over all the interior and exterior surfaces. The pumps drew water from an open tank through a standpipe. Several similar water pumps were operating under almost the same conditions with no observed failures.

The impellers were 10 in. in diameter and ½ in. wide. They were made from a cast bronze alloy and were contained in a cast iron pump casing.

Investigation. Visual examination of the impellers disclosed that the interior surfaces were extremely clean but were pockmarked over the whole area. The flange face on the suction side and the surfaces adjacent to those where material was missing showed evidence of cold work.

Micrographs of sections through the damaged surfaces showed a layer of distorted metal grains (see Fig. 9b). At higher magnification, slip lines were visible, indicating that severe cold work had occurred at the surface. There was no evidence of intergranular attack or dezincification.

The clean, pockmarked, severely eroded surfaces of the impellers are characteristic of cavitation damage. In this instance, cavitation damage could have been the result of (a) a turbulent flow pattern caused by the movement of the impellers in the liquid; or (b) excessive air in the system because the water in the supply tank was low, or because air had been drawn through a pump seal. Further investigation revealed that considerable quantities of air were being drawn into the system when the water in the supply tank was allowed to drop to a low level.

Conclusions. Metal removal and the microstructural damage evidenced by a shallow layer of severely worked grains at the damaged surface were caused by cavitation erosion. Cavitation was induced when a low level of water in the supply tank allowed large quantities of air to be drawn into the standpipe along with the water.

Corrective Measures. A water-level control was added to the piping system so that a sufficient head of water was maintained at the standpipe, and air was excluded from the pump inlet. No further failures occurred.

Cavitation can occur whenever local conditions combine to induce local vaporization in a liquid. In the following example, eccentric rotation of a heated cylinder that was cooled by water flowing between it and a surrounding nonrotating surface, combined with surface temperatures near the boiling point of the cooling water, led to erosion of the cylinder.

Example 2. Cavitation Erosion of a Water-Cooled Aluminum Alloy 6061-T6 Combustion Chamber (Fig. 10)

Equipment in which an assembly of in-line cylindrical components rotated in water at 1040 rpm displayed excessive vibration after less than an hour of operation. The

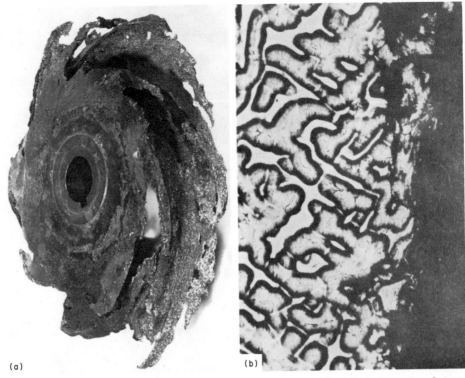

(a)   (b)

Fig. 9. (a) Water-pump impeller, made from a cast bronze alloy, that encountered considerable loss of material from cavitation damage. (b) Micrograph, at 100×, of an etched section from the impeller, which shows a layer of distorted metal grains at the surface subjected to cavitation. (Example 1)

(a)

(b)   (c)

Fig. 10. (a) An aluminum alloy 6061-T6 combustion chamber that was damaged by cavitation erosion during operation while rotating in water at a moderate speed. (b) and (c) Micrographs, at 100× and 500×, respectively, of cross sections of the chamber wall showing typical cavitation damage. (Example 2)

malfunction was traced to an aluminum alloy 6061-T6 combustion chamber (Fig. 10a) that was part of the rotating assembly.

The combustion chamber consisted of three hollow cylindrical sections that had diameters of 3 in., 2⅞ in., and 1³⁄₁₆ in., respectively (left to right in Fig. 10a).

Preliminary examination of the combustion chamber showed pitting on the water-cooled exterior surface in two approximately ¼-in.-wide bands that extended completely around the circumference of the chamber at axial locations of 1⅞ in. and 3⁹⁄₁₆ in. from the right end of the 2⅞-in.-diam section of the chamber as shown in Fig. 10(a). The pitting was more severe in the band at the 1⅞-in. location (particularly over about 180° of the circumference) than in the band at the 3⁹⁄₁₆-in. location.

Also, a circumferential groove about ½ in. wide and having a maximum depth of about 0.010 in. had been abraded on the 3-in.-diam section of the chamber along an arc of approximately 180° at the left edge in Fig. 10(a). At the point where this wear was observed, the combustion chamber was designed to have a nominal clearance from a concentric housing around it, with cooling water flowing through the intervening annular space. The region of maximum wear was on the same side of the chamber as was the region of severest pitting.

Operating Conditions. In operation, gases in the combustion chamber reached a very high temperature. The high thermal conductivity of the aluminum alloy, the rotation of the chamber, and axial flow of cooling water that was initially at room temperature provided efficient cooling of the chamber.

The 1³⁄₁₆-in.-OD shank served as the fuel inlet, and ignition took place within the main portion of the chamber. Accordingly, the shank was the coolest portion of the chamber and was not expected to be exposed to temperatures above about 95 C (200 F), even near the interior surface, on the basis of test data and calculations. Metal temperatures above about 175 C (350 F) were expected to be reached only to a very shallow depth on the interior surface in the hottest portions of the main body of the chamber, because of the high heat-transfer rate across the ⁵⁄₁₆-in.-thick wall.

Spectrographic analysis showed that the material of the chamber corresponded in composition to aluminum alloy 6061, as specified. Tests also showed that the chamber had been anodized.

Hardness measurements taken at intervals all around the circumference of the chamber near the more severe band of pitting averaged 83 Bhn, with the lowest reading being 75 Bhn. The average hardness on the exterior of the shank was 83 Bhn.

These hardnesses were substantially lower than the typical hardness of aluminum alloy 6061-T6, which is 95 Bhn.

Metallographic Examination. Three cross-sectional specimens were taken for metallographic examination. The first was taken through the most severely pitted area, and a portion of this specimen is shown at two magnifications in Fig. 10(b) and (c). This region was generally eroded to a depth of about 0.001 in., and some pits (not shown) were several thousandths of an inch deep. This also was the area where the highest surface temperature on the chamber wall would be expected. The second specimen was taken through the most severely abraded region on the 3-in.-OD section of the part. The third specimen was taken through the shank, which was not damaged in any way.

Examination of the three metallographic specimens at 800 diameters showed the structure to be essentially the same on each specimen and to contain a fairly dense distribution of a very fine precipitate of magnesium silicide (Mg_2Si) throughout the material. This constituent would be visible only

if aluminum alloy 6061 had been heated to temperatures above about 175 C (350 F), or if it had been improperly heat treated.

Conclusions. As a result of improper heat treatment, the combustion-chamber material was too soft for successful use in this application. Because even the external surface of the shank, which could not be heated above about 95 C (200 F) in use, was just as soft and showed the same distribution of Mg_2Si as did the hottest portion of the combustion chamber, overheating in service was ruled out as a possible cause of the observed low hardness.

Misalignment of the combustion chamber and one or both of the mating parts, to which the softness of the chamber material could have been a contributory factor, resulted in eccentric rotation and the excessive vibration that caused malfunction of the assembly. Contact against a surrounding member then caused the extensive abrasion shown at the left edge of Fig. 10(a). The pitting (which showed maximum severity on the same side of the chamber on which there was mechanical abrasion) was produced by cavitation erosion resulting from the combined effects of low hardness of the metal, cyclic pressure variation associated with the eccentric rotation (which induced the low pressures necessary for cavitation bubbles to form in the first place), and metal-surface temperatures near the boiling point of water at the hottest regions of the combustion-chamber exterior.

The operating characteristics of the defective combustion chamber were not sufficiently understood to explain the mechanism by which the cavitation erosion was concentrated at the two bands observed. Irregularities in the housing around the combustion chamber and temperature variation relating to the combustion pattern in the chamber were considered to be possible contributing factors to localization of the cavitation erosion.

Recommendation. The adoption of inspection procedures to assure (a) that the specified properties of aluminum alloy 6061-T6 were obtained, and (b) that the combustion chamber and adjacent components were aligned within specified tolerances, was recommended to prevent future occurrences of this type of failure on these assemblies.

In a similar situation, consideration also should be given to raising the pressure in the coolant, which would suppress the formation of cavitation bubbles.

Another failure by cavitation erosion, in which a change in flow direction induced cavitation, is described in Example 3 on page 3 in the article on Fundamental Sources of Failures.

When degradation of components in service appears to have been caused by the combined effects of cavitation (or liquid impingement) and corrosion in an aggressive medium, the relative importance of erosion and corrosion may be difficult to establish. This is particularly true of certain typical field problems such as erosion-corrosion of heat-exchanger tubes, valves and other devices, where the hydrodynamic intensity often is difficult to assess.

Prevention of Erosion Damage

Damage from liquid erosion can be prevented or minimized by (a) reducing the intensity of cavitation or liquid impingement; (b) using erosion-resistant metals; or, under certain conditions, (c) using elastomeric coatings.

Reduction of hydrodynamic intensity in devices subject to liquid impingement can be accomplished by reducing the quantity or size of liquid droplets in the gas stream or reducing flow velocity, or both. In modern low-pressure steam turbines, for example, the problem of liquid erosion is attacked simultaneously by (a) incorporating interstage moisture-removal devices, which reduce the amount of condensed water that can impinge on rotor blades in the following stage; (b) increasing the axial spacing between stator and rotor, resulting in smaller size and lower impact velocity of droplets; and (c) attaching shields of a Stellite alloy or hardened tool steel to the leading edges of rotor blades, or locally flame hardening the leading edges — either of which provides the region subject to the greatest damage with a highly erosion-resistant surface layer.

In devices subject to cavitation, it may be possible to reduce the hydrodynamic intensity simply by increasing the radius of curvature of the flow path or by removing surface discontinuities. Both of these factors can significantly reduce the probability of cavitation. Increasing the cross section of flow passages will reduce flow velocity, thus reducing the intensity of cavitation. Also, entrained gas in a cavitating liquid reduces collapse pressures by a cushioning effect; consequently, damage sometimes can be reduced by the injection of controlled amounts of air into the liquid. Air injection often is used to reduce damage to certain hydraulic structures, such as dam spillways. (More detail concerning cavitation in hydraulic equipment can be found in Chapter 11 of Ref 1.)

Use of Erosion-Resistant Metals. It may be impossible to reduce the hydrodynamic intensity significantly without seriously degrading performance. In such instances, the use of erosion-resistant metals may be the only practical solution to a problem of liquid erosion.

Many of the erosion-resistant metals can be applied as welded overlays, thus making salvage or repair of damaged surfaces easier, or surface treatment of new components less costly, than would be possible if the component had to be made wholly of erosion-resistant metal. It also is fortunate that liquid erosion is basically a surface phenomenon, thus making the use of erosion-resistant overlays effective in combating damage. The Stellite alloys and stainless steels are the alloys most widely used as overlays.

For example, Fig. 11 shows two portions of the leading edge of a blade from the last stage of a low-pressure steam turbine. One portion, shown at left in Fig. 11, was protected by an overlay of Stellite 6B, whereas the other portion, shown at right in Fig. 11, was unprotected type 403 (modified) stainless steel. The overlay, made of 0.04-in.-thick rolled strip and brazed onto the leading edge, resisted erosion quite effectively, whereas the unprotected base metal did not.

Both blade portions shown in Fig. 11 also illustrate the effect that low hydrodynamic intensity has on service life. Damage was most severe at the leading edge, where hydrodynamic intensity was greatest. Away from the leading edge, impact droplets were smaller, impact velocity was lower and impact occurred at oblique angles rather than at right angles, and thus damage was progressively less severe.

Many small parts are not amenable to protection by the use of erosion-resistant overlays. Therefore, the most effective means of combating erosion of small parts is to increase the hardness of the metal or to specify a more erosion-resistant metal.

Use of Elastomeric Coatings. Highly flexible materials, such as elastomers, are resistant to erosion, especially at low hydrodynamic intensities. In fact, under certain conditions the resistance of elastomers exceeds that of metals that have considerably greater mechanical properties. The resistance of elastomers to damage can be partly explained by the observed behavior of microjets during cavitation-bubble collapse near an elastomeric surface. In contrast to the tendency of microjets to be attracted toward inflexible metallic surfaces, microjets tend to be repelled from elastomeric or other highly flexible surfaces and dissipate their energy into the fluid rather than against the surface. Theoretical analyses using a simple, ideal fluid have verified that a flexible surface acts as a "free surface", repelling collapsing bubbles, which then are attracted to any nearby rigid surface.

Elastomers are capable of absorbing large amounts of energy by elastic deflection. This undoubtedly influences

The portion at left was protected by an overlay; the portion at right was unprotected. The overlay consisted of 0.04-in.-thick rolled strip of Stellite 6B and was brazed onto the leading edge of the blade. Compare amounts of metal lost from protected and unprotected portions.

Fig. 11. Two portions of a modified type 403 stainless steel steam-turbine blade that was damaged by liquid-impingement erosion (2.5×)

their erosion resistance. At low hydrodynamic intensities, impact stresses are attenuated, and the energy of individual impacts is dissipated within the elastomer without the generation of much internal energy in the form of heat. However, at high hydrodynamic intensities, an elastomer is less capable of dissipating heat and thus is subject to decomposition and other forms of thermal failure characteristic of these materials.

Some devices, particularly those that operate in regions of low hydrodynamic intensity, have successfully resisted erosion when covered with a layer of a flexible material. For example, polyurethane coatings are widely used to protect radomes and other aerodynamic surfaces of subsonic aircraft from rain erosion.

Flexible coatings, especially rubber, have significant disadvantages, being difficult to bond to some metals and complex shapes, and being susceptible to damage when short periods of high hydrodynamic intensity are encountered in an otherwise low-intensity environment. Intense cavitation sometimes destroys the bond between a relatively thin layer of rubber and the substrate.

References

1. Robert T. Knapp, James W. Daily and Frederick G. Hammitt, "Cavitation", McGraw-Hill, New York, 1970
2. R. T. Knapp and A. Hollander, Laboratory Investigations of the Mechanism of Cavitation, *Trans ASME*, Vol 70, 1948, p 419-435
3. B. Vyas and C. M. Preece, Residual Stresses Produced in Nickel by Cavitation, "Proceedings of the 4th International Conference on Rain Erosion and Allied Phenomena", A. A. Fyall (Ed.), Royal Aircraft Establishment, London, 1975
4. D. A. Woodford, Cavitation Induced Phase Transformations on Alloys, *Met Trans*, Vol 3, May 1972, p 1137-1145
5. Frank J. Heymann, Toward Quantitative Prediction of Liquid Impact Erosion, ASTM STP 474, American Society for Testing and Materials, Philadelphia, 1970, p 212-248

Selected References

"Symposium on Erosion and Cavitation", ASTM STP 307, American Society for Testing and Materials, Philadelphia, 1962

"Erosion by Cavitation or Impingement", ASTM STP 408, American Society for Testing and Materials, Philadelphia, 1967

"Characterization and Determination of Erosion Resistance", ASTM STP 474, American Society for Testing and Materials, Philadelphia, 1970

"Erosion, Wear, and Interfaces with Corrosion", ASTM STP 567, American Society for Testing and Materials, Philadelphia, 1974

A Discussion on Deformation of Solids by the Impact of Liquids, *Phil Trans Roy Soc London, Ser A*, Part No. 1110, 1966

J. M. Robertson and G. F. Wislicenus (Editors), "Cavitation State of Knowledge", American Society of Mechanical Engineers, New York, 1969

T. R. Shives and W. A. Willard (Editors), "The Role of Cavitation in Mechanical Failures", NBS Special Publication 394, U. S. Govt. Printing Office, Washington, D. C., 1974

P. Eisenberg, H. S. Preiser and A. T. Thiruvengadam, How to Protect Materials Against Cavitation Damage, *Mater Design Eng*, Mar 1967

Corrosion Failures

*By the ASM Committee on Failures by Corrosion**

CORROSION, which is the unintended destructive chemical or electrochemical reaction of a material with its environment, frequently leads to service failures of metal parts or renders them susceptible to failure by some other mechanism. This article deals with failures that proceed almost exclusively by corrosion *per se* at ordinary temperatures. Other articles in this volume discuss analysis and prevention of several types of failure in which corrosion is a contributing factor. These failure types, and the pages on which the articles that deal with them begin, are as follows: stress-corrosion cracking, page 205; liquid-metal embrittlement, page 228; hydrogen damage (hydrogen embrittlement), page 230; corrosion fatigue, page 240; erosion by liquids, page 160; fretting, page 154; and elevated-temperature failures, page 249.

The rate, extent and type of corrosive attack that can be tolerated in a part vary widely, depending on the specific application; whether the observed corrosion behavior was normal for the metal used in the given service conditions helps determine what corrective action, if any, should be taken.

All corrosion reactions are electrochemical in nature and depend on the operation of electrochemical cells at the metal surface. This applies even to generalized uniform "chemical" attack, where the anodes and cathodes of the cells are numerous, small and close together.

The analysis of corrosion failures and the development of suitable corrective measures require the application of the principles of chemistry, electrochemistry and metallurgy.

For more detailed discussions of the fundamentals and mechanisms of corrosion than are given in this article, the reader is directed to the Selected References listed at the end of the article (page 204). These references are categorized as to type of publication (books or periodicals) and subject coverage.

Factors That Influence Corrosion Failures

Several factors, and the possibility of interactions among them, must be considered by the failure analyst (*a*) in determining whether corrosion was the cause of, or contributed in some way to, a failure and (*b*) in devising effective and practical corrective measures.

The type of corrosion, its rate and the extent to which it progresses are influenced by the nature, composition and uniformity (or nonuniformity) of the environment and the metal surface that is in contact with that environment. These factors do not usually remain constant as corrosion progresses, but are affected by externally imposed changes and by changes that occur as a direct consequence of the corrosion process itself.

Other factors that have major effects on corrosion processes include temperature and temperature gradients at the metal-environment interface, the presence of crevices in the metal part or assembly, relative motion between the environment and the metal part, and the presence of dissimilar metals in an electrically conductive environment.

Processing and fabrication operations such as surface grinding, heat treating, welding, cold working, forming, drilling and shearing produce local or general changes on metal parts that, to varying degrees, affect their susceptibility to corrosion.

The specific application determines the amount of metal that can be lost before a part is considered to have failed by corrosion. In some applications, especially where uniform general attack occurs, a substantial reduction in thickness of a part can be tolerated. In applications where appearance is important or where discoloration or contamination of a food or other product in processing or storage are unacceptable, the dissolution of even a minute amount of metal constitutes failure (see Example 4 on pages 179 and 180 in this article).

Localized attack (as by pitting, for example) can penetrate the walls of vessels, piping, valves and related equipment to cause leakage that constitutes failure. Even relatively shallow localized attack can provide stress concentrations, or generate hydrogen on the metal surface, and result in failure by mechanisms other than corrosion.

Analysis of Corrosion Failures

In analysis of corrosion failures, the procedures described in the article on General Practice in Failure Analysis (see page 10) should be followed wherever they are applicable. An investigation should include a visit to the scene of the failure wherever possible; otherwise, the analysis of the failure is more difficult and more susceptible to error.

Not all corrosion failures require a comprehensive, detailed failure analysis. Often, the preliminary examination will provide enough information to show that a relatively simple procedure will be adequate. In general, the investigation should consider a broad range of possibilities without being so exhaustive as to be too costly or time-consuming.

Routine checks on whether the material used is actually that specified should not be ignored. For example, such checks have shown that "seamless" tubes that failed in service by developing longitudinal splits actually were welded tubes that corroded preferentially at the welds; "forgings" that failed in service actually were castings in which failure was initiated by corrosion at porous areas exposed at the surface of the metal; and "Monel" parts that corroded rapidly in an environment to which Monel is highly resistant actually were strongly magnetic and made of carbon steel. In another instance, failure of a braided copper wire was traced to the substitution of a carbon-black filler for the usual silica filler in a sheath covering the wire, causing galvanic action between the carbon and the copper in the presence of moisture.

*RAYMOND WARD, *Chairman,* Consultant – Materials, General Electric Co.; JAMES G. BIELENBERG, Senior Engineer, Central Research Laboratory, Airco, Inc.; HUGH CROWDER, Research Metallurgist, Production Research Div., Continental Oil Co.

C. R. DENABURG, Malfunction Investigation Staff, NASA, Kennedy Space Center; ALBERT HANSON, President, Hanson Materials Engineering Ltd.; VIRGIL J. KNIERIM, Staff Metallurgist, Corporate Engineering, Aeroquip Corp.; ALAN H. MILLER, Chief Materials Engineer, Materials Engineering Dept., Research and Advanced Product Development, DeLaval Turbine, Inc.; VITO PALOMBELLA, Materials and Processes Engineering, Grumman Aerospace Corp.; ROBERT M. ROSE, Professor, Dept. of Materials Science and Engineering, Massachusetts Institute of Technology; ROBERT E. SMALLWOOD, Engineering Dept., E. I. du Pont de Nemours & Co., Inc.

D. O. TAYLOR, Principal Engineer, Maintenance, Corporate Engineering Dept., Allied Chemical Corp.; WILLIAM L. WALKER, Principal Engineer, Materials and Process Development, Boiling Water Reactor Systems Dept., General Electric Co.

History of Failed Part

Before taking samples or carrying out tests that might destroy evidence relating to the failure, it is best to obtain and evaluate all available information that time permits about the circumstances of the failure, the history of the failed part, and the seriousness or potential seriousness of the failure.

Information about the type of environment to which the failed part was exposed is of primary concern. The corrosion behavior of the part is affected by both local and upstream chemical composition in the system, by whether exposure to the environment is continuous or intermittent, by temperature and by whether these and other factors varied during the service life of the part.

If available, engineering drawings, and material and manufacturing specifications for the part should be examined, with particular attention being paid to any part changes that may have been made. Missing information should be obtained from operating and inspection personnel, at the same time verifying the accuracy of any relevant documentary information, such as daily log sheets or inspection reports. The investigator should try to learn what, if any, tests or changes that could affect physical evidence relating to the failure may already have been made after the failure occurred.

Often, only a small part of the desired information will be available to the failure analyst, information obtained may be of questionable accuracy, or it may be impossible to verify some of the information that is obtained.

On-Site Examination

On-site examination is in general the same for corrosion failures as for other types of failures. The region of failure itself should be visually examined using hand magnifiers and any other suitable viewing equipment that is available.

The areas immediately adjacent to and near the failure, as well as related components of the system, should be examined for possible causative effects on the failure. Remote related equipment should be examined, especially in complex systems and where liquid or gases flow. Also, the possibility of the introduction of chemicals or other contaminants from upwind or upstream areas should be checked.

Photography. The failed component and related features of the system should be photographed before samples are removed. Color photographs are particularly useful when colored corrosion products are present; accurate color rendition is enhanced by use of a gray background, which is used as a guide in developing and printing.

Equipment useful for macroscale and microscale photography and metallographic work in the field and the laboratory is described in the Appendix that begins on page 26 in this volume.

The article "Photography of Fractured Parts and Fracture Surfaces", on pages 11 to 24 in Volume 9 of this Handbook, contains practical information about cameras, lighting arrangements, lighting techniques, types of films, selection of lens opening and exposure times, and processing of film — information that applies to photographing corroded surfaces as well as fracture surfaces.

Accessories useful in a preliminary examination include glass vials and plastic bags for holding samples, a stainless steel spatula for digging out soft corrosion products, and a file capable of cutting through hard scales. A magnet is useful for distinguishing austenitic from martensitic and ferritic stainless steels, as well as steels from nonferrous alloys.

On-Site Sampling

In doing on-site sampling, the investigator should be guided by the information already obtained about the history of the failure.

The bulk environment to which the failed part was exposed should be sampled, and suitable techniques should be used to obtain samples and make observations (such as pH, for instance) on the local environment at the point of failure.

In addition to taking samples from the failed area, samples from adjacent areas or from apparently noncorroded regions should be obtained for comparison purposes. New or unused parts can provide evidence of the initial or unexposed condition of the part.

Precautions. Removal of specimens, and samples of corrosion product, from the failed part requires careful consideration in the selection of locations and method of removal. Suitable precautions must be taken (a) to avoid the destruction of evidence that could be of value in investigating the failure, and (b) to avoid further damage to the part or to other related components and structures.

Torch cutting is frequently used for removal of specimens, because of its speed and convenience. Cuts should be made at a sufficient distance from the failure site to prevent alteration of the microstructure, thermal degradation of residues that may be present, and the introduction of contaminants. If an abrasive cutoff wheel or a saw is used, the same precautions to avoid overheating apply; also, coolants or lubricants that can contaminate or alter the part or any deposits present should not be used.

Protection of Samples. Small parts, and samples taken from large parts, can be protected during transportation to the laboratory by individual packaging.

Glass vials and polyethylene film and bags are useful. One method of retaining deposited material *in situ* is to tape a covering of inert plastic over the area.

Preliminary Laboratory Examination

The procedures followed in the preliminary laboratory examination will vary, depending on whether an on-site examination has already been done by the failure analyst and the completeness of any such examination. An on-site examination by a well-equipped investigator will have included much of the work that would otherwise have to be done in the preliminary laboratory examination.

When there has been no on-site examination by the analyst, records on the part and environment, the remainder of the failed part (or at the very minimum a good photographic record of it), along with undamaged or unused parts and related components, plus samples of the environment, will assist greatly in the performance of a complete and accurate failure analysis.

Preservation of Evidence. Whether or not an on-site investigation has been done, the course of action should be based on handling of all samples in such a way that maximum information can be gained before any sample is damaged, destroyed or contaminated to the extent that other potentially useful tests cannot be performed on it.

Also, a complete written and photographic record should be kept through all stages of the investigation. The information on photography given or referred to under "On-Site Examination" on this page is equally applicable to photography in the laboratory.

Visual Examination and Cleaning. Metal samples are first examined visually and with the aid of a hand magnifier or other suitable viewing aids. At this stage, features such as the extent of damage, general appearance of the damage zone, and the color, texture and quantity of surface residues are of primary interest. If substantial amounts of foreign matter are visible, cleaning is necessary before further examination. The residues can be removed in some areas, leaving portions of the failure region in the as-received condition to preserve evidence. When only small amounts of foreign matter are present, it is sometimes preferable to defer cleaning so that the surface can be examined with a stereomicroscope before and after cleaning, or to defer cleaning until necessary for surface examination at higher magnifications or for the preparation of metallographic specimens.

Washing with water or solvent, with or without the aid of an ultrasonic bath, is usually adequate to remove soft residues that obscure the view. Inhibited pickling solutions will remove adherent rust or scale. Usually, it is advisable to save the cleaning solutions for later analysis and identification of the substance removed. Alternatively, plastic replicas can be used for cleaning (as described on pages 14 and 15 in the article on General Practice in Failure Analysis); besides cleaning, the replicas retain and preserve surface contaminants, thus making them available for analysis.

Nondestructive Examination. For parts in which internal damage may have resulted from corrosion or the combined effects of corrosion, stress and imperfections in the metal, the application of nondestructive detection methods prior to cutting may be desirable. Radiography, ultrasonic flaw detection and measuring, liquid-penetrant inspection, magnetic-particle inspection, eddy-current testing, and holographic examination comprise the principal methods. The possible introduction of contamination on the test specimen in using some of these techniques should be recognized and considered prior to their use.

Microscopic Examination

Examination by both light microscopy and electron microscopy can be used to observe minute features on corroded surfaces, to evaluate microstructure of the metallic parts, and to observe the manner in which, and extent to which, the metal was attacked by the corrodent.

Corroded Surfaces. Viewing the cleaned surface with a stereomicroscope clearly shows gross topographic features such as pitting, cracking, or surface patterns that can provide information about failure mechanism — whether corrosion was the sole phenomenon involved; the type of corrosion; and whether other mechanisms, such as wear and fracture, were also operative.

If the features cannot be observed clearly using a stereomicroscope, instruments such as a deep-field photographic microscope or a scanning electron microscope, which produce images with a greater depth of field, often can resolve the features, especially on very rough surfaces. Transmission electron microscopy, using replicas, may be needed to resolve extremely fine features. These instruments, their capabilities and their limitations are described on page 26, pages 49 to 53 and pages 54 to 63, respectively, in Volume 9 of this Handbook.

Microstructure. Techniques of specimen preparation are described, and micrographs of both normal and abnormal structures for a wide variety of materials are presented, in Volumes 7 and 8 of this Handbook. Microscopic examination of polished, or polished-and-etched, sections can reveal not only microstructural features and additional damage such as cracking, but also the manner in which the corrodent has attacked the metal (such as grain-boundary attack or selective leaching).

It is desirable to retain the corrosion products if they possess sufficient coherence and hardness to be polished. One method of keeping the surface material in place is to impregnate the sample with a casting-type resin, which is allowed to harden before cutting samples. Polishing on napless cloths with diamond abrasives is recommended to secure maximum quality of edge retention.

Identification and Analysis

To establish what role, if any, corrosion played in a failure, the following must be identified and analyzed: (a) the metal or metals of which the failed part is made, (b) the environment to which the failed part was exposed, (c) inhomogeneities in the metal surface, and (d) foreign matter and metal surface layers. Procedures and equipment usually employed are described under "Chemical Analysis" beginning on page 24 in the article on General Practice in Failure Analysis. Spot tests often are used as a first step, and where equipment needed for other methods is not immediately available.

Both conventional techniques (such as wet chemical analysis, emission spectrography, x-ray diffraction, spectrophotometry, gas chromatography and x-ray fluorescence spectrography) and special techniques (such as electron microprobe analysis, ion microprobe analysis, Auger electron spectrometry, Mossbauer spectrometry, and electron diffraction) may be needed to completely define the composition and structure of various substances.

For an extensive compilation of standards on methods of analyzing metals, the reader is directed to Part 32 of the 1974 ASTM Standards (or subsequent annual editions). General reference books and periodical publications on chemical and instrumental analysis will provide guidance on the analysis of materials not covered in the ASTM Standards.

Metal of the Failed Part. Identification and analysis of the metal of which the failed part was made is usually routine. Ordinarily, the purpose is not to look for minor deviations from the chemical composition specified for the part, but rather to check for possible major deviations in composition and to make sure that the alloy specified was used.

However, for some austenitic stainless steels the corrosion resistance and other properties of welded joints require close control over the composition of the stainless steel and the weld metal.

Failure Environment. Both the bulk composition of the failure environment and the local composition at the metal-environment interface in the failure region are important in determining whether or how corrosion contributed to the failure. Composition of the environment can be determined chemically or spectroscopically.

Inhomogeneities in the Metal Surface. Serious corrosion damage can result from the presence of inhomogeneities in the surface of a metal part used in a corrosive environment. A classic example is severe local attack on a stainless steel because of the presence of embedded particles of "tramp" iron in the surface of the stainless steel.

Foreign Matter and Metal Surface Layers. Establishing whether a layer of material on the metal surface is merely a trace of innocuous soil, a residue of corrodents or of corrosion products, or a metal surface layer differing in composition from the bulk metal may present more of a problem in many failure analyses than analyzing the material, especially where a thorough on-site investigation cannot be carried out.

Corrosion Testing

Various types of testing techniques are used in investigating corrosion failures and in evaluating the resistance to corrosion of metals and alloys for service in specific applications. These include accelerated tests, simulated-use tests and electrochemical tests. Monitoring of performance in pilot-plant operations and in actual service is also done, usually in applications for which there is extensive knowledge and experience or where laboratory evaluation has given favorable results.

Accelerated tests are commonly used in investigating failures and evaluating corrosion resistance. Some accelerated test methods have been accepted as standard both by the military and by industry. To shorten testing time, corrosion is accelerated in relation to naturally occurring corrosion, usually by increasing temperature or using a more aggressive environment.

Because various factors that influence natural corrosion processes differ widely in time-dependence, the results of accelerated tests must be interpreted with extreme care, and can be related to expected actual service behavior only where close correlation with long-term service results has been established.

Simulated-use tests are frequently used in analyzing corrosion failures and evaluating the corrosion behavior of metals and alloys in specific applications. In these tests, either actual parts or test specimens are exposed to a synthetic or natural service environment.

A considerable number of laboratory corrosion tests that are not accelerated tests have been described in ASTM standards, in military specifications, and in NACE Standard TM-01-69, "Laboratory Corrosion Testing of Metals for the Process Industries". These procedures provide guidance in reproducing service conditions as accurately as possible and in interpreting and evaluating the test results in relation to service failures.

Electrochemical tests provide data that can (a) establish criteria for passivity or anodic protection against corrosion, and (b) determine critical breakdown or pitting potentials. Two general methods of electrochemical corrosion testing are used — controlled-current and controlled-potential methods. For either test method, ASTM G3 provides useful guidance and standardization of the manner of recording and reporting electrochemical measurements.

In the controlled-current method, the current (a measure of the corrosion rate) is controlled and the resulting corrosion potential is measured. A number of instruments are available for such tests, in which either logarithmic or linear polarization curves are developed. Both galvanostatic and galvanodynamic polarization measurements are used to plot anodic and cathodic polarization curves.

A limitation of controlled-current testing is that corrosion rates often change with time, and estimating continuing corrosion rates is not always accurate. Also, the applied current density in these tests depends on the absolute difference between the total oxidation and total reduction current densities. Consequently, if the total oxidation current density consists of two components, only one of which is corrosion, the apparent corrosion rate from the test will exceed the actual corrosion rate from weight loss.

In the controlled-potential method of electrochemical testing, the corrosion potential (oxidizing power) is controlled and the resulting corrosion current is measured. Equipment is available for both constant-potential (potentiostatic) and varying-potential (potentiodynamic) testing to determine over-all corrosion-rate profiles for metal-electrolyte systems over a range of potentials.

Sources for Corrosion-Test Procedures. In addition to the sources given above for procedures employed in simulated-use tests and electrochemical tests, the most frequently used tests are described briefly in the comprehensive and general reference books on corrosion listed on page 204 in this article.

Procedures for a substantial number of standard corrosion tests that are used by individual companies, governmental agencies and industrial, trade and standards organizations are available in specifications and standards issued by ASTM, the federal government, and NACE.

Extensive information on nearly all aspects of corrosion testing, as well as on the evaluation and interpretation of the effects of corrosion in tests and in service failures, is given in the "Manual of Industrial Corrosion Standards and Control" (ASTM STP 534), edited by F. H. Cocks, and the "Handbook on Corrosion Testing and Evaluation" by W. H. Ailor, Jr. (see the list of references under "Special Topics" on page 205).

A comprehensive list of standard corrosion tests from domestic and foreign sources and a number of the most widely used ASTM procedures are included in ASTM STP 534. The two books also list and describe corrosion tests not issued by a standards or governmental agency, but rather by trade associations and individual companies.

Corrosion Rates and Corrosion Types

To determine whether a corrosion failure was caused by the use of an unsuitable material, it is necessary to know whether the rate and type of corrosion were normal for the given metal-environment combination. The standard reference books on corrosion of metals listed at the end of this article provide information on this subject.

Volume 1 of this Handbook contains, on the pages cited, a substantial amount of data on corrosion rates and corrosion types in various environments for the following metals: mild steel (pages 257 to 280); cast irons (pages 359, 363 to 364, 371, 385 to 388, 395, and 402 to 406); steel castings (pages 432 to 465); stainless steels (pages 552 to 576); aluminum alloys (pages 916 to 938); copper alloys (pages 983 to 1052); lead alloys (pages 1056 to 1066); magnesium alloys (pages 1086 to 1112); nickel alloys (pages 1115 to 1130); titanium alloys (pages 1151 to 1156); zinc alloys (pages 1162 to 1172); precious metals (pages 1179 to 1196); galvanized steel (pages 1162 to 1169); and tin-coated steel (pages 1131 to 1143). Also covered in some detail in Volume 1 are: corrosion-resistant metals for atmospheric and marine service (pages 552 to 564); chemical-processing equipment at ordinary and high temperatures (pages 564 to 585); high-temperature petroleum-refinery applications (pages 585 to 603); high-temperature bolting applications (pages 604 to 611); and furnace parts and fixtures (pages 611 to 620).

Volume 2 of this Handbook contains information on the corrosion resistance of electroplated metals (pages 409 to 484), and metallic coatings applied by other processes (pages 489 to 530), along with descriptions of the processes.

An extensive compilation of data on corrosion rates is given in the "Corrosion Data Survey", N. E. Hamner (Ed.), 5th Edition, 1974, published by the National Association of Corrosion Engineers (NACE). This compilation is arranged by corrosive substances in alphabetical order (including about 1400 chemicals and chemical mixtures used in industry) and graphically shows corrosion rates for 26 classes of alloys and commercially pure metals, plus numerous special-use metals. For each corrodent-metal combination, the corrosion rates at various concentrations and temperatures are given. Special notes on susceptibility to pitting, intergranular and transgranular attack, stress corrosion, crevice corrosion, velocity and aeration effects are also included. Most of the data are for temperatures of 25 to 350 C (77 to 662 F), but, where appropriate, corrosion rates are given at temperatures to 849 C (1560 F) and as low as -250 C (-418 F). Also included in "Corrosion Data Survey" are corrosion rates in various atmospheres, eight types of waters, soils of various electrical resistivities, petroleum-refinery chemicals, boiler chemicals, cleaning solutions and lubricating oils, plus graphs for HCl, HNO_3, HF, H_2SO_4, $H_2SO_4 +$ HNO_3, NaOH and other acids and alkalis, that show concentration ranges of varying corrosivity and the metals suitable for each concentration range.

Comprehensive studies of the corrosion behavior and complications of corrosion-rate data of steel and other commercially important metals are reported in ASTM STP 445 (1969) for exposure to seawater and in ASTM STP 435 (1968) for exposure to different types of atmospheres.

Corrosion-rate data for tropical exposure of more than 50 metals, about half of which are ferrous metals, covering exposure to seawater, fresh water, mean tides, and marine and inland atmospheres, are given in "Corrosion of Metals in Tropical Environments, Part 10 – Final Report of Sixteen-Year Exposures", by C. R. Southwell and J. D. Bultman, NRL Report 7834, Jan 2, 1975. Corrosion-rate data for bimetallic couples are also presented.

This NRL report includes all data for exposure periods of 1, 2, 4, 8 and 16 years; interim and special reports (see Selected References at the end of this article) discuss the results for various classes of metals in greater detail. Corrosion damage is presented in terms of weight loss and average penetration for generalized attack, final steady-state corrosion rate in mils per year, average pitting penetration and maximum pit depth. One of the more significant aspects of the data concerns the extrapolation of corrosion-rate data. The varying shape of curves in which weight loss is plotted against exposure time shows clearly the misleading results that would be obtained by extrapolating the short-term corrosion rates linearly (secant rates) to predict long life. In a comparison of the data for 12 metals of different types, the one-year secant rates on the average were ten times the final tangential rate at 16 years, the eight-year secant rates were five times the final

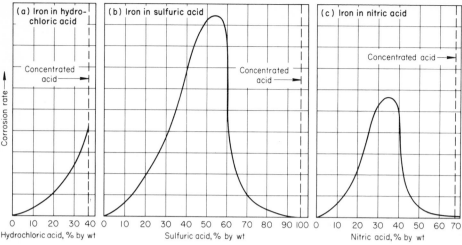

It should be noted that the scales for corrosion rate are not the same for all three charts.

As discussed in text, the corrosion rate of iron (and steel) in nitric acid in concentrations of 70% or higher, although low compared to the maximum rate, is still sufficient to make it unsafe to ship or store nitric acid in these metals. (Source of charts: M. Henthorne, "Corrosion Causes and Control", Carpenter Technology Corp., Reading, Pa., 1972, p 30)

Fig. 1. Effect of acid concentration on the corrosion rate of iron completely immersed in aqueous solutions of three inorganic acids at room temperature

tangential rate, and even the 16-year secant rates averaged more than twice the final tangential rate.

Analysis of Incomplete Data

If inconsistencies exist among the information and test results obtained in investigating a corrosion failure, consideration of additional factors and further examination and testing are called for. It is extremely difficult to duplicate exact environmental conditions and the factors that influence the initiation and progress of corrosion. Extraneous contamination that was introduced, or corrosion products that were formed, subsequent to failure may be misleading during failure analysis.

Also, some aspects of the condition and configuration of the part in the failure region, or interaction with other materials (including the possible interaction with other components of the system), and possible mechanisms and causative factors involved in the failure, may have been overlooked; or misleading preconceptions about the cause of failure and mechanism may have developed in the early stages of the investigation.

Important manufacturing records may no longer be available, raising questions related to initial heat treated condition, welding procedures, and cleaning practices, and making it impossible to arrive at anything but a speculation about the cause and mechanism of failure.

A correct conclusion as to the cause and mechanism of the failure must be based on positive supporting evidence, rather than merely on the absence of contrary evidence.

Contamination of failed parts or samples may make it impossible to arrive at positive conclusions in a failure analysis.

For example, the only parts or samples available may already have been contaminated with liquid penetrants or ultrasonic-testing couplants, cleaned with an organic solvent, and recontaminated with a cutting fluid during removal.

If liquid-penetrant testing has been done, it must be assumed that the surface has been wiped thoroughly and possibly wire brushed. Where such prior testing has been done, special problems are presented by the absence of any corrosion products or potential corrodents and the presence of extraneous materials, and much of the evidence on such a pretested sample or part is circumstantial and suspect.

In one instance, a failure analysis was attempted without any of the original surface left on the failed material. At every point where corrosion had occurred on the component in service, grinding had been performed in an attempt to remove what were thought to be "surface defects". Because of the absence of original surface material, the true cause and type of attack and the composition of the corrodent were never positively established.

Uniform Corrosion

Corrosion of metals by uniform chemical attack is the simplest and most common form of corrosion and occurs in the atmosphere, in liquids and in soil, frequently under normal service conditions. The rate of attack can be rapid or slow, and the metal surface can either be clean or be covered with corrosion products.

Selection of a metal that has a suitable resistance to the environment in which the specific part is used and the application of paints and other types of coatings are two common methods used to control uniform corrosion.

Uniform corrosion commonly occurs on metal surfaces having a homogeneity of chemical composition and of microstructure. Access to the metal by the attacking environment is generally unrestricted and uniform.

In uniform corrosion, electrochemical reaction between adjacent closely spaced microanode and microcathode areas is involved; consequently, uniform corrosion might be considered as localized electrolytic attack occurring consistently and evenly over the surface of a metal.

All metals are affected by this form of attack in some environments; the rusting of steel and the tarnishing of silver are typical examples of uniform corrosion. In some metals, such as steel, uniform corrosion produces a somewhat rough surface by removing a substantial amount of metal, which either dissolves in the environment or reacts with it to produce a loosely adherent, porous coating of corrosion products. In reactions such as the tarnishing of silver in air or the attack on lead in sulfate-containing environments, thin, tightly adherent protective films are produced, and the metal surface remains smooth.

Corrosion rate and expected service life can be calculated from measurements of the general thinning produced by uniform corrosion. However, since the rate of attack can change over a period of time, periodic inspection at suitable intervals is ordinarily done to avoid unexpected failures (see page 171 for sources of corrosion-rate data). The protection provided by paints and other resinous coatings, and their limitations, are discussed under "Use of Resinous and Inorganic-Base Coatings" in this article (see pages 194 and 195).

Modification of the environment by changing its composition, concentration, pH, and temperature, or by adding an inhibitor, are also effective and appropriate methods of controlling uniform corrosion in some situations.

Effect of Concentration. The effect on corrosion rate of increasing or decreasing the concentration of corrodent in the environment to which a metal part is exposed does not follow a uniform pattern — first, because of ionization effects in aqueous solutions and the effects of even trace amounts of water in nonaqueous environments; and second, because of changes that occur in characteristics of any film of corrosion products that may be present on the surface of the metal. Typical patterns of the types of corrodent-concentration effects on corrosion rate which may be encountered are illustrated in Fig. 1, which plots the variation of corrosion rate of iron as a function of the concentration of three common inorganic acids in aqueous solutions at room temperature.

The rate of corrosion of a given metal usually increases as the concentration of the corrodent increases, as shown in Fig. 1(a) for the corrosion of iron in hydrochloric acid. However, corrosion rate does not always increase with concentration of the corrodent; the effect often depends on the range of corrodent concentration, as shown in Fig. 1(b) and (c) for iron in sulfuric acid and in nitric acid, respectively.

Because corrosion is electrochemical and involves anodic and cathodic reactions, process variables influence corrosion rate if they influence one or both reactions.

For example, the main cathodic reaction for iron corroding in dilute inorganic acids is $2H^+ + 2e \rightarrow H_2\uparrow$. The more hydrogen ions available, the faster the rate of the cathodic reaction. In turn, this permits a high rate of anodic dissolution ($M \rightarrow M^{+n} + ne$). This is what happens throughout the concentration range in hydrochloric acid solutions.

In both nitric acid and sulfuric acid solutions, the hydrogen-ion concentration increases with acid concentration, but at the higher levels of acid concentration it decreases again. Iron may be used to handle concentrated sulfuric acid at ambient temperatures. Care must be taken to avoid any contamination with water, because this will dilute the acid and increase the rate of attack. Also, impurities in the acid or the iron can increase the rate of attack.

The corrosion rate of iron (and steel) at room temperature in nitric acid decreases with increasing concentration above about 35% because of the formation of a passive oxide film on the metal surface. However, this passive condition is not completely stable.

The rate of attack for concentrations of 70% or higher (although low compared to the maximum rate shown in Fig. 1) is still greater than 50 mils per year, making iron and steel unsuitable for use in shipping and storing nitric acid at any concentration (see also discussion under "General Corrosion" on page 200 in this article).

Nitric acid in bulk is usually stored and shipped in type 304 stainless steel, aluminum alloy 3003 or commercially pure titanium (grade 2).

Metals that have passivity effects (such as Monel 400 in hydrochloric acid solutions and lead in sulfuric acid solutions) corrode at an extremely low rate at low acid concentration at room temperature, but lose their passivity at a certain limiting acid concentration above which the corrosion rate increases rapidly with increasing acid concentration.

Effect of Temperature. In investigating the effect of temperature on the rate of

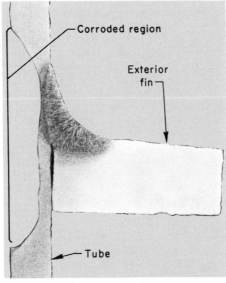

Fig. 2. Etched longitudinal section, at 3×, of a carbon steel steam tube that corroded on the inner surface more rapidly opposite the exterior heat-transfer fin than elsewhere along the tube

corrosion of a metal in a liquid or gaseous environment, the temperature that must be considered is that existing at the metal-corrodent interface, which temperature often differs substantially from the temperature of the main body of the corrodent.

This difference is especially important for heat-transfer surfaces, where the "hot-wall" effect causes a much higher corrosion rate than is ordinarily encountered in the solution being heated. A rise of 10 degrees C (18 degrees F) in bulk temperature of the solution can increase the corrosion rate by a factor of two or more. Hot-wall failures are fairly common in heating coils and heat-exchanger tubes.

An example of the hot-wall effect would be the corrosion rate of Hastelloy B in 65% sulfuric acid. At 121 C (250 F), the corrosion rate would be less than 20 mils per year. However, a Hastelloy B heating coil in the same solution might have a surface-wall temperature of 143 C (290 F) and a corrosion rate greater than 200 mils per year.

In some metal-corrodent systems, there is an approximately exponential rise in corrosion rate with an increase in temperature at the interface. In others, the corrosion rate is low for low corrodent concentrations at room temperature, and increasing the temperature up to a certain point has practically no effect on the corrosion rate, but the corrosion rate increases very rapidly at temperatures above that point.

Temperature changes sometimes affect corrosive attack on metals indirectly. In systems where an adherent protective film on the metal may be stable in a given solution at room temperature, the protective film may be soluble in the solution at

higher temperatures, with the result that corrosion can progress rapidly.

When boiling occurs in the solution, other factors also influence the rate of attack on a metal immersed in it. One factor may be simply an increase in velocity of movement of the liquid corrodent against the metal surface, increasing the corrosion rate. In some situations, more radical changes occur at the metal surface, such as the substitution of steam and spray in place of liquid as the corrodent or the formation of a solid film on the metal surface — either of which may completely alter the metal-corrodent interface conditions.

There are some exceptions to the general rule that increasing temperature increases the corrosion rate. One is the reduction in rate of attack on steel in water as the temperature is raised, because the increase in temperature decreases the oxygen content of the water, especially as the boiling point of the water is approached.

Other exceptions arise where a moderate increase in temperature results in the formation of a thin protective film on the surface of the metal or in passivation of the metal surface.

If thick deposits are formed on a heat-transfer surface, they have a twofold effect by (a) changing the metal surface temperature, and (b) making crevice corrosion possible.

Local differences in temperature on a heat-transfer surface exposed to steam can influence corrosion rates by causing differences in the duration of exposure to condensation. For example, the inner surface of a carbon steel tube that carried saturated steam at 234 C (454 F) corroded to a greater depth opposite exterior heat-transfer fins than elsewhere on the inner surface (see Fig. 2). The heat loss through the fins lowered the temperature of the inner surface of the tube in the area beneath the fins, resulting in the presence of condensate on this area for a greater percentage of the time, and a correspondingly greater loss of metal, than elsewhere on the inner surface. All corroded areas were fairly smooth.

Pitting Corrosion

Pitting of metals is extremely localized corrosion that generally produces sharply defined holes. The attack on the interior walls of the hole is usually reasonably uniform, but may be irregular where the specific conditions introduce a secondary intergranular attack. Every engineering metal or alloy is susceptible to pitting. Pitting occurs when one area of a metal surface becomes anodic in respect to the rest of the surface, or when highly localized changes in the corrodent in contact with the metal, as in crevices, cause accelerated localized attack.

In general, when pitting occurs on a freely accessible clean metal surface, a slight increase in corrosivity of the environment will cause general or uniform corrosion. Pitting on clean surfaces ordinarily represents the start of breakdown of passivity or local breakdown of inhibitor-produced protection.

When pits are few and widely separated, and the metal surface undergoes little or no general corrosion, there is a high ratio of cathode-to-anode area and penetration progresses more rapidly than when pits are numerous and close together.

Difficulty of Detection. Pitting is one of the most insidious forms of corrosion; it can cause failure by perforation while producing only a small weight loss on the metal. Also, pits are generally small, and often remain undetected. A small number of isolated pits on a generally uncorroded surface are easily overlooked. A large number of very small pits on a generally uncorroded surface may not be detected by simple visual examination, or their potential for damage may be underestimated. When pits are accompanied by slight or moderate general corrosion, the corrosion products often mask them.

Pitting is sometimes difficult to detect in laboratory tests and in service, because there may be a period of months or years, depending on the metal and the corrodent, before the pits initiate and develop to a readily visible size.

Delayed pitting sometimes occurs after an unpredictable period of time in service, when some change in the environment causes local destruction of a passive film. When this occurs on stainless steels, for example, there is a substantial increase in solution potential of the active area, and pitting progresses rapidly.

Stages of Pitting. Immediately after a pit has initiated, the local environment and any surface films on the pit-initiation site are unstable, and the pit may become inactive after just a few minutes if convection currents sweep away the locally high concentration of hydrogen ions, chloride ions, or other ions that initiated the local attack. Accordingly the continued development of pits is favored in a stagnant solution.

When a pit has reached a stable stage, barring drastic changes in the environment, it penetrates the metal at an ever-increasing rate by an autocatalytic process. In the pitting of a metal by an aerated sodium chloride solution, rapid dissolution occurs within the pit, while reduction of oxygen takes place on adjacent surfaces. This process is self-propagating. The rapid dissolution of metal within the pit produces an excess of positive charges in this area, causing migration of chloride ions into the pit.

Thus, in the pit there is a high concentration of MCl_n and, as a result of hydrolysis, a high concentration of hydrogen ions. Both hydrogen and chloride ions stimulate the dissolution of most metals and alloys, and the entire process accelerates with time. Since the solubility of oxygen is virtually zero in concentrated solutions, no reduction of oxygen occurs within a pit. Cathodic reduction of oxygen on the surface areas adjacent to pits tends to suppress corrosion on these surface areas. Isolated pits thus cathodically protect the surrounding metal surface.

Since the dense, concentrated solution within a pit is necessary for its continuing development, pits are most stable when growing in the direction of gravity. Also, the active anions are more easily retained on the upper surfaces of a piece of metal immersed in or covered by a liquid.

Some causes of pitting are local inhomogeneity on the metal surface, local loss of passivity, mechanical or chemical rupture of a protective oxide coating, galvanic corrosion from a relatively distant cathode, and the formation of a metal ion or oxygen concentration cell under a solid deposit (crevice corrosion).

The rate of pitting is related to the aggressiveness of the corrodent at the site of pitting and the electrical conductivity of the solution containing the corrodent. For a given metal, certain specific ions increase the probability of attack from pitting and accelerate that attack once initiated. Pitting is usually associated with metal-environment combinations in which the general corrosion rate is relatively low; for a given combination, the rate of penetration into the metal by pitting can be 10 to 100 times that by general corrosion.

With carbon and low-alloy steels in relatively mild corrodents, pits often are generally distributed over the surface and change locations as they propagate. If they blend together, the individual pits become virtually indistinguishable, and the final effect is a roughened surface but a generally uniform reduction in cross section. If the initial pits on carbon steel do not combine in this way, the result is rapid penetration of the metal at the sites of the pits and little general corrosion.

The most common causes of pitting in steels are (a) surface deposits that set up local concentration cells, and (b) dissolved halides that produce local anodes by rupture of the protective oxide film. Anodic corrosion inhibitors, such as chromates, can cause rapid pitting if present in concentrations below a minimum value that depends on the metal-environment combination, temperature and other factors.

Pitting occurs at mechanical ruptures in protective organic coatings if the external environment is aggressive, or if a galvanic cell is active.

Buried pipelines that fail because of corrosion originating on the outside surface usually fail by pitting corrosion. Figure 13 in this article shows the pitted external surface of uncoated carbon steel water-line pipe, in comparison to the smooth interior surface produced by severe erosion-corrosion, which was the primary cause of failure of the pipe.

With corrosion-resistant alloys, such as stainless steels, the most common cause of pitting corrosion is highly localized destruction of passivity by contact with moisture that contains halide ions, and in particular, chlorides (see Examples 11 to 13 in this article). Chloride-caused pitting of stainless steels usually results in undercutting, producing enlarged subsurface cavities or "caverns", as shown in Fig. 18 in this article.

Undercutting was also observed in the example that follows, in which rapid penetration of type 321 stainless steel occurred because of loss of passivity in a stagnant chloride-containing aqueous solution.

Example 1. Corrosion Failure by Pitting of Type 321 Stainless Steel Aircraft Fresh-Water Tanks Caused by Retained Metal-Cleaning Solution (Fig. 3)

Two fresh-water tanks of type 321 stainless steel were removed from aircraft service because of leakage. One tank had been in service for 321 hr, the other for 10 hr. The tanks were made of 0.032-in.-thick type 321 stainless steel. Pitting and rusting had occurred only on the bottom of the tanks near a welded outlet, where liquid could be retained after draining. Most of the pits were about 1/4 to 1/2 in. from the weld bead at the outlet.

Service History. Inquiry revealed that there had been departures from the specified procedure for chemical cleaning of the tanks in preparation for storage of potable water. First, the sodium hypochlorite sterilizing solution used was three times the prescribed strength. Second, although the tanks were drained after the required 4-hr sterilizing treatment, a small amount of solution remained in the bottom of the tanks and was not rinsed out immediately. Rinsing was delayed for 16 hr for the tank that failed after 321 hr of service and for 68 hr for the tank that failed after 10 hr of service, exposing the bottom surfaces of the tanks to hypochlorite solution that had collected near the outlet.

Chemical Tests. Samples of the tanks were subjected to a 5% salt-spray test for three days. No corrosion was observed. Additional samples, which were subjected to one cycle of the Huey test (boiling 65% nitric acid for 48 hr), showed no appreciable intergranular attack.

Samples of both tanks were tested for reaction with sodium hypochlorite at three strength levels:

1 The prescribed concentration of 125 ppm available chlorine
2 The triple-strength solution (375 ppm available chlorine) used in sterilizing both tanks
3 The full-strength solution (5% available chlorine) from the stock bottle.

The samples immersed in solution No. 2 rusted and discolored the solution in approximately 2 hr. Samples in solution No. 1 showed no corrosion for one to two days but a slight reaction after four to five days. Samples in solution No. 3 showed no corrosion after four to five days of immersion.

Samples from the tanks, including the heat-affected zones near the welds at the outlet, were pickled in an aqueous solution containing 15% by volume conc HNO_3 and 3% by volume conc HF to remove heat discoloration and scale and then immersed in the three sodium hypochlorite solutions for several days. None of the samples showed any sign of corrosion.

Metallographic inspection of specimens from the tanks disclosed a normal microstructure with no precipitated carbides. Cross sections through pits in the tanks showed subsurface enlargement of the pits, as shown in Fig. 3.

Conclusions. Oxidizing solutions such as hypochlorites, chromates and nitrates in certain concentration ranges cause rapid pitting of stainless steels. With greater concentration, passivation is complete; at lower concentrations, chloride does not penetrate the passive film. Apparently, the concentration of sterilizing solution used was in the range that promotes pitting.

Failure of the stainless steel tanks by chloride-induced pitting resulted from using an overly strong hypochlorite solution for sterilization and neglecting to rinse the tanks promptly afterward.

Failure to remove the scale from the heat-affected zone near the welds at the outlet, and then to passivate the interior of the tanks, may have accelerated the pitting, although severe pitting also occurred outside the heat-affected zones.

Corrective Action. Directions for sterilization and rinsing were revised. The instructions for diluting the hypochlorite solution were clarified, and the importance of using the proper strength solution was emphasized. Immediate rinsing after draining the solution was specified, using six fill-and-drain cycles and leaving the tank full of potable water as the final step.

To further improve resistance to chloride-induced pitting, it was recommended that welding be carefully controlled and adequately protected with inert gas to restrict heat effects to formation of a golden-brown to deep-purple discoloration on the metal, avoiding the formation of black scale. It was also recommended that scale and discoloration of the welds at the outlet and heat-affected zones be removed by abrasive blast cleaning and that the interior of the completed tanks be passivated, using either 22% nitric acid at 60 C (140 F) or 50% nitric acid at 52 C (125 F). Three rinse cycles of water immersion and drainage were stipulated, to be followed by final rinsing inside and out with fresh water and then oven drying.

Pitting of Various Metals. Despite their good resistance to general corrosion,

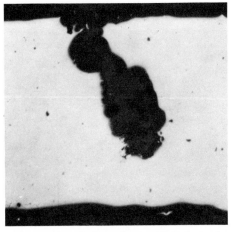

Fig. 3. Unetched section, at 95×, through the bottom of a type 321 stainless steel aircraft fresh-water storage tank that failed in service as a result of pitting, showing subsurface enlargement of one of the pits (Example 1)

stainless steels are more susceptible to pitting than many other metals. The stainless steels higher in chromium, nickel and molybdenum are also higher in resistance to pitting, but are not immune under all service conditions.

As a general guide, some alloys more resistant to both general corrosion and pitting are, in order of increasing resistance: (a) Hastelloy G, Incoloy 825, Carpenter 20 Cb-3 (wrought form), and Durimet 20; (b) Hastelloy C and Chlorimet 3; and (c) titanium.

Pitting failures of corrosion-resistant alloys are relatively uncommon in solutions that do not contain halides, although any mechanism that permits the establishment of an electrolytic cell in which a small anode is in contact with a large cathodic area offers the opportunity for pitting attack.

In active metals, such as aluminum and magnesium and their alloys, pitting also begins with the establishment of a local anode. However, a major effect on the rate of pitting penetration is that the corrosion products of these metals produce a high pH in the pit, thus accelerating the dissolution of the protective oxide film. Although the surrounding metal may be exposed to relatively pure water, the metal at the bottom of a pit corrodes at an appreciable rate, even in the absence of galvanic effects. Maintaining surface cleanness helps avoid pitting of these metals.

Pitting of aluminum and magnesium and their alloys in aqueous solutions is often accelerated by galvanic effects, which occur because these metals are anodic to most other metals, and by the effects of dissolved metallic ions and suspended particles in the solution. Pitting of these metals can be caused by even a few parts per billion of dissolved copper compounds, as well as by particles of

metallic iron (which produce both crevice and galvanic effects) embedded in or adhering to their surfaces.

General rules for avoiding pitting of any metal are as follows: (a) keep the surface clean, (b) avoid contact with stagnant solutions, (c) avoid galvanic couples, and (d) avoid rupture of any natural or applied protective coatings.

Selective Leaching

Selective leaching is the removal of an element from an alloy by corrosion. The most common example is dezincification, the selective removal of zinc in brasses. Many alloys are susceptible to selective leaching under certain conditions. The elements that are more resistant to the environment remain behind, provided that they have a sufficiently continuous structure to prevent them from breaking away in small particles.

Mechanisms. Two mechanisms have been described for selective leaching: (a) two metals in an alloy are dissolved, and one redeposits on the surface; and (b) one metal is selectively dissolved, leaving the other metals behind. Dezincification of brasses occurs by the first mechanism; the loss of molybdenum from nickel alloys in molten sodium hydroxide occurs by the second. In some alloys selective leaching takes place by either mechanism, depending on temperature and on the type, concentration and flow rate of the corrodent.

A special case of selective leaching is preferential attack on inclusions (see Example 4, pages 179 and 180).

The metal in the affected area becomes porous and loses much of its strength, hardness and ductility. Failure may be sudden and completely unexpected, because dimensional changes are not always substantial and the corrosion sometimes appears to be superficial, although the selective attack may have left only a small fraction of the original thickness of the part unaffected.

Table 1 lists some of the alloys for which selective leaching has been reported, together with the corrosive environments and the elements removed by leaching.

Dezincification occurs in brasses containing less than 85% copper. Zinc corrodes preferentially, leaving a porous residue of copper and corrosion products. Alpha brass containing 70% copper and 30% zinc (copper alloy 260) is particularly susceptible to dezincification when exposed in an aqueous electrolyte at elevated temperatures.

Dezincification proceeds as follows: (a) the brass dissolves, (b) the zinc ions stay in solution, and (c) the copper plates back on. Dezincification can proceed in the absence of oxygen, as evidenced by the fact that zinc corrodes slowly in pure

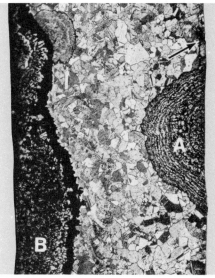

Area A shows plug-type attack on the nickel-chromium-plated outside surface of the brass pipe that initiated below a break in the plating (at arrow). Area B shows uniform attack on the bare inside surface of the pipe. (Etched in NH_4OH-H_2O_2; 85×)

Fig. 4. Micrograph showing difference in dezincification of inside and outside surfaces of a plated copper alloy 260 (cartridge brass, 70%) pipe for domestic water supply

Table 1. Combinations of Alloys and Environments Subject to Selective Leaching, and Elements Removed by Leaching

Alloy	Environment	Element removed
Brasses	Many waters, especially under stagnant conditions	Zinc (dezincification)
Gray iron	Soils, many waters	Iron (graphitic corrosion)
Aluminum bronzes	Hydrofluoric acid, acids containing chloride ions	Aluminum
Silicon bronzes	Not reported	Silicon
Copper nickels	High heat flux and low water velocity (in refinery condenser tubes)	Nickel
Monels	Hydrofluoric and other acids	Copper in some acids, and nickel in others
Alloys of gold or platinum with nickel, copper or silver	Nitric, chromic and sulfuric acids	Nickel, copper or silver (parting)
High-nickel alloys	Molten salts	Chromium, iron, molybdenum and tungsten
Cobalt-tungsten-chromium alloys	Not reported	Cobalt
Medium-carbon and high-carbon steels	Oxidizing atmospheres, hydrogen at high temperatures	Carbon (decarburization)
Iron-chromium alloys	High-temperature oxidizing atmospheres	Chromium, which forms a protective film
Nickel-molybdenum alloys	Oxygen at high temperature	Molybdenum

water. However, oxygen increases the rate of attack when it is present. Analyses of dezincified areas usually show 90 to 95% copper, with some of it present as copper oxide.

Dezincification may be either uniform or of the "plug" type (see Fig. 4). High zinc content in a brass favors uniform attack; relatively low zinc content favors plug-type attack. Composition of the liquid in contact with the metal has a greater effect on the type of dezincification, but the pattern of behavior is neither completely consistent nor fully understood. Slightly acidic water, low in salt content and at room temperature, is likely to produce uniform attack, whereas neutral or alkaline water, high in salt content and above room temperature, often produces plug-type attack.

Access of corrodent, flow rate, and other factors are sometimes involved. As shown in Fig. 4, plug-type attack occurred on the exterior of a nickel-chromium-plated brass pipe for domestic water supply where untreated municipal water leaking from the faucet packing gland ran down the pipe and attacked the brass through a break in the plating caused by mechanical damage. The water inside the pipe produced fairly uniform, layer-type dezincification on the pipe, which had an initial wall thickness of 0.030 in. Only about one-third of the original wall remained as sound metal in the corroded 0.024-in.-thick region shown in Fig. 4.

In the example that follows, uniform dezincification in copper alloy 270 (yellow brass, 65%) changed to the more rapidly penetrating plug-type attack after developing to a depth of about 0.010 in. into the metal.

Example 2. Failure of Copper Alloy 270 Innercooler Tubes for Air Compressors Because of Dezincification (Fig. 5)

After about 17 years in service, copper alloy 270 (yellow brass, 65%) innercooler tubes in an air compressor began leaking cooling water, causing failure and requiring the tubes to be replaced. The tubes were ¾

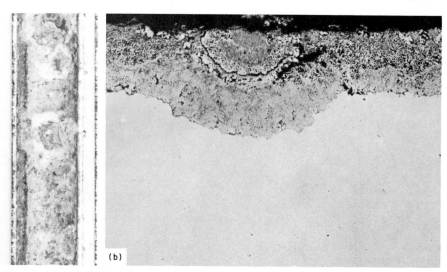

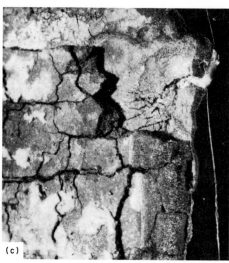

(a) Unetched longitudinal section through the tube. (b) Micrograph, at 75×, of an unetched specimen showing a thick uniform layer of porous, brittle copper on the inner surface of the tube and extending to a depth of about 0.010 in. into the metal, plug-type dezincification extending somewhat deeper into the metal, and the underlying sound metal. (c) Macrograph, at 9×, of an unetched specimen showing complete penetration to the outside wall of the tube and the damaged metal at the outside wall at a point near the area shown in the micrograph in (b).

Fig. 5. Copper alloy 270 (yellow brass, 65%) air-compressor innercooler tube that failed by dezincification (Example 2)

in. in diameter and had a wall thickness of 0.050 in. The cooling water that flowed through the tubes generally was sanitary (chlorinated) well water; however, treated recirculating water was used at times. Sections of 12 cooler tubes were sent to the laboratory for a determination of the cause and mechanism of failure.

Investigation. The tubes were sectioned longitudinally, as shown in Fig. 5(a), so that the inside surfaces could be examined. Visual examination of the inside surfaces disclosed a thick layer of porous, brittle copper. Figure 5(b) shows a uniform layer of the spongelike copper to a depth of about 0.010 in. on the inside surface, and a plug-type deposit that penetrated somewhat deeper into the tube wall; the sound metal underlying this damaged surface layer is also shown in Fig. 5(b). Figure 5(c) is a macrograph that shows the damaged metal at the outside wall of the tube at one of many points where the wall had been completely penetrated.

Spectrochemical analysis of the base material and the brittle layer disclosed that the tubes had been fabricated from copper alloy 270 (yellow brass, 65%) and that only a trace of the nominal 35% zinc remained in the brittle layer. It was concluded that failure of the tubes was the result of the use of an uninhibited brass that has a high zinc content and therefore is readily susceptible to dezincification.

Recommendation. The material for the tubes should be replaced with copper alloy 687 (arsenical aluminum brass), which contains 0.02 to 0.10% arsenic and is highly resistant to dezincification. Copper alloy 443 (inhibited admiralty metal) could be an alternative selection for this application; however, this alloy is not as resistant to impingement attack as copper alloy 687.

Before the failure analysis was completed, the innercooler was retubed using tubes made from aluminum bronze (copper alloy 614 or 628) and was put back into service. However, copper alloy 687 was the material used for all subsequent replacement tubes.

Copper alloys with high copper content, such as alloy 230 (red brass, 85%), are almost immune to dezincification in most water and salt solutions, as are inhibited brasses and other copper-zinc alloys containing 0.02 to 0.10% arsenic, antimony or phosphorus. Apparently, these inhibiting elements are redeposited on the alloy as a film and thereby hinder deposition of copper.

For severely corrosive environments where dezincification occurs, or for critical parts, copper nickels such as copper alloys 706 (10% Ni), 710 (20% Ni), and 715 (30% Ni) are used.

Graphitic Corrosion. Perhaps the second most frequently observed type of selective leaching is graphitic corrosion of gray iron, which occurs in relatively mild aqueous environments and on buried pipe. (Failure of a buried gray iron pipeline by graphitic corrosion is described in Example 10 on page 190.)

The graphite in gray iron is cathodic to iron and remains behind as a porous mass when iron is leached out. Graphitic corrosion usually occurs at a low rate. The graphite mass is porous and very weak, and graphitic corrosion produces little or no change in metal thickness. A corroded surface usually does not appear different from gray iron.

Graphitic corrosion does not occur in ductile iron or malleable iron, because no graphite network is present to hold together the residue. White iron has essentially no free carbon and is not subject to graphitic corrosion.

Detection of Selective Leaching. On many alloys selective leaching is not readily detected by visual examination. A copper flash is usually visible on dezincified copper alloys, but this is not positive evidence of dezincification because a copper flash can deposit from even small amounts of copper salts in aqueous solution without the occurrence of dezincification.

An area where selective leaching has occurred will sound dull when struck. However, severe intergranular corrosion may produce the same effect.

Metallographic examination will show the porous structure and different etching characteristics of the remaining metal. In some metals, selective leaching will not leave a porous surface layer but will cause a change in microstructure (for example, decarburization of high-carbon steel). The low strength and low hardness of the selectively leached layer are usually detectable. Often this layer can be scraped or chipped away.

Where other observations are inconclusive, a microprobe analysis can be made of the affected surface and original alloy; a loss in one or more elements will usually be very apparent. However, the electron microprobe is relatively insensitive to elements of lower atomic numbers.

Sometimes a layer is formed on an alloy that appears, even under metallographic examination, to be selectively leached. Microprobe analysis will tell if the layer is actually a new element introduced into the original alloy by diffusion — as, for example, carbon and iron diffusion into pure nickel in molten salts; or carbon and oxygen diffusion into titanium at elevated temperatures — but only at fairly high concentrations (chemical analysis or metallographic examination are needed to detect trace amounts).

Even without corrosion, some alloys will lose one element when heated in a vacuum. The remaining structure is similar to that resulting from selective leaching. Loss of zinc from brasses heated to 400 C (752 F) has been reported.

Intergranular Corrosion

Intergranular corrosion is preferential dissolution of the grain-boundary phases or the zones immediately adjacent to them, usually with slight or negligible attack on the main body of the grains. Grain-boundary materials in general are at least slightly more active chemically than the grains themselves, because they are areas of mismatch between the orderly and stable crystal lattice structure within the grains.

The preferential attack is enhanced by the segregation of specific elements or compounds, or enrichment of one of the alloying elements, in the grain boundaries, or by the depletion of an element necessary for corrosion resistance in the grain-boundary areas. Susceptibility to intergranular corrosion is usually related to thermal processing, such as welding or stress relieving, and can be corrected by a solution heat treatment (which redistributes alloying elements more uniformly), modification of the alloy, or the use of a completely different alloy.

When the attack is severe, entire grains may be dislodged because of complete deterioration of their boundaries. In the presence of residual or applied stress, failure by stress-corrosion cracking can occur before substantial intergranular attack has occurred.

Austenitic stainless steels become sensitized or susceptible to intergranular corrosion when heated in the temperature range of about 550 to 850 C (1000 to 1550 F). Heating at 650 C (1200 F) for 1 hr is often used for intentionally sensitizing stainless steel specimens for testing purposes.

The extent of the sensitization effect is a function of both time and temperature. Exposure to temperatures near the middle of this range for a few minutes is equivalent to several hours near the upper and lower limits. The limits of the "sensitizing" temperature range cannot be defined exactly, because they are influenced by the composition (especially the percentage of carbon and of carbide-forming elements such as titanium, columbium and columbium plus tantalum).

Also, whether "sensitizing" is damaging in a given instance depends on the requirements of the specific application and the environment and stresses to which it is exposed, and the prior thermal and mechanical working history of the alloy. Holding at temperatures as low as about 400 C (750 F) and as high as about 900 C (1650 F) for prolonged periods has been reported to cause sensitization of austenitic stainless steels.

Depletion of chromium in the grain-boundary areas is usually the cause of intergranular corrosion in austenitic stainless steels. Generally, more than 10% chromium is needed to give stainless steels corrosion resistance substantially greater than that of carbon and low-alloy steels.

In the sensitizing range, chromium carbides and carbon precipitate out of solution if the carbon content is about 0.02% or higher. The result is metal with lowered chromium content in the area immediately adjacent to the grain boundaries. The chromium carbide in the grain boundary is not attacked, but in many corrosive environments the chromium-depleted zone that is immediately adjacent to the grain boundary is attacked.

Type 304 (18-8) stainless steel usually contains from 0.06 to 0.08% carbon, and thus excess carbon is available for combining with the chromium and precipitating the carbide. Carbon diffuses towards the grain boundary readily at sensitizing temperatures, but chromium diffuses much more slowly.

The typical appearance of intergranular corrosion of stainless steels is as shown in Fig. 6 for an attack on sensitized type 304 stainless steel at 82 C (180 F) in water containing a low concentration of fluorides in solution.

Intergranular corrosion of the type shown in Fig. 6 is more or less randomly oriented and does not have highly localized propagation, as does intergranular stress corrosion in which cracking progresses in a direction normal to applied or residual stresses.

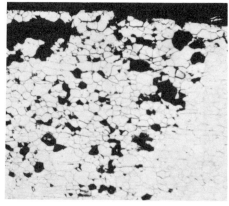

Fig. 6. Etched section, at 100×, through a sensitized type 304 stainless steel specimen, showing intergranular corrosion produced at 82 C (180 F) in water containing a low concentration of dissolved fluorides

One method of reducing the susceptibility of austenitic stainless steels to intergranular corrosion is to use solution heat treatment, usually by heating to 1066 to 1121 C (1950 to 2050 F) and immediately water quenching. By this procedure chromium carbide is dissolved and retained in solid solution, provided that cooling of the steel from the solution

heat treating temperature is done without delay and proceeds rapidly.

Solution heat treatment poses difficult problems on many welded assemblies and is generally impracticable on large equipment or in making repairs.

Using stainless steels that contain less than 0.03% carbon (extra-low-carbon grades) reduces susceptibility to intergranular corrosion sufficiently for serviceability in many applications. Somewhat better performance can be obtained from types 347 or 321 stainless steel, which contain sufficient titanium and columbium (or columbium plus tantalum), respectively, to combine with all of the carbon in the steel.

In the example that follows, severe intergranular corrosion was eliminated by replacing type 304 stainless steel with type 347 and stress relieving at 900 C (1650 F), followed by rapid cooling.

Example 3. Intergranular Corrosion of a Type 304 Stainless Steel Fused-Salt Pot Because Fabrication and Operating Conditions Sensitized the Metal (Fig. 7)

A fused-salt, electrolytic-cell pot containing a molten eutectic mixture of sodium, potassium and lithium chlorides, and operating at melt temperatures ranging from 500 to 650 C (930 to 1200 F), exhibited excessive

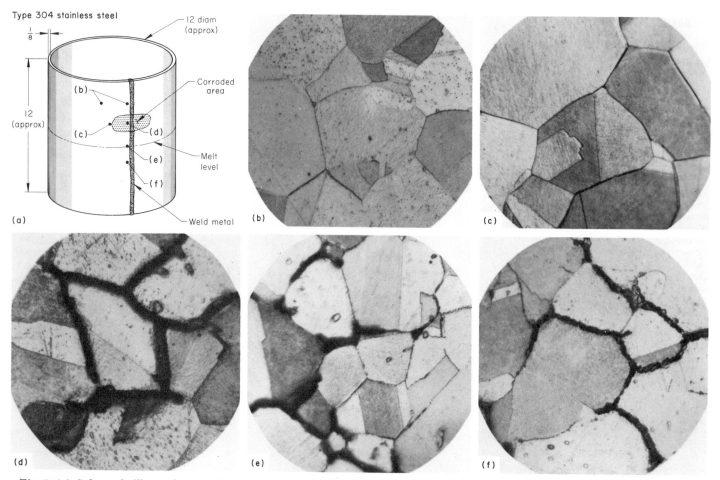

Fig. 7. (a) Schematic illustration of a fused-salt, electrolytic-cell pot of type 304 stainless steel that failed by intergranular corrosion as a result of metal sensitization. (b) to (f) Micrographs, at 500×, of corroded and uncorroded specimens taken from the correspondingly lettered areas on the pot shown in (a); specimens were etched in CuCl₂. (Example 3)

corrosion after two months of service. The pot, shown schematically in Fig. 7(a), was a welded cylinder with $\frac{1}{8}$-in.-thick type 304 stainless steel walls, and was about 12 in. in height and diameter. There were severe localized corrosion and horizontal cracking below and immediately above the level of the molten salts ("melt level") adjacent to a vertical weld.

Investigation. Six specimens were removed from the wall of the pot for evaluation. Their location with respect to the melt level and the vertical weld is shown in Fig. 7(a). The structures of the specimens are shown in Fig. 7(b) to (f). The surface of each specimen examined corresponded to the inner peripheral surface of the pot wall.

All the specimens exhibited carbide precipitation in the grain boundaries, with continuous networks in most instances. Two specimens were taken from the areas marked (b) in Fig. 7(a); both areas were 4 in. above the melt level, and were exposed to temperatures substantially below the melt temperature. One of these specimens (not shown in Fig. 7) was $2\frac{1}{4}$ in. from the weld and outside one heat-affected zone. The other, shown in Fig. 7(b), was in the heat-affected zone. Both were similar in microstructure and showed no evidence of intergranular corrosion.

As shown in Fig. 7(c), no grain-boundary attack was observed in the specimen taken from area (c) in Fig. 7(a), which is located $1\frac{3}{4}$ in. above the melt level (at temperatures slightly below the melt temperature) and outside the heat-affected zone. The specimen from area (d) in Fig. 7(a), which was the same distance above the melt level as specimen (c), but was within the heat-affected zone, exhibited severe grain-boundary attack (see Fig. 7d).

The specimens from areas (e) and (f) in Fig. 7(a), both of which had been sensitized in welding and were in direct contact with the fused salt, and thus exposed to temperatures of 500 to 650 C (930 to 1200 F) in service, exhibited extensive grain-boundary penetration (see Fig. 7e and f). Corrosion in these specimens was so severe that numerous regions were found where entire grains had fallen out, leaving behind microscopic cracks.

Conclusion. The pot failed by intergranular corrosion because an unstabilized austenitic stainless steel containing more than 0.03% carbon had been sensitized and placed in contact in service with a corrosive medium at temperatures in the sensitizing range.

Welding, followed by exposure in service to temperatures in the sensitizing range, caused severe intergranular corrosion in the heat-affected zone below the melt level (area f), at the melt level (area e), and $1\frac{3}{4}$ in. above the melt level (area d). Although carbide precipitation was present in the remaining three areas, intergranular corrosion did not occur in any of them because none of these areas was exposed to *both* the welding heat and temperatures in the sensitizing range in service.

Recommendations. Material for the pot should be changed from type 304 stainless steel to Hastelloy N (70% Ni, 17% Mo, 7% Cr, 5% Fe). Maximum corrosion resistance and ductility are developed in Hastelloy N when the alloy is solution heat treated at

1121 C (2050 F) and is either quenched in water or rapidly cooled in air.

An alternative, but less suitable, material for the pot was type 347 (stabilized grade) stainless steel. After welding, this stainless steel should be stress relieved at 900 C (1650 F) for 2 hr and rapidly cooled, to minimize residual stresses while avoiding sensitization.

Corrective Measures. Type 347 stainless steel was selected to replace type 304, primarily because it cost less and was more available than Hastelloy N. Manufacturing techniques were like those used previously, but included the recommended stress-relief heat treatment. The new pot performed satisfactorily for six months, after which the operation was discontinued.

Subsequent visual examination of the interior wall revealed no localized corrosion or cracking like that observed on the original pot; also, the general surface corrosion extended over wider areas but was much more uniform and was shallower.

Although satisfactory service was obtained for six months with the pot made of type 347 stainless steel, this alloy has only marginal behavior for this application, in which the melt temperature can reach 650 C (1200 F) on occasions, and the use of alloy Hastelloy N should be considered if trouble-free performance for longer periods of time should be required.

Nickel Alloys. Precipitation-hardenable nickel alloys corrode intergranularly in some environments. Inconel X-750 is susceptible to intergranular corrosion in hot caustic solutions, in boiling 75% nitric acid, and in high-temperature water containing low concentrations of chlorides or other salts. It can be made resistant to intergranular corrosion in these corrodents, but not necessarily in others, by heat treating the cold worked alloy at 900 C (1650 F).

Solid-solution nickel-base alloys such as Inconel 600 are subject to grain-boundary carbide precipitation if held at or slowly cooled through the temperature range of 540 to 760 C (1000 to 1400 F). If thus sensitized, they are susceptible to intergranular corrosion in the same types of corrodents as cited above for Inconel X-750.

Hastelloy B and C are susceptible after being heated at 500 to 705 C (930 to 1300 F), but are made immune to intergranular corrosion by heat treatment at 1150 to 1175 C (2100 to 2150 F) for Hastelloy B and at 1210 to 1240 C (2210 to 2260 F) for Hastelloy C, followed by rapid cooling in air or water.

Copper alloy 260 (cartridge brass, 70%) corrodes intergranularly in dilute aqueous solutions of H_2SO_4, $Fe_2(SO_4)_3$, $BiCl_3$ and other electrolytes.

Aluminum and its alloys are also subject to intergranular corrosion. High-purity aluminum corrodes at a rate roughly proportional to the cooling rate from about 600 C (1100 F), and to the iron content. The precipitated phases in high-strength aluminum alloys make

them susceptible to intergranular corrosion. The effect is most pronounced for alloys containing precipitated $CuAl_2$ and somewhat less for those containing $FeAl_3$, Mg_5Al_8, Mg_2Si, $MgZn_2$ and $MnAl_6$ along grain boundaries or slip lines. Solution heat treatment makes these alloys almost immune to intergranular corrosion but substantially reduces their strength.

Some magnesium alloys are similarly attacked unless solution heat treated, and die-cast zinc alloys are corroded intergranularly by exposure to steam and marine atmospheres.

Titanium. Intergranular corrosion (and, in the presence of tensile stress, stress-corrosion cracking) of titanium and some titanium alloys occurs in fuming nitric acid at room temperature. A small addition (about 1%) of NaBr acts as inhibitor. Commercially pure titanium is subject to similar corrosion and cracking in methanol solutions containing Br_2, Cl_2 or I_2; or Br^-, Cl^- or I^-. A small addition of water acts as an inhibitor.

Various titanium alloys, including Ti-8Al-1Mo-1V, when heated in air while in contact with moist sodium chloride (for example, from fingerprints) at temperatures of 260 C (500 F) or higher, undergo intergranular corrosion or stress-corrosion cracking, usually along grain boundaries. Pure titanium is resistant to both of these types of failure.

Selective Attack on Inclusions

Selective attack on inclusions by an environment to which the body of metal is resistant, wherein only small amounts of material (as compared to the massive attack usually encountered in selective leaching; see pages 175 to 177) are preferentially corroded away, is a special case of selective leaching. The inclusions provide small anodic areas surrounded by large cathodic areas.

Where the inclusions are in the form of elongated stringers and there is end-grain exposure to the environment, as in the following example, the attack is highly directional (unlike that shown in Fig. 6 and 7), and deep penetration of the metal is possible.

Example 4. Localized Corrosion of Inclusions in a Type 303 Stainless Steel Vending-Machine Valve That Was Exposed to Acidic Soft Drinks (Fig. 8)

After about two years in service, a valve in contact with a carbonated soft drink in a vending machine occasionally dispensed a discolored drink with a sulfide odor, causing complaints from customers.

Manufacturing specifications called for the valve body to be made of type 303 stainless steel, a free-machining steel chosen because of the substantial amount of machining necessary to make the parts. Other machine parts in contact with the drink were made from type 304 stainless steel or inert plastics.

According to the laboratory at the bottling plant, the soft drink in question was one of the most strongly acidic of the commercial soft drinks, containing citric and phosphoric acids and having a pH of 2.4 to 2.5.

Investigation. The body of the valve, through which the premixed drink was discharged to the machine outlet, had an abnormal appearance on some portions of the end surface that were continuously in contact with the liquid, even during idle periods. These regions showed dark stains and severe localized corrosive attack in the stained areas. The remaining portions of the valve surface and other metal parts that had also been in contact with the liquid appeared bright and unaffected.

Examination at low magnification confirmed the presence of severe highly localized attack in the stained areas.

The valve bodies were supplied by two different vendors. Chemical analysis of drillings from a corroded valve body supplied by vendor A, and from an unused valve body supplied by vendor B, showed that both parts met the composition requirements for type 303 stainless steel. This alloy had been specified for the valve bodies for at least nine years before complaints on its performance had come to the attention of the valve manufacturers.

Immersion Tests. Several of the valve bodies, one used and five unused, selected at random from parts on hand supplied by the two vendors, were cleaned in acetone and then continuously immersed in the highly acidic soft-drink mixture for several days. The results were as follows:

Body No.	Vendor	Initial condition	Effect of test on valve
1	A	Stained and corroded	None
2	B	Unused	Black stain(a)
3, 4	A	Unused	None
5, 6	B	Unused	None

(a) The test also discolored the mixture and gave it a pronounced sulfide odor, making it completely unpalatable.

Metallographic Examination. The valve body that was stained and corroded (from vendor A, No. 1 in the above table), the unused valve body that had stained in the immersion test (from vendor B, No. 2 in the above table), and an unused valve body from vendor A that had not been subjected to immersion testing, were all sectioned through the end that would be continuously exposed to the soft drink in the vending machine, and were examined metallographically at magnifications of 50 to 400 diameters. Numerous stringer-type inclusions of manganese sulfide were observed in each of the three metallographic specimens.

Figure 8 is a micrograph of an unetched specimen from the corroded region on the end of the used valve body (No. 1 in the immersion test); the corroded surface is an end-grain surface, and the corrosion began at the exposed ends of manganese sulfide stringer-type inclusions, which were anodic to the surrounding metal and readily attacked by the acidic soft drink.

The attack extended along the inclusion lines to a maximum depth of about 0.025 in., with the depth apparently depending on the length of the exposed sulfide stringers. A continuous line of attack that extended

Fig. 8. Micrograph, at 100×, of an unetched section through a type 303 stainless steel valve exposed to an acidic soft drink in a vending machine, showing localized corrosion along manganese sulfide stringer inclusions at the end-grain surface (Example 4)

at least 0.023 in. below the surface of the metal is shown in Fig. 8, which also shows the distribution and dimensions of the sulfide stringers generally characteristic of the three specimens that were examined metallographically.

No significant attack was found on the metallographic specimen taken from unused valve body No. 2 from vendor B, which had turned black during laboratory immersion in the soft-drink mixture.

Conclusions. The failure of valve body No. 1 occurred because (a) manganese sulfide stringers were present in significant size and concentration in the type 303 stainless steel used, and large stringers were exposed at end-grain surfaces of the valve body; (b) the beverage was sufficiently acidic (having a pH of 2.4 to 2.5) to cause staining and continuing preferential attack on the exposed sulfide stringers, which were anodic to the surrounding metal; and (c) after the machine stood unused overnight or over a weekend, there was occasionally enough attack on exposed sulfide stringers on the end surface of the valve body to produce a hydrogen sulfide concentration in the immediately adjacent liquid, thus making at least the first cup of beverage dispensed discolored and unpalatable.

Discussion. Type 303 stainless steel has only marginal corrosion resistance for this application, because of the size and distribution of sulfide stringers found in some lots of standard grades of this alloy. The sulfide stringers are anodic to the surrounding stainless steel, and are preferentially corroded away. This behavior can be considered a special case of selective leaching.

The inconsistent results obtained on immersing unused valve bodies 2 to 6 from

the two vendors in the beverage for several days were not surprising, in view of this marginal corrosion resistance, the locally varying distribution and dimensions of the sulfide stringers, and the use of only solvent cleaning before the immersion test.

The complete resistance of the stained and corroded valve body (No. 1 in the immersion tests) is not inconsistent with its past history. Any available sulfides on the corroded surface of the valve body could have already been consumed, and its passivity restored during exposure to the air after removal from service.

The extent of attack on the end-grain surface of the corroded valve body (see Fig. 8), and the failure of an unused valve body in the laboratory immersion test, make it highly probable that contamination of the soft drink by the corroded valve body occurred previously on one or more occasions during the year that it was in service without being reported to technically qualified personnel for investigation.

Recommendation. Specification of type 304 stainless steel (which contains a maximum of 0.030% sulfur) for these and similarly exposed metal parts was recommended to avoid possible adverse effects on sales, even if the failures were infrequent. This alloy is generally satisfactory for processing and dispensing soft drinks, and has been widely used for these purposes.

Concentration-Cell Corrosion

If a piece of metal is immersed in an electrolyte and there is a difference in concentration of one or more dissolved compounds or gases in the electrolyte, two areas of metal in contact with solution differing in concentration will ordinarily differ in solution potential, forming a concentration cell. Two electrically connected pieces of a given metal could also form a concentration cell in the same manner.

If the difference in potential is great enough, the more anodic area corrodes preferentially by concentration-cell corrosion. This type of corrosion can occur on a continuous, uniform, freely exposed surface at a rate depending on the difference in potential, the ratio of cathode area to anode area, the conductivity of the electrolyte, and the distance between the cathode and the anode.

In a drop of an electrolyte on a metal surface, the concentration of dissolved gases on the metal surface at the center of the drop would differ from that at the edges of the drop, in what is called a differential-aeration cell.

There are many other circumstances in which concentration cells are formed and cause corrosion. The rate of diffusion of air produces differential aeration in the layers of water or aqueous solutions just below the liquid level, and causes concentration-cell corrosion in this region on partly immersed metal parts.

Differential concentration cells in which a metal part is partly immersed in a liquid electrolyte above which the gaseous phase consists of a gas or gases other than air also are common. Concentration-cell corrosion may be controlled by diffusion effects of dissolved gases or other substances, especially when pitting-type concentration-cell corrosion proceeds in stagnant solutions.

Concentration-cell corrosion occurs on buried metals as a result of their being in contact with soils that have different chemical compositions, water contents, or degrees of aeration.

Crevice Corrosion

A crevice in a metal surface, at a joint between two metallic surfaces or between a metallic and a nonmetallic surface, or beneath a particle of solid matter on a metallic surface, provides conditions conducive to the development of the type of concentration-cell corrosion called crevice corrosion.

Pitting corrosion beneath solid particles on stainless steel hydraulic tubes is described in Example 11 in this article (see page 193). The corrosion processes in a pit that is fairly deep in comparison to its diameter, as illustrated in Example 11, are similar to those encountered in crevice corrosion.

Crevice corrosion can progress very rapidly (tens to hundreds of times faster than the normal rate of general corrosion in the same given solution). For example, a sheet of stainless steel can be cut (corroded) into two pieces simply by wrapping a rubber band around it and then immersing the sheet in seawater or dilute ferric chloride solution. The open surfaces will pit slowly, but the metal under the rubber band will be attacked rapidly for as long as the crevice between the rubber band and the steel surface exists.

In a metal-ion concentration cell, the accelerated corrosion occurs at the edge of or slightly outside of a crevice. In an oxygen-concentration cell, the accelerated corrosion usually occurs within the crevice between the mating surfaces.

Any layer of solid matter on the surface of a metal that offers the opportunity for exclusion of oxygen from the surface, or for accumulation of metal ions beneath the deposit because of restricted diffusion, is a probable site for crevice corrosion.

Differential aeration beneath solid deposits or at cracks in mill scale is a frequent cause of crevice corrosion in boilers and heat exchangers. Suitable water treatment to provide thin protective films, together with special attention to cleaning, rinsing and drying when boilers are shut down, minimizes the occurrence of crevice corrosion in such equipment.

Breaks ("holidays") in protective organic coatings or linings on vessels containing corrosive chemicals are also likely sites for the development of crevice corrosion.

Liquid-Level Effects. Crevice corrosion often occurs underneath deposits of solid substances that sometimes collect just above the liquid level on a metal part that is partly immersed in an electrolyte; the deposits usually remain moist or are intermittently moist and dry.

Where the liquid level fluctuates or where the liquid is agitated, the area of the metal that is intermittently wetted is called the "splash zone". Splash zones are encountered in all types of tanks and equipment containing liquids; corrosion occurring in these areas is called splash-zone corrosion.

A failure caused by this type of crevice corrosion occurred in a carbon steel tank that contained a saturated solution of sodium chloride (brine) at room temperature. When a pump, apparently in good condition, failed to deliver brine, inspection showed that a steel suction line, partly immersed in the liquid and used to transfer small amounts of brine as needed to other equipment, had corroded through in the intermittently wetted area. Further inspection showed that the tank also had been attacked in the intermittently wetted area. The corrosion problem was eliminated by replacing the steel suction line with a glass-fiber-reinforced epoxy pipe and by lining the tank with a coal-tar epoxy coating.

Rust films that have little opportunity to become dry do not develop protective properties. Such unfavorable conditions exist in the splash zone above the high-tide level along the seashore. The corrosivity of the moist rust films is aggravated further by the high oxygen content of the splashing seawater. Observations of old steel piling along the seashore usually reveal holes just above the water line, where the rate of corrosion is several times greater than that for continuous immersion in seawater.

Effects of Thermal Insulation. Thermal insulation may act as a diffusion barrier if once permeated by water, and concentration-cell corrosion may occur. In addition, some insulations contain halides in sufficient quantities that repeated leaching by water can build up concentrations on the metal surface to levels where serious corrosion can occur. This can be avoided by specifying that thermal insulation contain corrosion inhibitors, such as sodium silicate, or that the halide content be held to a very low level, or that the leaching action be prevented by coating the insulation with a waterproof compound or sheath.

It is also desirable to apply a protective paint coating to insulated vessels, especially those used to contain materials at low temperatures and subject to condensation of moisture on the vessel walls.

The thermal stability of the insulating materials exposed to high temperatures must be adequate for the application. The leaching of chlorides from a phenolic-resin binder in fiber-glass insulation and of hydrochloric acid from glass-wool insulation at elevated temperatures resulted in crevice-corrosion failure of stainless steel components (see Example 12 in this article).

Effect of Solid Deposits. In power-generation equipment, crevice-corrosion failures have occurred in main-station condenser tubes cooled with seawater, as a result of the formation of solid deposits and the attachment of marine organisms to the tube wall; these failures have occurred particularly in condensers tubed with stainless steel.

Crevice corrosion of heat-exchanger tubes made of copper alloy 706 (copper nickel, 10%) caused by particles of dirt in river water used as a coolant is described in Example 3 on page 549 in the article on Failures of Heat Exchangers.

Riveted and bolted joints must be considered as possible sites for crevice corrosion, and thus they require careful attention in design and assembly to avoid crevices, as well as provisions to ensure uniform aeration and moderate but not excessive flow rates at the joints. Replacement with welded joints can eliminate crevice corrosion, provided special care is taken in welding and subsequent finishing of the welds to provide smooth, defect-free joints.

Crater Corrosion. Type 347 stainless steel is sometimes subject to a type of crevice corrosion known as "crater corrosion", which occurs at the stop point of a weld. The failure is related to microsegregation of certain constituents in the pool of molten metal that is the last to solidify on a weld. In a manner similar to zone-melting refinement, the moving weld puddle continuously sweeps selected constituents ahead of it, and the concentration of these selected constituents in the puddle continuously increases until the welding is stopped and the puddle solidifies. The center of the stop point is attacked rapidly in oxidizing acids, such as nitric acid, in a form of self-accelerating crevice corrosion.

It is not necessary that the final solidification pool extend through the thickness of the part for full perforation to occur, as illustrated by the occurrence described in the following report:

Beveled weld-joint V-sections were fabricated to connect inlet and outlet sections of tubes in a type 347 stainless steel heat exchanger for a nitric acid concentrator. Each V-section was permanently marked with tube numbers by a small electric-arc pencil.

After one to two years of service, multiple leaks were observed in the heat-exchanger tubes. When the tubes were removed and examined, it was found that the general corrosion rate was normal for service of heat-exchanger tubes in a nitric acid concentrator, but that crater corrosion had perforated the tubes.

The crater corrosion occurred at two general locations. One location was at the stop point of the welds used to connect the inlet and outlet legs of the heat exchanger. The other location was at the stop points on the identifying numerals.

The material was changed to type 304L stainless steel, in which the zone-melting concentration does not take place.

Differential-Temperature Cells

In electrolytic cells of the differential-temperature type, the anode and cathode consist of the same metal and differ only in temperature. If the anode and cathode are areas on a single piece of metal (or on two electrically connected pieces of the same metal) immersed in the same electrolyte, corrosion proceeds as in any short-circuited galvanic cell.

For copper in aqueous salt solutions, the area of the metal at the higher temperature is the cathode and the area at the lower temperature is the anode. In the preferential attack on the anode, copper dissolves from the cold area and deposits on the warmer area. Lead acts similarly, but for silver the polarity is reversed, with the warmer area being attacked preferentially.

For steel immersed in dilute aerated chloride solutions, the warmer area is anodic to the colder area, but as the reaction progresses, the polarity sometimes reverses depending on aeration, solution velocity against the metal surface, and other factors.

Differential-temperature-cell corrosion occurs most frequently in heat-transfer equipment and piping, where substantial temperature differences exist between the inlet and the outlet portions exposed to the same electrolyte.

Galvanic Corrosion

When dissimilar metals are in electrical contact in an electrolyte, the less noble metal (anode) is attacked to a greater degree than if it were exposed alone, and the more noble metal (cathode) is attacked to a lesser degree than if it were exposed alone. This behavior, which is known as galvanic corrosion, can often be recognized by the fact that the corrosion is more severe near the junction of the two metals than elsewhere on the metal surfaces. Galvanic corrosion is usually the result of poor design and selection of materials, or the plating-out of a more noble metal from solution on a less noble metal.

The greater the difference in potential between the two metals, the more rapid will be the galvanic attack. The textbook electromotive-force series ranks the

Table 2. Galvanic Series in Seawater

Corroded end (anodic, or least noble)
Magnesium Magnesium alloys
Zinc Galvanized steel or galvanized wrought iron
Aluminum alloys 5052, 3004, 3003, 1100, 6053, in this order
Cadmium
Aluminum alloys 2117, 2017, 2024, in this order
Low-carbon steel Wrought iron Cast iron
Ni-Resist (high-nickel cast iron)
Type 410 stainless steel (active)
50-50 lead-tin solder
Type 304 stainless steel (active) Type 316 stainless steel (active)
Lead Tin
Copper alloy 280 (Muntz metal, 60%) Copper alloy 675 (manganese bronze A) Copper alloys 464, 465, 466, 467 (naval brass)
Nickel 200 (active) Inconel alloy 600 (active)
Hastelloy B Chlorimet 2
Copper alloy 270 (yellow brass, 65%) Copper alloys 443, 444, 445 (admiralty brass) Copper alloys 608, 614 (aluminum bronze) Copper alloy 230 (red brass, 85%) Copper 110 (ETP copper) Copper alloys 651, 655 (silicon bronze) Copper alloy 715 (copper nickel, 30%) Copper alloy 923, cast (leaded tin bronze G) Copper alloy 922, cast (leaded tin bronze M)
Nickel 200 (passive) Inconel alloy 600 (passive)
Monel alloy 400
Type 410 stainless steel (passive) Type 304 stainless steel (passive) Type 316 stainless steel (passive) Incoloy alloy 825
Inconel alloy 625 Hastelloy C Chlorimet 3
Silver
Titanium
Graphite
Gold
Platinum
Protected end (cathodic, or most noble)

metals according to their chemical reactivity, but applies only to the laboratory conditions under which the reactivity was determined. In practice, the solution potential of metals is affected by the presence of passive or other protective films on some metals, polarization effects, degree of aeration, complexing agents, and temperature.

Galvanic Series in Seawater. A galvanic series based on immersion in seawater is more generally applicable than

the electromotive-force series as an indication of the rate of corrosion between different metals or alloys when they are in contact in an electrolyte. In most electrolytes the metal close to the active end of the galvanic-series chart will behave as an anode, and the metal closer to the noble end will act as a cathode. The amount of separation between two metals in the chart is a rough measure of the difference in potential that can be expected and is usually related to the rate of galvanic corrosion between the two metals in a given electrolyte.

This galvanic series, which includes most of the industrially important metals, is given in Table 2. In most cases, metals from one group can be coupled with other metals from the same group without causing a substantial increase in the corrosion rate of the more active metal.

Passivity Effects. Because some alloys (most notably, the stainless steels) can be either passive or active, they may occupy two places in the galvanic series: a relatively noble position for the passive state, and a less noble position for the active state. Thus, such alloys can play complex roles in situations involving corrosion. Passivity is generally thought to be due to a tightly bound film of oxide on the metal surface, rendering the surface much less susceptible to further reaction. Destruction of the film (for example, by halide ions) will restore the metal to the active state; thus, for a passive alloy, hydrochloric acid is often more dangerous than nitric acid.

Similar considerations apply to many instances in which passivity is destroyed locally — as on sensitized stainless steel, where the grain boundaries have been depleted of chromium and are active, and the interior of the grains passive. Because any stainless steel in the active condition is widely separated in the galvanic series from the same alloy in the passive condition (see Table 2), this is just a special case of galvanic attack. With a large cathode area and a small anode area (the depleted region at the grain boundary), the attack can be especially severe in certain environments.

Selection of Compatible Metals. In the design of a product, selecting metals that will be in electrical contact in an electrolyte, without giving adequate consideration to the possibility of galvanic action between the metals, is a frequent cause of failure.

The coupling of aluminum with brass in equipment that was immersed in ground water resulted in the failure described in the following report:

A sump pump failed to operate, and the resultant flooding of a basement in a manufacturing plant caused extensive damage, when a float arm for a water-level-control device failed as a result of galvanic corrosion. In this device, brass stops were attached to an aluminum vertical rod (float arm) to control the off-on switch. The aluminum rod corroded severely just below the lower brass stop and broke off at this point.

The selection of these two metals for this application was a gross error by the manufacturer of the equipment, because aluminum is known to be strongly anodic to brass in nearly all aqueous environments (in seawater, the difference in corrosion potential between the two metals is 0.6 volt).

The aluminum float arm was replaced with one made of type 316 stainless steel, which has a corrosion potential close to that of brass. No further problems were encountered during the ensuing five years of service.

Another instance of galvanic corrosion because of a poor selection of material is described in the following example.

Example 5. Galvanic-Corrosion Failure of a Malleable Iron Latch in a Valve for an Automatic-Sprinkler System (Fig. 9)

One of three valves in a dry automatic-sprinkler system tripped accidentally, thus activating the sprinklers. A check of the system indicated that the two other valves were about to trip. Maintenance records showed that the three valves had been in service approximately 21 months.

The valve consisted of a cast copper alloy clapper plate that was held closed by a pivoted malleable iron latch, as shown in Fig. 9(a). The latch and top surface of the clapper plate usually were in a sanitary-water environment (stabilized, chlorinated well water having a pH of 7.3) under stagnant conditions. Process make-up water that had been clarified, filtered, softened and chlorinated, and had a pH of 9.8 was occasionally used in the system.

Water pressure on the bottom side of the clapper plate varied from 35 to 150 psi. During a fire emergency, heat detectors activated a switch, releasing a weight that pivoted the lip of the latch away from the clapper. Water pressure forced the clapper plate upward, allowing water to flow through the system.

Investigation. Visual examination of the latch and clapper plate showed corrosion at the contact surfaces between the clapper plate and the latch. Figure 9(b) shows the large amount of metal dissolved from the clapper latch, leaving only about half of the original amount of metal to hold the clapper in a closed position. Also visible in Fig. 9(b) are indications of crevice corrosion where the latch was hinged to the main body of the valve; this attack, however, did not contribute to the failure.

A micrograph of a section through the contact area of the malleable iron clapper latch (Fig. 9c) showed elongated grains and substantial deformation, as well as the pattern and depth of the corrosion, which had drastically weakened the remaining metal in the contact area. Other areas of the failure surface showed transgranular cracks.

Discussion and Conclusions. Corrosion of the malleable iron latch was by galvanic action and greatly reduced the shear load the latch was capable of withstanding. If the

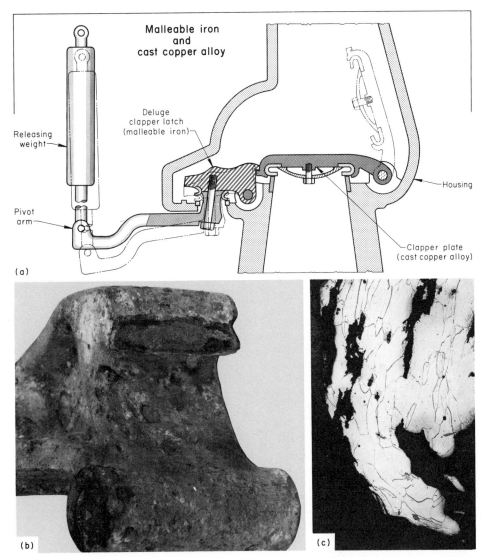

(a) Schematic illustration of sprinkler system, showing deluge clapper latch that failed. (b) Photograph of clapper latch, showing effects of galvanic attack at area of contact (near top) with cast copper alloy clapper plate, and crevice corrosion (at lower left). (c) Micrograph, at 250×, of a cross section of the failure area on the clapper latch, showing the pattern of the corrosion, and elongated grains in the microstructure (indicative of a ductile type of failure).

Fig. 9. Sprinkler system in which a malleable iron deluge clapper latch failed from galvanic attack caused by contact with a copper alloy clapper in stagnant water (Example 5)

latch were not properly adjusted or corrosion decreased the contact area considerably, the applied stress on actuation could exceed the shear strength of the material. In this instance, the contact area was reduced to about half its normal size, and the shear strength of the remaining metal was reduced by the penetrating galvanic corrosion.

When the sprinkler valve accidentally tripped, plastic deformation, characteristic of ductile failure, occurred.

Failure of the latch was caused by extensive loss of metal by galvanic corrosion and the sudden loading related to the tripping of the valve. The malleable iron latch had been corroded to such an extent that it failed mainly by plastic deformation. Failure in some regions of the contact area was by ductile (transgranular) fracture.

Corrective Action. The latch material was changed from malleable iron to silicon bronze (ASTM B198; copper alloy 872).

The use of silicon bronze prevented corrosion or galvanic attack, and the latch was kept properly adjusted to maintain an adequate contact area. The replacement latches were still in satisfactory condition after more than 14 years.

Ratio of Cathode Area to Anode Area. Breaks ("holidays") in organic protective coatings on an active metal component of equipment in which the remaining metal is made of a relatively noble or passive metal can result in extremely rapid galvanic attack, even in a weakly conductive electrolyte, because of a high ratio of cathode area to anode area.

In one instance of this type of behavior, a plant had replaced the leaking bottom of a type 316 stainless steel tank with a bottom of ASTM A285 steel and coated it with a vinyl paint system. The tank contained pure condensate, and

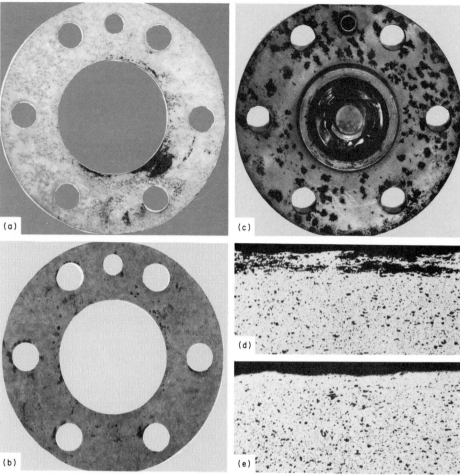

The galvanic attack occurred on the aluminum alloy spacer, shown in (a), when a vellum gasket, shown in (b), that separated the spacer from a nickel-plated steel housing, shown in (c), became saturated with moisture-containing molybdenum disulfide lubricant that acted as an electrolyte. (d) and (e) are micrographs, at 500×, of unetched specimens that were taken from, respectively, a corroded area and an uncorroded area of the aluminum alloy spacer.

Fig. 10. Components for the mounting surface of a hydraulic actuator that failed in service because of galvanic attack on the aluminum alloy spacer (Example 6)

thus no problems were anticipated. However, after about six months several small leaks were noted through the painted-steel bottom. Inspection revealed breaks in the vinyl-paint coating. The unfavorable cathode-to-anode ratio, approximately 1000 to 1, resulted in vigorous attack on the carbon steel at the holidays and caused pinhole failures.

Metals Embedded in Concrete or Plaster. Galvanic corrosion of embedded metals has caused failures of aluminum conduit in steel-reinforced concrete and failures of gypsum plaster on steel lath coupled with copper tubing.

Aluminum conduit embedded in steel-reinforced concrete that contained calcium chloride corroded galvanically in the ceiling of a newly constructed stadium. Cracks in the concrete ceiling began to appear within a few months after completion of the stadium, causing spalling of the concrete. Repair of these defects involved chipping away the surrounding concrete, removing the corroded aluminum conduit, replacing it with steel conduit, and recasting fresh

concrete. More than 15,000 ft of corroded aluminum conduit was replaced in this stadium.

The corrosion of steel tie wires in plaster that also contains copper tubing is another, although less frequent, example of damage to a cementing material caused by galvanic corrosion of embedded metals. In one instance, a gypsum-plaster suspended ceiling in a military hospital fell a few months after installation. In addition to the steel tie wires in the system (used to tie the pre-painted, and hence insulated, metal lath to the upper supporting members), the ceiling contained a grid network of copper tubing for hot-water radiant heating. Failure was caused by galvanic corrosion of the steel tie wires. Analysis of the fallen plaster showed that it unaccountably contained 4400 ppm of chloride ions.

In both of the systems described above, the mechanism of corrosion is similar. Both contain the essential components of a galvanic cell — two electrically coupled dissimilar metals immersed in an electrolyte.

During the time that the concrete is damp, the cement matrix of the concrete is a fairly good electrolyte. The steel and aluminum serve as electrodes, and, because of the different positions of these metals in the galvanic series, an electrical potential is developed between them. If an external connection is made between the steel and the aluminum, a current will flow in the circuit just as in any other short-circuited galvanic-cell battery. The aluminum becomes the anode and corrodes. The steel becomes the cathode and tends to be protected. The intensity and duration of the current flow depend on a number of variables. The mechanism of failure of the concrete is that the aluminum corrosion products occupy a larger volume than the metallic aluminum plus its corrodents. The increasing volume builds up an internal pressure around the conduit. If the conduit is thin-walled and deeply buried in strong concrete, the pressure may collapse the conduit. Otherwise, the concrete will crack.

In the gypsum-plaster system containing steel tie wires and copper tubing, similar actions apply. Copper becomes the cathode and is protected, while the steel becomes the anode and corrodes. When the steel tie wires in a plastered ceiling become sufficiently weakened by corrosion, the plaster (and metal lath) will fall under its own weight.

In the building-construction systems described, dissimilar metals will, for practical reasons, nearly always be in electrical contact, either externally to the cementing material or, more usually, both externally and internally. The galvanic-cell principle applies in both cases. The only difference is that when contact is internal, the corrosion will tend to be greater near the point of contact.

The degree to which the reaction of two dissimilar metals in a cementing material corrodes the anode depends on electrical conductivity (for cold-weather installation, up to 2% calcium chloride is added to concrete to speed up setting), proximity of the dissimilar metals, and ratio of anode area to cathode area.

If it is impossible to avoid the use of dissimilar metals in cementing materials, the following precautions should be observed:

1 The electrical conductivity of the cementing material should be kept to a minimum. The use of calcium chloride or other ionic compounds should be forbidden, and contamination of the cementing material, such as by use of seawater for mixing water, should be avoided. Abnormally delayed drying and subsequent exposure to moisture should also be prevented as far as possible.

2 Dissimilar metals should be spaced as far apart as practicable.

3 The ratio of anode area to cathode area should be at a maximum. Coating the

anode should be avoided, unless the coating is continuous or unless the intense localized corrosion that may occur at a few uncoated points can be tolerated. A strict rule in corrosion control is: If one of two dissimilar metals is to be coated, coat the cathode.

Effect of Time-Dependent Factors.

Some types of time-dependent changes that affect susceptibility to corrosion are readily overlooked, as in the galvanic-attack failure of a number of hydraulic actuators in the example that follows.

Example 6. Failure of Aluminum Alloy Spacers by Galvanic Attack (Fig. 10)

Immediately after installation, leakage was observed at the mounting surface (Fig. 10a) of several rebuilt hydraulic actuators that had been in storage for up to three years prior to installation. At each joint there was an aluminum alloy spacer (Fig. 10a) and a vellum gasket (Fig. 10b). The mounting flanges of the steel actuators (Fig. 10c) had been nickel plated. During assembly of the actuators, a lubricant containing molybdenum disulfide had been applied to the gaskets to serve as a sealer.

One actuator housing, several aluminum alloy spacers, and one used and one new vellum gasket were sent to the laboratory for examination.

Investigation. Visual examination of the components disclosed corrosion deposits and staining such as shown in Fig. 10(a), (b) and (c). The stained areas were dark in color and greasy to the touch. Samples of deposits scraped from the aluminum spacer and the vellum gasket were identified by x-ray diffraction as molybdenum disulfide (MoS_2). Deposits taken from the nickel-plated steel housing were not completely identified. Analysis indicated, however, that nickel formate dihydrate $Ni(CHO_2)_2 \cdot 2H_2O$ was one of the constituents. No molybdenum disulfide or nickel formate was found on the new gasket that was submitted for examination.

Metallographic examination of sections taken through a badly stained area on one of the aluminum alloy spacers showed that corrosion had penetrated to a depth of 0.0025 in. at some areas (see Fig. 10d and e).

Test for Galvanic Action. A test was conducted to determine if the corrosion on the aluminum alloy spacers was the result of galvanic action. Sections of the actuator housing, the vellum gasket and the aluminum alloy spacer were clamped with an insulated C-clamp. The vellum gasket was found to be electrically conductive, and a potential of 0.1 volt at 60,000 ohms was measured between the aluminum alloy spacer and the actuator housing. This voltage could be increased or decreased by changing the force applied by the C-clamp.

The C-clamp was removed, and the test pieces were baked in an oven at 232 C (450 F) for seven days. After baking, no potential could be detected between the test pieces when they were reclamped by the insulated clamp.

Visual examination of the test pieces revealed staining similar to that observed on the failed spacers. Metallographic examination of cross sections through stained areas

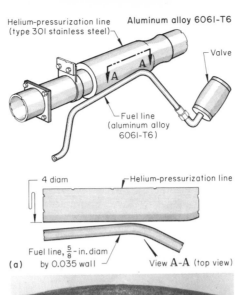

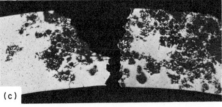

(a) Setup showing proximity of the fuel line to the helium-pressurization line, and in view A-A the point of contact (0.2-in. maximum separation) between the two components at which the failure initiated.

(b) Macrograph, at 2×, of the ½-in.-long crack at a 60° bend in the fuel line. Light area around the crack indicates lack of the protective chromate coating.

(c) Micrograph, at 25×, of a polished but unetched section through the crack, showing severe intergranular attack and extent of corrosion.

Fig. 11. Part of the propulsion system for a missile in which the aluminum alloy 6061-T6 fuel line failed from galvanic attack because of contact with a type 301 stainless steel helium-pressurization line (Example 7)

in the aluminum-spacer test pieces disclosed the presence of incipient corrosion.

Conclusions. Leakage was the result of galvanic corrosion of the aluminum alloy spacers while in storage. The molybdenum disulfide apparently was suspended in a volatile water-containing vehicle that acted as an electrolyte between the aluminum alloy spacer and the nickel-plated steel actuator housing.

Initially, there was no couple between the spacer and housing because the vellum gasket acted as an insulator, but the water-containing lubricant gradually impregnated the vellum gasket and established a galvanic

couple between the spacer and the housing. The staining of the nickel-plated steel housing and the presence of hydrated nickel formate deposits did not contribute to the leakage, but indicated some attack on the housing and helped to confirm the nature of the corrosion mechanism.

Corrective Measures. Use of the molybdenum disulfide lubricant as a gasket sealer was discontinued, and the actuators were assembled using dry vellum gaskets. A satisfactory seal was obtained with the dry vellum gaskets, and no delayed failures by leakage at the gaskets were observed on units assembled in this manner.

Accidental Contact of Dissimilar Metals.

Where dissimilar metals are used in complex equipment and structures exposed to the atmosphere, positive precautions must be taken in design and assembly to avoid accidental contact of the dissimilar metals. Such precautions are particularly important where the environment is aggressive and where a failure could have especially serious consequences, as in the example that follows.

Example 7. Failure of a Chromate Conversion-Coated Aluminum Alloy 6061-T6 Tube From Galvanic Attack (Fig. 11)

An audible leak in a vernier fuel line made of chromate conversion-coated aluminum alloy 6061-T6 tube (Fig. 11a) was observed when pressure was applied to the line during a propulsion leak check on a liquid-fueled missile. The missile had been exposed to the atmosphere about five miles from the ocean for eight months and then at the seacoast for another eight months. Previously, missiles of this type had been exposed outdoors at the seacoast site for considerable lengths of time without any failures during leak checks.

Visual and Macro Examination. A length of the fuel line including the failure region was removed and examined visually, and at low magnification. The outside of the tube was covered with a yellow-to-brown chromate conversion coating. The leak, viewed at a magnification of two diameters, appeared as an irregular ½-in.-long crack at a 60° bend in the fuel line (Fig. 11b).

When viewed at a magnification of 15 diameters, the crack was seen to extend completely through the wall of the tube. The chromate conversion coating on the tube had been worn away from the area around the crack, and there were light parallel transverse scratches in this area.

A considerable amount of metal had been corroded away immediately adjacent to the crack, and corrosion pits were observed around the crack and at two spots on the crack side of the tube and about ⅝ in. and ⅞ in. from the crack. A white powdery substance was present in the crack and the pits, and there was a ring of a dark deposit around each, at the periphery of the corroded area. Stains were also visible in and near the corroded regions.

There were a few small areas on the tube, a few inches from the point of failure, where the chromate coating was absent but at which there was no possibility of contact with or close approach to the stainless steel helium-pressurization line. No evidence of chemical attack was detected on these areas when they were examined at low magnification.

Analysis of Materials. The composition of the tube was found by spectrographic analysis to correspond to that of the specified material, aluminum alloy 6061. The white substance in the crack and the pits appeared to be aluminum oxide; chemical analysis of this substance could not be made, because it was not possible to isolate a sufficient amount. Chemical analysis of the dark deposit showed that it contained a relatively high concentration of iron.

Metallographic Examination. A transverse section taken through the crack and examined at 50 diameters in the polished but unetched condition showed severe intergranular attack at and near the crack, originating on the outside surface of the tube and extending more than $\frac{1}{8}$ in. from the crack. A section through the crack and the immediately adjacent region of deep intergranular attack is shown in Fig. 11(c).

Sections through the two pits $\frac{5}{8}$ and $\frac{7}{8}$ in. from the crack showed these pits to be about $\frac{1}{32}$ in. in diameter and to extend about halfway through the tube wall.

Microhardness measurements on the metallographic specimen averaged 108 Knoop (equivalent to a hardness of Rockwell E 11), which is typical of the specified T6 (solution heat treated and artificially aged) temper for aluminum alloy 6061. The thickness of the tube wall near the crack was verified to be the specified 0.035 in. by measurements on the metallographic specimen.

Origin of Wear at Leak. Review of the assembly drawings for the missile established that the aluminum alloy 6061-T6 fuel line in which the leak occurred passed near the 4-in.-diam helium-pressurization line, which was made of type 301 stainless steel (see Fig. 11a).

Examination of a number of missile assemblies revealed that on this missile two components were separated by 0.2 in. or less at the 60° bend in the aluminum alloy fuel-line tube (see view A-A in Fig. 11a). The fuel-line tube was unsupported for a distance of several inches from the bend in each direction. Further, the orientation of the tube at the bend was found to enable contact of the side of the tube that failed against the stainless steel helium-pressurization line. The stainless steel line showed no evidence of damage.

It appeared that the scratching of the aluminum alloy tube and the local removal of the chromate coating on the tube had resulted from rubbing of the tube against the stainless steel helium line. Galvanic attack on the aluminum alloy (anode) at the point of contact with the stainless steel (cathode) in the presence of moisture while at the seacoast location was concluded to be the probable cause of the severe intergranular corrosion. This attack weakened the fuel-line tube wall to such an extent that it failed during pressurization in leak testing.

Simulated-Conditions Tests. In an attempt to duplicate the failure, specimens simulating the suspected service condition were made by rolling pieces of type 301 stainless steel sheet into tubes having a diameter approximately the same as the helium line

and attaching chromated sections of the actual aluminum alloy 6061-T6 tube. The two members of each assembly were taped together, with a plastic shim placed between the two that separated the straight sections but allowed local contact at the 60° bend in the fuel-line tube.

One specimen was exposed in a 20% salt-spray cabinet for approximately 150 hr, and a second specimen was exposed on an atmospheric-corrosion-test rack at an ocean pier for about six weeks. The aluminum alloy tubes from the two specimens were then sectioned at the area of contact and examined metallographically. Severe pitting, penetrating to a depth of about one-third the wall thickness, and intergranular attack were found on the tube exposed in the salt-spray cabinet. Intergranular attack, about 0.007 in. deep, was found on the specimen exposed to the seacoast atmosphere. Almost no attack was found on sections of the aluminum alloy tube away from the area of contact, and no attack was observed on the stainless steel in either type of exposure.

In additional tests on modified assemblies, distilled water was placed between closely spaced parts with a dropper. Results showed that moisture could bridge across gaps of 0.030 in. and 0.060 in., but not across a gap of 0.090 in.

Conclusions. The laboratory tests and seacoast-atmosphere corrosion tests confirmed that the aluminum alloy fuel-line tube had been in contact with the stainless steel helium-pressurization line, that the chromate coating had been removed locally by abrasion, and that intergranular galvanic attack had weakened the aluminum alloy fuel-line tube sufficiently to permit failure during pressurization.

The absence of attack on nearby small areas of the aluminum alloy fuel-line tube where the chromate coating was absent, but where there had not been any contact with the stainless steel, ruled out possible galvanic action between a bare aluminum alloy surface (a small anodic area) and the surrounding chromate-coated area (a large cathodic area) during the prolonged seacoast exposure as a significant contributory factor in the failure.

Corrective Action. It was recommended that the aluminum alloy 6061-T6 vernier fuel lines on these missiles be inspected for contact with the stainless steel helium line and for corrosion in the suspect region, and that precautions be taken to prevent contact or close approach of the two parts. It was recommended also that a check be made to determine whether there were any other possible areas of contact that would need similar attention.

One corrective technique that was found to be effective in tests consisting of exposure of test assemblies for about 300 hr in a 20% salt-spray cabinet was installing an austenitic stainless steel clamp cushioned with silicone rubber around the aluminum alloy fuel line to provide separation. A similarly cushioned clamp made of cadmium-plated steel and tested in the same way showed severe corrosion of the clamp and two shallow pits on the aluminum alloy tube under the edge of the clamp. There was no corrosion of the stainless steel at either type of clamp in this test.

Velocity-Affected Corrosion in Water

The attack on metal immersed in water may vary greatly, depending on the relative velocity of movement of water against the metal surface. Where attack occurs, the effects of differences in water velocity are most pronounced for metals that show passivity behavior or form other protective films in water.

Effects in Slow-Moving and Stagnant Waters. Slow-moving and stagnant waters allow loosely adherent solid corrosion products to form on metal surfaces and aggravate corrosion. Also, in closed systems where a corrosion inhibitor is used, the effectiveness of the corrosion inhibitor is reduced where the water is stagnant or nearly so.

In designing for corrosion control, stagnant zones should be eliminated by the following methods:

1 Allowing free drainage of water and suspended solids.
2 Installing baffling to eliminate stagnant liquid zones
3 Increasing the frequency of cleaning
4 Providing gas-vent lines
5 Providing strainers or separators to remove foreign material (dirt).

Any of the common varieties of iron or steel, including low-carbon or high-carbon steel, low-alloy steel, wrought iron and cast iron, corrode in slow-moving fresh water or seawater at almost the same rate, equivalent to 0.005-in. penetration per year. At high temperatures, the rate increases, but it remains relatively low on an absolute scale; hence steel can be used for boilers in contact with deaerated water.

Commercially pure aluminum corrodes in aerated or deaerated fresh water at still lower rates than does iron, making it a suitable material for handling distilled water.

Swift-moving water may carry dissolved metal ions away from corroding areas before the dissolved ions can be precipitated as protective layers. Gritty suspended solids in water scour metal surfaces and continually expose fresh metal to corrosive attack.

In fresh waters, as water velocity approaches very high values, it is expected that corrosion of steel first increases, then decreases, and then increases again. This occurs because erosive action serves to break down the passive state.

The corrosion of steel by seawater increases as the water velocity increases. The effect of water velocity at moderate levels is indicated in Fig. 12, which shows that the rate of corrosive attack is a direct function of the velocity until some critical velocity is reached, beyond which there is little further increase in corrosion. At much higher velocities, corrosion rates may be substantially higher.

The effect of changes in water velocity on the corrosion resistance of stainless steels, copper alloys and nickel alloys shows much variation from alloy to alloy at intermediate velocities. Type 316 stainless steel may pit severely in seawater at velocities of less than 4 or 5 ft per second, but is usually very corrosion resistant at higher velocities. Copper alloy 687 (aluminum brass) has satisfactory corrosion resistance if the seawater velocity is less than 8 ft per second.

Stainless steels perform much better when in contact with seawater at high velocities (over 5 ft per second). This is probably because of the absence of adherent organisms or other deposits. The austenitic stainless steels containing molybdenum (such as type 316) are superior to other grades of stainless steel in slow-moving seawater.

Copper alloy 715 (copper nickel, 30%) has excellent resistance to swift-moving seawater and to many types of fresh water. Because copper alloy 715 also is subject to bio-fouling, velocities should be kept above 5 ft per second.

In seawater at high velocity, metals fall into two distinctly different groups: (*a*) those that are velocity limited (carbon steels and copper alloys), and (*b*) those that are not velocity limited (stainless steels and many nickel alloys).

Metals that are not velocity limited are subject to virtually no metal loss from velocity effects or turbulence short of cavitation conditions. The barrier films that form on these metals seem to perform best at high velocities with the full surface exposed and clean. It is in crevices and under deposits that form from slow-moving or stagnant seawater that local breakdown of the film, and pitting, begin.

Erosion-Corrosion. When movement of a corrodent over a metal surface increases the rate of attack due to mechanical wear and corrosion, the attack is called erosion-corrosion. It is encountered when particles in a liquid impinge on a metal surface causing the removal of protective surface films, such as air-formed protective oxide films or adherent corrosion products, and exposing new reactive surfaces that are anodic to uneroded neighboring areas on the surface. This results in rapid localized corrosion of the exposed areas in the form of smooth-bottomed shallow recesses.

Figure 13 shows the smooth surface produced by erosion-corrosion on the interior surface of a failed section of a buried low-carbon steel (0.20% C) water-supply pipe, and the pitted exterior of the uncoated pipe. The pipe was a 14-in.-diam, schedule 40, bypass line at a missile-launching facility; water flow was intermittent, usually about twice weekly for a total operating time of 3 hr per week at an operating pressure of about

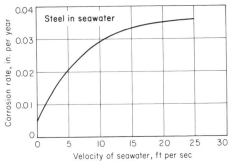

Fig. 12. Effect of velocity of seawater at atmospheric temperature on the corrosion rate of steel

185 psig. It was recommended that this section of pipe be replaced with pipe made from abrasion-resistant T-1 steel, which had originally been specified, or with pipe coated with an elastomer on both interior and exterior surfaces.

Nearly all flowing or turbulent corrosive media can cause erosion-corrosion. The attack may exhibit a directional pattern related to the path taken by the corrodent as it moves over the surface of the metal.

Impingement corrosion is a severe form of erosion-corrosion. It occurs frequently in turns or ells of tubes or pipes or on surfaces of impellers or turbines where impingement is encountered and erosion is more intense. It occurs as deep, clean, horseshoe-shaped pits with the deep, or undercut, end pointing in the direction of flow. Impingement-corrosion attack can also occur as the result of partial blockage of a tube. A stone, a piece of wood, or some other object can cause the main flow to deflect against the wall of the tube. The impinging stream can rapidly perforate tube walls. Water carrying sand, silt or mud will have an additional severely erosive effect on tubes.

Steam erosion is another form of impingement corrosion. It occurs when high-velocity wet steam contacts a metal surface. The resulting attack usually produces a roughened surface showing a large number of small cones with the points facing in the direction of flow.

In the example that follows, impingement corrosion was produced in a malle-

able iron elbow that was exposed alternately to rapid flow of steam at 150 psi and of cooling water at 130 psi.

Example 8. Impingement-Corrosion Failure of a Ferritic Malleable Iron Elbow (Fig. 14)

Leakage was detected in a malleable iron elbow after only 3 months in service. Life expectancy for the elbow was 12 to 24 months. The 0.824-in.-ID 90° elbow connected segments of ¾-in. pipe (0.824-in. ID, 0.113-in. wall) for a line through which steam and cooling water were alternately supplied to a tire-curing press. The supply line and elbow were subjected to 14 heating and cooling cycles per hour for at least 16 hr per day, or a minimum of 224 cycles per day. Steam pressure was 150 psi and water pressure was 130 psi. Based on pump capacity, the water-flow rate was estimated at 350 gal per minute. Water inlet temperature was 10 to 16 C (50 to 60 F); water outlet temperature was 50 to 60 C (120 to 140 F). The water had a pH of 6.9.

The elbow was cast from ASTM A47, grade 35018, malleable iron and had a hardness of Rockwell B 76 to 78. Composition of the iron was 1.95% C, 0.60% Mn, 1.00% Si, 0.15% S, 0.05% P, 0.17% Cu, 0.03% Cr, 0.02% Ni and 0.001% Mo.

Investigation. Specimens were cut from two areas on the elbow, one just below the point of leakage (at A in Fig. 14a) and another further downstream (at B in Fig. 14a). The deepest penetration in the first specimen was at the top, just below the point of leakage, where the wall thickness had been reduced to 1/16 in. Maximum wall thickness was 3/8 in.

Metallographic examination of the first specimen showed that moderate but irregular attack occurred (Fig. 14b). A small area of ferrite remained at the top, but the surface ferritic zone (light areas in Fig. 14b) had been eroded and corroded away on the remainder of the surface, exposing the pearlitic zone (dark areas in Fig. 14b). The interior of the specimen showed a ferritic malleable microstructure.

The second specimen, which showed no signs of attack, had a typical ferrite zone at the surface, then a subsurface pearlitic zone with about twice the thickness of the ferrite zone and a ferritic malleable microstructure in the interior of the specimen (Fig. 14c).

Conclusions. Examination of the micrographs (Fig. 14b and c) indicated that the elbows had been given the usual annealing and normalizing treatment for ferritizing malleable iron. This resulted in lower re-

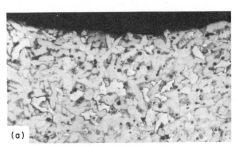
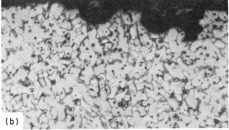

Fig. 13. Micrographs, at 115×, of etched specimens that show corrosion on the inside and outside surfaces of a buried 14-in.-diam low-carbon steel (0.20% C), schedule 40, water-supply pipe. (a) Smooth surface produced by erosion-corrosion on the inner surface; (b) pitting corrosion on the uncoated outer surface of the pipe.

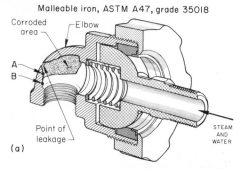

Malleable iron, ASTM A47, grade 35018

(a)

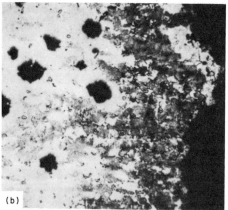

(b)

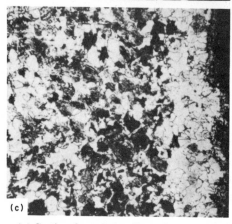

(c)

(a) Section through the elbow, showing extent of corrosion and point of leakage. A and B are locations of specimens shown in micrographs (b) and (c), respectively.

(b) Micrograph, at 67×, of a nital-etched specimen from location A (just below the failure area), showing ferritic surface (light areas) corroded away, exposing the subsurface pearlitic zone (dark areas).

(c) Micrograph, at 67×, of a nital-etched specimen from location B (an uncorroded area of the elbow), showing a typical ferrite zone at the surface, a subsurface pearlitic zone (with twice the thickness of the ferrite zone), and a ferritic malleable microstructure in the interior.

Fig. 14. Malleable iron elbow in which impingement corrosion caused leakage and failure at the bend (Example 8)

sistance to erosion and corrosion than pearlitic malleable iron.

Recommendation. It was recommended that replacement elbows be heat treated so as to produce a pearlitic malleable microstructure, which has longer life under the given conditions of service. (See page 378 in Volume 1 of this Handbook for a discussion of the heat treatment and properties of ferritic and pearlitic malleable irons.)

In piping systems, erosion-corrosion can be reduced by increasing the diameter of the pipe, thus decreasing velocity and turbulence. The streamlining of bends is useful in minimizing the effects of impingement. Inlet pipes should not be directed onto the vessel walls if this can be avoided. Flared tubing can be used to reduce problems at the inlet tubes in a tube bundle.

Cavitation erosion is the most severe form of erosion-corrosion. It occurs principally when relative motion between a metal surface and a liquid environment causes vapor bubbles to appear. When the bubbles collapse, they impose hammerlike blows simultaneously with the initiation of tearing action that appears to pull away portions of the surface. Although the tearing action can remove any protective oxide film that exists on the surface of a metal, exposing active metal to the corrosive influence of the liquid environment, corrosion is not essential to cavitation erosion, as discussed in the article beginning on page 160 in this volume.

Whenever high velocities give rise to extremely low-pressure areas, as in a jet or rotary pump, vapor bubbles collapse at high-pressure areas and destroy protective film on the metal surface or disrupt the metal itself.

Cavitation erosion occurs typically on rotors or pumps, on the trailing faces of propellers and of water-turbine blades, and on the water-cooled side of diesel-engine cylinders. Damage can be reduced by operating rotary pumps at the highest possible head of pressure in order to avoid formation of bubbles. For turbine blades, aeration of water serves to cushion the damage caused by the collapse of bubbles. Neoprene or similar elastomer coatings on metals are reasonably resistant to damage from this cause. To reduce cavitation damage to diesel-engine cylinder liners, the addition of 2000 ppm sodium chromate to the cooling water has proved effective, as has the use of Ni-Resist (high-nickel cast iron) liners.

Table 3 rates some metals frequently used in seawater in four groups on the basis of their resistance to cavitation erosion in seawater.

Bacterial and Bio-Fouling Corrosion

Biological organisms affect corrosion processes on metals by directly influencing anodic and cathodic reactions, by affecting protective surface films on metals, by producing corrosive substances and by producing solid deposits.

These organisms include microscopic forms such as bacteria and macroscopic types such as algae and barnacles. Microscopic and macroscopic organisms have

been observed to live and reproduce in mediums with pH values between 0 and 11, at temperatures between −1 and 82 C (30 and 180 F), and under pressures up to 15,000 psi. Thus, biological activity may influence corrosion in a variety of environments, including soil, inland water and seawater, crude oil and petroleum products, and in oil-emulsion cutting fluids.

Effects of Anaerobic Bacteria. Probably the most important anaerobic bacteria that affect the corrosion of buried steel are those of the sulfate-reducing type, which produce sulfides. They are often found in wet clay, boggy soils and marshes. The sulfide they produce accelerates the dissolution of iron and also retards cathodic reactions, especially hydrogen evolution.

Coating the buried structure with asphalt, enamel, plastic tape, or concrete is often done to prevent contact between the steel structure and the environment.

Table 3. Ratings of Some Metals for Resistance to Cavitation Erosion in Seawater(a)

Group I: Most resistant. Subject to little or no damage. Useful under extremely severe conditions.

    Stellite hard facing alloys
    Titanium alloys
    Austenitic and precipitation-hardening stainless steels
    Nickel-chromium alloys such as Inconel alloys 625 and 718
    Nickel-molybdenum-chromium alloys such as Hastelloy C

Group II: These metals are commonly used where a high order of resistance to cavitation damage is required. They are subject to some metal loss under the most severe conditions of cavitation.

    Nickel-copper-aluminum alloy Monel K-500
    Nickel-copper alloy Monel 400
    Copper alloy 955 (nickel-aluminum bronze, cast)
    Copper alloy 957 (nickel-aluminum-manganese bronze, cast)

Group III: These metals have some degree of cavitation resistance. They are generally limited to low-speed, low-performance applications.

    Copper alloy 715 (copper-nickel, 30%)
    Copper alloys 922 and 923 (leaded tin bronzes M and G, cast)
    Manganese bronze, cast
    Austenitic nickel cast irons

Group IV: These metals normally are not used in applications where cavitation damage may occur, except in cathodically inhibited solutions or when protected by elastomeric coatings.

    Carbon and low-alloy steels
    Cast irons
    Aluminum and aluminum alloys

(a) Applies to normal cavitation-erosion intensities, at which corrosion resistance has a substantial influence on the resistance to damage. Adapted from A. H. Tuthill and C. M. Schillmoller, "Guidelines for Selection of Marine Materials", Ocean Science and Ocean Engineering Conference, Marine Technology Society, June 1965, International Nickel Co., Inc.

Concrete is less satisfactory than the other coating materials in the presence of sulfur-oxidizing bacteria, because it also is rapidly attacked by the sulfuric acid environment.

Because it is not possible to completely avoid pinholes or breaks from accidental damage to coatings, cathodic protection of coated buried structures is necessary, to minimize or prevent microbiological corrosion. Substitute materials, such as asbestos and plastic pipe in place of steel pipe, also have been used as an effective means of preventing the detrimental effects of microbiological activity in certain undesirable soil locations.

Anaerobic bacteria also affect such operations as the secondary recovery of petroleum by waterflooding, which involves injection of very large amounts of water into the oil well. Even with closed systems using water from deep-source wells, localized pitting corrosion occurs and has resulted in complete wall perforation.

In one well, the corrosion product in the pits underneath a calcium-carbonate scale contained 31% iron sulfide. The source water contained 225 ppm sulfate. The bacterial action formed iron sulfide by the reaction: $4Fe + SO_4^{--} + 4H_2O \rightarrow 3Fe(OH)_2 + FeS + 2OH^-$. Thus, localized pitting corrosion resulted from direct anaerobic bacterial reduction of the sulfates at the metal surface.

Corrosion of water-injection lines can be controlled by the use of bactericides, but their effectiveness must be monitored with regularly scheduled microbiological tests and the use of corrosion-monitoring test equipment.

Effects of Aerobic Bacteria. Aerobic bacteria can oxidize elemental sulfur or sulfur-containing compounds to sulfuric acid. The reaction with elemental sulfur is: $2S + 3O_2 + 2H_2O \rightarrow 2H_2SO_4$.

These organisms thrive best at low pH and can produce localized sulfuric acid concentrations up to 5% by weight, creating extremely corrosive conditions. They are frequently found in sulfur fields, in oil fields, and in and about sewage-disposal piping that contains sulfur-bearing organic waste products. In sewage lines, sulfur-oxidizing bacteria cause rapid acid attack of cement piping.

Aerobic bacterial corrosion can occur in the operation of the source wells in a secondary-recovery waterflood program unless steps are taken to prevent leaking in packing glands and valves, to guard against aeration of the water supply.

A heavy hydrated iron oxide scale, together with a complete wall perforation in a 3½-in.-diam waterflood flow line, is shown in Fig. 15. Microbiological examination of a water sample from the line showed the concentration of aerobic viable bacteria to be 22,000 per milliliter after three days and 28,000 per milliliter

Fig. 15. Longitudinal section of a 3½-in.-diam pipe for an oil-well waterflood flow line that failed in service from oxide scaling and perforation caused by aerobic bacterial corrosion that was initiated by aeration of the water supply

after seven days. No sulfate-reducing bacteria were found.

The oxygen content of the water in waterflood systems should be monitored, and the water should be deoxygenated on the basis of corrosion-monitoring data. The most effective method involves elimination of the sources of aeration.

Corrosion in Water-Containing Fuels. Bacterial contamination also causes corrosion in integral fuel cells of jet aircraft, where attack occurs on structural surfaces of lower sump areas made of aluminum alloy.

Fungus or bacterial microorganisms originate in stagnant fuel in fuel dumps and are introduced into the aircraft during fuel transfer and transportation. The microorganisms (several hundred species have been identified) become attached to the structure and in the presence of water and fuel proliferate to form a tenacious mat.

The microorganisms survive at the fuel-water interface, and their biological by-products develop an acidic aqueous solution in the small amounts of water that are always present. The matlike formation retains water locally along with other foreign materials such as rust particles entrained with the fuel. Organic coating systems that are used are not completely impervious, and the corrosive solution eventually attacks the aluminum and causes perforation.

Solution of this problem in jet-aircraft fuel cells requires special fuel-handling and filtration equipment and techniques, together with frequent inspection and drainage of fuel cells.

Fouling by Marine Organisms ("Bio-Fouling"). Marine organisms such as barnacles and mussels attach themselves to any surface, grow and effectively seal off a small part of the surface from its environment, in what is called fouling, or "bio-fouling". Concentration cells form underneath the barnacles and produce deep pits.

Fouling on ship hulls is a function of environmental conditions. The most severe problem occurs in relatively shallow water, since in deeper water there are no natural surfaces, such as rocks in

the tidal zone, to which the organisms may adhere. Thus, harbor conditions are particularly conducive to the initiation of fouling on ship hulls. In general, warm water temperatures favor long breeding seasons and rapid multiplication of macroorganisms that cause fouling.

Relative motion between an object and water usually inhibits the attachment of organisms. Thus, rapidly moving vessels accumulate only small quantities of organisms, and the major portion of fouling occurs when the vessel is docked.

A similar velocity effect is also noted in heat exchangers employing seawater as a coolant. Rapid fluid flow tends to suppress fouling of heat exchangers, whereas rapid accumulation occurs at low fluid rates or during shutdown periods. Also, the nature of the surface strongly influences the attachment of macroorganisms. Smooth, hard surfaces offer an excellent point for adhesion, whereas rough, flaking surfaces inhibit adhesion. For example, the fouling of stainless steel and iron occurs initially at about the same rate in seawater. However, after some exposure, the surface of the iron is covered by a loosely adhering iron oxide and fouling is generally less on iron than on stainless steel after long exposure periods.

Copper and copper alloy 706 (copper nickel, 10%) are highly resistant to fouling in quiet seawater, whereas many of the more noble alloys foul, and pit deeply, in quiet seawater.

However, as velocities reach the range of 3 to 6 ft per second, fouling diminishes and pitting of the more noble alloys slows down and even ceases. As velocities continue to increase, the corrosion-barrier film is stripped away from copper and copper nickel, while the stainless steels and many nickel-base materials remain passive and inert. The complete reversal in the tolerance of metals for the marine environment as velocities change is the source of much seemingly conflicting information on actual experience with metals in marine service.

Control of Bio-Fouling. Fouling by organisms is most effectively inhibited by the use of antifouling paints. These paints contain toxic substances, usually copper compounds. They function by slowly releasing copper ions into the aqueous environment, which poisons the mussels, barnacles and other creatures. A similar technique is used in closed systems, where various toxic agents and algicides such as chlorine and chlorine-containing compounds are added to the environment. These methods work more or less successfully, depending on their application. However, under conditions conducive to the growth of aqueous organisms, periodic cleaning is almost always necessary to ensure unimpeded fluid flow and to prevent crevice attack.

Corrosion of Buried Metals

Major influences on the corrosion of uncoated metallic objects buried in the earth include: (a) galvanic effects; (b) chemical composition, oxygen content and pH of the soil; (c) alloy selection; and (d) stray currents.

Galvanic Effects. Failures of the threads in steel pipe have been encountered when brass valves have been screwed directly into the pipe. An insulating coupling should always be used to prevent this type of attack.

Early failure because of galvanic effects resulting from local variation in type of soil occurred in the example that follows.

Example 9. Failure of a Buried Type 304L Stainless Steel Drain Line by Galvanic Attack Because of Local Differences in Soil Composition

One of five underground drain lines intended to carry a highly acidic effluent from a chemical-processing plant to distant holding tanks failed in just a few months, before all the lines were completed. Type 304L stainless steel was selected from a number of alloys after extensive laboratory testing of corrosion resistance to the highly corrosive liquid. Each line was made of pipe $2\frac{7}{8}$ in. in diameter, and with 0.203-in. wall thickness to provide additional assurance of long life in contact with the corrosive effluent. Five small drain lines instead of just one large line were installed to reduce the risk of depending on one outlet to discharge effluent. (Inability to discharge effluent would make it necessary to shut down the plant.)

Pipelaying began at the processing building, the lengths of pipe being joined by shielded metal-arc welding. Soundness of the welded joints was determined by water back-pressure testing after several lengths of pipe had been installed and joined. Backfilling of the pipe trench was begun after several series of welding and back-pressure-testing cycles were complete.

Before completion of the pipeline, a pressure drop was observed during back-pressure testing. An extreme depression in the backfill near the beginning of the lines and near the building revealed the site of failure. A leak was found in one of the five pipes.

Investigation. The failed section of pipe was removed and found to have a hole approximately $\frac{3}{4}$ in. in diameter on the outside, narrowing down to a diameter of $\frac{1}{4}$ in. on the inside. Measurements showed that the voltage drop between the soil and the pipe averaged about 1.5 volts. The soil was not consistent in composition, but was a coarse intermixture of sandy loam and heavy clay, and the voltage drops between the pipe and these conglomerates varied greatly for the different types of soil.

The generally smooth contour of the hole in the pipe, together with the voltage-drop measurements, showed that the failure had resulted from galvanic corrosion at a point where the corrosivity of the soil was substantially greater than the average, resulting in a voltage drop near the point of failure of about 1.3 to 1.7 volts.

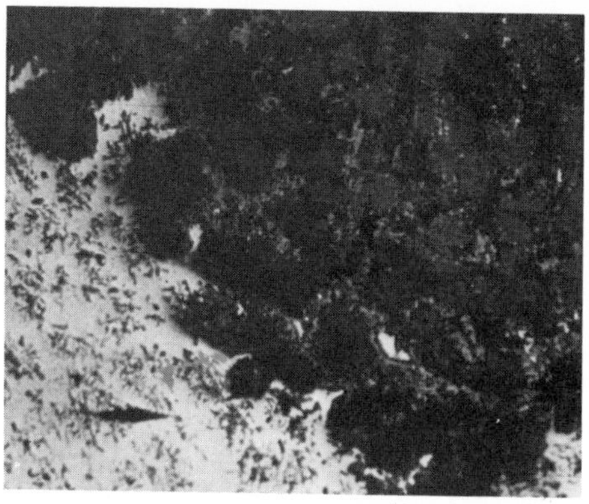

Fig. 16. Micrograph, at 75×, of an unetched specimen from a buried gray iron pipe that failed from graphitic corrosion. Graphitic corrosion near the failed area is at upper right; unaffected iron is at lower left. (Example 10)

Corrective Action. Because of the necessity for very high reliability of continued operation of the line without failure, three corrective measures were employed:

1 The pipelines were asphalt coated.
2 The pipelines were enclosed in a concrete trough with a concrete cover.
3 Magnesium anodes, connected electrically to each line, were installed at periodic intervals along their entire length to provide cathodic protection.

Effect of Soil Composition. Soil containing organic acids derived from humus is relatively corrosive to steel, zinc, lead and copper. The measured total acidity of such a soil appears to be a better index of its corrosivity than is pH alone. High concentrations of sodium chloride and sodium sulfate in poorly drained soil make the soil very corrosive. A poorly conducting soil, whether low in content of moisture or dissolved salts, or both, is generally less corrosive than a highly conducting soil. But conductivity alone is not a sufficient index of corrosivity; the anodic or cathodic polarization characteristics of a soil are also a factor.

Cinders constitute one of the most corrosive environments. It has been reported that in exposures of four or five years, corrosion rate in cinders for steel and zinc was five times, for copper eight times, and for lead 20 times as high as the average rates for the same metals in 13 different soils.

Pitting corrosion of steel and cast iron pipe is prevalent in areas where backfill has consisted of coal ashes, which normally contain sulfides. Corrosion may be a combination of galvanic (steel-to-carbon couple) corrosion and corrosion caused by the formation of weak sulfuric acid from the ashes. Backfill should always be well compacted to exclude air. The presence of moisture plus air results in oxidation of metallic objects, particularly those made from iron or steel.

Chemical pollution of the soil, such as from leaks or spills, often results in very aggressive corrosion of metallic objects like pipe and underground structures.

The soils of the east coast of Florida have a pH of about 6.5 to 8.3. The variation in silica sand, oyster and clam shells, imported clay and shale does not appear to have an appreciable effect on the corrosion rate of cast iron pipe and steel pilings. Cast iron pipes examined in one study were not significantly damaged by corrosion. Any pipe failures appear to have been caused by impact and overpressurization. Steel pilings in service for ten years were examined. The condition of the pilings was good, with little or no corrosion. The deepest pits were 0.050 in. over a 1-sq-in. area. These pits were found on a "spot" of exposed bare metal on a mill-scale surface. The pilings were of 16-in.-diam low-alloy steel pipe with a wall thickness of $\frac{3}{8}$ in.

Alloy Selection. Minor changes in composition and microstructure are not important to corrosion resistance. Hence copper-bearing steel, low-alloy steel, low-carbon steel, and wrought iron corrode at approximately the same rate.

Increase in chromium content of low-alloy steel decreases observed weight loss in a variety of soils; but above 6% Cr, depth of pitting increases. In 14-year tests, 12% Cr and 18% Cr steels were severely pitted. Type 304 stainless steel was not pitted or was only slightly pitted. Type 316 stainless steel did not pit in any of 15 soils to which the alloy was exposed for 14 years.

Zinc coatings are surprisingly effective in reducing weight loss and pitting rates of steel exposed to soils. A major source of protection appears to result from the alloy layer formed between zinc and the steel surface in hot dip galvanizing.

Copper, on the average, corrodes at about one-sixth the rate of iron, but in tidal marsh, for example, the rate is comparatively higher than in most other soils, being one-half that of iron.

Lead also corrodes less on the average than does steel. In poorly aerated soils or soils high in organic acids, the corrosion rate may be four to six times the average.

Zinc pitted completely through the specimen thickness in some soils. In five-year tests carried out in Great Britain, commercially pure aluminum was severely pitted in four soils, but was virtually unattacked in a fifth soil.

Gray iron in soils, as well as in water, is subject to graphitic corrosion, as is demonstrated in the next example.

Example 10. Failure of a Gray Iron Underground Gas-Transmission Pipe by Graphitic Corrosion in Moist Corrosive Soil (Fig. 16)

A gray iron pipe, used to convey natural gas underground, failed after about 26 years in service. The pipe was 8 in. in diameter, with a wall thickness of 0.35 in. The soil around the pipe was in relatively low land, consisting mostly of extremely moist clay-type soil. Expected life of the pipe would be about 35 years under normal undisturbed environmental conditions.

Construction work had been going on nearby for four months prior to failure; heavy blasting had been done to remove rock formations. Some time prior to the failure of the pipe, gas odors had been detected. Excavation found ruptured piping. Fortunately, the rupture was found early enough to prevent possible explosions by leakage of gas into industrial plants in the vicinity.

Investigation. Visual and low-magnification examination of the failed region indicated that the observed fracture was apparently related to the blasting. There were numerous pinholes within 20 in. of the fracture. The outside surface could be scratched away easily with a penknife, with the apparent corrosion near the fracture about ¼ in. deep. The corrosion product had the appearance of a heavy rust.

Chemical analysis of the soil surrounding the underground pipe indicated large amounts of calcium sulfate and mixtures of chlorides. The soil was a very moist clay. Metallographic examination of a section taken 5 ft away from the fracture exhibited graphite, type B graphite flakes, and primary ferrite with Brinell hardness values in the range of 135 to 160 Bhn. Metallographic examination of a section ½ in. away from the fracture revealed an area of graphitic corrosion, as shown in Fig. 16. (Graphitic corrosion is defined and discussed on page 177 in this article.)

Conclusions. Continuous exposure for 26 years in constantly moist soil that was high in calcium sulfate and chlorides would be expected to produce severe graphitic corrosion of gray iron. In some areas, the corrosion had penetrated completely through the 0.35-in.-thick wall, causing fine pit-holes and minor gas leakage. This crusty corrosion, although retaining the original shape of the pipe, was soft enough to be cut away with a penknife. Final failure or rupture occurred because of the underground shock of the nearby blasting operations.

Recommendations. It was recommended that the pipe be inspected at regular intervals, paying special attention to the section in low-lying moist areas. It was recommended also that reinforced coal-tar protective coatings be used in conjunction with cathodic protection.

Methods of Protection. Buried pipelines and tanks are susceptible to accelerated corrosion, depending on soil conditions and galvanic and stray-current effects, unless protected by a combination of cathodic protection and reinforced coal-tar or other suitable coatings. Protection ordinarily requires a cathode current density of 1 to 3 milliamp per square foot; the current density needed in specific applications must be determined by empirical testing.

Thick coatings of coal tar, with reinforcing pigments or inorganic fibers to reduce cold flow of the coating, when combined with properly designed and installed cathodic protection systems (see

"Cathodic Protection", on page 196) provide effective protection to buried steel at reasonable cost.

As a general rule, the use of coatings on buried structures without cathodic protection is not recommended; in aggressive soils and where microbiological corrosion occurs or where stray currents are encountered, service life frequently is shorter than that of uncoated structures, on which corrosion would not usually be highly localized.

Portland cement, and vitreous-enamel coatings, when free of pores, are protective, but are brittle and readily damaged mechanically.

Zinc coatings also are protective, but deteriorate more rapidly when galvanically coupled to large areas of bare iron, steel or copper, in which case insulating couplings should be used.

A soil high in organic acids can be made less corrosive by surrounding the metal structure with limestone chips. A layer of chalk ($CaCO_3$) surrounding buried pipes has been used in some soil formations that would be expected to produce microbiological corrosion.

Atmospheric Corrosion

The metals ordinarily used in equipment and structures corrode at a negligible rate when exposed to the atmosphere in the absence of moisture to serve as an electrolyte. For example, metal parts exposed in the desert air remain free from corrosion for long periods of time. Also, metal parts exposed to the air at temperatures below the freezing point of water or of aqueous condensates on the metal do not corrode to a significant extent, because ice is a poor electrolytic conductor.

Corrosivity of Different Atmospheres. The general corrosivity of rural, industrial and marine atmospheres in tem-

perate climates is compared in Table 4, which gives the average corrosion rates for a number of metals exposed for 10 and 20 years in the three types of atmospheres.

Three generalizations can be drawn from the data for the nonferrous metals in Table 4:

1 The industrial atmosphere is much more corrosive than the rural atmosphere (except on lead), and is more corrosive or at least as corrosive as the marine atmosphere.

2 The rural atmosphere is less corrosive (on some metals, much less) than the marine atmosphere, and the two atmospheres have low and approximately equal rates of attack on the more resistant metals.

3 The corrosion rate on a given metal shows only a slight increase or decrease between the 10-year and 20-year periods, with no apparent pattern.

For the most part, the corrosion rate is dependent on the chemical behavior of each metal in relation to the moisture content and the amount and nature of the particulate matter and of the gaseous impurities in a given type of atmosphere.

Corrosion-Product Films. One factor that accounts for many of the differences in corrosion rates in Table 4 is the formation of corrosion-product films that provide different amounts of protection against corrosion.

Only lead, which readily forms tightly adherent, insoluble, highly protective films in the air, is equally resistant to rural, industrial and marine atmospheres. These films usually consist mainly of oxycarbonates, but contain equally protective sulfates and oxychlorides in industrial and marine atmospheres.

The protection provided by corrosion-product films causes the corrosion rates given in Table 4 to level off to approximately steady-state values after an initial period of more rapid attack. The slopes

Table 4. Average Corrosion Rates of Various Metals Exposed for 10 and 20 Years to Three Types of Atmospheres(a)

| Metal | Corrosion rate, mil per year | | | | | |
| | Rural atmosphere(b) | | Industrial atmosphere(c) | | Marine atmosphere(d) | |
	10-year exposure	20-year exposure	10-year exposure	20-year exposure	10-year exposure	20-year exposure
Aluminum	0.001	0.003	0.032	0.029	0.028	0.025
Copper	0.023	0.017	0.047	0.054	0.052	0.050
Lead	0.019	0.013	0.017	0.015	0.016	0.021
Tin	0.018	...	0.047	0.052	0.091	0.112
Nickel	0.006	0.009	0.128	0.144	0.004	0.006
Monel 400(e)	0.005	0.007	0.053	0.062	0.007	0.006
Zinc, 99.9%	0.034	0.044	0.202	0.226	0.063	0.069
Zinc, 99.0%	0.042	0.043	0.193	0.218	0.069	0.068
Carbon steel(f)	...	...	0.48	...	...	...
Low-alloy steel(g)	...	...	0.09	...	...	...

(a) Adapted from H. H. Uhlig, "Corrosion and Corrosion Control", 2nd Ed., Wiley, 1971, p 166. Data on nonferrous metals from Symposium on Atmospheric Corrosion of Non-Ferrous Metals, ASTM STP No. 175, 1955. Data on steels from C. P. Larrabee, *Corrosion*, Vol 9, Aug 1953, p 259. (b) State College, Pa. (c) New York City, for nonferrous metals; Kearny, N. J., for carbon and low-alloy steels. (d) La Jolla, Cal. (e) 65% Ni, 32% Cu, 2% Fe, 1% Mn. (f) 0.2% C, 0.02% P, 0.05% S, 0.05% Cu, 0.02% Ni, 0.02% Cr. (g) 0.01% C, 0.2% P, 0.04% S, 0.03% Ni, 1.1% Cr, 0.4% Cu.

Table 5. Compositions of Steels for Which Corrosion Data Are Plotted in Fig. 17

Steel	C	Mn	P	S	Si	Cu	Ni	Cr	Mo
Open-hearth Cu steel	0.02	0.39	0.006	0.018	0.005	0.20	...	0.07	...
Bessemer Cu steel	0.10	0.40	0.112	0.059	0.018	0.21	0.003	0.03	...
3.2% Ni structural steel ..	0.19	0.53	0.016	0.022	0.009	0.07	3.23	0.10	...
High-strength low-alloy steels:									
Ni-Cu steel	0.05	0.36	0.054	0.016	0.008	1.14	1.99	0.01	...
Cu-Ni-Mn steel	0.09	0.86	0.008	0.025	0.019	1.41	0.95	0.03	0.09
Cr-Si-Cu-P steel	0.09	0.24	0.154	0.024	0.80	0.43	0.05	1.07	...

of the curves in Fig. 17 illustrate this behavior for steels exposed to an industrial atmosphere. Figure 17 also shows the effects of the compositions of the steels (see Table 5) on the protective characteristics of the rust film formed, with the greatest protection being provided by the films on the high-strength low-alloy steels.

General experience with atmospheric-exposure tests on steel and zinc has demonstrated that the conditions of exposure during the early stages of a test also have a major effect on the long-term corrosion behavior of the metals, further confirming the generally protective nature of the corrosion-product films.

In one series of tests, weight losses of zinc specimens exposed for several weeks to an industrial atmosphere depended primarily on the humidity and presence of moisture during the first few days of exposure and were affected less by conditions during the remainder of the test. A similar primary dependence on the initial exposure conditions has been observed on steel when the specimens were exposed for a year, with the exposures beginning in different months of the year. In winter the greater surface accumulation of combustion products, in particular sulfuric acid, produces a less protective initial corrosion product, which influences the subsequent corrosion rate.

One-year exposure of aluminum and aluminum alloys in an industrial atmosphere has resulted in substantially deeper pitting when begun in winter than in summer, but (unlike the results for steel and zinc) only slightly greater weight loss.

Passivity. Among the metals for which atmospheric corrosion rates are given in Table 4, nickel and aluminum have a natural passivity in uncontaminated air (steels and zinc can be passivated by chemical oxidizing treatments). The passivity of nickel is destroyed in the industrial exposure and that of aluminum is destroyed in both the industrial and the marine atmospheres.

The surface films generally considered to be the source of passivity are only about 30 angstroms or less in thickness, while ordinary corrosion-product films are several orders of magnitude thicker.

Rural atmospheres are generally free of the particulate matter and corrosive

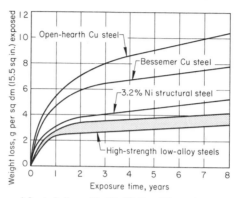

Adapted from H. H. Uhlig, "Corrosion and Corrosion Control", 2nd Ed., Wiley, 1971, p 165; and H. H. Uhlig (Ed.), "Corrosion Handbook", Wiley, 1948, p 124.

Fig. 17. Variation in weight loss of several steels with exposure time in a corrosive industrial atmosphere. See Table 5 for compositions of the steels.

gases found in industrial atmospheres, and this condition accounts for the low corrosion rates in rural atmospheres (see Table 4). The normal carbon dioxide content of air has little or no effect on metals exposed to the atmosphere. In some tests, carbon dioxide has been found to decrease the corrosion rate of steels, apparently by enabling the formation of rust films that are more protective than those formed in its absence.

Industrial atmospheres contain dust as a primary contaminant, in concentrations of about 2 mg per cubic meter for average city air to 1000 mg per cubic meter for heavily industrialized areas. It is estimated that more than 100 tons of dust per square mile settles in urban industrial areas in a month.

Dust deposited on metal surfaces in these areas generally contains particles of carbon and carbon compounds, metal oxides and metal salts (chiefly sulfates and chlorides) and sulfuric acid. The combination of moisture with dust particles bearing soluble contaminants produces crevice corrosion, by forming differential aeration cells and other types of concentration cells.

Most of the soluble contaminants are hygroscopic and absorb moisture from the air when the relative humidity is substantially less than 100%. The critical level of relative humidity (that at which moisture absorption takes place on metals exposed to even relatively mild industrial atmospheres) is usually about

50 to 70% for steel, copper, nickel, zinc and most metals that are used in structures and objects intended for industrial atmospheric exposure. This takes in account the effect of the normal fluctuations in temperature between day and night.

Gases such as sulfur trioxide, sulfur dioxide (which readily oxidizes to sulfur trioxide), hydrogen chloride, oxides of nitrogen, hydrogen sulfide and the halogens in the air accelerate the crevice-corrosion effects of moist dust deposits on these metals. Even at low concentrations, such gases also corrode these metals in the absence of dust deposits, if the humidity reaches or exceeds the critical level.

Metal surfaces located where they become wet but where rain cannot wash the surfaces may corrode more rapidly than if fully exposed. For example, the rusting of steel in partly sheltered locations in moist air containing oxides of sulfur, which form sulfuric acid, is apparently accelerated in a self-perpetuating sequence of reactions. The acid attacks the steel, producing iron sulfate that is retained on the moist rust and hydrolyzes to form more sulfuric acid and iron oxide, thus catalyzing the rusting process.

Marine Atmospheres. At and near the seacoast, the deposition of salt-water spray is the most corrosive aspect of marine atmospheric exposure. The rate of attack on exposed metals varies widely, depending on distance from the ocean, prevailing wind direction, relative humidity and temperature fluctuations that can produce condensation.

The penetration of protective film by chloride ions and the high solubility and hygroscopic nature of metal chlorides cause rapid corrosion on carbon and low-alloy steels. Zinc and cadmium plating extend the life of steel hardware to a useful but limited extent; large steel structures must be protected by painting.

The high conductivity of moisture containing dissolved salt accelerates crevice corrosion and galvanic corrosion, making the use of sealants mandatory at joints and the use of single-metal systems good practice.

Brasses undergo rapid dezincification unless alloyed with small amounts of arsenic, antimony or phosphorus in "inhibited" grades. Copper nickels, titanium and alloys such as Incoloy 800 perform well in marine atmospheres, but most metals corrode severely unless protected by organic coatings.

In general structural applications of aluminum alloys and stainless steels in thick sections, pitting and crevice corrosion are not usually serious problems (however, stress corrosion can cause problems as discussed in the article on Stress-Corrosion Cracking, which begins on page 205 in this volume). Pitting and crevice corrosion can produce rapid penetration and failure by leakage in thin-wall vessels, tubes and pipes made of these alloys.

The results of deposition of solids and of condensation of moisture on stainless steel hydraulic tubes on carrier-based aircraft at sea are described in the example that follows.

Example 11. Pitting-Corrosion Failure of Type 304 Stainless Steel Aircraft Hydraulic Tubes in a Marine Atmosphere (Fig. 18)

Frequent leaking in type 304 stainless steel hydraulic tubes was experienced in carrier-deployed naval bombers. Field reports described the failures as pinholes, large holes, cracks, ruptures and splits. The tubes ranged from $\frac{1}{4}$ to $\frac{1}{2}$ in. in diameter and had a wall thickness of 0.016 in.

A total of 62 tubes that had failed were removed from 44 aircraft; 30 of the tubes, from bomb-bay areas. Failed hydraulic tubes were removed from nine other locations within the aircraft, with a maximum of five coming from any single region. About one-third of the failures occurred in tube areas covered by identification labels.

All of the failures in bomb-bay areas were in bare areas of tubing that were not covered by identification labels. Leakage of tubes in bomb-bay areas occurred an average of about 450 hr (maximum, about 700 hr; minimum, 155 hr) after installation of the tubes, and after an average of about 200 hr (maximum, 320 hr; minimum, 16 hr) of aircraft service on a carrier.

Metallurgical Investigation. Samples of tubes that had failed in bare areas were examined at magnifications of 6 to 40 diameters. Extensive pitting was found, most of the pits being 0.0005 to 0.03 in. in diameter.

In some areas where the pitting was severe, several pits were joined together, giving the appearance of cracks parallel to the tube axis. The pits were on the outside surface in the top and bottom quadrants of horizontal sections of the tubes. No pits were found on the sides or on vertical sections.

Some tubes showed many rust spots about 0.064 in. in diameter, most of which had not progressed to the pitting stage. No corrosion was found on the inside surfaces except where the tube wall had been penetrated.

Other failed tubes showed little or no pitting of bare surfaces, but etched areas, scattered pits, clustered pits, cracks plus pits and some isolated cracks were found beneath identification labels. In many locations, the remains of the labels appeared wrinkled.

Metallographic examination of sections of failed tubes revealed that the average penetration of the pits was about halfway through the wall of the tube (Fig. 18a), with some pits forming "caverns" where penetration was nearly or fully complete (Fig. 18b and c).

No evidence of intergranular corrosion was found adjacent to the pits. The microstructure of the steel was normal, free of precipitated carbides and surface imperfections, and contained only innocuous non-metallic inclusions.

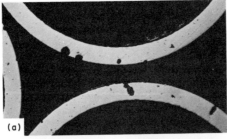

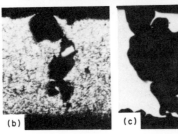

(a) Typical pits in the tubes, showing extent and depth of pitting. Unetched; 16×. (b) Etched pit at 65× showing incipient formation of a "cavern" and almost complete penetration of the wall of one of the tubes. (c) Pits that joined to form a "cavern", resulting in complete penetration of the tube wall. Unetched; 65×.

Fig. 18. Micrographs of transverse sections through type 304 stainless steel tubes that failed in the hydraulic systems of naval aircraft at sea from pitting corrosion (Example 11)

Chemical Tests. Chemical analysis identified the corrosion products from several pits as $Fe_2O_3 \cdot H_2O$ plus chloride ions. X-ray diffraction tests established that "dirt" present on one tube was silica (sand), sodium chloride and ferric oxide. Spectrographic analysis of the "dirt" showed a high concentration of silicon, substantial concentrations of sodium and calcium, and low concentrations of aluminum, chromium, iron and magnesium.

The pitted surface of one tube showed the presence of chlorides in the pits when it was tested by pressing it with filter paper impregnated with 10% silver nitrate and then exposing the paper to ultraviolet light.

Analysis of the metal from several failed tubes showed the average composition to be normal for type 304 stainless steel. Huey tests (five 48-hr cycles in boiling 65% nitric acid) revealed no intergranular attack and an acceptable rate of general corrosion of 0.017 in. per year.

Corrosion tests were done to simulate service exposure of the tubes to seawater spray and aircraft-carrier stack gases. In these tests, specimens of type 304 stainless steel tubing from stock were exposed to salt-water spray while in contact with iron granules. Pits developed beneath the granules, penetrating in one instance to 40% of the wall thickness of the tube.

In other tests on tubing from stock, particles of sand and iron were sealed beneath identification labels after the tubing and particles were sprayed with sodium chloride solution. Incipient pitting was observed beneath some of the labels, mostly where sand grains had been inserted. Rust was generally present beneath other labels.

A five-month exposure to marine atmosphere was conducted with a sample tube

from stock; the tube was supported horizontally. Two areas were covered with protective coatings (one with a lacquer-type primer plus two coats of white acrylic nitrocellulose lacquer and the other with a zinc chromate primer), and a third area was left bare. In each area, three labels were applied — one correctly, one with sand grains and iron particles sealed beneath it, and the third with a wrinkle or "tunnel" parallel to the tube axis.

The exposure did not result in penetration through the coatings, either beneath the labels or in the bare area. Some pits were found at the edge of the coatings.

Lines of pits were visible along the edges of the three labels on the bare tube area and along the "tunnel" of the wrinkled label. Extensive pitting like that found on the tubes that failed in service was observed on bare areas of the test specimens.

Conclusions. Failure of the hydraulic tubes occurred by leakage that resulted from complete penetration by pitting corrosion because of exposure to seawater spray and aircraft-carrier stack gases while the aircraft were parked on the carrier deck. (Bomb-bay and access doors were always left open, and the rear sections of the aircraft routinely overhung the water.)

The corrosion was initiated by concentration cells that were formed beneath identification labels and beneath particles of "dirt" on bare surfaces of the tubes. The corrosion was restricted to the top and bottom surfaces of the horizontal tubes because of the accumulation of "dirt" on the upper surface and the formation of droplets of condensate on the bottom. Where dirt or condensate did not collect, no corrosion of exposed surfaces occurred.

The pitting produced in the laboratory and in the marine-environment test was similar to that on the hydraulic tubes returned from service.

The identification labels provided sites for concentration-cell corrosion but did not contribute chemically to the attack.

Corrective Action. The following steps were taken to avoid or minimize pitting corrosion of the hydraulic tubes:

1 Bomb bays were reclassified as intermittently exposed areas like wheel wells and wing-fold joints; chemical cleaning and protective coating of all bomb-bay tubes in aircraft in service were requested, and cleaning and coating procedures were recommended.
2 A three-coat paint system was specified for more-complete protection of stainless steel hydraulic tubes in bomb-bay areas of future aircraft.
3 A zinc chromate primer coat was specified for stainless steel hydraulic tubes not in exposed areas.
4 It was recommended that the design of future aircraft be modified to permit the closure of bomb-bay and access doors while the aircraft are parked.
5 It was requested that titanium alloy Ti-3Al-2.5V be evaluated as a possible substitute for type 304 stainless steel for hydraulic tubes.

Tropical Atmospheres. The long-term-exposure tests reported by C. R. Southwell and J. D. Bultman in "Corrosion of Metals in Tropical Environments, Part 10 – Final Report of Sixteen-Year Exposures", NRL Report 7834, Jan 1975, included exposure to marine and inland (semirural) atmospheres in Panama.

More than 50 metals, about half of which were ferrous and half nonferrous metals, were studied individually in this test program, as well as many combinations of the metals in bimetallic couples. In general, corrosion rates were somewhat higher than for comparable nonindustrial atmospheres in temperate climates. Among the ferrous metals exposed, plain carbon steel corroded at a rate about one-third higher in the marine than in the inland environment, and similar increases prevailed for most of the wrought steels.

Tabulated summaries of results cover all of the metals and bimetallic couples exposed in all five environments: seawater, mean tide, fresh water and the marine and inland atmospheres. Time versus corrosion curves were presented for many metals.

Cast bronzes, which are frequently used in naval applications, showed very good long-term resistance to corrosion in all exposures and exceptionally high resistance at mean tide and in fresh water.

Commercially pure metals are best suited for evaluating alloys and the corrosiveness of environments. The lead, nickel, copper, zinc and aluminum curves showed a considerable variation in order of resistance in the different environments. Aluminum had the lowest corrosion rate in all exposures except for immersion in fresh water.

Curves for 15 structural ferrous metals in the marine and inland atmospheres showed a considerable advantage for the low-alloy "weathering" steels over plain carbon steels. A 5Cr-0.5Mo steel showed even higher resistance.

Copper-bearing steels were no more resistant than plain carbon steel in either atmosphere. Wrought iron was equal to carbon steel in the marine atmosphere but was slightly less resistant in the inland atmosphere.

The marine atmosphere was about 1.3 times as corrosive to wrought steels as the atmosphere at the inland location, but for cast iron and cast steel there was little difference.

A very large amount of bimetallic-corrosion information is presented in tabular summaries. Carbon steel was a very effective anode for more-noble metals; strips of steel effectively protected stainless steels, nickel and nickel alloys, copper, copper nickels, brasses and bronzes for periods in excess of eight years continuously submerged in seawater, and for 16 years at mean tide.

In fresh water, galvanic protection was not very effective; however, smaller-area anodes used to provide protection were significantly corroded by galvanic action in this medium.

Bimetallic-corrosion results for the atmospheric exposures revealed that the marine atmosphere caused four to eight times as much galvanic corrosion as the inland atmosphere.

The above are only a few general results from the large amount of data included. However, all the results from this extensive program have been condensed into the single report cited earlier, where any results of interest — such as those involving individual metals, groups of alloys, general corrosion, pitting, environmental effects or galvanic corrosion — can be studied.

Corrective and Preventive Measures

Where a corrosion failure has occurred, economical and practicable measures for prevention of future failures of the same type are required. The major types of corrective and preventive measures are:

1 Change in alloy, heat treatment or product form
2 Use of resinous and inorganic-base coatings
3 Use of inert lubricants
4 Use of electrolytic and chemical coatings and surface treatments
5 Use of metallic coatings
6 Use of galvanic protection
7 Design changes for corrosion control
8 Use of inhibitors
9 Changes in pH and applied potential
10 Continuous monitoring of variables.

Change in Alloy, Heat Treatment or Product Form

Where the environment cannot be changed to solve a corrosion problem, a change in alloy, heat treatment or product form may be required. Under some circumstances, both alloy and product form may be changed.

Extreme temperatures and high operating stresses favor the use of special-purpose cast alloys. For example, the tubes in gas reformers are usually made of cast heat-resisting alloys such as HK-40 or Super-Therm, to obtain maximum life at operating temperatures of 871 C (1600 F) to 1010 C (1850 F). Similarly, the use of high-alloy castings enables turbine engines to operate at higher temperatures (and, therefore, at higher efficiencies) than weldments would permit.

Solution annealing of austenitic stainless steels minimizes the risk of intergranular attack and stress-corrosion cracking. For stainless steel weldments that cannot be annealed and that are to be used in applications where either intergranular corrosion or intergranular stress-corrosion cracking is of concern, a quenching procedure can be used. In this procedure, the weld is rapidly quenched to prevent the precipitation of the chromium carbides. If the quenching procedure proves ineffective, either a

low-carbon or a stabilized stainless steel may be substituted, depending on the tensile requirements. Low-carbon stainless steels do not have tensile properties as high as those of either the standard or the stabilized stainless steels, particularly at elevated temperatures.

Selection of the proper alloy and product form requires a complete knowledge of the operating conditions, including chemical environment, and operating temperatures and stresses. Sometimes, intermediate stages of chemical reactions produce an environment that will cause failure of an alloy shown by laboratory testing to be resistant to the initial components and the end products. Thus it is advisable to field test where possible.

Useful guides in the selection of suitable materials to solve an existing corrosion problem include the references that discuss corrosion rates and types and the compilations of corrosion-rate data described under "Corrosion Rates and Corrosion Types" on page 171 in this article.

Accelerated and simulated-use testing, electrochemical testing and laboratory corrosion tests (see pages 170 and 171 in this article) are more definitive guides in material selection; monitoring in actual field service is often used to confirm the results of these tests.

Use of Resinous and Inorganic-Base Coatings

Acrylics, epoxies, phenolics, furanes and urethanes are used extensively for corrosion protection in the form of paints, potting compounds, adhesives, coatings and linings. Their chemical resistance makes them suitable for many applications.

However, especially for fairly corrosive immersion service, consideration must always be given to the possible presence of pinhole porosity in paint-type coatings, which may result in pitting and crevice corrosion, and to the possibility of accelerated galvanic attack where dissimilar metals are present (see discussion under "Ratio of Cathode Area to Anode Area" on page 183).

The versatility these organic compounds have for being formulated for different methods of application (as liquids, as solids applied by bonding, and as powders that can be fused) permits their extensive use in protection of metal structures and equipment against corrosion.

Some important applications include the following:

1 Acrylic, epoxy, phenolic, furane and urethane primers and paints can be used to coat any metal for atmospheric protection.
2 Clear acrylics and urethanes are used to protect surfaces that must remain visible, such as nameplates and dials.

3 Thick, viscous epoxy coatings are used to embed delicate electrical connections in printed-circuit boards.

4 Sealant materials, if properly applied, are highly effective in preventing crevice corrosion; if not properly applied, they can make it more likely to occur.

5 Elastomeric or solid-form sheets of rubber, polypropylene, polyvinyl chloride and other resins are used for corrosion-protective liners or containers of almost unlimited size or shape.

Certain primers that form cross-linked polymeric films have superior adhesion and thus minimize local rusting and underfilm (filiform) corrosion.

Zinc-Rich Coatings. Organic and inorganic coatings containing zinc dust give excellent protection to steel and galvanized structures. They provide sacrificial protection because the zinc particles are in intimate contact with one another, so that the coating film is electrically conductive. This is achieved by very high zinc loading with a relatively small amount of binder (such as an ethyl silicate). In order to protect the steel, the coating itself must be in electrical contact with the substrate and not insulated by any rust, scale, old paint, or pretreatment chemicals. Sand blasting to produce a near-white surface is generally the preferred surface preparation.

As the zinc is sacrificed, zinc corrosion products in the form of efflorescing salts — commonly called "white rust" — appear on the film, making the coating thicker and reducing its electrical conductivity. These products of corrosion then act as a barrier between the active zinc and the corrodents. However, if the coating is damaged, the fresh zinc metal that is exposed provides renewed anodic action. Essentially, then, a zinc-rich coating is a "self-healing" film, since any damage to the barrier reinitiates the anodic action.

The inorganic vehicles used in these coatings are usually ethyl silicates, which are available in both solvent-reducible and water-reducible types. The organic vehicles used include chlorinated rubber, styrene, epoxies, phenoxies, urethanes and silicones.

In a seacoast environment, the performance of zinc-rich coatings in inorganic vehicles is far superior to that of zinc-rich coatings in organic vehicles. One disadvantage of the coatings that are based on inorganic vehicles is that they require more-critical surface preparation than those based on organic vehicles.

When zinc-rich coatings are used as primers for a top coat of an essentially pore-free resinous coating, the difference between the two types of vehicle becomes much less dramatic, and neither zinc-rich undercoat has much effect when a large break in the film occurs. Both organic and inorganic vehicles are effective in healing small, narrow breaks in the film, and in preventing underfilm corrosion.

Use of Inert Lubricants

Certain chemically inert resins (such as silicones, esters and fluorocarbons) can serve both as effective lubricants and as corrosion-resistant coatings and linings. In seacoast environments, lubricants frequently must perform this dual role of lubrication and corrosion protection. The role of corrosion protection is often overlooked when selecting a lubricant for a specific function, as for wire rope on exposed sliding surfaces.

In a lubricant-testing program at an aerospace facility, 45 oils and greases of widely varying composition were evaluated for effective lubricity, corrosion protection, and conformance to specifications. Most of the lubricants performed satisfactorily except in providing corrosion protection. A total of four corrosion tests were performed in this program: (*a*) the bearing-in-the-bottle test (ASTM D1743), (*b*) 2541 hr in a humidity cabinet, (*c*) 1003 hr in a 5% salt-fog environment, and (*d*) a one-year exposure on a seaside test rack. The most severe of these tests was exposure on the seaside test rack. Some of the results of this test are described below:

Specialized Inert Lubricants. The highly specialized inert lubricants required by gaseous and liquid oxygen systems and by hypergolic systems (systems of two components that react explosively on contact) offered little corrosion protection to carbon steel test panels. This was probably caused by failure to include effective inhibitors in these lubricants for fear of sensitizing the lubricants to oxygen or hypergolics. However, one such grease, when provided with an organic-base inhibitor (in an amount less than 0.5%) that did not compromise the inertness of the grease to oxygen, performed quite well in the seaside corrosion test by protecting the carbon steel panel for a full year, permitting only minor corrosion.

Conventional petroleum-base lubricants varied widely in the seaside-exposure test. However, it was found that earth-gel-thickened greases performed very poorly in this test, possibly because the earth gel may be capable of transporting moisture and contaminants to the surface of the metal through the oil film. This was found to be true for greases based on petroleum oils, polychlorotrifluoroethylene oils, or silicone oils.

Thickened Greases. Some of the more effective corrosion-preventing greases were those thickened with lithium soaps, alkyl ureas, or organic polymers. Greases containing graphite or molybdenum disulfide varied widely between affording protection and accelerating corrosion, depending almost entirely on the effectiveness of the inhibitor.

Polychlorotrifluoroethylene lubricants must be employed with extreme caution, because they can detonate when in contact with aluminum or magnesium subjected to shear stresses.

Use of Electrolytic and Chemical Coatings and Surface Treatments

The major types of electrolytic and chemical coatings and surface treatments include anodizing, chemical conversion coatings, and passivation treatments. These processes vary widely in their effectiveness in protecting treated metals against corrosion. Anodic and chemical conversion coatings also serve as excellent bases for organic coatings.

Anodizing of aluminum and aluminum alloys provides effective protection in natural environments, but not against aggressive environments, especially acidic and alkaline environments. Military specification MIL-A-8625C requires 336 hr of exposure in a 5% salt-spray test with no surface degradation. Unanodized parts would show severe degradation in this time period.

Most aluminum components for aircraft applications are anodized for added corrosion protection; the anodic coating also serves as an excellent base for paint. The sulfuric acid method should not be used on assemblies that can entrap liquids; the chromic acid method must be used on such assemblies.

Anodizing is also done on magnesium alloys. It has little protective value against corrosion, but provides an excellent base for corrosion-resistant paints and other resinous coatings.

Chemical Conversion Coating. Chromate conversion coatings are extensively used on steel products that have been electroplated with cadmium or zinc, and they substantially improve the corrosion resistance. Similar coatings are also produced by electrolytic processing, with the parts being made the anode in the electrolytic chromating bath. Chromate coatings, however, are very thin and can readily be removed by abrasion or impact. Local bare areas then may corrode preferentially.

Chromate, phosphate and other conversion coatings are also used on aluminum, magnesium, steel and other metals, but primarily as a base to improve the adhesion and protective value of organic coatings to be applied over them.

Passivation is common practice in the manufacture of stainless steel components and assemblies.

Stainless steels, whether martensitic, ferritic or austenitic, often show rust spots on the surface after exposure to humid conditions. This results from the embedding of small particles of iron or steel in the surface from cutting, machining, fabrication and handling. If the particles are not removed, the stainless steel is susceptible to local rusting and pitting in the presence of moisture or other electrolytes.

Passivation involves the removal of particles of iron or steel by chemical methods (pickling) or by mechanical methods, and permits the formation of a very thin but highly effective passive film on the stainless steel surface on exposure to a clean, dry atmosphere. Pickling must be followed by thorough neutralization, rinsing and drying.

Special chemical passivating treatments produce an effective passive film more rapidly than does exposure to the atmosphere. The complete absence of rusting after the treated metal has been exposed to moisture or high humidity for 24 hr is an indication that the passivating treatment was effective.

Use of Metallic Coatings

A wide variety of metallic coatings are applied, mainly by electroplating, hot dipping, electroless processes, and cladding. Selective brush plating, spray metallizing, vacuum deposition, gas plating, and cathode sputtering are also used. Selection of a coating process is based on the availability of equipment, the criticality of the particular part, and the over-all cost of the type of protection needed.

Electroplated Coatings. Electrodeposition of zinc or cadmium is widely used to protect steel from corrosion. Zinc provides better performance in industrial areas; cadmium is preferred for marine environments. These coatings offer sacrificial protection to the steel substrate and will minimize dissimilar-metal effects when the coated part is joined to aluminum or magnesium. Tin, nickel, chromium and copper are other metals that are readily applied by electroplating, but coatings of these metals are much less effective than sacrificial coatings in providing corrosion resistance.

The possibility of producing hydrogen damage (hydrogen embrittlement) must be considered in applying electroplated coatings, especially on high-strength steels. (For additional information, the reader is referred to the article on Hydrogen-Damage Failures, which begins on page 230 in this volume.)

Sprayed Metal Coatings. Metal spraying can provide thick protective coatings. Multiple coating minimizes, but does not completely eliminate, the occurrence of voids and weak spots in the coatings. Zinc and aluminum coatings are commonly used.

Cladding can provide thick coatings that are free of even fine porosity and, with suitable selection of the cladding metal, give more effective protection against corrosion of the base metal. Cladding is costly, however, and cannot be applied to parts of all configurations.

Use of Galvanic Protection

Galvanic protection can be either cathodic protection (in which the object to be protected is made cathodic) or anodic protection (in which the object to be protected is made anodic). The method most commonly used is cathodic protection.

Cathodic protection may be of two different types: impressed direct current, or sacrificial anode.

In the impressed-direct-current type, the structure to be protected is made the cathode in a direct-current electrical circuit. The anode in the circuit is an auxiliary electrode, usually of iron or graphite, located some distance away from the structure to be protected. The positive terminal of the source of direct current is connected to the auxiliary electrode, and the negative terminal to the structure to be protected. Current then flows from the electrode through the electrolyte to the structure, and the structure does not corrode. The applied voltage need only be high enough to supply an adequate current density to all parts of the structure to be protected. Soils or waters of high resistivity will require higher voltages than those with lower resistivity, and higher voltages will be required when anode spacing is increased in soil or water with a given resistivity.

In the sacrificial-anode system, the structure to be protected is made the cathode in a galvanic-corrosion cell, and current is supplied by the corrosion of anodes that are commonly made of zinc or magnesium. Voltage and current are limited by the corrosion of the sacrificial anodes; the number and location of anodes are much more critical in this method than in the impressed-direct-current method. Periodic anode replacement may be required where corrosion rates of the structure would be high without cathodic protection.

The choice of the system (impressed direct current versus sacrificial anode) depends upon a variety of factors, including availability of direct current, corrosion rate of the unprotected structure, ease of anode replacement, and total lifetime system cost.

Cathodic protection is used to protect metals such as steel, copper, lead and brass against corrosion in all soils and in almost all aqueous mediums. Cathodic protection is ordinarily used in conjunction with resinous coatings, which greatly reduce the area to be cathodically protected and the current required.

Cathodic protection cannot be used to avoid corrosion above the waterline, because the impressed current cannot reach metal areas that are out of contact with the electrolyte. Nor does the protective current enter electrically screened areas such as the interior of water-condenser tubes (unless the auxiliary anode enters the tubes), even though the water box may be adequately protected.

For buried pipelines, cathodic protection costs far less than any other means offering equal assurance of protection. Assurance that no leaks will develop on the soil side of a cathodically protected buried pipeline has made it economically feasible, for example, to transport oil and high-pressure natural gas across half the continent of North America.

Stray currents are frequently encountered problems in cathodic-protection systems. Figure 19(a) shows an arrangement in which stray currents were produced when the owner of a buried tank installed cathodic protection, not knowing of the presence of a nearby pipeline. The pipeline rapidly failed by corrosion because of the stray currents. If the pipeline had been cathodically protected, stray-current attack could have caused the buried tank to fail. The stray-current problem shown in Fig. 19(a) was corrected by electrically connecting the tank and the pipeline by an insulated buss connection, and installing a second anode, as shown in Fig. 19(b). Here, both pipe and tank were protected without stray-current effects.

Anodic Protection. By imposing an external potential to make them anodic, some metals can be prevented from corroding in an electrolyte in which they would otherwise be attacked. This technique, which is called anodic protection, is applicable only to metals and alloys that show active-passive behavior. It has been applied to iron, titanium, aluminum and chromium, but mostly to steel and stainless steel. Anodic protection is not applicable to zinc, magnesium, cadmium, silver, copper and copper-base alloys.

In anodic as in cathodic protection, the corrodent must be an electrolyte. The passive potential is automatically maintained, usually electronically, by a potentiostat.

The anodic technique has been used for protecting mild steel against uniform corrosion in NH_4NO_3 fertilizer mixtures, carbon steel in 86% spent sulfuric acid at temperatures up to 60 C (140 F), and carbon steel in 0.1 to $0.7M$ oxalic acid at temperatures up to 50 C (120 F).

Since passivity of iron and the stainless steels is destroyed by halide ions, anodic protection of these metals is not possible in hydrochloric acid or in acidic chloride solutions. Also, if Cl^- should contaminate the electrolyte, the metal may corrode by pitting. In the latter circumstance, however, it is only necessary to operate in the potential range below the critical pitting potential for the mixed electrolyte.

Titanium, which has a very noble critical pitting potential over a wide range of Cl^- concentration and tempera-

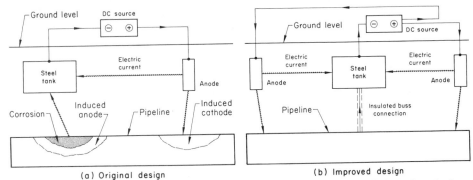

Fig. 19. (a) Original design of a cathodic-protection system for a buried steel tank that caused local failure of a nearby unprotected buried pipeline by stray-current corrosion. (b) Improved design; installation of a second anode and an insulated buss connection provided protection for both tank and pipeline, preventing stray currents.

ture, is passive in presence of Cl⁻ and can be anodically protected without danger of pitting, even in solutions of hydrochloric acid.

Current densities to initiate passivity are relatively high, but current densities for maintaining passivity are usually low. Corrosion rates are commonly in the range of 0.2 to 25 mdd.

Ability to maintain the desired potential accurately over the entire structure is very critical in anodic control. Fortunately, an anodic-protection system has high throwing power, and it is possible to protect quite complex structures with proper cathode placement. It is essential that the whole structure remain within the passive range. This may be difficult to achieve in deep crevices, and active corrosion could occur at the bottom of a crevice.

The cathode material must be one that does not suffer gross corrosion in the environment. A platinum-clad metal or a corrosion-resistant alloy is commonly used.

Operating costs for anodic protection are high, but they can be reduced by proper planning of the system and its operation. Once passivity has been achieved, it is often unnecessary to apply the current continuously. In some instances it may be possible to operate by applying the current for only about 1% of the time — 5 sec on, 500 sec off. In addition to saving power, this can be useful when there is more than one anodic protection system in the vicinity. By installing an automatic switching device, it is possible to protect two or more structures with one power unit.

The effect of agitation in anodic-protection systems is complex. In some systems agitation will lower current requirements by enhancing passivity, whereas in other systems it has the opposite effect.

The current required to maintain passivity is monitored during protection. A rise in the current shows that the corrosion rate is increasing and that corrective measures may be needed.

Applications of anodic protection have been simple (holding tanks), complicated (shell-and-tube heat exchangers), and novel (portable units for tank trucks and railroad cars).

Anodic vs Cathodic Protection. Anodic and cathodic protection tend to complement one another; each method has its advantages and disadvantages. Anodic protection can be used in corrosives ranging from weak to very aggressive; cathodic protection is restricted to moderately corrosive conditions because of its high current requirement, which increases as the corrosivity of the environment increases. Hence, it is not practical to protect metals cathodically in very aggressive mediums. Anodic protection, on the other hand, uses a very low applied current and can be utilized in strong corrosive mediums.

The installation of a cathodic-protection system is relatively inexpensive, because the components are simple and easily installed. Anodic protection requires complex instrumentation, including a potentiostat and reference electrode, and its installation cost is high. The operating costs of the two systems differ because of the difference in current requirements noted above. The throwing power of cathodic protection is generally low, thus requiring numerous closely spaced electrodes to achieve uniform protection. Anodic-protection systems have high throwing power; consequently, a single auxiliary cathode can be used to provide protection to extensive areas such as long lengths of pipe.

Anodic protection has two unique advantages. First, the current required is directly related to the rate of corrosion for the protected system. Thus, anodic protection not only protects but also offers a means for monitoring instantaneous corrosion rate. Second, operating conditions for anodic protection can be precisely established by laboratory measurements of polarization. In contrast, the operating limits for cathodic protection are usually established by empirical trial-and-error tests.

Design Changes for Corrosion Control

A simple change in design is sometimes the most appropriate way to eliminate a corrosion problem. Welded construction can eliminate the crevices normally found in bolted or riveted assemblies, thus preventing crevice corrosion. Modifying equipment to permit agitation of a mixture may prevent pitting attack under deposits that otherwise might settle out in a stagnant system.

The relocation of drain lines in such a way that complete drainage of a vessel is possible can eliminate pitting corrosion, which might occur in stagnant solutions.

When a solution containing dissolved ions that might cause corrosion at high concentrations is being heated, it is desirable to pass the solution through the tube side of the heat exchanger rather than the shell side. This procedure avoids possible concentration either in joints of tubes to tube sheets or in the vapor phase that usually exists in the shell side of heat exchangers even when special precautions are taken to eliminate it.

Drip lips on tank inlet lines are desirable so that any concentration of solutions (as by simple evaporation), which might cause corrosion, occurs on the extension of the inlet line rather than on the tank wall.

Cavitation, erosion, and impingement-corrosion problems can be minimized by providing for smooth flow of liquids or gases, without abrupt changes in direction or velocity. In some instances, it may be possible to transfer the corrosion to an acceptable location by a relatively simple design change, as in the following situation:

Frequent problems were encountered with rapid failure of the inlet line of a type 304L stainless steel continuous concentrator. The concentrator feed was 0.5M nitric acid containing approximately 10 grams per liter of a polyvalent metal ion; the concentration factor through the unit was approximately 10. The original inlet line, which was a simple flanged connection, failed by what appeared to be a combination of severe general corrosion and pitting attack that was limited to the first 6 to 12 in. of the line just ahead of the concentrator.

Corrosion tests revealed that the inlet line was the anodic member of a massive concentration cell made up of the solution circulating in the concentrator and the relatively dilute solution entering through the feed line.

It was decided to replace the entire unit with one made of titanium, but while the new unit was being fabricated a temporary correction was made. This consisted simply of extending the inlet line into the concentrator loop.

The severe concentration-cell corrosion then took place on the inlet-line extension, rather than on the inlet line itself. The unit performed satisfactorily under these conditions until it was replaced with the new titanium unit.

Redesign may lead to corrosion problems that were not previously present in the old equipment. The introduction of a stainless steel tank or agitator may cause galvanic corrosion of associated carbon steel components. The application of an organic coating on the interior of a carbon steel vessel may result in serious pitting problems at pinholes in the coating, whereas only mild general corrosion had been encountered before the coating was applied.

Occasionally, a change in design or materials for purposes of corrosion control may have serious effects that are not related to corrosion *per se*:

The material of construction of a concentrator handling a nitric acid solution was changed from type 304L stainless steel to unalloyed titanium because of corrosion problems with the stainless steel. No further corrosion problems were encountered with the unit, but the frequency of rejection of product batches because of excess silica content increased significantly, even though there was no significant increase in the silica content of the feed stream to the concentrator.

It was subsequently discovered that the silica in the feed stream deposited preferentially on the titanium surfaces and then broke loose, raising the silica content of a particular batch above the acceptable limit. No such deposition of silica had occurred on the stainless steel unit because the general corrosion rate before changing the material was such that the substrate metal was being continually but slowly dissolved.

Changes in design may necessitate a change in materials. For example, a decision to replace an existing shell-and-tube heat exchanger with a plate-type exchanger requires careful consideration. The plate-type exchanger has crevices, is highly stressed in the embossed areas, and is made of thinner material. Thus, materials that have been successful in the shell-and-tube exchanger may fail in the plate-type exchanger.

In other instances, a less expensive engineering material may give satisfactory life if design is revised to eliminate features such as crevices, pockets where scale or mud can accumulate, condensation points, areas of high velocity, phase separations within a vessel, and high stresses such as those imposed by improperly designed supports. A material may be satisfactory for a tank but fail as a heating coil because of the hot-wall effect. A pump may have an impeller made of a different alloy from that of the pump casing because of velocity effects. Here the engineer must consider the possibility of galvanic corrosion.

In making design changes to solve a corrosion problem, consideration must be given to the mechanical properties of the material involved as well as to the chemical resistance of the new material in the existing chemical environment.

Use of Inhibitors

Inhibitors, which are chemical substances added to a liquid (usually water or an aqueous solution) to prevent corrosion or to control it at an acceptably low rate, are used mainly in closed or recirculating systems. They are selected for their effectiveness in protecting the specific metal or combination of metals in a given system (for a list of inhibitors used to protect various metals in a variety of environments, see M. G. Fontana and N. D. Greene, "Corrosion Engineering", McGraw-Hill, 1967, p 200-202).

Inhibitors that function by stifling the anodic corrosion reaction are called anodic inhibitors; those that function by stifling the cathodic corrosion reaction are called cathodic inhibitors.

Anodic inhibitors may be divided into two types, oxidizing and nonoxidizing.

Inhibition by oxidizing inhibitors is not a direct function of oxidizing power. Thus, on steel, chromates and nitrites act in the absence of oxygen; molybdates and tungstates are effective as inhibitors only in the presence of air; and pertechnetates are good inhibitors at concentrations as low as 5 to 10 ppm, although permanganates have little inhibitive action.

Anodic inhibitors stifle the anodic reaction, usually forming sparingly soluble substances as adherent protective films. There often is no change in the appearance of the metal, although it carries a very thin film that may be isolated by the use of special techniques.

Salts such as hydroxides, silicates, borates, phosphates, carbonates and benzoates are effective on steel only in the presence of dissolved oxygen. The maintenance of inhibition by such materials is indicated by the more noble potential attained by the metal, which approaches that of the cathode.

When present in insufficient amounts, anodic inhibitors, except benzoate, can be dangerous because they permit the formation of small anodic areas without appreciably decreasing the amount of metal dissolution, and thereby produce intense local attack.

Cathodic inhibitors stifle the cathodic reaction, either by restricting the access of oxygen or by "poisoning" sites favorable for cathodic hydrogen evolution. Cathodic inhibitors that decrease the corrosive action of aqueous solutions on steel include salts of magnesium, manganese, zinc and nickel. The increase in alkalinity near the vessel walls by reduction of oxygen to OH^- leads to the precipitation of the hydroxides of these metals as a reasonably adherent porous deposit that retards the diffusion of oxygen to the steel.

The presence of calcium bicarbonate in water gives a general precipitate of calcium carbonate if the water is supersaturated, or gives a local deposit on or near cathodic areas where the pH is high. The addition of lime to water both raises the pH and serves as a cathodic inhibitor.

Cathodic inhibitors form a visible film on the metal, are not generally as efficient as anodic inhibitors, and do not completely prevent attack. On the other hand, cathodic inhibitors are less likely than anodic inhibitors to intensify attack if added in insufficient amounts. Many waters contain both magnesium and calcium salts as natural constituents with inhibitive possibilities.

Factors Affecting Inhibitor Systems. The successful application of inhibitors requires knowledge and understanding of their chemical behavior and of the corrosion processes in the system under consideration. A given substance may inhibit corrosion in one environment and increase it in another. The choice and concentration of inhibitor depend on the type of system, the composition of the water, the temperature, the rate of movement, the presence of residual or applied stresses, the composition of the metal, and the presence of dissimilar metals. The presence of natural crevices and loose scale and debris must also be taken into account.

Installations in which inhibitors are used vary from small, closed systems using recirculated water to large cooling systems using more than a million gallons of water per day. On economic grounds alone, the choice of inhibitor in large installations is relatively restricted. The concentration of inhibitor will, in general, be greater the higher the concentration of aggressive corrodents (such as chloride and sulfate) that interfere with the formation and maintenance of a passivating film on the metal.

Selection of Inhibitors. In choosing an inhibitor, the corrosion engineer must consider the difference in behavior of "safe" and "dangerous" inhibitors. Safe inhibitors reduce the total amount of corrosion without increasing the intensity on unprotected areas; dangerous inhibitors produce increased rates of attack on unprotected areas. Intensification of attack by dangerous inhibitors can be caused by a number of factors: lack of sufficient inhibitor, the presence of enough chlorides and sulfates to prevent complete protection, and the presence of crevices and dead-ends into which renewal of inhibitor by diffusion is not rapid enough.

Anodic inhibitors are, for the most part, dangerous inhibitors. Cathodic inhibitors are generally safe, but zinc sulfate (for use with steel), in high enough concentrations, results in intensified attack along the waterline.

Effect of Velocity in System. The amount of inhibitor required depends on the velocity of movement of the water or solution and the relative ratio of volume of liquid to area of metal surface. The higher the velocity of movement, the thinner the diffusion boundary layer and the greater the amount of inhibitor reaching the surface. The over-all effect of increasing the velocity is the same as increasing the concentration of inhibitor.

In addition, moving water is less likely to deposit debris and screen the surface from the action of the inhibitor. Since inhibition is a dynamic process, the inhibitor, at least initially, is being consumed in building up the cathodic or anodic film. Hence, the safe inhibitor concentration is influenced by the ratio of volume of liquid to area of metal exposed.

Great care is needed in applying the results of laboratory tests to industrial equipment. Apart from the factors already mentioned, an increase in temperature and the presence of dissimilar metals both require an increase in inhibitor concentration.

The condition of the metal surface and its accessibility to the inhibitor are also of the greatest importance. In industrial equipment containing water or aqueous solutions, there usually are crevices or re-entrant corners at which the replenishment of inhibitor is slow. Good design can reduce these to a minimum, but some sites of this type may be unavoidable and should be considered when applying inhibition. A higher concentration of inhibitor is required if the surface is rough, has been sand blasted or is covered with grooves and scratches. The same applies to surfaces under stress or on which impurities that could cause galvanic effects are present.

Compatibility of inhibitors with the liquid in the system, and with non-metallic materials with which the liquid may be in contact, must also be considered. The presence of organic matter may lead to the rapid depletion of oxidizing inhibitors such as chromate, and bacteria may flourish in nitrite and phosphate solutions.

Changes in pH and Applied Potential

Other changes in environment to reduce corrosion rates are sometimes more convenient than the addition of inhibitors. Also, the presence of inhibitors cannot be tolerated in potable and some process waters or aqueous solutions. Changing the pH of the water or aqueous solution, in conjunction with the application of a suitable external potential (as discussed in the section "Use of Galvanic Protection" on page 196 in this article), is often helpful in reducing corrosion rates.

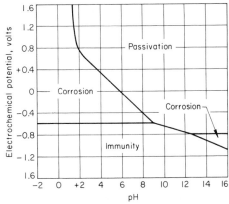

Fig. 20. Pourbaix diagram showing the theoretical conditions for corrosion, passivation and immunity of iron in water and dilute aqueous solutions

Pourbaix diagrams are sometimes used to provide guidance in making appropriate adjustments. These diagrams, which are derived from electrochemical measurements and thermodynamic data, are potential-pH diagrams that relate to the electrochemical and corrosion behavior of metals in water and in aqueous solutions.

Pourbaix diagrams show the conditions of potential and pH under which the metal either does not react (immunity) or can react to form specific oxides or complex ions. They do not provide information on rates of reaction.

Pourbaix diagrams indicate the conditions for which diffusion-barrier films may form on an electrode surface, but they provide no measure of how effective such barrier films may be in the presence of specific anions such as SO_4^{--} or Cl^-. Similarly, they do not indicate the detailed conditions under which non-stoichiometric metal compound films influence corrosion rates.

However, Pourbaix diagrams outline the nature of the stoichiometric compounds into which any less stable compounds may transform. They relate the possibility of corrosion to the pH of the corrodent and the potential difference between the pure metal and its ions in solution. They show under what pH-potential conditions corrosion might occur, and those under which it will not occur, thus providing guidance as to how corrosion can be minimized or avoided.

These diagrams are available for most of the common metals. A primary source is M. Pourbaix, "Atlas of Electrochemical Equilibria in Aqueous Solutions", Pergamon Press, New York, 1966. Additional diagrams and detailed discussions of the use of the diagrams can be found in current journals that deal with corrosion.

A Pourbaix diagram for iron in water and dilute aqueous solutions is shown in Fig. 20. Note that there are zones of corrosion, immunity from corrosion, and passivity.

Some metals besides iron for which Pourbaix diagrams have proved to be especially helpful include tantalum, titanium, aluminum and magnesium. The diagrams correlate well in a general way with the well-established facts that tantalum is relatively inert, titanium is resistant to a wide range of conditions, aluminum is amphoteric (and is attacked by acids and alkalis over a wide range of conditions), and magnesium is very active over a wide range of conditions.

Continuous Monitoring of Variables

Continuous monitoring of critical variables in both batch operations and process streams is a valuable tool in controlling the environment to avoid the development of unacceptably high corrosion rates. Some of the variables monitored and their applications are noted and described below.

Electrical Resistance (ER). Corrosion rate is indicated by the electrical resistance of wire made of a metal similar or identical to that present in the system. Electrical resistance (ER) has been used to indicate corrosion rates in liquid and vapor phases, but has a relatively slow response time. An example of the use of an ER probe would be in anhydrous hydrochloric acid in steel vessels. The presence of small amounts of water would increase the corrosion rate considerably, and an ER probe would indicate when a water leak has occurred.

Linear Polarization Resistance (LPR). Monitoring by LPR is based on the linear relationship that exists between a small amount of electrochemical polarization and the corrosion rate; the probe must be immersed in a conductive liquid phase. The LPR instruments have a relatively fast response time, and have been used in cooling-water systems to control the rate of inhibitor additions.

Electrical Conductivity. The corrosion rate of many metals in organic systems increases significantly if a corrodent is present and the electrical conductivity increases above 10^{-7} mho. Conductivity measurements have a very fast response time. They do not measure corrosion rates directly, but only changes in the properties of the environment. Conductivity gages have been used to monitor the presence of water in chlorinated hydrocarbons.

Continuous Chemical Analysis. Various types of instrumentation, such as infrared (IR), ultraviolet (UV), specific ion electrodes and gas chromatography, have been used to monitor or control the presence of various chemical substances in process streams. Measurements of pH would be included in this area. In some operations the amount of inhibitor added to a process batch or stream can be controlled by such instrumentation.

Temperature. Continuous monitoring and close control of temperature are readily done and are often needed to minimize corrosion.

Electronic Hydrogen Analysis. An electronic hydrogen probe can continuously monitor an environment that generates hydrogen by corrosion and be equipped to plot corrosion rate against time. A thin-wall probe made of the metal being monitored is connected to a getter-ion pump, which maintains a vacuum in the probe, into which some fraction of the corrosion-generated hydrogen diffuses. The pump current, which is proportional to the amount of hydrogen entering the probe, is monitored. The response time can be low enough that a change in corrosive conditions can be detected within a period of a few minutes. This technique has been used in the laboratory for hydrogen sulfide and oxygen corrosion research and inhibitor testing. It has been used in the field for monitoring corrosion of carbon and low-alloy steels in sour-gas pipelines, drilling mud, and refinery streams.

Carbon and Low-Alloy Steels

Carbon and low-alloy steels are ordinarily expected to corrode in service, and frequently fail from that cause. Uniform generalized corrosion can be predicted with reasonable accuracy in most systems and checked or monitored to prevent unexpected failures.

Pitting. The most common form of premature failure encountered in the carbon and low-alloy steels is pitting corrosion. Any condition that removes the moderately protective oxide film normally present on these materials may allow pitting corrosion to occur. Pitting rates under the least damaging conditions are usually about ten times the normal corrosion rate of the metal, and may be as high as 100 to 1000 times the uniform generalized corrosion rate.

On bare metal surfaces, there are three means of minimizing pitting attack: frequent cleaning, inhibition, and galvanic protection. A clean surface is much less likely than a contaminated surface to develop pitting attack, because there is free access of oxygen to a clean metal surface for the repair of ruptures in the oxide film. Also, there is little opportunity for formation of a small anode beneath a deposit while the remaining surface acts as a large cathode that intensifies the corrosion by galvanic action. The use of frequent cleaning to combat pitting corrosion is limited to surfaces that are accessible at suitable intervals for cleaning in some manner.

The use of inhibitors is limited to those systems for which an inhibitor compatible with the product is available, to closed systems, and to the use of specific inhibitors that can be disposed of or recovered economically from once-through systems. Poor control of anodic inhibitors can cause corrosion, instead of preventing it, with chromates being a prime example.

Galvanic protection can be either anodic or cathodic. The use of galvanic protection as a means of minimizing or preventing attack of steels by pitting and other forms of corrosion is described in this article under "Use of Galvanic Protection" (see page 196).

General Corrosion. Premature failure of carbon and low-alloy steels may occur from general corrosion in situations where the actual environment to which the material is exposed is significantly different from the environment in which it was designed to operate. While carbon steel exhibits a low corrosion rate in 100% sulfuric acid at ambient temperature, the rate increases very rapidly with dilution of the acid.

The rate of attack on iron and steel by nitric acid at concentrations of 70% by weight and higher is reported to be greater than 50 mils per year at room temperature (see Fig. 1), making it unsafe to ship or store the acid at any concentration in these metals. The rate of attack is increased by the presence of even low concentrations of nitrogen oxides in the acid.

In addition, differential aeration (see third and fourth paragraphs under "Concentration-Cell Corrosion", on page 180 in this article) causes concentration-cell corrosion just below the liquid level. On steel partly immersed in the acid, a vigorous self-accelerating attack has been observed to develop gradually at the liquid level in the presence of air.

Temperature Effects. Carbon steel may also show abrupt changes in corrosion resistance with increasing temperature and is susceptible to differential-temperature-cell attack in some applications (for example, in nonuniformly heated pipelines carrying 25 to 50% sodium hydroxide solutions).

Galvanic and stray-current corrosion accounts for a large number of failures of buried or submerged carbon and low-alloy steel components. Galvanic protection systems are usually employed in conjunction with heavy bituminous coatings to provide protection against breaks in the coatings (see the section "Use of Galvanic Protection" on page 196 in this article).

Importance of Oxide Film. Carbon and low-alloy steels are reactive metals on the thermodynamic scale and will corrode rapidly in the absence of the normally present thin film of iron oxide. Any conditions that prevent the formation and repair of this oxide film, or remove the film, can cause rapid corrosion of these materials.

Cast Iron

Cast iron varies greatly in its resistance to corrosion, depending on the type and composition of the metal and on the service environment. It is widely used in buried pipelines and in chemical-processing equipment.

Gray iron, particularly when exposed to underground corrosion or some other relatively mild form of attack, is subject to a selective process called "graphitic corrosion". The iron is selectively leached out, leaving a residue that has the shape of the original structure but the appearance of graphite and practically no mechanical strength. Superficial examination may not detect this situation, as in a gas or water pipe, and very hazardous circumstances may result. Details of graphitic corrosion are given on page 177 in this article. The interlocking network of graphite flakes retains its shape and integrity, but only as long as the network interlocks.

Malleable and Ductile Irons. When malleable and ductile irons corrode, both the graphite and the matrix are swept away by erosion-corrosion attack (see Example 8). Pearlitic malleable iron is more resistant to erosion-corrosion than ferritic malleable iron.

Cast iron equipment is sometimes used in chemical processes because of its low cost even though the corrosion rate is very high. Large gray iron kettles (8 in. in wall thickness) have been used in producing hydrochloric acid from the reaction of sulfuric acid with sodium chloride even though the corrosion rate exceeds 4 in. per year. Other materials of construction also have high corrosion rates in this application and are considerably more expensive.

High-silicon cast iron is used in a wide variety of highly corrosive chemicals, including sulfuric acid, hydrochloric acid, and hydrochloric acid plus oxidizing salts. (One notable exception is hydrofluoric acid, in which it is attacked at a substantial rate.)

High-silicon cast iron is one of the most universally resistant of the commercial (nonprecious) metals and alloys. However, it is very brittle, which limits its use in some equipment or requires special precautions to avoid severe impacts.

High-nickel cast irons, such as Ni-Resist austenitic iron, have been used to solve problems of severe corrosion and erosion-corrosion in pumps and related equipment exposed to seawater. Several compositions of high-nickel cast irons are described in ASTM A436-63.

Stainless Steels

The most important aspect of the corrosion of stainless steels is that they owe their corrosion resistance to a film of chromic oxide less than about 100 angstroms thick. In the absence of this oxide film, stainless steels corrode at rates comparable to those for carbon steels. Two of the major aspects of the corrosion-related behavior of the stainless steels are stress-corrosion cracking, which is discussed in another article in this volume (see page 205), and the closely related phenomenon of intergranular corrosion.

General Corrosion Behavior. The entire class of stainless steels is quite similar in general corrosion behavior. At chromium contents below about 12% the corrosion resistance is generally like that of other alloy steels. However, chromium content above about 13% makes these alloys resistant to attack by most mild corrodents and prevents rust in moist air.

The corrosion rate in aggressive corrodents such as nitric acid is reduced rapidly as the 13% Cr level is exceeded, but then declines more slowly until a content of about 18% Cr is reached; at this point there is another large reduction in corrosion rate in aggressive corrodents.

In general, stainless steels pit in halide solutions, corrode in a uniform manner in hydrochloric and sulfuric acids, and (if sensitized) corrode intergranularly in oxidizing acids such as nitric acid, but there are exceptions. The addition of 1 gram per liter of CrO_3 to a boiling solution of nitric acid will increase the corrosion rate of an 18 Cr – 8 Ni stainless steel by a factor of about 100, while the addition of about 1% nitric acid to a boiling solution of sulfuric acid will reduce the corrosion rate by a factor of about 100.

Pitting attack of stainless steels is a major problem and results from localized breakdown of the oxide film.

Pitting failures of stainless steels occur most frequently in heat exchangers operating in seawater, brackish water, or acid-polluted water. Usually, the unit appears to operate satisfactorily until one or more pumps are shut down and some area of the exchanger goes stagnant. Shortly after returning to operation, multiple tube leaks are a common occurrence, and the mode of corrosive attack is almost invariably pitting. Two cardinal rules for operation of stainless steels in salt water are to keep surfaces clean, and to keep the water moving.

Sensitization. A serious problem encountered with stainless steels is sensitization (see discussion on page 177 in this article), which makes them susceptible to rapid intergranular corrosion in certain environments in which they would be expected to be immune, and which occurs as a result of improper heat treating or welding.

In stainless steels in the as-welded condition, this attack occurs in a limited area within the heat-affected zone because of

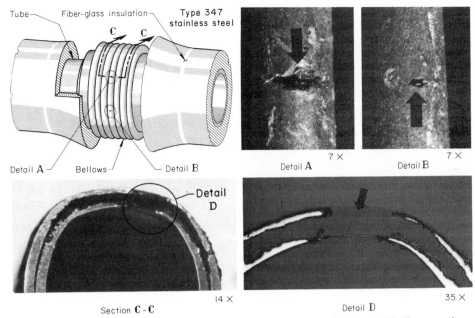

Fig. 21. Airplane air-duct assembly in which the type 347 stainless steel bellows section failed from corrosion because of decomposition of a phenolic binder in fiber glass used for insulation. Details A and B show corroded areas of the outer surface of the bellows, and pitting perforations (arrows). Section C-C shows fissuring of the bellows walls and extensive attack between them. Detail D shows more clearly the fissuring (arrow) and extensive attack exhibited in Section C-C. (Example 12)

loss of chromium level in the grain-boundary material by precipitation of chromium carbides. This form of attack can also occur if a component is heated in the temperature range of about 550 to 850 C (1000 to 1550 F), but the attack will be distributed uniformly over the heat treated surface.

All sensitization can be eliminated by solution heat treating at 1050 to 1100 C (1920 to 2010 F) and cooling rapidly; and sensitization associated with welding can be eliminated by using a low-carbon alloy such as type 304L or a stabilized alloy such as type 347.

Types of Preferential Attack. Another form of sensitization-related corrosion occasionally encountered in as-welded type 347 is known as knifeline attack. In this form of attack, a very thin layer of metal immediately adjacent to the fusion line of a weld is preferentially corroded in an intergranular manner. In addition to knifeline attack, type 347 also shows preferential corrosion at the stopping point of weld beads (crater corrosion), and end-grain corrosion, with all three types of attack usually occurring only in strongly oxidizing environments.

Knifeline attack can be eliminated by reheating the weldment to a temperature of about 1060 C (1940 F) and then quenching. No heat treatment is known to eliminate the end-grain attack on type 347, or on types 304 and 316, which also are susceptible to this form of corrosion. End-grain attack can be avoided by not exposing the ends of bar stock or tubing, or the parting lines of forgings, to corrodents. When a design cannot accom-

plish this, the exposed ends should be fused with a gas tungsten-arc welding torch, or covered with weld-metal deposit.

Severe general corrosion, when encountered at ordinary temperatures in stainless steels, suggests the presence of either hydrochloric or dilute sulfuric acid. Very low concentrations of these acids cause severe attack in the absence of an oxidizer, such as nitric acid.

Severe general intergranular attack can occur in noncorrosive environments if grain-boundary diffusion of readily soluble elements such as sulfur has occurred at high temperatures during the fabrication process.

Leaching of Corrodents From Coverings. Stainless steels are susceptible to pitting and crevice corrosion in environments containing moisture and halides. The mechanism of attack is the same, with the pits or crevices becoming anodic to the larger cathodic open surface. In the two examples that follow, the extraction of chlorides from insulating material covering the metal was the cause of failure by pitting. In the first of these examples, the chlorides were produced by thermal decomposition of the phenolic resin binder in fiber-glass insulation.

Example 12. Corrosion of Type 347 Stainless Steel From Decomposition of Phenolic Binder in Fiber-Glass Insulation (Fig. 21)

Leakage was detected in an air duct (Fig. 21) during a leak test. The part was installed on an airplane that had a reported operating time of 1224 hr. The welded duct assembly contained three double-wall bellows made of type 347 stainless steel, two of which were covered with insulating fiber glass. The third bellows joint was not covered. The remainder of the assembly was type 321 stainless steel tubing, all of which was covered with fiber-glass insulation. The insulating material was MIL-B-5924.

The duct was sent to the laboratory to determine the cause of leakage.

Preliminary Examination. The insulation was split longitudinally and opened to expose the entire duct assembly. The bellows joints and tubing that had been covered with the fiber glass showed extensive general corrosion and severe pitting; the bellows that had not been covered by insulation was free from corrosion. Close examination of the duct disclosed perforations in the convolutions of the corroded bellows adjacent to a 90° bend; the perforations are shown at arrows in details A and B in Fig. 21. These were the origin of leakage detected during the test. There was extensive corrosive attack between the convolutions in the area of the perforations.

Microscopic examination of sections through the bellows revealed (besides the perforations) corrosion pitting that almost completely penetrated the 0.005-in.-thick outer convolution, fissuring on the outer surface, and extensive attack between the bellows walls such as is shown in section C-C and at arrow in detail D in Fig. 21. There was no surface attack on the inner surface of the bellows; the perforations and pitting all originated on the outer surface.

The microstructure of the stainless steel in the bellows was satisfactory.

Chemical Analysis and Tests. Chemical analysis showed that the composition of the bellows material was normal for type 347 stainless steel. Chemical tests disclosed the presence of water-soluble chloride ions in the fiber-glass material. The absence of magnesium ions, which are always present in seawater, eliminated the possibility of chloride contamination of the insulation by the marine environment.

Discussion. Only those sections of the duct that were covered with fiber-glass insulation experienced corrosion.

Investigation revealed that the fiber glass contained a resin binder that was manufactured by a reaction between phenol and formaldehyde usually in the presence of a hydrochloric acid catalyst. The finding of chloride ions in the binder indicated that some of the catalyst could have entered into the reaction mixture.

Because the binder decomposes at temperatures above 230 C (450 F), the recommended maximum temperature for the fiber glass was 230 C (450 F); in operation, temperatures of the duct ranged from 230 to 340 C (450 to 650 F).

Based on the above characteristics of the fiber glass, it appeared likely that corrosion occurred in the following manner:

1 The phenolic-resin binder provided a source of water-soluble chloride ions.
2 The chloride ions combined with water from condensation associated with intermittent elevated-temperature operation.
3 The aqueous chloride solution, confined by the insulation cover, caused general corrosion of the stainless steel duct.
4 Chloride-ion concentration, subsequent hydrolysis and acid formation probably accelerated attack and pit growth.
5 Decomposition of the phenolic binder at

temperatures above 230 C (450 F) most likely resulted in such by-products as phenol, formic acid and formaldehyde that, in combination with the chlorides, contributed to the corrosion.

Laboratory corrosion testing was conducted to verify the apparent mechanism of attack. A new, uncorroded type 347 stainless steel bellows was sectioned longitudinally. One half of the bellows was immersed in an aqueous solution prepared with chlorides extracted from a new, unused piece of MIL-B-5924 fiber glass; the other half was immersed in distilled water as a control. Both samples were subjected to heating and cooling cycles in a beaker capped with a steam-condensing system. The samples were examined periodically for evidence of corrosion. After six days, the sample in the chloride solution showed general surface corrosion; the control sample was free from attack. At this point, testing was discontinued.

Conclusions. Water-soluble chloride ions, provided by decomposition of the phenolic-resin binder in the fiber-glass insulation at the normal operating temperatures of 230 to 340 C (450 to 650 F), were primarily responsible for surface corrosion and pitting of the stainless steel duct and tubing.

Recommendations. All stainless steel ducting that was insulated with MIL-B-5924 fiber glass should be inspected for general corrosion and corrosion pitting. Replacement of excessively corroded ducting should be done at the earliest opportunity.

The use of MIL-B-5924 insulating fiber glass on high-temperature stainless steel ducting should be discontinued because: (a) the phenolic binder provides a source of corrosive water-soluble chloride ions, and (b) the binder breaks down above 230 C (450 F), producing corrosive decomposition products.

Corrective Measure. The use of a fiber glass with a silicone-resin binder that is stable at temperatures above 370 C (700 F) was adopted for high-temperature applications with good results.

In the next example, glass-wool insulation that did not contain a resinous binder, but that was exposed to high temperatures in service, released hydrochloric acid and caused failure.

Example 13. Failure of a Stainless Steel Hot-Air Line Because of the Release of Hydrochloric Acid From Glass-Wool Insulation at 370 C (700 F)

A stainless steel hot-air line was removed from service in an aircraft because of pitting and rusting of the exterior surface over most of the areas covered by glass-wool thermal insulation. The line was made from 0.040-in.-wall, 2½-in.-OD type 321 stainless steel welded tubing.

Preliminary Examination. Inspection of the tube at magnifications of 10 and 40 diameters disclosed fissuring and pitting of the tube wall. Rusting was general near the welded seam and was found in scattered spots up to ⅛ in. in diameter over most of the remainder of the surface. Spot tests indicated the presence of chloride ions and scattered areas of acidity but revealed no other elements that would be indicative of exposure to seawater.

Testing and Analysis. The composition and microstructure of the line were normal for type 321 stainless steel. A sample of the glass-wool insulation removed from the corroded line was tested and found to contain chloride ions. Another sample showed a chloride-ion content of 0.33% on extraction with dilute nitric acid.

A nitric-acid-extraction test of unused insulation from stock yielded a negative result. Another sample from stock was slowly heated in a tube through which an air stream was passed. The volatile decomposition products from the insulation were absorbed in a dilute ammonia solution, which was subsequently found to contain chloride ions. A small quantity of moisture that had condensed at the outlet of the combustion tube proved to be strongly acidic.

Conclusions. The following conclusions may be drawn concerning the cause of failure:

1 The failure of the stainless steel hot-air line was caused by corrosion by hydrochloric acid and water that were evolved from the thermal insulation.
2 The glass-wool insulation released hydrochloric acid only when heated. Because the hot-air line reached a temperature of 370 C (700 F) in service, adequate heat for release of chloride ions was available.
3 The source of the chloride ions was probably a chlorinated compound used in the glass-wool finish.

Remedial Action. It was recommended that only chloride-free insulation be used for the hot-air lines.

Hot-Salt Corrosion. At elevated temperatures, the stainless steels are subject to what is called "hot-salt corrosion". This is a rapid, localized but uniform corrosion attack caused by molten salts that act as a flux, continuously removing the protective oxide film. One aggressive mixture that has caused problems with jet-engine components is made up primarily of sodium sulfate contaminated with sodium chloride. Solutions to a hot-salt corrosion problem are to eliminate the corrodent, to change the material to one resistant to such attack, or to apply a resistant coating.

Heat-Resisting Alloys

Heat-resisting alloys include several groups: (a) solid-solution nickel-base alloys, (b) precipitation-hardenable nickel-base alloys, (c) iron-nickel-chromium and iron-chromium-nickel alloys, and (d) cobalt-base alloys.

Hot Corrosion. One problem peculiar to heat-resisting alloys in many applications is "hot corrosion"; this term refers to any corrosion behavior in which the rate of attack is significantly accelerated over and above that expected from oxidation. Difficulties from hot corrosion have been experienced in gas turbines and jet engines (particularly those operating in marine atmospheres) and in petroleum-refining and petrochemical equipment.

The two most common types of hot corrosion are vanadium corrosion and sulfidation; both originate in impurities in the petroleum-base fuel or feed stock. In both types, the impurity results in molten compounds on the metal surface. If vanadium is present, V_2O_5 or complex sodium vanadates ($nNa_2O \cdot V_2O_5$) or sodium vanadylvanadates ($nNa_2O \cdot V_2O_4 \cdot mV_2O_5$) may form. If sulfur is present, the deposit depends on the source of sulfur and operating conditions. For turbines operating on "sour" (high-sulfur) fuel in salt air, the result is Na_2SO_4.

In both of these types of hot corrosion, the threshold temperature for damage corresponds fairly well to the melting point of the compound. The molten compound fluxes, destroys or disrupts the normal protective oxide. In petroleum processing, such as cracking and reforming, sulfur may be present in the feed in many forms, including organic sulfur compounds and hydrogen sulfide. The damage mechanisms in such cases are often analogous to oxidation, but are much more rapid because mass transport is much more rapid through sulfide scales, which are not very protective.

Remedial measures for hot corrosion consist of (a) the elimination whenever possible of the impurities in fuel or feed; (b) limiting operating temperatures; (c) selection of more-resistant alloys; and (d) the use of protective coatings. High-chromium stainless steels and aluminum diffusion coatings have met with some success where hydrogen sulfide is the problem; in turbines and aircraft applications in general, aluminum coatings over a Ni-Al-base layer are used to minimize or prevent sulfidation corrosion. The main method of coping with vanadium corrosion is to avoid using vanadium-bearing fuel in turbines operating above the threshold temperature.

Behavior at Room Temperature. The heat-resisting alloys as a group have excellent corrosion resistance at ordinary temperatures, and suitably resistant alloys for even the most aggressive environment at room temperature and moderately elevated temperatures usually can be found among them.

Aluminum and Aluminum Alloys

Aluminum and aluminum alloys develop a protective oxide film that, in most atmospheric exposures, prevents or retards corrosion. However, this film, like most surface coatings, is often not complete in its coverage. In seacoast areas where salt-water deposits occur, localized corrosion of aluminum will occur at small breaks or defects in the protective film, and this localized corrosion may result in the development of large pits. Pitting is a characteristic form of corrosion in aluminum alloys, as is its related form, crevice corrosion. Crevice corrosion occurs at laps, seams, and between faying surfaces, where the access of oxygen is restricted. Both pitting and crevice corrosion can result in severe localized metal removal, and thus in structural damage.

The seacoast environment also contributes to the occurrence of stress-corrosion cracking among the heat treatable, high-strength aluminum alloys (see page 211 in this volume). A form of corrosion sometimes encountered in these alloys is exfoliation, which causes separation of layers in sheet, plate, forgings (see Example 22 on page 310), and extrusions. Exfoliation corrosion, which is relatively common in seacoast areas, begins at exposed edges, where residual stress promotes delamination. Accumulation of the voluminous corrosion products also serves to propagate exfoliation by a wedging action.

Galvanic corrosion, from the contact of aluminum alloys with more noble metals, can be very damaging structurally if salt is available to contribute to the electrical conductivity of moisture films in contact with the metal couple.

Corrosion control for aluminum alloys is best begun with alloy selection. If strength considerations permit, the strain-hardenable alloys of the 1100, 3000 or 5000 series should be utilized, because they are generally resistant to corrosion and almost nonsusceptible to stress-corrosion cracking. Among the heat treatable grades, alloy 6061 performs well. The methods used to minimize or prevent corrosion failures involve the application of surface treatments or coatings. These are of four general types: (a) cladding with a thin surface layer of almost pure aluminum, (b) anodizing to obtain a relatively thick surface layer of aluminum oxide, (c) treatment to obtain a surface layer of chemically combined corrosion-inhibiting compounds, and (d) paint systems (usually two or more coats) utilizing a zinc chromate primer. The selection of the most suitable protective system depends on the configuration of the part, on the alloy, and on the severity of the exposure.

Copper and Copper Alloys

Copper and copper alloys have excellent corrosion resistance in many environments. Copper forms many commercially useful alloys that differ widely in composition and hence in corrosion resistance; selection of the most suitable copper alloy for use in a specific application must be made with care.

Copper has good resistance to corrosion by sulfide-free hydrocarbons, dry gases and nonoxidizing acids and salts, but does not resist corrosion by oxidizing acids or salts, ammonia, and moist halogens or sulfides. Copper usually corrodes by general thinning (erosion-corrosion) and by pitting when exposed to wet steam traveling at high velocities or when exposed to fresh waters at velocities above 4 ft per second and to seawater at velocities above 3 ft per second.

Copper-zinc alloys have better physical properties than copper alone, and they are also more resistant to impingement attack; hence, brasses are used in preference to copper for condenser tubes. Among the brasses, resistance to impingement attack increases with the zinc content of the alloy.

Corrosion failures of brasses usually occur by selective leaching (dezincification), pitting and stress-corrosion cracking.

Cartridge brass, 70% (copper alloy 260), which is used where easy machining and casting are desirable, gradually dezincifies in seawater and in soft fresh waters. This tendency is retarded by the addition of 1% Sn, the resulting alloy being called admiralty metal. The addition of 0.02 to 0.10% arsenic, antimony or phosphorus (inhibited admiralty metal) further retards the rate of dezincification and permits the use of these alloys in condenser tubes.

In this application, conditions favoring dezincification are contact with slightly acid or alkaline water not highly aerated, low rates of flow of the circulating liquid, relatively high tube-wall temperatures, and permeable deposits or coatings over the tube surface.

Inhibited naval brasses, which contain a nominal 0.8% tin and 0.02 to 0.10% arsenic, antimony or phosphorus and have a higher zinc content than admiralty metal, are somewhat lower in resistance to impingement attack and dezincification. They are used in marine hardware, ship-propeller shafts, and condenser plates.

Aluminum bronzes have good resistance to erosion-corrosion and to stress-corrosion cracking, and can be used at elevated temperatures. Selection of alloy and sequence of mechanical working and thermal treatments must be made with care for good performance in exposure to steam. With inhibitors, aluminum bronzes have excellent resistance to brackish water, to clear and polluted seawater, and to many types of fresh water. These alloys are subject to biofouling, however, and therefore the water velocity should be kept above 5 ft per second.

Silicon bronzes are resistant to many organic acids and compounds, to dry gas and to a number of inorganic compounds. They have good resistance to both fresh and salt water, but they should never be used with ammonia, which induces stress-corrosion cracking.

Copper nickels contain iron to form protective films that improve the resistance to impingement corrosion.

Copper nickel, 10% (copper alloy 706), has been used for years by the power and marine industries. The alloy has excellent resistance to clean flowing seawater at velocities up to 8 ft per second and to brackish water at velocities up to 5 to 6 ft per second. It is extensively used in the food-processing industry and in the conversion of saline water. This alloy, like other copper alloys, is attacked by oxidizing acids and salts and by sulfur. It is subject to corrosive attack by pitting and general thinning.

Copper nickel, 30% (copper alloy 715), has excellent resistance to rapidly moving seawater and to many types of fresh water. The cooling-water velocities should be kept above 5 ft per second to avoid bio-fouling. It is widely used in the power and marine industries and for condenser service in naval use. It is used in oil refineries and in chemical plants for its high corrosion resistance. Copper nickel, 30%, is the most resistant of all the copper-base alloys to stress-corrosion cracking, but it can be corroded by general metal thinning and pitting.

Selective leaching of this alloy can occur under conditions of high heat flux in condensers when the water velocity is low (less than about 5 ft per second). In wet or dry steam at low velocity it usually corrodes at rates less than 0.1 mil per year. A modified copper nickel, 30%, containing about 3% chromium, is used where higher yield strength is required.

Erosion-Corrosion. The movement or turbulence of water at the inlet ends of condenser tubes frequently leads to localized corrosion, commonly called inlet-end corrosion, which is a form of erosion-corrosion. It results in clusters of deep pits, which are usually undercut on the downstream side and often take the shape of a horseshoe that surrounds a raised point of relatively unattacked metal. The attacked areas are usually bright and free from scale, corrosion products or other visible films.

The harmful effects of turbulence, aeration, and high velocity of the circulating water in promoting erosion-corrosion of the tube walls may be minimized by using copper nickels, limiting velocity to a relatively safe value, controlling turbulence, eliminating entrained or separated air, eliminating debris in the circulating water, and using plastic inserts at the inlet ends of tubes. The plastic inserts must be tightly fitted to the tubes in order to avoid the possible development of crevice corrosion.

Nickel and Monels

Nickel has the best resistance to strongly alkaline solutions of all the common metals, but it is readily attacked by strong oxidizers. It has good corrosion resistance in dilute nonoxidizing acids if the solution is deaerated, but it has poor resistance to complexing agents such as ammonia. Nickel is resistant to most waters, including seawater, but may pit deeply in stagnant waters or in the presence of biological fouling. Alkaline hypochlorites also pit nickel.

Monels have corrosion resistance similar to that of nickel in most environments. Monels are readily attacked by strong oxidizers and are corroded most rapidly in aerated solutions. Corrosion rates in aerated nonoxidizing acids may be over 100 times those in unaerated solutions. Monels are not resistant to strong hot caustic solutions or to ammonium hydroxide in concentrations greater than 3%.

Monels are resistant to flowing seawater and brackish water, but pit in stagnant waters. Both nickel and copper are selectively leached by various media. Oxidizing conditions, and exposure to ammonia, mercury, and sulfur or sulfur-bearing reducing environments at temperatures of more than about 315 C (600 F), should be avoided.

Titanium

Commercially pure titanium is outstanding among structural materials in its resistance at ordinary temperatures to strongly oxidizing acids, aqueous chloride solutions, moist chlorine gas, sodium hypochlorite, seawater, and brine solutions. It resists many other corrosive substances well enough to be used in contact with them. Titanium alloys generally are less resistant to corrosion than commercially pure titanium.

Titanium is corroded by hydrofluoric, hydrochloric, sulfuric, oxalic and formic acids, but attack may be inhibited by additions to the solution (except for hydrofluoric acid). When titanium is passivated (as is usual), it is the noble metal in a galvanic couple with all other structural alloys except the Monels and stainless steels.

Pure titanium is the preferred material of construction for much of the equipment built to handle industrial brines. It is used for pumps, piping, thermowells, heat exchangers, crystallizers, evaporators, condensers and many other items that are subject to the corrosive action of these brines.

Crevice Corrosion and Pitting. In brine solutions, however, titanium may suffer crevice corrosion and pitting at sufficiently high temperatures. In 50% sodium chloride solutions, the temperature threshold for pitting is between 126 and 131 C (258 and 268 F). Special titanium alloys have been developed that extend this temperature threshold for brine solutions to higher levels.

Crevice corrosion can occur where the pH of the solution in the crevice drops below 1.5 to 2.0, as can occur in cleaning titanium equipment with sulfamic acid solutions.

Cathodic attack of titanium may occur if it is coupled to a less noble metal and picks up hydrogen. When titanium is made the cathode in a reducing environment in which it has only marginal stability, hydrogen discharged on the surface destroys the thin protective film. The corrosion rates of both titanium and aluminum when coupled in dilute oxalic or sulfuric acids are accelerated. Titanium when made a cathode is also known to absorb hydrogen, forming a brittle hydride layer which spalls with time. Spalling of this hydride film on a corrosion coupon may appear at first glance to be due to direct dissolution, since the coupon loses weight.

Harmful Alloying Elements and Corrosive Substances. Some alloying elements affect the corrosion resistance of titanium alloys adversely. Iron is probably the most critical element. High iron content (over 0.20%) lowers the corrosion resistance to nitric acid. Multivalent oxidizing metallic ions are powerful inhibitors against corrosion of these alloys. Most other soluble ions either improve the corrosion resistance or have little effect.

However, concentrations of fluoride ions as low as 100 ppm significantly lower the corrosion resistance of titanium and its alloys, which are also attacked at significant rates by reducing acids and, at temperatures above 80 C (175 F), hot alkaline solutions.

Selected References

Comprehensive Reference Books

L. L. Shreir (Ed.), "Corrosion: Volume 1, Corrosion of Metals and Alloys; Volume 2, Corrosion Control", John Wiley & Sons, Inc., New York, 1963, 1117 pages and 869 pages, respectively

U. R. Evans, "The Corrosion and Oxidation of Metals", Edward Arnold & Co., London, 1960, 1094 pages; First Supplementary Volume, St. Martin's Press, New York, 1969

H. H. Uhlig (Ed.), "Corrosion Handbook", John Wiley & Sons, Inc., New York, 1948, 1188 pages (includes corrosion-rate data compilation)

General Reference Books

M. Henthorne, "Corrosion Causes and Control", Carpenter Technology Corp., Reading, Pa., 1972, 72 pages

H. H. Uhlig, "Corrosion and Corrosion Control", 2nd edition, John Wiley & Sons, Inc., New York, 1971, 419 pages

J. F. Bosich, "Corrosion Prevention for Practicing Engineers", Barnes & Noble, Inc., New York, 1970, 250 pages

M. G. Fontana and N. D. Greene, "Corrosion Engineering", McGraw-Hill Book Co., New York, 1967, 391 pages

F. L. LaQue and H. R. Copson, "Corrosion Resistance of Metals and Alloys", 2nd edition, Reinhold Publishing Corp., New York, 1963

Periodical Publications

Corrosion, National Association of Corrosion Engineers, Houston, Texas; monthly

Materials Performance, National Association of Corrosion Engineers, Houston; monthly

Corrosion-Rate Data Compilations

C. R. Southwell and J. D. Bultman, "Corrosion of Metals in Tropical Environments, Part 10 – Final Report of Sixteen-Year Exposures", NRL Report 7834, Jan 1975

N. E. Hamner (Ed.), "Corrosion Data Survey", 5th edition, National Association of Corrosion Engineers, Houston, Texas, 1974, 283 pages

I. Mellan, "Corrosion Resistant Materials Handbook", 2nd edition, Noyes Data Corp., Park Ridge, N. J., 1971

J. P. Polar, "A Guide to Corrosion Resistance", Climax Molybdenum Co., 1961, 270 pages

E. Rabald, "Corrosion Guide", 2nd edition, Elsevier Publishing Co., London, 1968

Discussions of Corrosion Phenomena Including Corrosion-Rate Data Compilations

C. R. Southwell *et al*, Corrosion of Metals in Tropical Environments, Part 9 – Structural Ferrous Metals 16-Years' Exposure to Sea and Fresh Water, *Materials Protection*, Vol 9, No. 1, 1970, p 14-23

C. R. Southwell *et al*, Corrosion of Metals in Tropical Environments, Part 8 – Nickel and Nickel-Copper Alloys 16-Years' Exposure, *Materials Protection*, Vol 8, No. 3, 1969, p 39-44

C. R. Southwell *et al*, Corrosion of Metals in Tropical Environments, Part 7 – Copper and Copper Alloys 16-Years' Exposure, *Materials Protection*, Vol 7, No. 1, 1968, p 41-47

C. R. Southwell *et al*, Corrosion of Metals in Tropical Environments, Part 6 – Aluminum and Magnesium, *Materials Protection*, Vol 4, No. 12, 1965, p 30-35

A. L. Alexander *et al*, Corrosion of Metals in Tropical Environments, Part 5 – Stainless Steels, *Corrosion*, Vol 17, 1961, p 345t

C. R. Southwell *et al*, Corrosion of Metals in Tropical Environments, Part 4 – Wrought Iron, *Corrosion*, Vol 16, 1960, p 512t

B. W. Forgeson *et al*, Corrosion of Metals in Tropical Environments, Part 3 – Underwater Corrosion of Ten Structural Steels, *Corrosion*, Vol 16, 1960, p 105t

C. R. Southwell, *et al*, Corrosion of Metals in Tropical Environments, Part 2 – Atmospheric Corrosion of Ten Structural Steels, *Corrosion*, Vol 14, 1958, p 435t

B. W. Forgeson *et al*, Corrosion of Metals in Tropical Environments, Part 1 — Test Methods Used and Results Obtained for Pure Metals and a Structural Steel, *Corrosion*, Vol 14, 1958, p 73t

Metal Corrosion in the Atmosphere, STP 435, ASTM, Philadelphia, 1968

Corrosion in Specific Applications

W. E. Berry, "Corrosion in Nuclear Applications", John Wiley & Sons, Inc., New York, 1971, 572 pages

Materials Performance and the Deep Sea (Symposium), STP 445, ASTM, Philadelphia, 1969

G. Butler and H. C. K. Ison, "Corrosion and Its Prevention in Water", Reinhold Publishing Corp., New York, 1966, 281 pages

A. H. Tuthill and C. M. Schillmoller, "Guidelines for Selection of Marine Materials", Ocean Science and Ocean Engineering Conference, Marine Technology Society, June 1965, International Nickel Co., Inc.

Corrosion of Various Metals

L. Colombier and J. Hockmann, "Stainless and Heat Resisting Steels", St. Martin's Press, New York, 1968 (translated by Scripta Technica, Ltd.; printed in Great Britain by Fletcher and Son, Ltd., Norwich, England)

H. Leidheiser, Jr., "The Corrosion of Copper, Tin, and Their Alloys", John Wiley & Sons, Inc., New York, 1971, 411 pages

H. Godard, W. B. Jepson, M. R. Bothwell and R. L. Kane, "The Corrosion of Light Metals", John Wiley & Sons, Inc., New York, 1967, 360 pages

J. G. Parr and A. Hanson, "An Introduction to Stainless Steel", American Society for Metals, Metals Park, Ohio, 1965, 147 pages

Special Topics Dealing With Corrosion

J. B. Mohler, Corrosion of Coated Metals, *Metal Finishing*, Vol 73, No. 4, 1975, p 33-35 and p 38 (first in a series of six articles on this subject)

F. H. Cocks (Ed.), "Manual of Industrial Corrosion Standards and Control", STP 534, ASTM, New York, 1974, 311 pages

W. H. Ailor, Jr., "Handbook on Corrosion Testing and Evaluation", John Wiley & Sons, Inc., New York, 1971, 873 pages

"Laboratory Corrosion Testing of Metals for the Process Industries", NACE Standard TM-01-69

R. M. Burns and W. W. Bradley, "Protective Coatings for Metals", 3rd edition, Reinhold Publishing Corp., New York, 1967, 735 pages

I. A. Levin, "Intercrystalline Corrosion and Corrosion of Metals Under Stress", Plenum Press, New York, 1962

Stress-Corrosion Cracking

*By the ASM Committee on Failure by Mechanical-Environmental Processes**

STRESS-CORROSION CRACKING is a mechanical-environmental failure process in which sustained tensile stress and chemical attack combine to initiate and propagate fracture in a metal part. Stress-corrosion cracking is produced by the synergistic action of sustained tensile stress and a specific corrosive environment, causing failure in less time than would the separate effects of the stress and the corrosive environment if simply added together.

Failure by stress-corrosion cracking frequently is caused by simultaneous exposure to a seemingly mild chemical environment and to a tensile stress well below the yield strength of the metal. Under such conditions, fine cracks can penetrate deeply into the part while the surface exhibits only faint signs of corrosion. Hence, there may be no macroscopic indications of an impending failure.

In addition to stress-corrosion cracking, there are several other processes that cause failure of metal parts by the conjoint action of mechanical stress and corrosion. These include hydrogen damage (hydrogen embrittlement), corrosion fatigue, liquid-metal embrittlement, and fretting, which are discussed in other articles in this volume.

Sources of Stresses in Manufacture

The principal sources of high local stresses in manufacture include (*a*) thermal processing, (*b*) stress raisers, (*c*) surface finishing and (*d*) fabrication.

Thermal Processing. One of the most frequently encountered sources of

*ROGER W. STAEHLE, *Chairman*, International Nickel Professor of Corrosion Science Engineering, Department of Metallurgical Engineering, Ohio State University; CHARLES H. AVERY, Chief Metallurgical Engineer, Truesdail Laboratories, Inc.; CEDRIC D. BEACHEM, Micromechanical Criteria Branch, Engineering Materials Div., Naval Research Laboratory; A. P. BOND, Research Supervisor, Climax Molybdenum Co. of Michigan; WALTER K. BOYD, Manager, Corrosion and Electrochemical Technology Section, Battelle – Columbus Laboratories; PHILIP J. CHARLEY, President, Truesdail Laboratories, Inc.; FRANKLIN H. COCKS, Associate Professor, Department of Mechanical Engineering and Materials Science, Duke University.

CARL J. CRON, Union Oil Research Center, Union Oil Co. of California; OWEN F. DEVEREUX, Associate Professor of Metallurgy, University of Connecticut; JOHN H. DUMBLETON, Associate Professor of Materials Science, Department of Materials Science and Metallurgical Engineering, University of Cincinnati; D. J. DUQUETTE, Associate Professor of Metallurgical Engineering, Rensselaer Polytechnic Institute; STEPHEN FLOREEN, Research Fellow, Paul D. Merica Research Laboratory, International Nickel Co., Inc.; LESLIE D. KRAMER, Advanced Materials Engineer, Steam Turbine Div., Westinghouse Electric Corp.; LOREN L. LANIER, Central Engineering Laboratories, FMC Corp.; DONALD O. SPROWLS, Section Head, Stress Corrosion Section, Chemical Metallurgy Div., Alcoa Laboratories.

EARL C. SUTHERLAND, Vice President, MEI-Charlton, Inc.; WILLIAM WIEBE, Senior Research Officer, Structures and Materials Laboratory, National Aeronautical Establishment, National Research Council, Canada; EDWARD A. DURAND, *Secretary*, Senior Editor, Metals Handbook, American Society for Metals.

thermal-processing stresses is welding. Shrinkage of weld metal during cooling, and the restraint imposed by the adjacent metal and by rigid welding fixtures, can produce residual tensile stresses as high as 30,000 to 40,000 psi. Other thermal-processing effects that often produce stresses during manufacture include solidification of castings (especially those having large differences in section thickness and those made with cast-in inserts) and improper heat treating practices (failure to preheat, when required; overheating during austenitizing or solution treating; failure to provide required temperature uniformity in furnaces; use of quenching practices too severe for a specific alloy or part shape; and undue delay in transferring workpieces from the quenchant to the tempering furnace).

Stress raisers that result from various types of deficiencies in manufacture often contribute to mechanical-environmental failures. Some common types of such stress raisers are: (a) geometrical stress raisers or notches related to design, (b) notches caused by accidental mechanical damage or electric-arc strikes, (c) cracks produced by incorrect heat treatment (such as quench cracks) or by deficiencies in welding and in associated preweld and postweld treatments, (d) inclusions and hydrogen blisters, (e) interfaces in layer-type bonded materials (applied by cladding, rolling, electroplating, spraying, brazing or soldering), (f) interfaces in case hardened steels, and (g) severe surface irregularities produced in grinding and rough machining.

Surface Finishing. Residual tensile stresses that are damaging or potentially damaging in conjunction with environmental attack are produced in many different types of surface-finishing treatments. These treatments include electroplating, electrical discharge machining and (under some conditions) conventional grinding and machining. When hydrogen is produced in the finishing process and diffuses into the metal, internal stresses can be produced.

Shot peening and surface rolling often are used to produce compressive stresses in metal surfaces, but the magnitude of stress imposed by peening is sometimes not great enough to overcome the effects of extremely high local tensile stresses.

Fabrication. High residual tensile stresses sometimes result from bending, stamping, deep drawing and other cold forming operations. Residual tensile stresses of 30,000 to 60,000 psi have been measured on the surfaces of cold bent steel tubes. Expansion rolling of boiler and heat-exchanger tubes into holes in the tube sheets produces tensile stresses that may be damaging (see Example 3 in this article). Another source of residual tensile stresses is straightening to remove deformation caused by heat treatment.

Under some circumstances, severe uniform cold working improves the resistance of a metal to stress-corrosion cracking. For example, cold drawn steel wire is more resistant to stress-corrosion cracking than is oil-tempered wire having equal mechanical properties. Also, cold reduction of low-carbon steel to 50% or less of its original thickness makes it relatively immune to cracking in boiling nitrate solutions at 100 to 200 C (212 to 392 F) for thousands of hours. (Use of cold reduction to improve resistance of silicon bronzes to cracking is described in Example 3 on page 287 in the article on Failures of Cold Formed Parts.)

Assembly. Fit-up and assembly operations often are sources of tensile stresses. Press fitting, shrink fitting and assembly by welding are among the major operations in this category. Dimensioning an interference fit so as to keep the amount of interference small is desirable in order to avoid creation of tensile stresses that could lead to stress-corrosion cracking, but this procedure makes the assembly likely to fail by mechanisms such as fretting, fatigue and corrosion fatigue; accordingly, a compromise in dimensioning often is the safest procedure. An interference fit of a bushing in a hole was the source of stresses that resulted in service failure by stress-corrosion cracking of a high-strength aluminum alloy part in a marine atmosphere (see Example 7 in this article).

Forming operations used in assembly to retain components can produce residual tensile stresses that can induce stress-corrosion cracking, particularly when the parts are used or stored in a corrosive atmosphere. In the following example, copper alloy ferrules that had not been stress relieved after drawing and were assembled in a fuse by crimping failed by stress-corrosion cracking.

Example 1. Stress-Corrosion Cracking of Copper Alloy 270 Ferrules in Storage and in Service in Chemical Plants

A substantial number of copper alloy 270 (cartridge brass, 70%) ferrules for electrical fuses cracked while in storage and while in service in paper mills and other chemical-processing plants. The ferrules, made by three different manufacturers, were of several sizes. One commonly used ferrule was 1⅜ in. long by 3 in. in diameter and was drawn from 0.020-in.-thick strip.

Investigation. Ferrules from fuses in service and storage in different types of plants, plus ferrules from newly manufactured fuses, were evaluated by visual examination, by determination of microstructure, by examination of any existing cracks, and by the mercurous nitrate test for copper and copper alloys (ASTM B154). This is an accelerated test to detect residual stress in copper and copper alloy stock and in fabricated parts that might bring about failure of the material by stress-corrosion cracking. Ferrules that had been stress relieved after

forming, but not assembled to fuses, passed the B154 test; similar unassembled ferrules that had not been stress relieved after forming cracked before the required 30-min immersion period was completed.

The mercurous nitrate test also showed that ferrules crimped to fuses were susceptible to cracking whether or not they had been stress relieved after forming. This last observation established that the crimping operation in assembly produced residual stresses, even on stress-relieved ferrules, that were high enough to make the ferrules susceptible to stress-corrosion cracking. The cracks introduced during forming that were found in ferrules on fuses in service or storage were of the multiple-branched type characteristic of stress-corrosion cracking. The higher incidence of cracking of ferrules in the paper mills was apparently related to a higher concentration of ammonia there, in conjunction with a humid atmosphere.

Conclusions. The ferrules failed by stress-corrosion cracking resulting from residual stresses induced during forming and the ambient atmospheres in the chemical plants. The humid, ammonia-containing atmosphere in the paper mills was the most detrimental.

Corrective Measures. The fuses were specified to meet the requirements of ASTM B154. The three manufacturers used different methods to solve the problem. One changed to copper ferrules and fastened them to the fuse tube with epoxy cement (copper has insufficient strength for crimping). Another changed the ferrule material to a copper-iron alloy. The third manufacturer began using copper alloy 230 (red brass, 85%) and subjecting the crimped ferrules to a stress-relief anneal using an induction coil, and made long-range plans to change to plated steel ferrules.

The use of pipe-threaded fittings in making connections to an aluminum alloy 2024-T431 valve body in a missile launch unit produced excessive stress in the threads and resulted in failure of the valve body by stress-corrosion cracking in a service environment of hydraulic fluid that contained small amounts of moisture and chloride. Similarly, stresses on tapered threads on a cast aluminum-zinc alloy connector exposed to a semi-industrial atmosphere caused failure by stress-corrosion cracking in less than one month. This connector had been overtorqued during tightening to seal the assembly for a preservice hydrostatic test. In both instances, the substitution of straight-threaded for pipe-threaded connections to reduce the stresses was one of the recommended corrective measures.

Sources of Stresses in Service

Stresses in addition to those that a metal part or assembly was designed to withstand are introduced in service in various ways. Of major concern in connection with failure by mechanical-environmental processes is the combined effect of stress raisers and environment.

Stress raisers frequently are introduced in service by damage from accidental mechanical impact or local electrical arcing. Stress raisers or notches also frequently result from local wear, fretting, erosion, cavitation and spalling.

Stress raisers also can result from any form of localized corrosion, such as pitting, selective leaching, intergranular attack, and concentration-cell, crevice, or galvanic corrosion. In Example 9 in this article, dezincification of copper alloy fittings provided stress raisers that led to failure by stress-corrosion cracking.

Environmental effects of various types introduce stresses in service. Exposure of metal parts to high and low temperatures, which often is accompanied by nonuniform heating rates and sharp thermal gradients, is a major source of stress in service.

In heat exchangers, for example, thermal gradients can create strains having equivalent elastic stresses ten to twenty times greater than residual or applied stresses. If the environment on the cold side of the heat exchanger is conducive to stress corrosion, these thermal stresses can produce cracking on this side. Because of the general distribution of the thermal stress, the result is extensive cracking and sometimes complete fragmentation.

In a type 321 stainless steel ammonia converter in which the temperature produced by the chemical reaction was 910 C (1670 F), the temperature of boiler feedwater in an integral cooling jacket surrounding the converter was 205 C (400 F). The water jacket had deaerator tubes at the top to remove any steam formed in the jacket, but the tubes did not have sufficient capacity to carry away all the steam formed in the jacket. The resulting accumulation created a steam pocket and a vapor-liquid interface at a level opposite the 910 C (1670 F) interior of the converter, and leaks developed at and near the level of the interface.

Removal and examination of portions of the wall in the damaged area revealed the presence of extensive stress-corrosion cracking that had completely penetrated the wall from the water side. The tensile stress on the water side of the wall at the vapor-liquid interface was calculated to be about 13,000 psi; the boiler feedwater in the cooling jacket contained 1 ppm or less of chlorides.

To correct the problem, it was recommended either that tail gas, which also required heating, be fed through the jacket instead of boiler water, or that the deaerator tubes be of a size to ensure flooding of the hot wall at all times.

Diffusion of carbon, gaseous carbon compounds, hydrogen, nitrogen, oxygen and other gases from the environment into the interior of metal parts also is a major source of stress in service.

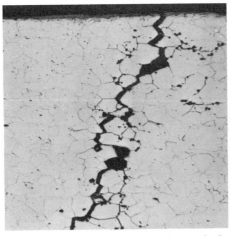

Fig. 1. Micrograph, at 100×, of an etched section through a sensitized specimen of type 304 stainless steel, showing intergranular stress-corrosion cracking produced at 82 C (180 F) in water containing 70 ppm of dissolved chlorides

The formation of corrosion products by local attack in confined spaces produces high stress levels in metals because the corrosion products occupy a larger volume than the metal from which they are formed. The wedging action of corrosion products in cracks and between tight joints in assemblies has been known to generate stresses of 4000 to 7000 psi and to initiate and propagate failure by mechanical-environmental processes. Where lamellar structures are subject to chemical attack, or where weak lamellar structures are subject to stress from entrapped solid or gaseous corrosion products, exfoliation occurs; blisters are produced by gaseous corrosion products entrapped locally just below the surface of a metal part.

Cyclic Stresses. The sources and effects of cyclic stress in service are described in the article on Fatigue Failures (pages 95 to 125 in this volume). The relation of cyclic stress to mechanical-environmental failure is discussed in the article on Corrosion-Fatigue Failures (pages 240 to 249).

Cyclic stresses of mechanical origin generally arise from rotary or reciprocating motion of mechanical devices, either from normal operation or from abnormal effects such as vibration and resonance. Other major sources of cyclic stresses in service are fluid-flow effects (including the von Karman effect and cavitation) and thermal effects.

Crack Initiation and Propagation

The site of initiation of a stress-corrosion crack may be submicroscopic and determined by local differences in metal composition, thickness of protective film, concentration of corrodent, and stress concentrations. A pre-existing mechanical crack or other surface discontinuity, or a pit or trench produced by chemical attack on the metal surface, may act as a stress raiser and thus serve as a site for initiation of stress-corrosion cracking. Laboratory investigation has shown that generally there is some localized plastic deformation before cracking occurs.

The tip of an advancing crack has a small radius, and the attendant stress concentration is great. Using audio-amplification methods, it has been shown in certain materials that a mechanical step or jump can occur during crack propagation. In fact, in one test (Ref 1), "pings" could be heard with the unaided ear. In this test, it was demonstrated that the action of both stress and corrosion is required for crack propagation. An advancing crack was stopped when cathodic protection was applied (corrosion was stopped, but the stress condition was left unchanged). When cathodic protection was removed, the crack again started to propagate. This cycle was repeated several times. In this test, the progress of the crack was photographed and projected at the actual speed of propagation.

The role of tensile stressing is important in rupture of protective films during both initiation and propagation of cracks. These films may be tarnish films (such as those on brasses), thin oxide films, layers richer in the more noble element of a binary alloy (such as a copper-gold alloy), or other passive films. Breaks in the passive film or enriched layer at various points on the surface initiate plastic deformation or incipient cracking.

Breaking of a film ahead of an advancing crack permits crack propagation to continue in the metal. Rapid local breaking of the film without particles of film filling the exposed crack is required for rapid crack propagation. Intergranular cracking occurs when grain-boundary regions are anodic to the main body of the metal, and therefore less resistant to corrosion, because of precipitated phases, depletion, enrichment, or adsorption.

General Features of Stress-Corrosion Cracks

Stress-corrosion cracks ordinarily undergo extensive branching and proceed in a general direction perpendicular to the stresses contributing to their initiation and propagation. Figure 1 shows intergranular stress-corrosion cracking in a specimen of sensitized type 304 stainless steel, which occurred at 82 C (180 F) in water containing 70 ppm of dissolved chlorides. (Compare this cracking with the randomly oriented intergranular attack on the nonstressed specimen of the same alloy shown in Fig. 6 on page 178.)

There are exceptions to the general rule that stress-corrosion cracks are branched. For example, some non-branched cracks have been observed along with branched cracks in structural steel exposed to contaminated agricultural ammonia (see Fig. 2).

The surfaces of some stress-corrosion cracks resemble those of brittle mechanical fractures although they actually are the result of local corrosion in combination with tensile stress. In some metals, cracking propagates intergranularly, and in others, transgranularly. In certain metals, such as high-nickel alloys, iron-chromium alloys, and brasses, either type of cracking can occur, depending on the metal-environment combination.

Features of stress-corrosion-cracked surfaces revealed by macroscopic and microscopic examination are discussed under "Macroscopic Examination" on page 215 and "Microscopic Examination" on page 216.

Theories of Stress-Corrosion Cracking

Several theories have been advanced to explain in detail the mechanism of stress-corrosion cracking. Two major theories are the electrochemical and stress-sorption theories.

Electrochemical Theory. According to the electrochemical theory, galvanic cells are set up between metal grains and anodic paths are established by heterogeneous phases. For example, the precipitation of $CuAl_2$ from an Al-4Cu alloy along grain boundaries produces copper-depleted paths in the edges of the grains. When the alloy, stressed in tension, is exposed to a corrosive environment, the ensuing localized electrochemical dissolution of metal, combined with localized plastic deformation, opens up a crack. With sustained tensile stress, protective films that form at the tip of the crack rupture, causing fresh anodic material to be exposed to the corrosive medium, and the stress-corrosion cracking is propagated.

Supporting this theory is the existence of a measurable potential in the metal at grain boundaries, which is negative (or active) with respect to the potential of the grains. Furthermore, cathodic polarization will stop the cracking.

This theory has been extended to include metals that do not form intermetallic precipitates, but for which phase changes or segregation of alloying elements or impurities can occur during the process of plastic deformation of metal at the crack tip, the resulting composition gradient then setting up galvanic cells.

Stress-Sorption Theory. According to the stress-sorption theory, stress-corrosion cracking generally proceeds by weakening of the cohesive bonds between surface-metal atoms through adsorption of damaging substances in the environ-

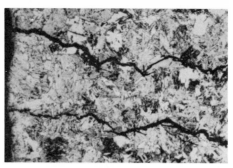

Fig. 2. Micrograph, at 75×, of a picral-etched specimen of structural steel that was exposed to contaminated agricultural ammonia, showing nonbranched stress-corrosion cracks

ment. Because chemisorption is specific, damaging components are also specific. The surface energy of the metal is said to be reduced, increasing the probability that the metal will form a crack under tensile stress. Adsorption of any kind that reduces surface energy should favor crack formation.

Only a monolayer of adsorbate is needed to markedly decrease the affinity of surface-metal atoms for each other or for atoms of substances in the environment. The only adsorbates presumed to be effective are those that reduce the attractive force of adjoining metal atoms for each other.

Inhibiting anions compete with particles of damaging substances for adsorption sites, thereby making it necessary to apply a more positive potential to the metal to reach a concentration of damaging substances that is adequate for adsorption and resulting cracking of the metal.

Special Characteristics of Stress-Corrosion Cracking

In extensive empirical investigations, several special characteristics of stress-corrosion cracking have been observed. Although the electrochemical and stress-sorption theories and modified versions of them generally are in accord with most of the facts, no single theory that has

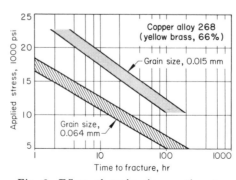

Fig. 3. Effect of grain size on time to fracture in ammonia atmosphere, for copper alloy 268 (yellow brass, 66%) at various values of applied stress (Ref 2)

been proposed to date completely explains all these special characteristics, which include the following:

1 Only certain specific environments contribute to this type of failure for a given metal or alloy, with no apparent general pattern.
2 Pure metals are much less susceptible to this type of failure than are impure metals, but pure binary alloys, such as copper-zinc, copper-gold and magnesium-aluminum alloys, generally are susceptible.
3 Cathodic protection has been successful in preventing initiation of stress-corrosion cracking and in stopping propagation of cracking that has already progressed to a substantial extent.
4 Addition of soluble salts containing certain specific anions can inhibit the crack-producing effect of a given environment on a given alloy.
5 Certain aspects of the metallurgical structure of an alloy (such as grain size, crystal structure and number of phases) influence the susceptibility of the alloy to stress-corrosion cracking in a given environment.

Susceptibility of Metals to Stress-Corrosion Cracking

Stress-corrosion cracking can be produced in most metals under some conditions. Susceptibility of a given metal to stress-corrosion cracking in a specific environment depends on its over-all and local chemical composition and on its metallurgical structure. The sensitization behavior of the various classes and individual types of stainless steels is a good example of such a dependency.

Effects of Composition. In considering the effects of metal composition on susceptibility to stress-corrosion cracking, the presence of alloying elements and impurities in low concentrations (and even in trace amounts) also must be considered. In general, binary alloys that contain only very small amounts of elements other than the two major constituents are quite susceptible to failure by stress-corrosion cracking.

High-purity metals generally are much less susceptible to this type of failure than most commercial grades of metals and alloys. In fact, pure metals were long considered immune to stress-corrosion cracking on the basis of experience and several theories of the mechanism of this failure process. However, it was later shown that stress-corrosion cracking can be produced in almost any alloy or pure metal in certain environments and at a corrosion potential specific to the metal-environment combination. One example is the stress-corrosion cracking of 99.999% pure copper in aqueous ammoniacal solutions containing $Cu(NH_3)_4^{++}$ complex ions.

Commercial grades of low-carbon steels, high-strength steels, austenitic stainless steels and other austenitic alloys (especially if in the sensitized condition), high-strength aluminum alloys, and brasses and certain other copper alloys are among the metals in which stress-corrosion cracking frequently occurs (see Tables 1 and 2 on the next two pages, and the sections of this article on various classes of metals, on pages 217 to 225.

The effect of interstitial elements on susceptibility of metals to stress-corrosion cracking is adequately shown by the behavior of austenitic stainless steels containing trace amounts of elemental nitrogen when exposed to a boiling aqueous solution of magnesium chloride. Below 500 ppm of nitrogen, no cracking occurs; above 500 ppm, cracking occurs with great rapidity. The cracking is transgranular; hence, the effect of the nitrogen must be attributed either to an influence on the slip process or to the stability of the protective film.

Similar effects are observed in a broad range of alloys when cracking is intergranular. In this circumstance, it is reasonable to assume that impurities are concentrated in grain boundaries and that the chemical reactivity is associated with this segregation.

Depending on the chemical interaction between these enriched grain boundaries and the environment, certain chemical reactions occur preferentially at the boundaries. This reactivity influences both the susceptibility of an alloy to stress-corrosion cracking and the paths followed by any cracks that develop.

The concentration of impurities in grain boundaries discussed in the above two paragraphs does not refer to grain-boundary precipitation effects, but rather to concentration of impurities that remain in solid solution at the grain boundaries and make the local chemical composition substantially different from that of the bulk of the material in the grains.

Effects of Metal Structure. In general, any metal with a small grain size is more resistant to stress-corrosion cracking than the same metal having a large grain size. This relation, which applies whether crack propagation is intergranular or transgranular, is shown in Fig. 3 for copper alloy 268 (yellow brass, 66%) in ammonia.

Elongated grain structures characteristic of high-strength wrought aluminum alloy mill products markedly affect the path of stress-corrosion cracking in susceptible alloys and tempers. Alloy 7075-T6, for example, in the form of sheet and plate has a high resistance to stress-corrosion cracking when stressed in the direction of rolling or in the long-transverse direction, but has a relatively low resistance when stressed in the short-transverse direction (normal to the plane of the plate). A high resistance in the short-transverse direction can be obtained, however, by an extended stabilization treatment to obtain a T7-type (lower strength) temper.

In some metals, stress-corrosion cracking follows special crystallographic planes. For example, stress-corrosion cracking of titanium proceeds at a slight angle to the basal plane. If the basal plane is perpendicular to the potential plane of crack propagation, resistance to stress-corrosion cracking is at a maximum.

Two-phase brasses (those containing more than about 40% zinc) may crack merely in water. Single-phase brasses are resistant to cracking in water, and the presence of a corrodent such as ammonia or an amine is necessary to cause cracking in them.

Crystal structure also has an effect on stress-corrosion cracking. For instance, ferritic stainless steels (body-centered cubic) are much more resistant to stress-corrosion cracking when exposed to chlorides in aqueous solutions than are austenitic stainless steels (face-centered cubic). The resistance of ferrite-containing cast austenitic stainless steels to cracking when exposed to 205 C (400 F) to condensate from water containing 800 ppm of chloride is roughly proportional to the volume percentage of ferrite, because pools of ferrite in the austenite matrix interfere with or block the propagation of stress-corrosion cracks.

Paths of Stress-Corrosion Cracking

In wrought high-strength heat treatable aluminum alloys, paths of stress-corrosion cracks are always intergranular, because the thermal treatments required to achieve high strength never completely eliminate the electrochemical potential between grain boundaries and grain centers. Stress-corrosion cracking in high-strength aluminum alloys is probably the most widely known example of the effect of grain orientation on the path of cracking. Where the grains are substantially elongated in the rolling direction, stress-corrosion cracks cannot easily propagate perpendicular to this direction but propagate very rapidly parallel to the rolling direction. However, newer alloys and tempers have been developed to provide a high resistance to stress-corrosion cracking when rolled, extruded or forged products are stressed in the short-transverse direction.

In wrought austenitic stainless steels, crack paths usually are transgranular if proper heat treatment has been employed. However, if thermal processing has produced sensitization because of carbide precipitation, stress-corrosion cracking frequently progresses intergranularly because the chromium-depleted zones along the boundaries of a grain are anodic to the main body of the grain. In wrought martensitic stainless steels (such as types 403, 410 and 431), intergranular cracking is the rule when heat treatment procedures, although not necessarily improper, result in similar carbide precipitation.

The path of stress-corrosion cracking in some metals is not governed completely by composition and structure of the metal but also is influenced by the environment. For instance, the path of cracking in copper-zinc alloys can be made transgranular or intergranular by adjusting the pH of aqueous solutions in which these alloys are immersed.

Stress Effects in Stress-Corrosion Cracking

Stress-corrosion cracking occurs only in the presence of tensile stresses, which may be externally applied or residual; purely compressive stresses do not contribute to this type of failure. The length of time required to produce cracking is shorter for higher stresses.

Directionality Effects. The relation between the direction of stressing and the grain direction of the metal influences stress-corrosion cracking. Transverse stressing is considerably more detrimental than longitudinal stressing, and short-transverse stressing is more detrimental than long-transverse stressing. In aluminum alloy 7075-T6 extrusions, for example, the threshold stresses in the longitudinal, long-transverse, and short-transverse directions are 60,000, 32,000 and 7000 psi, respectively. For forgings, stressing across a flash line generally is regarded as at least as severe as stressing in the short-transverse direction.

Threshold stress (the minimum stress at which the probability is extremely low that cracking will occur) depends on temperature, on the composition and metallurgical structure of the alloy, and on the composition of the environment. In some tests, cracking has occurred at an applied stress as low as about 10% of the yield strength; for other metal-environment combinations, threshold stress is about 70% of yield strength.

The effect of alloy composition on threshold stress is typified by the graph in Fig. 4, which illustrates the relation between applied stress and average time to fracture in boiling 42% magnesium chloride solution for two 18-8 stainless steels (types 304 and 304L) and two high-alloy stainless steels (types 310 and 314). As indicated by the nearly level portions of the curves, the threshold stress in this environment is about 35,000 psi for high-alloy stainless steel and about 12,000 psi for 18-8 stainless steel.

Threshold Stress Intensity. For most metal-environment combinations that are susceptible to stress-corrosion cracking,

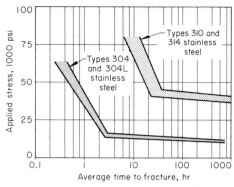

Effect is shown by relation of applied stress to average time to fracture for two 18-8 stainless steels (types 304 and 304L) and two high-alloy stainless steels (types 310 and 314) in boiling 42% magnesium chloride solution.

Fig. 4. Effect of alloy composition on threshold stress (Ref 3)

there appears to be a threshold stress intensity, K_{Iscc}, below which stress-corrosion cracking does not occur. Average values of this parameter for maraging steels heat treated to various yield strengths and then exposed to aqueous environments are given on page 221 in this article, along with a general description of the relation of rate of cracking to stress intensity for maraging steels and for other high-strength steels. For more information on stress intensity and the role of fracture mechanics in studying the kinetics of stress-corrosion cracking, see the section on Stress-Corrosion Crack-Growth Rate on page 35 in the article "Toughness and Fracture Mechanics", and Ref 4 in the present article.

Effect of Environments

The onset of stress-corrosion cracking often depends on subtleties of environment composition, and alloy composition and structure. Frequently, minor changes in the environment or the alloy can prevent cracking. Hence, the relations between environments and alloy types presented in this section provide only general guidelines as to the probability of stress-corrosion cracking.

Specific Ions and Substances

Stress-corrosion cracking often is caused by specific ions that are present as impurities in the environment. For example, even when in the solution heat treated or the annealed condition, austenitic stainless steels crack in aqueous solutions that contain as little as 2 ppm of chloride at 200 C (390 F). Sensitized austenitic stainless steels crack at room temperature in water containing about 100 ppm of chloride or 2 ppm of fluoride. Some copper alloys crack in environments that contain ammonia in similarly low concentrations.

The dependence of the general pattern of stress-corrosion cracking on the pres-

ence of one or more specific corrosive substances sometimes is called the "specific-ion effect". The presence of ions known to induce cracking in a given type of alloy is widely used as a criterion for predicting whether or not cracking will occur. For example, the presence of chlorides in contact with austenitic stainless steels is always regarded as hazardous. Although this is a reasonable criterion for predicting stress-corrosion cracking, it is known that specific ions are not always required and that environments as simple as pure water, dry hydro-

Table 1. Specific Ions and Substances That Have Been Known To Cause Stress-Corrosion Cracking in Various Alloys When Present at Low Concentrations and as Impurities

Damaging specific ions and substances	Alloys susceptible to stress-corrosion cracking	Temperature
Halogen Group		
Fluoride ions	Sensitized austenitic stainless steel	Room
Gaseous chlorine	High-strength low-alloy steel	Room
Fused chloride salt	Zirconium alloys and titanium alloys	Above melting point of fused salts
Gaseous iodine	Zirconium alloys	300 C (570 F)
Gaseous HCl and HBr	High-strength low-alloy steels (rapid crack growth)	Room
Halides in aqueous solutions	High-strength aluminum alloys	Room
	High-strength steels	Room
	Austenitic stainless steels	Hot
Oxygen Group (H₂O-O₂-H₂ Systems)		
O₂ dissolved in liquid H₂O	Sensitized stainless steels	300 C (570 F)
Gaseous hydrogen at ambient pressure	High-strength low-alloy steels	Room
Gaseous hydrogen at high temperature and pressure	Low-strength and medium-strength steels	> 200 C (> 390 F)
Gaseous H₂O ....,	High-strength aluminum alloys	Room
Gaseous H₂O-O₂-H₂	High-strength uranium alloys	.....
Hydroxides (LiOH, NaOH, KOH)	Carbon steels; Fe-Cr-Ni alloys (caustic cracking)	> 100 C (> 210 F)
Oxygen Group (S, Se, Te Systems)		
Polythionic acids (H₂SₙO₆)	Sensitized stainless steels, sensitized Inconel 600	Room
H₂S gas	High-strength low-alloy steels	Room
Sulfide impurities in aqueous solutions	Medium-strength to high-strength steels (accelerated hydrogen-induced cracking)	Room
MnS and MnSe inclusions	High-strength steels (initiation sites for cracking)	Room
SO₂ gas with moisture	Copper alloys	Room
Nitrogen Group		
N₂O₄ liquid	High-strength titanium alloys	50 C (120 F)
Fuming nitric acid	Pure titanium; high-strength aluminum alloys	> 100 C (> 210 F)
Nitrates in aqueous solution	Carbon steels	> 100 C (> 210 F)
Nitrogen oxides with moisture ...	Copper alloys	Room
Aerated aqueous NH₃ and ammonium salts in aqueous solution	Copper alloys	Room
Nitrogen, phosphorus, arsenic, antimony and bismuth, as alloying species in metal	Stainless steels (in presence of Cl⁻) and copper alloys (in presence of aerated aqueous NH₃); accelerated cracking	Room
Arsenic, antimony and bismuth, as ions in aqueous solutions ..	High-strength steels; accelerated hydrogen entry and hydrogen-induced cracking	Room
Carbon Group (C, Si, Ge, Sn, Pb)		
Carbonate ions in aqueous solutions	Carbon steel	100 C (210 F)
CO-CO₂-H₂O gas	Carbon steel	.....
Lead ions in aqueous solutions ...	High-nickel alloys	.....

gen, and other pure substances can contribute to stress-corrosion cracking.

The combination of oxygen and chlorides in trace concentrations in alkaline phosphate-treated boiler water is sufficient to cause stress-corrosion cracking of austenitic stainless steels in areas exposed to steam and intermittently wetted by boiler water.

Aircraft parts, both of steel and of aluminum alloys, have failed because of the mildly corrosive action of the atmosphere; water vapor and trace contaminants in air can initiate and propagate stress-corrosion cracking and cause premature failure of such parts. Marine and industrial environments containing small quantities of halide ions are particularly aggressive in causing cracking of high-strength steels, corrosion-resistant steels and aluminum alloys.

Specific ions and substances that are known to have caused stress-corrosion cracking of various alloys when present in low concentrations and as impurities are conveniently classified on the basis of the periodic table. Table I lists these damaging specific ions and substances, which are classified as the halogen group, the oxygen group (H_2O-O_2-H_2 systems and S, Se, Te systems), the nitrogen group and the carbon group. For each damaging substance, the alloys that are susceptible to stress-corrosion cracking and the approximate temperature or temperature range at which cracking has been observed is given. Stress-corrosion cracking will not always occur for each listed combination of damaging species, alloy type and temperature, but these combinations should be considered suspect when the possibility of this type of failure is being assessed.

In environments containing the damaging species of the halogen group, stress-corrosion cracking can be caused by these species in the gaseous molecular form, in acids, in fused salts and as ions in aqueous solutions.

The data presented in Table 1 for the oxygen group demonstrates that simple environments, not necessarily specific ions, are sufficient to cause stress-corrosion cracking. The oxygen group is divided into two systems. The first system includes the species based on water, oxygen, hydrogen and combinations thereof, and is treated separately because these species are so widely present in environments to which alloys are exposed. Caustic cracking of low-carbon steels in boilers by hot solutions containing sodium hydroxide, which is listed in this system, is described on page 217 in this article. In the second system of the oxygen group, the substances that cause cracking most frequently are those that contain sulfur.

The nitrogen group includes as damaging species some substances that are

present not in the environment but as alloying species in stainless steels and copper alloys. These alloying species are the elements nitrogen, phosphorus, arsenic, antimony and bismuth. The other damaging species in the nitrogen group are present in the environment.

Service Environments

Commercial and consumer equipment generally is operated in two classes of service environments: "controlled" environments and "noncontrolled" environments. In controlled environments, the composition of the fluid is controlled; these environments include working (energy-transfer) fluids, and process streams and batches in the chemical and food industries. In operations of this type, the composition of the environment is controlled either to meet and maintain product-quality requirements or to prevent corrosion of containers and other types of equipment.

Noncontrolled environments include those to which products of the transportation and manufacturing industries are exposed. Here, structures are exposed to a broad range of environments that can be anticipated by the design engineer but very rarely controlled. As a prerequisite to investigating the possibility of stress-corrosion cracking, the properties of a noncontrolled environment should be defined as accurately as possible.

Even in controlled environments, unexpected impurities sometimes are introduced by accidents or improper operation, and stress-corrosion cracking can be caused by transient as well as prolonged periods of deviation from normal operating conditions and from normal composition of the environment.

Atmospheric environments contain a variety of damaging or potentially damaging chemical substances. Some of the substances in the atmosphere that contribute to stress-corrosion cracking, the alloys they affect, and their special characteristics are given in Table 2.

The example that follows illustrates the effects of a moist chloride-containing atmosphere on aluminum alloys.

Example 2. Stress-Corrosion Cracking of Aluminum Alloy Fittings in a Marine Atmosphere Because of Improper Alloy Selection (Fig. 5)

During a routine inspection, cracks were discovered in several aluminum alloy coupling nuts (Fig. 5a) on the fuel lines of a missile. The fuel lines had been exposed to a marine atmosphere for six months while the missile stood on an outdoor test stand near the seacoast. A complete check was then made, both visually and with the aid of a low-power magnifying glass, of all coupling nuts of this type on the missile.

One to three cracks were found in each of 13 nuts; two of these nuts had been supplied by one vendor and the other 11 had been supplied by another vendor. There were no leaks at any of the cracked nuts, and further checking using liquid-penetrant techniques did not reveal any additional cracks.

Subsequent examination of the remaining missiles on test stands at this site showed that some coupling nuts of this type on each of the missiles that had been exposed to the atmosphere for more than about a month had cracked in a similar manner.

Macroexamination. The thirteen cracked coupling nuts, which were on $1/4$- to $3/4$-in.-OD fuel lines, were removed for further inspection. The nuts had been anodized and then dyed for identification.

Visual and low-magnification examination showed that the cracks had originated in the round section at the threaded end and had propagated parallel to the axis of the nut across one of the flat surfaces. An actual-size view of one of the cracked nuts, and a view of the crack at six diameters, are shown in Fig. 5(a) and (b), respectively.

Analysis of Materials. Spectrographic analysis of the 13 cracked nuts identified the material as aluminum alloy 2014 or 2017. (The composition ranges of these two alloys overlap, which prevented exact identification by spectrographic analysis.) Chemical analysis of a white deposit removed from one of the cracks showed the presence of a high concentration of chloride.

Metallographic examination of mounted specimens in the polished and polished-and-etched conditions revealed that the cracks were similar to stress-corrosion cracks observed previously in aluminum alloys of this type — primary and secondary intergranular cracks showing intergranular corrosion. A cross section taken through the failure re-

Table 2. Substances in Atmospheric Environments That Contribute to Stress-Corrosion Cracking of Various Alloys

Damaging substance	Alloy	Special aspects
Oxygen	Copper alloys	Depends on oxygen concentration
Hydrogen sulfide	Many commercial alloys	Sources: anaerobic bacteria; breakdown of organic products
Oxides of nitrogen	Carbon steels; copper alloys	The oxides produce nitric acid and nitrates
CO or CO_2, plus moisture	Carbon steels	. . . . .
Ammonia	Copper alloys	. . . . .
Arsenic and antimony compounds	Many commercial alloys	Contained in insecticides and other sprays
Sulfur dioxide	Copper alloys	The oxide produces H_2SO_3, H_2SO_4
Chlorides plus moisture	(a)	Marine exposure

(a) Aluminum alloys, austenitic stainless steels, titanium alloys, high-strength steels

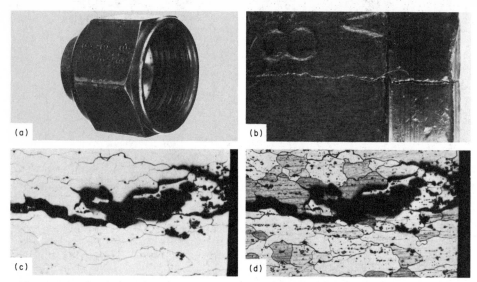

Fig. 5. (a) *Aluminum alloy coupling nut that cracked by stress corrosion in a marine atmosphere. (b) View of the crack at 6×. (c) and (d) Micrographs, at 100×, of a section through the crack near the origin, showing appearance before and after etching.*
(Example 2)

gion of one nut, near the origin of the crack, is shown in Fig. 5(c) as it appeared before etching and in Fig. 5(d) after etching. The microstructure and longitudinal (axial) grain orientation identified the material of the nuts as bar stock.

Discussion. Tightening of the nuts resulted in sustained tensile stresses in the material. These were in the form of hoop stresses, which were higher than those encountered in most applications of this type of coupling nut because the parts had to be "liquid oxygen clean" (completely free of lubricants or organic materials) and the nuts therefore had to be tightened to high torque in order to obtain liquid-tight seals.

Conclusions. Cracking of the aluminum alloy coupling nuts was caused by stress corrosion. Contributing factors included use of a material (aluminum alloy 2014 or 2017) that is susceptible to this type of failure, sustained tensile stressing in the presence of a marine (chloride-bearing) atmosphere, and an elongated grain structure transverse to the direction of stress. The elongated grain structure transverse to the direction of stress was a consequence of following the generally used procedure of machining this type of nut from bar stock.

Corrective Measures. The material specification for new coupling nuts for this application was changed to permit use of only aluminum alloys 6061-T6 and -T651 and 2024-T6, -T62 and -T851. (For identification purposes, the anodic coating on coupling nuts of the new materials was dyed a different color from that used on the aluminum alloy 2014 or 2017 nuts.) Alloy 6061 is not susceptible to stress-corrosion cracking, and alloy 2024 in the tempers selected has been shown to withstand much higher transverse tensile stresses than can alloy 2014-T6 in alternate-immersion tests in 3.5% sodium chloride solution. These tests have shown excellent correlation with exposure to marine atmospheres. The 7xxx-series aluminum alloys, which generally are less resistant to corrosion and stress corrosion, are not acceptable materials for use in fluid-connection fittings.

It was recommended that specified procedures be followed closely in tightening both the alloy 2014 or 2017 nuts still in service or on hand and the new nuts. Because proper tightening alone would not eliminate failures of the 2014 or 2017 nuts, it also was recommended that any of these nuts that were exposed to marine atmospheres be inspected for cracks at least once every two weeks, and that those exposed to inland atmospheres be inspected at least once a month. Visual inspection using a low-power magnifying glass and adequate lighting was to be supplemented by liquid-penetrant inspection of any nuts that were suspect.

Application of protective organic coatings to the alloy 2014 or 2017 nuts also was considered as a means of minimizing stress-corrosion cracking, but such coatings could not be used on nuts for liquid-oxygen service.

Subsequently, shear failures occurred in the shoulders of 6061-T6 nuts during the tightening operation, and alloy 2024-T6 became the preferred material. Failure of the 6061-T6 nuts was attributed to the lower strength of this alloy, the high-torque tightening required for "liquid oxygen clean" nuts, and thin shoulder webs permitted by wide tolerances on the shoulder dimensions.

Working Fluids. Some types of working fluids are the liquids and gases used in power-production systems. An important example is pure water used in production of electricity by steam-turbine systems. In such systems, water is converted to steam, and the expanded steam is passed through a turbine and subsequently condensed.

Such environments usually are treated with corrosion inhibitors to minimize attack of structural materials. A common method is to maintain pH within a range where iron-base alloys are stable by adding such chemicals as phosphates, alkali or ammonium hydroxides, or amines. In addition to control of the pH of such

working fluids, additions of reducing substances such as hydrazine and sodium sulfite are made to maintain a low concentration of oxygen, because oxygen accelerates corrosion.

Other heat-transfer fluids include liquid sodium, which is used in liquid-metal-cooled fast-breeder nuclear reactors, and high-temperature gases such as helium, nitrogen, and carbon dioxide, which are used in gas-cooled reactors. Any of these heat-transfer fluids may contain impurities that are possible causes of stress-corrosion cracking.

Another type of heat-transfer fluid is the water used in cooling towers. Failure by stress-corrosion cracking of copper alloy fittings in a system of this type is described in Example 9 in this article.

In addition to the use of working fluids under essentially steady-state conditions in normal operation, transient changes in the composition of fluids can produce chemical effects that lead to stress-corrosion cracking. Such transient changes can be caused by leakage in condensers, pumps, valves, seals and fittings (for instance, leakage of chlorides into a condenser cooled by seawater).

Temporary use of a substitute working fluid in a given application also can have unexpected harmful effects. A stress-corrosion failure related to occasional use of a fluid different from that normally employed in a heat exchanger is described in the example that follows.

Example 3. Stress-Corrosion Cracking of Copper Alloy Tube Sheet Because of Retubing Stresses and Occasional Presence of Ammonium Compounds (Fig. 6)

Tube sheets of an air-compressor aftercooler (see Fig. 6a) were found to be cracked and leaking about 12 to 14 months after they had been retubed. Most of the tube sheets had been retubed several times previously because of tube failures. (The tube failures were not related to the tube-sheet failures.) Sanitary (chlorinated) well water generally was used in the system, although filtered process make-up water (river water) containing ammonia was used occasionally.

The tube sheets were 2 in. thick. The tubes, which were ¾ in. in outside diameter and 0.050 in. in wall thickness, had been expansion rolled into the holes in the tube sheets.

Examination of Failed Part. One of the cracked tube sheets was removed and submitted for laboratory examination. Chemical analysis showed that the tube sheet was made of copper alloy 464 (naval brass).

Metallographic examination of sections cut parallel and perpendicular to the tube-sheet surface revealed cracks that had penetrated through more than 90% of the tube-sheet thickness. The cracks had propagated intergranularly through the beta phase, as shown in Fig. 6(b), which is a micrograph of a section taken parallel to the tube-sheet surface. Some dezincification of the beta

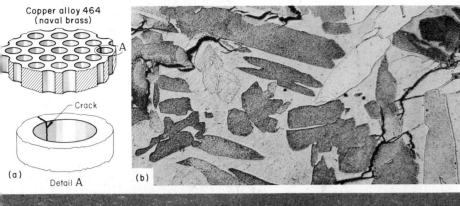

Fig. 6. (a) *Tube sheet from an air-compressor aftercooler that failed by stress-corrosion cracking.* (b) *Micrograph, at 250×, of a specimen etched in 10% ammonium persulfate solution, showing intergranular crack propagation.* (c) *Macrograph, at 5×, of an unetched specimen, showing multiple branching of cracks.* (Example 3)

phase also can be seen in this micrograph. Figure 6(c) is a macrograph of a section through a crack that was more than 1 in. deep and that shows multiple branching.

Test for Residual Stresses. Sample sections of the tube sheet were submitted to the ASTM B154 mercurous nitrate test, which is an accelerated test for detecting the presence, in copper or copper alloy products, of residual stresses that might cause stress-corrosion cracking in storage or in service. Cracks induced in the sample sections during the test indicated the presence of high residual stresses in the tube sheet.

Discussion. The presence of ammonia in the river water used occasionally and the presence of residual internal stresses provided the conditions necessary for stress-corrosion cracking of the tube sheets. The multiple branching of the cracks was characteristic of stress-corrosion cracking, and the intergranular crack propagation corresponded to the usual course of stress-corrosion cracking in brass in the presence of ammonia.

Conclusions. The tube sheets failed by stress-corrosion cracking as a result of the combined action of internal stresses and a corrosive environment. The internal stresses had been induced by retubing operations, and the environment had become corrosive when ammonia was introduced into the system by the occasional use of process makeup water. The slight amount of dezincification observed did not appear to have contributed substantially to the failures.

Corrective Measure. It was made a standard procedure to stress relieve tube sheets before each retubing operation. The stress relieving was done by heating at 274 C (525 F) for ½ hr, followed by slow cooling for 3 hr to room temperature. No stress-corrosion-cracking failures occurred in this equipment during a period of several years since the adoption of stress relief before retubing.

Process streams and batches differ from working fluids in that they usually are chemicals, foods, or other materials that are being processed into some final product form. The process streams and batches in themselves may not be aggressive with respect to stress-corrosion cracking, but may become aggressive if damaging impurities are introduced.

Leached Substances. Stress-corrosion cracking of a metal frequently is caused by damaging substances that have been leached from nonmetallic materials in contact with the metal. Sometimes the substances that cause cracking are products of thermal decomposition of a material that is innocuous unless heated to its decomposition temperature.

Damaging substances, such as chlorides or sulfur compounds, can be leached from concrete, gasket materials, insulating materials, and polyvinyl chlorides and similar plastic materials.

Moisture can leach chlorides from the calcium chloride frequently added to concrete to aid in curing. Sulfur compounds and chlorides can leach from gasket materials under conditions of pressure and elevated temperature.

Gasket materials include those composed of asbestos, cork, cellulose or other organic fibers, in combination with various binders or impregnants, and the vulcanized elastomeric materials that are used for automotive applications.

The binders used in asbestos and fiberglass insulation frequently contain chloride compounds and are leached in the presence of moisture at room temperature or at elevated temperatures, depending on composition. (Example 5 on page 219 in this article describes stress-corrosion

cracking of stainless steel piping that resulted from leaching of chlorides from insulation in the presence of moisture.)

Polyvinyl chloride materials usually are harmless unless they are heated above the decomposition temperature, or are exposed to ultraviolet radiation.

Concentration of Crack-Inducing Substances. In any environment (liquid, gas or moist solid), substances capable of inducing stress-corrosion cracking frequently are present at harmless levels, either as normal components or as impurities. However, several factors that are related to design or to service conditions can cause these substances to concentrate locally and produce stress-corrosion cracking.

Intermittent wetting and drying is a major cause of concentration of damaging and potentially damaging soluble substances in films of moisture on metal surfaces. Where a dilute aqueous solution is transmitted to a metal surface by capillary action through an absorbent fibrous material, the process is called "wicking". Tests have been done on the effect of temperature on the time required to produce stress-corrosion cracking in 0.062-in.-thick type 304 stainless steel U-bends in a wicking experiment. Cracking was found to occur at much lower temperatures when alternate wetting and drying was used than when the specimens were kept wet continuously.

In service, intermittent wetting and drying often is caused by changes in weather, rise and fall of tides, and fluctuations in levels of liquids in storage. Also, intermittent condensation and drying occurs on metal surfaces in many service environments because of fluctuations in temperature. If soluble substances are available, solutions sufficiently concentrated to cause stress-corrosion cracking are readily produced on the metal surfaces.

This phenomenon was found to have caused stress-corrosion-cracking failure of carbon steel cables on a bridge over a river, where the cables were exposed to an industrial atmosphere that contained ammonium nitrate. The cables, which contained 0.7% carbon, failed after 12 years of service. Tests showed that when specimens from the cables were stressed in tension while immersed in $0.01N$ ammonium nitrate or sodium nitrate at room temperature, they failed after 3½ to 9 months. No cracking was produced in similar tests in distilled water and in $0.01N$ solutions of sodium chloride, ammonium sulfate, sodium nitrate and sodium hydroxide.

In the following example, a highly concentrated solution was produced by dissolution of ammonium nitrate dust on local areas of a steel tank where occasional exposure to moist air permitted condensation to occur intermittently.

Example 4. Stress-Corrosion Cracking of Carbon Steel Hoppers by Ammonium Nitrate Solution (Fig. 7)

After 10 to 20 months of service, the carbon steel hoppers on three trucks used to transport bulk ammonium nitrate prills developed extensive cracking in the upper walls. The prills were used in blasting operations and required transportation over rough roads to a mining site.

The prills were discharged from the steel hoppers using air superchargers that generated an unloading pressure of about 7 psi. A screw conveyor at the bottom of the hopper assisted in the unloading operation. Each hopper truck held from 10 to 13 tons of prills when fully loaded and handled approximately 100 tons per month.

The interior surfaces of all three hoppers had been painted — one before placement in service, the second after 7 days of service and the third after 60 days of service. All exterior surfaces were covered with a gray epoxy coating of the type used at the prill-manufacturing plant. There were no specifications for the interior coatings, but one appeared to be a fluorocarbon and another an aluminum-pigmented coating.

Investigation. The walls of the hoppers were made of 0.105-in.-thick flat rolled carbon steel sheet of structural quality, conforming to ASTM A245.

Visual inspection of the internal surfaces of the hoppers revealed extensive rusting under the paint, especially along edges and at corners. This inspection also revealed that most of the cracking was confined to the top areas of the hoppers, around manholes and at circumferential welds in the sheet-steel walls.

The cracking occurred in areas where bare steel had been exposed by chipping and peeling of paint. The cracks were 2 to 8 in. long and were located in or adjacent to welds. Some cracks were perpendicular to the weld bead, but most followed the weld. In one hopper, cracks were found along the full length of approximately 20 intermittent welds that attached internal bracing to the walls. All cracks in the hopper walls could be seen from the outside, where they appeared as straight lines of rust breaking through the gray external coating.

A rectangular section that included a weld was removed from the upper front edge of the wall of one hopper for metallurgical examination. A transverse section approximately 1/8 in. from the weld was mounted to permit examination of both the interior and exterior edges of the hopper wall. Examination of metallographic specimens after polishing and etching with nital revealed an extensive pattern of intergranular cracking (see Fig. 7) that had originated at the interior surface.

Ammonium nitrate solutions of certain concentrations are known to crack steel. A concentrated nitrate solution was produced on the upper walls of the carbon steel hoppers by dissolution of ammonium nitrate dust in atmospheric water vapor that had condensed when moist air had entered the hoppers during unloading and during standby periods in which the manhole covers were left open.

Conclusion. Failure of the hoppers was the result of intergranular stress-corrosion

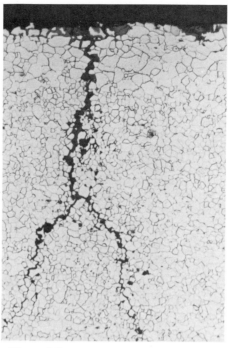

Fig. 7. Micrograph, at 100×, of a nital-etched specimen of ASTM A245 carbon steel, showing stress-corrosion cracking that occurred in a concentrated solution of ammonium nitrate (Example 4)

cracking of the sheet-steel walls because of contact with a highly concentrated ammonium nitrate solution.

The solution was produced by dissolution of ammonium nitrate dust in condensed atmospheric water vapor that formed intermittently on the upper walls of the tank.

Corrective Measure. A three-coat epoxy-type coating with a total dry thickness of 0.013 in. was applied to the interior surfaces of the hoppers.

Although high stress levels in the steel resulting from welding, unloading, and traveling on uneven roads contributed to the cracking, it was more economical to properly coat the interior surfaces of the steel hoppers than to design for minimum stress levels or to make a change in material. For instance, equivalent aluminum hoppers would cost approximately 2½ times as much as the carbon steel hoppers, and stainless steel hoppers would cost five times as much.

Gradual concentration of a damaging substance on a metal surface can result from diffusion effects caused by an imposed electric field or an electric field produced by corrosion processes, or by some other local condition, and can lead to stress-corrosion cracking in gases, liquids, and moist solid environments such as soil, concrete or plaster.

Concentration also can occur because of part shape — especially on assemblies in which close fit of parts creates crevices. Crevices provide both sites and proper conditions for concentration of impurities on metal specimens in aqueous media. Such crevices are common in assemblies using gaskets or sealants. Because of tightness of such crevices, it is impossible for impurities to be removed from them. The impurities thus are concentrated by leaching, decomposition or corrosion, and frequently result in stress-corrosion cracking. In heated crevices, such as in tube sheets of steam generators, impurities are concentrated when water flashes to steam, and stress-corrosion cracking may occur if hydroxides are present.

Dried processing chemicals on metal surfaces (such as those that remain on poorly rinsed surfaces after pickling, cleaning and similar operations) are available for corrosion attack at a later time when the surfaces are exposed to their normal environments. One example is the effect of residual fluoride on zirconium in corrosion testing. When zirconium specimens exposed to fluoride solutions in corrosion tests are properly cleaned after removal from the solutions, they gain weight at a low rate when subsequently exposed to high-temperature water; however, when there is sufficient residual fluoride, the specimen loses weight because of corrosion that can initiate stress-corrosion cracking.

Pre-Service Environments

Many stress-corrosion-cracking failures are caused by exposure of metal equipment to corrosive environments before the equipment is put into service. These environments include those associated with fabrication, testing, shipment, storage and installation.

Fabrication Environments. Substances to which metal parts and equipment are exposed during fabrication and processing often leave residues on the metal surfaces or introduce impurities into the metal. Stress-corrosion cracking caused by these residues or impurities frequently begins, and occasionally results in failure during the production process. Sometimes impending failure is discovered during fabrication; at other times, it is not discovered until the equipment is in service.

Examples of sources of such deleterious impurities are (a) machining lubricants; (b) "protective" coatings; (c) fumes from adjacent processing lines; (d) atmospheric impurities; (e) welding flux; (f) cleaning solutions; (g) inspection environments, such as liquid penetrants; (h) containers for processing; (i) lubricants, such as copper and lead, used in tube drawing; and (j) plating and chemical-surface treatment solutions.

Testing Environments. In product research and development, metal parts and assemblies are tested to determine load capacity and conformance to other requirements. Failures sometimes are initiated and/or propagated by test environments, such as in hydrostatic testing of pressure vessels, piping and related equipment. For instance, a titanium alloy Ti-6Al-4V vessel that was to contain

N_2O_4 in service failed after about 13 hr of hydrostatic testing at about 43 C (110 F) at 75% of yield stress. Here, the testing environment, which closely simulated the service environment, was the cause of failure. In this instance, failure was fortuitous, since it established that the material-environment combination was not suitable for reliable performance in the intended application.

Other environmental impurities that may be harmful in hydrostatic testing include microbiological and bacterial contaminants, chlorides and fluorides. Stress-corrosion cracking of titanium in methanol was first observed when methanol was used as a medium for hydrostatic testing.

Shipping and Storage Environments. During shipping or storage, parts and assemblies may or may not be protected from the atmosphere. There have been instances in which allegedly protective materials have in fact contained species that caused, rather than prevented, stress-corrosion cracking. Where suitable protection is not provided, the components can be continually or intermittently in contact with impurities in the surroundings. For instance, metal parts shipped by sea are in danger if not fully protected from chlorides.

Thus, to prevent initiation and propagation of stress-corrosion cracking during shipment or storage, expected exterior environments and "protective" systems must be thoroughly evaluated and effective protective measures taken.

Example 2 in this article describes stress-corrosion cracking of aluminum alloy couplings, which occurred in a missile that was on a test stand near the seacoast for several months. The combination of tensile stresses and marine atmosphere caused the failure.

Installation Environments. During installation of equipment, critical materials often are exposed to damaging or potentially damaging environments. Some of these environments are: (a) welding flux, (b) marking materials, (c) lubricants (applied to moving parts, and to large bolts during installation), (d) machining oils, (e) test environments and (f) contaminants from fingerprints. Sometimes, installation procedures such as bolting or crimping inadvertently introduce residual stresses that can lead to stress-corrosion cracking in service.

Procedures for Analyzing Failures

The procedures for analyzing failures suspected to have occurred by stress-corrosion cracking are in general the same as those described in the article on General Practice in Failure Analysis, which begins on page 10 in this volume.

Ideally, the failed part should be brought to the laboratory immediately after failure, with no further disturbance and with all of the physical evidence intact. The part should be accompanied by a complete record of the manufacturing and environmental history and results of prior testing. Attention also must be given to chemical environments to which the part was exposed during manufacturing, shipment, storage and service — particularly to such factors as concentration, temperature, pressure, acidity or alkalinity, normal or accidentally introduced impurities, cyclic conditions, and any deliberate or accidental changes in the control of these factors.

On-site examination provides an opportunity for observing and testing environmental conditions and mechanical processes involved. The relation of the failed part to the over-all operation, and possible sources of stress, generally can be established. Photographs and sketches are indispensable for recording location of failure, extent of fracture or cracking, presence of corrosion products or foreign deposits, evidence of mechanical abuse, and other significant details.

Sampling. The samples required may be failed parts, related parts, specimens removed from parts, and the environment to which the failed parts were exposed. Selection of samples and removal of specimens should be carefully planned, keeping in mind the main objectives of the investigation.

Suitable precautions must be taken to avoid the following: (a) destruction of evidence (for example, corrosion products or other surface deposits) that could be of value in investigating the failure; (b) overheating, contaminating and damaging the part and adjacent and remote related components and structures; and (c) contamination of samples of the environment.

In sampling the environment to which the failed part was exposed, the investigator should be guided by the information already obtained about operating conditions and history of the failure. The general environment should be sampled. Also, appropriate techniques should be used to obtain samples of, and characterize (by pH and the presence of specific contaminants, for instance), the environment in immediate contact with the failure region. For general guidance on chemical substances and environments likely to cause stress-corrosion cracking in specific metals, see "Effect of Environments", beginning on page 210.

Following visual examination, the fracture surface should be stripped with cellulose acetate tape to entrap any fracture-surface deposits. The tape can be used for later microanalysis, with the aid of an electron microprobe or a scanning electron microscope with an energy-dispersive system, or other suitable analytical equipment.

After stripping, the fracture surface should be cleaned (ultrasonically, if possible) and degreased in reagent-grade acetone, which leaves minimal amounts of organic residues on the surface while removing almost all traces of cellulose acetate from stripping.

Observation of Fracture-Surface Characteristics

Crack patterns, initiation sites and topography of crack surfaces, and evidence of corrosion all provide clues as to the causes, origins and mechanisms of fractures.

Crack Patterns. As discussed on page 207 in this article and illustrated in Fig. 1, stress-corrosion cracking almost without exception is characterized by multiple branching. The nature of the crack patterns is best observed by microscopic examination of sections in the failure region.

Initiation Sites and Topography of Crack Surfaces. These features are crucial in determining the causes and mechanisms of fractures. When a primary fracture has been damaged or corroded, secondary cracks and incomplete primary cracks are opened to expose their surfaces for examination.

Corrosion of Fracture Surfaces. The techniques for determining the presence of corrodents and corrosion products and for identifying them are noted on page 170 in the article "Corrosion Failures" and described more fully on page 24. Besides establishing the presence and identity of these substances on the fracture surface, an investigation (often extensive) of the environment and service history of the part must be carried out to determine the exact role (if any) of these substances in the failure.

Where information on the environment and service history of the part are incomplete, or where abnormal transient conditions may have existed, results of the investigation may be inconclusive. In some circumstances, tests that simulate service, and investigations of the effects of variations in composition of the environment and in operating conditions, are warranted.

Macroscopic Examination

Macroscopically, fractures produced by stress-corrosion cracking always appear brittle, exhibiting little or no ductility even in very tough materials; in this way they resemble corrosion-fatigue fractures. Many transgranular stress-corrosion cracks characteristically change fracture planes as they propagate, producing flat facets. Both these flat facets and the grain facets of intergranular stress-corrosion cracks ordinarily are observable at low magnification.

The fracture surfaces usually contain easily identifiable regions of crack initia-

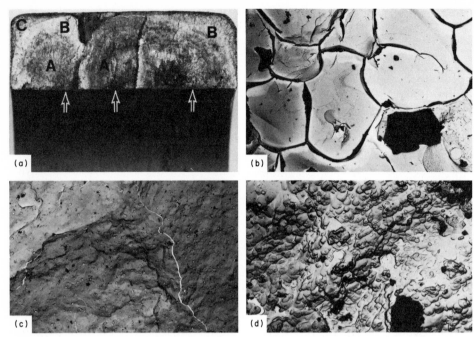

(a) Fracture surface, at 1.35×. Arrows show locations of multiple crack origins. Areas at A and B are respectively representative of early and advanced stages of stress-corrosion-crack growth; region of final, fast fracture is at C. (b) TEM fractograph from area A, at 1350×, showing mud-crack pattern. (c) TEM fractograph from an area marked B, at 1700×, showing intergranular separation. (d) TEM fractograph from area C, at 3400×, showing dimples in region of ductile, final fracture. (TEM fractographs are of plastic-carbon replicas.)

Fig. 8. Macrograph and TEM fractographs of the fracture surface of an aluminum alloy 7075-T6 aircraft landing-gear component that failed by stress-corrosion cracking

tion, slow crack propagation and final rupture. Final rupture usually occurs by tensile overload. Thus, the area of final fracture often shows some evidence of ductility such as a shear lip or a herringbone pattern emanating from the zone of slow cracking.

The area of slow crack growth often contains corrosion products or is stained or otherwise discolored with respect to the area of final, fast fracture. However, the presence of staining or corrosion products on the fracture surface is by no means positive proof of stress-corrosion cracking. Some stress-corrosion-cracking fractures are not stained or discolored, especially in materials with good corrosion resistance; in addition, many fractures become corroded before inspection can be accomplished.

The zones of slow propagation of stress-corrosion cracks usually are much rougher in appearance than those of corrosion-fatigue cracks and do not contain fatigue beach marks or macroscopic evidence of cold work. However, if either the stress component is removed or the environment becomes inactive, crack propagation will discontinue until these factors again become operative. This sometimes results in macroscopic markings similar in appearance to the beach marks characteristic of fatigue fractures.

Both types of fracture can, and often do, initiate at corrosion pits or other stress raisers on the surface of the part. However, if the environment is suffi-

ciently corrosive and if tensile stresses are present, stress-corrosion cracking can be initiated even on smooth surfaces, whereas corrosion fatigue always is initiated at a stress raiser.

Fractures caused by either of these mechanisms always initiate at the surface of the part or at some location where the aggressive species can contact the metal. By corollary, if the crack is found to have a subsurface origin, corrosion fatigue and stress-corrosion cracking usually can be eliminated as possible causes of failure.

Cracks produced by stress corrosion and by some hydrogen-damage processes generally have macroscopically rough fracture features, which usually are discolored from reaction with the environment. These mechanisms are easily recognized as macroscopically different from corrosion fatigue, but identifying the exact mechanism by macroexamination alone is not always possible. These cracks do not always have distinct origins; there may be much pitting in the region of crack initiation, and the crack may exhibit branching in this region.

Microscopic Examination

Careful correlation of microscopic fracture-surface topography with macroscopic fracture-surface features is essential. The crack-initiation region and the directions of crack growth must be identified accurately so that information concerning the sequence of events and the

micromechanisms of fracture, as observed by electron microscopy, can be correlated with the circumstances of crack initiation and the mechanism of crack propagation. Frequently, several different fracture micromechanisms are observed on a single fracture surface. Accordingly, correct identification of the initiating fracture mechanism and of any changes in micromechanism during fracture propagation is of vital importance in arriving at a correct understanding of the failure. This is demonstrated in the following report:

An aluminum alloy 7075-T6 aircraft landing-gear component that was stressed only by loads from the dead weight of the aircraft and exposed to a corrosive marine environment failed by stress-corrosion cracking. The fracture surface, showing the locations of multiple crack origins and areas representing three stages of crack propagation, is presented in Fig. 8(a). The areas of the early stages of crack growth were heavily coated with gray corrosion products, which were thickest in the crack-nucleation regions indicated by the arrows in Fig. 8(a).

Figure 8(b) is a TEM fractograph of a two-stage plastic-carbon replica and reveals a mud-crack pattern from a region representing an early stage of crack growth (area A in Fig. 8a). Mud cracks are replicated cracks in a layer of corrosion products on a fracture surface, but sometimes are misinterpreted as intergranular. At the lower right corner of Fig. 8(b) is a particle of corrosion product (dark) extracted from the surface and retained in the replica.

As crack growth progressed, the concentration of corrosion products decreased, and curved macroscopic crack-progression lines were evident in areas representing the latter stages of crack growth (areas marked B in Fig. 8a). These lines are a form of beach mark and, at first glance, could lead to the erroneous conclusion that the component failed by fatigue. However, microfractographic examination established the actual mechanism at this stage of fracture propagations. Figure 8(c), which is a TEM fractograph of a portion of one of the areas marked B in Fig. 8(a), shows clear evidence of intergranular separation.

The dimpled surface visible in Fig. 8(d), which is a TEM fractograph of area C in Fig. 8(a), was the region of final, fast fracture by ductile rupture.

It is difficult to distinguish between service failures by stress-corrosion cracking and by hydrogen damage solely from microfractographic evidence. Fractures of both types mainly follow intergranular paths, although stress-corrosion cracking sometimes is transgranular, and the surfaces of both types of fracture may be substantially corroded. Also, hydrogen evolution during stress-corrosion cracking may be a factor in the cracking process, so that the combination of hydrogen embrittlement and corrosion at the crack tip may be instrumental in producing grain-boundary separation.

Chemical Analysis

Chemical analysis is used in investigating cracking failures that may have been caused by stress-corrosion cracking or other mechanical-environmental failure processes to help determine the cause and mechanism of failure. Chemical analysis of the environment, the metal, and surface deposits or scale on the metal is discussed on pages 24 and 25 in this volume.

Impurities and substances present at low concentrations or in trace amounts in the environment are of special interest where stress-corrosion cracking is a possibility, because they are the substances that usually induce this type of failure. Identification of the chemical compounds present in any surface deposits on the metal is important in determining the identity of corrodents and the nature of the damaging corrosion processes. However, great care should be taken to ensure that surface deposits are representative of the service environment, and are not residues of extraneous materials introduced during operations such as liquid-penetrant or magnetic-particle inspections performed after the failure.

In analyzing stress-corrosion-cracking failures, the nominal chemical composition of the metal usually is of less concern than the substances present at low concentrations or in trace amounts (usually as impurities) and than the structure of the metal.

Metallographic Analysis

Aspects of metallographic analysis that require special attention include the following:

1 Preferred grain orientation such that the direction of maximum stress is perpendicular to elongated grain faces
2 The possible existence of highly hardened surfaces resulting from improper machining practices, wear or localized working, which can initiate stress-corrosion cracks in high-strength materials
3 The possibility that impurities have been dissolved in the surface layers as a result of high-carbon or high-sulfur activity in the environment
4 The possibility that processing has introduced hydrogen into the metal, which can result in hydrogen-induced delayed fracture
5 Detailed analysis of grain-boundary regions to determine whether composition or structure was not controlled or was changed such that the grain boundaries are preferential regions for stress-corrosion attack (sensitization of austenitic stainless steel has such an effect)
6 The possibility that an impurity may be present that is not specified for the alloy and that would render the alloy particularly susceptible to stress-corrosion cracking. (This might include, for example, the presence of arsenic or antimony in stainless steel — elements for which chemical analysis usually is not conducted.)

It is not sufficient to consider only nominal chemical composition in assessing potential for stress-corrosion cracking; the possibility of surface contamination or changes in surface mechanical properties, as well as other structural changes resulting from heat treatment, also must be carefully considered.

Simulated-Service Tests

Once the cause and mechanism of a failure have been established, it is desirable to experimentally verify the conclusions so that appropriate corrective measures can be taken. These tests should simulate as closely as possible the environmental and mechanical conditions to which the failed part was subjected in service. Ideally, this involves testing a part in service; however, such testing frequently is not feasible because of factors such as length of time to failure or extraneous damage caused by failure of the part. Thus, simulated-service tests may have to be performed in the laboratory. The following should be carefully considered:

Environmental factors:

1 Temperature, which may be steady or fluctuating, and may also affect stress.
2 Single-phase or two-phase environment, which may involve alternate wetting and drying.
3 Composition, including major and minor environmental constituents, concentration and changes thereof, dissolved gases, and pH.
4 Electrochemical conditions, which may involve galvanic coupling or applied cathodic protection.

Mechanical factors:

1 Loading, which may be static or cyclic. If cyclic, mean stress may be zero, tensile or compressive; also, if cyclic, stress-wave shape and period must be defined.
2 Surface damage, which may occur by fretting or abrasion.

Combined mechanical and environmental factor:

Surface damage, which may occur by cavitation or liquid-impingement erosion.

The common methods for evaluating the susceptibility of metals to stress-corrosion cracking are described in Ref 5 and 6.

Test Conditions. When running simulated-service tests, exact duplication of service conditions cannot always be achieved. Also, the size and shape of the failed part may not be conducive to laboratory testing. In this circumstance, carefully selected test specimens should be machined from the original part, if possible, incorporating any design features that may have contributed to the failure, such as sharp bend radii or crevices.

Because many parts fail only after long periods of time, it is often not feasible to perform a simulation test of similar duration. In these instances, the tests may be accelerated by increasing the stress, temperature or concentration of the corrodent. However, changing these conditions may produce a type of failure completely different from that observed in service. Increasing the stress may produce failure by overload rather than stress-corrosion cracking, and increasing the temperature or concentration of the corrodent may produce general corrosion or pitting corrosion rather than stress-corrosion cracking. Meaningful accelerated testing is accomplished largely by trial and error.

Once failure of the test part or specimen has occurred, the failure must be investigated, using appropriate techniques to ensure that the failure mechanism and appearance are representative of that previously encountered.

Wrought Carbon and Low-Alloy Steels

Susceptibility to stress-corrosion cracking of carbon steels, which usually contain at least 0.10% carbon, generally increases as carbon content decreases. However, decarburized steel and bulk pure iron are resistant to cracking; thus, susceptibility must be at a maximum at some concentration of carbon between 0% and about 0.10%. The exact carbon content at which cracking occurs most readily is not known, but the susceptibility to cracking is high in steels containing 0.05% carbon (Ref 7).

The nature and concentration of other alloying elements in low-carbon steels have less effect on general susceptibility to stress-corrosion cracking than does microstructure.

Surveys of the stress-corrosion behavior of high-strength low-alloy steels in a variety of environments have shown that the strength of the steel is the most important single indication of sensitivity to stress-corrosion cracking. Steels with yield strengths of about 200,000 psi or higher are especially susceptible to this type of failure.

Caustic Cracking in Boilers. Caustic cracking of steel is a serious stress-corrosion problem and causes many explosions and failures of other types in steam boilers. The general conditions that cause caustic cracking are reasonably well understood, but failure by such cracking is still a problem.

Caustic-cracking failures frequently originate in riveted and welded structures near faying surfaces where small leaks permit soluble salts to build up high local concentrations of caustic soda and silica. Crack propagation ordinarily is intergranular. Failures of this type have been produced at concentrations of sodium hydroxide (NaOH) as low as 5%, but usually a concentration of 15 to 30% NaOH, plus a small amount of oxygen, is required to induce caustic cracking. Failures usually take place when the operating temperature is in the range of 200 to 250 C (about 390 to 480 F). The concentration of NaOH necessary for producing cracking increases as temperature decreases.

Cracking occurs where corrosion potential is such that only part of the steel surface is covered with an oxide film. Cracking can be prevented by anodic protection, which forms a continuous and more stable oxide film, or by cathodic protection, which completely reduces the oxide film.

Reducing pH, and adding strong oxidizing agents to passivate the steel surface, are common modifications of boiler-water treatment that are used to prevent caustic cracking. Inhibitors such as nitrates, sulfates, phosphates, and tannins have been used. However, adjustment of boiler-water composition and addition of inhibitors should be done only if the chemical behavior of the materials involved is fully understood and only after suitable laboratory testing, because adjustment of boiler-water composition can destroy the effectiveness of many inhibitors.

Common practice for most steam boilers is to control pH and to monitor the water supply or maintain an effective concentration of inhibitors.

Reducing grain size has been found to be helpful in decreasing the susceptibility to caustic cracking of the low-carbon steels generally used in boilers. Minor changes in steel composition are of little value, because they do not alter sensitivity at grain boundaries — areas that are preferentially attacked in caustic cracking. Stress relieving after welding is advisable in order to avoid excessive residual stress around the welds.

Cracking in Nitrate Solutions. Stress-corrosion cracking of carbon and low-alloy steels in nitrate solutions has occurred in tubing and couplings used in high-pressure condensate wells, and in storage tanks containing radioactive wastes.

Cracking in nitrate solutions follows an intergranular path. Boiling solutions of several nitrates, including NH_4NO_3, $Ca(NO_3)_2$, $LiNO_3$, KNO_3, and $NaNO_3$, have been found to produce cracking. In general, more acidic solutions have more potent effects. The threshold stress necessary to produce cracking decreases with increasing concentration of the nitrate in the solution. This threshold stress can be quite low. For example, exposure to boil-

ing $4.0N$ solutions of the above nitrates has produced cracking in some carbon and low-alloy steels at tensile stresses lower than 10,000 psi. Decreasing temperature increased time to failure. By extrapolation of these test results, it can be estimated that failure would occur in about 1,000 hr at room temperature. Room-temperature tests of bridge-cable wire in $0.01N$ nitrate solutions have produced failures after exposure for several months.

Decreasing pH enhances nitrate cracking, and resistance to cracking can be improved by raising pH. Sodium hydroxide, which causes caustic cracking by itself, can be added to nitrate solutions to retard cracking. The reverse is also true: nitrate additions retard caustic cracking. Cathodic protection can prevent stress-corrosion cracking in many nitrate solutions. Anodic polarization is harmful. In addition to sodium hydroxide, several other inhibitors prevent cracking.

In low-carbon steels, carbon content has a strong effect on susceptibility to nitrate-induced cracking. Initiation of stress-corrosion cracking is minimized when carbon content is lower than 0.001% (extremely low) or higher than about 0.18%. The threshold stress for cracking is low at carbon contents of about 0.05%, but increases at carbon contents above about 0.10%. Accordingly, decarburization of steel surfaces can lead to cracking in nitrate solutions. This effect of carbon content applies primarily to crack initiation. A stress-corrosion crack that starts in a decarburized surface layer will continue to propagate into the higher-carbon interior region of the metal. Tests performed on notched specimens have shown that pre-existing cracks will propagate in steels of high carbon content.

Crack initiation and propagation in nitrate solutions appear to be closely related to carbon, and possibly nitrogen, in grain-boundary regions. It has been suggested that cracking proceeds by a mechanism in which carbon-rich areas act as cathodes that sustain dissolution of the adjacent ferrite. As would be expected, changes in composition or processing history of the steel so as to alter carbon distribution can appreciably influence susceptibility to stress-corrosion cracking. Strong carbide-forming elements such as chromium, tantalum, columbium and titanium generally are helpful in improving resistance to cracking. Reducing grain size and cooling slowly after annealing are helpful also. Steels with pearlitic or coarse, spheroidized microstructures usually are less susceptible to cracking than steels containing fine carbides. Moderate cold working may increase susceptibility to cracking, but severe cold working is beneficial.

Just as in caustic cracking, full stress-relief annealing after welding can prevent cracking of welded assemblies, which may contain fairly high residual stresses in the as-welded condition.

Cracking in Ammonia. Carbon steel tanks containing ammonia have developed leaks because of stress-corrosion cracking. In one instance, cracking developed in the interior surface of the head regions of tanks having cold formed heads, but not in tanks that had been stress relieved after fabrication. Thus, residual tensile stresses, in combination with the applied stresses, evidently were sufficient for cracking to occur. Crack growth in the tanks that failed was slow, and the average service time before detection of leakage was three years.

It has been shown that both plain carbon steels and quenched and tempered low-alloy steels are susceptible to stress-corrosion cracking in ammonia. In this investigation, both intergranular and transgranular cracking occurred in the quenched and tempered steels, but only intergranular cracking in the carbon steels. The higher-strength steels were more susceptible to cracking.

These failures were not produced in pure ammonia, but occurred in the ammonia mixed with air, or with air plus carbon dioxide. The presence of water vapor delayed but did not prevent cracking. Cracking of this type occurs by a mechanism that is not fully understood, and there is no known means of preventing it.

Cracking in Other Environments. Stress-corrosion cracking of carbon and low-alloy steels also has occurred in other environments, including: carbon dioxide and carbonate solutions; mixtures of water, carbon monoxide and carbon dioxide; mixtures of ammonia, hydrogen, hydrogen sulfide, hydrogen cyanide and carbon dioxide; hydrogen cyanide; organic liquids, including methanol, butyl alcohol, acetone and carbon tetrafluoride; phosphorus trifluoride; sodium phosphate; nitric acid; sulfuric acid; and ferric chloride. In general, little is known about the conditions necessary for either initiation or prevention of stress-corrosion cracking in these environments.

Austenitic Stainless Steels

Although the stress-corrosion cracking of austenitic stainless steels has been studied extensively, it is not possible to predict the exact conditions under which failure will or will not occur. However, certain behavior patterns have been noted.

Austenitic stainless steels should be quenched rapidly from high temperatures to avoid sensitization. Slow cooling from about 850 C (1560 F) to about 550 C

(1020 F) in heat treatment or welding increases susceptibility to intergranular stress-corrosion cracking (or to intergranular corrosion), but rapid cooling through this range prevents such damage. The extent of damage is a function of both time and temperature. In general, the damage is attributable to the precipitation of chromium carbides at grain boundaries, resulting in a depletion of chromium in the matrix. The limits of the so-called sensitizing-temperature range cannot be defined exactly, because they are influenced by the composition of the stainless steel (especially the percentages of carbon and of stabilizing carbide-forming elements or combinations of elements such as titanium, columbium, and columbium plus tantalum).

Also, whether sensitizing is damaging in a given instance depends on the requirements of the specific application, on the environment and stresses to which the steel is exposed, and on the prior thermal and mechanical working history of the steel. Holding at temperatures as low as about 400 C (about 750 F) and as high as about 900 C (about 1650 F) for prolonged periods has been reported to cause sensitization of unstabilized austenitic stainless steels.

In austenitic stainless steels, stress-corrosion cracking proceeds transgranularly in solutions containing chlorides. It appears that cracking in chlorides usually occurs only at temperatures above about 70 C (about 160 F). Heat transfer intensifies stress-corrosion problems, probably by making concentration of chlorides at the metal surface possible. Even without apparent concentration, very low chloride content is sufficient to cause cracking, especially at higher temperatures. (The effect of nitrogen content on stress-corrosion cracking of austenitic stainless steels in the presence of magnesium chloride is discussed on page 209). As the nickel content of austenitic stainless steels is increased above about 10%, resistance to cracking in solutions containing chlorides is improved. Failure of type 316 stainless steel piping because of accidental exposure to condensate that contained chlorides is described in the example that follows.

Example 5. Stress-Corrosion Cracking of Type 316 Stainless Steel Piping Because of Chlorides Leached From Insulation (Fig. 9)

A 750-ton-per-day ammonia unit was shut down following a fire near the outlet of the waste heat exchanger. The fire had resulted from leakage of ammonia from the type 316 stainless steel outlet piping.

As Fig. 9(a) shows, the outlet piping immediately downstream from the waste heat exchanger was comprised of an 18-in.-diam flange, an 18-to-14-in.-OD reducing cone, a short length of 14-in.-OD pipe and a 14-in.-OD 90° elbow, all joined by circumferential welds. The flange was made from a casting, and the reducing cone, pipe and elbow were made of 1/2-in.-thick plate. A 13-in.-OD by 1/16-in.-thick liner wrapped with insulation was welded to the smaller end of the reducing cone. All of the piping up to the flange was wrapped with insulation.

Investigation. Visual examination disclosed cracks through the weld joining the flange and cone and into the base metal on either side. The cracks extended only a short distance into the flange, but well into the reducing cone. Cracks also were found in a short section of the longitudinal weld in the 14-in.-OD pipe between the cone and the elbow.

The piping assembly was cut into the individual components for ease of examination. The components were then liquid-penetrant inspected.

At the flange end of the cone, there were numerous cracks across the inner top surface from the 8 o'clock position to the 4 o'clock position. The area across the bottom of the cone, from the 4 o'clock position to the 8 o'clock position, was free of cracks. Only one of these cracks was visible on the outer surface. On the inner surface this crack extended across the weld metal and into the flange, but on the outer surface it did not entirely penetrate the weld metal. Also, the crack was shorter and discontinuous on the outside, indicating that it had originated at the inner surface. Figure 9(a) shows several of the cracks on the inner surface of the cone.

Visible cracks in the pipe section were confined to a 2- to 3-in.-long area in the longitudinal weld. Most of these cracks were in a generally transverse direction in the weld metal but did not appear to extend beyond the weld metal. This area also had a blue tint as a result of the fire, which was reported to have reached behind the insulation.

Analysis of the insulation wrapped around the liner revealed chlorides in the form of NaCl, at a concentration of 190 to 300 ppm, produced by selective leaching.

Metallographic examination of specimens from the cracked area of the cone shown in Fig. 9(b) revealed that both the weld joining the flange and the cone (Fig. 9c) and the base metal of the cone (Fig. 9d) contained several branched, transgranular cracks, all of which had originated at the inner surface. These cracks were characteristic of stress-corrosion cracking in austenitic stainless steel.

A macrograph of a cross section through the longitudinal weld in the pipe section is shown in Fig. 9(e). Cracks in this weld were much different from those in the weld joining the flange and cone. The cracks were in the outside surface, relatively straight and shallow, and nonbranched. At higher magnification (see Fig. 9f and g), it could be seen that the cracks were intergranular and lined with scale. These characteristics indicated that the cracks had been formed at high temperature.

Discussion. The branched, transgranular cracks in the flange-to-cone weld and in the base metal of the cone were characteristic of stress-corrosion cracks. Stress-corrosion cracking in type 316 stainless steel is most commonly caused by aqueous chlorides. Concentrated caustic also can cause this type of damage, but would not have been present in the waste heat exchanger. There were two possible sources of chlorides; boiler feedwater and insulation. The boiler feedwater was an unlikely source because it was monitored regularly to guard against chlorides. However, the insulation material between the cone and its inner liner was known to contain leachable chlorides.

Chlorides will not cause stress-corrosion cracking unless an aqueous phase is present, and thus the temperature of the outlet stream must have dropped below the dew point at some time. It is also possible that absence of insulation at the flange caused a cool spot at which condensation could occur.

Conclusions. The outlet piping failed in the area of the flange-to-cone weld by stress-corrosion cracking as the result of aqueous chlorides; the chlorides were leached from the insulation around the liner by condensate. The cracks in the longitudinal weld in the pipe section were caused by exposure of the weld metal to the high temperature of the fire behind the insulation.

Recommendations. To prevent future failures, it was recommended that the chlorides be eliminated from the system, the temperature of the outlet stream be maintained above the dew point at all times, or the type 316 stainless steel be replaced with an alloy more resistant to chloride attack. Use of a more resistant alloy, such as Incoloy 800, is the most reliable approach.

Austenitic stainless steels also are susceptible to stress-corrosion cracking in caustic environments. Both transgranular and intergranular failures have been observed. Fortunately, the conditions leading to caustic cracking are more restrictive than those leading to chloride cracking. Temperatures near or above the boiling point at ambient atmospheric pressure are required, and very concentrated caustic solutions usually are required.

Austenitic stainless steels have also suffered intergranular stress-corrosion cracking in polythionic acids ($H_2S_nO_6$; $n = 2$ to 5). Sensitized steels are most susceptible, but transgranular cracking of nonsensitized steels is also possible. Proper care to prevent the entry of moisture during shutdown prevents formation of polythionic acid in refinery equipment and is the most effective measure used in the petroleum industry for prevention of this type of failure.

Intergranular stress-corrosion cracking of austenitic stainless steels in boiling-water nuclear reactors has been reported. In most instances, the steel was sensitized, but cracking also has occurred in heavily cold-worked steels free of grain-boundary carbides.

The usual preventive measures (stress relief and cold reduction or peening to produce residual compressive stresses) are helpful in preventing stress-corrosion cracking of austenitic steels. Measures aimed at preventing chloride concentration at the metal surface also are helpful.

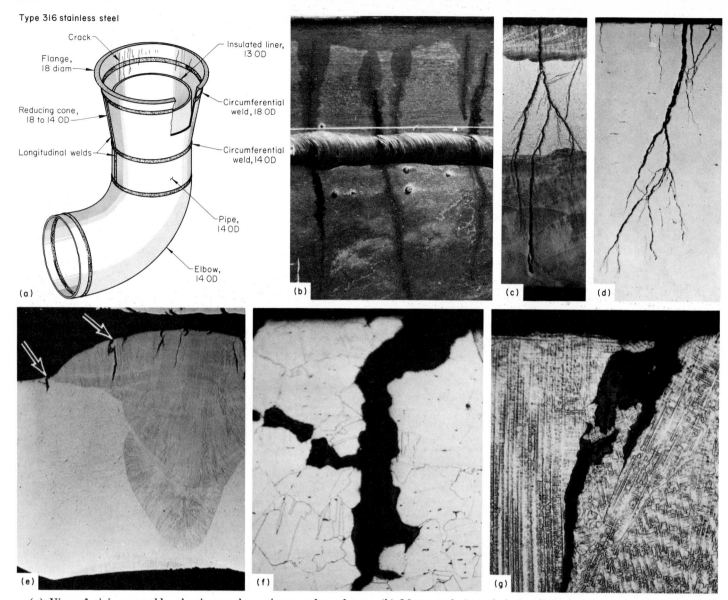

(a) View of piping assembly, showing cracks on inner surface of cone. (b) Macrograph (actual size) of failure region at flange-to-cone weld. (c) Macrograph, at 5×, of a longitudinal section (etched in oxalic acid) through flange-to-cone weld, showing branched cracks. (d) Macrograph, at 10×, of an unetched section through cone base metal near flange-to-cone weld, showing branched cracks. (e) Macrograph, at 10×, of an unetched section through longitudinal weld, showing shallow, nonbranched cracks. (f) and (g) Micrographs, at 100×, of sections (etched in oxalic acid) through weld shown in view (e) and through adjacent base metal, respectively, exhibiting intergranular scale-lined cracks.

Fig. 9. Type 316 stainless steel piping that failed by stress-corrosion cracking at welds; cracking was caused by exposure to condensate containing chlorides leached from insulation (Example 5)

It is advisable to use insulation materials that do not yield aggressive solutions by leaching, or to incorporate a suitable inhibitor in the insulation. Sensitization of the steel should be avoided even in environments that do not cause intergranular corrosion in the absence of stress. Welding practice should be adjusted to minimize residual stress and sensitization in the heat-affected zone.

Ferritic Stainless Steels

Fully ferritic stainless steels are highly resistant to stress-corrosion cracking in the chloride and caustic environments that crack the common austenitic stainless steels. However, laboratory investigations have shown that additions of small amounts of nickel or copper to ferritic steels may make them susceptible to cracking in severe environments. This is especially true for as-welded steels. Nevertheless, cracking in chloride or caustic environments in service occurs very rarely.

Ferritic stainless steels with chromium contents of 14% or more are subject to embrittlement at temperatures from about 370 to 540 C (about 700 to 1000 F). Embrittlement results in loss of room-temperature toughness.

Martensitic and Precipitation-Hardening Stainless Steels

Higher-strength martensitic and precipitation-hardening stainless steels are subject to stress-corrosion cracking and, to a greater degree, hydrogen damage. Actually, failure of these alloys under conditions that appear conducive to stress-corrosion cracking is so similar to failure caused by hydrogen damage that it often is questionable whether distinguishing between the two mechanisms is meaningful. Susceptibility to failure is determined primarily by metallurgical structure.

As expected, increasing yield strength of martensitic and precipitation-hardening stainless steels increases the probability of cracking. The environments that cause failure are not specific; almost any corrosive environment capable of causing hydrogen evolution can cause cracking also. Even as mild an environment as fresh water at room temperature may cause failure in especially susceptible alloys.

In the next example, a 17-4 PH (type 630) stainless steel part that had been sensitized by aging at too low a temperature failed by stress-corrosion cracking in high-purity water.

Example 6. Stress-Corrosion-Cracking Failure of a Sensitized 17-4 PH Stainless Steel Valve Stem in High-Purity Water (Fig. 10)

A 3.5-in.-diam valve stem made of 17-4 PH (type 630) stainless steel, which was used for operating a 24-in. gate valve in a steam power plant, failed after approximately four months of service, during which it had been exposed to high-purity water at about 177 C (350 F) and 1600 psi. The valve had been subjected to 25 hot cycles to 302 C (575 F) and 1825 psi by the manufacturer and to occasional operating tests at 260 C (500 F) during service. Valve stems of 17-4 PH stainless steel had given satisfactory performance in similar service conditions. The bottom of the stem, from which the valve gate was suspended, was in the shape of a T.

Manufacturing History. The valve stem was forged from 6-in.-square billet stock and is reported to have been solution heat treated at 1038 ± 14 C (1900 ± 25 F) for ½ hr and either air quenched or oil quenched to room temperature. It was then rough machined and afterward was inspected by magnetic-particle, liquid-penetrant and ultrasonic methods. At this stage, the stem reportedly was aged at a temperature from 552 to 593 C (1025 to 1100 F) for 4 hr before final machining. The final hardness to be expected from this treatment is less than Rockwell C 35. Final inspection was done by the liquid-penetrant method.

Laboratory Examination. Each of the two surfaces of the fracture showed a semicircular stain (see Fig. 10a) in a large area where fracture had propagated along prior austenite grain boundaries without deformation. The stains remained even after ultrasonic cleaning in a solution of detergent in hot water.

Also shown in Fig. 10(a) is a narrow cup-and-cone shear-type area of failure that extends almost all the way around the entire circumference of the fracture surface. This portion of the fracture was transgranular, with some deformation, but not enough to affect outside-diameter measurements ¼ in. away. In one narrow region of the periphery, intergranular fracture extended to the surface with no cup-and-cone shearing; intergranular stress-corrosion cracking may have begun here. This point also coincided with the junction of the stem with a tapered fillet at the T-head, which could have been a site of stress concentration.

Microscopic examination of the structure adjacent to the fracture revealed a pattern of typical stress-corrosion cracks that radiated from the fracture surface along the grain boundaries (see Fig. 10b). A macro-etched cross section displayed a region of coarse-grained material (ASTM No. 2 grain size) surrounded by a structure of finer and more uniform grain size that extended to the

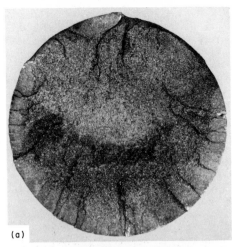

(a)

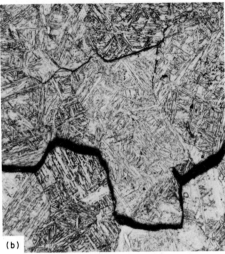

(b)

(a) A fracture surface of the valve stem, at 0.7×, showing stained area and cup-and-cone shearing at perimeter. (b) Micrograph, at 50×, showing secondary intergranular cracks branching from fracture surface.

Fig. 10. Power-plant gate-valve stem, made of 17-4 PH stainless steel, that failed by stress-corrosion cracking in high-purity water (Example 6)

surface. The coarse grain size was abnormal, suggesting that the solution heat treatment that should have followed forging may have been either omitted or carried out at too high a temperature. In either circumstance, coarse grain size would be conducive to low ductility.

The matrix was found to contain small areas of ferrite, which in turn contained fine precipitate. This type of structure has been found in specimens that have been slowly (furnace) cooled through the range of 454 to 399 C (850 to 750 F) after aging. Brinell hardness readings along the length of the stem indicated a uniform hardness throughout. Hardness readings taken from a cross section of the stem ¾ in. from the fracture surface averaged Rockwell C 42.

Because the hardness seemed too high for the reported aging temperature, a reheat treatment was undertaken as a double check. A portion of the failed stem was re-solution treated at 1038 C (1900 F) for 1 hr, oil quenched, and then sectioned to permit aging at a variety of times and temperatures.

The hardness values resulting from these aging treatments were as follows:

Aging treatment	Rockwell C hardness
1 hr at 482 C (900 F), air cool	44
4 hr at 496 C (925 F), air cool	41
4 hr at 524 C (975 F), air cool	39
1 hr at 552 C (1025 F), air cool	39
2 hr at 552 C (1025 F), air cool	37
4 hr at 552 C (1025 F), air cool	35

These results indicated that the stem had been aged at 496 C (925 F) or less, rather than at the reported 552 to 593 C (1025 to 1100 F).

Conclusion. Failure was by progressive stress-corrosion cracking that originated at a stress concentration, followed by ultimate shear of the perimeter when the effective stress exceeded the yield strength of the structure. Heat treatment had been improper, creating a structure having excessive hardness, inadequate ductility, and unfavorable sensitization to stress-corrosion cracking.

Corrective Measures. To prevent failures of this type in other 17-4 PH stainless steel valve stems, the following heat treatments were recommended: After forging, solution heat treat at 1038 C (1900 F) for 1 hr, then oil quench. To avoid susceptibility to stress-corrosion cracking, age at 593 C (1100 F) for 4 hr, then air cool.

Maraging Steels

Stress-corrosion cracking of maraging steels has been studied extensively, using U-bends, unnotched tensile specimens, machined notched specimens and fatigue-precracked fracture-toughness-test specimens. As with high-strength steels, the more severe the notch, the greater the susceptibility to stress-corrosion cracking.

Effect of Stress Intensity. As yield strength is increased, the threshold stress intensity needed for stress-corrosion cracking of maraging steels in aqueous environments decreases, as shown in the following tabulation of average values:

Yield strength, psi	Threshold stress intensity, psi · in.$^{\frac{1}{2}}$
200,000	100,000
250,000	40,000
300,000	10,000

This general trend of decreasing threshold values with increasing yield strength is similar to what is observed for other high-strength steels. At a given yield strength, maraging steels generally have somewhat higher threshold values than other high-strength steels.

Crack-growth rates for maraging steels usually show the three-stage curve characteristic of other high-strength steels. At lower stress intensities, rate of cracking increases exponentially with stress intensity. At higher stress intensities, a plateau is reached at which crack-growth rate is constant with increasing stress in-

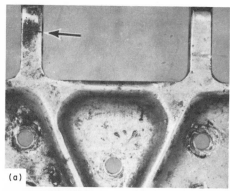

(a)

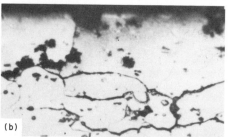

(b)

(a) Hinge bracket, shown at actual size; arrow indicates crack. (b) Micrograph, at 250×, of a section etched in Keller's reagent, showing secondary cracking adjacent and parallel to the fracture surface.

Fig. 11. Aluminum alloy 2014-T6 hinge bracket that failed by stress-corrosion cracking in service (Example 7)

tensity. At still higher stress intensities, near the values for fracture toughness in air, there is a further increase in rate of stress-corrosion cracking with stress intensity (see Ref 4). Crack-growth rate at a given stress intensity increases as yield strength increases.

Path of cracking usually is intergranular along prior austenite grain boundaries. Transgranular cracking has occurred also, and may preferentially follow the martensite-platelet boundaries. Whether or not the crack path depends on stress intensity, as in low-alloy steels, is not clear.

Microscopic branching of the main crack into two cracks inclined to the plane of the precrack occurs frequently, but the conditions that cause branching are not known. Crack branching in specimens broken in air has been reported and is believed to be associated with banding of the microstructure. Thus the appearance of crack branching by itself cannot be taken as proof of stress-corrosion cracking.

Effects of Environment. For smooth specimens tested in water, adding Cl⁻ ions and increasing pH from 9 to 13 accelerates stress-corrosion cracking, probably by accelerating pitting. With precracked specimens, these variables generally have much less effect. Cathodic protection has not been found to be a consistently effective way to prevent stress-corrosion cracking of maraging steels.

Effects of Heat Treatment. High annealing temperatures that coarsen the microstructure are deleterious. Underaging heat treatments generally are deleterious also. Overaging heat treatments have produced mixed results. Generally, the best practice is probably to use a low annealing temperature and the standard maraging heat treatment.

Effects of Cold Working and Prestressing. Cold working either before or after aging improves resistance to stress-corrosion cracking. Prestressing so as to leave residual compressive stresses at the notch roots is helpful also.

Effects of Composition. Variations in major alloying elements have little or no effect on cracking behavior. Of the minor elements, carbon and particularly sulfur are very deleterious. Marked improvement in resistance to cracking can be obtained if concentration of these elements is held to very low levels.

Prevention of Stress-Corrosion Cracking. As with other high-strength steels, there is no completely satisfactory way to prevent stress-corrosion cracking in maraging steels other than by reducing the strength level. In some instances, cathodic protection, surface coatings and prestressing can prevent stress-corrosion cracking, but techniques such as these must be used with care.

Aluminum Alloys

Stress-corrosion cracking occurs in high-strength aluminum alloys in ordinary atmospheric and aqueous environments. Both initiation and propagation of cracking are accelerated by moisture, temperature, chlorides and other industrial contaminants.

Although proper selection of both material and structural design and regular inspection in service normally prevent such failures from operating stresses, there are some factors that may be overlooked. The loading conditions responsible for corrosion-fatigue cracking generally are known, but the stress situations that generally cause initiation of stress-corrosion cracking are not known to the designer because they usually involve sustained tensile stresses that are not anticipated and cannot be measured with precision.

These situations frequently result from poor fit-up during assembly of structural components, or from residual stresses introduced into individual components during operations such as cold forming, welding, and quenching or straightening after heat treatment.

In the failure described in the example that follows, stresses produced by an interference fit of a bushing in a hole in an aircraft fitting contributed to failure of the fitting, which was exposed to a marine atmosphere.

Example 7. Stress-Corrosion Cracking of Forged Aluminum Alloy 2014-T6 Aircraft Hinge Brackets Because of Stresses From Interference Fit of a Bushing (Fig. 11)

Forged aluminum alloy 2014-T6 hinge brackets in naval-aircraft rudder and aileron linkages were found cracked in service. The cracks were in the hinge lugs, adjacent to a bushing made of cadmium-plated 4130 steel.

Investigation. Examination of the microstructure in a lug of a typical failed hinge bracket revealed intergranular corrosion and cracking in the region of the cracks discovered in service. The fracture was neither located along the flash line nor oriented in the short-transverse direction, both of which are characteristic of most stress-corrosion failures of forgings.

It was evident from the interference fit of the bushing in the hole of the lug that a hoop stress of sustained tension existed in the corroded area. The over-all condition of the paint film on the hinge bracket was good, but the paint film on the lug was chipped. Figure 11(a) shows the crack in the lug (arrow) and Fig. 11(b) shows branched secondary cracking adjacent to and parallel to the fracture surface.

Conclusions. Failure of the hinge brackets occurred by stress-corrosion cracking. The corrosion was caused by exposure to a marine environment in the absence of paint in the stressed area. The stress resulted from the interference fit of the bushing in the lug hole.

Corrective measures taken to prevent further failures were:

1 All hinge brackets in service were inspected for cracks and for proper maintenance of paint.
2 Aluminum alloy 7075-T6 was substituted for alloy 2014-T6, to provide greater strength. (Surface treatment for the 7075-T6 brackets was sulfuric acid anodizing and dichromate sealing.)
3 The interference fit of the bushing in the lug hole was discontinued. The bushings, with a sliding fit, were cemented in place in the lug holes.

Excessively high stresses in service sometimes result from mechanical stress raisers inherent in the design of the part or from stress raisers caused by localized corrosion, as in the following example.

Example 8. Stress-Corrosion Cracking of a Forged Aluminum Alloy 2014-T6 Aircraft Lug, Which Initiated at Local Corrosion (Fig. 12)

During a routine shear-pin check, the end lug on the barrel of the forward canopy actuator on a naval aircraft was found to have fractured. The lug was forged from aluminum alloy 2014-T6.

Investigation. As shown in Fig. 12(a), the lug had fractured in two places; the original crack occurred at the top, and the final fracture occurred at a crack on the left side of the lug. The surface of the original crack was flaky with white deposits that appeared to be corrosion products. Apparently, the origin of the failure was a tiny region of pitting corrosion on one flat surface of the lug (back surface in Fig. 12a; arrows there show location of pitting-corrosion region).

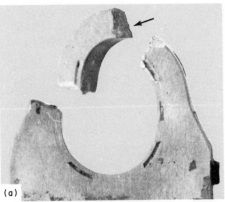

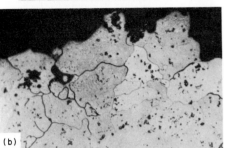

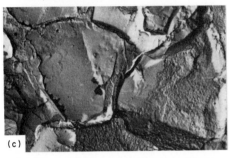

(a) View of the lug at 2×. Fracture at top was the initial fracture; arrow points to location of tiny region of pitting corrosion (on back side of lug) at which failure originated. Final fracture is at left. (b) Micrograph, at 140×, of an etched (Keller's reagent) section through surface of initial fracture, showing branched cracking. (c) TEM fractograph, at 2770×, showing corroded areas and features typical of stress-corrosion cracking.

Fig. 12. Forged aluminum alloy 2014-T6 actuator-barrel lug that failed by stress-corrosion cracking (Example 8)

The opposite flat surface (front in Fig. 12a) had a shear lip at the fracture edge.

A metallographic section through the initial fracture displayed intergranular branched cracking that had originated at the fracture surface, which was also intergranular (Fig. 12b). Electron-microscope fractography confirmed the intergranular nature of the fracture, revealing evidence of corrosion and typical characteristics of stress-corrosion cracking (Fig. 12c).

The bolt from the failed lug gave no indication of excessive loading and showed no evidence of deformation.

Conclusions. The cause of failure was stress-corrosion cracking resulting from exposure to a marine environment. The fracture occurred in normal operation at a point where damage from pitting and intergranular corrosion acted as a stress raiser, and not because of overload. The pitting and intergranular attack on the lug were evidence

Table 3. Ratings of Resistance to Stress-Corrosion Cracking (SCC) of Wrought Commercial Aluminum Alloys

Alloy series	Type of alloy	Strengthening method	Tensile strength, psi	SCC rating(a)
1xxx	Al	Cold working	10,000 to 25,000	A
2xxx	Al-Cu-Mg (1-2.5% Cu)	Heat treatment	25,000 to 45,000	A
2xxx	Al-Cu-Mg-Si (3-6% Cu)	Heat treatment	55,000 to 75,000	B
3xxx	Al-Mn-Mg	Cold working	20,000 to 40,000	A
5xxx	Al-Mg(1-2.5% Mg)	Cold working	20,000 to 42,000	A
5xxx	Al-Mg-Mn (3-6% Mg)	Cold working	42,000 to 55,000	B
6xxx	Al-Mg-Si	Heat treatment	22,000 to 55,000	A
7xxx	Al-Zn-Mg	Heat treatment	55,000 to 73,000	B
7xxx	Al-Zn-Mg-Cu	Heat treatment	75,000 to 90,000	B

(a) A = No known instance of stress-corrosion cracking in service or in laboratory tests. B = Stress-corrosion cracking has occurred in service with certain alloys and tempers; service failures can be avoided by careful design and assembly and proper selection of alloy and temper.

that the surface protection of the part had been inadequate as manufactured or had been damaged in service and not properly repaired in routine maintenance.

Recommendations. To prevent future failures of this type, the lug and barrel should be anodized in sulfuric acid and given a dichromate sealing treatment, followed by application of a coat of paint primer plus a lacquer top coat.

During routine maintenance checks, a careful examination should be made for damage to the protective coating, and any necessary repairs should be made by cleaning, priming and painting. Severely corroded parts should be removed from service.

Effect of Alloy Selection. High-purity and commercially pure aluminum and the relatively low-strength aluminum alloys are not susceptible to stress-corrosion cracking. Failures by this mechanism are associated chiefly with heat treated wrought products of the higher-strength alloys used in load-carrying structures, such as Al-Cu, Al-Zn-Mg, Al-Zn-Mg-Cu, and Al-Mg (3% or more Mg) alloys. With these alloys, processing and heat treatment must be controlled to ensure high resistance to stress-corrosion cracking. The relative resistance to stress-corrosion cracking of various wrought aluminum alloys in relation to strength is given in Table 3.

Effect of Direction of Stressing. Cast products are isotropic with regard to cracking, and directionality is generally not important in the performance of sheet (except in structural applications, such as the stressed skins of aircraft wings), but resistance to cracking of wrought products can vary markedly with direction of stressing. Service failures of extrusions, rolled plate and forgings have been caused chiefly by tensile stresses acting in the short-transverse direction relative to the grain structure. It is important to consider the direction of stress relative to the grain structure when designing structural components and performing failure analyses. Exceptions may occur in thin forged sections that recrystallize during solution heat treatment and have low directionality.

Effect of Precipitation Heat Treatment. For thick wrought sections, special precipitation heat treatments, such as those that produce T7 tempers in Al-Zn-Mg-Cu alloys and T8 tempers in Al-Cu alloys, have been developed to provide relatively high resistance to stress-corrosion cracking in the more critical short-transverse stressing direction. Evaluation of the resistance of improved alloys and tempers in accelerated corrosion tests, however, can be markedly influenced by test procedures, and reliance should therefore be placed mainly on exposure to outdoor atmospheres or other service environments.

Effects of Temperature. The resistance of the non-heat-treatable Al-Mg alloys, and of the naturally aged (T3 and T4 tempers) heat treated Al-Cu alloys, to stress-corrosion cracking can be adversely affected in structures subjected to elevated temperatures. The effects depend on the specific alloy and temper, on temperature, and on time at temperature.

Relative ratings of resistance to stress-corrosion cracking for various alloys and tempers are published by the Aluminum Association in Aluminum Standards and Data, and more detailed guidelines for comparing the high-strength alloys, tempers and product forms with respect to stressing direction are presented in MIL-Handbook-5.

Copper and Copper Alloys

Copper and copper alloys have excellent corrosion resistance in many industrial environments, in seawater and in marine atmospheres, but are susceptible to stress-corrosion cracking in some important industrial environments. These environments include those containing ammonia, citrate, tartrate, moist SO_2, and mercury.

Effect of Environment. Stress-corrosion cracking in copper alloys occurs most frequently in environments that contain ammonia or amines, in either aqueous solutions or moist atmospheres. Cracking occurs at room temperature and at stress

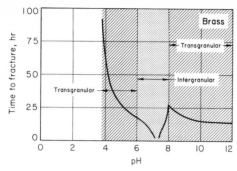

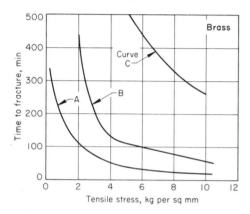

Fig. 13. Effect of pH on time to fracture by stress-corrosion cracking of brass in ammoniacal copper sulfate solution at room temperature

Curve A: Partly immersed in concentrated ammonium hydroxide. Curve B: Exposed to the vapor of concentrated ammonium hydroxide. Curve C: Exposed to a gaseous mixture of ammonia, oxygen, carbon dioxide and water vapor.

Fig. 14. Effect of initial tensile stress on time to fracture by stress-corrosion cracking at room temperature of brass in three corrosive environments

levels as low as 1% of the tensile strength of the alloy.

In aqueous solutions, pH has a strong influence on susceptibility to cracking and on whether crack paths are intergranular or transgranular, as shown for brass in ammoniacal copper sulfate solution in Fig. 13. Cracking occurs most rapidly in nearly neutral solutions, where the crack path is intergranular. The crack path is transgranular in both alkaline and acidic solutions, and the alloy is highly resistant to cracking when pH is less than 4.

Failure of copper and copper alloys will occur at low stresses in aqueous solutions and moist atmospheres. Figure 14 plots the relation between time to fracture at room temperature and initial tensile stress for brass partly immersed in concentrated ammonium hydroxide (curve A), exposed to the vapor of concentrated ammonium hydroxide (curve B), and exposed to a gaseous mixture of ammonia, oxygen, carbon dioxide and water vapor (curve C).

The presence of oxidizing substances such as dissolved oxygen and cupric, ferric and nitrate ions accelerates stress-

corrosion cracking of copper alloys in ammoniacal aqueous solutions. In stress-corrosion tests in which brass was exposed for 20 days to atmospheres containing (by volume) 0.1 to 1% sulfur dioxide, the specimens cracked, but similar specimens that had been pretreated with the inhibitor benzotriazole were unaffected. Pretreatment of brass specimens with benzotriazole failed to prevent cracking in tests in which the stressed specimens were exposed for 72 hr in an atmosphere containing (by volume) 2% ammonia and in an aged solution of ammonium hydroxide. Aqueous solutions of mercurous nitrate are widely employed in testing copper alloys for the presence of residual stresses that make the alloys susceptible to stress-corrosion cracking.

Effect of Alloying Elements. High-purity copper is almost immune to stress-corrosion cracking in most environments and in the practical range of service stresses. However, intergranular cracking of high-purity copper has been observed under some conditions, apparently as a result of segregation of trace impurities at the grain boundaries.

The resistance of copper to stress-corrosion cracking is greatly reduced by the presence of low concentrations of arsenic, phosphorus, antimony and silicon as alloying elements. Time to fracture for copper containing various concentrations of these alloying elements when stressed at an applied tensile stress of 10,000 psi is plotted in Fig. 15. As the concentration of each alloying element is increased, time to failure at first decreases, reaching a minimum between about 0.1 and 1%, and then increases.

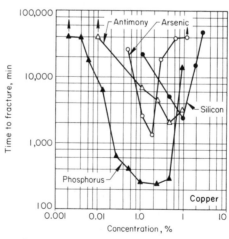

Effect of presence of low concentration of arsenic, phosphorus, antimony and silicon on time to fracture of copper by stress-corrosion cracking under an applied tensile stress of 10,000 psi in a moist ammoniacal atmosphere. Composition of test atmosphere was 80% air, 16% ammonia, and 4% water vapor; temperature was 35 C (95 F), which was above the dew point.

Fig. 15. Effects of arsenic, phosphorus, antimony and silicon on stress-corrosion cracking of copper

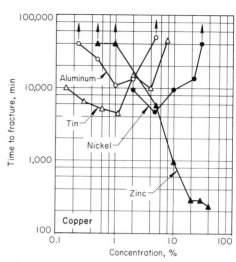

Effect of presence of low-to-moderate concentrations of aluminum, nickel, tin and zinc on time to fracture of copper by stress-corrosion cracking under an applied tensile stress of 10,000 psi in a moist ammoniacal atmosphere. Composition of test atmosphere was 80% air, 16% ammonia, and 4% water vapor; temperature was 35 C (95 F), which was above the dew point.

Fig. 16. Effects of aluminum, nickel, tin and zinc on stress-corrosion cracking of copper

Results of similar tests on copper containing higher concentrations of the alloying elements aluminum, nickel, tin and zinc are plotted in Fig. 16. Except for zinc, a minimum time to fracture is reached between about 1 and 5%; time to failure for copper containing zinc does not show a minimum for concentrations of 0.5 to 40%, but decreases with increasing zinc content for the concentration range shown in Fig. 16.

The effect of zinc content on susceptibility of copper-zinc alloys to stress-corrosion cracking when exposed to cooling-tower water containing amines and dissolved oxygen is discussed in the next example. The alloys that failed in this application had nominal zinc contents of 25, 26 and 40%. Two replacement cast silicon bronzes that gave satisfactory service contained less than 5 and 1.5% zinc; a satisfactory replacement wrought silicon bronze contained less than 1.5% zinc.

Example 9. Failure of Copper-Zinc Alloy Cooling-Tower Hardware Because of Stress-Corrosion Cracking and Dezincification (Fig. 17)

After 14 months of service, cracks were discovered in castings and bolts used to fasten together braces, posts and other structural members of a cooling tower, where they were subjected to externally applied stresses.

Selected specimens were removed and then examined in a laboratory to determine the nature and extent of the failures. A total of 35 samples of cracked hardware (21 castings and 14 bolts and nuts) from different zones of the cooling tower were removed for examination. The castings were made of copper alloys 862 and 863 (manganese bronze). The bolts and nuts were made of copper alloy 464 (naval brass, uninhibited). The water that was circulated through the tower had high concentrations of oxygen, carbon dioxide and chloroamines.

Investigation. Twenty-one representative castings, 16 of which had failed in service, were submitted for laboratory examination. After a preliminary examination, the castings were divided into two categories: those that had completely separated into two or more parts in service, and those that had not completely fractured but that contained cracks.

Fig. 17(a), (b) and (c) are photographs showing some of the castings that broke into two or more parts in service. The casting

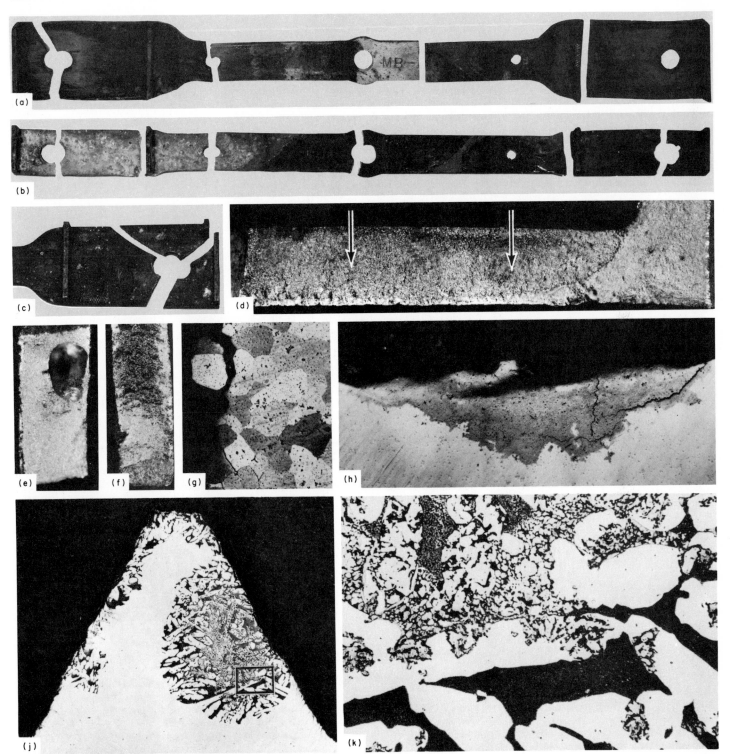

(a), (b) and (c) Photographs, at 1/3×, showing some of the castings that broke into two or more parts in service; in (b), separations other than those second from left and second from right were produced in laboratory bend tests. (d) Fractograph, at 2.5×, of a broken casting, showing area of stress-corrosion crack that occurred in service (arrows) and area of ductile fracture produced in a laboratory bend test.

(e) Fractograph, at 2.5×, showing a gas pocket in a bend-test specimen.

(f) Fractograph, at 2.5×, showing dross inclusions and porosity. (g) Mi-

crograph, at 100×, of a section (etched in NH₄OH) through a fracture surface, showing intergranular fracture path. (h) Micrograph, at 100×, of an unetched section through an area of plug-type dezincification; note cracks in deposit. (j) Micrograph, at 50×, of an unetched section through a partly dezincified bolt thread, showing initial attack in beta phase and subsequent attack in alpha (white) phase. (k) Micrograph, at 500×, of area enclosed in the rectangle in view (j), showing more clearly the sequence of attack in this two-phase structure.

Fig. 17. Copper-zinc alloy cooling-tower hardware that failed by stress-corrosion cracking and dezincification (Example 9)

pictured in Fig. 17(a) broke apart in four places. In Fig. 17(b), the separations second from the left and second from the right are complete breaks that occurred in service. The casting shown in Fig. 17(c) broke into three pieces in service.

Some of the castings had broken completely and were so badly corroded that it was impossible to gain information concerning the failure mechanism. Five of the castings appeared to be sound.

The unfailed fittings and unfailed areas of the other fittings were subjected to laboratory bend tests, which produced the two end and two central fractures shown in Fig. 17(b) and the fractures of which surfaces are shown in Fig. 17(d), (e) and (f).

The fractures resulting from the bend tests were of three types:

1 Fractures of samples in which cracking had been initiated in service
2 Brittle fractures through apparently sound areas containing large dross inclusions, some as great as 90% of the cross-sectional area
3 Ductile fractures through apparently sound areas containing small casting defects.

Figure 17(d) is a macrograph of a surface of a stress-corrosion crack (arrows) that had propagated most of the way through the casting. The lighter area along the lower edge and at the right was a ductile fracture produced in a bend test in the laboratory. Evidence of corrosion and dezincification was found in the upper parts of the fracture surface.

Gas pockets, or blowholes, such as the one shown in the fractograph in Fig. 17(e), in otherwise ductile metal were also the cause of fracture of laboratory bend-test specimens.

Figure 17(f) is a fractograph of a fracture surface containing large dross inclusions and extreme shrinkage porosity. The dark-gray area at bottom has been completely dezincified.

Figure 17(g) is a micrograph of a section through a fracture surface of a broken brace-connection casting, showing an intergranular fracture path.

A micrograph of a section through a local area of plug-type dezincification is shown in Fig. 17(h). The copper in the corrosion product was redeposited in a porous, friable and weak mass on the metal surface. Cracks are clearly in evidence in the deposit.

A review of the fractures in 15 of the hardware castings showed that 26 fractures had occurred in service by stress-corrosion cracking and dezincification and that four had been produced in laboratory bend tests. One service fracture and six laboratory fractures had occurred in areas that had been weakened by inclusions or shrinkage porosity. Two of the laboratory fractures had taken place near letter impressions that reduced the cross-sectional area. Ductile fracture had occurred in 14 instances during laboratory bend testing. One ductile fracture had occurred in an area containing blowholes.

Bolting Material. Only two of the 14 cracked bolts had broken during service. One had broken through the threaded portion, and one through the shank adjacent to the bolt head. Both fractures were brittle in nature. Laboratory bend tests failed to reveal other brittle areas in the bolts.

Corrosion attack in the form of dezincification was found at the innermost extremities of forging laps near the bolt heads and in the threaded sections. A micrograph of a section through one of the bolt threads that had been dezincified is shown in Fig. 17(j). Initial attack occurred in the beta phase followed by attack in the alpha (white) phase. The sequence of attack in the two-phase structure is more easily observed in Fig. 17(k), which shows at higher magnification the area enclosed in the rectangle in Fig. 17(j).

Conclusions. The castings and bolts failed by stress-corrosion cracking caused by the combined effects of dezincification damage and applied stresses.

Although the fracture surfaces of the failed castings were badly damaged, laboratory examination revealed the numerous areas containing stress-corrosion cracking. Brittle fractures at dross inclusions showed evidence of dezincification, and ductile fractures were produced in the castings during bend tests.

The bolts tested in the laboratory generally were of sound material, although evidence of dezincification was found in threads and at the bases of small forging laps.

Corrective Measures. Because of the susceptibility of copper-zinc alloys that contain relatively high percentages of zinc (manganese bronze castings and naval brass bolting materials) to stress-corrosion cracking in the recirculating water in the cooling tower, the castings were replaced with copper alloy 872 (cast silicon bronze) castings. Replacement bolts and nuts were made from copper alloy 651 or 655 (wrought silicon bronze).

The castings were inspected after 11 months of service, and no evidence of stress-corrosion cracking was found. Visual examination after approximately 24 months of service revealed some red stain on the surfaces of the castings and bolts. Metallographic examination revealed the stains to be superficial. Bend tests indicated that there had been no loss of strength in the material and that no cracks had developed.

The replacement hardware made of silicon bronze was in service for more than 16 years with no reported failures.

Magnesium Alloys

Commercial alloys of magnesium generally are resistant to failure by stress-corrosion cracking in their major applications, in which they are exposed to the atmosphere.

Effects of Environment and Alloy. Exposure to the atmosphere has been shown to have little effect on stress-corrosion cracking of magnesium alloys, whether in marine, industrial or rural environments. High-purity magnesium, and magnesium alloys containing manganese, rare earths, thorium, or zirconium, can be made to fail by stress-corrosion cracking only by exposure to corrodents such as dilute aqueous fluoride solutions at stresses higher than those encountered in normal service. Experience and testing of the commonly used commercial alloys

have shown that in atmospheric exposure, only wrought ZK60A (5.5% Zn, 0.45% Zr min) and the alloys containing more than approximately 1.5% aluminum are significantly susceptible to stress-corrosion cracking.

Effect of Product Form. When judged on the basis of safe stress as a fraction of tensile yield strength, castings are less susceptible to stress-corrosion cracking than wrought products of the same composition. Although wrought magnesium alloy products usually show some anisotropy in their mechanical properties, their resistance to stress-corrosion cracking is not appreciably influenced by the direction of applied stress in relation to the direction of working.

Test Methods. There is no standard accelerated test recommended for assessing the susceptibility of magnesium alloys to stress-corrosion cracking; generally, exposure of stressed specimens to the atmosphere has been used to determine stress-corrosion susceptibility of specific products. In most tests, spring-loaded "constant tension" fixtures have been used, and results of these tests have been supplemented by atmospheric tests on structures designed to simulate fabrication stresses.

Path of cracking in magnesium alloys generally is transgranular; but in Mg-Al alloys, intergranular cracking sometimes occurs. The crack path may change with changes in environment for a given alloy and processing and with changes in alloy processing for a given alloy composition and environment.

Causes and Preventive Measures. Stress-corrosion failures of magnesium alloy structures in service, which are infrequent, usually are caused by residual tensile stresses introduced during fabrication. Sources of such stresses are restrained weldments, interference fits and casting inserts.

Effective preventive measures include (a) stress-relief annealing of structures that contain residual stresses produced by welding or other methods of fabrication; (b) cladding with a metal or alloy that is anodic to the base metal; and (c) applying protective inorganic coatings or paint, or both, to the surface.

Nickel and Nickel Alloys

Commercially pure wrought nickel is not subject to stress-corrosion cracking in any of the chloride salts and has excellent resistance to all the nonoxidizing halides. Oxidizing acid chlorides, such as ferric, cupric and mercuric, are extremely corrosive and should be used only in low concentrations with wrought nickel. Stannic chloride is less strongly oxidizing, and dilute solutions at room temperature are resisted by commercially pure wrought nickel.

The susceptibility of austenitic Ni-Cr alloys to transgranular cracking in chloride solutions generally decreases as the nickel content of the alloy is increased. Inconel 600, which has a minimum nickel content of 72%, is virtually immune to chloride-ion stress-corrosion cracking. This alloy is subject to stress-corrosion cracking in high-temperature caustic alkalis in high concentrations. When the alloy is used in this type of service environment, it should be fully stress relieved prior to use, and operating stresses should be kept to a minimum. Stress-corrosion cracking may occur also in the presence of mercury at elevated temperatures. The recommendation given for caustic-alkali service should be followed if the alloy is used in an application that involves contact with mercury at elevated temperatures.

Inconel 601 has exhibited good resistance to stress-corrosion cracking in various corrosive mediums, including 45% magnesium chloride and 10 to 98% concentrations of sodium hydroxide.

Titanium and Titanium Alloys

Titanium is an inherently active metal that forms a thin protective oxide film. The apparent stability and high integrity of the film in environments that cause stress-corrosion cracking of most structural alloys make titanium and its alloys resistant to stress-corrosion cracking in boiling 42% magnesium chloride and boiling 10% sodium hydroxide solutions, which are commonly used to induce stress-corrosion cracking in stainless steels.

Effects of Environment and Temperature.
A number of environments in which some titanium alloys are susceptible to stress-corrosion cracking, and the temperatures at which cracking has been observed, are listed in Table 4. Some of these environments are discussed in the paragraphs that follow.

Red fuming nitric acid causes stress-corrosion cracking of titanium alloys in the absence of water; the presence of 1.5 to 2% water inhibits cracking. For some alloys, cracking occurs only in the presence of nitrogen dioxide.

Hot Dry Chloride Salts. Hot-salt stress-corrosion cracking of titanium alloys is a function of temperature, stress, and time of exposure. In general, hot-salt cracking has not been encountered at temperatures below about 260 C (500 F); greatest susceptibility occurs at about 290 to 425 C (about 550 to 800 F), based on laboratory tests. Time to failure decreases as either temperature or stress level is increased. All commercial alloys, but not unalloyed titanium, have some degree of susceptibility to hot-salt cracking.

Cadmium. Titanium alloys crack when in contact with liquid cadmium at a tempera-

Table 4. Environments and Temperatures That May Be Conducive to Stress-Corrosion Cracking of Titanium Alloys

Environment	Temperature
Nitric acid, red fuming	Ambient
Hot dry chloride salts	260-480 C(a)
Cadmium, solid and liquid ..	Ambient to 400 C(b)
Chlorine	Elevated
Hydrogen chloride	Elevated
Hydrochloric acid, 10%	Ambient to 40 C(c)
Nitrogen tetroxide	Ambient to 75 C(d)
Methyl and ethyl alcohols ..	Ambient
Seawater	Ambient
Trichloroethylene	Elevated
Trichlorofluorethane	Elevated
Chlorinated diphenyl	Elevated

(a) 500-900 F. (b) 750 F. (c) 100 F. (d) 165 F.

ture of 320 C (610 F) or higher if the protective oxide film on the titanium alloy is ruptured. These alloys will crack at ambient temperatures when solid cadmium is pressed tightly against the titanium alloy with sufficient force to rupture the oxide film (thus permitting direct metal-to-metal contact), and provided that the titanium alloy is under relatively high tensile stress.

Chlorine, Hydrogen Chloride and Hydrochloric Acid. In these environments, the mechanism of cracking is not completely understood, although it appears that both oxygen and water must also be present for cracking to occur.

Nitrogen tetroxide containing small amounts of dissolved oxygen causes cracking of titanium and some titanium alloys. No cracking occurs if the nitrogen tetroxide (N_2O_4) contains a small percentage of nitric oxide (NO). The cracking may be transgranular or intergranular, or both, depending on alloy composition.

Methyl and ethyl alcohols containing small amounts of water, chloride, bromide and iodide promote cracking at ambient temperatures. Greater concentrations of water inhibit cracking. Higher alcohols may induce cracking, but to a lesser extent; the longer the chain, the less reactive the alcohol becomes.

Seawater. Using standard smooth-surface U-bend and four-point loaded specimens, no susceptibility of titanium and its alloys to cracking in seawater and other chloride-containing solutions is found. Under plane-strain conditions using prenotched fatigue-cracked specimens, susceptibility to crack propagation depends on alloy composition and heat treatment. For example, alloys containing more than 6% aluminum are especially susceptible to rapid crack propagation in seawater. Tin, manganese, cobalt and oxygen have adverse effects, but isomorphous beta stabilizers such as molybdenum, columbium, or vanadium reduce or eliminate susceptibility to cracking.

References

1. W. M. Pardue, F. H. Beck, M. G. Fontana, Propagation of Stress-Corrosion Cracking in a Magnesium-Base Alloy as Determined by Several Techniques, *Trans ASM*, Vol 54, 1961, p 539-548

2. H. H. Uhlig, "Corrosion and Corrosion Control", 2nd Edition, John Wiley & Sons, Inc., New York, 1971
3. M. G. Fontana and N. D. Greene, "Corrosion Engineering", McGraw-Hill Book Co., New York, 1967
4. B. F. Brown (Ed.), "Stress-Corrosion Cracking in High-Strength Steels and in Titanium and Aluminum Alloys", Naval Research Laboratory, Washington, D. C., 1972
5. W. H. Ailor, Jr., "Handbook on Corrosion Testing and Evaluation". John Wiley & Sons, Inc., New York, 1971
6. M. Henthorne, "Corrosion Causes and Control", Carpenter Technology Corp., Reading, Pa., 1972
7. K. Bohnenkamp, Caustic Cracking of Mild Steel, p 374-383 in "Fundamental Aspects of Stress Corrosion Cracking" (conference held at the Ohio State University, Sept 11-15, 1967), R. W. Staehle, A. J. Forty and D. van Rooyen (Editors), National Association of Corrosion Engineers, Houston, Texas, 1969

Selected References

J. Hochmann, J. Slater and R. W. Staehle (Editors), "Stress-Corrosion Cracking and Hydrogen Embrittlement of Iron Base Alloys" (conference held at Unieux-Firminy, France, June 12-16, 1973), National Association of Corrosion Engineers, Houston, Texas (in publication by NACE, as of 1975)

F. H. Cocks (Ed.), "Manual of Industrial Corrosion Standards and Control", STP 534, ASTM, 1974

N. E. Hamner (Ed.), "Corrosion Data Survey", 5th Edition, National Association of Corrosion Engineers, Houston, Texas, 1974

M. G. Fontana and R. W. Staehle (Editors), "Advances in Corrosion Science and Technology", Vol 3, Plenum, New York, 1973

H. L. Craig (Ed.), "Stress Corrosion Cracking of Metals — A State of the Art", STP 518, ASTM, 1972

J. C. Scully, "The Theory of Stress Corrosion Cracking in Alloys", North Atlantic Treaty Organization, Brussels (1971)

H. Leidheiser, Jr., "The Corrosion of Copper, Tin, and Their Alloys", John Wiley & Sons, Inc., New York, 1971

R. D. Barer and B. F. Peters, "Why Metals Fail", Gordon and Breach Science Publishers, Inc., New York, 1970

R. W. Staehle, A. J. Forty and D. van Rooyen (Editors), "Fundamental Aspects of Stress Corrosion Cracking" (conference held at the Ohio State University, Sept 11-15, 1967), National Association of Corrosion Engineers, Houston, Texas, 1969

C. D. Beachem, "Microscopic Fracture Processes", Chapter 4, p 243-350, in H. Liebowitz (Ed.), "Fracture, Vol I, Microscopic and Macroscopic Fundamentals", Academic Press, Inc., New York, 1968

A. S. Tetelman and A. J. McEvily, Jr., "Fracture of Structural Materials", Chapter 9, "Fracture Under Static Loading", John Wiley & Sons, New York, 1967

H. Godard, W. B. Jepson, M. R. Bothwell and R. L. Kane, "The Corrosion of Light Metals", John Wiley & Sons, Inc., New York, 1967

"Stress Corrosion Testing", STP 425, ASTM, 1967

Hugh L. Logan, "The Stress Corrosion of Metals", John Wiley & Sons, Inc., New York, 1966

J. A. Whittaker, "A Survey on the Stress Corrosion of Copper Based Alloys", International Copper Research Association, New York, 1965

J. K. Stanley, The Current Situation on the Stress-Corrosion and Hydrogen Embrittlement of High Strength Fasteners, Paper No. 72-385, AIAA/ASME/SAE Conference held at San Antonio, Texas, Apr 10-12, 1972, American Institute of Aeronautics and Astronautics, New York

Liquid-Metal Embrittlement

By the ASM Committee on Failure by Mechanical-Environmental Processes*

LIQUID-METAL EMBRITTLE-MENT, as discussed in this article, is the decrease in strength or ductility of a solid metal caused by contact with a liquid metal. Liquid-metal embrittlement results in either (*a*) a decrease in tensile elongation prior to failure or (*b*) fracture without plastic deformation at stress levels below the normal yield strength of the material. Initiation of embrittlement may occur instantaneously upon contact of the solid by the liquid metal or may be delayed until wetting of the solid metal takes place.

A normally ductile metal subjected to tensile stress while in contact with a liquid metal may fracture at an abnormally low stress with little or no ductility. Unlike initiation of fracture by corrosion or stress corrosion, initiation of fracture by liquid-metal embrittlement is not time dependent. It begins immediately on application of the stress if wetting has occurred, and the crack continues to grow as long as (*a*) there is sufficient liquid metal present to cover at least part of the fracture surfaces and (*b*) some vapor reaches the crack tip.

Differences From Stress-Corrosion Cracking

Probably because of the specificity of embrittling agents for any given class of alloys, many correlations and analogies between liquid-metal embrittlement and stress-corrosion cracking have been proposed. Analogies regarding temperature dependence, grain size, crack-growth velocity, stress, alloy composition and other parameters are deceptive, and may lead to erroneous conclusions in failure analysis.

Some of the major differences between liquid-metal embrittlement and stress-corrosion cracking are:

1 Stress-corrosion cracking proceeds under the influence of positively and negatively charged ions in aqueous solution that interact with solid metals and with each other in a manner related to their aqueous ionic condition. The interaction between liquid and solid metals in liquid-metal embrittlement is completely different in nature.
2 In aqueous environments, dissolution of atoms from the metal surface requires a greater change in free energy than does dissolution in liquid-metal

*See page 205 for committee list.

environments. Furthermore, the strain energy of a dislocation, which is about 5% of the total free-energy change for dissolution of an atom in an aqueous environment, is approximately equal to the free-energy change for dissolution of an atom in a liquid metal. Thus, dissolution from a point where a dislocation intersects a free surface in contact with the liquid metal can occur as a result of very little additional energy.
3 In stress-corrosion cracking (but not in liquid-metal embrittlement), for every dissolution step a reduction or cathodic step must occur. The reduction rate often may control the anodic process. For example, the rate of stress-corrosion cracking of austenitic stainless steel in neutral chloride solutions is controlled by the availability of a reducible substance (oxygen).

Mechanism

The following conditions generally are accepted as prerequisites for the occurrence of liquid-metal embrittlement:

1 The metals involved do not form stable high-melting intermetallic compounds.
2 The metals have no significant mutual solubility.
3 The surface of the solid metal must be wettable by the liquid metal.

To date, no detailed and comprehensive explanation of the mechanism of liquid-metal embrittlement has been advanced. In general, the present theories postulate a reduction in the surface energy of the solid by the liquid and access of the liquid to the crack tip. However, a model involving vapor transport, which was developed from studies on embrittlement of steels, appears to be applicable to embrittlement of other metals also.

Tests in which high-strength low-alloy steels were exposed under stress to both liquid and solid cadmium have shown that exposure of the bulk solid metal to a liquid metal (as by immersion or general condensation) is not necessary for embrittlement to take place. Embrittlement can occur by transport to the crack tip of atoms of the embrittling metal in the vapor phase, even at temperatures well below the melting point of the embrittling metal.

Test exposure of notched specimens of 4340 steel, vacuum arc-remelted D-6ac steel, and 200B maraging steel to cadmium has produced intergranular cracking at temperatures of 205 C (400 F) and

230 C (450 F) — well below the melting point of cadmium (321.1 C or 610 F).

To eliminate any possibility of hydrogen embrittlement, the test specimens, which had been heat treated to a tensile strength of 220,000 to 240,000 psi, were vacuum metallized (instead of electroplated) with cadmium.

Except in one of three specimens of 200B maraging steel, no cracking was observed after more than 200 hr at a temperature of 163 C (325 F) under a stress of 75% of the notched tensile strength. However, when the steel specimens were subsequently tested at higher temperatures (but substantially below the melting point of cadmium) while being stressed at 65% of their notched tensile strength, (*a*) intergranular cracking occurred in D-6ac specimens after 55 hr at 230 C (445 F) and after 71 hr at 205 C (400 F), (*b*) intergranular cracking and complete fracture occurred in a 4340 steel specimen after 82 hr at 230 C (450 F), and (*c*) intergranular cracking took place in two specimens of 200B maraging steel after 55 hr at 230 C (450 F) and after 75 hr at 205 C (400 F).

Tests were done also on notched specimens electroplated with cadmium. On some of these specimens, the notches were masked with neoprene during electroplating to provide cadmium-free notches; on others, electroplated cadmium was removed from the notches by machining before testing. For complete results of these tests, which provided additional evidence supporting the vapor-transport mechanism for liquid-metal embrittlement, see Ref 1.

Also, embrittlement of leaded 4145 steel (0.30% Pb) at temperatures as low as 205 C (400 F), substantially below the melting point of lead (327.5 C or 621.5 F), has been observed in tests described in Ref 2. In this investigation also, embrittlement was attributed to transport of lead atoms in the vapor phase to the crack tip.

Further studies (Ref 3 and 4) have shown liquid-metal embrittlement to be common in a wide variety of leaded carbon and alloy steels having a wide range of carbon contents. The following model of the fracture process was developed. In leaded steels, the lead normally is present as a boundary phase surrounding nonmetallic inclusions. When the specimen is loaded beyond the yield stress, microcracks are initiated at the inclusions. At temperatures above its melting point, the lead proceeds part of the way down the crack as a liquid, aided by surface-tension effects, and completes its movement to the crack tip as a vapor. At temperatures below the melting point, the lead travels by vapor transport alone. Studies of failures in jet engines have confirmed this model, and two techniques for alleviating the embrittling effect have been developed. These techniques are prior cold deformation of leaded steels and addition of rare-earth metals such as cerium to leaded steels.

An intriguing aspect of liquid-metal embrittlement is the specificity of the embrittling agents. For example, gallium causes severe embrittlement of aluminum alloys but has little or no effect on plain carbon steel, magnesium, and copper alloys.

Susceptibility of Various Metals

Carbon and low-alloy steels, stainless steels, aluminum and aluminum alloys, copper and copper alloys, magnesium alloys, nickel and nickel alloys, and titanium and titanium alloys differ in susceptibility to embrittlement by contact with liquid metals as discussed below.

Carbon and low-alloy steels have been found to be susceptible to liquid-metal embrittlement in a number of molten metals other than cadmium, which has been discussed previously. The degree of embrittlement is greater for steels that have been heat treated or alloyed to produce higher strength. For example, mercury-sodium amalgams will embrittle high-strength steel at room temperature but have no effect on plain carbon steels such as 1010.

Studies conducted on several low-carbon and low-alloy steels at temperatures from 260 to 815 C (500 to 1500 F) have revealed that embrittlement of these steels is caused by contact with the following metals in the liquid state: brass, aluminum bronze, copper, zinc, lead-tin solders and indium. In addition, the embrittling effect of lithium at its melting point (180.5 C or 356.9 F) is well documented in the literature. Failure of welded 4130 steel occurs within one minute at an applied stress of only 15,000 psi in the presence of molten lithium.

Stainless steels generally are quite resistant to liquid-metal embrittlement and sustain little or no degradation in properties when contacted by liquid metals that severely embrittle plain carbon and low-alloy steels.

Aluminum and Aluminum Alloys. Although liquid-metal embrittlement of aluminum alloys is not common, it can result in rapid failure. Mercury, gallium, indium, tin and alkali metals (except lithium) are embrittling agents, whereas lead, bismuth and cadmium are not.

Several aluminum alloys, including 1100, 2024, 3003, 5083, 5454, 6061, 6063, 6066, 7001, 7075 and 7079, have shown some degree of embrittlement by mercury. In general, the higher the strength of the alloy, the more severe the embrittlement. Exposure to mercury of aluminum alloy structures containing even quite low tensile stress can result in failure by liquid-metal embrittlement. Failures have resulted from accidental spillage of mercury from pressure gages or broken thermometers.

In structures not subject to fatigue loading, components made of 5*xxx* and 6*xxx* aluminum alloys that are not susceptible to stress-corrosion cracking may fail catastrophically if exposed to mercury. After such a failure, elimination of mercury contamination of other components or adjacent structures must be complete.

In failure analysis when the presence of mercury is suspected, visual and macroscopic examination of the corroded or fracture surfaces can be very helpful in detecting the presence of tiny globules of the liquid metal.

Copper and Copper Alloys. Brasses and bronzes are particularly susceptible to liquid-metal embrittlement by mercury. In general, cracking follows an intergranular path. The time to failure is dependent on the stress level. No effective inhibitor of embrittlement of brass and bronze by mercury has been found, but additions of tin or silicon appear to lessen the degree of embrittlement.

Brasses also are susceptible to liquid-metal embrittlement by tin, lead, and their alloys, even at very low stresses.

Copper and copper alloys other than brass are embrittled by bismuth, bismuth-lead alloys rich in bismuth, lithium, and, under some conditions, mercury. The cracks caused by exposure of these metals in the solid state to liquid metals are usually intergranular. Stress-corrosion cracking in copper alloys may be either intergranular or transgranular, depending on pH, alloying concentrations, and variations in environmental species.

Magnesium alloys are relatively insensitive to embrittlement by liquid metals. Liquid sodium and liquid zinc are the only low-melting-point metals that cause embrittlement of magnesium.

Nickel and nickel alloys, although rapidly corroded by mercury or lead, show little or no embrittlement. Similar observations have been recorded for cobalt exposed to bismuth and cadmium.

Titanium and Titanium Alloys. Mercury embrittlement of titanium has occurred when titanium was deformed while immersed in mercury. Molten cadmium embrittles titanium; in addition, brittle fracture of several titanium alloys in intimate contact with solid cadmium has occurred at ambient temperatures. The oxide film on titanium must rupture before embrittlement can occur.

References

1. J. F. Hildebrand, Cadmium Embrittlement of High Strength, Low Alloy Steels at Elevated Temperatures, *Materials Protection and Performance,* Vol 12, No. 9, Sept 1973, p 35-40
2. S. Mostovoy and N. N. Breyer, The Effect of Lead on the Mechanical Properties of 4145 Steel, *Trans Am Soc Metals,* Vol 61, No. 2, June 1968, p 219-232
3. N. N. Breyer and P. Gordon, Lead Induced Brittle Failures of High Strength Steels, *Proceedings of the Third International Conference on the Strength of Metals and Alloys,* Cambridge, England, Aug 1973
4. W. R. Warke and N. N. Breyer, Effect of Steel Composition on Lead Embrittlement, *J Iron Steel Inst,* Oct 1971, p 779-784

Selected References

C. M. Preece, Adsorption-Induced Embrittlement of Metals, *Research/Development,* Vol 23, No. 10, Oct 1972, p 30-34
S. J. Matthews, M. O. Maddock and W. F. Savage, How Copper Surface Contamination Affects Weldability of Cobalt Superalloys, *Welding J,* May 1972, p 326-328
W. Rostoker, J. M. McCaughey and H. Marcus, "Embrittlement by Liquid Metals", Reinhold Publishing Corp., New York, 1960

Hydrogen-Damage Failures

*By the ASM Committee on Failure by Mechanical-Environmental Processes**

HYDROGEN DAMAGE (hydrogen embrittlement) is a mechanical-environmental failure process that results from the initial presence or absorption of excessive amounts of hydrogen in metals, usually in combination with residual or applied tensile stresses. It occurs most frequently in high-strength steels and certain other high-strength alloys. Cracking caused by this process is often referred to as hydrogen-stress cracking and hydrogen-induced cracking.

Hydrogen damage in one form or another is a problem with many types of alloys, and in some instances severely restricts the use of certain materials. Because of the ready supply of hydrogen available in such environments as water, moist air, hydrocarbons, acids and hydrogen sulfide, and in chemicals during processing, pumping or storage, hydrogen damage can develop in a wide variety of environments and circumstances.

Embrittlement by hydrogen damage manifests itself as a decrease in tensile ductility (reduction in area in laboratory testing), a decrease in notched tensile strength, and delayed failure by fracture under static loading. Yield strength is not significantly affected.

In the absence of a sharp initial crack, hydrogen-induced fracture caused by the diffusion of hydrogen into the metal often initiates at subsurface sites where triaxial stress is highest. When the critical stress is exceeded, a crack initiates and propagates through the region of high hydrogen concentration.

If a sharp crack is already present, such as a fatigue or stress-corrosion crack, the hydrogen cracking may initiate at the tip of the pre-existing crack. In quenched-and-tempered steels, hydrogen cracking usually follows prior austenite grain boundaries.

In metals that have high notch sensitivity, the extent of crack growth is usually quite small, and the probability of detecting a crack before complete failure occurs is thus also small.

In some types of hydrogen damage, cracking is promoted by high internal pressure caused by the combination of atomic hydrogen into molecular hydrogen gas at internal discontinuities or inclusions in the interior of the metal. It has

been suggested that hydrogen enhances cracking because hydrogen absorption at these sites lowers the surface energy required for cracks to grow. Another suggestion is that hydrogen reduces the bonding energy of the metal lattice sufficiently to allow cracking.

Types of Hydrogen Damage

Specific types of damage by hydrogen, some of which occur only in specific alloys or groups of alloys, are:

1 Cracking from hydrogen charging
2 Hydrogen-induced blistering
3 Hydrogen-induced cracking from decarburization
4 Cracking from hydrogen-induced slow-strain-rate embrittlement
5 Hydrogen-induced cracking from static fatigue
6 Cracking from hydride formation
7 Cracking from exposure to molecular hydrogen gas
8 Cracking from exposure to hydrogen sulfide
9 Cracking from exposure to water and dilute aqueous solutions.

Exposure to molecular hydrogen gas, hydrogen sulfide, and water and dilute aqueous solutions also can produce stress-corrosion cracking in certain metals (see discussion under "Specific Ions and Substances", and Table 1, on page 210 in this volume).

Three characteristics of hydrogen damage are: (*a*) subsurface hydrogen pressure in the metal, or deleterious effects of hydrogen or its reaction products, or both, are primary factors in producing cracking; (*b*) the "specific ion" effect that characterizes stress-corrosion cracking is absent; and (*c*) response to changes in environmental factors, such as applied potential (see "Laboratory cracking tests" on page 238), differs from that of stress-corrosion cracking.

Cracking From Hydrogen Charging

In hydrogen charging, atomic hydrogen is introduced into metals by processes such as pickling, electroplating, galvanic coupling to a more anodic metal, cathodic-protection reactions, and stray currents. Corrosion reactions that generate hydrogen at metal surfaces also result in hydrogen charging (see discus-

sion under "Cracking From Water and Dilute Aqueous Solutions", page 233).

In addition, metal specimens for use in studying hydrogen embrittlement are intentionally charged with atomic hydrogen by electrolysis or electroplating at controlled current densities and by other means.

If enough hydrogen is absorbed and diffuses into the metal lattice, the metal can become embrittled. Embrittlement may occur when a critical amount of hydrogen precipitates out of solution within the metal as hydrogen gas at voids or points of weakness in the metal.

The presence of certain chemical substances that prevent the formation of hydrogen-gas molecules increases the concentration of atomic hydrogen that can be absorbed by the metal during charging. These substances, which are called cathodic poisons, include phosphorus, arsenic, antimony, sulfur, selenium, tellurium, and the cyanide (CN^-) ion.

The highest attainable pressure of gaseous hydrogen in voids is approximately 13,000 atm. This pressure can be attained by intense electrolytic charging of iron samples in sulfuric acid solutions containing arsenic.

Pickling and Electroplating. Hydrogen diffuses into the metal during pickling and plating operations. Pickling alone is not a serious problem (unless internal voids or other imperfections lead to local formation of molecular hydrogen), because much of the absorbed hydrogen gradually diffuses out of the metal. Heating at 150 to 200 C (300 to 390 F) speeds up the removal of hydrogen. Also, the addition of suitable inhibitors to the pickling solution eliminates or minimizes attack on the metal and the consequent generation of hydrogen.

Plating solutions and plating conditions selected to produce a high cathode efficiency minimize the amount of hydrogen generated on the metal surface that can be absorbed into the metal. However, electroplated and other metallic coatings act as barriers to effusion of hydrogen, and elevated-temperature baking after plating is required for removal of the hydrogen. Baking for 3 or 4 hr at 190 C (375 F) usually suffices, unless the coating is cadmium, through which hydrogen diffuses less readily than through other

*See page 205 for committee list.

electrodeposited metals. Raising the baking temperature to accelerate effusion is not possible without reducing the protective qualities of the cadmium plate. Thus, baking time is lengthened.

Procedures for prevention of hydrogen damage in electroplating and preparation for electroplating are described in ASTM Standards. Salt baths that are operated at about 210 C (410 F) can be used for descaling titanium alloys, superalloys and refractory metals, to avoid the possibility of hydrogen charging associated with pickling.

Galvanic Coupling and Cathodic Protection. The galvanic coupling of metals that differ significantly in solution potential can lead to hydrogen embrittlement. For example, the galvanic coupling of a high-strength steel to a more active metal (zinc, magnesium or aluminum) could result in hydrogen absorption by the steel. In such a couple, the steel is the cathode and hydrogen is produced at the cathode in an electrochemical reaction. In a similar manner, cathodic protection of a high-strength steel could result in hydrogen embrittlement.

Stray currents sometimes cause embrittlement by increasing the corrosion rate in a localized region and thereby producing substantial amounts of hydrogen. Cracking is likely to occur if the localized corrosion causes hydrogen accumulation in or near a highly stressed area of the metal.

Hydrogen-Induced Blistering

Hydrogen-induced blistering is most prevalent in low-strength alloys, and is sometimes observed in metals that have been cleaned by pickling. During pickling, atomic hydrogen generated at the metal surface is absorbed by the metal. If enough hydrogen is absorbed, subsurface cracks may be formed in regions where hydrogen is highly concentrated.

If these cracks are just below the surface, the hydrogen-gas pressure in the cracks can lift up and bulge out the exterior layer of metal so that it resembles a blister. The equilibrium pressure of the molecular hydrogen in the void, which is in contact with the atomic hydrogen in the surrounding metal, is great enough to rupture any metal or alloy.

Figure 1 is a micrograph of a cross section through a 1020 steel specimen that shows subsurface inclusions where molecular hydrogen precipitated at the matrix-particle boundaries, causing a hydrogen blister.

The absorbed hydrogen can come from any source. Corrosion-generated hydrogen causes blistering of steel in oil-well equipment and petroleum storage and refinery equipment.

In a completely different type of corrosive environment, severe blistering was

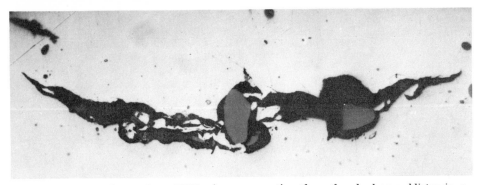

Fig. 1. Micrograph, at about 385×, of a cross section through a hydrogen blister in a 1020 steel specimen and the subsurface inclusion at which molecular hydrogen precipitated at the matrix-particle boundaries, causing the blister

produced on the interior surface of a low-carbon steel tank used to transport concentrated sulfuric acid. Slight dilution of the acid had resulted in chemical attack on the 7/32-in.-thick tank wall and diffusion of atomic hydrogen into the steel, where the atomic hydrogen formed molecular hydrogen and built up sufficient pressure to cause severe blistering within 1/16 in. of the inside surface of the tank wall. In the absence of significant internal discontinuities in which it could collect, the hydrogen probably would have diffused completely through the tank wall without producing blistering. Microscopic examination of specimens of the steel a short distance from the blistered region established that the metal had a normal, partly spheroidized structure and was free from defects; bend tests showed that it had satisfactory ductility.

The occurrence of corrosion-generated hydrogen blistering can be minimized by the use of metals that are chemically resistant to the environment and free from significant internal imperfections, and by making allowance for environmental contamination that is known to occur in the specific application.

Hydrogen-Induced Cracking From Decarburization

One way in which decarburization, the selective removal of carbon from a metal, occurs is by chemical reaction with an environment that contains hydrogen or hydrogen compounds. This type of hydrogen damage is most commonly found in steels that are subjected to elevated temperatures in petrochemical-plant equipment. As the reaction continues, a decarburized layer on the surface of the metal grows to increasing depths. Cracking may develop in the metal under tensile stress, or the progressive weakening of the metal as the decarburization progresses may result in failure by some other mechanism (see API Publication 941, July 1970).

Under certain circumstances, heat treatment in atmospheres of pure hydrogen also can cause decarburization. An

example is the annealing of electrical steels and special high-nickel alloys at about 1100 C (2000 F) in a hydrogen atmosphere that has too high a dew point.

Hydrogen at a dew point of −45 C (−50 F) does not decarburize hypoeutectoid steels. Also, the decarburizing effect of hydrogen on these steels at temperatures below 700 C (1300 F) is negligible, even at fairly high dew points. Data on behavior of hypereutectoid steels are conflicting; some sources report severe decarburization; others report little or none.

The reaction of hydrogen with carbide in steel to form methane and thereby to decarburize the steel is generally dependent both on temperature and on dew point and should not be generalized. Furthermore, although moist hydrogen is strongly decarburizing, it should not be assumed that the contribution of water to the methane reaction is dependent on dissociation of the water in contact with the hot steel surface. This concept is based on the assumption that water in contact with the hot steel surface dissociates readily; empirical evidence does not support this assumption. If the concept were valid, moisture problems in reasonably tight heat treating furnaces would be essentially self-solving. This is not borne out in practice.

In annealing of stainless steels in an atmosphere of completely dissociated ammonia at about 980 to 1100 C (1800 to 2000 F), decarburization does not occur unless the dew point is too high. At a dew point of −50 C (−60 F) or lower, this atmosphere does not decarburize, even though it contains 75% hydrogen.

Although hydrogen can, under certain conditions of temperature and dew point, severely decarburize steel, the decarburization of steel is not dependent on the presence of hydrogen and will occur in a variety of hydrogen-free heat treatment atmospheres, including atmospheres of oxygen, air and carbon dioxide, and in molten salts, such as molten potassium chloride.

Hydrogen cracking from decarburization has been observed in boiler tubes, as discussed on pages 531 to 533.

Decarburization usually is easily observed on a metallographic cross section of the alloy. Controlling decarburization is generally best done by using an alloy that has low susceptibility to this type of attack. In low-alloy steels, carbides can be stabilized by the addition of chromium and molybdenum, which improves the resistance to decarburization in heat treatment environments (and subsequent cracking in service), and the resistance to decarburization and cracking in high-temperature service environments containing hydrogen.

Hydrogen-induced cracking also may occur in steel if the steel contains absorbed hydrogen and is cooled too rapidly after prolonged exposure to elevated temperatures. The excess hydrogen then cannot escape during cooling and produces cracking.

Cracking From Hydrogen-Induced Slow-Strain-Rate Embrittlement

Alloys containing excess hydrogen may become embrittled during plastic deformation. Several important factors in hydrogen-induced slow-strain-rate embrittlement are strain rate, stress and temperature, and the crack-initiation and crack-propagation processes.

Effect of Strain Rate. If the strain rate is relatively high, there may be little or no decrease in macroscopic plasticity because of hydrogen, whereas at lower rates, a pronounced embrittlement from hydrogen may be detected.

Qualitatively, this effect of strain rate can be associated with the rate of hydrogen movement. The occurrence of embrittlement may require a significant movement and concentration of hydrogen. Grain boundaries are sites where hydrogen often accumulates and causes premature fracture.

If the strain rate is too high, the alloy may fracture before any significant diffusion of hydrogen can take place. Thus, both hydrogen-free and hydrogen-containing specimens would have comparable ductilities at fracture. With lower strain rates, however, the hydrogen diffuses with sufficient rapidity to cause embrittlement.

Effect of Stress. There is usually a minimum value of applied stress below which failure does not occur in a given material. Applied stresses in the presence of hydrogen that are as small as 40% of the yield strength can cause failure in only a few hours under sustained load.

In welded or heat treated parts, particularly those of complex shape, the sum of residual and applied stresses often approaches the yield strength of the material, making the parts readily susceptible to cracking by hydrogen-induced slow-strain-rate embrittlement.

Effect of Temperature. At high temperatures, an alloy may be soft enough to withstand any embrittlement caused by hydrogen and thus show no loss in ductility. At low temperatures, the rate of diffusion of hydrogen may be too slow to allow any localized buildup of hydrogen during testing, and again there may be no difference in ductility between hydrogen-free and hydrogen-containing specimens.

For most metals, maximum susceptibility to hydrogen cracking occurs at about room temperature. The slower hydrogen-diffusion rate at temperatures well below room temperature prevents hydrogen buildup at the crack tip from reaching the level necessary for crack propagation to be affected.

At temperatures in excess of about 120 C (250 F), the hydrogen in solid solution tends to be homogenized. This counters the stress-induced hydrogen diffusion, and consequently the local buildup of hydrogen concentration needed to cause embrittlement may not occur.

Crack initiation and propagation during slow-strain-rate embrittlement is influenced by a combination of hydrogen content and applied stress. The time required for initiation of a crack (incubation period) is greatly affected by the hydrogen content. The incubation period depends on the time necessary for the hydrogen to concentrate in regions of high triaxial stress, and thus to provide the driving force for the diffusion of hydrogen in the metal.

Propagation of the crack can occur only when there is a sufficiently high concentration of hydrogen in front of the crack. Cracking rate is controlled by the diffusion of hydrogen to the vicinity of the crack tip. Final, fast fracture may occur in a ductile or a brittle manner, depending on the toughness of the metal.

Hydrogen-Induced Cracking Under Static Fatigue

Some of the most serious problems associated with hydrogen damage occur as delayed failures under constant load in service — often called static-fatigue failures. Failures of this type occur after a part has originally passed inspection but during service develops hydrogen cracking while subject to a steady load, eventually fracturing suddenly in a brittle manner.

Hydrogen Absorption. In hydrogen-induced cracking under static fatigue, the hydrogen is already present in the metal before the part is exposed to the steady load that results in fracture.

Two common methods of hydrogen introduction are (a) use of damp charge materials during melting and (b) melting or welding in moist environments. Hydrogen is readily absorbed by many molten metals; if excessive hydrogen is picked up during melting or welding, the metal can become supersaturated with hydrogen when it is cooled to room temperature.

Sometimes, as in steel ingots, the decrease in hydrogen solubility during cooling will cause the formation of hydrogen gas within the ingot, producing cracking at sites of high hydrogen concentration in the solidified metal. The cracks, which are usually short and discontinuous, have shiny surfaces and are called "flakes", "fisheyes", "shatter cracks" or "snowflakes".

Static-fatigue tests simulate hydrogen-induced-cracking failures. In these tests, specimens of the failed alloy are usually precharged with hydrogen and then loaded, under either constant deflection or constant load. The time to failure of the specimens is then determined.

For a given level of hydrogen there is usually a minimum stress value below which failure will not occur. At higher stresses the time to failure is shortened, but even at very high stresses there is usually some minimum time before failure takes place. Increasing the level of hydrogen in the alloy usually shortens the failure time and lowers the minimum stress that is necessary to produce failure.

Various methods have been employed to measure crack-growth rates during tests of this kind. Also, fracture-toughness specimens loaded to various stress intensities have been tested for static fatigue behavior. Ordinarily, increasing stress or stress intensity accelerates the rate of crack growth. Frequently, cracking appears to take place in discrete bursts that are interspersed with periods of inactivity during which cracking does not occur. This behavior generally is attributed to a sequence involving hydrogen diffusion to the region around the existing crack tip, further cracking in this region and then diffusion of hydrogen to the region around the new crack tip.

Cracking From Hydride Formation

Embrittlement and cracking of a number of the transition, rare-earth and alkaline-earth metals (and the alloys of these metals) result from hydride formation. Metal hydrides are formed in these metals and alloys by the chemical combination of hydrogen with a metal in which it is in solid solution or with alloying elements in that metal. The hydride-forming metals of industrial concern include titanium, tantalum, zirconium, uranium, thorium, and alloys of these metals. The presence of hydrides in the microstructure of these metals can cause significant increases in strength and large losses in ductility and toughness (see "Titanium and Titanium Alloys" on page 236, and "Transition and Refractory Metals and Alloys" on page 237, for a discussion of the embrittlement and cracking of hydride-forming alloys).

As in other types of alloys, excess hydrogen is readily picked up during melting or welding, and hydride formation takes place during subsequent cooling. The use of vacuum melting and the modification of compositions can reduce susceptibility to hydride formation. Hydrogen can often be removed by annealing in a vacuum. Welding generally requires the use of inert-gas shielding to minimize hydrogen pickup.

The hydride particles often have the form of platelets and show preferred orientation within the parent lattice, depending primarily on the metal or alloy composition. Applied stresses also can alter hydride-precipitation behavior.

Cracking From Molecular Hydrogen Gas

Steel vessels and other equipment that contain hydrogen gas at high pressures are susceptible to failure by hydrogen cracking, with failure occurring most readily at ambient temperatures. Crack-growth rates increase exponentially with hydrogen-gas pressure.

Because molecular hydrogen cannot diffuse into the metal lattice, it is assumed that atomic hydrogen must be formed on the metal surface, although the mechanism by which this behavior occurs has not been determined.

Numerous tests have demonstrated that high-pressure hydrogen can drastically lower the tensile ductility or toughness of various metals. Slow crack growth at low stress intensities in statically loaded fracture-toughness specimens also has been observed.

Generally, high-strength steels and high-strength nickel alloys display severe degradation of properties in hydrogen gas; austenitic stainless steels, aluminum alloys and alloy A-286 show very little embrittlement in this environment; and most other engineering metals and alloys are affected to an intermediate degree.

Cracking From Hydrogen Sulfide

Gases or liquids that contain hydrogen sulfide can be extremely embrittling and can cause premature failures in high-strength alloys. In high-strength steel at normal operating temperatures, the hydrogen sulfide reacts with the steel to form atomic hydrogen, which then is absorbed at the metal surface and diffuses into the interior. Sulfur accelerates the hydrogen absorption. Embrittlement and cracking in steel can develop from the presence of only a few parts per million of hydrogen sulfide. Hydrogen damage by exposure to hydrogen sulfide is a serious problem in petrochemical equipment used to store and handle the so-called sour, or hydrogen-sulfide-containing, oils.

Sulfides from the atmosphere that are dissolved in moisture on a steel structure can cause failure of the steel by hydrogen damage. Hydrogen sulfide from slag in concrete similarly results in failure of steel rods that are buried in concrete.

Cracking From Water and Dilute Aqueous Solutions

Slow generalized corrosion or localized corrosion of commonly used metals and their alloys in water and dilute aqueous solutions, accompanied by diffusion of atomic hydrogen into the metal, can produce cracking by internal precipitation of molecular hydrogen at an internal imperfection, such as a void, or at an internal stress raiser. The corrosive solutions can range from high-purity water and natural waters to dilute solutions of acids, bases and salts. Failure by this mechanism can occur in several steels (especially high-strength steels), several stainless steels, and other engineering metals (such as aluminum, copper, nickel and their alloys) in which the atomic hydrogen does not react with metallic elements in the matrix.

Failures of carbon and low-alloy steel boiler tubes caused by hydrogen that was produced in a corrosion reaction are described on pages 531 to 533. Other components that were similarly exposed to water also have failed in service.

Carbon and Low-Alloy Steels

Carbon and low-alloy steels, especially when the tensile strength of the steel is above about 150,000 psi, are subject to failure by all of the types of hydrogen damage listed on page 230 in this article except hydriding. Failure by hydrogen damage (except by blistering or decarburization) is seldom encountered in carbon and low-alloy steels that have tensile strengths below about 100,000 psi.

Hydrogen damage or embrittlement caused by exposure to hydrogen gas, hydrogen sulfide, and aqueous environments so closely resembles stress-corrosion cracking that it sometimes is classified as stress-corrosion cracking.

Cracking by Hydrogen Gas. Hydrogen-damage failures of steel bourdon tubes operating with internal pressures of hydrogen of 12,000 to 15,000 psi have occurred often. Steel pressure vessels containing hydrogen gas also have failed by hydrogen damage. The severity of hydrogen damage increases with the hydrogen-gas pressure.

Premature failures and low ductility are observed in tensile testing of steel exposed to hydrogen gas. Delayed fracture in statically loaded specimens tested in hydrogen also occurs. The crack-growth rate in statically loaded specimens has been found to increase exponentially with hydrogen-gas pressure.

Maximum sensitivity to cracking in hydrogen occurs at or near room temperature, although cracking occurs also at lower and higher temperatures.

Dilution of the hydrogen gas with inert gases does not prevent cracking, but slight dilution with oxygen can completely stop cracking, apparently because preferential adsorption of oxygen occurs at the steel surface and prevents hydrogen absorption.

Sensitivity to cracking in hydrogen gas increases markedly as the strength level of the steel is increased. Both transgranular and intergranular cracking occur, the former primarily at high stress intensities, and the latter at low stress intensities.

Cracking in Hydrogen Sulfide. Sulfides from the atmosphere that are dissolved in moisture on a steel structure can cause failure of the steel by hydrogen damage. Collapse of the Point Pleasant, West Virginia, bridge began by failure of a 1060 steel eyebar. Sulfur compounds were found on the fracture surface and are believed to have played an important role in the crack growth in the eyebar.

It is now generally accepted that hydrogen is responsible for the cracking, with sulfur promoting hydrogen absorption. Atomic hydrogen is formed at the steel surface by the corrosion reaction:

$$Fe + H_2S \rightarrow FeS + 2H$$

Increasing concentrations of hydrogen sulfide shorten the times to failure, but failures may still develop at concentrations of only a few parts per million. The concentration of hydrogen sulfide that is required for failure decreases as the strength and hardness of the steel are increased. The minimum threshold stress necessary for cracking is likely to increase as the concentration of hydrogen sulfide decreases. Water ordinarily must be present for hydrogen sulfide cracking to occur. In one recent study, however, a precracked steel specimen with a yield strength of 220,000 psi underwent crack growth in dry hydrogen sulfide gas.

Cracking has often been transgranular with cleavage regions on the fracture surface. Intergranular cracking also has been reported, and it is likely that the crack path depends on the stress intensity and microstructure. Microscopic crack branching sometimes occurs.

Lowering the pH significantly enhances cracking. Increasing temperature generally retards cracking by homogenizing the hydrogen and thus avoiding high local concentrations.

Cold working of the steel prior to exposure increases residual stress, thereby reducing the resistance to sulfide cracking. At equal yield strengths, steels with quenched-and-tempered martensitic microstructures have greater resistance to cracking than steels with normalized-and-tempered martensitic or bainitic microstructures. There is little difference in resistance between martensitic and bainitic structures. The presence of retained austenite is helpful, possibly because it either absorbs hydrogen or slows down crack growth.

The effects of individual alloying elements on cracking susceptibility is controversial. In particular, conflicting results have been reported concerning the effects of carbon, chromium and nitrogen. Strong carbide-forming elements, such as molybdenum, vanadium and titanium, appear helpful. Sulfur and phosphorus are detrimental.

Both weld metal and heat-affected zones are often susceptible to cracking, probably because of the more susceptible microstructures and higher hardnesses often found in these regions.

The National Association of Corrosion Engineers has attempted to define steels that are resistant to cracking, in essence stating that hardness should not exceed Rockwell C 22. There is evidence supporting this statement, but several studies have reported hydrogen sulfide cracking of steels lower in hardness. At present it does not appear possible to define a strength level below which steels are completely immune to hydrogen sulfide cracking.

Cracking in Aqueous Environments. Susceptibility to hydrogen-induced cracking of steels in water and dilute aqueous solutions is directly related to the tensile strength of the steel. Generally, steels appear resistant to hydrogen-induced cracking in water at tensile strengths below 100,000 psi. Between 100,000 and 150,000 psi, steels are usually resistant or only slightly susceptible to cracking. Above about 150,000 psi, however, most steels are susceptible, and with increasing strength the susceptibility increases markedly. The strength appears to influence not only the minimum stress or stress intensity to initiate cracking, but also the crack-growth rate.

Hydrogen-induced cracking of steel in aqueous environments is thought to be caused by embrittlement in which hydrogen atoms are formed at the steel surface by corrosion and are absorbed by the steel. The cracking is usually intergranular along the prior austenite grain boundaries, although transgranular cracking sometimes occurs. There is evidence that the crack path depends on the stress intensity at the crack tip, being intergranular at lower stress intensities and transgranular at higher stress intensities. Measurements of crack velocity versus stress intensity usually show a three-stage curve. At low stress intensities, the crack rate increases exponentially with the stress intensities. At intermediate stress intensities (stage II), the crack-growth rate remains constant, probably controlled by some rate-limiting transport process. At high stress intensities, the growth rate again increases with stress intensity until mechanical overload fracture takes place.

Crack branching sometimes takes place during stage II crack propagation.

Changes in environment influence hydrogen-induced-cracking behavior. Generally, the environment has a more pronounced effect at lower strength levels and in unnotched specimens. Increasing chloride ion concentration increases crack-growth rate, especially in dilute solutions.

Temperature has no effect on the threshold value, but increasing temperature increases the stage II crack-growth rate. Arrhenius plots of the temperature dependence of the crack-growth rate have yielded activation energies comparable to those for hydrogen diffusion in steels, in agreement with a hydrogen-embrittlement mechanism of cracking.

Impressed cathodic potentials are deleterious. The pH has almost no effect, except that a pH as low as about 1.0 reduces the threshold stress intensity for cracking. Finally, the presence in solution of "cathodic poisons", such as phosphorus, arsenic, selenium, tellurium and sulfur, which promote hydrogen absorption by the steel, greatly enhances the cracking rate. These two observations are also consistent with a hydrogen-embrittlement-cracking mechanism.

Cracking of high-strength steels can occur in moist air, especially if there is local condensation on the steel surface.

As the strength level of the steel increases, the sensitivity to minor variations in the environment is likely to diminish. Sharply notched specimens are also generally less sensitive to the external environment. Local corrosion taking place within the notch can produce pH and potential conditions at the notch tip that are much different from those at the surface of a specimen. Hydrogen generation at the notch root, and consequently crack propagation, may take place even though hydrogen generation would not be predicted from the conditions at the exterior surface. This can lead to hydrogen-induced cracking when it would not be expected. Thus, for instance, anodic potentials can produce such cracking because surface pitting is produced and hydrogen generated within the pits causes cracking.

Changes in the composition and microstructure of the steel can sometimes alter resistance to hydrogen-induced cracking. Increasing carbon and manganese contents reduces resistance. The effects of other alloying elements are less clear, although more highly alloyed steels usually are more resistant than low-alloy quenched-and-tempered steels. Changing the microstructure from tempered martensite to lower bainite gave significantly lower crack-growth rates in one comparison. Ausforming, marquenching, and reducing the prior-austenite grain size have been helpful in some instances. Generally, for steels with yield strengths less than 200,000 psi, increasing fracture toughness increases the threshold stress intensity for hydrogen-induced cracking.

The only completely effective way to prevent hydrogen-induced cracking of high-strength steels in aqueous environments is to reduce the strength level. Various coating or paint systems have been used successfully in some instances, but there is always the possibility that defects in these protective coatings will lead to cracking. Effective inspection procedures to detect such flaws before they become critical are necessary if failures are to be avoided.

Hydrogen-induced cracking of welds has not been extensively studied, but the evidence suggests that at comparable strength levels the weld metal generally has poorer cracking resistance than the base metal. Cracking may also develop in the heat-affected zone if the hardness in this region is higher than that in the base metal.

Stainless Steels

The susceptibility of the different classes of stainless steels (austenitic, ferritic, martensitic and precipitation-hardening) to failure by hydrogen damage varies widely.

Austenitic Steels. Although austenitic stainless steels are highly susceptible to stress-corrosion cracking, they are almost completely resistant to failure by hydrogen damage. A major factor in the resistance of these steels to hydrogen damage is that they have a face-centered-cubic structure that is relatively impermeable to diffusion of atomic hydrogen. The resulting low content of hydrogen in the metal lattice allows only minimal reduction in ductility.

Ferritic Steels. When in the annealed condition, ferritic stainless steels are extremely resistant to hydrogen damage, because of their low hardness. However, when hardened by cold working or when in the as-welded condition, they are susceptible to failure by hydrogen damage.

Martensitic and Precipitation-Hardening Steels. The higher-strength stainless steels of these types are subject to hydrogen embrittlement. The cracking is mostly transgranular; in martensitic stainless steels it may follow prior austenite grain boundaries.

As yield strength is increased, the chances of hydrogen-induced cracking are greatly increased. The metallurgical structure has a secondary effect on susceptibility to hydrogen embrittlement.

Environments that cause failure in martensitic and precipitation-hardening steels are difficult to predict. Almost any corrosive environment capable of causing hydrogen evolution may cause cracking in these steels. Even a mild environment, such as fresh water at room temperature, may cause failure in especially susceptible alloys.

Failure may be prevented by the use of coatings that limit hydrogen entry, removal of hydrogen introduced during processing (such as by pickling and electroplating), and use of an appropriate heat treatment. Unfortunately, heat treatment to maximize resistance to hydrogen damage severely limits the strength that can be obtained.

The applicability of these preventive measures for precipitation-hardening stainless steel bolts that cracked because of hydrogen embrittlement is illustrated in the example that follows.

Example 1. Hydrogen-Embrittlement Cracking of 17-4 PH Stainless Steel Bolts (Fig. 2)

During a routine inspection, one of eight 17-4 PH (type 630) stainless steel precision bolts that clamped two aluminum alloy 7075-T6 flanges together in an assembly was found to be broken, as shown in Fig. 2(a). The seven other bolts were neither broken nor cracked, but three bolts on an identical assembly and two of twelve bolts on a similar assembly, all in the same system, were found to be cracked.

The bolts, which had washer heads, were 5/16 in. in diameter by 4¾ in. long, and had been heat treated to condition H900. In assembly, the bolts were coated with a special lubricant under the head and on the threads and were tightened to a torque of 295 to 305 in.-lb.

The system in which the bolts were used had been in standby service in a warm seacoast environment for about nine months prior to the inspection. Although no system malfunction occurred, a broken bolt could have prevented proper operation had the system been activated.

Investigation. All six of the failed bolts had cracked in the centerless-ground shank between the head and the threads. In two bolts, cracking occurred between 1 in. and 1½ in. from the head, whereas in the four other bolts, cracking occurred between ½ in. and 1½ in. from the threads. All cracks were approximately normal to the bolt axis.

The fracture surfaces of the broken bolts were mainly flat with a slight shear lip near the shank surface for about half the circumference. There was no evidence of extensive corrosion, or even staining; only scattered blackened pitting was present on the shanks of all the bolts.

The broken bolt and one of the cracked bolts were examined by electron fractography and microscopic examination of cross sections through the fractures. The results of

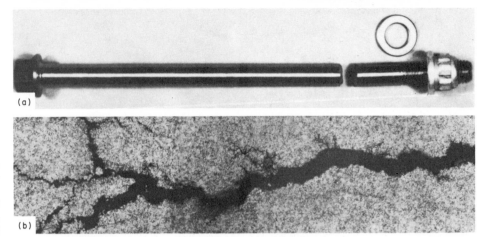

Fig. 2. (a) *Precision bolt of 17-4 PH (type 630) stainless steel that cracked from hydrogen embrittlement when exposed for about nine months in a warm seacoast atmosphere and in contact with aluminum alloy 7075-T6. (b) Micrograph, at 75×, of an etched section through a secondary crack, showing transition from unbranched cracking (right) to branched cracking (left). (Example 1)*

electron fractography were largely inconclusive, the only significant observation being corrosion nuclei in isolated areas on the fracture surfaces of both bolts.

On a cross section through a secondary crack immediately adjacent to the main fracture in the broken bolt, the latter stages of crack growth exhibited crack branching (see Fig. 2b). However, almost no branching occurred over the major portion of the crack. The crack in the second bolt was essentially unbranched. Cracking was intergranular.

In previous testing of 17-4 PH (type 630) stainless steel, stress-corrosion cracking could not be produced in a 3.5% sodium chloride solution, whereas hydrogen embrittlement was produced by attaching a piece of aluminum to the stress-corrosion specimen. Dissimilar-metal corrosion was considered capable of generating sufficient hydrogen to embrittle 17-4 PH (type 630) stainless steel in the H900 condition, which was the material and heat treatment used for the bolts. Hydrogen-induced cracking in these tests progressed intergranularly, with no significant branching.

Conclusions. Cracking of the bolts occurred by hydrogen embrittlement. Hydrogen was generated by the corrosion reaction that resulted in pitting of the shank below the head in each bolt. Because of the high diffusion rate of hydrogen in the stressed metal, pitting was not necessarily associated with the fracture origins.

Recommendations. Both short-range and long-range remedial actions were recommended. In systems already in the field, it was recommended that the bolts be liberally coated with the lubricant used at installation to prevent corrosion and to use only minimum torque in assembling the units (to reduce the operating stress).

Until a change in bolt material could be made, it was recommended that the 17-4 PH (type 630) stainless steel be heat treated to the H1000 condition, which would result in a slight reduction of strength in the bolt material, but would greatly increase its resistance to hydrogen-induced delayed failure.

As a long-range solution, it was recommended that the bolt material be changed

to A-286, an iron-base heat-resisting alloy, cold worked about 50% and aged at 650 C (1200 F). In this condition, A-286 has slightly greater strength than 17-4 PH (type 630) stainless steel in condition H900.

Maraging Steels

Many studies have been made in which maraging steels were precharged with hydrogen or tested in hydrogen gas. Generally, maraging steels are embrittled by precharging with hydrogen. The severity of embrittlement increases with increasing hydrogen content and increasing yield strength of the steels.

The cracks in precharged specimens are either intergranular cracks along the prior austenite grain boundaries or transgranular quasicleavage cracks. At comparable strength levels and hydrogen contents, the maraging steels are less embrittled than quenched-and-tempered high-strength low-alloy steels. It appears that the low carbon content of the maraging steel and the trapping of hydrogen at innocuous sites in the maraging steel microstructures are the factors responsible for the greater resistance of these steels to hydrogen embrittlement.

Tensile tests in hydrogen gas at 10,000 psi have shown that maraging steel with 250,000-psi yield strength suffers a severe loss in ductility. Static tests under constant gas pressure have produced delayed failures due to hydrogen. The degree of embrittlement of maraging steels in these tests was comparable to those of other steels of comparable strengths. Crack-growth-rate measurements on precracked specimens statically loaded in hydrogen gas have shown cracking rates very similar to those found in a 4130 steel. The cracking rates increased with the stress intensity. The higher the yield strength of the maraging steel the greater was the cracking rate at a given stress intensity.

Hydrogen can be removed from maraging steels by baking. Baking can be done at 150 to 205 C (300 to 400 F) or higher without changing the microstructure or the properties of these steels.

Heat-Resisting Alloys

In general, hydrogen embrittlement has not been a serious problem with heat-resisting alloys. However, experiments have shown that certain nickel-base alloys (for instance, alloy 718, alloy IN-100, Waspaloy and Haynes 188) are susceptible to embrittlement when exposed to highly oxidizing environments, or to pure hydrogen at a pressure of 5000 psi and a temperature of 680 C (1250 F). No analyses of fracture paths or fracture-surface appearance were conducted in these experiments.

Failures may be encountered occasionally at ambient temperatures, as in the delayed failure of an iron-base heat-resisting alloy by hydrogen-induced static fatigue, which is described in the following example.

Example 2. Hydrogen-Induced Delayed Failure of Unitemp 212 Bolts (Fig. 3)

On two occasions, two different ¼-in.-diam bolts, similar to those shown in Fig. 3(a), fractured in static service. The two bolts, made of Unitemp 212, an iron-base heat-resisting alloy, were used in a support structure on a missile. One bolt had been exposed in a seacoast climate for nine months and the other for nine days. Cadmium-plated nuts were used with the bolts.

Investigation. Both bolts fractured along a plane that was approximately normal to the axis of the bolt in a location close to that of the last full thread, as shown in cross section in Fig. 3(b). The fracture surfaces were flat and fine-grained, and exhibited little or no shear lip.

Metallographic examination of the bolt that failed after nine days of exposure revealed a clean, mainly austenitic microstructure, with evidence of cold work at the rolled threads. The fracture was essentially transgranular; there was no secondary cracking or crack branching and no evidence of corrosion.

Electron fractography revealed that both bolts fractured mainly by quasicleavage (see Fig. 3c). There was no evidence of corrosion on the fracture surface of the bolt that broke after nine months of exposure, and only traces of corrosion were found on the fracture surface of the other bolt.

For comparison of the fracture features, two new bolts were broken under overload, one by deliberately applying excessive torque to a nut and the other by loading in a tensile-testing machine with the axis of the bolt inclined at about 10° to the load axis. The bolt that was broken by deliberate overtorque exhibited mainly cleavage and quasicleavage fracture features that were coarser than those on the failed bolt; the bolt that was broken in asymmetric tension exhibited mainly dimples.

Conclusions. On the basis of the electron-fractographic studies, it was concluded that

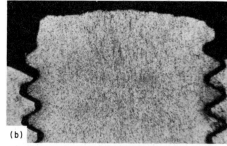

(a) Type of bolts that failed, shown at ¾×. (b) Macrograph, at 9×, of a cross section through a failed bolt that broke in the unthreaded shank (at top here) near the last full thread. (c) TEM fractograph, at 7000×, of a plastic-carbon replica of a fracture surface of a bolt, showing quasicleavage.

Fig. 3. Unitemp 212 bolts that failed in service from hydrogen-induced delayed cracking (Example 2)

fracture in service progressed transgranularly mainly by quasicleavage, with no secondary cracking or crack branching, to produce delayed failure under static loading. The fracture surfaces did not resemble those of new bolts broken under overload.

Failure was ascribed to hydrogen embrittlement, even though the source of hydrogen could not be established with certainty. It was considered possible that the bolts had been solution heat treated in an atmosphere containing hydrogen and that quenching from the solution-treatment temperature could cause retention of some hydrogen in the bolts. Alternatively, hydrogen could have been retained in the cadmium-plated nuts and diffused into the bolts under a stress gradient.

The fracture surfaces of both bolts were remarkably clean, indicating recent failures.

Recommendations. As a short-term solution, it was recommended that the bolts be installed using minimum specified torque, that only nuts of the same material be used (to minimize the possibility of galvanic corrosion), and that a liberal coating of lubricant be applied at assembly (to exclude moisture from the surface).

As a long-term solution, it was recommended that the bolt material be changed to A-286, another iron-base heat-resisting alloy, cold worked about 50% and aged at 650 C (1200 F).

Aluminum and Aluminum Alloys

Hydrogen damage occurs occasionally in aluminum and aluminum alloys, but it is not a serious problem.

Voids may form in aluminum during solidification from a melt. These voids can affect both cast and wrought products. In ingot for wrought products, the presence of hydrogen gas in voids inhibits healing on subsequent working and is responsible for such defects as bright flakes in thick sections and blisters in the surface of annealed or heat treated material. The principal effect of bright flakes is a reduction in short-transverse elongation.

Hydrogen damage has not been considered an industrial problem with aluminum alloys. Studies on the possibility of the occurrence of hydrogen damage in aluminum alloys have shown that dry gaseous hydrogen does not cause any significant hydrogen damage in aluminum alloys, but that stress-corrosion cracking of Al-Zn-Mg alloys in moist gases probably does involve hydrogen damage.

Titanium and Titanium Alloys

Hydrogen damage in titanium alloys results from embrittlement due to absorbed hydrogen. Hydrogen may be supplied by a number of sources, including water vapor, pickling acids, and hydrocarbons. The amount of absorption depends primarily on the titanium oxide film on the titanium surface, and an adherent unbroken film can significantly retard hydrogen absorption.

Titanium and titanium alloys will become embrittled by hydrogen at concentrations that cause a hydride phase to precipitate in the lattice structure. The precise level of hydrogen at which a separate hydride phase is formed depends on the composition of the alloy and upon previous metallurgical history. In commercial unalloyed material this hydride phase is normally found at levels of 150 ppm of hydrogen; however, hydride formation has been observed at levels as low as 40 or 50 ppm of hydrogen.

At temperatures near the boiling point of water, the diffusion rate of hydrogen into the metal is relatively slow, and the thickness of the layer of titanium hydride formed on the surface rarely exceeds about 15 mils, because spalling takes place when the hydride layer reaches thicknesses in this range.

Hydride particles form much more rapidly at temperatures above about 250 C (480 F), because of the decrease in hydrogen solubility within the titanium lattice. Under these conditions surface spalling does not occur, and the formation of hydride particles through the entire thickness of the metal results in complete embrittlement and high susceptibility to failure. This type of embrittlement is often seen in material that has absorbed excess hydrogen at elevated temperatures, such as during heat treatment or welding, and then has formed hydride particles during cooling.

There have been instances of localized hydriding in environments where titanium has otherwise given good performance. Investigations of such instances suggest that the localized hydriding is the result of the impurity content of the titanium (particularly the iron content) and the amount of surface contamination introduced during fabrication.

There is a strong link between surface iron contamination and hydriding of titanium. Severe hydriding has been noted in high-pressure dry gaseous hydrogen around particles of iron present on the surface. Anodizing in a 10% ammonium sulfate solution removes surface contamination and leads to thickening of the normal oxide film.

In chemical-plant service where temperatures are such that hydrogen can diffuse into the metal if the protective oxide film is destroyed, severe embrittlement may occur. For instance, in highly reducing acids where the titanium oxide film is unstable, rapid hydriding will occur. Hydrogen pickup has also been noted under high-velocity conditions where the protective film is eroded away as rapidly as it forms.

Hydrogen contents of 100 to 200 ppm may cause severe losses in tensile ductility and notched tensile strength in titanium alloys. Delayed brittle fractures under sustained loading also may take place. The sensitivity to hydrogen embrittlement from hydriding varies with alloy composition, and is reduced substantially by alloying with aluminum.

Care should be taken to minimize hydrogen pickup during fabrication. Welding operations generally require inert-gas shielding to minimize hydrogen pickup. Hydrogen can be removed from titanium by annealing in vacuum.

Transition and Refractory Metals and Alloys

Tantalum, zirconium, uranium, thorium, and alloys of these metals, when exposed to hydrogen, can sustain severe damage due to hydride formation.

Tantalum absorbs hydrogen at temperatures above 250 C (480 F), resulting in the formation of tantalum hydride. Hydrogen absorption also can occur if tantalum is coupled to a more active metal in a galvanic cell, particularly in hydrochloric acid.

As little as 100 ppm of hydrogen in tantalum will cause severe embrittlement by hydride formation.

Zirconium and zirconium alloys are highly susceptible to embrittlement by hydride formation. Absorption of gaseous hydrogen into zirconium and its reaction with zirconium to produce the hydride, ZrH_2, occurs with extreme rapidity at 800 C (1470 F). This hydride is brittle and may be crushed to a powder. The hydrogen may be pumped off to leave a powder of metallic zirconium.

Zirconium alloys can pick up substantial amounts of hydrogen during exposure to high-pressure steam. Zirconium with 2.5% columbium will corrode in water at 300 C (570 F) at a rate of approximately 2.5×10^{-3} cm per year and pick up hydrogen at the rate of 2 to 4 mg/cm^2 per day.

Hydrogen can be removed from zirconium and zirconium alloys by vacuum annealing.

Uranium, uranium alloys and thorium are susceptible to hydrogen embrittlement. The hydrides in thorium have been identified as ThH_2 and Th_4H_{15}. The hydride in uranium is UH_3. Even in pure water, 15 to 20% of the hydrogen produced by reaction of uranium with the water may enter the surface of gamma-phase uranium-molybdenum alloys.

Failure Analysis

The basic principles that are common to all failure analyses are described in the article that begins on page 10 in this volume. Investigative techniques directed more specifically toward the mechanical-environmental failure processes, including hydrogen damage or embrittlement, are discussed on pages 215 to 217 in the article on Stress-Corrosion Cracking. Several test methods that have been developed for the study of hydrogen-embrittlement phenomena and the prediction and monitoring of hydrogen-affected behavior of metals under specific conditions are described in ASTM STP 543 (1974).

History of the Metal or Part. Initially, in such a failure analysis, it is necessary to determine: (a) whether the metal or part has a known susceptibility to hydrogen-induced cracking; (b) whether the failed part was exposed to a source of hydrogen that would enable the absorption of atomic hydrogen into the metal lattice in solid solution: and (c) whether the part was subjected to noncyclic tensile stresses.

Crack Origin. When hydrogen-induced cracking results from blistering or from static fatigue, it always originates in the interior of the part or specimen. Hydrogen-induced cracking of other types can originate either in the interior or at a stress raiser on the surface. In metals of relatively low strength and hardness, and in high-strength metals that are not subjected to significant externally imposed or residual tensile stresses, cracking almost always originates in the interior of the part or specimen. In high-strength metals that are subjected to externally imposed or residual tensile stresses, especially if a severe stress raiser (such as a sharp fatigue or stress-corrosion crack) is present at the surface, cracking is likely to originate at the surface.

Crack Pattern. Almost without exception, a single crack that shows no significant branching is produced in hydrogen-induced cracking. Cracking can be intergranular or transgranular, or change from one to the other as cracking progresses. However, many metal-environment combinations are known to show a specific crack pattern for hydrogen-induced cracking. For example, in quenched-and-tempered steels, a hydrogen-induced crack usually follows the prior austenite grain boundaries.

Microscopic examination is used to determine the microscopic features of fracture surfaces in laboratory studies of hydrogen-induced cracking and in the investigation of service failures.

Hydrogen-induced cracking that originates at the surfaces of parts in an aqueous solution usually progresses by intergranular fracture in the early stages of crack propagation, with the mode of cracking changing to cleavage or microvoid coalescence as the stress intensity increases and cracking approaches final, fast fracture.

Figure 4 shows the results of this behavior in the fracture of precracked test specimens of quenched-and-tempered 4315 steel (yield strength, 172,000 psi) that were coupled to pieces of magnesium and subjected to a constant load, while immersed in a 3½% solution of sodium chloride.

In the failure analysis reported below, fractographic examination at 3000 diameters was the final step in the investigation of a transverse fracture of a tubular piston rod from a hydraulic actuator used on an aircraft:

The piston rod was made from AMS 6415H (MIL-S-5000, condition C), which corresponds approximately in composition to 4340 steel.

The fracture surface of the failed piston rod (see Fig. 5a) indicated that the crack had apparently initiated at a sharp fillet, indicated by arrows A in Fig. 5(a), that had been created during the internal machining of the tubular rod.

The crack apparently progressed radially outward in all directions. The rate of crack growth was greater in the general directions of the arrows than in the directions perpendicular to them, as evidenced by the large shear lips at the B's in Fig. 5(a). A shear lip (the area of final, fast fracture) extended around the entire outer circumference of the fracture surface, conclusive evidence that the crack had initiated around the internal circumference of the rod wall. No macroscopic deformation of the rod was found.

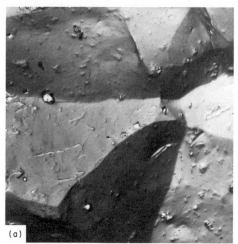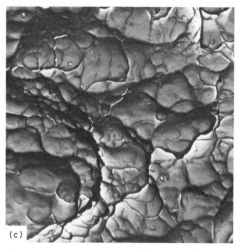

Fig. 4. TEM fractographs of two-stage replicas of fracture surfaces of precracked test specimens of quenched-and-tempered 4315 steel (yield strength, 172,000 psi) under constant load and coupled to magnesium while immersed in a 3½% solution of sodium chloride, showing progression of hydrogen-induced cracking as stress in- *tensity increases. (a) Intergranular cracking in the early stage of hydrogen-induced cracking; magnification, 2900×. (b) Progression to cleavage cracking as stress intensity increases; magnification, 4100×. (c) Progression to microvoid coalescence with further increase in stress intensity; magnification, 2900×.*

Examination by electron fractography indicated that the fracture was intergranular over the entire flat area of the fracture surface (see Fig. 5b).

Because the rod had been cadmium-plated during fabrication, it was concluded that embrittlement by hydrogen that was introduced into the rod during the plating process was the prime cause of the fracture.

Deposits on Fracture Surfaces. Corrosion products ordinarily are not present, or are present in trace amounts only, on the surfaces of hydrogen-damage fractures unless the surfaces have been exposed to corrosive environments. Foreign matter, if present, is in trace amounts only unless the fracture surfaces have been exposed to contaminants. Highly sensitive techniques have been developed for detection and identification of trace deposits on fracture surfaces.

Fractographic techniques and equipment that can be used at lower sensitivity are suitable for the detection and identi-fication of larger than trace deposits of foreign matter at or near the metal surface in surface-originated cracks where the metal has been exposed to a corrosive atmosphere. Table 1 lists methods used for the detection and the determination of average chemical composition, crystal structure, and shapes of foreign particles on fracture surfaces.

Laboratory cracking tests are used to verify the presence of hydrogen damage or to distinguish between hydrogen damage and stress-corrosion cracking. One method of distinguishing between hydrogen embrittlement and stress-corrosion cracking in laboratory tests is observation of the effects of small impressed electric currents on time to failure (in a static test) or on rate of crack growth. If cracking has occurred by stress corrosion, impressing a small anodic current will accelerate cracking. With hydrogen embrittlement, cracking will be accelerated by impressing a small cath-odic current. (See M. G. Fontana and N. D. Greene, "Corrosion Engineering", McGraw-Hill, 1967, p 113-114.)

As an illustration of the usefulness of impressed currents, consider the behavior of metals that, when stressed, crack on exposure to many different corrosive aqueous solutions. For instance, a stressed high-strength carbon steel or a stressed martensitic stainless steel immersed in either dilute sulfuric or hydrochloric acid may crack within a few minutes. These cracks have the outward appearance of stress-corrosion cracks, but they are hydrogen induced, because when the immersed steel is polarized by an impressed cathodic current, cracking occurs in an equal or shorter period of time. This behavior is contrary to stress-corrosion behavior; for example, austenitic stainless steels in boiling magnesium chloride solution are protected from stress-corrosion cracking by impressing a cathodic current.

Another means of identifying hydrogen damage is use of dilute sulfuric acid containing a few drops of a "cathodic poison" to accelerate hydrogen absorption by the metal (see H. H. Uhlig, "Corrosion and Corrosion Control", 2nd edition, Wiley, 1971, p 142-143).

It is difficult and sometimes impossible to distinguish with certainty between hydrogen-induced and stress-corrosion-cracking failures that have occurred in service by exposure to hydrogen gas, hydrogen sulfide, and water and dilute aqueous solutions. Several basic characteristics to be observed in investigating failures of these types are (a) history of the metal or part, (b) crack origin, (c) crack pattern, (d) evidence of little or no corrosion on the fracture surfaces, and (e) microscopic features. Observation of hydrogen involvement in one or more of these characteristics does not necessarily

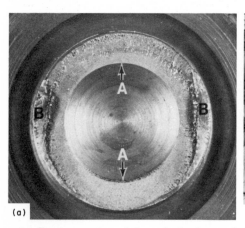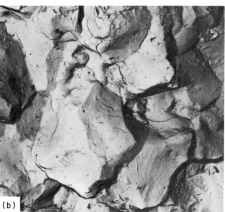

(a) Fracture surface of the rod, showing crack that initiated at a sharp fillet (arrows A), and large shear lips at the B's. (b) TEM fractograph, at 3000× (two-stage plastic-carbon replica), showing intergranular fracture that extended across the entire flat area of the fracture surface.

Fig. 5. Tubular piston rod of AMS 6415H (MIL-S-5000, condition C) for a hydraulic actuator, which fractured in service because of hydrogen embrittlement

establish that a given fracture resulted from hydrogen-induced cracking. However, if hydrogen is involved in most of these characteristics, if contrary indications are absent, and if evidence is available that rules out other possible explanations, it generally can be concluded that failure occurred by hydrogen-induced cracking.

Prevention of Failures

The effectiveness of a proposed change in part design or material in preventing hydrogen damage can be determined, and any possible harmful effects on the changed part can be detected, by processing sample parts using modified procedures and evaluating the reaction of the parts under simulated or actual service conditions. Accelerated tests also can be used, but the results of accelerated tests must always be interpreted with special care because generally they are less reliable than results of actual service tests for predicting service performance.

Test procedures have been developed especially to (a) evaluate relative susceptibility of metals to hydrogen damage or embrittlement, (b) measure hydrogen-pickup rate during processing, (c) determine the concentration of hydrogen in metals, and (d) study various hydrogen-embrittlement effects. These procedures are described in detail in ASTM STP 543 (1974).

The sensitivity and reliability of these procedures have been thoroughly evaluated. They have proved useful in comparing metals, protective coatings and processing methods and in evaluating effects of a wide variety of factors on hydrogen absorption and on embrittlement behavior.

Some of the most useful capabilities of procedures described in ASTM STP 543 include: (a) effects of impurities in high-pressure hydrogen exposure and effects of irradiation can be tested; (b) the degree of embrittlement of actual parts can be assessed in the shop and in the field; and (c) embrittlement occurring during processing can be monitored, and the processing can be controlled so as to minimize embrittlement.

Changes in Processing. The addition of inhibitors to processing solutions to prevent attack on the base metal can be used to eliminate hydrogen evolution and consequent absorption of atomic hydrogen into the metal lattice. Suitable changes in electroplating-bath composition, bath temperature, and current density, to enable operation at high cathode efficiency, can greatly reduce the pickup of hydrogen by the metal during electroplating.

Electroplating with a different metal that reduces hydrogen input to the base metal is practicable in some applications.

Table 1. Methods Used for Detection and Identification of Foreign Particles of Different Sizes on Fracture Surfaces

Average chemical composition	Type of method used for determining: Crystal structure	Shape
Particles Larger Than 2.5 Mm		
Wet chemical analysis; mass spectroscopy; emission spectroscopy; x-ray fluorescence; electron microprobe analysis	X-ray diffraction; electron diffraction	Scanning electron microscopy (SEM); stereomicroscopy; metallographic light microscopy
Particles of Intermediate Size		
Mass spectroscopy; emission spectroscopy; electron microprobe analysis	X-ray diffraction; electron diffraction	Scanning electron microscopy (SEM); transmission electron microscopy (TEM)
Particles Smaller Than 10 Microns		
Auger electron spectrometry; ion-scattering spectroscopy; x-ray photoemission	Electron diffraction	Scanning electron microscopy (SEM); transmission electron microscopy (TEM)

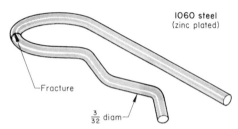

Fig. 6. Zinc-plated 1060 steel retainer clip that failed in service because of delayed fracture by hydrogen embrittlement (Example 3)

The addition of a baking operation after electroplating, or a change in an existing postplating baking operation by increasing the baking time, raising the baking temperature and shortening the interval between plating and baking, sometimes enables quicker and more complete removal of absorbed hydrogen from the base metal without significant adverse effects on the electrodeposit, as in the example that follows.

Example 3. Delayed Failure of 1060 Steel Retainer Clips Because of Hydrogen Embrittlement (Fig. 6)

After a relatively short service life, a substantial number of retainer clips of the type shown in Fig. 6 fractured spontaneously. The clips were formed from hardened 1060 steel wire, then acid cleaned and finally zinc plated in a cyanide solution.

Occasionally, this type of clip had fractured from cracks produced during forming. These fractures, which contained traces of zinc plate, were at a different location on the clip from the one at which the service fractures occurred.

Investigation. The service fractures were mainly brittle and were free of zinc plate on the fracture surface. Because of the delayed nature of cracking and the absence of zinc plate, hydrogen embrittlement was suspected. Consequently, several samples of the clips were baked at 177 C (350 F) for 8 hr, and several at 260 C (500 F) for 8 hr. These samples, along with several samples in the as-received condition, were mounted on a 3/8-in.-square bar and exposed at room temperature.

After a relatively short exposure time, all the as-received clips broke at the location shown in Fig. 6. After 200 hr, 60% of the clips that had been baked at 177 C (350 F) had cracked. However, one benefit of baking was observed — the cracks had propagated only part of the way through the clips. After more than 400 hr, none of the clips that had been baked at 260 C (500 F) had cracked.

Conclusion. Failure occurred in service because of embrittlement by hydrogen that had been introduced in either the acid-cleaning or zinc-plating process.

Recommendation. Baking at 260 C (500 F) for 8 hr following the zinc-plating operation was recommended. Baking at 177 C (350 F), although it had reduced the incidence of delayed failure and had restricted the depth of crack propagation, was considered ineffective for these retainer clips.

Change in Alloy. Changing to an alloy that is not susceptible to hydrogen embrittlement is often possible. In many applications, a lower-strength metal will function just as well mechanically as a higher-strength metal, and the use of such a metal can eliminate a hydrogen-embrittlement problem.

Reduction of Stress. Lowering the stress below the threshold value for hydrogen embrittlement will prevent cracking. This may be done by annealing (for residual stresses), thickening the section, or reducing the load.

Change in Design. Design changes, such as eliminating sharp corners that act as stress raisers, increase resistance to hydrogen-induced cracking. Elimination of sites for crevice corrosion accompanied by production of damaging amounts of hydrogen also is helpful.

Heat Treatment. In high-strength steels, tempering at a higher temperature for a longer time may help reduce hydrogen content. This would lower the strength level and also result in a much tougher and more hydrogen-embrittlement-resistant material.

Surface-preparation techniques that impart residual compressive stresses to the surface are used to improve resistance to cracking when susceptible metals are subjected to the combination of hydrogen embrittlement and residual or applied tensile stress. These techniques include shot peening, grit blasting, and face milling.

Coatings and linings can be applied to the surface of the metal to shield it from a corrosive environment (see pages 194 to 196 in the article on Corrosion Failures, in this volume).

Change in Welding Procedures. Low-hydrogen welding rods should be specified for welding if hydrogen embrittlement is a problem. Also, it is important to maintain dry conditions in storing the rod before use and during welding, because water and water vapor are major sources of hydrogen. Preheating and postheating are also important when welding high-strength steels to prevent creation of high residual stresses or microcracks.

Inspection and Maintenance Procedures. Carefully planned and closely supervised inspection methods can detect existing cracks and preventive maintenance can be utilized to prevent catastrophic failures.

Selected References

J. Hochmann, J. Slater and R. W. Staehle (Editors), "Stress-Corrosion Cracking and Hydrogen Embrittlement of Iron Base Alloys", conference held at Unieux-Firminy, France, June 12-16, 1973, National Association of Corrosion Engineers, Houston, Texas (in publication by NACE, as of 1975)

I. M. Bernstein and A. W. Thompson (Editors), "Hydrogen in Metals", American Society for Metals, Metals Park, Ohio, 1974

L. Raymond (Ed.), "Hydrogen Embrittlement Testing", STP 543, ASTM, Philadelphia, 1974

N. E. Hamner (Ed.), "Corrosion Data Survey", 5th Edition, National Association of Corrosion Engineers, Houston, Texas, 1974

F. H. Cocks (Ed.), "Manual of Industrial Corrosion Standards and Control", STP 534, ASTM, New York, 1974

J. K. Stanley, The Current Situation on the Stress-Corrosion and Hydrogen Embrittlement of High Strength Fasteners, Paper No. 72-385, AIAA/ASME/SAE Conference held at San Antonio, Texas, April 10-12, 1972, American Institute of Aeronautics and Astronautics, New York

W. H. Ailor, Jr., "Handbook on Corrosion Testing and Evaluation", John Wiley & Sons, Inc., New York, 1971

H. H. Uhlig, "Corrosion and Corrosion Control", 2nd edition, John Wiley & Sons, Inc., New York, 1971

R. W. Staehle, A. J. Forty and D. van Rooyen (Editors), "Fundamental Aspects of Stress Corrosion Cracking", conference held at the Ohio State University, Sept 11-15, 1967, National Association of Corrosion Engineers, Houston, Texas, 1969

C. D. Beachem, "Microscopic Fracture Processes", Chapter 4, p 243-350, in H. Liebowitz (Ed.), "Fracture, Vol I, Microscopic and Macroscopic Fundamentals", Academic Press, Inc., New York, 1968

M. G. Fontana and N. D. Greene, "Corrosion Engineering", McGraw-Hill Book Co., New York, 1967

A. S. Tetelman and A. J. McEvily, Jr., "Fracture of Structural Materials", Chapter 9, "Fracture Under Static Loading", John Wiley & Sons, New York, 1967

A. S. Tetelman, "Fracture of Solids", section titled "The Hydrogen Embrittlement of Ferrous Alloys", Interscience Publishers, New York, 1963

M. Szczepanski, "The Brittleness of Steel", Chapter 5, "Hydrogen Embrittlement", John Wiley & Sons, Inc., New York, 1963

Corrosion-Fatigue Failures

By the ASM Committee on Failure by Mechanical-Environmental Processes*

CORROSION FATIGUE is the combined action of repeated or fluctuating stress and a corrosive environment to produce cracking. Usually, an aggressive environment has a deleterious effect on fatigue life, producing failure in fewer stress cycles than would be required in a more inert environment. In certain instances, however, such as exposure of nickel-base superalloys to high-temperature oxidizing environments, an aggressive environment can slow the fatigue-fracture process, increasing the number of stress cycles to failure.

The basic principles of fatigue in metals are discussed in the article that begins on page 95 in this volume; corrosion is discussed in the article that begins on page 168. The present article describes the interaction of these two processes, especially the influence of environment on crack initiation and propagation under cyclic or repeated loading. It is important to recognize that corrosion fatigue is not necessarily involved if cyclic stress and exposure to a corrosive medium occur successively or alternately. Furthermore, corrosion does not always reduce fatigue life, and cyclic stressing does not always increase rates of corrosion.

The microscopic processes by which a fatigue crack is initiated in the presence of an aggressive chemical substance, and by which the environment affects growth of the crack, are not completely understood. Many different models of these processes have been proposed to explain the macroscopic effects that are observed. No single model proposed to date adequately explains all the observed effects. In fact, it appears likely that different processes are responsible for the behavior observed with various combinations of material and environment.

In corrosion fatigue, the magnitude of cyclic stress and the number of times it is applied are not the only critical loading parameters. Time-dependent environmental effects also are of prime importance. When failure occurs by corrosion fatigue, stress-cycle frequency, stress-wave shape and stress ratio must be known to satisfactorily define the loading conditions. (For a discussion of concepts and terms related to fatigue, see pages 95 and 96 in this volume.)

Effects of Cyclic Stress

The service life of a component or structure often is determined by the number of stress cycles required for a crack to initiate plus the number of stress cycles required for the crack to grow to critical size before final fracture occurs. Nominal section stress is not of great value in defining the conditions under which a crack will grow, although it may prove adequate for defining the conditions of crack initiation. Local stress is important for both crack initiation and crack growth. During crack growth, however, local stress is further affected by the crack itself — a significant stress concentrator. The local stress at the tip of a crack can be defined most effectively by the use of linear-elastic fracture mechanics, as discussed on page 31 in the article on Toughness and Fracture Mechanics, in this volume. By describing local stress in terms of applied stress intensity, it is possible to predict when a growing fatigue crack of subcritical size will reach critical size. Thus, sudden final fracture of a cracked component can be avoided by removing the part from service before the crack reaches critical size.

Effect of Frequency. In nonaggressive environments, the cyclic frequency generally has little effect on fatigue behavior. On the other hand, in aggressive environments fatigue strength is strongly dependent on frequency. An observed dependence of fatigue strength or fatigue life on frequency often is considered definitive in establishing corrosion fatigue as the mechanism of a failure.

The frequency dependence of corrosion fatigue is thought to result from the fact that interaction of a material and its environment is essentially a rate-con-

*See page 205 for committee list.

trolled process. Low frequencies, especially at low strain amplitudes or when there is substantial elapsed time between changes in stress levels, allow time for interaction between material and environment; high frequencies do not, particularly when high strain amplitude is involved also. However, high frequencies or high strain rates induce internal heating, which may alter material properties or increase the corrosion rate at the crack tip.

With environments that have a deleterious effect on fatigue behavior, there may exist a critical range of frequencies of loading in which the mechanical-environmental interaction is significant. Above this range the effect usually disappears, while below the range the effect sometimes diminishes.

Effect of Stress Amplitude. In general, a low amplitude of cyclic stress favors relatively long fatigue life, permitting greater opportunity for involvement of the environment in the failure process. Where stresses are sufficiently high to cause significant macroscopic plastic deformation, environmental interaction may be insignificant.

Stress amplitude must be considered together with mean stress and frequency. Low stress levels may allow adequate time for environmental interaction, but if the frequency is high, the crack tip may not be exposed to the environment. Typical behavior, illustrating the effect of frequency and/or stress as discussed above, is illustrated in Fig. 1.

Effect of Mean Stress. When a static tensile stress is imposed on a sinusoidally varying stress of equal amplitude, the maximum stress in the material is doubled and the mean stress is raised from zero to a value equal to the static stress. A growing fatigue crack is held open for the entire cycle, rather than for only half of it, because the stress is always tensile. Also, the crack is opened wider because the peak stress is higher than when the mean stress was zero. Thus, tensile mean stresses not only raise the general level of stress intensity at the crack tip, but also increase the likelihood that the environment will penetrate to the crack tip.

Effect of Stress-Wave Shape. The shape of the cyclic-stress wave influences the effect of a surrounding aggressive environment. Prolonged exposure at peak stress contributes to accelerated failure. In corrosion fatigue, a primary concern is whether stress-corrosion cracking may occur. In a system that is susceptible to stress corrosion, cracking can occur at any load above the critical stress intensity for stress-corrosion cracking (K_{Iscc}); in other words, holding times during the high-load portion of the stress cycle are detrimental. Also, as mentioned previously, the portion of the

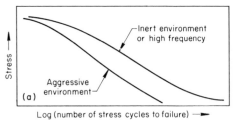

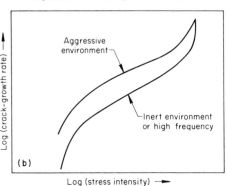

Fig. 1. Typical fatigue behavior in aggressive environment compared with fatigue behavior in inert environment or at high frequency, shown (a) as an S-N curve and (b) as variation of crack-growth rate with stress intensity

stress cycle during which loading is tensile represents the period during which a growing crack is open and susceptible to penetration by the environment.

A second consideration in evaluating the effect of stress-wave shape is the portion of the wave during which the stress is increasing. In one investigation, it was found that the detrimental effect of an environment at loads below K_{Iscc} occurred only during the increasing-load portion of the stress cycle. From this, it may be inferred that cyclic loading under a triangular, trapezoidal, positive-slope-sawtooth or sinusoidal stress wave is more likely to effect a reduction in fatigue life in detrimental environments than is cyclic loading under a negative-slope-sawtooth or square wave.

Effects of Environment

Nucleation and propagation of corrosion-fatigue cracks in service are influenced by corrosive environments — mainly, bulk aqueous solutions or environments produced by continuous or periodic condensation of vapor.

Effect on Fatigue Strength. For any given material, the fatigue strength, or fatigue life at a given value of maximum stress, generally decreases in the presence of an aggressive environment. The effect varies widely, depending primarily on the characteristics of the material-environment combination. The environment affects crack-growth rate or probability of fatigue-crack initiation, or both. For many materials, the stress range required to cause fatigue failure

diminishes progressively with time and with number of cycles. This effect is illustrated in Fig. 1(a) as a progressively wider separation between fatigue curves for inert and aggressive environments with increasing life or decreasing stress.

Corrosion-fatigue tests on smooth specimens of high-strength steel indicate that very large reductions in fatigue strength or fatigue life can occur in salt water. For instance, the fatigue strength at ten million cycles could be reduced to as little as 10% of that in dry air. In these tests, the main role of the environment was corrosive attack of the polished surface, creating local stress raisers that initiated fatigue cracks. Salt water also increases the crack-growth rate in steels.

In the following example, corrosion by water-contaminated hydraulic oil, which reduced fatigue strength to about one-fourth of that expected in the absence of corrosion, caused failure of an alloy steel aircraft shaft.

Example 1. Corrosion-Fatigue Cracking in an AMS 6415 Steel Aircraft Shaft Caused by Simultaneous Cyclic Stressing and Attack by Contaminated Hydraulic Oil (Fig. 2)

The hollow, splined alloy steel aircraft shaft shown in Fig. 2(a) cracked in service after more than 10,000 hr of flight time. The crack was detected during a routine overhaul about 1000 hr after the previous overhaul.

In operation, the shaft was subjected to complex loading that consisted mainly of steady radial and cyclic torsional loading and reversed cantilever bending. The inner surface of the hollow shaft was continuously exposed to hydraulic oil at temperatures of 0 to 80 C (about 30 to 180 F).

The shaft was specified to be machined from an AMS 6415 steel forging (approximately the same composition as 4340 steel) and then quenched and tempered to a hardness of Rockwell C 44.5 to 49. After tempering, the tapered interior of the 6-in.-diam shank (see Fig. 2a) was machined to close tolerances and had a smooth finish.

Investigation. Preliminary visual and low-magnification examination of the shaft revealed a crack about 1¾ in. long on the tapered interior of the shank, as shown in Fig. 2(a). The crack extended deep into the part and penetrated completely through the shank in one region. Scattered pitting-type corrosion had occurred on the interior surface of the shank, and corrosion pits were visible along the cracks. The pitting corrosion indicated that a corrosive substance, probably water in the hydraulic oil, had been present in service. No material or fabrication defects were detected, nor was there any other service damage that could be related to the failure.

Chemical analysis showed that the steel conformed in composition to the requirements of the specified material, AMS 6415 steel. Hardness measurements were within the range required for this part. The microstructure was free from any abnormalities or defects.

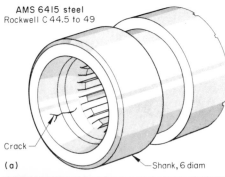

AMS 6415 steel
Rockwell C 44.5 to 49

Crack

(a)

Shank, 6 diam

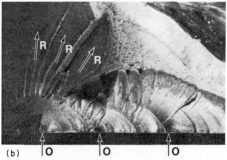

(b)   O   O   O

(a) View of a portion of the shaft, showing the location of the corrosion-fatigue crack, on the tapered interior of the shank.

(b) Light fractograph, at about 4½×, showing fracture origins at corrosion pits (arrows O) and direction of fast fracture (arrows R). Region where crack was opened in the laboratory, by sawing and then breaking by hand, is shown at upper right corner.

Fig. 2. Hollow, splined alloy steel shaft that failed by corrosion fatigue in aircraft service because of exposure to hydraulic oil that was contaminated with water (Example 1)

Visual and low-magnification (15 to 30 diameters) examination of the fracture surfaces showed that the failure had originated at several corrosion pits. Several small corrosion-fatigue cracks had propagated from these nuclei and joined to form a single corrosion-fatigue crack in the tapered shank, as shown in Fig. 2(b). Specific features and successive stages in the development of the crack, together with a region of fast, brittle fracture through the remaining ⅛ in. of shank thickness, are shown in this fractograph.

Conclusions. The shaft cracked in a region subjected to severe static radial, cyclic torsional and cyclic bending loads. Cracking originated at corrosion pits on the smoothly finished surface and propagated as multiple small corrosion-fatigue cracks from separate nuclei. After progressing separately to a substantial depth, the small cracks combined into a single larger crack that enlarged until the normal service stresses produced brittle cracking through to the opposite surface.

The originally noncorrosive environment (hydraulic oil) became corrosive in service because of the introduction of water into the oil. Corrosion pits acted in combination with cyclic torsional and reversed-bending stresses to cause corrosion-fatigue cracking.

Recommendations. It was recommended that additional precautions be taken in operation and maintenance to prevent the

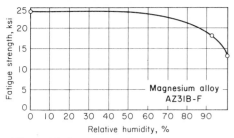

Fig. 3. Fatigue strength (at ten million cycles) of magnesium alloy AZ31B-F, plotted as a function of relative humidity. Tests were conducted in tension-tension fatigue at about 3 Hz with a stress ratio, R, of 0.25.

use of oil containing any water and to prevent the introduction of water through filling spouts or air vents. Also, polishing to remove pitting corrosion (but staying within specified dimensional tolerances) was recommended as a standard maintenance procedure for shafts with long service lives. Inspection and polishing should be incorporated into normal overhaul procedures.

Stainless steels have a lower fatigue strength in seawater than in fresh water, probably because of the presence of chloride ions in seawater. Chlorides are known to produce stress-corrosion cracking in austenitic stainless steels, and therefore might be expected to also affect fatigue strength.

Although high-purity aluminum is known to pit in aqueous chloride solutions, its fatigue strength is relatively unaffected by such environments. On the other hand, aluminum alloys are highly susceptible to corrosion fatigue. For instance, the small amount of water vapor normally present in the atmosphere severely reduces the fatigue life of several aluminum alloys. The fatigue life in ambient air has been observed to be only about one-tenth the fatigue life in vacuum, or in air at a relative humidity of less than ten per cent. Water mainly affects crack-growth rate, but a reduction in crack-initiation time has been observed in sodium chloride solutions.

The fatigue strengths of alloys of many other systems are reduced by aggressive environments; this appears to be true particularly for those systems that are susceptible to stress-corrosion cracking, although susceptibility to stress-corrosion cracking is not a prerequisite for corrosion fatigue. Some typical effects are shown in Fig. 3 for magnesium alloy AZ31B-F (3Al-1Zn-0.2Mn) extruded and machined rod that was tested in air with

Table 1. Corrosion-Fatigue Limits for Lead Alloys in Air and in a 38% H₂SO₄ Solution

Alloy	Corrosion-fatigue limit, psi	
	In air	In 38% H₂SO₄
Pure lead	430	0
Pb-0.05Te-0.06Cu ..	600	400
Pb-1Sb	860	740
Pb-9Sb	2050	1850

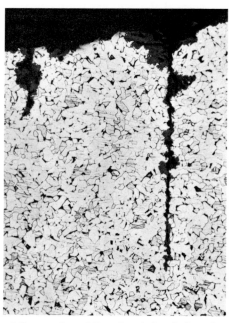

Micrograph, at 250×, of a nital-etched section through corrosion-fatigue cracks that originated at hemispherical corrosion pits in a carbon steel boiler tube. Corrosion products are present along the entire length of the cracks.

Fig. 4. Corrosion-fatigue cracks in carbon steel

varying relative humidity, and in Table 1 for a series of lead alloys tested in air and in a 38% solution of sulfuric acid in water. (In another series of tests, pure lead achieved two to four times longer fatigue life in oil than in air, indicating that air, or perhaps the moisture in air, accelerates fatigue failure substantially for lead alloys.)

Effect on Crack Initiation. Surface features at origins of corrosion-fatigue cracks vary with the alloy and with specific environmental conditions. In carbon steels, cracks often originate at hemispherical corrosion pits and often contain significant amounts of corrosion products (see Fig. 4). The cracks are predominantly transgranular, may exhibit a slight amount of branching, and, except where they intersect the free surface, resemble fatigue cracks that are not environmentally induced. Surface pitting is not a prerequisite for corrosion-fatigue cracking of carbon steels; corrosion-fatigue cracks sometimes occur in the absence of pits.

In aluminum alloys exposed to aqueous chloride solutions, corrosion-fatigue cracks frequently originate at sites of pitting or intergranular corrosion. Stage I crack propagation is normal to the axis of principal stress. This is contrary to the behavior of fatigue cracks initiated in dry air, where initial (stage I) growth follows crystallographic planes. As shown in the fractographs in Fig. 5, the river patterns normally observed in stage I propagation in dry air (Fig. 5a) are suppressed by aerated chloride solutions (Fig. 5b). Initial corrosion-fatigue cracking normal to the axis of principal stress also occurs in aluminum alloys exposed to humid air, but apparently pitting is not a requisite for crack initiation.

Corrosion-fatigue cracks in copper and various copper alloys initiate and propagate intergranularly, as shown in Fig. 6. Corrosive environments have little effect on the fatigue life of pure copper, although they change the fatigue-crack path from transgranular to intergranular. Alternatively, copper-zinc and copper-aluminum alloys exhibit a marked reduction in fatigue resistance, particularly in aqueous chloride solutions. This type of failure is difficult to distinguish from stress-corrosion cracking except that it may occur in environments that normally do not cause failures under static stress, such as sodium chloride or sodium sulfate solutions.

Environmental effects usually can be identified by the presence of corrosion damage or corrosion products on fracture surfaces or within growing cracks. Exceptions to this rule are alloys that are subject to hydrogen damage. For example, corrosion-fatigue cracking of high-strength steel exposed to a hydrogen-producing environment (such as water vapor) may be difficult to identify from macroscopic or microscopic observations of a fracture surface; the fracture-surface features produced by crack initiation and propagation do not differ significantly from those produced by fatigue in nonaggressive environments. For similar reasons, corrosion fatigue may be difficult to distinguish from some forms of hydrogen damage, particularly hydrogen-induced slow-strain-rate embrittlement and static fatigue.

Effect on Crack Propagation. The current emphasis in corrosion-fatigue testing is measurement of rates of fatigue-crack propagation in different environments. Indications are that an environment affects the rate at which fatigue cracks propagate in most metals, and that even for a single alloy system this environmental effect is complex. In a given alloy, crack-growth rates can vary widely with variations in stress factors such as stress state, stress-intensity range, and stress-wave shape and frequency, in addition to varying as the result of environmental effects.

Crack propagation in steels may be intergranular or transgranular, although the latter is more likely. Extensive corrosion often damages fracture surfaces and can make positive identification of the fracture mechanism difficult. The environment also may alter the mode of crack propagation; in hydrogen, for example, fatigue-crack growth by quasicleavage has been observed, which is considerably different from the typical mode of fatigue-crack propagation. Quasicleavage also has been observed on fracture surfaces of high-strength maraging steels fatigued in aqueous solutions.

As with mechanical-fatigue cracking, corrosion-fatigue cracking in aluminum alloys propagates transgranularly; thus, grain directionality does not appreciably influence crack propagation. This is in contrast to propagation of stress-corrosion cracks in susceptible wrought aluminum alloys, which is markedly influenced by grain directionality.

Influence of Chemical Activity of Environment. In contrast to stress-corrosion cracking, the phenomenon of corrosion fatigue does not depend on the presence of a specific corrosive substance; the sole requirement is that a substance be sufficiently corrosive to the material. Accordingly, increasing chemical activity (for example, by lowering the pH of a solution or by increasing corrodent concentration) generally decreases resistance of a material to corrosion fatigue, whereas decreasing the chemical activity improves resistance to corrosion fatigue.

The fatigue behavior of low-carbon steel in contact with a neutral solution is directly related to the concentration of dissolved oxygen in the solution, but only when the oxygen concentration is below 0.2 atm. Completely eliminating oxygen from the solution eliminates corrosion fatigue of low-carbon steel — presumably because corrosion is thereby reduced to a level at which it does not have an influence on fatigue behavior.

The chemical composition of solutions inside growing corrosion-fatigue cracks is expected to be similar to that observed for stress-corrosion cracks. In stress corrosion, the solution in the cracks is more acidic than the bulk environment because of crevice effects. However, under cyclic loading the walls of corrosion-fatigue cracks exert a pumping, recirculating action on the solution contained in the cracks; thus, the solution within these cracks may more nearly resemble the bulk environment than does the solution contained within stress-corrosion cracks.

Anodic polarization of steels, aluminum alloys and copper alloys decreases resistance to corrosion fatigue, whereas cathodic polarization increases resistance. Accordingly, bimetallic couples, which create anode-cathode relationships, decrease resistance to corrosion fatigue when the cyclically stressed material is the anode and increase resistance when the stressed material is the cathode. Corrosion-fatigue rates under these conditions ordinarily are directly related to the magnitude of the galvanic effect.

The effect of corrosive environments on corrosion fatigue caused by thermal cycling has not received much attention. For some materials, a corrosive environment may improve corrosion-fatigue resistance, especially when a coherent bulk oxide bridges a crack or blunts the crack tip. Conversely, when thermal cycling cracks an oxide scale, exposing the underlying metal to the environment, corrosion-fatigue resistance usually is reduced.

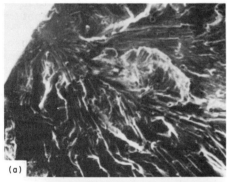

Fig. 5. SEM fractographs, at 140×, of fatigue-fracture surfaces of aluminum alloy 7075-T6, showing that river patterns produced in dry air (a) are suppressed in an aerated 3% NaCl solution (b)

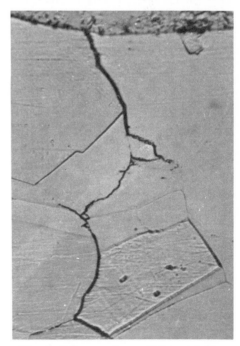

Fig. 6. Micrograph, at 500×, of intergranular fatigue cracking in a Cu-8Al alloy tested in 3% NaCl solution

Fig. 7. SEM fractograph (secondary-electron image), at 60×, of a single-origin corrosion-fatigue crack in type 403 stainless steel exposed to steam, showing rubbed origin (at arrow) and beach marks

Analysis of Corrosion-Fatigue Failures

General procedures and techniques for analysis of failures, regardless of mechanism, are discussed in the article that begins on page 10 in this volume. Additional information, particularly regarding collection, identification and analysis of corrosion products and examination of corroded surfaces, is contained in the article on Corrosion Failures, which begins on page 168. In this section, only those aspects of failure analysis that bear directly on the identification of corrosion fatigue as the mechanism of failure are discussed.

Macroscopic Examination of Fractures

After historical information about the failure has been obtained, and after on-site examination has been performed and samples for laboratory investigation have been collected, detailed examination usually begins with visual and low-magnification examination of the failed part, with special attention to features of exposed fracture surfaces. Because analysis of fracture-surface deposits can be vital to the identification of corrosion fatigue, the first step in the macroscopic investigation should be stripping the fracture surface with cellulose acetate tape or plastic replicating material to entrap any deposit for later microanalysis. Then, whether complex electron optics or simple photographic documentation is to be used, the piece should be cleaned and degreased in an ultrasonic cleaner containing reagent-grade acetone, or similar organic solvent, as the tank medium. The main advantage of reagent-grade acetone is that it leaves a minimal amount of organic residue on the fracture surface yet removes almost all traces of cellulose acetate left from stripping.

(a)

(b)

(a) Light fractograph, at 7.5×, showing primary origin (at arrow) and three secondary origins (along right edge below primary origin). (b) SEM fractograph (secondary-electron image), at 50×, of area surrounding primary origin (in circle). White areas are corrosion pits; black areas, one of which is indicated by arrow, are remnants of corrosion product left after the fracture surface was electrolytically cleaned.

Fig. 8. Two views of the fracture surface of a forged type 630 (17-4 PH) stainless steel steam-turbine blade that failed by corrosion fatigue originating at severe corrosion pitting

Also, acetone is an excellent solvent for wet magnetic-particle suspensoid and most liquid penetrants, which often are used in the field for nondestructive detection of cracks. If the part is too large or otherwise not amenable to ultrasonic cleaning, solvent may be sprayed onto the surface of the part using a squeeze

bottle or an aerosol can; the solvent should not be applied with a brush.

Instrumentation. By far the most useful instrument for macroscopic examination is a good binocular microscope, preferably one with a "zoom-type" objective lens. Many corrosion-fatigue cracks characteristically change fracture planes, or may be intergranular; thus, a laboratory microscope must be capable of providing a three-dimensional field of view that is not distorted by lens aberrations.

A scanning electron microscope also is valuable for macroscopic examination. Corrosion-fatigue fractures often are sufficiently rough that a standard optical binocular microscope cannot focus the entire area of view, but a scanning electron microscope has a greater depth of field. In addition, most scanning electron microscopes have controls for continuous "zoom" from magnifications of 25 to 3000 diameters.

Most environmentally affected fracture surfaces exhibit a tenacious oxide formed on the metal substrate, which interferes with direct observation. Very often, excellent macroscopic examination of these surfaces can be conducted using the backscattered electron image of a scanning electron microscope. The only possible disadvantage of the backscattered electron image is that re-entrant angles ordinarily resolved by the secondary-electron image generally cannot be seen using backscattered electrons. The secondary-electron image on unprepared fracture surfaces often will "charge up" and obscure portions of an oxidized fracture, but the surface often can be sputtered with a film of a conductive material, such as carbon, to minimize this effect.

Fracture Origins. Origins of corrosion-fatigue fractures typically are surrounded by crack-arrest lines, or beach marks, as shown in Fig. 7 and in Fig. 2. Often there are several origins, particularly when fracture has been initiated by pitting (see Fig. 8). Occasionally, no well-defined origin can be resolved.

Features at the origin of a corrosion-fatigue fracture often are indistinct because the compression portion of each stress cycle has forced mating fracture surfaces together and formed an extremely rubbed, discolored origin, as shown at the arrow in Fig. 7. Also, the area of the origin is exposed to the environment for the longest time, and thus may exhibit more extensive residues of a corrosion product than the rest of the fracture surface. A corrosion product at fatigue origins can be misleading when viewed macroscopically. The oxide may be flat and tenacious, globular, or nodular. At magnifications of less than 60 diameters, globular or nodular oxide particles are easily mistaken for intergranular facets; thus, no conclusions should be drawn until other metallographic or fractographic techniques confirm the mechanism of crack initiation. Occasionally, oxidation is so severe that no information other than location of origin can be obtained.

Other features that can be observed macroscopically are secondary cracks, pits, and fissures, all of which often are adjacent to the main origin of a particular fracture. In corrosion-fatigue failures, cracks and fissures adjacent to the primary origin are indicative of a uniform state of stress at that location. Therefore, the primary fracture simply propagated from the flaw that either induced the most severe stress concentration or was exposed to the most aggressive local environment. Sometimes, the primary fracture is related more to corrosion sites resulting from heterogeneous microstructure than to the stress distribution.

In the next example, corrosion fatigue was identified as the mechanism of failure by macroscopic examination of the fracture surface and was confirmed by microscopic examination of a section through the fracture origin plus knowledge of the service conditions.

Example 2. Corrosion-Fatigue Fracture of an H21 Tool Steel Safety-Valve Spring in Moist Air (Fig. 9)

The safety valve on a steam turbogenerator was set to open when the steam pressure reached 348 psi. The pressure had not exceeded 260 psi when the safety-valve spring shattered into 12 separate pieces, two of which are shown in Fig. 9(a). The steam temperature in the line varied from about 330 to 400 C (about 625 to 750 F). Because the spring was enclosed and mounted above the valve, its temperature probably was slightly lower.

The 7¾-in.-OD by 12-in.-long spring was made from a 1⅜-in.-diam rod of H21 hot work tool steel and had been in service for about four years, subjected to mildly fluctuating stresses.

Investigation. Visual examination of the broken spring revealed that all the individual fractures had thumbnail-shape origins along the top surface of the wire, as shown in Fig. 9(b). The origins were typical of fatigue, but the remaining portions of the fractures were brittle. The shape of the fracture surfaces and the fact that the spring had shattered into 12 pieces suggested that the spring had been uniformly loaded, predominantly in torsion, but that the fatigue cracks had introduced stress raisers at multiple points.

Chemical analysis of the metal in the spring disclosed that it was within the composition range for H21 tool steel, except that the tungsten content was 7.8% instead of the usual 9 to 10%.

Sections were taken approximately 90° to the fracture surface and through the origins of three of the fractures. Examination of these sections revealed corrosion pits

(a)

(b)

(a) Photograph, at about 0.3×, of two of the 12 pieces into which the spring shattered.
(b) Light fractograph, at about 0.7×, showing typical corrosion-fatigue origin (at arrow) and brittle final fracture.

Fig. 9. Safety-valve spring, of H21 tool steel, that fractured from corrosion fatigue in moist air (Example 2)

adjacent to the fracture surfaces, with cracks emanating from the bases of some of them. In one section, a corrosion pit approximately 0.045 in. in diameter had initiated two cracks 0.028 and 0.060 in. deep. The cracks contained an iron oxide corrosion product that enclosed spheroidal carbide particles.

The microstructure of the spring consisted of spheroidal carbide particles in a matrix of tempered martensite. The surface of the spring had been decarburized, and the surface grains were larger than those in the interior. This condition probably resulted during heat treatment and may or may not have accelerated the rate of corrosion.

Conclusion. The spring failed by corrosion fatigue that resulted from application of a fluctuating load in the presence of a moisture-laden atmosphere.

Corrective Action. All safety valves in the system were replaced with new, open-top valves that had shot peened and galvanized steel springs. No further failures occurred for more than four years following this action. Both the zinc coating, which provided galvanic protection for the spring, and the open-top valve construction, which allowed free circulation of air with a reduced concentration of moisture, were considered instrumental in eliminating corrosion fatigue of these valve springs.

As an alternative course of action, the valve springs could have been made from a corrosion-resistant metal — for instance, a series 300 austenitic stainless steel or a nickel-base alloy such as Hastelloy B or C.

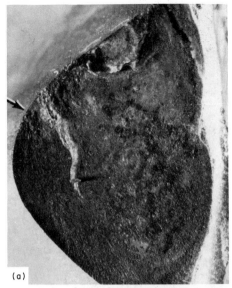

(a)

INTERGRANULAR ORIGIN

(b)

(a) Light fractograph, at 7½×, of corrosion-fatigue crack. Arrow indicates origin; white area along right edge is overload fracture produced during laboratory examination.
(b) Light fractograph, at 60×, of intergranular stress-corrosion crack (outlined by arrows) that initiated the corrosion-fatigue crack.

Fig. 10. Fracture surface of a type 403 stainless steel steam-turbine blade. Fracture originated in a weld that had not been stress relieved.

Crack propagation by corrosion fatigue sometimes proceeds from cracks or pits that were started by another mechanism. For example, the fracture shown in Fig. 10 was initiated by stress-corrosion cracking, but crack propagation occurred by corrosion fatigue. In instances where stress-corrosion cracking and corrosion fatigue are competing mechanisms, as might be expected in a component exposed to both cyclic loading and static tensile loading in a corrosive environment, the mechanism of propagation is determined by the stress-intensity factor and the time of exposure. Corrosion fatigue is favored either at high cyclic frequencies or when K_{Ii} is less than K_{Iscc}. Stress-corrosion cracking will predominate when cyclic frequencies are low and K_{Ii} is greater than K_{Iscc}.

Both corrosion fatigue and mechanical fatigue may exhibit multiple origins that ultimately join to form a single crack front on a single plane. However, it is sometimes possible to distinguish corrosion fatigue from purely mechanical fatigue by the number of cracks propagating through the part. Frequently, several corrosion-fatigue cracks form and propagate simultaneously along parallel paths, as shown in Fig. 11. On the other hand, mechanical-fatigue cracks may initiate at several points in the same general region on a part, but usually one crack becomes dominant, or several cracks join to form a single front, before cracking has progressed very far into the part.

Final Fracture. The region of fast fracture usually is macroscopically distinct from the region of slow crack propagation. The region of slow crack propagation almost always exhibits signs of corrosion, whereas the fast-fracture region is corroded only when sufficiently exposed to the environment following rupture. For example, the white area along the right edge of the fracture surface in Fig. 10(a) is a clean overload fracture produced by breaking a cracked blade in the laboratory during failure analysis. More often, complete separation occurs in a service environment, and there is at least a slight amount of corrosion on the overload portion of the fracture surface.

Microscopic Examination of Fractures

Studies of fracture surfaces are really studies of fracture paths. Many of the features found at high magnification bear little resemblance to those found at low magnifications, primarily because local factors that influence the fracture process (environment, stress state and magnitude

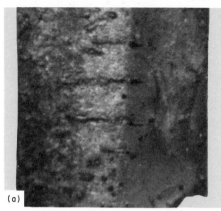

(a)

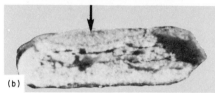

(b)

(a) Macrograph, at about 8×, showing multiple corrosion-fatigue cracks that propagated along parallel paths.

(b) Light fractograph, at about 8×, of a fracture surface adjacent to the region shown in (a); arrow indicates origin.

Fig. 11. Corrosion-fatigue cracking in oval wire of hardened 1065 steel

of stress at the crack tip, plus microstructure) are different from their macroscopic counterparts.

Most corrosion-fatigue fractures start as small flaws and grow as stress intensity increases, as the environment at the crack tip alters, and as the plastic zone ahead of the crack front increases in size. In many instances, crack initiation occurs at low stress under dominant crystallographic influences, producing clear-cut cleavage-type or intergranular fracture with a minimum of observed plasticity. As the crack grows, more plasticity is associated with the cracking process, more grains become involved in

producing each fracture-surface feature, and the fine-scale features become less distinctly crystallographic. Thus, a typical crack begins at a local stress raiser, grows as a crystallographic crack and subsequently changes to a noncrystallographic crack as it propagates through the component.

Both transmission and scanning electron microscopes are widely used in failure analysis. Detailed information on these instruments, together with examples of fractographic features that can be resolved by high-magnification fractography, is presented in Volume 9 of this Handbook. It often is important to recognize features that can be produced during overload fracture or fatigue without concurrent environmental effects, because it is sometimes the absence of these features that identifies an environmentally assisted fracture.

Microfractographic features that are clear indicators of fatigue include: striations (Fig. 12a); "tire tracks" (Fig. 12b); and plateaus separated by shear steps or tear ridges, or both (Fig. 12c). Any or all of these features may be absent on a fatigue-fracture surface. When fracture occurs by corrosion fatigue, these features may be indistinct or may be obscured by corrosion products. For example, fatigue in a mildly corrosive service environment produced the features shown in Fig. 12(a); the striations are somewhat indistinct, and residues of corrosion product appear as black spots in the fractograph. On the other hand, the features in Fig. 12(c), which were produced in a less aggressive laboratory environment, are more clearly delineated. Striations are almost never observed on the surfaces of fatigue fractures produced in high vacuum, which indicates that mild environmental interaction may be responsible for the formation of striations.

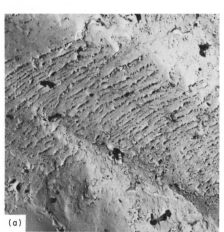

(a)

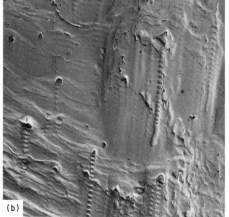

(b)

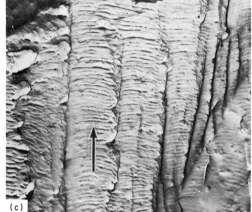

(c)

(a) Fatigue striations, and corrosion products (black spots), on a fracture surface of an aluminum alloy 2014-T6 aircraft wheel that cracked in service; shown at 3500×. (b) "Tire tracks" caused by surfaces rubbing together as fatigue crack opened and closed; shown at 18,000×.

(c) Plateaus (patches of fatigue striations) separated by shear strips and tear ridges on a fracture surface of 5-in.-thick aluminum alloy 2024-T851 plate that was fatigue tested in air; shown at 2000×. Arrow indicates direction of crack propagation.

Fig. 12. TEM fractographs of plastic-carbon replicas, showing fracture-surface features that are clear indicators of fatigue

Determination that a fracture has been initiated by corrosion fatigue does not necessarily involve identification of fine-scale fatigue features on the fracture surface. Figure 13(a) is a light fractograph of a broken Ti-6Al-4V aircraft compo-

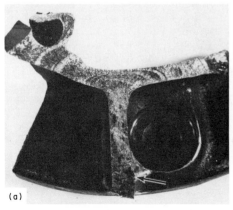

(a) Light fractograph, at 2×, showing predominantly intergranular fracture; thumbnail-shape area indicated by arrow is primary origin of corrosion fatigue. (b) TEM fractograph of a plastic-carbon replica, at 5000×, showing absence of striations in fatigue area. (c) TEM fractograph of a plastic-carbon replica, at 4500×, showing dimples on a grain facet.

Fig. 13. Features on the fracture surface of a broken Ti-6Al-4V aircraft component

nent. Fracture was initiated by corrosion fatigue at the thumbnail-shape area indicated by the arrow. At least three other, smaller thumbnail-shape areas were found on the periphery in the general region of the primary origin. These areas had macroscopic and microscopic features that were identical to those of the primary origin. As shown in Fig. 13(b), clearly defined striations were not observed in the fatigue areas. The remainder of the fracture was intergranular with the grain facets exhibiting dimpled rupture (see Fig. 13c).

In the fractograph in Fig. 14(a), which shows the fracture surface of a sand cast magnesium alloy AZ91C-T6 aircraft-generator gearbox, the beach marks appear to represent the deposit of corrosion products at successive positions of the crack front. Extensive corrosion in the region of crack initiation at a series of filing or grinding grooves in a fillet, indicated by the arrow in Fig. 14(a), had removed all of the fracture features (see Fig. 14b). Although corrosion obscured much of the fine fracture detail over most of the fracture surface, fatigue striations were seen in regions corresponding to later stages of crack growth (Fig. 14c).

Although fatigue striations usually are well formed in most metals, they often are not very well formed in steels. In addition, steels are particularly susceptible to atmospheric corrosion. Thus, even if exposed for only a short time to humid air, minute features on the fracture surfaces of a steel component may be masked. Longer exposure to humid air, or exposure to a more oxidizing atmosphere such as hot exhaust gases, may destroy much of the detail or may cover the fracture surface with a tenacious crystalline oxide. Sometimes, fatigue in steels is intergranular; Fig. 15 shows an intergranular corrosion-fatigue fracture in 4340 steel that occurred during testing in humid air.

Artifacts. Mishandling of fractured parts or use of poor technique in prepar-

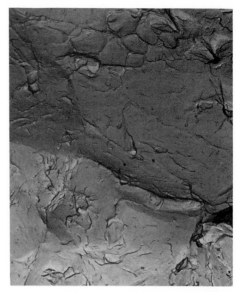

Fig. 15. TEM fractograph, at 3000×, showing surface of intergranular corrosion-fatigue fracture in 4340 steel that occurred during testing in humid air

ing replicas for examination by electron microscopy can result in artifacts, which interfere with proper interpretation of fracture features. Two types of artifacts that could be misinterpreted as fatigue striations are shown in Fig. 16; other artifacts are shown on page 62 in Volume 9 of this Handbook.

Selection of proper magnification can be important to proper identification of fracture features. Thus, it is important to view a fracture surface at several different magnifications to ensure resolution of significant details. For instance, the mating fracture surfaces of a specimen of 2024-T3 aluminum alloy that was broken by fatigue in air are shown in Fig. 17 at a magnification of 3000 diameters. The fractograph in Fig. 17(a) shows real fatigue striations, whereas Fig. 17(b) shows slip-band cracks (at arrows). At a lower magnification — 500 diameters, for example — the true striations might not be discernible and the slip-band cracks

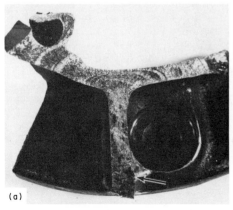

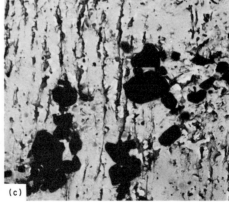

(a) Light fractograph, at 1.2×, showing origin (arrow) and beach marks. (b) TEM fractograph (plastic-carbon replica), showing lack of fracture detail at origin; 2700×. (c) TEM fractograph (plastic-carbon replica), showing fatigue striations formed during later crack-growth stages; 5000×.

Fig. 14. Fracture-surface features of a sand cast magnesium alloy AZ91C-T6 aircraft-generator gearbox that failed by corrosion fatigue

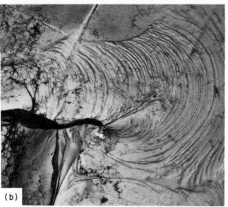

(a) Linear structure formed by removing plastic replica from fracture surface before plastic has hardened. (b) Artifact formed when plastic is incompletely dissolved, then redeposited on carbon replica.

Fig. 16. TEM fractographs, at 2000×, showing two types of artifacts in plastic-carbon replicas that can be misinterpreted as fatigue striations

might be interpreted as striations. Thus it might be presumed, based on an incorrect interpretation at low magnification, that fatigue occurred under a relatively high applied stress, because the "striations" would be widely spaced.

Corrective Measures

The results of failure analysis, including duplication of the original failure by either in-service or laboratory testing of a similar part, should establish and confirm the mode of failure. Further analysis and testing should reveal the basic reasons for the failure and establish whether initial material selection or original design, or possibly both, were inappropriate, and whether incorrect fabrication or unusual service conditions contributed to failure.

Once the cause of failure has been determined, a temporary or permanent solution can be considered. Both temporary and permanent solutions for corrosion fatigue involve one or more of the following: reduction or elimination of cyclic stress, increasing corrosion-fatigue strength of the material, and reduction or elimination of corrosion. These objectives are accomplished by changes in material, design or environment.

For permanent solutions, if a new material is selected (either the same alloy with a different heat treatment or fabrication method, another alloy from the same system, or an alloy from a completely different system), basic compatibility with design requirements and with the environment to be encountered in service usually must be proved by testing. If changes in design or in mode of fabrication are selected, test specimens should reflect these changes. Any environmentally affected properties must be checked in both the test environment and the service environment. Any alteration of the environment should be tested at this stage as well. Finally, the ultimate test of a revamped component is its service life in comparison with the life of the component that it replaced.

Temporary solutions, which usually are intended to remove at least one of the causes of failure, cannot always be thoroughly tested prior to implementation. It may be possible to reduce operating stress or increase corrosion-fatigue strength so that a replacement part will have a longer service life. It also may be possible to coat the part to prevent access of corrosive environment, at least temporarily, or to modify the environmental or electrochemical conditions. Testing of temporary solutions should be done under conditions as close to actual service conditions as possible. Comparison of these tests with those of the original part will provide a quick indication of the effectiveness of the solutions and a revised estimate of service life.

Operating stress may be lowered by reducing either the mean stress or the amplitude of the cyclic stress. This almost always involves a change in component design. Sometimes, only a minor change is required, such as increasing a fillet radius to reduce the amount of stress concentration at a critical location. In other instances, more extensive changes are required, such as significantly increasing cross-sectional area or adding a strengthening rib. If failure has occurred because of stress raisers introduced during manufacture, changes in manufacturing specifications and quality requirements may be necessary.

Shot peening usually is effective in prolonging fatigue life in air by introducing residual compressive stresses in a metal surface, thus reducing the mean tensile stress at potential crack-initiation sites. In more aggressive environments, however, shot peening may have only limited value, because general corrosion can eventually remove the surface layer and thus the beneficial compressive residual stresses.

Nitriding, which also introduces compressive residual surface stresses, can improve corrosion-fatigue resistance of steels, particularly when relatively short

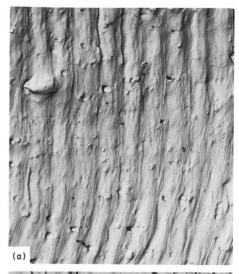

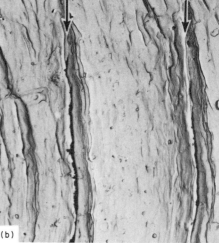

(a) Real fatigue striations (one per cycle). (b) Slip-band cracks (at arrows) that formed on only one fracture surface after passage of the fatigue-crack front and that could be misinterpreted as striations at lower magnification.

Fig. 17. TEM fractographs, at 3000×, of plastic-carbon replicas of the mating fatigue-fracture surfaces of a specimen of aluminum alloy 2024-T3 tested in air

life is required. For applications requiring extended life, other measures are more effective.

Material strength generally is increased by alloying, changes in heat treatment, or selection of a material from a different alloy system. Because corrosion may reduce the fatigue strength of a material to only a small fraction of its fatigue strength in air, alloying additions or heat treatments that only increase strength, without altering the corrosion resistance of the material, may be of marginal value. Conversely, alloying that improves corrosion resistance can be effective in combating corrosion fatigue. For instance, chromium steels generally are more resistant than carbon steels.

Corrosion effects can be lessened by alloying, by providing galvanic protection, or by altering or removing a corrosive environment. Galvanic protection by sacrificial anodes or applied cathodic currents has been successful in reducing the influence of corrosion on fatigue of metals and alloys exposed to aqueous environments, except in alloys such as high-strength steels that are subject to hydrogen-induced delayed cracking. In similar instances, anodic polarization has been used for protection of stainless steels. With passive alloys, or alloys that can be polarized to produce passive behavior, crevices must be avoided because corrosion within crevices actually may proceed more rapidly due to the anode-cathode relationship. For instance, in a part made of low-carbon steel, an area under an O-ring can fail by corrosion fatigue in a caustic solution with a pH of 12 at a location where only low cyclic stresses exist. Where pitting corrosion has occurred, corrosion pits may act as stress raisers and thus accelerate fatigue failure.

Inhibitors sometimes are added to the environment or included in organic coatings to eliminate corrosion fatigue. The effect of inhibitors is believed to depend solely on their ability to reduce corrosion rates to acceptable values.

Corrosion fatigue cannot occur if there is no contact between the surface of a susceptible material and a corrosive environment; however, ordinary fatigue can occur. In most instances, the environment cannot be prevented from contacting the component, and thus coatings are necessary. Continuity of the coating is important; organic coatings such as paint or plastic are only physical barriers (unless they contain inhibitors), and therefore must be absolutely continuous to be effective. Density and thickness of coatings also are significant factors in the prevention of corrosion fatigue. Noble-metal coatings can be effective, but only if they remain unbroken and are of sufficient density and thickness. The relatively low corrosion-fatigue strength of carbon steel is reduced still further when local breaks in a coating such as nickel occur. Presumably, noble-metal coatings that contain residual compressive stresses are more effective than coatings that contain residual tensile stresses.

Elevated-Temperature Failures

*By the ASM Committee on Analysis of Elevated-Temperature Failures**

IN SERVICE at elevated temperature, the life of a metal component subjected to either vibratory or nonvibratory loading is predictably limited. In contrast, at lower temperatures, and in the absence of a corrosive environment, the life of a component in nonvibratory service is unlimited, provided that the operational loads do not exceed the yield strength of the metal. Stress imposed at elevated temperature produces a continuous strain in the component and results in creep. Creep, by definition, is time-dependent strain occurring under stress. After a period of time, creep may terminate in fracture by stress rupture (also called creep rupture).

The conditions of temperature, stress and time under which creep and stress-rupture failures occur depend on the metal or alloy and on the service environment. Consequently, elevated-temperature failures may occur over a wide range of temperatures. In general, however, creep occurs in any metal or alloy at a temperature slightly above the recrystallization temperature of that metal or alloy; at such a temperature, atoms become sufficiently mobile to allow time-dependent rearrangement of structure.

It has been suggested that, for a given metal, "elevated temperature" begins at about one-half the absolute melting temperature of that metal, but this is an oversimplification. Actually, the temperature at which the mechanical strength of a metal becomes limited by creep rather than limited merely by yield strength is not directly related to melting temperature; consequently, "elevated temperature" must be determined individually for each metal or alloy on the basis of behavior. Elevated-temperature behavior begins approximately at 205 C (400 F) for aluminum alloys, 315 C (600 F) for titanium alloys, 370 C (700 F) for low-alloy steels, 540 C (1000 F) for austenitic, iron-base high-temperature alloys, 650 C (1200 F) for nickel-base and cobalt-base high-temperature alloys, and 980 to 1540 C (1800 to 2800 F) for refractory metals and alloys.

The principal types of elevated-temperature failure are creep and stress rupture, low-cycle or high-cycle fatigue, thermal fatigue, tension overload, and combinations of these, as modified by environment. Generally, the type of a failure is established by examination of fracture surfaces and comparison of component operating conditions with available data on creep, stress-rupture, tension, elevated-temperature-fatigue, and thermal-fatigue properties. This analysis is usually sufficient for most failure investigations, but a more thorough analysis may be required when stress, time, temperature and environment have acted to change the metallurgical structure of the component (see discussion in the section headed "Metallurgical Instabilities", on pages 252 to 254 in this article).

Creep

Some typical creep curves are plotted in Fig. 1. Most creep curves consist of three distinct stages; these stages are shown schematically in Fig. 2. Following initial elastic strain resulting from the immediate effects of the applied load, there is a region of increasing plastic strain at a decreasing strain rate (first-stage, or primary, creep). Following first-stage creep is a region of nominally constant rate of plastic strain (second-stage, or secondary, creep). Finally, there is a region of drastically increased strain rate with rapid extension to fracture (third-stage, or tertiary, creep).

*ERNEST A. SCHOEFER, *Chairman*, Consulting Engineer; JOSEPH ALIOTTA, Manager, New Products, Engelhard Minerals and Chemicals Corp.; DONALD L. BAGNOLI, Senior Project Engineer, Materials Research Section, Exxon Research and Engineering Co.; J. G. BYRNE, Dept. of Materials Science and Engineering, University of Utah.

RICHARD S. DEFRIES, Physical Metallurgist, Benet Weapons Laboratories, Watervliet Arsenal; MATTHEW J. DONACHIE, JR., Senior Materials Project Engineer, Materials Engineering and Research Laboratory, Pratt and Whitney Aircraft Div., United Aircraft Corp.; GLENN A. FRITZLEN, Manager of Quality Assurance, Stellite Div., Cabot Corp.; JOHN KILDSIG (retired), formerly Supervisor, Development Laboratory, Ma-

terials Engineering, Detroit Diesel Allison Div., General Motors Corp.; K. C. LOWSTETTER, Technical Director, Engineered Products Div., Abex Corp.; BRUCE W. MCLEOD, Chicago District Manager, Rolled Alloys, Inc.; RONALD C. MOORHEAD (deceased), formerly Chief Metallurgist, Duraloy Co.; ROBERT SHERMAN, Senior Research Engineer, Southwest Research Institute.

JAMES H. STEWART, Owner-Director, Industrial Radiography Laboratory; EDWARD T. VITCHA, Manager, Materials Engineering, Valve Div., TRW Inc.; D. E. WENSCHHOF, Technical Service Representative, Huntington Alloy Products Div., International Nickel Co., Inc.; PAUL M. UNTERWEISER, *Secretary*, Senior Editor, Metals Handbook, ASM.

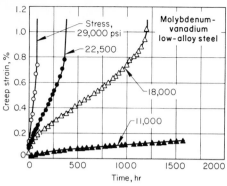

Fig. 1. Creep curves for a molybdenum-vanadium low-alloy steel under tension at four stress levels at 600 C (1112 F)

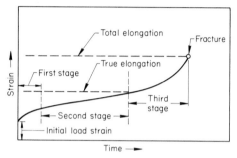

Fig. 2. Schematic tension-creep curve, showing the three stages of creep

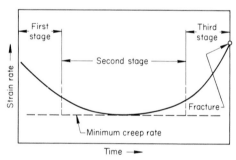

Fig. 3. Relationship of strain rate, or creep rate, and time during a constant-load creep test. The minimum creep rate (MCR) is attained during second-stage creep.

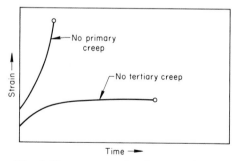

Fig. 4. Creep curves showing no primary creep and no tertiary creep

The region of initial strain under load has not been given a numerical stage designation because it is common practice to ignore this contribution to total strain when plotting creep curves. Consequently, creep curves generally show only the time-dependent plastic strain that follows the initial elastic (and possibly plastic) strain. However, although this procedure is acceptable for purposes of research or investigation, the initial strain, which may amount to a substantial fraction of the total strain, is not omitted from design studies and should not be omitted from a failure analysis. Thermal expansion may impose additional strain and also must be considered.

Primary creep, also known as transient creep, represents a stage of adjustment within the metal during which rapid, thermally activated plastic strain, which occurs in the first few moments after initial strain, decreases in rate as crystallographic imperfections within the metal undergo realignment. This realignment leads to secondary creep.

Secondary creep is an equilibrium condition between the mechanisms of work hardening and recovery; it is also known as steady-state creep. A constant creep rate that is the lowest for the metal under given service conditions of stress, temperature and environment is assumed to be characteristic of this stage. This constant creep rate is generally known as the minimum creep rate (MCR) and is widely employed in research and engineering studies. Minimum creep rate does not, in fact, continue for a significant period of time. From Fig. 3, which illustrates the variation of strain rate with time in a constant-load creep test carried to fracture, it is apparent that strain rate commences at a high value but then decreases rapidly until a minimum is reached. This minimum is within the range of steady-state creep although it amounts to no more than a bottoming-out of the strain-rate – time curve, and is followed promptly by an increase in strain rate that continually increases until the metal fractures. Secondary creep, therefore, is essentially a transition between primary and tertiary creep even though it often occupies the major portion of the duration of the creep test. On the strain-rate – time curve, this transition zone in creep-resistant materials is sufficiently flat so that the minimum creep rate is applicable to virtually all of secondary creep. Minimum creep rate can be related empirically to rupture life.

Tertiary Creep. Primary creep has no distinct end point, and tertiary creep has no distinct beginning. Tertiary creep refers to the region of increasing rate of extension that is followed by fracture. Principally, it may result from metallurgical changes (such as recrystallization under load) that promote rapid increases in deformation, accompanied by work hardening that is insufficient to retard the increased flow of metal. In service or in creep testing, tertiary creep may be accelerated by a reduction in cross-sectional area resulting from crack-ing or localized necking. Environmental effects (such as oxidation) that reduce cross section also may increase tertiary-creep rate. In many commercial creep-resistant alloys, tertiary creep apparently is caused by inherent deformation processes and will occur at creep strains of 0.5% or less.

In designing components for service at elevated temperatures, data pertaining to the elapsed time and extension that precede tertiary creep are of the utmost importance; design for creep resistance is based on such data. However, the duration of tertiary creep also is important, because it constitutes a safety factor that may allow detection of a failing component prior to catastrophic fracture.

Modified Creep. Under certain conditions, some metals may not exhibit all three stages of plastic extension. For example, at high stresses or temperatures, the absence of primary creep is not uncommon, with secondary creep or, in extreme cases, tertiary creep following immediately upon loading. At the other extreme, notably in cast alloys, no tertiary creep may be observed and fracture may occur with only minimum extension. Both of these phenomena are illustrated by the creep curves in Fig. 4.

Stress Rupture

A component under creep loading will eventually fracture (rupture), provided the strain occurring during creep does not relieve the stress. Although time-versus-extension data for plotting of a creep curve can be measured during a stress-rupture test, often only the stress, temperature, time to fracture, and total elongation (stress-rupture ductility) are recorded.

Stress-Rupture Fracture. Depending on the alloy, stress-rupture fracture (creep fracture) may be macroscopically either brittle or ductile. Brittle fracture is intergranular and occurs with little or no elongation or necking. Ductile fracture is transgranular and typically is accompanied by discernible elongation and necking. Intergranular cracking may not be readily discernible on the surface of a part; however, if the oxide scale developed during elevated-temperature stressing in air is removed, such cracking usually will be visible (for an illustration of surface cracking by stress rupture, see Fig. 23 in the article on General Practice in Failure Analysis, on page 23 in this volume). It can be readily seen in a polished longitudinal section and may extend beyond the fracture zone. Internal cracking in a boiler tube that ruptured at high temperature is illustrated in Fig. 4 on page 528 in the article on Failures of Boilers. Fractographs of some stress-rupture fractures will exhibit both transgranular

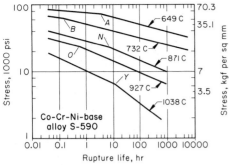

Fig. 5. Logarithmic plot of stress-rupture stress versus rupture life for Co-Cr-Ni-base alloy S-590. The significance of inflection points A, B, N, O and Y is explained in the text.

and intergranular fracture paths. In such instances, it is usually found that the transgranular fractures were initiated by prior intergranular fissures that decreased the cross-sectional area and raised the stress.

Intergranular fractures typically start at grain-boundary triple points — intersections of single boundaries with free surfaces, intersections of single boundaries with second phases, or intersections of two or more boundaries. Wedge-shape cracks form at triple points. Voids, or creep cavities, can form along grain boundaries, particularly those having high densities of precipitated second-phase particles, without the need for intersecting boundaries. This process is called "cavitation creep". The presence of grain-boundary voids in the microstructure on either side of an elevated-temperature fracture is evidence that it is a stress-rupture fracture (see Fig. 24 on page 23 in the article on General Practice).

The type of fracture depends not only on temperature but also on strain rate. At constant temperature, the occurrence of either transgranular or intergranular fracture depends on strain rate. Conversely, at constant strain rate, the type of fracture depends on temperature. In general, lower creep rates, longer rupture times or higher temperatures promote intergranular fractures.

Other significant microstructural features are also associated with stress-rupture fracture. When intergranular cracking occurs, not only do the crack paths follow grain boundaries at and beneath the fracture surfaces, but also the grains appear equiaxed even after considerable plastic deformation and total elongation. In contrast, transgranular fracture results in severely elongated grains in the vicinity of the fracture. The degree of elongation varies with certain metallurgical factors — notably, prior condition of the metal and its susceptibility to recrystallization or grain-boundary migration under given service or test conditions.

Stress-Rupture Curves. The creep curve serves to describe the behavior of material under one set of conditions. It is desirable to portray graphically the stress-rupture behavior over a wide range of conditions both for design purposes and for improved metallurgical knowledge of the failure process. Logarithmic (log-log) plots of stress-rupture stress (σ) versus rupture life (RL) do provide an indication of metallurgical instabilities. These instabilities are delineated by the occurrence of new straight-line segments of changed slope on the log-log plot, as shown by inflection points A, B, N, O and Y in Fig. 5. Stress rupture is a variable-rate process; straight lines on log σ-log RL plots are simply approximations to a continuously varying line.

Stress-Rupture Ductility. The two common measures of ductility are elongation and reduction in area. In the standard tension-creep curve, as shown in Fig. 2, there are actually two measures of elongation that are of interest. First, there is *true* elongation, which is defined as the elongation at the end of the second stage of creep. Second, there is *total* elongation, which is the elongation at fracture (and which may be measured as total strain, or the last creep reading recorded prior to fracture). In some instances, elongation at fracture is mainly extension caused by crack separation. In others, it is mainly necking extension or extension resulting from other tertiary-creep processes. True elongation, on the other hand, nominally consists of extension resulting from nonlocalized creep processes only, although it frequently includes some elongation due to intergranular void formation.

Ductility data from stress-rupture tests are generally erratic, even in replicate tests; they are more erratic for castings than for wrought products. In some metals and alloys, the values of total elongation follow a smooth curve that either increases or decreases with increasing rupture time and temperature.

Table 1. Typical Elevated-Temperature Ductility of a 1.25Cr-0.5Mo Low-Alloy Steel and Type 316 Stainless Steel

Time to rupture, hr	Total elongation in 1½ in., %	Reduction in area, %
1.25Cr-0.5Mo Low-Alloy Steel at 538 C (1000 F)		
8.7	19.6	41
47.0	12.1	29
259.4	14.0	20
660.6	10.5	13
2162.0	17.6	32
Type 316 Stainless Steel at 704 C (1300 F)		
3.1	26.6	26
3.7	24.4	27
37.5	17.8	28
522.6	56.2	41
881.6	39.4	33

However, many metals exhibit an apparently unpredictable series of maximums and minimums that are essentially without significance.

Data on typical total elongation and reduction in area for a low-alloy steel at 538 C (1000 F) and a stainless steel at 704 C (1300 F) are given in Table 1. These ductility data do not reflect the microstructural changes occurring in these alloys at the test temperatures. Despite obvious difficulties in interpretation of ductility data, it is common practice to plot total elongation versus rupture life. The open circles in Fig. 6 represent such data for Co-Cr-Ni-base alloy S-590 at 732 and 927 C (1350 and 1700 F). At both temperatures, considerable scatter of data points is observed.

It is claimed that true elongation gives a more accurate representation of the ductility behavior of metals than does total elongation. As shown by the solid circles in Fig. 6, the variation of true elongation with rupture life for alloy S-590 follows a smooth curve, with true elongation decreasing with decreasing strain rate (longer rupture life). On the other hand, total elongation for alloy S-590 exhibits no clear-cut correlation with rupture life.

The large differences between total and true elongation, such as those shown in Fig. 6, are a function of crack volume and distribution in tertiary creep. The differences in crack initiation and growth can make only relatively small differences in rupture time but account for large differences in total elongation. Replicate tests may thus exhibit large differences in total elongation, but very small differences in true elongation.

Stress-rupture ductility is an important factor in alloy selection. In conventionally cast nickel-base superalloys, for example, a stress-rupture ductility of about 1% is common at 760 C (1400 F), compared to values above 5% for the strongest wrought superalloys. Because

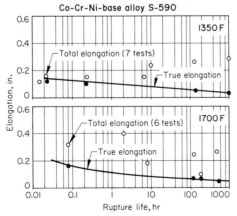

Fig. 6. Relation of elongation and rupture life for Co-Cr-Ni-base alloy S-590 tested at two temperatures

component designs are frequently based on 1% creep, a low stress-rupture ductility may preclude use of an alloy to its full strength potential. As shown by the schematic creep curves in Fig. 7, a higher rupture ductility for the same load and temperature conditions means a higher safety margin. Premature failures have resulted from lack of ductility during tertiary creep. Thermal-fatigue resistance also may be related to rupture ductility. Generally, superalloys with the highest ductilities for a given strength level show the greatest resistance to thermal fatigue.

Stress Concentration. Both strength and stress-rupture ductility must be considered in the design of components for service at elevated temperatures. Normally, these properties are determined quantitatively by smooth-bar stress-rupture tests. In most service applications, components are subjected to complex stresses, including stress concentrations arising from inherent flaws in the metal as well as those stemming from design. Results of smooth-bar tests do not account for such stress conditions. Fortunately, these conditions can be partly reproduced in the laboratory by use of the notched-bar test. Notched-bar stress-rupture tests are of principal interest because of the relationship between stress-rupture ductility and the ratio of notched-bar to smooth-bar stress-rupture strength.

Brown and Sachs* discovered that alloys with smooth-bar stress-rupture ductilities of less than 5% (as measured by reduction in area) usually were notch sensitive whereas alloys with smooth-bar stress-rupture ductilities above 5% rarely were notch sensitive. Later, a better correlation was obtained by Brown, Jones and Newman† by direct use of notched-bar stress-rupture ductility (also measured by reduction in area); on the basis of this correlation, notch sensitivity was determined to occur at notched-bar stress-rupture ductilities below 3%.

In components that contain notches, stress-rupture behavior is determined by notch configuration and by the ductility available to relieve the stress concentration at the roots of notches. For materials ordinarily used in high-temperature components, a ratio of notched-bar to smooth-bar stress-rupture strength of less than 1 to 1 is indicative of marginal ductility. Obviously, notch configuration can affect the notch sensitivity of

*W. F. Brown, Jr., and G. Sachs, "A Critical Review of Notch Sensitivity in Stress Rupture Tests", National Advisory Committee for Aeronautics, TN 2433, Aug 1951

†W. F. Brown, Jr., M. H. Jones and D. P. Newman, "Influence of Sharp Notches on the Stress-Rupture Characteristics of Several Heat-Resisting Alloys", in Symposium on Strength and Ductility of Metals at Elevated Temperatures, STP No. 128, ASTM, Philadelphia, 1952

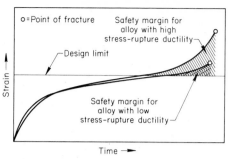

Fig. 7. Schematic creep curves for alloys having low and high stress-rupture ductility, showing the increased safety margin provided by the alloy with high stress-rupture ductility

real structures (notch sensitivity increases with notch sharpness). However, it is doubtful that a simple relationship is entirely satisfactory for applying data on stress-rupture ductility to all types of high-temperature structures.

Elevated-Temperature Fatigue

In service, the steady loads, or strains, to which components are subjected are often accompanied by mechanically induced cyclic loads that are responsible for failure by fatigue. The fatigue properties of metals are normally presented on an S-N curve, which plots maximum stress against the number of cycles before fracture. The effect of temperature on fatigue strength is marked: fatigue strength decreases with increasing temperature. However, the precise relationship between temperature and fatigue strength varies widely, depending on the alloy and the temperature to which it is subjected.

The fatigue behavior of structures that are loaded in combined steady-state and vibratory loading is complex. Combined creep – fatigue loads result in substantially decreased life at elevated temperatures compared with that anticipated in

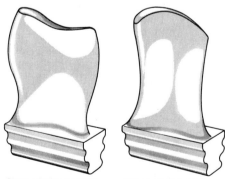

Shape during heating   Shape during cooling

Fig. 8. Schematic portrayal of the expansion, contraction and distortions in shape that occur in the airfoils of turbine blades as a result of cyclic heating and cooling or of uneven heating. Failure by fracture in thermal fatigue is caused by these cyclic thermal stresses.

simple creep loading, and this effect must be considered in failure analysis.

Thermal Fatigue

Mechanical vibration is not the only source of cyclic loads. Transient thermal gradients within a component can induce plastic strains, and if these gradients are applied repeatedly, the resulting cyclic strain can induce component failure. This process is known as thermal fatigue. The effects of the strains that are induced by thermal transients on the airfoils of blades for gas-turbine engines are illustrated schematically in Fig. 8. The thermal strains are generated in the airfoils because the outer surfaces change temperature more rapidly than the metal within. These effects of thermal fatigue may develop in airfoils after a relatively short service life (10,000 to 100,000 cycles). In turbine airfoils, creep strains are superimposed on thermal strains and thus account for a further reduction in life expectancy.

Cracking can occur in many structures during high-temperature operation. An example is the cracking that occurs in heat treating fixtures, as mentioned on page 259, under "Heat treating fixtures".

Thermal-Fatigue Fracture. Thermal-fatigue cracks initiate along the surface and progress inward. They are oriented normal to the surface and may occur singly or in multiples. Because the crack initiates externally, the amount of corrosion or oxidation along the surface of a thermal-fatigue crack is inversely proportional to the depth of the crack. In stress-rupture cracks, on the other hand, oxidation is more uniform. Thermal-fatigue cracks may progress intergranularly, but more often they progress transgranularly. Although the surface of a thermal-fatigue crack is relatively planar, it may be either dendritic (for cast alloys) or smooth (for wrought alloys) in texture.

Excessive creep produces numerous subsurface cracks, whereas thermal fatigue produces surface-oriented cracks that usually are relatively few in number. Typically, fracture surfaces of components cracked in stress rupture are irregular and discontinuous, in contrast to the planar, continuous surfaces of thermal-fatigue fractures.

Metallurgical Instabilities

Stress, time, temperature and environment may act to change the metallurgical structure during testing or service and thereby contribute to failure by reducing strength. (Some changes may enhance strength.) These structural changes are also referred to as metallurgical instabilities and, although they influence all types of failure, are most conveniently described in terms of their influence on stress-rupture properties. A sharp change in the slope of a log σ versus log RL curve (that is, a "break" in the curve) may be ascribed to metallurgical instability. Sources of instabilities include transgranular-intergranular fracture transition, recrystallization, aging or overaging (phase precipitation or decomposition of carbides, borides or nitrides), intermetallic-phase precipitation, delayed transformation to equilibrium phases, order-disorder transition, general oxidation, intergranular corrosion, stress-corrosion cracking, slag-enhanced corrosion and contamination by trace elements.

Transgranular-Intergranular Fracture Transition. The primary metallurgical factor in stress-rupture behavior is the transition from transgranular fracture to intergranular fracture (frequently called the equicohesive transition). The temperature at which the transition occurs is called the equicohesive temperature (ECT). The transition occurs because the properties of grain-boundary regions differ from those of grains. At low temperatures, grain-boundary regions are stronger than grains, and thus deformation and fracture are transgranular. At high temperatures, grain boundaries are weaker than grains, and deformation and fracture are largely intergranular.

The equicohesive temperature varies with exposure time and stress. For each combination of stress and rupture life, there is a temperature above which all stress-rupture fractures will be intergranular. For shorter rupture lives and lower stresses, this transgranular-to-intergranular transition will occur at higher temperatures, and for longer rupture lives and higher stresses, at lower temperatures. This effect is illustrated by points A and B in Fig. 5 (points N, O and Y represent other types of metallurgical instability). Under certain conditions, features of both transgranular fracture and intergranular fracture will be found; consequently, an analysis of rupture-life data or component failure is not complete without a thorough metallographic examination to establish initial failure mechanism.

Aging and Overaging. Age-hardening alloys are characteristically unstable; structurally, they are in a state of transition to stable (equilibrium) condition. Consequently, under creep conditions, it is likely that additional temperature-induced and stress-induced atomic migration will cause aging to continue, resulting in reduced strength. The extent and nature of this change will depend on several factors, including the condition of the alloy prior to creep, and the temperature, stress and time of exposure.

Some of the more common high-temperature structural alloys that harden as

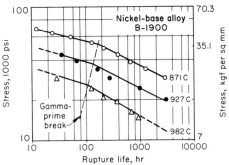

Fig. 9. Logarithmic plot of stress-rupture stress versus rupture life for nickel-base alloy B-1900. The increasing slope of the curves to the right of the gamma-prime break is believed to be caused by gamma-prime coarsening that is the result of overaging.

a result of decomposition of highly supersaturated solid solutions include the Nimonic alloys (Ni-Cr-Al-Ti alloys), austenitic steels that do not contain strong carbide formers, and secondary-hardening ferritic steels. These alloys are widely used for their creep resistance, but are not immune from reduced rupture life due to overaging.

Chief among the age-hardening phases precipitated in nickel-base systems is the gamma-prime (γ'), $Ni_3(Al,Ti)$ phase. When a high-strength nickel-base alloy is exposed for 1000 to 2000 hr to stress at elevated temperatures, a considerable amount of gamma-prime coarsening may occur. The rupture life of a typical cast high-strength nickel-base alloy, B-1900, at three different temperatures is plotted in Fig. 9. The dashed line in Fig. 9 designated "Gamma-prime break" indicates the beginnings of slight increases in slope of the curves, which are believed to be caused by gamma-prime coarsening by overaging. Actually, the coarsening was not apparent in the microstructure at the points where the breaks occur but was observed metallographically after longer tests were completed.

Intermetallic-Phase Precipitation. Topologically close-packed (TCP) phases,

such as sigma, mu and Laves phases, form at elevated temperatures in austenitic high-temperature alloys. Not all of the effects of such phases on rupture life are well known. The effect of sigma-phase formation on the stress-rupture life of nickel-base alloy U-700 at 815 C (1500 F) is shown in Fig. 10. A pronounced "break" was found in the slope of the rupture curve, starting at about 1000 hr. The difference between the extrapolated and actual life at 30 ksi was about 5500 hr, representing a decrease of about 50% in expected life. Sigma phase not only was identified in this alloy system, but also was clearly associated with the failure, because the voids formed by creep occurred along the periphery of sigma-phase particles. In contrast, however, it was found that sigma did not have a similar effect on alloys 713C and U-520. Sigma phase, therefore, does not seem to have a universally deleterious effect on stress-rupture behavior. The amount, location and shape of sigma-phase precipitation determine whether sigma strengthens or weakens an alloy, or whether it has no effect.

The inconsistency of the effect of sigma-phase formation on creep and stress-rupture properties may arise from the simultaneous presence of other phases, such as carbide. The shape and distribution of carbide particles can influence crack initiation and propagation (and hence the resultant stress-rupture ductility and rupture life) in a pronounced manner. It is improbable that sigma phase affects ductility to a significant degree at low strain rates. Consequently, sigma need not always result in deterioration of creep and stress-rupture properties unless it is present in relatively large amounts. Because the presence of sigma does not automatically result in decreased rupture life, it is imperative that careful metallographic work be carried out on failures to ensure discrimination between sigma-promoted failures and other types of failures in which sigma or other TCP phases are merely present.

Carbide Reactions. A variety of types of carbides are found in steels and superalloys. Although temperature and stress affect both carbides found within grains and grain-boundary carbides, the effects on grain-boundary carbides are usually a much more significant factor in altering creep behavior. The presence of carbides is considered necessary for optimum creep and stress-rupture behavior in polycrystalline materials; however, subsequent alteration in their shape, or breakdown and transition to other carbide forms, may be sources of property degradation.

In acicular form, grain-boundary carbides do not appear to act as brittle notch formers that might directly affect rup-

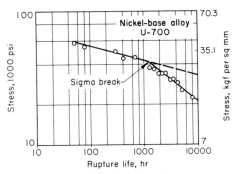

Fig. 10. Logarithmic plot of stress-rupture stress versus rupture life for nickel-base alloy U-700 at 815 C (1500 F). The increasing slope of the curve to right of the sigma break is caused by sigma-phase formation.

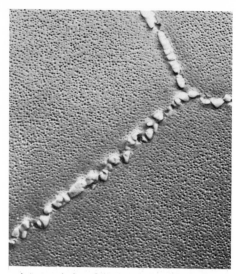

A transmission electron micrograph, at 4000×. Before replication, specimen was electropolished in a solution containing (by volume) 100 parts hydrochloric acid, 50 parts sulfuric acid and 600 parts methanol.

Fig. 11. Grain-boundary carbide films in a Waspaloy forging, which substantially reduced stress-rupture life

ture life at elevated temperatures. However, they may reduce impact strength. Indirectly, compositional changes in the vicinity of carbides can alter rupture strength. In general, M_6C carbides in acicular form are not believed to greatly affect the properties of nickel-base high-temperature alloys unless the alloying elements involved in the carbide reaction markedly alter the matrix composition.

Carbide films formed at grain boundaries can decrease rupture life. Figure 11 is an electron micrograph of grain-boundary carbide films in a Waspaloy forging; these films substantially reduced the stress-rupture life of the alloy.

Interaction of Precipitation Processes. Frequently, carbide and TCP phases do not react independently; in fact, they may interact with each other as well as with other precipitating phases. The relation between sigma, carbide, nitride and ferrite precipitation from austenite has been studied in 18Cr-8Ni stainless steels with high and low chromium contents and high and low carbon-plus-nitrogen contents. Stress-rupture curves for these alloys are presented in Fig. 12 and 13. The curves in Fig. 12 reflect the effects of varying chromium content when the carbon-plus-nitrogen content is both low (0.05 wt %) and constant. The curves in Fig. 13 reflect the effects of varying carbon-plus-nitrogen content when the chromium content is both high (20 wt %) and constant.

The curves in Fig. 12 indicate that ferrite forms in alloys with low interstitial content when the chromium content is high (20 wt %) or low (17 wt %). However, high chromium content promotes sigma formation. Ferrite and

sigma are interrelated; precipitation of ferrite ultimately promotes formation of sigma. By modifying the composition of the steel, both ferrite and sigma formation can be inhibited.

A significant feature in Fig. 12 is the evidence that small amounts of ferrite or sigma may enhance rupture life, although increased amounts formed by long exposure result in deterioration. The strengthening action of sigma can be seen by comparing the curves after the ferrite breaks in Fig. 12. The slope of the sigma-prone 20% Cr alloy is less than that of the 17% Cr alloy, indicating that the rate of strength decrease with time is less when small amounts of sigma are acting to dispersion harden the alloy. Eventually, the small initial grain-boundary precipitates of sigma agglomerate, and larger acicular sigma also forms, causing a reduction in strength.

Environmentally Induced Failure

A critical factor in the performance of metals in elevated-temperature service is the environment and resulting surface-environment interactions. In fact, the most important source of elevated-temperature failure requiring premature replacement of a component is environmental degradation of material. Control of environment or protection of materials (by coatings or self-protective oxides) is essential to most elevated-temperature applications.

General oxidation can lead to premature failure; grain-boundary oxidation may produce a notch effect that also can limit life. Some environments may be more harmful than others; attack of fire-side surfaces of steam-boiler tubes by ash from vanadium-bearing fuel oils can be quite severe. Vanadium-ash attack, and hot corrosion in general, are equally harmful in gas turbines. For example, Inconel 700 is used for gas-turbine blades under such conditions, and it is reported that significant loss in rupture life occurs because of hot corrosion at 700 to 750 C (1292 to 1382 F). Some steels and high-temperature alloys exhibit lower stress-rupture lives in vacuum than in air.

Salt-containing atmospheres exert a deleterious effect on other materials besides steels and high-temperature alloys. For example, hot-salt (stress) corrosion can be induced in titanium alloys kept in contact with salt during high-stress exposure at elevated temperatures. The resistance of titanium alloys to hot-salt corrosion is frequently determined by exposing specimens to salt while creep testing them for a fixed time (100 hr, for example) at the temperature of interest. Subsequent tensile testing reveals susceptibility to hot-salt-corrosion cracking. Hot-salt-corrosion effects normally are not observed in titanium at temperatures below about 288 C (550 F), and in some alloys, the threshold (crack – no-crack) line is essentially equivalent to the line for 0.1% creep in that alloy for the same

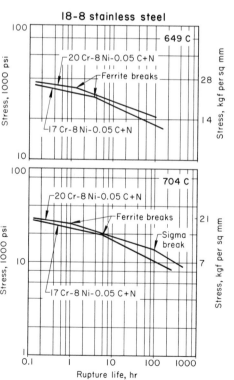

Fig. 12. Effects of varying chromium content on stress-rupture life of an 18-8 stainless steel with low carbon-plus-nitrogen content

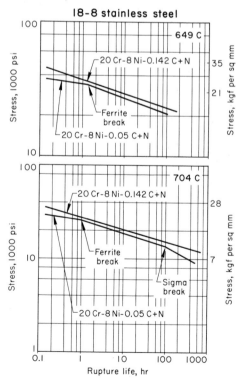

Fig. 13. Effects of varying carbon-plus-nitrogen content on stress-rupture life of an 18-8 stainless steel with high chromium content

Fig. 14. Both sides of two IN-713 turbine blades removed from service because of severe hot corrosion. Note the swelling at the trailing edge on the concave sides (at right in a and c), and the splitting and flaking along both leading and trailing edges on the convex sides (b and d). See also Fig. 15.

exposure time. Thus, in creep tests no hot-salt instability may be observed. Furthermore, actual components are not likely to be exposed to heavy salt-containing deposits. If they are exposed to such an atmosphere, cyclic-temperature rupture testing indicates that an incubation time exists for the occurrence of hot-salt-corrosion instability in titanium.

Corrosion and Corrosion-Erosion

The alloys used in the hot sections of gas-turbine engines are normally exposed to environments that promote corrosion and corrosion-erosion. Consequently, these alloys are selected on the basis of high strength and resistance to surface degradation due to operating environment.

With improvements in the design of gas-turbine engines, gas and metal temperatures were necessarily increased to improve efficiency. The maximum temperatures, however, were primarily limited by the high-temperature strength of the alloys used for turbine applications. In nickel-base high-temperature alloys, increased strength at elevated temperature was attained by lowering the chromium content and by increasing the aluminum and titanium contents to form high volume percentages of the strengthening precipitate gamma prime. However, the decrease in chromium content also resulted in a reduction of the hot-corrosion resistance of these alloys. Cobalt-base alloys, which also are used for gas-turbine rotors, are susceptible to hot corrosion in a manner similar to the nickel-base high-temperature alloys, although to a lesser degree.

Hot corrosion of nickel-base and cobalt-base alloys is accelerated oxidation caused by the presence of sodium chloride and sodium sulfate, usually from operation near seawater. The main sources of elements in these compounds are the fuel used in the engine and the sea salt in the air. Numerous concepts of the mechanism of hot corrosion have been developed. According to one, a molten sulfur-bearing slag forms on the surface of the engine components, fluxing the normally protective oxide scales on the alloys and resulting in accelerated oxidation.

With the introduction of the lower-chromium, higher-strength nickel-base alloys, hot corrosion became the major

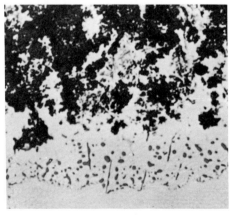

At top are mixed oxides and an alloy-depleted nickel matrix. At center are sulfide particles in an alloy-depleted matrix. At bottom is the gamma matrix with gamma-prime precipitate. Ferric chloride No. 2 etchant; 1000×.

Fig. 15. Microstructure of one of the IN-713 turbine blades in Fig. 14, showing corrosion products

cause for the premature removal of first-stage and second-stage turbine blades and vanes in gas-turbine engines. Higher-chromium, lower-strength alloys had previously been used with very few reports of sulfidation, probably because the problem was not recognized and because of lower engine-operating temperatures.

Figure 14 shows both sides of two IN-713 turbine blades that were removed from service because of severe corrosion. These blades show evidence of hot corrosion — the characteristic swelling, together with splitting and flaking along the leading and trailing edges of the airfoil. Metallographic examination of these blades revealed four zones: an oxide layer on the outside surface, then an oxide layer intermingled with alloy-depleted nickel matrix, then a zone of chromium sulfide particles in an alloy-depleted matrix, and finally a zone of normal gamma-prime precipitation from the gamma matrix. These zones, except for the outer oxide layer, are shown in Fig. 15 for one of the blades in Fig. 14. Electron-microprobe analysis of the oxidized layer showed that the sulfur was associated with chromium in an alloy-depleted zone, and that the depleted matrix metal was intermixed with the oxides.

Accelerated hot corrosion has been produced during engine testing by injecting simulated sea salt through the fuel nozzles to provide a salt concentration of 0.75 ppm and operating the engine at takeoff temperatures. The appearance and surface condition of uncoated IN-713 turbine blades after 45 cycles of this hot-corrosion test were very similar to those of blades returned from service.

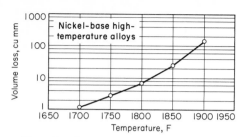

Fig. 16. Average volume loss of ten nickel-base high-temperature alloys as a function of hot-corrosion-test temperature. The alloys were tested in a laboratory test rig, using sodium sulfate as the corrodent.

In another laboratory hot-corrosion test, a regression equation relating loss in base-metal volume to alloy composition was derived for nickel-base alloys. Chromium was shown to be beneficial to hot-corrosion resistance, whereas molybdenum was detrimental. The severity of hot corrosion increased with temperature throughout the entire testing range (927 to 1038 C, or 1700 to 1900 F) in an approximately logarithmic manner, as shown in Fig. 16. Limited testing at 1093 C (2000 F) indicated that severity of hot corrosion continued to increase up to this temperature.

Engines returned from service, accelerated hot-corrosion engine tests, and laboratory hot-corrosion-rig tests have shown that high-temperature alloys with the high strength necessary to resist the stresses developed during engine operation were usually low in chromium and did not have adequate resistance to hot corrosion. There are several possible solutions to the problem, including development of an alloy that can resist hot corrosion, use of protective coatings on the turbine components, and utilization of air-cooling techniques to lower the operating temperature of component parts. Although there have been advances in the development of alloys with improved hot-corrosion resistance, the most effective protection is now being achieved primarily by the application of protective coatings. Hollow, air-cooled components are being utilized in higher-temperature locations of some gas-turbine engines, but even these parts have to be coated for protection against hot corrosion.

Protective coatings provide a partial solution to the hot-corrosion problem, supplementing the inherent corrosion resistance of most high-temperature alloys. Aluminide-type coatings successfully extend the life expectancies of gas-turbine-engine blades and vanes, as shown in Fig. 17. Principal processes for applying aluminum-rich coatings are pack cementation, hot dipping, slurry, and electrophoresis; coatings applied by these processes usually are diffused at elevated temperatures. Regardless of the methods used for applying them, basic similarities exist among all of the aluminide coatings. They are composed predominantly of Ni-Al on nickel-base alloys or Co-Al on cobalt-base alloys, with minor additions of an alloying element, usually chromium. Another class of high-temperature coatings is obtained by applying corrosion-resistant alloys, such as Co-Cr-Al-Y and Fe-Cr-Al-Y, to the surfaces of turbine components by means of electron-beam vapor deposition.

A nickel-aluminum protective coating on a nickel-base alloy will degrade by hot corrosion and will spall during subsequent operation. The surface appearance of an aluminide-coated IN-713 turbine blade after accelerated hot-corrosion testing in an engine is shown in Fig. 17(c). The concave and convex surfaces have bulged and flaked as a result of hot corrosion. Metallographic examination shows that the coating was slightly degraded by hot corrosion (see Fig. 17d). Nevertheless, the life of a coated blade represents about a four-to-one improvement over that of an uncoated blade.

Hot corrosion also can attack a coating in a localized area, as shown in Fig. 18. Localized attack may result from variations in the chemical composition of the

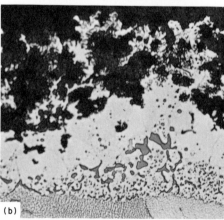

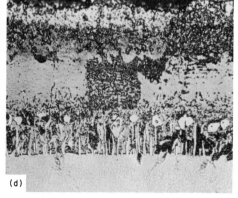

(a) Uncoated turbine blade after 118 programed cycles. Magnification, 1.8×. (b) Micrograph showing severe degradation of the uncoated blade by hot corrosion. Ferric chloride No. 2 etchant; magnification, 450×. (c) Aluminide-coated blade after accelerated hot-corrosion testing in an engine. Magnification, 1.8×. (d) Micrograph showing only slight degradation of the aluminide coating. Ferric chloride No. 2 etchant; magnification, 450×.

Fig. 17. Effect of an aluminide-type (Ni-Al) coating on the hot-corrosion resistance of an IN-713 turbine blade compared with that of an uncoated blade

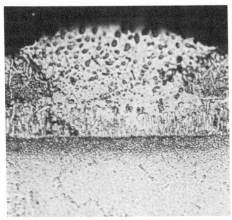

Fig. 18. Micrograph showing localized degradation of the aluminide coating on an Inconel 738 turbine blade after accelerated hot-corrosion testing in an engine. (Etched in FeCl₃+HCl+H₂O; 500×)

coating or from localized concentration of the corrodents. In addition, corrosion-erosion degradation of the coating can occur at one specific location, such as the leading edge of a turbine blade, because of exposure to the high-temperature, high-velocity gases in the turbine. Subsequent attack of the base metal occurs, requiring premature removal of the component from the engine. An example of corrosion-erosion is shown in Fig. 19.

Coating cracks that result when a coating is strained beyond its ductility limit also can cause premature failure of a turbine blade, because hot corrosion or oxidation, or both, can penetrate to the base metal and eventually cause spalling of the coating. Figure 20 shows hot-corrosion and oxidation attack of the base metal at the bottom of a crack in the aluminide coating of a turbine blade.

In an oxidizing atmosphere, aluminide coatings form a protective aluminum-oxide layer on the blade surface. The cyclic operation of a gas-turbine engine causes the oxide to spall off, and subsequently the coating forms another protective layer of aluminum oxide. The rate of coating degradation is dependent on the operating environment and will vary for each coating-alloy combination.

General Oxidation

Oxidation, and all other reactions of metals with gaseous environments, have long been recognized as severe limitations to the utilization of metals at high temperatures. The development of alloys, therefore, is usually aimed at improving oxidation resistance, as well as improving mechanical properties.

Table 2 provides suggested maximum temperatures for operation of wrought stainless steel components in oxidizing atmospheres without excessive scaling. These temperatures may require modification, depending on the severity of the oxidation rate as influenced by the type

of atmosphere and by other factors that can increase the loss of metal. The scaling-temperature or operating-temperature limits given are based on arbitrary standards and indicate approximately the temperatures at which, after prolonged heating in a strongly oxidizing atmosphere, a scale will form of sufficient thickness to cause flaking or spalling. These stainless steels oxidize superficially at lower temperatures, forming a series of temper colors, until a thin, more or less adherent layer of scale is formed. This action proceeds very slowly until the scaling temperature is reached, whereupon progressive thickening of the scale layer, with spalling, causes much more rapid deterioration of the metal, thus reducing the service life or making mandatory the selection of a more highly alloyed material for economical and continued operation. Because of their lower coefficient of thermal expansion, the ferritic stainless steels may be damaged less by scale formation and subsequent flaking during repeated heating and cooling than austenitic steels.

Carburization

The problem of carburization of steel — particularly, carburization of stainless steels used in elevated-temperature furnace environments — is common to many industrial applications. Typical is the occurrence of carburization, with or without oxidation, in stainless steel resistance-heating elements and various components and fixtures of heat treating furnaces. The simultaneous carburization and oxidation of stainless steel heating elements results in a form of attack sometimes referred to as "green

Fig. 19. Macrograph (at 4×) showing corrosion-erosion on leading edge of an aluminide-coated MAR-M 246 alloy turbine blade after simulated flight testing

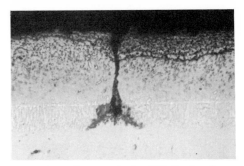

Fig. 20. Micrograph (at 500×) showing hot-corrosion and oxidation attack at the bottom of a crack in the aluminide coating of a turbine blade. (Specimen was etched in FeCl₃-HCl-methanol.)

rot". Basically, this form of attack results from precipitation of chromium as chromium carbide, followed by oxidation of the carbide particles, and is common to nickel-chromium and nickel-chromium-iron alloys.

Another typical industrial example involves the carburization of certain petrochemical-plant components, such as heater tubes. These tubes may be subjected to carburization or carburization-oxidation, or both. These two processes generate uneven volume changes, which result in very high internal stresses, together with metal loss due to corrosion-erosion or with embrittlement due to carbon pickup and consequent carbide formation. Ultimately, the corrosion or corrosion-erosion results in a loss of supporting thickness in the structural member, or the carbide formation results in a loss of ductility that renders the component susceptible to brittle fracture. Heavy carburization also eliminates the possibility of repair welding.

Effect on Stainless Steels. Diffusion of carbon in stainless steel results in the formation of additional carbides; these carbides may take the form of M_7C_3, $M_{23}C_7$ or M_3C_2. A typical example of a microstructure developed in stainless steel as a result of carburization is shown in Fig. 21(a); islands of massive carbides have formed in the austenite matrix. In

Table 2. Suggested Maximum Temperatures for Operation of Wrought Stainless Steel Components in Oxidizing Atmospheres Without Excessive Scaling

AISI type of steel	Temperature, max C	F
(7Cr-Mo)	650	1200
(9Cr-Mo)	675	1250
302, 304	900	1650
302B	980	1800
309	1095	2000
310	1150	2100
316, 321, 347	900	1650
403, 410	705	1300
430	845	1550
442	955	1750
446	1095	2000
501	620	1150

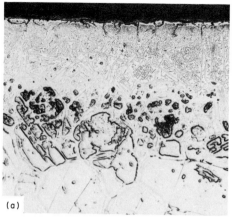 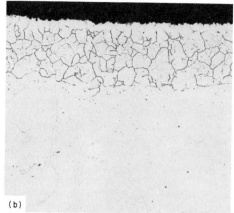

Fig. 21. Micrographs, at 50×, showing (a) *effect of carburization on the microstructure of stainless steel and* (b) *microstructure of the same steel prior to carburization. In the carburized steel, massive carbides are formed by the reaction of carbon with chromium, which depletes the matrix of chromium in regions adjacent to the carbides. (Both specimens were etched in a mixture of 10 ml HNO₃, 20 ml HCl, 20 ml glycerol, 10 ml H₂O₂ and 40 ml water.)*

the same steel prior to carburization, carbides are small and are restricted to the grain boundaries, as shown in Fig. 21(b). In the carburized steel, chromium has migrated to the carbides, depleting the matrix. As chromium depletion progresses, the relative percentages of nickel and iron increase. These changes can be readily detected by electron-microprobe scanning.

The primary significance of carburization is to be found in the changes in properties that it effects. There is a slight increase in the creep strength of the carburized alloy, together with a change in volume that results from an increased amount of carbide, which has a lower density than that of the original alloy. A density gradient, predicated on carbon content, develops across the carburized zones and into those zones that have not been carburized. In stainless steel heater tubes used in petroleum refineries, carburization occurs on the interior walls of

the tubes. This leads to the development of an inner layer of carburized metal and an outer layer of uncarburized metal, each with a different density and a different coefficient of thermal expansion. During thermal cycling, these differences promote the generation of high thermal stresses that can result in tube failure at elevated temperatures. Thermal stresses due to carburization can also be generated in weld metals, as is evidenced by the creep fissuring in the carburized weld metal extending to uncarburized base metal in Fig. 22.

In addition to its adverse effects on density and thermal expansion, carburization of stainless steels also contributes to embrittlement by producing a high volume percentage of carbide and an increased susceptibility to attack by oxidation. Oxidation attack is promoted by the depletion of chromium from the matrix by preferential formation of chromium carbides. The attack occurs when metal surfaces are simultaneously or intermittently exposed to heavily carburizing and oxidizing environments. Under these conditions, it is thermodynamically possible for the dual action of carburization and oxidation to weaken the metal. Specifically, in carburized metal, oxidation attack occurs at grain boundaries. Loss of grain-boundary strength is followed by detachment of grains and subsequent erosion. This form of attack slowly eats away the metal grain by grain; an example is shown in Fig. 23, where the original wall thickness of the tube has been reduced by approximately one-third.

Carburization is also a problem in various nuclear applications in which stainless steel tubing is used in contact with carburizing environments. These environments may be gaseous (CO-CO₂) or a liquid, such as liquid sodium, which is capable of transporting carbon. Both

types of environment can promote carbide formation and severe embrittlement.

"Metal dusting", a type of attack somewhat similar to oxidation attack of carburized metal, has occurred in petrochemical-plant equipment. Metal dusting can be distinguished from conventional oxidation attack of carburized metal as a result of the fact that it occurs randomly in localized areas and progresses more rapidly. An example of metal-dusting attack is shown in Fig. 24; note the evidence of random pitting on the interior wall of the tube. The cause of this highly accelerated attack is believed to be related to the high, localized stresses surrounding the pits — the stresses resulting from volumetric changes.

Metal dusting generally takes place at temperatures from 482 to 816 C (900 to 1500 F), although it has occurred at temperatures as high as 1093 C (2000 F) in strongly reducing atmospheres such as those containing large amounts of hydrocarbon gases. Atmospheres that are alternately oxidizing and reducing appear to promote metal dusting, whereas those containing sulfur-bearing compounds, such as hydrogen sulfide, deter it.

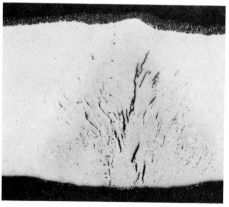

Macrograph, at about 1⅓×, is of a specimen etched in a mixture of 10 ml HNO₃, 20 ml HCl, 20 ml glycerol, 10 ml H₂O₂ and 40 ml water.

Fig. 22. *Section through a stainless steel weld (bottom), showing typical creep fissuring in carburized weld metal and extending to uncarburized base metal*

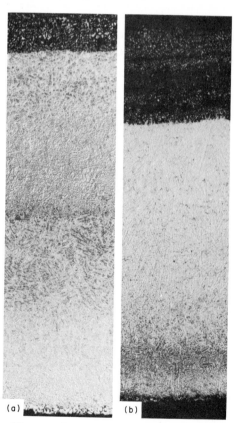

Macrographs, at 4×, are of specimens etched in a mixture of 10 ml HNO₃, 20 ml HCl, 20 ml glycerol, 10 ml H₂O₂ and 40 ml water.

Fig. 23. *Wall of a stainless steel tube after* (a) *one year and* (b) *several years of exposure to carburizing and oxidizing conditions. The wall thickness in macrograph* (b) *has been reduced by about one-third by grain detachment and by subsequent erosion.*

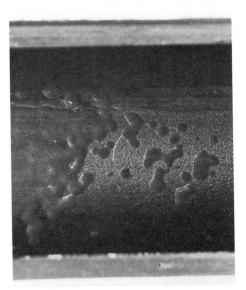

Fig. 24. "Metal dusting" attack on the inner wall of a stainless steel tube

Detection in Austenitic Alloys. Several methods for detecting carburization in austenitic alloys have been explored. The most successful of these is a method for detecting magnetic changes; specifically, carburization is measured and defined by measuring changes in magnetic permeability, with the aid of a magnetic eddy-current device. When an austenitic alloy is carburized, metallurgical changes result in the formation of a new matrix composition — a magnetic iron-nickel-chromium alloy. The matrix alterations that occur are proportional to the magnetic change, and thus carburization and magnetic measurements can be directly related. As shown in Fig. 25 for a tube cast from HK-40 alloy, the actual percentage of chromium depleted from the matrix is proportional to the magnetic permeability. The effectiveness and accuracy of the magnetic method depend on the development and use of standard reference specimens — carburized specimens made from the same alloy and having the same wall dimensions as the tubes or other components being tested.

Heat treating fixtures, such as trays and baskets, that are used in carburizing and carbonitriding atmospheres usually fail as a result of carburization where the cross section is relatively thin. When the trays or baskets, which are used to contain or support parts, are subjected to cyclic quenching in a liquid medium, there is also the possibility of failure by thermal fatigue. In fact, fixtures with heavier cross sections are more likely to fail as a result of thermal fatigue than as a result of carburization when they are subjected to both cyclic quenching and a carburizing atmosphere. Failure caused by carburization generally occurs at room temperature when the component embrittled by chromium carbide breaks as a result of impact or jarring. Failure

from thermal fatigue is generally characterized by gradual crack growth that proceeds with each thermal cycle until final fracture occurs. Such fracture usually occurs at the central portion of a fixture.

Those furnace trays and containers made of relatively thin sheet, about 11 gage (0.120 in. thick), are not subjected to very high thermal stresses during quenching from austenitizing temperatures (about 815 to 925 C, or 1500 to 1700 F) and are more susceptible to failure by embrittlement caused by carburization. Failures of furnace pans used in shaker-hearth furnaces are exceptional in that they generally fail in thermal fatigue. The high thermal stresses to which they are subjected arise from the loading of cold workpieces onto the pans. However, at the time of failure, the pans generally are severely carburized.

Also subject to failure by thermal fatigue in carburizing and carbonitriding applications are heat treating furnace baskets made of round bar. The likelihood of failure by thermal fatigue increases with an increase in the diameter of the bar used to construct the basket.

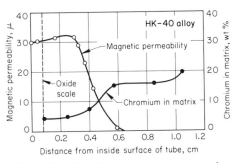

Fig. 25. Relation between magnetic permeability and chromium content of the matrix of a cast HK-40 alloy tube after carburization

Under identical service conditions, however, alloys with a lower mean thermal coefficient of expansion, such as Inconel 600 and 601, Hastelloy X and RA 333, will fare better than those alloys with a slightly higher mean thermal coefficient of expansion, such as Incoloy 800 and RA 330. The effect of section size on resistance to thermal fatigue is illustrated by the macrographs in Fig. 26. These macrographs show two RA 330 alloy bars — one ⅜ in. in diameter and the other ½ in. in diameter — taken from the same furnace basket after many service cycles of heating and quenching. Obviously, the ⅜-in.-diam bar exhibited the better resistance to thermal fatigue.

The effect of carbonitriding atmospheres on heat treating fixtures made of heat-resisting alloys is usually more severe than that of carburizing atmospheres. Consequently, in order to obtain longer service life, high-temperature alloys with higher chromium and silicon contents, such as RA 333 (25% Cr, 1.25% Si), are preferred for carbonitriding service. The alloys with higher chromium and silicon contents also resist carburization more effectively. For example, type 446 stainless steel (25% Cr) is more resistant to carburization than type 430 stainless steel (17% Cr) under identical conditions of environmental exposure. At a given nickel content, alloys with a high chromium content, such as RA 333 (25% Cr) and the cast HL alloy (30% Cr), can be expected to resist carburization to a greater extent than can alloys with lower chromium contents.

Carbon-Nitrogen Interaction

Centrifugally cast furnace tubes of alloys HK-40 (26% Cr, 20% Ni) and HL-40 (30% Cr, 20% Ni) have been used

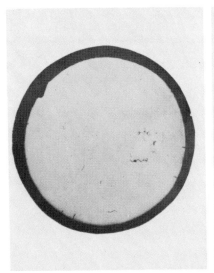
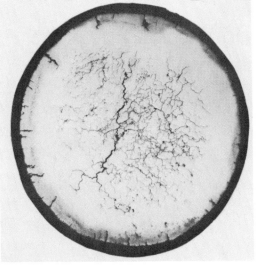

Fig. 26. Effect of section size on resistance to thermal fatigue. These macrographs of RA 330 alloy bars, ⅜ and ½ in. in diameter, that were taken from the same furnace basket, show evidence of carburization, but only the ½-in.-diam bar exhibits severe cracking due to thermal fatigue. (Etched in mixed acids; about 5×)

extensively in ethylene-pyrolysis furnaces for many years. In service, thick deposits of carbon or coke form on the intertube walls, and it is necessary periodically to burn these deposits away by means of steam-air decoking. Examination of failed furnace tubes has established an interaction between carbon diffused from the surrounding furnace atmosphere and nitrogen already present in the tubes. Metallographic examinations and chemical analyses have shown that a high nitrogen content can cause microscopic voids along grain boundaries, which in turn lead to premature failure by stress-rupture cracking. Void formation occurs only when carbon and nitrogen exceed a certain critical level.

It has been determined that, in general, the inward diffusion of carbon from the carburizing atmosphere forces the migration of nitrogen present in the tube toward the outside surface. However, there may be exceptions. In one hydrogen-reformer furnace, for example, there was a joint inward diffusion of carbon and nitrogen because the methane-gas feed contained 18% nitrogen. Analyses showed that the tubes contained 0.83% C and 0.156% N at the inside surface and only 0.42% C and 0.094% N at the outside surface.

Contact With Molten Metal

Molten metals used in coating and in other industrial processes, such as aluminum, copper, zinc, and their alloys, cannot be contained in vessels made of high-temperature alloys. Molten lead is the exception, provided the lead is covered with a protective layer of powdered charcoal. When molten lead is not protected from air, a lead oxide forms; this oxide is highly corrosive to most high-temperature alloys. Among the alloys that have been used successfully to contain molten lead, however, are Inconel 600 and RA 330.

Molten zinc, which is used in hot dip galvanizing of fabricated articles, is commonly contained in tanks or vats made from carbon steel plate of boiler-plate quality. Aside from strength, the principal requirement of a galvanizing-tank material is the ability to resist the corrosive attack of molten zinc. When a layer of flux is maintained on the surface of the bath, a collar of firebrick or other suitable ceramic material normally surrounds and abuts the top 6 or 7 in. of the tank, to retard heat transfer in this area and thus reduce attack by the flux on the steel tank wall. The remainder of the interior of the tank, however, is directly exposed to the molten zinc. In the example that follows, premature failure of a galvanizing vat was traced to improper welding of the vat rather than to inadequacy of the steel plate from which the vat was constructed.

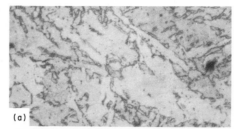

(a) Submerged-arc weld in a galvanizing vat that failed by molten-zinc corrosion along elongated ferrite bands such as those shown. (2% nital; 100×)

(b) Multiple-pass manual shielded metal-arc weld in a test specimen, which resisted molten-zinc corrosion and which shows a refined microstructure. (2% nital; 100×)

Fig. 27. Microstructures of weld metals in T joints of ASTM A285, grade B, steel (Example 1)

Example 1. Failure of a Carbon Steel Galvanizing Vat Caused by Faulty Welding (Fig. 27)

A steel galvanizing vat at a shipbuilding and ship-repair facility failed after only three months of service. The source of the failure was a leak that spilled 15,000 lb of molten zinc into the firebox and onto the floor. The vat, which measured 10 ft by 4 ft by 4 ft, was made of ¾-in.-thick carbon steel plate (ASTM A285, grade B). Welded joints were of "T" construction; each fillet weld (⅝ in.) was made in a single pass, using semiautomatic submerged-arc welding. Full fillet-to-fillet penetration was not obtained.

Investigation. When the failed vat was examined visually, severe channeling and pitting attack were observed on the inside fillet welds. Chemical analysis of the weld metal and the plate indicated that the welds contained considerably more silicon than the plate. The micrograph in Fig. 27(a) is of a specimen taken from an area adjacent to an area of channeling, and exhibits elongated ferrite bands. The damage was most severe along the ferrite bands, possibly because silicon was dissolved in the ferrite and thus made it more susceptible to attack by the molten zinc. To verify this assumption, two T joints were made in ½-in.-thick ASTM A285, grade B, steel plate. One joint was welded using the semiautomatic submerged-arc process with one pass on each side. A second joint was welded manually by the shielded metal-arc process using E6010 welding rod and four passes on each side; the refined microstructure of this weld is shown in Fig. 27(b). Chemical analyses of the welds indicated that the silicon content of the manual (shielded metal-arc) weld was 0.54%, whereas that of the semiautomatic (submerged-arc) weld was 0.86%.

After being weighed, the specimens were submerged in molten zinc for 850 hr, after

which they were again weighed, polished and examined under the microscope. The specimen welded by the submerged-arc process exhibited a weight loss 12 times that of the shielded metal-arc welded specimen; the bulk of corrosive attack was directed toward the silicon-rich ferrite bands.

In comparing the two welding processes, it was determined that the flux used in submerged-arc welding was high in silicon and that the large amount of weld metal deposited in a single pass remained molten long enough to dissolve much larger amounts of silicon than could be dissolved in manual shielded metal-arc welding. Furthermore, the coating on the welding rods used in shielded metal-arc welding was relatively low in silicon content, and because completion of the weld required four manual passes, the lesser amount of weld metal deposited during each pass solidified quickly, thereby limiting dissolution of silicon. Finally, each pass served to refine the ferrite grain developed in a previous pass, thus avoiding ferrite banding.

Corrective Measures. Based on the test results, the original welds were removed from the vat, and the vat was rewelded using the manual shielded metal-arc process with at least four passes on each side. The vat was returned to service and, after nine years, was reported to be operating successfully with little or no evidence of pitting.

Molten lead can be contained in tanks fabricated from high-temperature alloys, including austenitic stainless steels, provided the lead is covered by a layer of charcoal to prevent a severe oxidizing reaction. In the following example, premature failure of a stainless steel lead-containing tank was traced to the high moisture content of the charcoal cover.

Example 2. Premature Failure of a Type 309 Stainless Steel Pan for a Lead Bath (Fig. 28)

Severe reduction of wall thickness was encountered at the liquid line of a lead-bath pan (Fig. 28) that was used in a continuous strip or wire oil-tempering unit. Replacement of the pan was necessary after six months of service. The pan, 270 in. long, 24 in. wide and 15 in. deep with a 1-in. wall thickness, was a type 309 stainless steel weldment. Previously, the pans were cast from the same alloy.

Operating temperatures of the lead bath in the pan ranged from 804 C (1480 F) at the entry end to 843 C (1550 F) at the exit end.

Investigation. Visual examination of the pan disclosed that thinning of the walls (shaded area in perspective view of Fig. 28) was most severe at the surface of the molten lead along the length of the pan, except for the last 36 in. In this area, very little reduction in wall thickness had occurred.

Because the failed pan had been taken out of service, operating conditions were reviewed by examining a second pan of welded construction that had been in service for about three months. This pan was found to have a thin, uneven layer of coarse coke over its entire length, except for the last 36 in. at the exit end, which was covered with

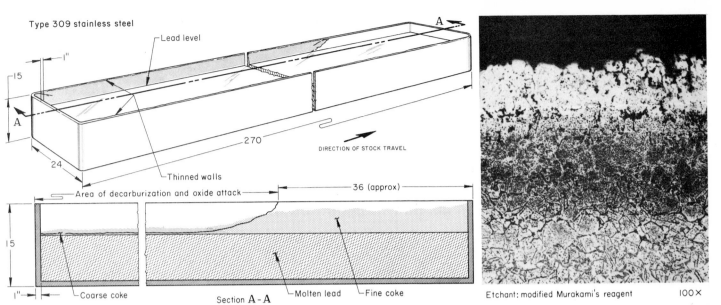

Type 309 stainless steel

Lead level

15

I"

A

A

24

270

DIRECTION OF STOCK TRAVEL

Thinned walls

Area of decarburization and oxide attack

36 (approx)

15

I"

Coarse coke

Section A-A   Molten lead   Fine coke

Etchant: modified Murakami's reagent   100×

Fig. 28. Stainless steel pan (top) for a molten-lead bath that failed as a result of wall thinning (shaded area) caused by oxidation and decarburization; section taken through a second pan (section A-A), showing the relation of the thinned region to coke level; and a micrograph of a section taken through the failure area (Example 2)

a layer of fine coke approximately 6 to 8 in. deep (see section A-A in Fig. 28). The thin layer of coke at the entrance end required frequent replenishing from a pile of damp, coarse coke. In contrast, the exit end of the pan required less-frequent replenishing because of the greater depth of coke and the drag-out of the coarse coke. Like those of the failed pan, the sidewalls of the second pan also exhibited a pattern of thinning.

Moisture content of the coarse coke in the supply pile was 12% and of the fine coke, 7%. Coke ready for shipping normally contains 2 to 3% water.

Metallographic examination of specimens taken from a greatly thinned area of the failed pan, when etched with Murakami's reagent [10 g $K_3Fe(CN)_6$, 10 g NaOH, 100 ml H_2O], disclosed solid decarburization to a depth of approximately 0.005 in. and heavy intergranular oxide attack. Beneath the decarburized layer was a carburized zone approximately 0.010 in. deep. The core area of all specimens had uniformly distributed acicular carbide. When specimens were etched with modified Murakami's reagent [15 g $K_3Fe(CN)_6$, 2 g NaOH, 100 ml H_2O], sigma phase was found to occur uniformly throughout the core material, appearing as a gray constituent that in general followed the grain boundaries (see micrograph in Fig. 28). This phase generally causes embrittlement; however, its effect was negligible in this application.

Only traces of decarburization and oxide attack were observed at the exit end of the pan, where wall thinning at the liquid line was slight. Attack of the metal was confined to the liquid line, and did not extend up the sidewall as in the more severely attacked areas. The carburized layer was narrower and closer to the surface.

Discussion. Type 309 stainless steel is susceptible to carburization and embrittlement in the temperature range of 760 to 816 C (1400 to 1500 F). The carbon diffuses inward from the surface and forms chromium carbide. Carbide formation results in depletion of chromium from the austenite

matrix and buildup of carbides at the grain boundaries. The lower chromium content at the grain boundaries makes the steel susceptible to intergranular oxide attack. This type of attack was observed in all the specimens that were taken from areas in which the sidewalls of the pan were greatly reduced in thickness.

The high water content in the coke ensured the presence of a moist, strongly oxidizing and decarburizing environment at the metal surface — a result mainly of reactions between water and carbon, which produce hydrogen and carbon monoxide, and between carbon, carbon monoxide and oxygen, which produce carbon dioxide. The strongly decarburizing effect of moist hydrogen explains the observed carbon depletion at the surface, whereas the other environment constituents — mainly carbon and oxygen and their reaction products — account for the observed carburization and oxidation.

Conclusion. Thinning of the pan walls at the surface of the molten lead resulted from using coke of high moisture content and from the low fluctuating coke level. In comparison, the exit end of the pan, where the coke level was high, encountered much less reduction in wall thickness.

Recommendations. The use of dry (2 to 3% moisture content) coke would reduce the supply of oxygen attacking the grain boundaries and also the hydrogen that readily promoted decarburization.

Maintaining a thick layer of coke over the entire surface of molten lead in the pan would exclude atmospheric oxygen from the grain boundaries.

Molten Iron. Over limited time intervals, permanent molds also serve as containers for molten metals. In the following example, it was determined that failure of a permanent mold after limited service life was caused by excessive pouring temperature of the metal in combination with inadequate thickness of mold-wash coating.

Example 3. Failure of a 4130 Steel Mold for Centrifugal Casting of Gray and Ductile Iron Pipe (Fig. 29)

The forged 4130 steel cylindrical permanent mold shown in Fig. 29 was used for centrifugal casting of gray and ductile iron pipe. In operation, the mold rotated at a predetermined speed in a centrifugal casting machine while the molten metal, flowing through a trough approximately 19 ft long, was poured into the mold, beginning at the bell end. The mold continued to spin while moving at a steady rate away from the end of the trough, so that the spigot end of the mold was poured last. After the pipe had cooled to 760 to 871 C (1400 to 1600 F), it was pulled out from the bell end of the mold and the procedure was repeated. When pulling of the pipe became increasingly difficult, examination revealed that the mold contained three spall pits about $\frac{1}{4}$ in. by $\frac{7}{16}$ in. by $\frac{3}{32}$ in. deep located 17 to 22 in. from the spigot end.

The pits were found after 277 pipes had been cast. The average performance for molds of this size was about 2100 castings. Normal pouring temperatures were 1288 C (2350 F) for gray iron and 1371 C (2500 F) for ductile iron.

Investigation. Visual inspection of the bore of the mold revealed three large score marks originating at the spalls. The spalls were not all located at the same distance from the end face of the spigot, but were helically distributed on the inner surface at the 1:00, 6:30 and 11:00 o'clock positions. The spall at the 6:30 o'clock position was the most inward. All score marks terminated within 32 in. of the spigot end. A large number of small high spots, which were quite shiny in appearance, were observed around the entire bore of the mold 10 to 20 in. from the spigot end face. The remainder of the bore appeared to be in fairly good condition.

Chemical analysis showed that the metal in the mold was within specification for 4130 steel, except that the manganese con-

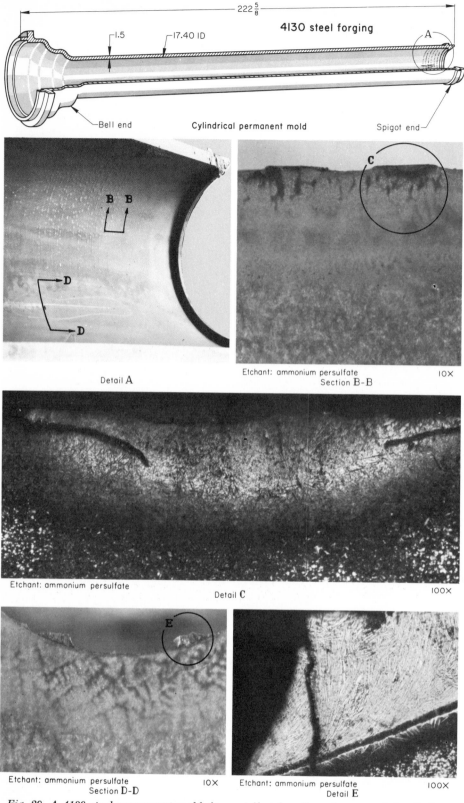

Detail A

Etchant: ammonium persulfate   10X
Section B-B

Etchant: ammonium persulfate
Detail C   100X

Etchant: ammonium persulfate   10X
Section D-D

Etchant: ammonium persulfate   100X
Detail E

Fig. 29. A 4130 steel permanent mold, for centrifugal casting of gray and ductile iron pipe, that failed because of localized overheating (at spigot end), caused by splashing of molten metal. The overheating resulted in mold-wall spalling and scoring, details of which are shown in the photographs. (Example 3)

The mold sections were then cut to obtain specimens as follows:

1 One 10-in.-long transverse specimen of good metal (no bore defects) from the mold section located 32 to 42 in. from the spigot end

2 Longitudinal specimens adjacent to areas of score marks at both the 11:00 and 1:00 o'clock positions

3 One longitudinal specimen 8 in. long that included the spigot end of mold

4 One transverse specimen across the score marks located at the 6:30 o'clock position

5 Transverse specimens through shiny spots.

Several specimens were polished and etched with ammonium persulfate, $(NH_4)_2S_2O_8$, for macroscopic examination. All specimens exhibited a heat-affected zone on the bore approximately $\frac{1}{8}$ in. deep, beginning $5\frac{3}{8}$ in. from the spigot end and extending about 24 in. toward the bell end. At this point the heat-affected zone was shallower but still present. The 10-in.-long specimen of good metal (no bore defects) had a heat-affected zone that was 0.010 to 0.015 in. deep.

Several specimens were etched in 3% nital for 20 sec for metallographic examination at magnifications of 3, 10 and 100 diameters.

The specimen of good metal exhibited a structure of bainite, which is typical for 4130 steel and indicative of a correct and effective heat treatment. Metal at the bore surface showed indications that the temperature there had exceeded the tempering temperature of the mold and may have been higher than 649 C (1200 F).

A section taken through an area of the mold containing shiny spots is shown as section B-B in Fig. 29. Here, shiny spots appear as two dark plateaus separated by depressions. A heat-affected zone 0.10 to 0.12 in. deep is visible. Detail C in Fig. 29, an enlarged view of the area at upper right in section B-B, shows a crescent-shaped area that consists of (from top) tempered martensite, a near-white arc of untempered martensite, and a banded, gray and black mixture of tempered and overtempered material in the form of globular pearlite. The cracks in the martensite are indicative of the presence of very high stresses. Propagation of similar cracks in other martensitic areas resulted in spalling, with some of the untempered structure being exposed on the surface of the bore.

A micrograph of a section through a scored, spalled area is shown as section D-D in Fig. 29. Overheated material was in evidence at the left edge of the depressed spall mark, the bottom of which was about 0.090 in. below the original bore surface. On the surface of the depression are several protuberances. Examination at a magnification of 100 diameters (see detail E, Fig. 29) revealed the protuberances to be gray iron welded to the bore surface. The first layer (approximately 0.003 in. thick) beneath the gray iron had an untempered martensitic structure. Between this layer and the original quenched-and-tempered bainite structure there was a high-carbon-diffusion area of undetermined structure, about 0.040 in. thick, followed by a band approximately 0.060 in. thick that exhibited an overtempered structure of ferrite and pearlite. Thus, at this point, overheating had penetrated approximately 0.190 in. beneath the bore surface.

tent was 0.04% above maximum. Scleroscope hardness values ranged from 36 to 42, with a mean of 39.5.

The mold was sectioned transversely at 32 and 42 in. from the spigot end. These two sections were then split longitudinally at the 3:00 o'clock and 9:00 o'clock positions to provide access to the bore. Detail A in Fig. 29 shows the spall at the 6:30 o'clock position and typical shiny spots. The two other spalled areas were similar in appearance.

Within the figure labels: 4130 steel forging; 222⅝; 1.5; 17.40 ID; Bell end; Cylindrical permanent mold; Spigot end; A

The defects in the bore (spalled and scored areas, shiny areas, and overheated surfaces) were found near the spigot end, where hot metal impinged on the bore surface. Temperature of the molten metal was probably kept rather high, resulting in relatively deep overheating of metal in the mold at the bore surface. The overheating may have been accentuated by an inadequate thickness of insulating mold-wash coating.

Conclusions. Failure of the mold surface was the result of localized overheating caused by splashing of molten metal on the bore surface near the spigot end. The remainder of the mold wall being cold caused very rapid heat extraction, and thus created localized spots of martensitic structure. Because of very high stresses in the hard martensitic structure, spalls and score marks resulted. Apparently, the mold-wash compound (bentonite mixture) near the spigot end was too thin to provide the proper degree of insulation and to prevent molten metal from sticking to the bore surface.

Recommendations. To reduce failure of centrifugal casting molds it was recommended that the pouring temperatures of the molten metal be reduced and that a thicker insulating coating (bentonite mixture) be sprayed onto the mold surface.

Contact With Molten Salts

The life of high-temperature alloys in contact with molten salts is usually erratic. For example, thermocouple-protection tubes under similar service conditions may survive a hundred immersions before replacement is necessary or may fail after only five or ten immersions. Failure of components exposed to molten salts usually occurs by perforation or by structural disintegration. Intergranular attack and chromium depletion often accompany failure in molten salts. Failure sometimes is related to operating variables, including hot spots, lax control of temperature, accumulation of sludge, and method of salt replenishment. Type 446 stainless steel protection tubes that provided acceptable life and those that failed prematurely have been subjected to exhaustive investigation, but no correlation could be found between any of the variables investigated that would account for the marked differences in service life. Salt pots used in heat treating applications also exhibit erratic service behavior, as described in the following example.

Example 4. Failure of Three Wrought Heat-Resisting Alloy Salt Pots Due to Intergranular Corrosion and Chromium Depletion (Fig. 30)

Over a period of about 1½ years, three RA 330 alloy salt pots from a single heat treating plant were submitted to failure analysis. All of the pots, which had ⅜-in.-thick walls, were used primarily to contain neutral salts at temperatures from about 815 to 900 C (1500 to 1650 F). However, some cyaniding was also performed in these pots, which, when not in use, were idled at 760 C (1400 F). It was reported that sludge was removed from the bottom of the pots

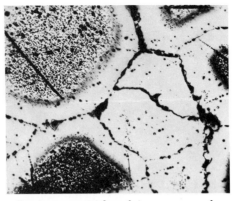

Specimen was taken from an area where chromium content was only 11.9% instead of the normal 19%. Note the chromium-depleted grain boundaries, and the depth of penetration of intergranular oxidation attack. (Etched in 10% oxalic acid; magnification, 60×)

Fig. 30. Microstructure of a specimen from an RA 330 alloy salt pot that failed because of intergranular corrosion and chromium depletion (Example 4)

once a day. Normal pot life varied from about 6 to 20 months.

The pots were removed from the furnace and rotated 120° every three weeks in order to ensure that no single location was overheated for a prolonged period of time. At the time of rotations, pots were also inspected visually.

The pots were fired by four natural-gas burners, which were mounted tangentially, with two burners located approximately one-third of the way up the pot and the remaining burners located two-thirds of the way up from the cylindrical side weld at the bottom head of the pot. The two sets of burners were located at right angles to each other. The distance from the gas flames to the outside surface of the pot varied from 4 to 6 in., and there was supposedly no flame impingement.

Pot No. 1 failed at the knuckle radius of the flanged and dished head of the pot — an area well away from the locations of the burners. The grain size of the RA 330 alloy was determined to be ASTM No. 0 and, at the outset, it was thought that the coarse grain size may have contributed to failure by providing less resistance to intergranular attack than would be provided by a finer-grained material. Chemical analyses of material were made at several locations in the vicinity of the failure. Although analyses of most elements corresponded closely with the nominal RA 330 composition, chromium contents varied markedly.

The nominal chromium content of RA 330 alloy is 19%. Analysis of metal taken from an inside surface halfway up the pot indicated a chromium content of only 11.9%. A micrograph of the chromium-depleted structure observed in this area is shown in Fig. 30. X-ray analysis of the outer surface of the pot indicated a chromium content of 18.6%. Further analyses of drillings taken from an inside surface near the location of failure indicated a chromium content of only 5.7%. It was concluded that most of the pot was inherently sound and free of mill-related defects, but that contamination of the molten salts may have been responsible for the severe corrosive

attack and chromium depletion, particularly in the grain boundaries, in the general area where failure occurred.

Pot No. 2 was returned about a year after the failure of pot No. 1. The second pot failed at two locations: one near the liquid-air interface and the second in the head area at the bottom of the pot. A micrograph revealed that attack near the liquid-air interface was intergranular and extensive. Attack was so severe that the alloy would no longer conduct electricity, thus making spectrographic analysis impossible. Chemical analyses of drillings obtained at the liquid-air interface indicated chromium contents of 9.7% at the inner surface, 13.4% at the center section, and 11.1% on the outer surface; the chromium depletion at the outer surface was presumed to have been caused by high-temperature oxidation resulting from the initial heating of the salt pot by the combustion of natural gas. The chromium content of a specimen taken from the bottom of the pot was 10.7% at the inner surface, 11.4% at center, and 16% on the outer surface. It was concluded that the cause of failure was severe intergranular corrosion accompanied by substantial chromium depletion.

Pot No. 3 was returned a few months after the return of the second pot. This pot had been used exclusively for cyaniding at a temperature of 871 C (1600 F). Severe scaling was noted on the sides of the pot, and wall thickness had decreased from ⅜ to about 1/16 in. at some locations. A micrograph revealed that severe attack had occurred at both the inner and outer walls of the pot. The inner wall showed evidence of severe intergranular corrosion accompanied by chromium depletion. There was also evidence of pronounced carbon buildup on the inner wall.

Chemical analysis indicated that the chromium content of the alloy at a central portion of the pot was only 9.7%. Depletion of chromium and, to a lesser extent, depletion of silicon were comparable to those observed in the other failed pots. However, grain size in the third pot was relatively fine (ASTM No. 5 to 6), thereby discounting the theory that coarse grain size was a principal cause of erratic service life or premature failure.

Conclusions. The cause of failure of each of the three salt pots was severe intergranular corrosion accompanied by substantial chromium depletion.

Salt baths composed of molten barium chloride are commonly used for austenitizing high speed tool steels and, for this application, may be operated at temperatures as high as 1290 C (about 2350 F). The containers used at these temperatures are usually made of, or lined with, a suitable refractory material. However, the electrodes used for heating the baths and the thermocouple-protection tubes used in the baths are made of high-temperature alloys. The alloys generally selected for protection tubes are type 446 stainless steel and a nickel-base alloy containing 75% Ni, 15% Cr and about 8% Fe. Metallurgically, these alloys are notably dissimilar. Type 446 stainless steel contains 25% Cr, a relatively low alloy content. However, users of this steel report that it is well suited for service in molten barium chloride at temperatures above 1095 C (about 2000 F) because of its low residual nickel content. Others prefer the nickel-base alloy. The following example describes premature failure of electrodes of this nickel-base alloy that were used in a barium chloride bath.

Example 5. Failure of 75Ni-15Cr-8Fe Alloy Electrodes in Molten Barium Chloride (Fig. 31)

A pair of 75Ni-15Cr-8Fe alloy electrodes failed after 2½ to 3 weeks in a molten barium chloride bath at 1095 to 1260 C (about 2000 to 2300 F), where they were used for austenitizing of high speed steels. In this application, normal electrode service life was 2 to 3 months, and the normal mode of failure was uniform corrosion beneath the salt line. In contrast, the electrodes that failed prematurely failed by corrosive attack that penetrated the electrode at random locations. Some pieces of electrode broke off and fell to the bottom of the salt pot.

The severity of corrosive attack is illustrated in Fig. 31(a), which shows a piece of the electrode that was retrieved from the salt bath. The micrograph in Fig. 31(b) shows that corrosive attack occurred within grains as well as along the grain boundaries. It was noted that portions of electrode exposed below the salt line were strongly magnetic, whereas those exposed above the salt line were nonmagnetic. Analysis of surface drillings taken from magnetic specimens showed a chromium content of only 1.6%, indicating severe chromium depletion. The chromium content of nonmagnetic specimens was 15.8%.

Techniques for Analyzing Elevated-Temperature Failures

Although components that fail at elevated temperatures may, and often do, exhibit certain metallurgical, physical or fractographic characteristics that are dis-

tinctive, it is generally conceded that the procedures and techniques that are employed in analyzing elevated-temperature failures are similar to those employed in the analysis of failures that are not related to temperature. These procedures and techniques are described in detail in the article on General Practice in Failure Analysis, which begins on page 10 in this volume.

At the outset, it is essential to recognize that not all causes of failure at elevated temperatures are related to temperature. Obviously, damage caused by careless or improper handling, errors in design or fabrication, faulty material, or tension overload can promote premature failure. All these factors should be considered as part of the service history of the component. Also, a complete history of the base metal should be developed, including chemical composition and all related material-specification requirements. Service history, wherever possible, should include data on elapsed time in service, operating temperatures, stress or loading conditions, environmental factors, and pertinent design factors such as notches and other mechanical stress raisers.

Among the laboratory failure-analysis techniques that have been applied to elevated-temperature failures are the following:

1 Visual examination by eye, low-power magnifying glass or binocular microscope at magnifications of 1 to 30 diameters
2 Photomacrography of portions of the failed part and failed surfaces
3 Electron fractography, using a scanning electron microscope or a transmission electron microscope
4 Nondestructive inspection, using ultrasonic, fluorescent-liquid-penetrant, magnetic-particle, eddy-current, radiographic or other techniques
5 Measurement of residual stress by x-ray diffraction
6 Bulk chemical analysis

7 Determination of mechanical properties and physical properties, including hardness
8 Determination of microstructure, using light microscopy (100 to 1500 diameters) or using replicas and the transmission electron microscope (3300 to 10,000 diameters)
9 X-ray-diffraction analysis or chemical analysis of surface compounds or contaminants
10 Analysis of selected phases or regions by electron microprobe, ion microprobe, or Auger spectroscope
11 Phase extraction by electrochemical methods and analysis by x-ray and chemical methods.

Only rarely would a complete evaluation of an elevated-temperature failure require the use of more than five or six of the above techniques. Nevertheless, all available procedures should be considered when a definitive analysis is mandatory.

Equipment and Tests for Analysis of Failures at Elevated Temperatures

The equipment and tests used in analysis of elevated-temperature failures, or used to supplement failure analysis, range from the simple to the highly complex and from the general to the highly specialized. The number of special tests applied to specific products and components alone, although incalculable, can be assumed to be very large. The coverage afforded such equipment and tests in this section, therefore, constitutes a selected sampling only.

Some Basic Tests. Magnetic tests are widely used in the analysis of failures involving normally nonmagnetic nickel-containing heat-resisting alloys and austenitic stainless steels. Many of these alloys become magnetic as a result of chromium depletion caused by oxidation or carburization, or both. Consequently, when these alloys are tested with a magnet and show evidence of magnetism, some insight into the possible causes of failure is afforded, and additional tests can be selected more judiciously on the basis of this initial evidence.

Macroetching of cross sections constitutes another simple test; it is useful in detecting the voids and cracks that are characteristic of thermal-fatigue failures. When thermal fatigue is severe, sectioning alone will serve to reveal the characteristic signs. Metallographic examination is helpful in detecting microstructural changes and corrosion products associated with common modes of failure. Microconstituents and corrosion products then can be identified more positively by chemical analysis, x-ray diffraction, or electron-microprobe analysis.

Various types of tests that simulate service conditions, or that exceed them

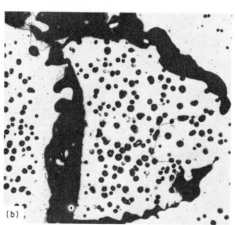

Fig. 31. (a) Piece of a 75Ni-15Cr-8Fe alloy electrode retrieved from a molten barium chloride bath, showing the extent of corrosive penetration. (b) Metallographic section, etched with mixed acids, showing a view at 210× of a corroded area about ⅛ in. from the outer face of the electrode. (Example 5)

in severity, are helpful in reconstructing failures under carefully controlled conditions. For example, failures of engine poppet valves can be reconstructed in a special fatigue-testing machine that simulates loading, operating temperatures and corrosive atmospheres. All known conditions of bending, overloading and overheating can be readily reproduced. This same machine is used to predict valve life under extreme conditions and to evaluate experimental valve alloys and coatings. Thermal-fatigue failures can be simulated in a test rig that advances and retracts a standard engine valve alternately from the flame of a torch to a water-cooled copper chill block under controlled conditions of heating, cooling and cycling. The first visual evidence of cracking constitutes failure.

Tests for Gas-Turbine Components

Several specialized rigs have been developed for testing gas-turbine blades, vanes and disks under simulated operating conditions. Several of these test rigs are described in the following sections.

Thermomechanical Fatigue Tests. Thermal fatigue is a major contributor to the failure of gas-turbine-engine components — notably, the airfoils of turbine blades and vanes, which are subjected to high mechanical and thermal strains. These strains, together with other operating conditions, have been successfully reproduced in thermal-mechanical strain-cycling tests performed in a closed-loop, servohydraulic fatigue-testing machine (see Fig. 32). Strain and temperature can be programed for running a variety of thermomechanical strain cycles. Load, strain and temperature are recorded on a digital data-acquisition system and punched on paper tape for plotting of mechanical strain versus temperature and stress versus strain in various cycles. Initiation and propagation of cracks in the components tested are monitored in periodic inspections by taking plastic replicas of the affected surfaces. In the testing machine, the specimen is surrounded by an induction heating coil that facilitates rapid heating of the specimen to temperatures as high as 1205 C (2200 F). Air jets force-cool the specimen at a rate that permits completion of the heating-cooling cycle in about 2 min. Strain cycling is normally controlled to equal the heating cycle (about ½ cycle per minute). Dwells (extended heating cycles) can be readily introduced when extended creep-interaction studies are to be made. Test conditions are such that failures always occur in low-cycle fatigue, usually at less than 5000 cycles.

Fluidized-Bed Thermal-Fatigue Tests. Fluidized beds, consisting of high-temperature, air-fluidized zircon sand, have been used to evaluate the thermal-fatigue capability of alloys for gas-turbine blades

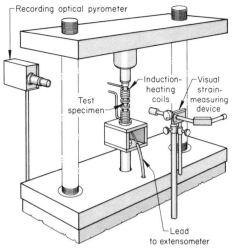

Fig. 32. Closed-loop, servohydraulic fatigue-testing machine used in thermomechanical fatigue testing

and vanes. The beds, which can be used for testing either specimens or small components (small enough not to disturb the heat-transfer characteristics of the beds), can operate at temperatures as high as 1093 C (2000 F) or as low as −73 C (−100 F). Specimens or parts are inserted alternately and automatically into the hot and cold beds in accordance with a desired cycle frequency. The strain cycle developed depends on the temperature of the test bed, on the alloy, and on the design of the specimen or component. The strain cycle cannot be programed independently. Test conditions result in failure in low-cycle fatigue — usually at less than 10,000 cycles.

The carrousel-type thermal-fatigue-test rig shown in Fig. 33 is also used for testing turbine blades and vanes. This rig is capable of testing eight specimens at one time. During each half-cycle, four specimens are being heated to the desired temperature while the other four are being cooled. During the next half-cycle, the rig turntable rotates one-eighth of the way around, and the heating and cooling conditions imposed on the test specimens are reversed. Because the rig rotates 360°, all eight specimens are heated by each of

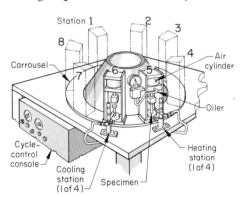

Fig. 33. Carrousel-type rig for thermal-fatigue testing. See text for description of operation.

four air – city-gas – oxygen burners; consequently, any variations in burner patterns are averaged out on all test specimens in like manner.

Test temperatures are measured by optical pyrometer, and the test temperature is the maximum recorded on a specimen at the end of each heating cycle. Each test cycle consists of rapid heating, usually in less than 1 min, to the desired test temperature followed by cooling in an air blast for the same period of time. Heating is concentrated at the center of the test specimen or turbine component in order to develop the high localized thermal stresses that cause cracking. With experience, cracking can be observed visually during cycling, at which time the number of cycles is read on an automatic counter and recorded. Alternatively, test specimens are subjected to fluorescent-liquid-penetrant inspection every 100 cycles to detect indications of thermal cracking.

Metallographic examination of the thermal cracks produced in the test rig has shown that they are very similar to those produced during engine operation. A typical thermal-shock crack produced on the trailing edge of a turbine blade is shown in Fig. 34.

The carrousel-type thermal-fatigue-test rig is also used to evaluate various turbine-blade alloys and coatings. Standard and hollow tensile-type test bars can be tested in the stressed condition, simulating the centrifugal forces imposed on rotating parts during engine opera-

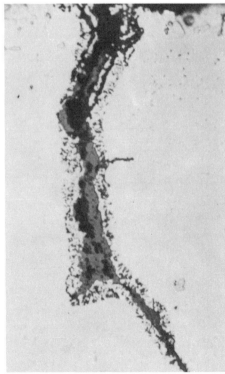

Fig. 34. Crack produced on the trailing edge of a turbine blade by thermal shock (500×; unetched)

tion. These stresses are imposed by air cylinders that maintain a constant stress during thermal expansion or contraction.

Simulated-Bolthole Test. The purpose of bolthole testing is to evaluate resistance to cracking at or around boltholes in tension-tension low-cycle fatigue at various elevated temperatures. The bolthole specimen is a plate with a simulated bolthole at its center. Half-bolthole specimens are also tested. In these, the half-bolthole is located at one edge of the test plate and is readily accessible for producing replicas following crack initiation and propagation.

The test rig is hydraulically loaded and is programed for rates ranging from ¼ cycle to 15 cycles per minute. This test was developed for evaluating boltholes in gas-turbine-engine disks, which operate at lower temperatures than turbine blades and vanes. The rig is capable of inducing vibratory and steady-state loads over a range of temperatures, thus simulating actual engine conditions.

Ferris-Wheel Disk Test. The ferris-wheel disk test makes it possible to subject full-scale gas-turbine-engine disks to simulated low-cycle fatigue conditions. The test rig, with a disk in position, is shown in Fig. 35. The disk is loaded hydraulically by extensions connected to each attachment. A common manifold is used to ensure equal distribution of loads around the circumference of the disk during loading or unloading cycles. The larger test rigs have a total radial-load capacity of 4,000,000 lb, a cyclic rate of 8 to 20 cycles per minute, and a temperature range from room temperature to 482 C (900 F). A special type of nondestructive inspection is used to ensure detection of the first indication of a crack. The procedure consists of interrupting the test periodically, applying fluorescent-liquid penetrant to suspect areas, then cycling slowly several times at half the normal test load, wiping the area to which the penetrant was applied, resuming the slow, half-load cycling, and inspecting under ultraviolet light. Cracks appear as pinpoints or lines that dim under load as penetrant is drawn into the crevice, and that brighten as the load is released and the closing crevice squeezes out the penetrant.

Spin Test. Gas-turbine-engine disks and blades also can be tested by applying centrifugal loads in a spin test (see Fig. 36). Disks may be spun at speeds and temperatures sufficient to cause creep or even stress rupture. Blades may be tested for creep under high centrifugal loads. The spin-test rig and pit permit rotation of a bladed disk at any speed or temperature up to those at which the disk or blade will burst. The disk is suspended in an evacuated pit and is driven by an 8-in. or 14-in. steam turbine. Heat is provided to the disk by either pan-type re-

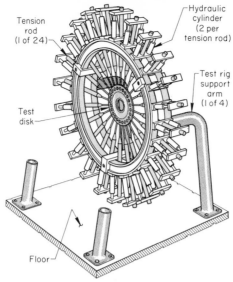

Fig. 35. Ferris-wheel rig for testing gas-turbine-engine disks under simulated conditions of low-cycle fatigue

sistance heaters, pan-type induction heaters, or resistance-type oven heaters.

Oxidation-Corrosion Tests. Oxidation-corrosion burner rigs have been developed to test turbine-blade alloys and coatings under environmental conditions and temperatures encountered in gas-turbine engines. These test rigs (see Fig. 37) are capable of testing eight to twelve specimens under engine conditions at temperatures from 788 to 1260 C (1450 to 2300 F).

The basic steady-state oxidation test simulates cruising conditions, but higher-than-cruising temperatures are obtainable to accelerate degradation. A burner, using jet-engine fuel, is controlled to maintain specimen temperatures by adjusting fuel pressure. Specimen temperatures are monitored and maintained by

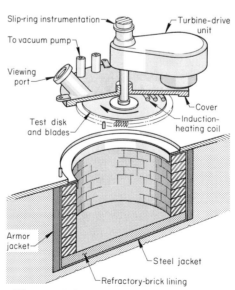

Fig. 36. Spin-test rig and pit used for creep testing of gas-turbine engine disks and blades

an optical pyrometer. The specimens are of a modified airfoil configuration — that is, they have simulated leading and trailing edges. The specimens are weighed before and after each test and are evaluated on the basis of weight loss. Often, oxygen penetration also is evaluated as a means of determining over-all metal attack in oxidation-corrosion tests.

A wider range of corrosion studies of alloys and coatings can be made by modifying the burner nozzle to permit the introduction of contaminants through the throat of the nozzle into the burner flame. As is common practice in oxidation testing, uncoated specimens are weighed before and after testing, and weight loss is the criterion of failure. When coated specimens are tested, they are inspected visually, and corrosive attack of the base metal is the indicator of failure.

Oxidation-corrosion rigs may have the capability of thermal cycling and thus be able to duplicate more accurately the thermal conditions in an engine. For example, a typical blade-corrosion-test cycle consists of 3 min at 843 C or 1550 F (idling), 2 min at 1010 C or 1850 F (take-off), then removal from the flame for 2 min (engine shutdown). Typical steady-state oxidation testing is conducted at a constant 1093 C (2000 F).

Test for Resistance to Hot Corrosion by Sulfidation-Oxidation. A hot-corrosion-test rig used in testing the sulfidation-oxidation resistance of turbine blades consists principally of two chambers, one for heating and one for cooling. However, the rig is modified to spray a solution of deionized water contaminated with sulfur on the rotating test specimens during the cooling portion of a cyclic hot-corrosion test. The test fixture, which is shown in Fig. 38, has been adapted for evaluation of either eight airfoil or "paddle-type" test specimens or 16 turbine blades.

The heating chamber is lined with firebrick and is heated by two city-gas burners on opposite sides of the chamber. Air-fuel mixtures are adjusted to maintain oxidizing conditions in the heating chamber. In a typical test, 16 turbine blades mounted on a special fixture and rotated by a motor at a speed of 1800 rpm are heated in the heating chamber to a predetermined temperature in the range of 927 to 1093 C (1700 to 2000 F). To ensure accurate and reproducible temperature control, the maximum temperature is always measured at the tips of the rotating specimens by an optical pyrometer. Following heating, the specimens and fixture are retracted into the cooling chamber, where the specimens are sprayed with an aspirated solution of deionized water containing 1.4% sodium sulfate, equivalent to a sulfate-ion concentration of 1.0%.

Each test cycle consists of a 1½-min heating cycle followed by a ½-min cooling and spraying cycle.

When test blades are to be evaluated by the weight-loss method, a test consists of 500 cycles, and the blades are weighed before and after testing. The surface oxide is removed by immersing the blades in molten potassium hydroxide before final weighing. Weight loss can be plotted as a function of time and temperature. When the blades are to be evaluated metallographically, they are examined with a binocular magnifier after each 100 cycles, and when a total corrosion area of approximately 0.005 sq in. (0.05 by 0.1 in. on each side of the blade) is observed, the blade is removed from the rig, sectioned, and examined metallographically.

The hot-corrosion attack produced on turbine blades in the test rig is basically comparable to that produced in service in commercial or military engines or in hot-corrosion-test engines, as shown by the micrographs in Fig. 39.

Cascade Tests. Because oxidation-corrosion burner test rigs usually operate at 1 atm pressure, they cannot provide the close simulation of engine conditions desired for some tests. To overcome this limitation and to provide for simulated testing of actual engine components, thermal-fatigue-test rigs of the cascade type have been developed. In these rigs, as many as six turbine airfoils can be subjected to normal engine gases under conditions that are more severe than those imposed by the oxidation-corrosion test rig. In addition to providing variations in pressure, the cascade rigs can impose thermal shocks that are more severe than those encountered in normal operation.

A typical rig consists of standard engine fuel nozzles, ignition equipment, and a rotary-vane air supply that blows air to a burner using jet-type (JP) fuel. The engine burner can supply the hot gases that are applied to the test vanes at elevated-temperature differentials. The exhaust from the burner is directed through water-cooled ductwork over the test vane and out to an atmosphere discharge. Automatic cycling equipment turns the fuel to the burner on and off, making it possible to evaluate, on a cyclic basis, the resistance of vanes to oxidation-corrosion, cracking, melting or fracturing.

One type of high-pressure cascade-type thermal-fatigue-test rig has the capability of testing at an absolute pressure of about 300 psi and at a range of gas-stream temperatures from 400 to 1760 C (750 to 3200 F). The major components of the annular six-vane cascade rig are (a) a preburner, (b) a main burner with a water-cooled tubular transition duct, coupled with a lower air-cooled section, (c) a vane-cascade pack with individual

vane-cooling air supply, and (d) an exhaust duct. Choked-flow venturis have been installed in the air-supply lines of the burner to provide constant air-flow conditions during cyclic operation. The burner supplies hot gases at pressures up to 685 psia at a flow rate of 25 lb per second. Airfoil metal temperatures are monitored by means of both a fixed probe and a traversing probe. Standard test instrumentation is provided throughout the rig.

Thermal-Shock Test. A thermal-shock testing machine, a diagram of which is shown in Fig. 40, employs cast or machined triangular test specimens with ½-in. sides to evaluate the resistance of alloys and coatings to thermal cracking. The specimen is shifted between a heating source and a forced-air cooling vent in accordance with a predetermined cycle. Heating is accomplished with a gas-air flame that can be adjusted to produce either oxidizing or reducing conditions. Both heating and cooling temperatures are automatically recorded. The test is discontinued when the first crack appears on the knife-edge surface of the test specimen.

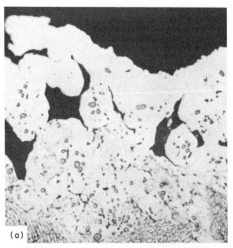
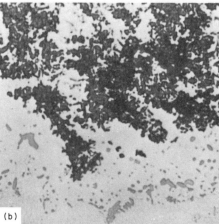

(a)

(b)

Fig. 39. Hot-corrosion attack produced on (a) an uncoated IN-713 specimen in a laboratory test rig and (b) an IN-713 blade that was removed from a service engine. This comparison indicates that the laboratory test rig is capable of simulating service conditions.

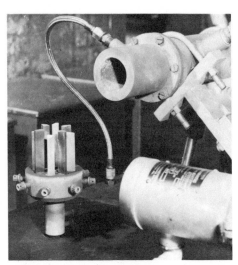

Fig. 37. Oxidation-corrosion test rig used for evaluation of turbine-blade alloys and coatings

Fig. 38. Fixture and test blades used in a rig for hot-corrosion testing to evaluate sulfidation-oxidation resistance of turbine blades or airfoil test specimens

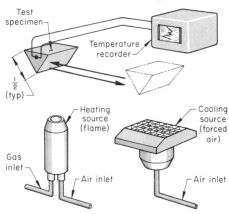

Fig. 40. Diagram of a thermal-shock testing machine used to evaluate the resistance of alloys and coatings to thermal cracking

Tests for Cannon Tubes

Most failures of cannon tubes occur at ambient temperature and are caused by overpressures, in-bore detonations, fatigue or erosion. The high-temperature failures that do occur are in thin-wall tubes where rapid firing rates cause the tube to overheat and to fail by bulging due to yielding or creeping — singly, or in combination. Erosion is caused when the hot gases heat the metal at the bore surface of the tube to its melting point and the high pressures from the propellant force the molten metal from the tube. Most weapons are test fired at their maximum firing rates to determine the maximum operating temperatures for testing purposes. Then, the various cannon-tube alloys are tested at these temperatures in order to reproduce actual operating conditions. The standard short-time tensile tests (usually 15 min for gun tubes) are generally conducted in the transverse direction to simulate the actual mode of failure.

Three other special high-temperature tests for cannon tubes are the high-temperature hydrodynamic tension test; the high-temperature, high-pressure fatigue test; and the erosion test. These tests, and the equipment used, are described in the paragraphs that follow.

High-Temperature Hydrodynamic Tension Test. The load in a cannon tube is applied at a rapid rate by the exploding propellant. Thus it was found necessary to determine the transverse yield strength of several prospective high-strength cannon-tube alloys as a function of strain rate over the range of strain rates from 10^{-4} to 10 in./in./sec. The effects of strain rates on yield strength as a function of composition, microstructure and yielding mechanism were investigated.

A hydrodynamic loading unit was built that is capable of loading a tensile specimen to a force of 60,000 lb in 0.5 millisecond. It is capable of elastic strain rates of up to 10 in./in./sec and plastic strain rates of 50 in./in./sec. The various high-strength and ultrahigh-strength alloy steels investigated exhibited increases in 0.2%-offset yield strength varying from 4 to 11% over the 10^{-4} to 10 in./in./sec range of strain rates. This increase is a function of both the composition and microstructure of the alloy. Coupled with the variable-strain-rate loading equipment is a high-rate heating system to reproduce the temperatures encountered in the thin-wall tubes. This system is capable of heating a 0.250-in.-diam tensile specimen to about 870 to 1095 C (1600 to 2000 F), depending on the resistivity of the specimen. Heating can be at any desired constant rate up to 17 C (30 F) per second, with higher heating rates obtainable on smaller specimens. The specimen can be held at peak temperature for any desired time prior to testing or loading, or both, at a specified strain rate.

High-Temperature, High-Pressure Fatigue Test. Because of the experimental difficulties involved, there are insufficient experimental data on the fatigue

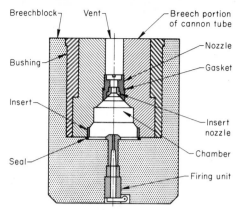

Fig. 41. Breech assembly that was developed for testing the high-temperature-erosion characteristics of low-alloy steels used in cannons

behavior of cannon tubes under conditions of repeated high-pressure cycling at elevated temperatures. To reproduce high-temperature, high-pressure fatigue-failure conditions and to generate the fatigue data necessary for design of thin-wall pressure vessels for high-temperature service, a system was developed for testing of pressurized cylinders at a maximum temperature of 815 C (1500 F) and a maximum pressure of 10,000 psi. The system consists of a hydraulically driven displacement ram that compresses the gas entrapped in the test cylinder. The cylinder is heated by a zoned electric furnace, and a controlled region is maintained at the test temperature. A control system provides remote operation, automatic fail-safe shutdown at cylinder failure or system malfunction, and monitoring of cylinder temperature and pressure. A start-up time of approximately 2 hr is used to make necessary settings and bring the cylinder to test temperature. Under initial test conditions of 705 C (1300 F) and 5000 psi, a continuous cyclic rate of 12 cycles per minute has been achieved and maintained for a 24-hr period. The major components of the system are: the test cylinder, the hydraulic system, the pneumatic system, the temperature-control system, and the operating controls.

Erosion Test. Lengthening of the vent in a cannon tube permitted the development of a test for the high-temperature-erosion characteristics of low-alloy steels differing slightly in chemical composition and mechanical properties. The test assembly, shown in Fig. 41, consists of a cannon breechblock and a small part of the cannon tube, which contains the nozzle and nozzle insert of the alloy to be tested. Calculated amounts of powder are placed into the breech chamber and fired to produce the required pressure and temperature in the nozzle insert of the material to be tested. After each firing, the nozzle insert is inspected and weighed to determine the erosion loss.

Causes of Premature Failure

Although components employed in elevated-temperature applications can fail prematurely because of inherent defects, many premature failures result from misuse. Misuse need not be intentional; often, it is inadvertent or accidental. For example, a premature failure caused by excessive operating temperature may be traced to failure of a temperature controller or to breakdown of a cooling system. The introduction of unanticipated contaminants to the elevated-temperature environment, which results in accelerated corrosion, may also be inadvertent or unavoidable. On the other hand, some premature failures at elevated temperature can be traced to mechanical abuse at room temperature.

Exceeding normal operating temperature is one of the most common causes of premature failure in virtually all elevated-temperature applications. For example, when nickel-base high-temperature alloys are employed in turbine-rotor applications, the normal operating temperatures range from 815 to 871 C (1500 to 1600 F), although short-time operation at 927 C (1700 F) to obtain maximum power is permissible. These temperature limits are imposed because the strength and stability of these alloys at elevated temperatures depend on preservation of particles of gamma-prime precipitate in the solid-solution gamma matrix, as well as the preservation of carbide particles in the grain boundaries. Exceeding prescribed temperature limits results in a reduction in the number of particles of both gamma prime and carbide, resulting in a marked deterioration in elevated-temperature properties — notably creep and stress-rupture properties. The effects of an increase in temperature from 982 C (1800 F) to 1204 C (2200 F) on the microstructure of MAR-M 246, a nickel-base alloy, are delineated in the series of micrographs presented in Fig. 42. Excessive temperature also can develop high thermal stresses that result in thermal-fatigue cracking. Other harmful effects that can result from excessive operating temperatures include severe grain coarsening, excessive oxidation or erosion, increased hot-corrosion rate, melting and abnormal dimensional growth.

The example that follows describes an application in which overheating caused localized melting that resulted in failure.

Example 6. Failure of a Hastelloy X Reactor-Vessel Wall Caused by Overheating

A portion of the wall of a reactor vessel used in burning impurities from carbon particles failed by localized melting. The vessel was made of nickel-base alloy Hastelloy X (22% Cr, 9% Mo, 18% Fe). Considering the service environment, melting could have been caused either by excessive carburization (which would have lowered the melting point of the alloy markedly) or by overheating.

Investigation. A small specimen containing melted and unmelted metal was removed from the vessel wall and examined metallographically. It was observed that the interface between the melted zone and the unaffected base metal was composed of large grains and enlarged grain boundaries. An area a short distance away from the melted zone was fine-grained and relatively free of massive carbides.

Conclusion. The vessel failed by melting that resulted from heating to about 1230 to 1260 C (2250 to 2300 F), which exceeded normal operating temperatures, and carburization was not the principal cause of failure.

In the following examples, failure of a high-temperature-alloy component was caused by localized overheating in conjunction with the introduction of a metallic contaminant, and failure of an aluminum component resulted from localized overheating caused by a fire.

Example 7. Failure of a Nickel-Base Alloy Muffle for a Brazing Furnace, Caused by Localized Overheating and Contamination by Copper

A brazing-furnace muffle, 13¼ in. wide by 10⅜ in. high by 78 in. long, was fabricated from nickel-base high-temperature alloy sheet and installed in a gas-fired furnace used for copper brazing of various assemblies. The operating temperature of the muffle was reported to have been closely controlled at the normal temperature of 1177 C (2150 F); during brazing, a hydrogen atmosphere was employed. After about five months of continuous operation, four or five holes developed on the floor of the muffle, and the muffle was removed from service.

Investigation. Copper was found in areas near the holes on the floor; a specimen taken from one of these areas was analyzed by the x-ray fluorescent method and was found to have an abnormally high copper content. Metallographic examination of a cross-sectional specimen, also from the failed area, revealed the presence of a microconstituent foreign to the alloy; this constituent, probably a nickel-copper intermetallic phase, was observed in the grain boundaries throughout the entire thickness of the muffle floor. The concentration of this phase was heaviest at the inner surface and decreased progressively toward the outer surface. The presence of a dendritic structure in some areas was indicative that some melting had occurred. Melting was also observed in areas that were remote from the locations of failure.

Conclusion. The muffle failed by localized overheating in some areas to temperatures in excess of 1260 C (2300 F). The copper found near the holes had dripped to the floor from assemblies during brazing. The copper diffused into the nickel-base alloy and formed a grain-boundary phase that was molten at the operating temperature. The presence of this phase caused localized liquefaction and weakened the alloy sufficiently to allow formation of the holes.

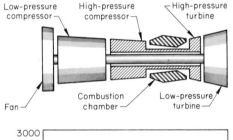

Heating conditions and times were: (a) 1800 F, 15 min; (b) 1950 F, 15 min; (c) 2000 F, 1 min; (d) 2100 F, 1 min; (e) 2100 F, 15 min; (f) 2200 F, 1 min. All specimens were air cooled from the testing temperatures. These are TEM micrographs of single-stage, positive replicas, as seen at 2500×.

Fig. 42. Effect of increasing temperatures from 1800 to 2200 F on the microstructure of nickel-base alloy MAR-M 246. Note that gamma-prime precipitate, clearly visible as tiny particles in (a), goes into solution at a progressive rate with increasing temperatures, (b) through (f).

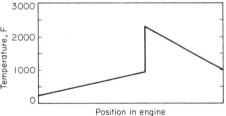

Fig. 43. Principal sections of a gas-turbine engine and their approximate operating temperatures as related to their position in the engine

Example 8. Failure of an Aluminum Alloy 2024-T62 Bracket Caused by Localized Overheating and Grain-Boundary Melting

An aircraft engine in which an in-flight fire had occurred was dismantled and examined. A fractured actuator arm of an aluminum alloy 2024-T62 bracket assembly, one of several failed components, was of prime interest because of apparent heat damage.

Investigation. A scanning electron microscope (SEM) was used to compare laboratory-induced fractures made in the same actuator arm at room and elevated temperatures with the service fracture. The service fracture exhibited grain separation and loss of delineation of grain boundaries due to

melting. The SEM revealed deep voids between grains and tendrils that connected the grains, which resulted from surface tension during melting. Microscopic examination of a polished and etched section through the fracture surface verified intergranular separation and breakdown of grain facets. The absence of any reduction in thickness of the actuator arm at the point of fracture, along with evidence of intense heat at this location, indicated that little stress had been applied to the part.

Conclusion. Comparison of the service fracture and the laboratory-induced fractures, in conjunction with macroscopic and metallographic observations, showed that the bracket assembly had failed because of melting by an intense, localized flame.

Gas-Turbine Components

The principal sections of a gas-turbine engine and their approximate operating temperatures are shown in Fig. 43. Because operating temperatures range from ambient to above 1204 C (2200 F), engine components are made of a variety of metals. Steels and titanium alloys are used for the relatively cool components, such as those in the fan and low-pressure compressor sections. Nickel-base, iron-nickel and iron-base high-temperature alloys are used for "warm" parts, such as shafts, turbine disks, high-pressure compressor disks and cases. Nickel-base and cobalt-base high-temperature alloys are used for hot parts, such as burners, turbine blades and vanes.

Hot Components. Turbine blades and vanes are designed for high load-carrying capacity at elevated temperatures. First-stage turbine vanes are exposed to hot gases from the burner having temperatures in excess of 1204 C (2200 F); consequently, airfoil metal temperatures may exceed 982 C (1800 F). These vanes and first-stage blades must be cooled. Metal temperatures in later stages may not exceed 649 to 760 C (1200 to 1400 F), and thus these blades and vanes can operate without being cooled. Nevertheless, creep is a problem in that blades and vanes will stretch. Stretch is acceptable, provided that it remains within the limits established by engine design. Occasionally, however, components will be exposed to excessive temperatures and will stretch beyond limits. Creep damage of a cobalt-base alloy vane that re-

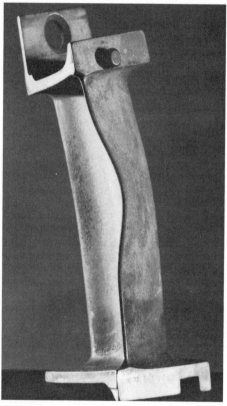

Fig. 44. Creep damage (bowing) of a cobalt-base alloy turbine vane, which resulted from overheating

sulted from overheating is shown in Fig. 44; the reduction in creep strength at the higher temperatures resulted in bowing. Excessive creep can also result in damage to sections other than the airfoil. For example, as shown in Fig. 45, shroud wear can result when blades are used past their allowable creep limits. Figure 45 also shows notch wear, which results from rubbing of the turbine shrouds. Notch wear is undesirable because it can lead to "untwisting" of turbine blades.

Wrought turbine blades also may stretch excessively as a result of improper heat treatment. Extensive creep damage to a turbine blade that was improperly heat treated and then tested to failure in an experimental engine is shown in Fig. 46. The stretching and necking due to creep are readily apparent, and the shroud at the blade tip quite obviously has been worn off.

Intergranular cracking is an indicator of creep damage even when very little change has occurred in the external dimensions of the component. In fact, when a component is heat treated improperly, the creep stretch obtained is above average. In cast alloys, cracking is more likely to result before much stretch is apparent. Figure 47 shows a cast nickel-base alloy turbine blade that was run in an experimental engine to produce cracking. The intergranular cracking produced was extensive, and, as is typical of creep and stress-rupture failure, the surfaces along the cracks were oxidized and alloy depleted.

Creep and stress rupture are not the only causes of cracking in turbine blades and vanes; fatigue is a fairly common cause. A fatigue fracture that developed in a cast cobalt-base alloy turbine blade is shown in Fig. 48. The fatigue fracture progressed from the trailing edge, resulting in a decrease in effective cross-sectional area and subsequent fracture due to ductile tension overload.

Components of the burner section are susceptible to thermal-fatigue cracking — which, like fatigue cracking, also pro-

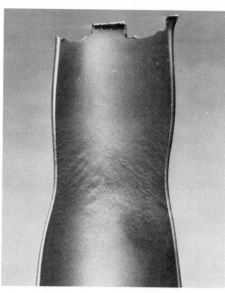

Fig. 46. Stretching and necking due to creep in a nickel-base alloy turbine blade that was improperly heat treated and then tested to failure in an experimental engine. Note also the wear at the blade tip. Blade is shown at approximately actual size.

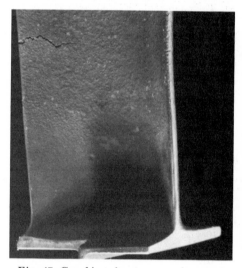

Fig. 47. Cracking due to creep in a cast nickel-base alloy turbine blade (1½×)

duces cracks that may be difficult to distinguish from cracking produced by creep and stress rupture. Cracks induced by thermal fatigue in a forward liner, which produced typical coarse, oxidized fracture surfaces, are shown in Fig. 49; one extends from a keyhole slot and another is evident adjacent to an airhole. Among the other types of burner-component failures encountered are distortion, extreme oxidation, and melting.

Warm Components. At lower temperatures, ranging from about 427 to 705 C (about 800 to 1300 F), steel and nickel-base alloy components are subjected to high loads, and wherever stress concentrations are high, fatigue is the most common mechanism of failure. Fatigue is induced in several ways. For example,

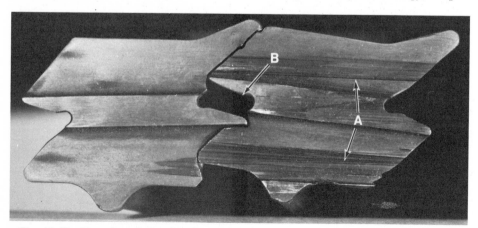

Fig. 45. Turbine shroud showing tip wear (at A) and notch wear (at B) that resulted when blades were used past their allowable creep limits

Fig. 48. Fatigue fracture in a cast cobalt-base alloy turbine blade, at about 3.3×. The fracture surface indicates that fatigue progressed from the trailing edge of the blade, terminating in overload fracture at the leading edge (at left).

Fig. 51. Galling and cracking (at arrow) on the root-attachment surface of a titanium alloy compressor blade, shown at 1½×. The damage was the result of severe loading and vibration.

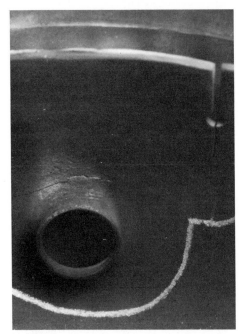

Fig. 49. Thermal-fatigue cracks on the internal surface of a nickel-base alloy forward liner of a gas-turbine burner, shown at 1½×. One crack extends from a keyhole slot and another can be seen in the area adjacent to an airhole.

Fig. 50 shows cracking in the rivet slot of a nickel-base alloy disk that was induced in low-cycle fatigue by thermal straining. In disks, low-cycle fatigue stems from stresses imposed by the combined effects of centrifugal loading by blades, the body load of the disk, and the thermally induced load between disk rim and bore. Discontinuities, such as rim slots and boltholes, are typically the sites for initiation of low-cycle fatigue.

Among the cracks that are not initiated by fatigue are those that originate during

forging. Generally, these cracks are detected by inspection techniques. Occasionally, however, forging cracks may be so small or so masked as to escape detection, and they may not become visible until after several cycles of service operation. Cracks can interact with fatigue loads to propagate after relatively few cycles. Sometimes, interactions can be produced between types of fatigue processes, namely low-cycle fatigue and high-cycle fatigue. Under laboratory conditions, a crack can be initiated in low-cycle fatigue and then, after a given number of cycles, be propagated in high-cycle fatigue. The crack can then be further propagated by alternating periods of low-cycle and high-cycle fatigue. It is also possible for a crack to be initiated *and* propagated by low-cycle fatigue for some finite number of cycles and then to be further propagated by high-cycle fatigue.

Cool Components. At still lower temperatures, up to 427 C (800 F), there may be failure of other components, principally those fabricated from titanium alloys. In the operation of certain components, such as compressor-blade attachments, galling can occur on the root-attachment surface as a result of severe loading and vibration (see Fig. 51). The blade shown in Fig. 51 had multiple fatigue origins on the fracture surface; these resulted from galling. Galling is not restricted to blades; it can sometimes occur also on disk-rim slots. Figure 52 is a close-up of a fracture through a disk and shows fatigue progressing from an origin in galled material produced by locking-tab contact with the disk.

Examples. The following five examples are reports of failure analyses of three different types of turbine-engine components — spacers, vanes and blades.

Fig. 52. Surface of a fatigue fracture in the galled rim-slot area of a titanium alloy disk, shown at ½×. Fatigue progressed from an origin in the galled material that was produced by locking-tab contact with the disk.

Example 9. Failure of an AMS 5661 (Incoloy 901) Alloy Turbine Spacer by Cracking of the Radial Rim (Fig. 53)

A turbine spacer made of AMS 5661 alloy (Incoloy 901) was removed from service because of a crack in the forward side of the radial rim. This alloy contains approximately 43% Ni, 13% Cr, 6% Mo, 2.5% Ti, remainder Fe. Axially, the crack extended for a distance of 5/8 in. across the spacer rim; radially, it extended to a depth of 1/4 in. into the web section.

Investigation. The spacer was sectioned to expose the fracture surfaces of the crack; these surfaces showed features of fatigue starting from the forward rim side adjacent to, and at, the inside surface of the rim. The fatigue features progressed aft for a distance of about 0.350 in. before changing to features of a tension fracture. Figure 53(a) is a light fractograph of the crack showing macroscopic features near the origin, which is at left in the fractograph.

Fig. 50. Low-cycle fatigue cracking induced in the rivet slot of a nickel-base alloy turbine disk by thermal straining (3×)

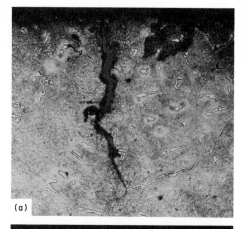

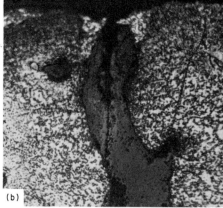

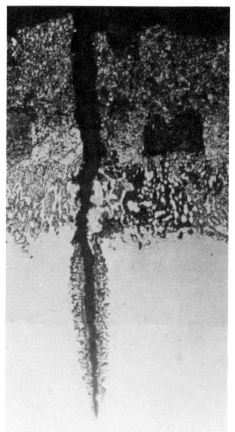

(a) A fracture surface of the turbine spacer at 9×, showing the fatigue crack, which progressed aft from the forward side of the rim. (b) and (c) TEM fractographs at 5000× and 10,000×, respectively, showing the irregular striations indicative of fatigue. The striations are indistinct because of rubbing between the mating surfaces.

Fig. 53. Turbine spacer, of AMS 5661 alloy (Incoloy 901), that was removed from service because of cracking of the radial rim (Example 9)

Replica studies of the fracture, using a transmission electron microscope, revealed striations that indicated a fatigue-type failure progressing from the forward side of the rim (see Fig. 53b and c). A striation count, conducted at a magnification of 10,000 diameters, showed that the fatigue had progressed at a rate of 180 cycles per 0.001 in. at a locale 0.010 in. from the forward face of the rim and at a rate of 100 cycles per 0.001 in. at a locale 0.080 in. from this face.

Metallographic examination of a cross section of the fracture on the forward side of the rim in the fatigue-origin area indicated that separation was transgranular, which is typical of fatigue cracking. The microstructure was normal for AMS 5661. Further testing revealed that the chemical composition, hardness, tensile strength, and stress-rupture properties of the material

The airfoil segment was from a turbine vane cast from cobalt-base alloy AMS 5382 (Stellite 31). Specimen was etched in FeCl₃-HCl-methanol. The microstructure shows evidence of age hardening by intragranular precipitation of carbide particles.

Fig. 54. Micrographs at (a) 100× and (b) 500× of an airfoil segment, showing thermal-fatigue cracks emanating from a leading edge and progressing along grain boundaries (Example 10)

conformed with the requirements of the AMS 5661 specification.

Conclusion. Cracking on the forward rim of the spacer occurred in fatigue that initiated on the forward rim face and that progressed into the rim and web areas. Because there was no apparent metallurgical cause for the cracking, the problem was assigned to engineering.

Example 10. Failure of AMS 5382 (Stellite 31) Alloy Turbine Vane by Cracking of the Airfoil Section (Fig. 54)

A turbine vane made of cast cobalt-base alloy AMS 5382 (Stellite 31) was returned from service after an undetermined number of service hours because of crack indications on the airfoil sections. This alloy contains approximately 25.5% Cr, 10.5% Ni and 7.5% W and is cast by the precision investment method.

Investigation. Metallographic examination revealed that the cracks were thermal-fatigue cracks and had emanated from the leading edges of the airfoil and progressed along grain boundaries, as shown in Fig. 54. The microstructure also showed evidence of age hardening by intragranular precipitation of carbide particles that was

Fig. 55. Micrograph, at 500×, of an aluminide-coated MAR-M 246 nickel-base alloy turbine blade, showing a crack in the coating that progressed inward in fatigue. Specimen was etched with FeCl₃ plus HCl in methanol. (Example 11)

induced by engine operating temperatures. Bend tests conducted on specimens removed from the airfoil section of a vane indicated extreme brittleness; the specimens fractured with no measurable bend radius — a condition attributed to age hardening.

In addition, the airfoil sections exhibited an unusual type of selective subsurface oxidation. This condition appeared to be related to the intragranular carbides. It was also determined that extensive residual tensile macrostresses could have contributed to cracking at the leading edges.

Conclusion. Cracking of the airfoil sections was caused by thermal fatigue and was contributed to by (*a*) low ductility due to age hardening, (*b*) subsurface oxidation related to intragranular carbides, and (*c*) high residual tensile macrostresses. No further conclusions could be drawn because of the lack of detailed service history.

Example 11. Cracking of Aluminide Coating on a Nickel-Base Alloy Turbine Blade (Fig. 55)

Following a programed engine test, the turbine blades in a turbine wheel were inspected by the fluorescent-liquid-penetrant method, and several blades exhibited crack indications in the aluminide coating on the airfoil. The blades were made of cast MAR-M 246 nickel-base alloy (9% Cr, 10% Co, 10% W, 5.5% Al, 2.5% Mo, 1.5% Ti, 1.5% Ta). Metallographic examination re-

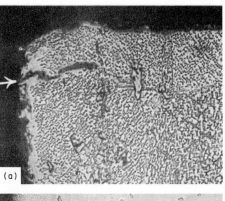

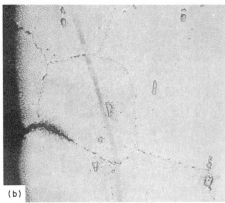

(a) An uncoated blade, at 2.7×, showing splitting along the leading edge, and swelling on the surface, of the airfoil.

(b) Section taken through the leading edge of an uncoated blade, etched in FeCl₃ plus HCl in methanol, showing a discontinuous surface layer of solid oxide at the blade tip, a layer of oxides

in alloy-depleted nickel-base material, and gray globules of chromium sulfide.

(c) and (d) Sections taken through the leading edges of aluminide-coated blades, etched in FeCl₃ plus HCl in methanol. Corrosion in (c) has penetrated up to the base metal, and in (d) has penetrated into the base metal.

Fig. 56. Uncoated and aluminide-coated IN-713 turbine blades that failed by hot corrosion in a marine environment (Example 12)

(a) Longitudinal section at 500×, taken through origin of failure (at upper left corner) of fractured blade, showing the fracture surface in profile at top, oxidation on blade surface at left, and oxide-filled crack at arrow.

(b) Section at 250× taken through the leading edge of another blade, showing oxide-filled crack following a grain boundary.

Specimens taken from both blades were etched in FeCl₃ plus HCl in methanol.

Fig. 57. Micrographs of two turbine blades that failed by thermal fatigue (Example 13)

vealed a coating crack that had progressed in fatigue into the base metal. The coating crack is shown in Fig. 55. Secondary coating cracks were detected adjacent to the primary crack, indicating that the aluminide coating had been strained beyond its ductility limit. The thickness of the coating and the chemical composition of the base metal were found to conform to specification requirements. Nevertheless, the solution to the problem was found in the development and application of a more ductile coating.

Example 12. Premature Failure of IN-713 Turbine Blades by Corrosion (Fig. 56)

Aluminide-coated and uncoated IN-713 turbine blades were returned for evaluation after service in a marine environment because of severe corrosion. Based on service time, failure of these blades by corrosive deterioration was considered to be premature.

Investigation. The airfoils of the uncoated blades exhibited splitting along the leading edges and swelling on the surfaces, indicative of severe hot corrosion, as shown in Fig. 56(a). Metallographic examination of an uncoated blade confirmed hot-corrosion damage by revealing the characteristic sulfidation-oxidation attack of the base metal (see Fig. 56b). The outer surface at

the leading and trailing edges showed a discontinuous layer of solid oxide; the next layer, varying considerably in depth, was composed of oxides intermingled with alloy-depleted nickel-base material. A third layer was an alloy-depleted zone containing gray globules of chromium sulfide adjacent to the normal IN-713 structure. These corrosion products did not readily flake from the surface of the blade, because of the composition of the mixed oxides and that of the alloy-depleted base metal.

The response of the aluminide-coated blades to the hot-corrosion environment of the turbine rotor varied considerably. Metallographic examination of two blades from a high-temperature region of the rotor revealed that, although both blades were attacked by corrosion, attack of one blade was limited to the coating whereas attack of the other blade penetrated both coating and base metal (see Fig. 56c and d). In contrast, an uncoated IN-713 blade operating at a lower temperature in the same rotor showed only slight hot-corrosion attack on the airfoil surface, and an aluminide-coated blade in the same locale was relatively unaffected — indicating that the severity of hot-corrosion attack increases with temperature. Because none of the blades showed evidence of a structural change, such as

partial solution of precipitated gamma prime, it was not possible to estimate the temperatures to which the blades had been subjected.

Conclusions. The blades failed by hot-corrosion attack. Variation in rate of attack on coated blades was attributed to variation in integrity of the aluminide coating, which had been applied in 1966, when these coatings were relatively new. It is evident that maintaining the integrity of a protective coating could significantly increase the life of a nickel-base-alloy blade operating in a hot and corrosive environment.

Example 13. Premature Failure of a Turbine Blade by Thermal-Fatigue Fracture (Fig. 57)

During disassembly of an engine that was to be modified, a fractured turbine blade was found. When the fracture was examined at low magnification, it was observed that a fatigue fracture had originated on the concave side of the leading edge and had progressed slightly more than halfway from the leading edge to the trailing edge on the concave surface before ultimate failure occurred in dynamic tension.

Investigation. The fracture was examined by scanning electron microscopy to determine the fracture characteristics at the origin and at the transition from fatigue to tensile fracture at the concave surface. This study revealed that the fatigue fracture was initiated at an intergranular crack in the concave side of the leading edge. Oxidation of the fracture surface at the origin prevented replication for fractography by transmission electron microscopy.

Metallographic examination of a longitudinal specimen cut through the fracture-origin area revealed several oxide-filled cracks (characteristic thermal-fatigue cracks) below the fracture surface (see Fig. 57a). In high-temperature alloys, surface oxidation at elevated temperatures can deplete alloying elements (notably chromium) in the base metal, thereby reducing the strength of the metal and making it susceptible to thermal-fatigue cracking.

Some thermal-fatigue cracks are intergranular and originate at points where grain boundaries intersect the surface. Figure 57(b) shows a thermal-fatigue crack at the edge of another turbine blade from the same rotor; note that it is an oxide-filled intergranular crack. The oxide prevents the crack from closing, and additional stresses are imposed on the crack tip, which may accelerate intergranular cracking or act as a stress raiser for nucleation of a transgranular fatigue crack.

In none of the blades examined was there evidence of sustained metal temperatures in excess of 1038 C (1900 F). The microstructures of the blades in the airfoil sections were essentially identical to those in the base sections.

Conclusions. Application of a protective coating to blades, provided the coating was sufficiently ductile to avoid cracking during operation, would be beneficial by preventing surface oxidation. Such a coating also would alleviate thermal differentials, provided the thermal conductivity of the coating exceeded that of the base metal. It was also concluded that directionally solidified blades could minimize thermal-fatigue cracking by eliminating intersection of grain boundaries with the surface. However, this improvement would be more costly than applying a protective coating.

Steam-Turbine Components

Large numbers of thick-wall, low-alloy steel castings are used in steam-turbine power-generating equipment; among the common cast components are casings, cylinders, valve chests and throttle valves. The following example describes the analysis of the failure of a thick-wall casing; in this analysis, extensive use was made of fractography.

Example 14. Failure of a Thick-Wall Cast Steel Casing for a Steam Turbine by Cracking (Fig. 58)

When a crack developed in a cast steel steam-turbine casing, a small section of the casing was removed by torch cutting to examine the crack completely and to determine its origin. The crack was discovered during normal overhaul of the turbine. The chemical composition and processing of the casting were in accordance with ASTM A356, grade 6. Actual composition of the

(a) Segment removed from the casting, showing the fracture surface at right. A large porosity defect can be seen at the upper right corner, near the broken-open tapped hole. (b) to (e) TEM fractographs at 7500× of four locations on the fracture surface. Intergranular modes of fracture are shown in (b) and (c), whereas a transgranular mode, typical of corrosion fatigue, is shown in (d). The fractograph in (e) was taken in the region of crack arrest and indicates an intergranular mode of fracture.

Fig. 58. Cast steel (ASTM A356, grade 6) turbine casing that failed by cracking (Example 14)

casing was 0.18% C, 0.60% Mn, 0.47% Si, 0.016% P, 0.01% S, 0.49% Mo and 1.13% Cr, which was within limits of the specification. The mechanical properties of the casting — yield strength, 50,770 psi; tensile strength, 70,930 psi; elongation, 29.5%; reduction of area, 70.5% — exceeded the requirements of the specification. Charpy V-notch impact-energy values for specimens taken from the casting were 10.75 ft-lb at 25 C (77 F), 6.5 ft-lb at 0 C (32 F), and 4.0 ft-lb at −17.8 C (0 F).

When the fracture surface was examined visually, an internal-porosity defect was observed adjoining the tapped hole. A second, much larger cavity was also detected (see upper right portion in Fig. 58a).

Metallographic Examination. An examination of the microstructure revealed a concentration of precipitates at slip planes within grain boundaries. It is known that fatigue produces an increase in the concentration of point and line defects in the active slip planes, and that these defects assist diffusion. Therefore, precipitation, which is a diffusion-controlled process, will be more advanced in the slip bands of a material subjected to fatigue. In this instance, the fatigue was thermal fatigue caused by repeated temperature changes in the turbine over a period of about ten years. These temperature changes were more frequent

than usual because the turbine was on standby service for several years.

In regions near the main fracture surface, small subsidiary cracks — both transgranular and intergranular — were noted. At surfaces contacted by steam, there was evidence of stress-corrosion cracking and intergranular attack.

Electron Fractography. Replica impressions were taken at eight locations on the main fracture surface for examination in an electron microscope. Depending on location, there was evidence of either intergranular or transgranular cracking. For example, Fig. 58(b) and (c) indicate an intergranular mode of cracking, whereas Fig. 58(d), taken farther down the fracture surface, indicates a transgranular mode typical of corrosion fatigue. Figure 58(e), which was taken from the region of crack arrest, indicates a completely intergranular mode.

Conclusions. Failure occurred through a zone of structural weakness that was caused by internal casting defects and a tapped hole. The combination of cyclic loading (thermal fatigue), an aggressive service environment (steam), and internal defects resulted in gradual crack propagation, which at times was intergranular — with or without corrosive attack — and at other times was transgranular.

Valves in Internal-Combustion Engines

Valves in internal-combustion engines are subjected to elevated temperatures and high loads. Among the types of failures encountered in valves are those caused by burning (rapid oxidation by hot gases), fatigue, thermal fatigue, corrosion, overstressing, and combinations of these factors. Burning is the most common mode of valve failure. The next most significant mode of valve failure is fatigue at the junction of the stem and head, the point at which the hot gases from the combustion process impinge on the valve stem during the exhaust cycle. The temperatures in this area normally range from about 730 to 760 C (about 1350 to 1400 F), and loads, which are due to firing pressure and valve-spring pressure, are low.

The fracture surface of a typical failed valve stem, showing multiple crack-initiation points, is shown in Fig. 59. The crack propagated by fatigue through three-quarters of the stem before final, fast fracture occurred in a single cycle. The source of stress concentration was a metallurgical notch resulting from a crack caused by oxidation.

If, in addition to normal loading, a bending load is imposed on a valve, the combined stresses may lead to failure at the point of maximum temperature and stress, as in the following example.

Example 15. Failure of a Truck-Engine Valve of 21-2 Steel That Resulted From Bending Loads at High Temperature (Fig. 60)

The exhaust valve of a truck engine failed after 488 hr of a 1000-hr laboratory endurance test; nonleaded gasoline was used during the entire test period. The valve was made of 21-2 valve steel (21% Cr, 2% Ni, 8% Mn, 0.5% C, 0.3% N) in the solution-treated and aged condition, and was faced with Stellite 12 alloy (30% Cr, 8% W, 1.35% C, rem Co). The failure occurred by fracture of the underhead portion of the valve.

X-ray analysis of the stem portion of the valve confirmed that the composition of the 21-2 valve steel was acceptable (19.48% Cr, 2.04% Ni, 8.7% Mn). Hardness measurements and examination of the microstructure in the stem region indicated that the valve had been correctly heat treated.

Macroscopic Analysis. When the valve was examined, there was no evidence of severe wear of the valve-seat face, and seat recession appeared uniform. The fractograph in Fig. 60 shows the valve-stem fracture surface, which clearly exhibits beach marks typical of fatigue fracture. The presence of several fatigue-crack origins concentrated on one side of the fracture surface (see arrows in Fig. 60) suggests that loading was not applied uniformly. This hypothesis is supported by the change in curvature of the beach marks, which became concave, indicating unidirectional bending with low nominal stress and a mild stress concentra-

Fig. 59. Fracture surface of a typical valve stem failure with multiple-crack-initiation points

Fig. 60. Fracture surface of a 21-2 steel valve stem at 4½×, showing several crack origins (at arrows) on one side, fatigue beach marks and the final fracture zone (at bottom) (Example 15)

tion. The position and appearance of the zone of final, fast fracture are characteristic of this stress state and mode of loading.

Metallographic Examination. A longitudinal section of the stem, taken through the fracture surface, was examined metallographically. The area of the stem in which the fatigue cracks nucleated exhibited corrosion pits. Such pits act as notches and are likely sites for nucleation of fatigue cracks. The corrosion pits were the result of intergranular attack by the corrosive environment and the depletion of chromium from the grain-boundary areas. Depletion of chromium ultimately resulted in formation of microcracks.

A second type of corrosive action also occurred and resulted in the formation of nodule-type oxides of chromium. The nodules formed at regular intervals in both the stem and the underhead region. The material adjacent to the oxides was not depleted of chromium, indicating a different type of corrosive attack. Corrosion pitting and chromium depletion produce a more severe notch than does oxide formation, be-

cause nodular oxide formation is intragranular. Although the nodules extended over a large area, their notch intensity was insufficient to nucleate cracks.

When the microstructure near the stem surface was examined, it was apparent that carbide spheroidization had occurred. Also, there was a coarsening of the carbide network within the austenite grains. The microstructure indicated that the underhead region of the valve was heated to about 930 C (about 1700 F) during operation. The cause of fatigue fracture, therefore, was a combination of nonuniform bending loads and overheating.

Electron-microprobe analysis was conducted on the valve stem to determine the nature of the corrosion products and to verify the absence of lead. The results showed the nodules to be chromium-rich oxides. The fact that no chromium depletion was observed adjacent to the nodules suggests that other elements — notably manganese and iron — were oxidized and subsequently scaled off, leaving the remaining material rich in chromium. The microprobe study also confirmed that the gasoline used was lead-free.

Electron-microprobe analysis was also conducted at the sites of microcrack formation. The results indicated increases in sulfur and oxygen contents and depletion of chromium and manganese. In several areas, segregates of manganese and sulfur were detected, indicating the presence of manganese sulfide inclusions in the material. These were attributed to contamination of the engine oil.

Conclusion. Failure of the valve stem occurred by fatigue as a result of a combination of (*a*) a nonuniform bending load, which caused a mild stress-concentration condition; and (*b*) a high operating temperature (about 930 C, or 1700 F) in a corrosive environment.

An intake valve for a diesel engine failed chordally in fatigue while operating at an excessive temperature. The valve was made of Silcrome XB (SAE HNV6) steel (0.8% C, 0.4% Mn, 2.3% Si, 20% Cr, 1.3% Ni). The force that caused the failure was the firing pressure on the top head side of the valve. The stem and remnant of the head of the failed valve are shown in Fig. 61(a); multiple initiation sites can be seen on the underhead side of the valve. The valve underhead is shown at higher magnification in Fig. 61(b). Numerous striations radiating outward from an initiation point can be seen; these features are typical of fatigue fracture. Hardness tests provided evidence that the valve had been operating at about 790 C (1450 F). Normally, the maximum operating temperature for this valve material is about 625 C (1160 F).

Thermal fatigue, often referred to as "valve guttering", is another common mode of failure for valves used in gasoline or diesel-fueled engines. Thermal fatigue in poppet valves begins with crack initiation, usually at sharp corners in the valve facing material, which is applied to

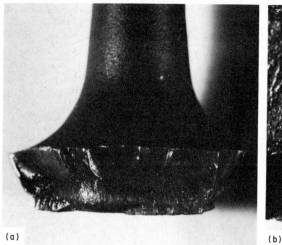

(a)

(b)

Fig. 61. (a) *View at about 2× of a portion of the stem and a remnant of the head of an intake valve that failed chordally in fatigue while operating at an excessive temperature. Multiple initiation sites can be seen on the underhead side of the valve. (b) Fracture surface of the valve, at 7½×; typical of fatigue failure, striations radiate outward from a fracture-initiation point (at arrow).*

increase corrosion resistance and combat wear. Thermal stress arises from a cooling action that results from the seating of the valve face on the cylinder head. The operating temperature of the valve head may range from about 705 to 760 C (1300 to 1400 F), but the valve face is cooled to about 650 C (1200 F) by contact with the cooler cylinder. The temperature gradient produces tangential stresses in the valve face. As the valve alternately opens and closes, cyclic heating and cooling leads to crack initiation and propagation.

With continued cycling, crack propagation leads eventually to gas leakage. Ultimately, the escaping gas raises the temperature in the crack zone to about 1925 C (3500 F) — the combustion temperature. Oxidation and erosion progress at a rapid rate, and failure is detected as a result of loss of compression.

Valve life can be extended either by reducing thermal stresses, which improves fatigue life, or by selecting valve materials with greater dynamic ductility, which would increase the number of service cycles to failure.

The poppet valve of which the head is shown in Fig. 62(a) failed after more than 5000 hr of engine operation, or about 600 million cycles. Hot gases from the combustion processes oxidized and eroded a path through the valve-seat facing alloy, Stellite F (SAE VF5), and into the valve base material, 21-12N (SAE EV4) steel. Some of the cracks that developed on the valve seat are shown in Fig. 62(b). At higher magnification, Fig. 62(c) shows two cracks that propagated through, and parallel to, dendrites in the welded structure of the VF5 facing alloy.

Molten-Solids Failures. The addition of tetraethyl lead, an antiknock agent, to gasoline contributes to the failure of valves by a mechanism known as "molten-solids failure". The function of the additive as an antiknock agent depends on the oxidation of tetraethyl lead to lead oxide and lead. However, in addition to these products, intermediate compounds of lead also are formed, and these react with scavenging agents (halogens and sulfates) and metallic additives (barium and calcium) in the engine lubricating oil.

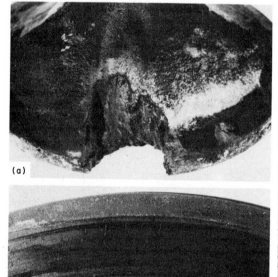

(a)

(b)

(c)

Fig. 62. (a) *Head of a poppet valve, at ½×, that failed by a mode of thermal fatigue known as "valve guttering". Severe oxidation-erosion of the valve seat was caused by the hot gases of the combustion process. (b) Actual-size view of a portion of the overhead side of the failed valve, showing several fine cracks that developed at sharp corners in the valve-seat facing material, Stellite F (SAE VF5) alloy. (c) Micrograph, at 40×, of an etched longitudinal section through a portion of the head of the failed valve, showing cracks that propagated through, and parallel to, dendrites in the welded structure of the valve-seat facing alloy.*

At elevated temperature, these intermediate compounds of lead act as liquid-phase corrodents of the protective oxide scale that forms on valves. Constant fluxing of the oxide scale reduces the oxidation resistance of the valve alloys, so that oxidation proceeds at a markedly accelerated rate. In addition, lead oxide also reacts directly with the valve alloys to produce low-melting eutectics. Typical low-melting eutectics include $PbO \cdot SiO_2$, $PbO \cdot MoO_3$, and compounds of tungsten, boron and aluminum. The resulting oxidation attack is both intergranular and intragranular.

Petroleum-Refinery Components

Some petroleum-refining operations involve the use of, or production of, hydrogen at high pressures and at temperatures of 232 C (450 F) or above. These service conditions lead to the deterioration of steel and result in the failure of components, notably pressure vessels. It has been observed that under certain conditions of temperature and hydrogen partial pressure, atomic hydrogen permeates and decarburizes steel by reducing iron carbide (Fe_3C) to form methane (CH_4). The methane does not diffuse from the steel, and its pressure may exceed the cohesive strength of the steel and cause fissuring between grains. When fissuring occurs, the ductility of the steel is significantly and permanently lowered. The severity of hydrogen attack increases with increasing temperature and hydrogen partial pressure.

Usually, hydrogen attack occurs in three stages. First, atomic hydrogen diffuses into the steel; second, decarburization occurs; and finally, intergranular fissuring occurs. A steel that has undergone only the first stage of hydrogen attack suffers a loss in ductility that is considered to be temporary, because ductility can be restored by heat treating

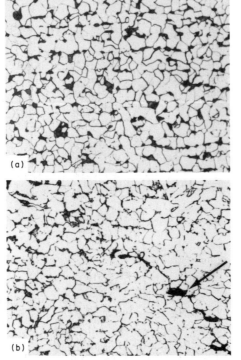

Fig. 63. Comparison of the normal microstructure of a low-carbon steel (a) with that of the same low-carbon steel following hydrogen attack (b). Arrow in (b) points to a fissure generated by entrapped methane.

at a relatively low temperature. Permanent, irreversible embrittlement results when the attack has progressed to the second or third stage. Consequently, the term "hydrogen attack" is intended to denote the permanent embrittlement that occurs in the second and third stages.

In Fig. 63, the typical structure of a low-carbon steel is compared to that having undergone the microstructural changes associated with hydrogen attack. Hydrogen attack has transformed the pearlite colonies to ferrite by reducing iron carbide to form methane. In turn,

the internal pressure generated by the entrapped methane has exceeded the strength of the steel and resulted in formation of the fissure shown in Fig. 63(b). Because a loss in ductility actually precedes a change in microstructure, bend tests and tensile tests are the most sensitive indicators of hydrogen attack.

Components of Steam Reformers

Reformers are used to produce a hydrogen-rich synthesis gas from a mixture of steam and natural gas or steam and another hydrocarbon gas at high pressures and elevated temperatures. A typical reformer consists of a brick-lined furnace or combustion chamber containing a series of oil-fired or gas-fired burners that heat cast heat-resistant alloy tubes containing the steam-gas mixture and a suitable catalyst such as nickel or nickel oxide. The steam-gas mixture, preheated to 427 to 649 C (800 to 1200 F), is introduced to the tubes, which in turn are heated to 705 to 1038 C (1300 to 1900 F). Thus, the mixture is catalytically and endothermically *reformed* to synthesis gas, which is then fed into waste-heat-recovery equipment for further processing.

Furnace Tubes. Surveys of operating plants have indicated that stress rupture is the principal mode of failure in cast heat-resistant alloy steam-reformer furnace tubes. The stress pattern developed in the wall of the reformer tube during service ultimately results in fissuring in the region extending from the inside surface to midwall; there is no fissuring at the outside surface. The sequence of steam-reformer tube failure has been studied systematically by examining specimens taken from tubes that have been subjected to varying amounts of service. The first signs of creep damage can be observed metallographically, as shown in the micrograph of an HK-40 alloy tube in Fig. 64(a). These early signs

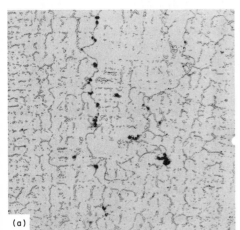
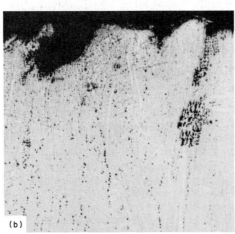
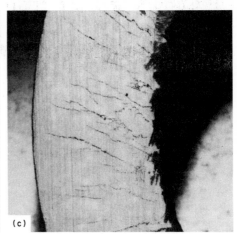

(a) Micrograph, at 50×, of an unetched specimen, showing early signs of creep damage in the form of microvoids (black dots) at two grain boundaries. (b) Macrograph, at 7×, of an unetched specimen, showing the extensive network of microvoids present after about 50% of total service life. (c) Macrograph, at 2×, of an unetched specimen, showing the advanced stage of cracking present after about 75% of total service life.

Fig. 64. Three stages of creep damage in steam-reformer furnace tubes made of HK-40 alloy

are observed after a tube has completed about 25% of its total service life. Creep damage in the form of microvoids, as shown in Fig. 64(b), becomes readily visible to the unaided eye after completion of about 50% of total service life. At this stage, the creep voids are becoming aligned and are beginning to form fissures. Finally, after completion of about 75% of total service life, cracks develop through most of the tube wall, as shown in Fig. 64(c). Nondestructive testing techniques have been developed to detect the various stages of tube damage.

Overheating of tubes will result in a reduction in service life. As shown in Fig. 65, when a tube is subjected to a service temperature 56 C (100 F) above the prescribed (base) temperature, its service life will be reduced by approximately 90%. Control of furnace temperature, therefore, is of prime importance in ensuring normal tube life. Evidence of overheating can be detected in the microstructure of the affected tube, thus providing a useful standard in failure analysis. For example, Fig. 66 presents the microstructure of two HK-40 alloy tubes that failed by stress rupture. The first tube (Fig. 66a) failed after 70 months of service, whereas the second (Fig. 66b) failed after only 57 months. Note that the microstructure of the second tube shows a greater amount of primary carbide than the microstructure of the first tube. The amount of primary carbide in the microstructure increases with an increase in service time or service temperature. Consequently, because the second tube failed after a shorter service life (57 versus 70 months), its failure was temperature related. It was estimated that this tube had been operating at a service temperature 28 C (50 F) above the prescribed temperature.

Outlet Piping. A steam-reformer outlet-piping system, operating at 816 C (1500 F), failed after a service life of about one year. As described in the following example, the principal causes of failure were sensitization and the development of cracks at welds.

Example 16. Failure of an Incoloy 800 Piping System by Cracking in Weld Heat-Affected Zones (Fig. 67)

The outlet-piping system of a steam-reformer unit failed by extensive cracking at four weld locations, identified as A, B, C and D in Fig. 67. The system, which was assembled by welding, consisted of Incoloy 800 (32% Ni, 21% Cr, 0.05% C) pipe and fittings. The exterior surfaces of the system were insulated with rock wool that did not contain weatherproofing. On-site visual examination and magnetic testing indicated severe external corrosion of most of the piping. The insulation formed a bond with corroded surfaces and was difficult to remove. The system showed extensive cracking in weld heat-affected zones.

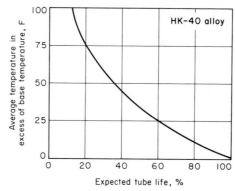

Fig. 65. Effect of exceeding prescribed (base) service temperature on the expected life of cast HK-40 alloy steam-reformer furnace tubes

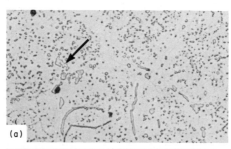

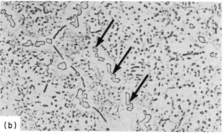

The structure in (a) shows fewer particles of primary carbides than that in (b), indicating that it was subjected to a lower service temperature. Primary-carbide particles are shown by arrows. (Etchant: 10 ml HNO_3, 20 ml HCl, 20 ml glycerol, 10 ml H_2O_2, 40 ml water; 250×)

Fig. 66. Comparison of microstructure of two HK-40 alloy steam-reformer furnace tubes that failed in stress rupture

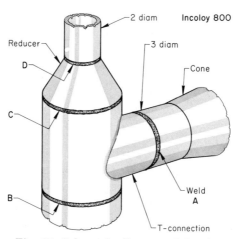

Fig. 67. Schematic diagram of Incoloy 800 outlet-piping system for a steam-reformer unit, showing the four welds (A, B, C and D) that failed by cracking (Example 16)

Investigation. Representative specimens of the piping, typical in terms of both external corrosion and cracking, were examined. A specimen taken from area A in Fig. 67 indicated that corrosion extended to a depth of 1/8 in.; cracks were seen at the edge of the cover bead and in the heat-affected zone of the weld. Metallographic examination of the cracked region showed that cracking was intergranular and that adjacent grain boundaries had undergone deep intergranular attack. Examination at higher magnification of areas in the vicinity of attack revealed heavy carbide precipitation, primarily at grain boundaries, indicating that the alloy had been sensitized. Sensitization resulted from heating during welding.

Further analysis, using the electron-microprobe technique, showed that the outside surface of the tube did not have the protective chromium oxide scale normally found on Incoloy 800. The inside surface of the tube had a thin chromium oxide protective scale that attached to the base metal at the grain boundaries.

Conclusions. The deep oxidation greatly decreased the strength of the weld heat-affected zones and cracking followed. A detailed stress analysis showed that failures had occurred in the areas of highest stress in the reducer and the T connection — namely, areas A, B, C and D in Fig. 67.

Gas-Line Flange. The next example reports on the failure of a stainless steel flange for a steam-reformer gas line. This flange, which replaced one that had a service life of 4 1/2 years, failed after only 30 days of service, because it had not been solution annealed after forging and prior to installation.

Example 17. Premature Cracking of a Type 321 Stainless Steel Flange for a Steam-Reformer Gas Line Because of Failure to Solution Anneal

A 400-lb replacement flange made of type 321 stainless steel was installed at the exit end of a waste-heat boiler — part of the steam-reformer gas section of an ammonia plant. This 16-in.-ID flange, which was welded to an insulated pipe, failed in a brittle manner by cracking after a service life of only 30 days. The crack occurred at a considerable distance from the weld area, indicating that any association between the crack and the heat-affected zone of the weld was unlikely. The operating temperature at the flange did not exceed about 480 C (about 900 F) in service.

Investigation. Specimens from the flange were analyzed for chemical composition and subjected to standard mechanical-property tests, and were found to be within ASTM specification limits. However, when specimens were impact tested, it was determined that their impact strength was below normal. Metallographic examination revealed the presence of stringers of sigma phase in the matrix conforming with the forging direction, which accounts for the low impact strength.

Because the operating temperature of the flange was below the sensitizing-temperature range in which sigma phase is known to form in nonstabilized stainless steels, it as determined that sigma phase was resent in the alloy at the conclusion of the orging operation. Failure to solution anneal the flange by heating to 1038 to 1052 C (1900 to 1925 F) and water quenching to liminate the sigma phase resulted in a ange that was in unsuitable metallurical condition. Cracking, therefore, was ttributed to the embrittling effects of the igma phase in combination with high exansion stresses. (Sigma phase in type 321 tainless steel is shown in micrograph 1133 n page 141 in Volume 7 of this Handbook.)

Components of Heat Treating Furnaces

Of the several types of heat treating urnace components exposed to gaseous nvironments at elevated temperatures, adiant tubes, which are in effect the urnace heating elements, are sometimes ubjected to the most severe service. The adiant tubes used in carburizing and ardening furnaces are representative of omponents subjected to this degree of ervice. As described in the following xample, these tubes may operate normally at temperatures as high as 1038 C 1900 F) and may be exposed to atmospheres that are alternately carburizing nd oxidizing.

Example 18. Failure of Radiant Tubes in a Batch-Carburizing Furnace (Fig. 68)

Three radiant tubes, made of three diferent high-temperature alloys, were removed from a carburizing furnace after aproximately 8½ months of service when hey showed evidence of failure by collapsing (telescoping) in a region 12 in. from he tube bottoms in the vicinity of the urners. The affected areas of the three ubes, which vary in degree of corrosion lamage sustained, are shown in Fig. 68(a).

The tubes had an original wall thickness of 0.120 in. and were made of three different lloys: Hastelloy X (48% Ni, 22% Cr, 18.5% Fe, 9% Mo), RA 333 alloy (45% Ni, 25% Cr, 18% Fe, 3% Mo, 3% W, 3% Co, 1.5% Mn, 1.25% Si, 0.05% C) and experimental alloy 634 (which contained 72% Ni, 4% Cr and 3.5% Si). The three radiant ubes had been operated at a temperature of about 1038 C (1900 F) in order to maintain furnace temperatures of 899 to 927 C (1650 to 1700 F). The normal life of radiant tubes in this furnace ranged from 6 to 20 months.

Investigation. Specimens for metallographic examination were removed from the heavily corroded area of each tube. Micrographs taken from areas near the surfaces of the three tubes are presented in Fig. 68(b) to (d). As shown in Fig. 68(b), the tube made of alloy 634, which contained the highest nickel and lowest chromium contents of the three alloys, suffered severe oxidation in the form of heavy surface scale. A micrograph of the Hastelloy X tube is shown in Fig. 68(c). This alloy contained the second-highest nickel content (48%) and 22% Cr; the micrograph shows heavy carburization and considerable subsurface oxidation. A micrograph of the RA 333 alloy tube is shown in Fig. 68(d) and exhibits

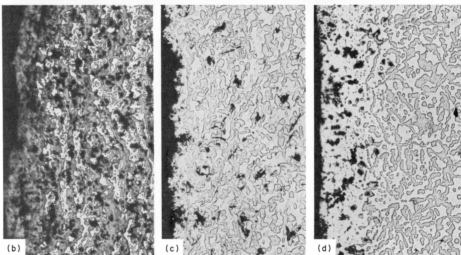

(a) View at ⅓× of corroded portions of tubes made of Hastelloy X (top), experimental alloy 634 (center), and RA 333 alloy (bottom). (b), (c) and (d) Micrographs at 100× of unetched sections from corroded portions of the tubes: (b) alloy 634 tube, showing heavy scale; (c) Hastelloy X tube, showing heavy carburization and severe subsurface oxidation; and (d) RA 333 alloy tube, showing heavy carburization and slight subsurface oxidation.

Fig. 68. Three radiant tubes that failed by corrosion during use in a carburizing furnace (Example 18)

heavy carburization but only slight evidence of subsurface oxidation. This alloy contained 25% Cr and only 45% Ni. In radiant tubes, selective oxidation is a far more serious problem than carburization. Measurement of the sound wall thickness (metal carburized but not oxidized) remaining in each of the three tubes confirmed the evidence shown in the micrographs: in the alloy 634 tube it was 0.067 to 0.087 in.; in the Hastelloy X tube, 0.087 to 0.114 in.; and in the RA 333 alloy tube, 0.110 in.

Conclusion. From the information obtained in the investigation described above, it was decided that tube life might be extended by selecting an alloy, such as RA 333, with a higher chromium content and with an additional element, like silicon, resistant to carburization-oxidation.

Radiant tubes occasionally are subjected to service temperatures much higher than normal. In the example that

follows, radiant tubes locally reached temperatures of about 1177 to 1204 C (2150 to 2200 F) as a result of poor positioning of the burner. This local overheating, in combination with corrosion from high-sulfur refractory cement, caused failure of a tube.

Example 19. Corrosion Failure of an RA 333 Alloy Radiant Tube in a Furnace Because of High-Sulfur Packing and Local Overheating (Fig. 69)

One of 14 vertical radiant tubes in a heat treating furnace failed prematurely when a hole about 2 by 5 in. corroded completely through the tube wall, as shown in Fig. 69. The radiant tubes were arranged in rows of seven along each side of the furnace and were spaced on 12-in. centers. They were made of RA 333 alloy, a wrought nickel-base heat-resisting alloy containing 45% Ni,

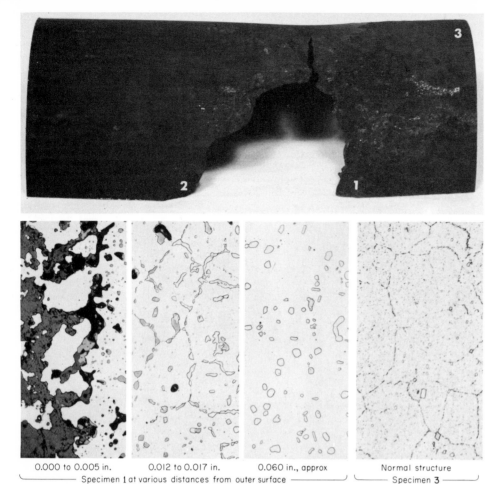

| 0.000 to 0.005 in. | 0.012 to 0.017 in. | 0.060 in., approx | Normal structure |

Specimen 1 at various distances from outer surface ———————— | Specimen 3

Fig. 69. At top is a section of radiant tube (at 0.7×) made of RA 333 nickel-base alloy that corroded in a heating furnace, showing hole corroded in tube wall and locations where three metallographic specimens were removed. Below are micrographs at 250× of specimens etched with mixed acids, showing microstructure of specimen 1 at various depths in corroded region and normal microstructure of specimen 3. (Example 19)

25% Cr, 18% Fe, 3% Mo, 3% W, 3% Co, 1.5% Mn, 1.25% Si and 0.05% C.

The tube was 72 in. long by 3½ in. in outside diameter and had a wall thickness of about 0.120 in. Failure occurred where the tube passed through the refractory hearth (floor) of the furnace.

When the furnace was examined, large amounts of soot were observed at various locations, especially on the hearth near the vertical tubes and covering the refractory-cement packing that sealed the tubes to the hearth. Preliminary examination *in situ* of the 14 tubes showed some pits on the outer surfaces of several tubes just below the roof of the furnace.

Service History. The furnace had been rebricked when new radiant tubes were installed. The tubes had been in service for only five months when the failure occurred, although similar radiant tubes used under the same operating conditions in an identical furnace at the same plant had had average service lives of 24 to 30 months, with a maximum life of about five years.

The two furnaces were used exclusively for clean hardening of H13 tool steels and similar alloy steels in an endothermic atmosphere at about 1010 C (1850 F). Although the atmosphere was neutral with respect to the work, it had a carburizing potential with respect to the radiant tubes.

Sampling. A 7-in.-long sample piece that contained the failure region (see Fig. 69) was cut from the failed tube for examination. Specimens for spectrographic analysis were taken from near the hole in this sample (a heavily scaled and corroded region) and from an apparently unaffected portion of the sample. In addition, a quantity of loose scale was scraped from the heavily scaled region to be analyzed chemically for sulfur. Specimens for metallographic examination (specimens 1, 2 and 3) also were cut from the sample in the locations shown in Fig. 69.

Visual Examination. Scaling and corrosion on the outside surface of the failed tube were observed around the hole in the tube and were most severe immediately adjacent to the hole. In this region, the severe attack extended about 6 in. around the circumference of the tube.

Less-severe scaling and pitting extended slightly above the hearth. The upper end of the sample was covered with a glossy adherent oxide layer.

The lower end of the sample (the portion below the hearth) did not bear any visible signs of attack or deterioration. The outside surface at this end of the sample was coated with a light layer of soot in some areas. Wiping away the soot revealed undisturbed surface scratches and other fabrication

marks, but there was no evidence of scaling in this region. The remainder of the failed tube (above the sample) showed no evidence of damage or deterioration.

Because of the pits observed on several tubes at the roof line in the preliminary examination, and because of the severity of the attack on the failed tube at the hearth, the 13 remaining tubes were removed from the furnace. Ten of these tubes were found to be pitted to varying degrees in the region that had been enclosed within the bricked roof of the furnace, and pinhole penetration was detected at a few isolated points on two or three of these tubes in the regions that were pitted.

Further examination and testing were restricted to the failed tube and the refractory cement.

Spectrographic and Chemical Analysis. The composition of the failed tube was found by spectrographic analysis to be normal for RA 333 alloy. Chemical analysis of scale taken from the heavily corroded outside surface of the tube near specimen 1 (see Fig. 69) showed that the scale contained 0.25% sulfur. The refractory cement used around the tubes when they were installed was not analyzed, but was described by the supplier to be a type having a relatively high sulfur content.

Metallographic examination was performed on specimen 1, which had been taken from the region just above the hole in the tube, as shown in Fig. 69. Examination of a cross section of the tube wall taken from specimen 1 showed that several distinct zones existed at different depths inward from the outside surface, as shown in the three photomicrographs at the bottom left in Fig. 69. (Specimen 2 showed a generally similar pattern of microstructure and was not photographed.)

The micrograph at the extreme left, extending a depth of 0.005 in. inward from the surface (from which the loose scale had first been removed) showed the outermost portion to be a carbon-depleted corrosion zone. The outer 0.005 in. consisted mostly of sulfide (gray constituent), remnants of the austenitic matrix (off-white) and small amounts of a silicate phase (black constituent).

The second micrograph of specimen 1 in Fig. 69 shows a region 0.012 to 0.017 in. in from the outer surface of the tube. This region had a fine grain size (ASTM No. 4 to 7) and was heavily carburized, showing extensive carbide separation along the grain boundaries (light-etching constituent) and a few scattered small gray particles of sulfide and black particles of silicate.

The third micrograph of specimen 1 in Fig. 69 shows a carburized, coarse-grained (ASTM No. 000 to 3) structure at a depth of approximately 0.060 in. (the midpoint of the wall thickness), in which the carbide was present as scattered small globular and elongated particles. The carbon content at this level was substantially lower than at the level shown in the second micrograph of specimen 1.

The micrograph of specimen 3 (an apparently unaffected region away from the failure region, as shown in Fig. 69) corresponded to the normal fine-grained microstructure of the alloy (ASTM grain size No. 4 to 7, but predominantly No. 5 to 7).

Discussion. Extreme grain coarsening was observed in the corroded region of the failed tube at the approximate midpoint of the 0.120-in. wall thickness (third micrograph of specimen 1, as shown in Fig. 69) and extending inward to the interior or fireside wall of the tube. The microstructure in this region of the tube was evidence that local overheating to about 1177 to 1204 C (2150 to 2200 F) had occurred in service.

The exceptional severity of the local overheating on this tube within the hearth (as compared to the 13 other tubes) apparently resulted from failure to position the burner so as to heat the tube uniformly around its circumference and high enough to avoid concentrating heat on the portion of the tube within the refractory hearth. As on all of the tubes, the insulating packing and brick of the hearth interfered with loss of heat by radiation, which was unhindered on the portions of the tubes that were freely exposed to the furnace atmosphere.

Within the hearth, the metal of the tube wall near its outer surface and in the corroded area, as illustrated by the second micrograph of specimen 1 in Fig. 69 (labeled 0.012 to 0.017 in.), showed no grain coarsening. The metal near the outer surface (which was exposed to soot and to the endothermic atmosphere), before being overheated, had apparently undergone sufficient grain-boundary carburization to prevent subsequent grain growth in the outer half of the wall. In the inner half of the wall, grain growth from overheating occurred before sufficient grain-boundary carburization took place to impede grain growth. This early grain growth resulted in the type of coarse-grained carburized structure shown in the third micrograph of specimen 1 in Fig. 69 (labeled 0.060 in., approx).

The attack observed on ten of the tubes where they passed through the roof of the furnace resulted from attack by the sulfur in the refractory cement, in combination with a local tube temperature estimated to be about 1121 C (2050 F) in this region. The attack was less severe than that observed at the hearth region on the failed tube, where the tube temperature reached about 1177 to 1204 C (2150 to 2200 F) because of improper burner placement and adjustment.

The formation of a glossy adherent oxide, as observed on intermediate-temperature areas of the 7-in. specimen removed from the failed tube, is a phenomenon that is frequently encountered on nickel-base heat-resisting alloys when they are exposed to temperatures at which their oxidation resistance is marginal.

Conclusions. The premature failure of the tube by perforation at the hearth level resulted from (a) corrosion caused by sulfur contamination from the refractory cement in contact with the tube, and (b) severe local overheating at the same location.

Corrective Action. All of the tubes were replaced. To lengthen the service life of the replacement tubes, a low-sulfur refractory cement was used in installing them, and burner positioning and regulation were controlled more closely, so as to avoid excessive heat input at the hearth level. The replacement tubes had a life well in excess of two years, which was normal for RA 333 alloy tubes in this application.

Cement-Mill Equipment

An important part of the cement-making process involves roasting or firing the raw materials in a horizontal rotating kiln. In this operation, equipment failures are frequent and in most instances result from abrasion at elevated temperatures coupled with some corrosion (corrosion is rarely a major factor). In time, abrasion thins out guides, crosses and other components to the extent that they must be replaced. Cast HH alloy (25% Cr, 12% Ni) is widely used in kiln components because it provides good high-temperature strength and abrasion resistance at a reasonable cost.

Incinerator Equipment

Municipal and industrial incineration plants have become more numerous in an increasing effort to control pollution and waste disposal and to develop additional sources of combustible gases for heating. In many of these plants, waste materials are charged into the top zone of refractory-lined circular furnaces. Rotating, bladed rabble arms force the refuse through the various stages of burning, and the ash is discharged at the bottom of the furnace. The rabble arms and blades rotate around a vertical axis and are forced-air cooled to maintain a temperature in the range of 427 to 760 C (800 to 1400 F).

Cast HH alloy is the material most commonly used in incinerator furnace components. Because of the abrasiveness and corrosiveness of the refuse, components usually fail as a result of corrosive wear. Some of the refuse and the products formed during incineration remove the protective oxide skin that normally forms on stainless alloys and thus accelerate wear and corrosion. Among the corrosive materials common to incinerators are

(a) chlorides, which are released when chlorinated plastics such as polyvinyl chloride are burned, (b) lead and zinc compounds that arise from volatilization of metal scrap, and (c) sulfur compounds and salts. Some corrosive gases, low-melting chlorides, and sulfur-containing salts exert a fluxing action on the protective films on metal surfaces.

Ordnance Hardware

During test firing, 81-mm mortar tubes bulged because of the pressures and temperatures that were developed during firing. When bulging occurred, the mortar tubes could no longer be used. The cause of these failures was apparent: the alloy from which the tubes were made did not have sufficient yield strength at the maximum tube operating temperature of 621 C (1150 F). The following example is not concerned with failure analysis of the bulged tubes, but rather with an evaluation that was conducted to select a suitable tube material.

Example 20. Evaluation of Alloys for Use in 81-Mm Mortar Tubes (Tables 3, 4, 5 and 6)

When bulging occurred in mortar tubes made of British I steel (see Table 3 for chemical composition) during elevated-temperature test firing, a test program was formulated to evaluate the high-temperature properties (at 538 to 649 C, or 1000 to 1200 F) of the British I steel and of several alternative alloys. These alloys included a maraging steel (18% Ni, grade 250), a vanadium-modified 4337 gun steel (4337V), H19 tool steel, and high-temperature alloys René 41, Inconel 718 and Udimet 630. The compositions of these alloys are given in Table 3, and the heat treatments that the alloys were given prior to being tested for evaluation are presented in Table 4. All the alloys evaluated either had been used in mortar tubes previously or were known to meet the estimated requirement of

Table 3. Compositions of Alloys Evaluated for Use in Mortar Tubes (Example 20)

Alloy	C	Mn	Si	Cr	Ni	Mo	Fe	Other
Maraging steel ..	0.02	0.08	0.06	...	18.5	4.7	70.0	0.3 Ti, 7.7 Co, 0.04 Al
4337V gun steel .	0.32	0.59	0.22	0.94	2.3	0.58	94.0	0.12 V
British I steel ...	0.45	0.62	0.30	2.8	0.43	0.90	94.0	0.20 V
Inconel 718	0.05	0.01	0.10	18.2	53.0	3.1	18.0	1.1 Ti, 5.4 Cb+Ta, 0.5 Al
H19 tool steel ...	0.40	0.29	0.23	4.1	...	0.44	86.0	4.1 Co, 4.0 W, 2.1 V
Udimet 630	0.03	0.15	0.10	17.3	57.0	2.9	17.5	1.0 Ti, 0.10 Co, 0.6 Al
René 41	0.09	0.04	0.10	18.8	55.0	9.8	1.4	3.2 Ti, 11.3 Co, 1.6 Al

Table 4. Heat Treatments of Mortar-Tube Alloys Prior to Evaluation (Example 20)

Alloy	Heat treatment (AC = air cool; FC = furnace cool; OQ = oil quench; ST = solution treat; WQ = water quench)	Hardness, R_C
Maraging steel	ST at 1500 F 1 hr, AC. Age at 925 F 3 hr, AC.	50
4337V gun steel	Austenitize at 1575 F 4 hr, OQ. Temper at 1100 F 5 hr, WQ.	40
British I steel	Austenitize at 1680 F 5 hr, OQ. Temper at 1130 F 5 hr, AC.	40
Inconel 718	ST at 1800 F 4 hr, AC. Age at 1325 F 16 hr, FC at 100 F/hr to 1150 F, hold 8 hr, AC.	40
H19 tool steel	Austenitize at 2125 F 1 hr. Triple temper at 1200 F 1 hr, AC.	44
Udimet 630	ST at 1875 F 4 hr, AC. Age at 1400 F 8 hr, AC. Age at 1200 F 10 hr, AC.	44
René 41	ST at 1975 F 4 hr, AC. Age at 1400 F 16 hr, AC.	37

Table 5. Transverse Yield Strength of Mortar-Tube Alloys After Cycling Between Room Temperature and Test Temperature (See Also Tables 3, 4 and 6) (Example 20)

No. of 15-min cycles	Transverse yield strength, 1000 psi(a)	
	At 1100 F	At 1150 F
Maraging Steel		
1	60, 61, 61	37, 40, 42
5	54, 57, 59	27, 35, 36
10	55, 66, 68	38, 39, 42
25	54, 59, 60	40, 43, 45
4337V Gun Steel		
1	73, 78, 79	50, 51, 54
5	68, 71, 78	48, 49, 52
10	73, 73, 75	41, 43, 47
25	48, 61, 69	33, 41, 41
British I Steel		
1	74, 77, 80	55, 57, 66
5	70, 71, 71	52, 55, 58
10	64, 68	43, 51, 52
25	61, 64, 68	47, 51, 52
Inconel 718		
1	124, 137	117, 118, 130
5	119, 133	116, 119, 130
10	119, 122, 129	111, 113, 116
25	115, 116, 128	107, 110, 115
H19 Tool Steel		
1	80, 85, 90	65, 81, 93
5	84, 92, 96	81, 81, 82
10	84, 90, 90	74, 81, 88
25	72, 86, 96	74, 77, 79
Udimet 630		
1	143, 144, 144	142, 143, 148
5	139, 139, 142	136, 140, 145
10	141, 141, 143	140, 142, 142
25	146, 147, 148	139, 142, 145
René 41		
1	97, 101	97, 100, 107
5	97, 108, 109	99, 100, 100
10	97, 99, 104	92, 94, 97
25	96, 103, 106	100, 103, 104

(a) Values are for two or three specimens tested at each number of cycles.

Table 6. Ductility of Mortar-Tube Alloys at 1100 F After Cycling Between Room Temperature and 1100 F (See Also Tables 3, 4 and 5) (Example 20)

No. of 15-min cycles	Ductility, as measured by:	
	Elongation, %(a)	Reduction in area, %(a)
Maraging Steel		
1	33.6, 34.8, 47.9	87.5, 90.3, 96.0
5	42.1, 45.7, 55.0	91.6, 94.8, 97.2
10	35.0, 43.3, 50.7	90.0, 93.1, 97.7
25	45.0, 52.9, 58.2	92.9, 94.7, 96.6
4337V Gun Steel		
1	16.8, 19.0, 25.0	65.0, 71.4, 76.8
5	19.3, 21.4, 24.7	76.5, 77.5, 79.6
10	18.6, 21.0, 21.8	71.6, 71.9, 75.4
25	21.8, 23.2, 34.7	70.7, 78.3, 84.4
British I Steel		
1	15.4, 16.1, 16.9	34.6, 35.8, 40.9
5	20.0, 21.4, 22.2	43.6, 58.4, 67.0
10	25.6, 29.2	68.8, 70.4
25	20.4, 33.2	66.0, 79.9
Inconel 718		
1	9.3	21.7
5	12.8, 18.3	23.2, 27.5
10	12.5, 15.4, 18.3	20.7, 23.2, 25.6
25	10.7, 17.1, 21.8	26.1, 26.6, 29.5
H19 Tool Steel		
1	3.6, 5.4, 8.3	7.1, 8.1, 12.5
5	6.4, 7.6, 8.3	9.7, 11.4, 12.0
10	6.1, 6.8, 9.3	10.9, 12.5, 13.5
25	6.8, 7.6	11.2, 12.0
Udimet 630		
1	5.4, 5.7, 6.4	10.3, 12.0, 12.0
5	4.3, 6.8, 6.8	7.1, 12.0, 13.5
10	2.9, 5.7	3.8, 9.2
25	2.9, 5.0	7.1, 9.2
René 41		
1	3.5, 4.3	4.9, 6.5
5	3.6	3.8
10	1.8, 4.0	4.3, 5.4
25	3.3	3.5

(a) Values are for one, two or three specimens tested at each number of cycles.

temperature for 15 min in an electric furnace mounted on the tensile-testing machine. Specimens tested at 593 and 621 C (1100 and 1150 F) were cycled 1, 5, 10 and 25 times; each cycle comprised heating in an electric furnace for 4 min to equalize the temperature of the bar, holding at temperature for 15 min, and cooling in still air. In each group, the last cycle was performed during hot tensile testing.

Test Results. Table 5 shows how transverse yield strengths of the alloys vary with cycling from room temperature to 593 and 621 C (1100 and 1150 F). Ductility of alloys cycled between room temperature and 593 C (1100 F), as measured by elongation and reduction in area, is shown in Table 6. The alloys fall in this order of decreasing strengths: Udimet 630, Inconel 718, René 41, H19 tool steel, British I steel, 4337V gun steel, and maraging steel. When cycled between room temperature and 538 to 649 C (1000 to 1200 F), only Udimet 630, Inconel 718, and René 41 retained yield strengths over the minimum of 80,000 psi at 621 C (1150 F). Also, these three alloys maintained high strengths over the tested range whereas the others decreased in yield strength as cycling progressed.

In general, the decrease in yield strength with time was greater at higher temperatures. However, short-time exposure at a given temperature lowered yield strength appreciably, while longer exposures had less effect. In fact, some alloys actually increased in yield strength with time at temperature. This phenomenon, more noticeable in the highly alloyed grades, may be due to the development of a critical size of precipitates either during aging of the precipitation-hardening alloys or by tempering at elevated temperature. The large decrease in yield strength at elevated temperatures is due to overaging in the maraging steel, and to overtempering in H19, British I steel, and 4337V.

Tensile tests revealed the following order of decreasing ductility: maraging steel, 4337V, British I steel, Inconel 718, H19 tool steel, Udimet 630 and René 41. Ductility of the maraging steel, 4337V, and British I steel rose with decreasing yield strength or increasing temperature whereas ductility of H19, René 41, Inconel 718, and Udimet 630 remained constant from room temperature to 649 C (1200 F).

Data revealed that the impact-toughness values of 4337V and Inconel 718 were, respectively, 950 and 1210 in.-lb per square inch at −40 C (−40 F) and 1550 and 1110 in.-lb per square inch at room temperature, or about triple the values for maraging steel, Udimet 630, and René 41. Note that impact-toughness values for the three nickel-base alloys are about the same at −40 C (−40 F) as at room temperature. From limited fatigue data, it appears that Inconel 718 is superior to René 41 in fatigue strength at 649 C (1200 F).

Conclusions. Because the mortar tubes made with maraging, 4337V and British I steels bulged when test fired in earlier field tests, a suitable tube material should have a minimum yield strength of 80,000 to 85,000 psi at 538 to 621 C (1000 to 1150 F). The evaluation indicated that H19 tool steel, René 41, Inconel 718, and Udimet 630 alloys met this requirement. However, the proper-

a minimum yield strength of 80,000 psi at 621 C (1150 F).

Test Program. Tests were made to determine (a) transverse yield strength (at 0.1% offset) and ductility at room temperature, and at 538, 593, 621 and 649 C (1000, 1100, 1150 and 1200 F); (b) transverse yield strength and ductility at 593 and 621 C (1100 and 1150 F) on specimens cycled 1, 5, 10 and 25 times for 15 min at temperature; and (c) impact and fracture toughness at −40 C (−40 F) and at room temperature. Fatigue-strength data were also obtained from manufacturers.

With the exception of the vanadium-modified 4337 gun steel (4337V) and the British I steel (which were air melted and vacuum degassed), all alloys came as vacuum-melted bar stock (induction or arc remelted, or both) in sizes equal to that of the 81-mm mortar tube. Transverse disks cut from each bar were machined into three tensile and two V-notch Charpy specimens for each test condition.

For the elevated-temperature tests, tensile-test bars were pulled after being held at

ties of H19 tool steel were marginal, and this alloy was not considered suitable for use in mortar tubes.

Because the remaining three alloys had uniform high yield strength at elevated temperatures, other criteria were used to determine their suitability. Udimet 630 had the highest yield strength (140,000 psi) with low ductility (6% elongation) and low toughness. Also, it was not readily available and was second most expensive of the three alloys. René 41 was the most expensive of the alloys, was also limited in availability, and had the lowest yield strength (100,000 psi), lowest ductility (4%), lowest toughness, and lowest fatigue strength.

Based on the test data, therefore, Inconel 718 was considered best suited for 81-mm mortar tubes. It had an optimum combination of elevated-temperature yield strength, ductility, impact toughness, and fatigue strength. Widespread industrial usage ensured its availability. Although a high-cost material, it was less expensive than the two alternative alloys.

Platinum and Platinum-Rhodium Components

Industrially, platinum and platinum-rhodium crucibles are used as containers for melting glass, for growing single crystals, and for making determinations of ash content in the cement and flour industries. Platinum and platinum-rhodium wires are used in thermocouples for sensing temperatures in the range of 400 to 2400 C (752 to 4352 F) in furnaces and other types of heating equipment. Because of the very high cost of platinum and its alloys, crucibles and thermocouples made of these materials should be properly used and cared for to ensure maximum service life. Failure analysis is helpful in providing guidance for proper selection of alloys for, and proper care of, crucibles and thermocouples.

Crucibles. Based on analysis of several hundred failures, it is possible to summarize the causes of failure in crucibles. About 85% of all crucible failures result from the formation of low-melting eutectics and brittle intermetallic compounds along grain boundaries, which arise from interaction with metallic vapors such as those of tin, arsenic, antimony, lead and silicon (three failures of this type are described in the examples that follow); the remaining 15% are the result of miscellaneous causes. Approximately 60% of all thermocouple failures result from mechanical breakage caused either by excessive loading at operating temperature or by grain-boundary embrittlement; the remaining 40% are caused by deterioration of thermoelectric properties.

Examples 21, 22 and 23. Crucible Failures Resulting From Formation of Low-Melting Eutectics and Brittle Intermetallics

Example 21. Pt-3.5Rh Crucible Liner. Several Pt-3.5Rh crucible liners used for melting leaded glass failed prematurely. A specimen from one of the liners was removed in the vicinity of the glass-melt line where fracture occurred. A micrograph showed grain-boundary voids near the fracture surface and along the inside surface of the crucible at and below the glass-melt line, suggesting an interaction of the liner material with the molten glass. A spectrographic analysis of the metal along the fracture surface detected excessive amounts of lead and cadmium.

The presence of grain-boundary voids and excessive amounts of lead and cadmium is indicative of the formation of grain-boundary eutectics. Fracture at and immediately above the melt line indicates that oxides of lead and cadmium were reduced at the melt line and that the resulting metal vapors reacted with the liner. Premature failure could have been avoided if sufficient partial pressure of oxygen had been maintained above the melt line (glass-vapor interface) and if the melt had been well stirred.

Example 22. Platinum Crucible. A platinum crucible used for melting glass failed after one hour of service at 1300 C (2372 F) in a furnace heated by silicon-carbide glow bars. The failure occurred when an attempt was made to pour the glass, which was greenish in color and very fluid. The composition of the glass included oxides, carbonates and fluorides of sodium, aluminum, silicon, arsenic, barium and lithium. A micrograph of a specimen taken from the bottom of the crucible showed a continuous low-melting eutectic to be the cause of failure.

Example 23. Pt-20Rh Crucible. A slag, composed of CaS, CaO, MgO, SiO_2 and Al_2O_3, was heated to 1427 C (2600 F) in a graphite crucible in an electric furnace maintained under argon atmosphere. The slag was then transferred to a Pt-20Rh crucible, whereupon it started to foam almost immediately. When the procedure was repeated, two holes developed in the bottom of the crucible.

Investigation. The failed crucible displayed honeycomb remnants of the slag, which had a distinctive odor of hydrogen sulfide. In addition to the holes in the bottom of the crucible, there was a grayish nodule. A micrograph of a specimen removed in the area of the nodule showed a dendritic-type structure. A microhardness survey indicated that the hardness of the dendritic-type structure in the nodule area was 640 dph, whereas the hardness of the Pt-20Rh alloy was only 110 dph. A spectrographic analysis of the failed area revealed the presence of excessive amounts of iron (>200 ppm), silicon (>300 ppm), magnesium (>100 ppm), aluminum (>100 ppm), and sodium (80 ppm).

Study of service conditions, spectrographic analysis, and metallographic examination indicated that low-melting eutectic had formed as a result of interaction of the slag with the crucible metal.

Conclusion. Apparently, the melting of oxides in an inert atmosphere generated a reducing reaction because of a lack of oxygen replacement. Consequently, elemental silicon, magnesium, aluminum, iron and sodium were generated. These elements formed low-melting eutectics and intermetallics with platinum, which were responsible for the failure.

Corrective Action. Although melting the slag in an oxidizing atmosphere would prevent the reduction of oxides and avoid future catastrophic failure, chemical-composition requirements of the slag would not allow this corrective action. The alternative solution was to use either a rhodium or an iridium crucible, because these metals form fewer low-melting eutectics and intermetallics under inert atmosphere and have superior resistance to all known impurities that readily attack platinum, platinum-rhodium alloys, and platinum-iridium alloys.

About 15% of all crucible failures result from causes other than the formation of low-melting eutectics and intermetallics. One cause is hammering the crucible in order to restore its shape after it has distorted as a result of thermal cycling. Hammering often results in cracking. Another cause of failure can be traced to the differences in thermal-expansion coefficients that exist between the crucible material and the substance being heated and cooled in it. This problem arises when glass is melted in Pt-10Rh and Pt-20Rh crucibles, the latter of which are selected for their rigidity and resistance to deformation in thermal cycling. This problem can be solved by using platinum crucibles of a thicker gage; unalloyed platinum has better ductility than the Pt-Rh alloys and can better accommodate differences in coefficients of thermal expansion.

Thermocouples. By definition, a thermocouple is a device for measuring temperatures and consists of two dissimilar metals that produce an electromotive force roughly proportional to the temperature difference between their hot and cold junctions. Thermocouples made of platinum and a platinum-rhodium alloy usually fail as a result of mechanical breakage or deterioration of thermoelectric properties, both of which involve contamination. Grain growth also can be a contributing factor in mechanical failure of thermocouple wires — especially, unalloyed platinum wires — after prolonged service at elevated temperatures. Small strains in the wire contribute to grain growth.

Platinum/platinum-rhodium thermocouples are generally used at temperatures up to 1800 C (3272 F) in oxidizing atmospheres and require several precautions to avoid premature failure. The user should always observe the service-temperature ranges and comparative emf values of the various noble-metal thermocouples given in Fig. 70. Even at room temperature, platinum is a very soft metal and is commonly fractured by rough usage. At elevated temperatures, the strength of platinum is very low; therefore, platinum wire should not be subjected to high-temperature loading. Figure 71 shows the "bamboo-type" surface that develops on platinum wire and that results in grain-boundary fracture because of excessive loading at elevated temperature. If loading is unavoidable, a mechanically stronger thermocouple, such as Pt-6Rh/Pt-30Rh, should be used. The addition of rhodium increases the stress-rupture strength of the wire.

Thermocouples containing platinum should not be used in reducing atmospheres in refractory-lined furnaces, because they can be contaminated by pickup of silicon from the refractory lining. The solubility of silicon in platinum is low, and a low-melting eutectic is formed with only a very small silicon content. Contamination will occur even when the platinum is not in contact with the silicon-bearing material, because, in a reducing atmosphere, the silicon can be transferred through the vapor phase.

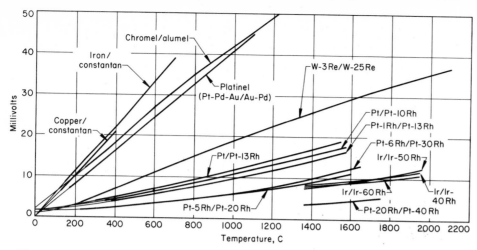

Fig. 70. Service-temperature ranges and comparative electromotive-force values, in millivolts, for various thermocouple materials

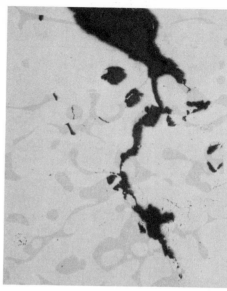

Fig. 72. Micrograph at 100× of an unetched specimen from a platinum thermocouple that was exposed to silicon contamination, showing network of platinum-silicide second phase (gray), and voids (black) where the eutectic melted

Fig. 71. Photograph at 40× of "bamboo-type" surface that developed on the platinum leg of a thermocouple as a result of excessive loading at elevated temperatures

Figure 72 shows the typical structure that results from silicon contamination. The presence of the platinum-silicide network eventually leads to localized melting and catastrophic failure.

When temperatures must be checked in a refractory-lined furnace containing a reducing atmosphere, the risk of premature failure can be minimized by protecting the thermocouple with an impervious sheath, ensuring free access of air within the sheath to maintain oxidizing conditions in the event of leakage. Sheathing will also protect the thermocouple from other volatile impurities, including volatile metals, that adversely affect mechanical strength and thermoelectric properties.

One type of sheathed thermocouple is shown in Fig. 73. It consists of a platinum or platinum-rhodium sheath surrounding Pt/Pt-Rh wires embedded in compacted magnesium oxide (MgO) or aluminum oxide (Al_2O_3). This type of sheathed thermocouple is widely used in a variety of protective furnace atmospheres and as an immersion thermocouple in the glass industry.

In general, observing the following precautions will ensure the accuracy and extend the life of thermocouples. A single length of double-bore insulating tubing should be used along the entire sheathed length of the thermoelements. Ample air space should be provided between the inner sheath and the outer tube of the double-bore tubing. If this is not practical, a type of sheathed thermocouple, such as that shown in Fig. 73, should be used. After they are placed in

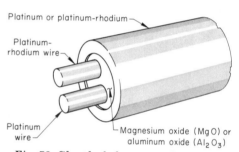

Fig. 73. Sheathed thermocouple consisting of a platinum or platinum-rhodium sheath surrounding Pt/Pt-Rh wires embedded in compacted magnesium oxide or aluminum oxide

service, thermocouples should be disturbed as little as possible, and their mountings should provide for uniform movement of the thermocouple wires when they expand or contract.

ANALYSIS AND PREVENTION OF SERVICE FAILURES: PRODUCTS OF PRINCIPAL METALWORKING PROCESSES

CONTENTS

Failures of Cold Formed Parts

THE TERM "cold formed" can have a broad meaning, depending largely on the products or product forms to which it is applied. The principal restriction is that cold forming applies to forming below the recrystallization temperature of the specific metal — most often, at or near room temperature when forming begins. Depending mainly on the severity of forming, the temperature of the work metal may increase as much as several hundred degrees Fahrenheit during the forming operation. In some instances heat is applied to the work metal before forming begins, to increase its formability.

Some metals (certain magnesium alloys, for example) have poor formability at room temperature, but formability is greatly increased by preheating to temperatures as low as 120 C (250 F). Sometimes, higher preheating temperatures are used — often as high as 425 C (800 F), but sometimes higher for forming some of the more difficult-to-form alloys. This practice is arbitrarily termed as "warm forming" or "hot forming".

Flat rolled materials (sheet, strip and plate) and wire are the product forms most often used to produce cold formed parts, although bars, bar shapes, and extrusions are other product forms commonly subjected to cold forming. Springs are the product most commonly formed from wire; springs are dealt with in a separate article beginning on page 487 in this volume. Examples in the present article are confined to products produced from flat rolled metal.

Unique Characteristics That Relate to Failure. In general, parts produced by cold forming are susceptible to the same causes of service failure as are parts produced from the same metal compositions

but by other shaping processes. There are, however, some unique characteristics of cold formed parts that may influence their susceptibility to failure.

First, cold forming of any metal part deforms the grains; the amount of deformation depends on the severity of forming. Severe deformation of the grains in locations of sharp bends or where the metal has become stretched, as in deep drawn parts, results in a condition that is more vulnerable to failure from mechanisms such as corrosion and fatigue. Susceptibility to corrosion is easily demonstrated by observing simple parts formed from low-carbon steel and exposed to the weather. Almost always it will be observed that the severely deformed areas will rust before areas on the same part that have been subjected to little or no deformation. This condition prevails even when there are no signs of cracks in severely deformed areas. Thus, it follows that severely deformed areas are extremely susceptible to stress corrosion.

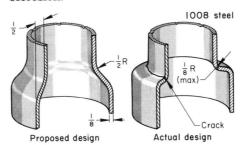

Cracking occurred because the generously radiused fillet in the proposed design was reduced during die maintenance to improve metal flow over the die ring. The sharper-radius fillet in the actual design acted as a stress raiser.

Fig. 1. Drawn 1008 steel container that failed by fatigue cracking that originated at a sharp-radius fillet

Frequently, there are fine cracks in certain areas of formed parts where deformation was severe. Although for many applications such cracks are harmless, they help to accelerate any type of corrosion, and they also will initiate fatigue cracks if the part is subjected to repeated stress.

Sharp radii or lack of generous fillets in drawn parts sometimes leads to failure. This occurred for the drawn container illustrated in Fig. 1. Although the engineering drawing for this container showed a large radius at the fillet at the change in diameters and a relatively long transition ("Proposed design" in Fig. 1), the dimensions were not specific. During routine die maintenance to improve metal flow over the die ring, the die radius was reduced to about 1/8 in. and the transition was shortened, as shown in the "Actual design" view in Fig. 1. This resulted in a sharp fillet along the most highly stressed location on the step: The sharp fillet had no effect on short-time hydrostatic strength; however, it constituted a stress raiser at which a fatigue crack initiated and propagated as a result of pressure fluctuations (see Fig. 1). After a number of such containers had accumulated a large number of pressure cycles, field failures were encountered because of fatigue cracks through the wall of the container. Corrective action included enlarging the die radius and instructing the incoming-inspection department that the radius in question must be checked on all new parts.

Other characteristics that are generally unique to cold formed parts include certain types of tool marks — specifically, indentations at inside bend radii, scoring that may occur during deep drawing or forming, and scoring on outer surfaces such as often occurs when forming in a press brake using V-dies.

The common orange-peel effect (which results when a very coarse-grained metal is stressed beyond its yield strength) increases vulnerability to corrosion, and can help to initiate fatigue cracks if the part is subjected to repeated stress.

Corner thinning causes concentration of stress flow lines at corners, which may help to cause failure by one or more mechanisms.

Another unique characteristic of cold formed parts involves local areas that have become severely work hardened, such as those areas that have been thinned by stretching or localized compression. Such areas are vulnerable to stress cracking.

Many formed parts are plated to protect them from corrosion. This often causes difficulties, because the open areas of the part where there was little or no deformation usually receive the thickest plating whereas severely formed areas may be plating-starved (the inside corners of a box-shaped part, for example). Thus, some formed parts are more susceptible to various forms of corrosion simply because the more vulnerable areas were not sufficiently protected.

Prevention of Failures. To a great extent, measures for preventing failures in formed parts are not different from the generally well-known preventive or corrective measures employed for parts that were shaped by other means; such measures include alloy-composition changes, design changes, elimination of surface discontinuities, and use of (or change of) heat treating procedures.

There are, however, because of the unique characteristics of formed parts discussed above, some preventive procedures that apply for forming parts from flat rolled metal. Regardless of the metal being formed, there are several interrelated factors concerned with selecting the metal for formability. This subject is discussed in detail in various articles in Volume 1 of this Handbook. It is essential, not only for manufacturing reasons, but also for prevention of failure in service, that the grade of metal be selected for maximum formability.

Grain size is of special importance, and generally increases in degree of importance as the metal being formed becomes thinner. As a rule, the finer the grain, the better the formability. In some instances of coarse-grained metal, the locations where forming was the most severe may have only a very few highly deformed grains in a given cross section. Therefore, it is important to select a fine-grained metal, but this is not always sufficient; it may be necessary to follow forming with full annealing (recrystallization), or at least with a stress-relieving heat treatment.

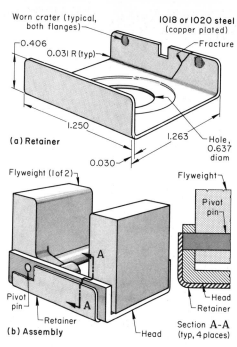

Fig. 2. Fatigue-fractured low-carbon steel retainer (a) for the pivot pins of a flyweight assembly (b) used in an aircraft-engine governor (Example 1)

Certain precautions must be taken in specifying a recrystallization-annealing treatment because of the possibility of producing very large grains, which may result in undesirable properties for some applications. Example 6 discusses a failure that was caused by a recrystallized structure containing some very large grains. Here, critical strain for recrystallization was achieved near the neutral axis in a cold bent tube; subsequent solution annealing caused huge grains to grow in the region of critical strain. Besides regions near the neutral axis in tube bends, critical strain is achieved (a) in the transition region from a bend radius to a straight section in parts formed from sheet, strip or wire; (b) near the neutral axis in some bent structural shapes such as I-beams or channels; and (c) in some deep drawn parts. Information on recrystallized structures and the prevention of excessive grain growth may be found in the articles beginning on pages 221 and 225 in Volume 8 of this Handbook.

Various metals have their own specific peculiarities. For instance, in forming of certain stainless steels or iron-base heat-resisting alloys, severe forming encourages grain-boundary carbide precipitation if the metal is reheated to a temperature within the sensitizing-temperature range (399 to 871 C; 750 to 1600 F). In the sensitized condition, the metal is extremely vulnerable to stress-corrosion cracking (see Example 2). Such a condition can be corrected only by the use of a recrystallizing anneal after forming, or it can be avoided by using a grade of

stainless steel that is less susceptible to sensitization.

The six examples that follow describe difficulties encountered, and corrective measures taken or recommended, for parts formed from carbon steel, a heat-resisting alloy, silicon bronze, and aluminum alloys.

Example 1. Fatigue Failure of a Low-Carbon Steel Channel-Shaped Retainer Because of Vibration (Fig. 2)

The governor on an aircraft engine failed and was returned to the manufacturer to determine the cause of failure. Upon disassembly of the unit, it was discovered that the retainer for the flyweight pivot pins (see Fig. 2) was broken.

The channel-shaped retainer (Fig. 2a) was made of 0.030-in.-thick 1018 or 1020 steel. The part was plated with copper, which acted as a stop-off during carburizing of the offset, circular thrust-bearing surface surrounding the 0.637-in.-diam hole (Fig. 2a). The surface was case hardened to a depth of 0.002 to 0.005 in., then austempered to obtain a minimum hardness of 600 Knoop (1-kg load).

Considerable vibration was created in the installation because of the design of the mechanical device used to transmit power to the governor. Figure 2(b) illustrates how the pivot pins for the flyweight were retained. The pins were permitted to slide axially through a small amplitude. The sources of stress were vibration and centrifugal force, which hammered the pins against the retainer.

Investigation. Part of one flange broke completely off the retainer, as shown in Fig. 2(a). The characteristic features of the fracture surfaces on the loose piece were obliterated by severe postfailure damage. Most of the fracture surfaces on the retainer, however, suffered negligible damage subsequent to failure.

The loose piece from the retainer became engaged with some mechanical members of the governor, which resulted in failure. The pivot pin extended out against the wall of the cast aluminum housing that encased the governor and eroded away part of the wall. If the loose piece had not caused the damage that resulted in failure of the mechanism, failure could have been caused by the accumulation of aluminum chips.

Microscopic examination of the fracture surface indicated that cracking was initiated at the edge of the retainer in the area of the 0.031-in. bend radius and progressed along the bend radius approximately half the length of the part, then extended across the flange.

The 0.031-in. bend radius (approximately $1t$) acted as a stress concentrator at the point of fracture initiation.

Ductility of the metal in the retainer was found to be excellent when the remaining part of the flange was intentionally bent.

Craters 0.082 to 0.096 in. in diameter (see Fig. 2a) were formed at four locations on the retainer by the impact action of the pivot pins. In each crater there was a slight rim of jagged metal that had been extruded out of the crater, and the copper plating had been worn through at the bottom of the crater. Copper plating on the

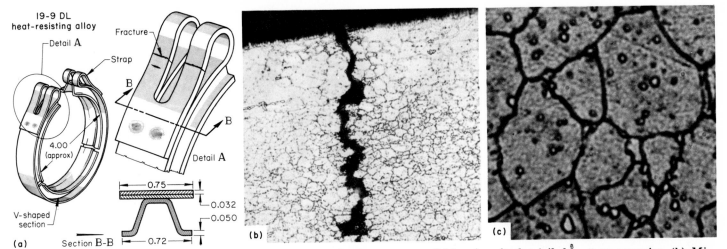

Fig. 3. (a) *Heat-resisting alloy clamp, for securing the hot ducting system on fighter aircraft, that failed by stress corrosion. (b) Micrograph, at 540×, of a section through the fracture area, showing an intergranular crack. (c) Micrograph, at 2700×, of a specimen of the work metal, showing carbide precipitation at grain boundaries and within grains. The specimens shown in micrographs (b) and (c) were etched electrolytically in oxalic acid. (Example 2)*

underface of the retainer also had been worn through by the motion between the retainer and the mating part.

On the edge of the hole in the bottom of the retainer there was evidence of motion between the shaft and retainer. Spline teeth on the shaft had formed impressions 0.005 in. deep on the edge of the hole. The wear resistance of the thrust-bearing surfaces around this hole was judged to be satisfactory, as indicated by the absence of excessive wear.

Conclusion. Failure of the retainer was the result of fatigue caused by excessive vibration in the flyweight assembly. Impact of the pivot pins on the retainer also contributed to failure.

Corrective Measures. The flyweight assembly was redesigned, and the channel-shaped retainer was replaced with a spring-clip type of pin retainer. The spring clip extended around the ends of the head and was held in place by notches in each end of the head.

Example 2. Stress-Corrosion Failure of a Strap-Type Clamp Made of 19-9 DL Heat-Resisting Alloy (Fig. 3)

The clamp shown in Fig. 3(a) was used for securing the hot ducting system on fighter aircraft. The strap was 0.032 in. thick, and the V-section was 0.050 in. thick; both were made of 19-9 DL heat-resisting alloy (0.3 C, 1.1 Mn, 0.6 Si, 19 Cr, 9 Ni, 1.25 Mo, 1.2 W, 0.4 Cb, 0.3 Ti, rem Fe). The operating temperature of the duct surrounded by the clamp was 425 to 540 C (800 to 1000 F). The life of the clamp was expected to equal that of the aircraft. After two to three years of service, the clamp fractured in the area adjacent to the slot near the end of the strap (see Fig. 3a) and was returned to the manufacturer to determine the cause of fracture.

Investigation. Micrographic examination was made of a section through the strap near the fracture area and including a secondary crack that was intergranular. This section, shown in Fig. 3(b), revealed a region of large grains at the surface that was about 0.002 in. deep. The large grains could have been the result of a sizing pass

on the hot rolled surface. Knoop microhardness values (50-gram load) were 345 (Rockwell C 25.6) for the metal in the core, and 370 (Rockwell C 28.6) for the metal near the surface.

Electrolytic etching of the work metal in oxalic acid revealed carbide precipitation at the grain boundaries (Fig. 3c) throughout the material but more prevalent in the area of large grains.

Annealing a portion of the clamp, by heating at 982 C (1800 F) and water quenching, removed the intergranular network of carbides.

Conclusions. The clamp fractured by stress-corrosion cracking because the work metal was in a sensitized condition. Sensitization occurred as a result of long-term exposure to the service temperature; the effects of sensitization were intensified as a result of cold forming. Fracture of the strap occurred along the grain boundaries, because the material was weakened by intergranular carbide precipitation.

Recommendation. Failure of the clamp could have been prevented by using a work metal that was less susceptible to intergranular carbide precipitation.

Example 3. Effect of Alloy Selection and Part Design on Stress-Corrosion Cracking of Formed Silicon Bronze in Marine-Air Atmosphere (Fig. 4)

Electrical-contact-finger retainers blanked and formed from annealed copper alloy 655 (high-silicon bronze A) failed prematurely by cracking while in service in switchgear aboard seagoing vessels. In this service, they were sheltered from the weather but were subject to indirect exposure to the sea air.

About 50% of the contact-finger retainers failed after five to eight months of service aboard ship. Figure 4(a) shows one of the contact retainers that failed and the location of the crack.

Nine contact fingers were mounted in each of the two slots of each retainer, and a bank of four to eight retainers held the electrical contacts for a typical circuit-breaker system. When a retainer cracked, the usual consequences were open circuits

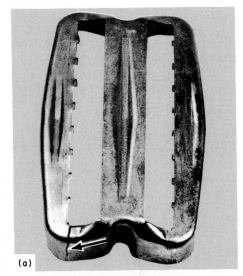

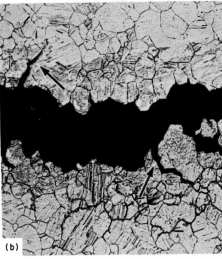

Fig. 4. (a) *Silicon bronze contact-finger retainer that failed from stress-corrosion cracking at corner (arrow) in shipboard service. (b) Microstructure of a specimen taken from failure region, showing secondary cracks (arrows). Specimen was etched in 50% NH₄OH, 50% H₂O₂ (3%); 250×. (Example 3)*

Aluminum alloys 2024 (alclad) and 6061

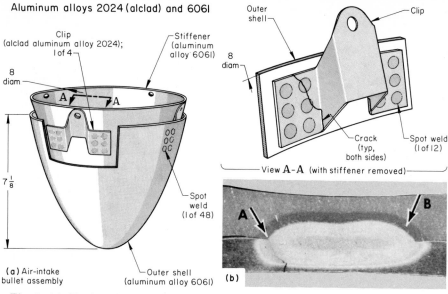

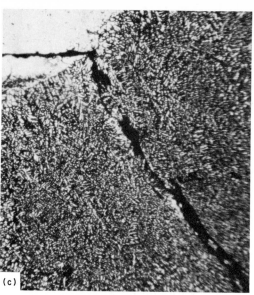

Fig. 5. (a) Engine-air-intake bullet assembly, of aluminum alloy components, that failed because of fatigue fracture of spot welded attachment clips (note typical location of cracks in view A-A). (b) Macrograph, at 10×, showing crack (at A) initiating at notch of spot weld and faying surfaces of outer shell (at top) and clip (at bottom). Also shown are excessive penetration in the clip, excessive indentation of the shell, and the large heat-affected zone (at B) in the shell. (c) Micrograph, at 150×, showing region at crack origin. Specimens in (b) and (c) were etched in Keller's reagent. (Example 4)

across some contacts, short circuits and arcing, with resultant overloading and damage to adjacent circuits as well.

Work-metal composition was found by emission spectrographic analysis of failed retainers removed from the vessels to be within the prescribed range for copper alloy 655.

Examination of Crack Region. On each defective retainer examined, a single crack was visible to the unaided eye (Fig. 4a). Each crack was on an end of the retainer, extending between an outer corner of one of the rectangular slotted openings and the periphery of the retainer, and nearly in line with the lengthwise direction of the slot.

Viewing with a low-power stereomicroscope showed that each crack had originated at a slot corner and progressed outward and through the side walls, extending almost or completely to the outermost edge of the retainer. Examination of crack regions at higher magnifications, using a light microscope, showed faceted, intergranular fracture patterns and extensive side cracking. Corrosive attack and corrosion products were not visible, and no signs of incipient cracking could be detected on the three other corners of cracked retainers by microscopic examination of the surface.

The results of the preceding examination of the cracks were confirmed by microscopic examination of polished-and-etched specimens taken from the failure regions of several of the cracked retainers. When observed at a magnification of 250 diameters, each of the specimens examined showed an intergranular crack pattern and a microstructure closely resembling that shown in Fig. 4(b).

Cause of Failure. It was concluded that the cracking was produced by stress corrosion as the combined result of (a) residual forming and service stresses, (b) the concentration of tensile stress at outer square corners of the pierced slots, and (c) preferential corrosion attack along the grain

boundaries as a result of high humidity and occasional condensation of moisture containing a fairly high concentration of chlorides (seawater typically contains about 19,000 ppm of dissolved chlorides) and traces of ammonia. Exposure to significant concentrations of ammonia and other corrodents could also have occurred while the vessels were in harbor in industrial locations.

The absence of general surface attack, and the formation of faceted, intergranular fracture patterns and extensive side or branch cracking, were consistent with the characteristic pattern for failure by stress-corrosion cracking for this alloy.

The occurrence of cracking on only one corner of a retainer apparently reflected a characteristically uneven distribution of stress on the four corners on the workpiece during forming and in service, by which one corner was more highly stressed than the three others. Cracking on one corner appeared to relieve the stress on the other corners.

Corrective Measures. Three changes were made to improve the resistance of the contact-finger retainers to stress-corrosion cracking. The slots were redesigned to have inside corner radii of $\frac{1}{8}$ in., to reduce the stress concentration associated with the square corners in the original design, and the formed retainers were shot blasted to remove uneven surface tensile stresses and put the surface layer in compression.

In addition, the work metal was changed to a different type of silicon bronze — namely, copper alloy 647. This alloy has a nominal alloying content of 2% nickel and 0.6% silicon, instead of the nominal 3% silicon content in the alloy 655 originally used for the contact-finger retainers.

Selection of copper alloy 647 was made on the basis of tests for formability and resistance to stress-corrosion cracking (moist ammonia atmosphere) done by the manufacturer on contact-finger retainers after the service failures were encountered.

All of the alloy 655 retainers in shipboard service were replaced with retainers made to the improved design, using alloy 647. The parts were blanked and formed in the solution heat treated and 37% cold reduced temper (as-purchased condition), aged after forming, and then shot blasted.

Over a period of several years, only a few isolated stress-corrosion-cracking failures of the replacement retainers were observed, and these occurred on other types of ships where there was exposure to high concentrations of ammonia and high humidity.

Discussion. Of various copper alloys considered for the retainers, all except alloy 647 had to be formed in the annealed temper, with consequent lower strength and excessively unbalanced stress distribution, whereas alloy 647 could be formed without difficulty in the half-hard (37% cold reduced) condition. Retainers made from alloy 647, although not completely immune from stress-corrosion cracking in the tests by the manufacturer, were much less susceptible to this type of failure than retainers made from alloy 655.

The excellent formability of 37% cold reduced alloy 647 was a key factor in the successful use of this alloy for the retainers. Cold reduction, either alone or in combination with artificial aging, has been found in other investigations (J. A. Whittaker, "A Survey on the Stress Corrosion of Copper Based Alloys", published by International Copper Research Assn.; and Robertson, Grenier, Davenport and Nole, p 273-294 in AIME Metallurgical Society Symposium on Physical Metallurgy of Stress Corrosion Fracture, 1959) to minimize the susceptibility of alloy 647 and other silicon bronzes to stress-corrosion cracking. Better resistance as annealed and greater improvement by cold reduction were found for alloy 647 than for alloy 655.

Plastic deformation produced slip planes, lattice rotation and curved bands in the grains, thus providing many new sites for ttack that were "blind alley" paths for preferential corrosion. These alternate paths allowed only limited penetration of the new sites and also decreased corrosion attack at grain boundaries.

Example 4. Fatigue Failure of an Aluminum Alloy Assembly at Spot Welds Because of Improper Heat Treatment (Fig. 5)

Postflight inspection of a gas-turbine aircraft engine that had experienced compressor stall revealed that the engine-air-intake bullet assembly shown in Fig. 5(a) had dislodged and was seated against the engine-inlet guide vanes at the 3 o'clock position. The engine was restarted, operated at 95% rotational speed, and immediately shut off when the port fire-warning light came on.

Compressor stall (surge) is a condition that can occur in engines that are improperly adjusted or have been abused. Repeated conditions of surge during operation, which this particular engine had experienced, and the attendant transient vibratory loads can cause extensive damage to the engine components.

The bullet assembly consisted of an outer shell and a stiffener (inner shell), both of 0.050-in.-thick aluminum alloy 6061 specified to be in the T6 temper and to have hardness of Rockwell 15-T 76 to 84, and four attachment clips, of 0.040-in.-thick alclad aluminum alloy 2024 specified to be in the T42 temper and to have hardness of Rockwell 15-T 78 to 84. Each clip was joined to the outer shell by 12 spot welds (see Fig. 5a), and was also joined to the stiffener (by spot welds not shown in Fig. 5). Service life of the assembly was about 680 hr.

Investigation. The outer shell of the assembly had separated from the stiffener, because of fracture of the four attachment clips through the shell-to-clip spot welds (see view A-A in Fig. 5a).

Visual examinations of the fracture surfaces, both with the unaided eye and with a low-power binocular microscope, were not definitive, because the legs of the clip that were attached to the shell were severely mutilated, indicating a large degree of relative movement between the clip and the shell either during or subsequent to complete separation.

Dye-penetrant inspection of the assembly revealed cracks in the clip spot welds on the shell, adjacent to the fractures, and also in the spot welds joining the clip to the stiffener. Microscopic examination of sections through the cracked spot welds revealed that the cracks had originated at the edge of the weld nugget and at the faying surfaces of the shell and the clip, as shown in Fig. 5(b) and (c). The shape of the weld nugget at this point created a region of peak stress. The cracks propagated through the spot weld and progressed in a transgranular manner through the clip.

The microstructure of the aluminum alloy 6061 in the shell and stiffener, combined with a hardness of Rockwell 15-T 50 to 52 (required: Rockwell 15-T 76 to 84) indicated that the material was in the annealed (O) temper, rather than the T6 temper as specified by the engineering drawing.

The metallurgical properties of the clad aluminum alloy 2024-T42 clip were satis-factory with respect to microstructure, and to hardness (required: Rockwell 15-T 78 to 84; observed: Rockwell 15-T 81 to 84). The chemical compositions of the alloy 2024 clip and the alloy 6061 shell and stiffener were satisfactory.

As Fig. 5(b) shows, the spot welds joining the clip to the outer shell exhibited excessive penetration (0.030 in.) of the 0.040-in.-thick clip, and excessive indentation of the shell; also, a large heat-affected zone (0.010 in. deep) was present at the portion of the weld in the shell. These conditions were the result of spot welding the shell in the annealed condition. During welding, the weld zones distorted under the welding pressure and increased the contact area, which changed the current distribution and resulted in low or inconsistent weld strength.

Conclusion. The outer shell of the bullet assembly separated from the stiffener because the four attachment clips fractured through the shell-to-clip spot welds. Fracture occurred by fatigue that initiated at the notch created by the intersection of the faying surfaces of the clip and shell with the spot weld nuggets. The 6061 aluminum alloy shell and stiffener were in the annealed (O) temper, rather than T6 as specified. This resulted in excessive penetration and indentation during spot welding and was a contributing factor in the bullet-assembly failure.

Recommendations. The shell and stiffener should have been heat treated to the T6 temper after forming. A review of the spot welding operation also may have been desirable; in this review, the size and shape of the electrode face that made contact with the shell and stiffener should have been considered, as well as the magnitudes of welding current and of current-on time.

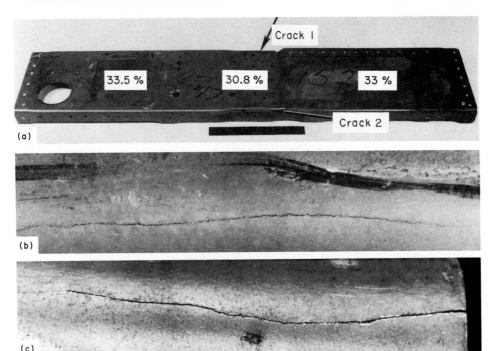

(a) Deck plate, at about 15% of actual size, showing location of cracks at opposing flange joggles. Percentages are IACS values of electrical conductivity as measured at three locations. (b) Detail of crack 1 in the plate, at 2×. (c) Detail of crack 2 in the plate, at 3×.

Fig. 6. Aircraft deck plate, formed from aluminum alloy 7178-T6, that failed in service by fatigue cracking (Example 5)

Example 5. Aluminum Alloy 7178-T6 Aircraft Deck Plate That Failed in Service by Fatigue Cracking (Fig. 6)

Two cracks were discovered in a deck plate of an aircraft during overhaul and repair after 659 hr of service. As shown in Fig. 6, the cracks were on opposite sides of the deck plate in the flange joggles. The plate had been formed from 7178-T6 aluminum alloy sheet.

Visual Examination. Inspection of the deck plate disclosed that the fastener holes adjacent to each crack (five holes transverse to and three holes parallel to the length of the plate, as shown in Fig. 6) had been slightly elongated.

The deck plate was cut to expose the crack surfaces, and several fracture origins were found, all adjacent to the undersurface of the deck plate. The evidence indicated that both cracks had initiated in the inner curve of the flange joggles.

Metallurgical Examination. The crack surfaces were replicated by a two-stage plastic-carbon technique, with chromium shadowing at 45°. The predominant features of electron-microscope fractographs made of the replicas were fatigue striations at the fracture origins.

Microscopic examination of sections through the fractures showed that fracture had been transgranular and that several secondary transgranular cracks existed in the curved inner surface of the flange. These were parallel with the main cracks and originated from surface defects. These defects could have been shallow corrosion pits, perhaps produced during cleaning, or could have been notches originating in the forming operation — the examination did not determine which. In other respects, the structure was normal in both areas.

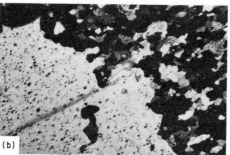

Fig. 7. (a) "Blowout" in an aluminum alloy 6061-T6 connector tube from a water-cooling system that appears to involve the loss of a single large grain. (b) Micrograph at 65× of the structure near the neutral axis of the bend; the huge grain at lower left (light area) occupied almost the entire wall thickness of the tube and was 0.2 to 0.3 in. long. (Example 6)

The condition of the plate was checked by hardness tests and by measurements of electrical conductivity. Hardness values ranged from Rockwell B 92 to 93. The electrical-conductivity values extended from 30.8 to 33% IACS, as shown in Fig. 6(a). The values for both hardness and electrical conductivity were satisfactory, indicating that the deck plate had been properly heat treated.

Conclusions. The following conclusions were drawn concerning the cause of failure of the deck plate:

1 The failure was caused by fatigue cracks originating in the inside curved surface of the flanges.
2 The fatigue cracks had initiated in surface defects caused by either corrosion pitting or forming notches, acting in combination with lateral forces evidenced by the moderate distortion of the fastener holes.

Recommendations. The following steps were recommended to prevent further cracking of deck plates:

1 Eliminate the surface defects by revised cleaning and/or forming procedures.
2 Alleviate the lateral forces by reviewing the design and making appropriate revisions.

Example 6. Failure by Blowout of Aluminum Alloy 6061-T6 Connector Tubes From a Water-Cooling System (Fig. 7)

Several of the aluminum alloy 6061-T6 drawn seamless tubes connecting an array of headers to a system of water-cooling pipes failed from causes described as "blowouts", circumferential tears, and longitudinal cracks. The aluminum alloy was supplied to conform with the requirements of ASTM B235-52T, GS11A, chemical specification, but at present would be covered by ASTM B234.

The tubes were 1.0-in.-OD tubes with a wall thickness of 0.65 in., and were supplied in the O temper. They were bent to the desired curvature (approximately 2½-in. centerline bend radius), preheated at 510 C (950 F) for ½ hr, and then solution treated for ½ hr at 520 C (970 F) and water quenched. They were then aged at 177 ± 3 C (350 ± 5 F) for 8 to 10 hr. Before shipment, the tubes were pressure tested at 1000 psi and dimensionally inspected.

Visual Examination. Some of the tubes failed by "blowout" of a section of the wall; some blowouts produced edges with sharp cleavage planes typical of a shear failure in a single crystal. Figure 7(a) shows an exam-

ple believed to involve the loss of a single large grain. The edges of other blowouts were rough and jagged, as though caused by rapid fatigue. All tube blowouts were found in, or adjacent to, the bends, and in most instances cracks extended from the blowouts through the full wall thickness. The size of the blowouts varied from about ⅛ by ⅜ in. to a maximum of ¾ by 2 in.

Other failures involved circumferential tears in which the fractures were extremely ragged and appeared to follow the boundaries between very large grains and adjacent very small ones; these fractures also were associated with tube bends. Incipient failures were also discovered in the form of both longitudinal and circumferential cracks that varied in size from a small fraction of an inch to several inches along the tube length, in or close to the bends.

The tubes exhibited a number of defects on the internal surface, including striations, cold shuts, hairline cracks emanating from cold shuts, and both circumferential and longitudinal cracks in the bends. It appeared that the tubes as-received possessed numerous stress raisers in the inner surface.

Macroetching revealed that the structure of the tubes had completely recrystallized in heat treatment. The macrostructure of the straight sections was uniformly fine-grained. In the bends there were exceedingly large grains in regions near the neutral axis, in some cases adjacent to very small grains. The size of the very large grains was commensurate with the postulate that some of the blowouts involved single grains that occupied the full wall thickness of the tube.

Laboratory Investigations. Spectrographic analysis of six specimens revealed that the tubes conformed to the ASTM specification except for the magnesium content, which ranged from 1.1 to 1.3%. This degree of excess beyond the specified range of 0.8 to 1.2% Mg did not appear to be serious or to explain the failures.

Rockwell hardness tests, microhardness tests and tension tests of material from the failed tubes gave results that were typical of aluminum alloy 6061-T6. However, flattening tests on the tubing (using strip specimens cut from the tubing), slow-bend tests, notched bend tests, and a bend test in which the specimens were bent by hand around a relatively small radius, indicated that the tubing material was notch sensitive and had a type of low ductility that had not been

detected in the tension tests. Specimens aluminum alloy 6061-T6 sheet were n notch sensitive and had a much great ductility in all the bend tests.

Microscopic examination confirmed th presence of extremely coarse grains in th bends of the tube connectors, in contrast a uniformly fine grain size in the straig sections. In some instances, coarse grai were measured as large as 0.2 to 0.5 in. diameter. The evidence indicated that th bending operation achieved a critical de gree of strain near the neutral axis of th tube. With less than this amount of strai no grain growth would occur on heating t the solution treatment temperature, as wa the case with some of the neutral-axi grains. Regions receiving the critical strai or slightly more would experience maxi mum grain growth on solution treatmen The portions of the tube at 90° to the neu tral axis received the maximum amount o cold work and therefore recrystallized bu did not undergo any appreciable chang in grain size. The wide variation in grai sizes observed near the neutral axis i illustrated in Fig. 7(b).

Conclusions. The following deduction were made concerning the connector-tub failures:

1 The bending of the connector tubes in th annealed condition induced critical strai near the neutral axis of a tube, which re sulted in excessive growth of individua grains during the subsequent solutio treatment.
2 The wide variation in grain size within th bends was considered unfavorable for re sistance to flexural fatigue.
3 The procedures used in fabricating the con nectors created many defects on the interio surfaces, which were potential stress raiser and possible origins of fracture.
4 The specific cause of the notch sensitivit and brittle behavior was not evident excep insofar as discontinuities on the inside sur face and the heterogeneous grain size ma have been contributing factors. In any event, the slow-bend tests offered a means of detecting notch-sensitive material on a sampling basis.

Corrective Measures. The following measures were adopted to ensure freedom from further connector-tube failures:

1 The connector tubes were bent in the T4 temper, as early as possible after being quenched from the solution temperature. The tubes were stored in dry ice after the quench until bending could be done. The tubes were aged immediately after being formed.
2 Flattening and slow-bend tests were specified to ensure that the connector tubes had satisfactory ductility.
3 Macroetching of random samples was instituted, and a limit on the maximum acceptable grain size was imposed.
4 Limits were placed on the number and size of permissible surface defects.

Representative samples of connector tubes supplied under the revised specifications were sectioned and examined metallographically. It was determined that the new tubes had a uniformly fine grain size, throughout the entire length. The grain size in the bends of the new tubes was two to three times as fine as the grain size in the straight sections of the original tubes.

The improved quality of the new connector tubes was effective in securing trouble-free operation.

Failures of Forgings

By Vito J. Colangelo and Peter A. Thornton*

A FORGING is a metal mass that has been worked or wrought to a configuration attained by controlled plastic deformation, by hammering, pressing, upsetting, rolling, extruding, or by a combination of two or more of these processes. Forgings may be produced from many metals and their alloys, including aluminum, copper, steel, titanium, heat-resisting alloys, and refractory metals. Forgings range in size from large open-die forgings to minute close-tolerance, no-draft forgings such as those used in making instruments. Forgings may be produced by hot working, warm working, cold striking or coining. The information in this article, however, deals principally with forgings produced by hot working.

When a metal part is hot worked, the individual grains are deformed; the deformed grains then immediately begin to recrystallize — that is, break up and form new grains. The hotter the metal, the more plastic it is and the more easily it deforms. At excessively high temperatures, however, grain growth, incipient melting, phase transformation and changes in composition occur.

At lower hot forging temperatures, the metal is more difficult to forge; however, the grain size that results may be finer and the metal may have better mechanical properties. If the forging temperature is reduced still further, below the recrystallization temperature, the deformed grains will not break up and form new grains, but instead will remain deformed. When the metal is in this condition, cracking may occur.

Imperfections From the Ingot

Except for forged powder metallurgy parts, all forgings originate from cast ingots. Many large open-die forgings are forged directly from ingots. Most closed-die and upset forgings are produced from billets, rolled bar stock, or preforms. Regardless of the number of hot working operations that take place, many of the imperfections found in forgings, and problems that occur in service, can be attributed to conditions that existed in the ingot.

* Dr. Colangelo is Senior Metallurgist, and Mr. Thornton is Materials Engineer, with Advanced Engineering Div., Benet Weapons Laboratory, Watervliet Arsenal.

Several examples in this article are based on reports from contributors other than the authors.

Segregation. The elements in a cast alloy are seldom distributed uniformly. Even unalloyed metals contain random amounts of various types of impurities in the form of tramp elements or dissolved gases; these impurities likewise are seldom distributed uniformly. Thus, the composition of the metal or alloy will vary from location to location. Deviation from the mean composition at a particular location in a forging is an imperfection termed segregation. In general, segregation is the result of solute rejection at the solidification interface during casting. For instance, gradation of composition with respect to the individual alloying elements exists from the cores of dendrites to the interdendritic regions. Segregation thereby produces a material having a range of compositions that do not have identical properties.

Forging can partly correct the results of segregation by recrystallizing or breaking up the grain structure to promote a more homogeneous substructure; however, the effects of a badly segregated ingot cannot be totally eliminated.

The presence of localized regions in metals that deviate from the nominal composition can affect corrosion resistance, forging and joining (welding) characteristics, mechanical properties, fracture toughness and fatigue resistance. In heat treatable alloys, variations in the composition can produce unexpected responses to heat treatments that result in hard or soft spots, quench cracks or other defects. The degree of degradation depends on the alloy plus a number of processing variables. Most metallurgical processes operate on the basis that the metal composition is nominal and reasonably uniform.

Ingot Pipe. Another common imperfection in ingots is the shrinkage cavity, commonly known as pipe, often found in the upper portion of the ingot. During freezing of the metal, shrinkage occurs and eventually there is insufficient liquid metal near the top end to feed the ingot. As a result, a cavity forms, usually approximating the shape of a cylinder or cone — hence, the term "pipe". To improve the feeding characteristics of the metal, hot tops (insulating refractories or exothermic materials) are employed, especially during the late stages of solidification. This technique keeps the metal in the hot-top region liquid as long as possible, thereby minimizing this shrinkage in the upper portion of the ingot.

Forging Bursts. During forging operations, substantial tensile stresses are produced in addition to the applied compressive stress. Where the material is weak, possibly from pipe, porosity, segregation or inclusions, the tensile stresses can be sufficiently high to tear the material apart internally, particularly if the forging temperature is too high (Ref 2). Such imperfections are known as forging bursts. Similarly, if the metal contains low-melting phases resulting from segregation, these phases may rupture during forging.

High hydrogen content in steel originates from moisture entrapped during melting and casting. The presence of hydrogen in steel forgings can produce defects called flakes. These are small cracks opened up by hydrogen that has diffused into grain boundaries and into boundaries between inclusions and the matrix. However, the metal can often possess a high hydrogen content without the presence of voids or flakes. In this instance, the hydrogen causes embrittlement of the metal along selective paths, which can drastically reduce the resistance of a forged part to crack propagation resulting from impact, fatigue or stress corrosion.

Nonmetallic inclusions, which originate in the ingot, are likely to be carried on to the forgings, even though several intermediate hot working operations may be involved. Also, additional inclusions (specifically, oxides) may develop in the billet or in subsequent forging stages.

Two kinds of nonmetallic inclusions are generally distinguished in metals: (a) those that are entrapped in the metal inadvertently, and which originate almost exclusively from particles of matter that are occluded in the metal while it is molten or being cast; and (b) those inclusions that separate from the metal because of a change in temperature or composition (Ref 1). Inclusions of the latter type are produced by separation from the metal when it is in either the liquid or the solid state. Oxides, sulfides, nitrides or other nonmetallic compounds form droplets or particles, when these compounds are produced in such amounts that their solubility in the matrix is exceeded. Because these compounds are products of reactions within the metal, they are normal constituents of it and conventional melting practices cannot *completely* eliminate such inclusions. However, it is desirable to keep

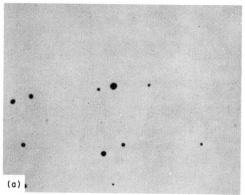
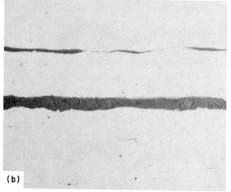
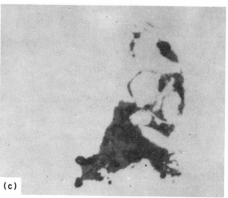

Fig. 1. Typical nonmetallic inclusions found in steels. (a) Oxide inclusions in cast low-alloy steel; magnification, 100×. (b) Large non-metallic stringer-type inclusions in low-carbon steel; magnification, 75×. (c) Complex inclusion showing extreme irregularities in shape; magnification, 1000×. All of these specimens were unetched.

the type and amount of inclusions to a minimum so that the metal is relatively free from those that cause the most problems. Typical nonmetallic inclusions found in steels are illustrated in Fig. 1.

Of the numerous types of imperfections encountered in forgings, nonmetallic inclusions appear to be the most frequent cause of service failures. In many applications, it is the presence of these inclusions that lowers the properties of a metal to withstand applied loads, impact forces, cyclical or fatigue loading, and sometimes corrosion and stress corrosion. Nonmetallic inclusions can easily become stress concentrators because of their discontinuous nature and incompatibility with the surrounding composition. This combination may very well yield a flaw of critical size that, under appropriate loading conditions, results in complete fracture of the forged part.

Anisotropy Caused by Forging

Preferred orientations can develop when a metal is plastically deformed by mechanical working. Preferred orientations consist of (a) crystallographic texturing, produced by crystallographic reorientation of the grains during severe deformation; and (b) mechanical fibering, which is brought about by the alignment of nonmetallic inclusions, voids, chemical segregation, and second-phase constituents in the main direction of mechanical working (Ref 3). Both types of preferred orientations cause the mechanical and physical properties of a metal to exhibit different properties in different directions (anisotropy).

Direct metallographic evidence of mechanical fibering is often present in the form of slag stringers in wrought iron, or in the form of pearlite banding, elongated grain structures, and flow lines in steels, which are revealed by deep etching the forging (Ref 4). Whenever any of these obvious displays of structural anisotropy are observed, there are usually measurable differences in strength and duc-

tility in test specimens that are oriented parallel and transverse to the direction of working.

Probably the most dramatic evidence for mechanical-fibering effect is in the area of fracture phenomena — that is, those that occur in laboratory testing, service failures, or during deformation in processing. Anisotropy of fracturing in wrought products is extremely widespread, occurring in both ductile and brittle materials and including some that are essentially pure metals. The literature contains numerous reports of investigations concerning anisotropy and mechanical properties. The results of a few of the more specific investigations are reported in Ref 5 to 8.

Mechanical Defects Caused by Forging

Forging can produce mechanical defects, such as laps and seams. Laps, which are also called folds, occur as the result of a protrusion of hot metal being folded over and forged into the surface. The oxide present on the internal surface of the lap, or fold, prevents the metal in the crevice from joining. A discontinuity with a sharp root is thus created, resulting in stress concentration.

Seams are similar to laps in nature and effect. They appear as closed-up surface cracks and are attributable to hot surface tears in the original ingot and to embedded scale that has been torn out leaving a cavity with oxidized walls. Seams may also result from defects in the ingot, such as blowholes near the surface that become oxidized and thus are prevented from healing during further work. Seams are difficult to detect on certain types of forgings.

Internal discontinuities in forgings caused by faulty forging techniques often appear as cracks or tears, and they may result either from forging with too light a hammer or from continuing forging after the metal has cooled down below a safe forging temperature.

Causes of Failure in Forgings

A failure in a forging may have been caused by material characteristics, deficiencies in design, improper processing or fabrication, or deterioration resulting from service conditions.

Analysis of the failure to determine the causes responsible can provide an insight into design problems or material limitations so that corrective measures can be applied and future problems eliminated.

The failure may be attributable to one of several fundamental mechanisms — brittle fracture, fatigue, wear or corrosion. The failure may result from the independent action of any of these mechanisms, but most often the final failure results from the combined action, either simultaneously or sequentially, of more than one mechanism. This is demonstrated in the examples of failure analysis presented throughout this article.

Relationship of Design and Failure

Few industrial products are designed to last forever; some are purposely designed to serve for relatively short periods of time (Ref 9). However, one of the first design decisions to be made when any new item is being considered for production is its expected service life. Later, when the item has passed through the various stages of development and production into service, one of the considerations that will determine if it is a successful design or not is whether it actually achieves this intended life.

Failures of a product are generally distributed over a period of time and follow a pattern. Initially, the rate of failure is high, followed by, in successful designs, a longer period during which failures occur at a low and fairly regular level. Finally, the rate of failure rises steadily. Therefore, with a product that is produced in quantity, the occasional failure of different parts may not be cause for serious concern, but repeated failures of a particular component usually indicate a design weakness or faulty manufacturing technique.

Investigations into the failure of forgings usually reveal that more than one basic mechanism has contributed to the over-all failure. For instance, fluctuating stresses may result in the development of a fatigue crack that ultimately leads to failure. With this relationship in mind, failures associated with design may be broadly classed under the following headings:

1 Basic faults in design concept
2 Employment of wrong materials
3 Improper specification of welding design and procedure
4 Fatigue due to stress raisers
5 Neglect of the factors associated with brittle fracture and fatigue fracture
6 Lack of consideration for operating environment (may result in corrosion fatigue and stress-corrosion cracking)
7 Neglect in the provision of suitable fittings and safety devices in the detailed design.

Role of Stress Concentration. Fatigue fractures due to the stress-concentrating effects of sharp corners, small radii and abrupt changes in section size constitute a large percentage of design-induced failures. Parts and assemblies usually contain notches, fillets, holes and similar irregularities that concentrate and increase stress. Machined components may have severe stress raisers formed by tool tears. Even ordinary tool marks can result in serious damage to a component if they occur in a region of high stress, such as a fillet (Ref 10). The pattern of varying stresses across a notched cylinder in tension is shown in Fig. 2. The longitudinal and tangential normal stresses (σ_L and σ_T) and the maximum shear stress (τ_{max}) peak at the root of the

notch, while the radial normal stress (σ_R) peaks below the root of the notch. More-severe notches intensify these maximums. Thus the presence of any notch, whether intentional or accidental, must be carefully considered because service stresses are usually highest at the surface.

Just below the base of the notch, the maximum shear stress drops to a low level (Fig. 2). Therefore, when plastic flow begins at the root surface of a notch, an even greater degree of triaxiality occurs. This is due to additional tangential and radial restraint, causing an increased σ/τ ratio just below the notch surface. Under a static load, highly stressed metal yields plastically at a notch root or hole edge, thereby conveying the high stresses on to other sections until fracture occurs. However, under fatigue or repeated loads most of the material is stressed below its elastic limit, yielding locally on a much smaller scale. Then, highly localized deformation may start a crack before the stress pattern changes to relieve concentrated stresses.

In the next example, fatigue cracking that originated at a sharp fillet illustrates the effect of stress raisers in forgings.

Example 1. Fatigue Fracture of a 4150 Steel Plunger Shaft That Initiated at a Sharp Fillet (Fig. 3)

Plunger shafts of breechblock assemblies for 40-mm guns were involved in a series of fracture failures. The fractures consistently occurred at two different locations on the shafts, both of which are shown in Fig. 3(a) — the shaft fillet (arrow at A) and either side of a machined notch (arrows at B). The material specification for the shafts required 41xx series steel with a carbon content of 0.38 to 0.53%, a hardness of Rockwell C 35 to 40 for the shaft, and a hardness of Rockwell C 50 to 55 for the notch (which was case hardened).

The plunger was subjected to sliding and torque when the breechblock mechanism was actuated. This motion probably resulted in some bending loads. Also, the loads were cyclically imposed when the gun was fired.

Investigation. Chemical analysis of the shaft material showed it to be of 4150 steel and within the required range of chemical composition. The hardness was measured as Rockwell C 30 to 34 on the shaft and 50 to 55 on the notch.

Inspection of a fracture surface at site A (Fig. 3b) revealed the classical beach marks indicative of fatigue loading. The curvature of these marks implied that some torsional loading was also involved. A large number of ratchet marks appear at the outer edge of the fracture surface, which indicates multiple fatigue origins with a high stress concentration due to the sharp radius. The final-fracture area is near the surface (OD) opposite the initiation site, so the stress that caused failure was probably not much above the fatigue strength of the material. This near-to-normal stress allowed for slow crack growth until fracture occurred.

Several shafts had broken at the notch. The surfaces of these fractures also had a fatigue-fracture appearance (see Fig. 3c). The fractures had originated in the sharp fillets along the edges of the notch; these fillets are indicated by arrows B in Fig. 3(a). Also evident on the fracture surface were machining marks, which had added to the stress concentration at the fillets.

Several shafts that had broken at the shaft fillet (site A) were inspected by the magnetic-particle method. Cracks were found in the fillets of the notch (sites B) in some of these shafts.

The ends of the plunger shafts, shown as C in Fig. 3(a), were significantly deformed by peening. The peening had been caused by impact of a cam against the shaft end during the sliding sequence of firing. Shaft hardness was found to be slightly lower than the minimum required by the specification, indicating improper heat treatment. However, the peening was not halting the operation of the breechblocks and was considered to be of secondary importance.

Conclusion. All the fractures were fatigue-induced failures due to sharp fillets. The stress-concentrating effects of the fillets caused fatigue cracks to initiate and grow under cyclic loading until the crack depth was critical, causing the shaft to fail and rendering the assembly inoperative.

Corrective Measure. The cause of the failures was eliminated by increasing the radii of the notch and shaft fillets, thereby reducing the effects of stress concentration to an acceptable level.

(a) Fracture sites on the plunger shaft: shaft fillet (at A), and machined notch (at B). Shaft end (at C) was deformed by peening but did not fracture. (b) Fracture surface at A, showing the characteristic beach marks of a fatigue failure. (c) Fracture surface at B, showing fatigue marks that initiated at the notch.

Fig. 3. Plunger shaft of 4150 steel that failed in service from fatigue fractures in two locations (Example 1)

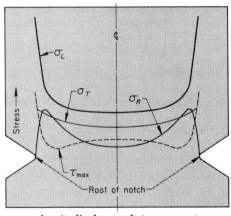

σ_L = longitudinal normal stress; σ_T = tangential normal stress; σ_R = radial normal stress; τ_{max} = maximum shear stress. The height above the notch root of any point on the curves indicates the relative magnitude of stress at that radial position.

Fig. 2. Schematic illustration of stress patterns in a notched cylinder in tension (Ref 10)

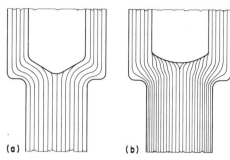

Fig. 4. Comparison of (a) desirable and (b) undesirable flow patterns in a forging

Role of Anisotropy. Anisotropy, which results from crystallographic texturing and from mechanical fibering (Ref 12), plays an important role in the final properties of forgings. Ductility, yield strength and, to a lesser extent, tensile strength, are the properties most affected by crystallographic texturing. The yield strength in the transverse direction (perpendicular to the main direction of working) usually is less than the yield strength in the longitudinal direction.

The occurrence and severity of mechanical fibering vary with the type (composition) of metal used and the amount of forging involved (Ref 13). Differences in the etching reaction of the aligned constituents will reveal flow lines associated with mechanical fibering. The flow lines in forgings should be aligned in the direction of maximum stress, because forgings exhibit the greatest strength in that direction. If this is done, the greatest stresses on a component act *along* the fibers, rather than across them. A comparison of desirable and undesirable flow patterns in a forging is shown in Fig. 4. In contrast to the pattern in Fig. 4(a), where the flow lines are mainly parallel to free surfaces, the pattern in Fig. 4(b) contains a large number of flow lines that intersect the surface at the bottom of the recess. This condition creates many potential crack-initiation sites that, under appropriate service conditions, could result in brittle or ductile fracture, fatigue fracture, or stress-corrosion cracking.

Efficient design of structural components requires the use of the lightest, least expensive materials that will safely carry the applied loads. Anisotropy therefore is an important design consideration, not only for safety reasons but also as a means of reducing the weight of a given component. For example, longitudinally oriented, forged material is more efficient from the standpoint of strength-to-weight ratio versus stress concentration than transversely oriented material from the same forging. If this efficiency can be utilized in the initial design, the best combination of material and processing is achieved.

Failures Related to Material Selection

Selection of the correct material for a particular forging is interrelated with the design. Selection of material is based on the stresses, temperature extremes, and corrosive environments to which the component will be subjected. In the following example, failure in valve stems for a cannon assembly was attributed to poor choice of material.

Example 2. Fracture of 17-4 PH Stainless Steel Poppet-Valve Stems Due to Incorrect Material Selection (Fig. 5)

A series of poppet-valve stems fabricated from 17-4 PH stainless steel (see Fig. 5) failed prematurely in service during the development of a large-bore (152-mm) cannon-tube assembly. The poppet valves were components of the scavenging system that evacuated the bore after each firing cycle. The function of the valve is to open and close a port, and thus the valve is subjected to impact and tensile loading.

Investigation. The stems had fractured in the upper threaded portion, as shown in Fig. 5. The threads of the stems exhibited slight corrosion. Also, a few thread crests were flattened, and machining scratches existed on the sides of some threads. Damaging as they were, these defects did not appear to have originated the failure.

Because the valve stem was subjected to heating from the firing cycles, the microstructure of the failed stem was compared with that of a new part, never in service. There was no significant difference between microstructures in the new and in the used stems. The microstructures were found typical of a martensitic precipitation-hardening stainless steel in the H900 condition.

Hardness was the only mechanical property that could be measured in the stems, because they were small. Requirements called for a hardness of Rockwell 15N 80 to 85. Actual values were Rockwell 15N 84.0, 81.8 and 84.5.

Finally, a stress analysis was conducted on the root of the first thread in the valve stem (region of fracture). Results of the analysis showed an approximate tensile stress of 175,000 psi. Therefore, an overstressed condition existed because the yield strength of 17-4 PH stainless steel is approximately 170,000 psi.

Conclusion and Recommendation. In service, the valve stems were impact loaded to stresses in excess of their yield strength. That they failed in the threaded portion also suggests a stress-concentration effect.

However, drastic changes in design can be avoided by selecting a higher-strength material and one with greater impact strength. For the stems, and without consideration of dimensional changes to the stems, it was recommended that they be manufactured from an alloy such as PH 13-8 Mo (H1000), which can be processed to a yield strength of 200,000 psi, with impact strengths in the order of 60 ft-lb at room temperature. Thus, a better combination of tensile and impact properties is possible, without serious loss of corrosion protection.

Failures Related to Fatigue

Forged components such as automobile axles, shafts, bolts and gears are cyclically loaded at nominal stresses that should be considerably lower than the yield strength of the material. However, unpredicted stresses in service may diminish the service life of such components by causing fatigue failures.

The progress and extent of a fatigue crack vary according to the nature and degree of loading. With alternating tension and compression or bending stresses, the crack propagates in a plane perpendicular to the principal stress. An axle journal fractured by reversed-bending fatigue is shown in Fig. 6(a). Figure 6(b) shows characteristic fatigue beach marks on the fracture surface, terminating at

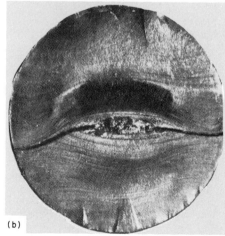

(a) Axle shaft showing fracture at the journal. (b) Fracture surface of the axle shaft showing fatigue beach marks with zone of final fast fracture near the center.

Fig. 6. Axle shaft that fractured at the journal from reversed-bending fatigue (Ref 11)

17-4 PH stainless steel
Rockwell 15N 80 to 85

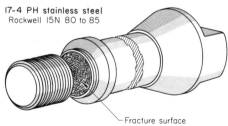

Fracture surface

Fig. 5. Stainless steel poppet-valve stem from a large-bore cannon tube that fractured in service (Example 2)

about the center of the axle shaft. A typical rotational-bending fracture surface is shown in Fig. 7. This fracture also contains evidence of a final fracture when fatigue cracking progressed to the critical stage. Rotational-bending fatigue fractures usually originate at several points

distributed around the circumference. Often these origins, lying close together, link together to form a single crack.

Notches considerably reduce resistance to fatigue-crack initiation. Resistance becomes less as the sharpness of the notch is increased. Stress concentrations amounting to two or three times the nominal stress can easily exist at notches. Abrupt changes in cross section, sharp edges, threads, grooves, and boring marks can all act as notches. A fatigue crack that originated at a sharp keyway is shown in Fig. 8.

Unfortunately, the higher the strength of a steel, the higher is its notch sensitivity. Therefore, the advantage of a high-strength steel can be nullified or even disadvantageous when the steel is used in an inappropriate design or is improperly machined and notches are incorporated in the structure.

Failures Related to Nonmetallic Inclusions

Nonmetallic inclusions, both endogenous and exogenous, generally originate in the ingot (casting) stage. The number of inclusions, their physical properties (especially plasticity) and their size, shape and position all influence mechanical properties (Ref 14). One study demonstrated that the local constraint of the matrix by hard inclusions during tensile loading can produce severe stress concentrations that depend on the elastic moduli, size, shape and orientation of the inclusions (Ref 15).

Kiessling has treated the problem of inclusions from a compatibility standpoint, wherein inclusions that have a low index of deformability may induce cracks in two ways (Ref 16). The first depends on the inability of inclusions to transfer stresses existing in the matrix. Therefore, critical peak stresses can be reached around these inclusions while the metal is being worked; that is, inclusions have a direct nucleating effect on

crack initiation during fatigue-loading conditions. Second, if the inclusions have a low index of deformability, they may cause microcracks at the metal/inclusion interface during hot or cold working of the metal. This type of microcrack, already present in the metal at the beginning of service, may then be the origin of later fatigue fracture. In analyzing such a fracture, it is difficult to determine whether it was induced through crack nucleation at the inclusion during service, or through propagation of a pre-existing microcrack.

From all experimental evidence, it seems clear that inclusions that are brittle compared with the matrix and retain their shape during working processes are much more detrimental to the fatigue properties than inclusions that deform plastically during hot working.

Sulfide inclusions have a high index of deformability at all temperatures. Cracks are not developed at the metal/inclusion interface during working, and the inclusions change their shape according to the same pattern as the surrounding matrix. Oxide inclusions are in general harmful to the fracture properties, but differences exist between various oxide inclusions, and their size and position are also important. Those most detrimental to the fatigue and fracture properties are the spherical, nondeformable calcium-aluminates, and Al_2O_3 inclusions. Both these inclusion types retain their shape during forging.

In conjunction with these hard inclusion phases, fragmentation is frequently encountered if the degree of working is severe. The following example (Ref 17) illustrates a typical problem resulting from discontinuous slag inclusions.

Example 3. 1035 Steel Stub Axles That Were Rejected Because of Slag Inclusions (Fig. 9)

An automobile manufacturer rejected several stub axles of 1035 steel because of what appeared to be short longitudinal cracks in the surfaces of the pins (Fig. 9a).

Fig. 7. Surface of a typical rotational-bending-fatigue fracture, with final fracture located just left of center (Ref 11)

Fig. 8. Surface of a typical fatigue fracture. Arrow points to origin of fatigue crack at a sharp keyway.

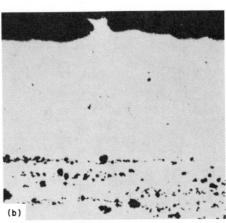

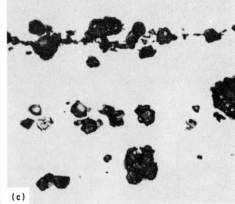

Fig. 9. Automobile stub axle, of 1035 steel, that was rejected because of slag inclusions at and below the surface. (a) View of axle showing slag inclusions at surface (encircled). (b) and (c) Longitudinal sections (unetched) showing inclusions at 100× and 500×, respectively. (Example 3; Ref 17)

The cracks were found initially when six axles were examined for defects by magnetic-particle testing.

Investigation. Further magnetic-particle inspections conducted on the six axles showed large quantities of short straight lines in the surfaces of the pins that at first were interpreted as cracks. Metallographic examination showed, however, that these lines were not cracks, but were slag inclusions at the surface and just below the surface. Those inclusions at the surface had been cut during machining. The inclusions consisted of multiphase spinels within a transparent glassy matrix, which resembled slaglike material such as is used in channel bricks. Coarse slag streaks like these are often called sand spots because they are friable and trickle out when the metal is worked. In Fig. 9(b) and (c), slag streaks are shown at two different magnifications in the longitudinal (working) direction. The inclusions were crumbled (fragmented) during forging but were not deformed. The particles consisted primarily of aluminum oxide or of silicates rich in aluminum oxide. Inclusions of this type could not be found in the interior of the cross section; only oxide and sulfide inclusions of normal size were found in the interior.

Conclusion was that the inclusions consisted of pieces of fireclay from channel brick that were flushed into the ingot mold. Although no true cracks were present, rejection of the stub axles was nevertheless justified. Slag streaks could reduce the strength of the stub axles and could also lead to the formation of fatigue fractures during operation.

Many investigations conducted on failed pressure vessels have revealed the presence of large exogenous nonmetallic inclusions that were nucleation sites for crack formation. Most often, these failures occur during the final stages of processing. The example that follows illustrates the damaging effect of nonmetallic inclusions on fracture properties of high-strength alloy steel.

Example 4. Thick-Wall Pressure Vessel, of Vanadium-Modified 4340 Steel, That Cracked From Exogenous Inclusions During Proof Firing (Fig. 10)

During the proof-firing tests of an alloy steel (4340 modified with vanadium additions) tubelike pressure vessel, magnetic-particle inspection indicated a crack on the inner surface of the vessel. The crack was oriented longitudinally (along the forging direction). At the time the crack was discovered, eight firing cycles had been completed.

Investigation. First, a chemical analysis and a mechanical-property evaluation were made near the crack. Composition was within the specified ranges for the material. Mechanical properties were as follows: yield strength (0.1% offset), 176,000 psi; tensile strength, 182,000 psi; elongation, 13%; reduction in area, 45%; Charpy impact strength (−40 F), 25 ft-lb. These properties met the specified requirements.

Next, a segment of the vessel containing the crack was sectioned, exposing the crack and resultant fracture surface. A large

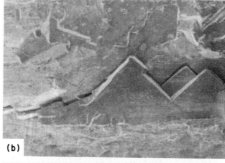
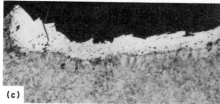

(a) Macrograph of a portion of the pressure-vessel wall, showing the inclusion as a shiny area (at arrow). (b) Scanning electron micrograph, at 13×, of the inclusion, showing the angular shape. (c) Micrograph, at 50×, of a 2%-nital-etched section through the pressure-vessel wall at the inclusion (light area near top).

Fig. 10. Metallographic evidence of an inclusion in the wall of a vanadium-modified 4340 steel pressure vessel (Example 4)

shiny area was observed just below the inner surface, as shown in Fig. 10(a).

The dark-gray surrounding area is contamination from firing. A closer look at the shiny area by scanning electron microscopy (SEM) showed it to be a very angular and faceted inclusion, taking on an almost intergranular appearance (Fig. 10b). Polished-and-etched metallographic specimens revealed that the included material did not etch along with the steel matrix, as shown in Fig. 10(c). Also, the inclusion contained, and was surrounded by, large amounts of small dark particles. Electron-microprobe analysis identified these dark particles as aluminum oxides. The large light portion in Fig. 10(c) contained iron, manganese, chromium and nickel in amounts approximately the same as the base material. From these data and observations, the inclusion was tentatively identified as an iron compound with a carbon content probably lower than that of the base steel. Also, a micro-hardness transverse across the inclusion into the matrix indicated that the inclusion material was somewhat softer than the steel (approximately 400 Knoop, versus 490 Knoop for the steel matrix). Severe etching did not reveal any grain structure in the region of the crack. It did, however, outline large faceted grain boundaries like those observed in the scanning electron micrograph shown in Fig. 10(b).

Discussions with the vendor of the steel revealed that during the vacuum degassing process the stream of molten steel occasionally broke up and sprayed on the pouring cap of the ingot, forming protuberances. As this process continued, the steel protuberances (resembling icicles) grew larger until some were inadvertently broken off. When these steel icicles fell into the ingot, they were trapped in the solidifying steel and apparently did not remelt. Further investigation also showed that an oxide was formed in conjunction with the iron compound, which could interfere with the remelting process and keep the inclusion intact.

Conclusion. The inclusion was identified as an iron compound that contained large amounts of small aluminum oxide particles. The inclusion formed like an icicle during vacuum degassing and inadvertently fell into the solidifying ingot. Consequently, the inclusion was forged into the tube. Except for this inclusion, the material had very acceptable mechanical properties. The localized area of nonmetallic material was responsible for the crack. In fact, an inclusion aggregate such as that in the vessel acts much like a crack because it creates a discontinuity in the forging. Under stress, the fracture toughness of the steel was exceeded at the inclusion and the material cracked.

Numerous failures of diesel-engine crankshafts have been attributed to fatigue fractures that were initiated by oxide-type inclusions in the transition zone of the induction hardened surface and the core. In the following example, the effect of subsurface inclusions on fatigue properties in a crankshaft is discussed.

Example 5. Crankshaft of 1050 Steel That Fractured in Fatigue Because of Subsurface Inclusions (Fig. 11)

A 1050 steel crankshaft 34¼ in. long with 2½-in.-diam journals, and weighing 69 lb, fractured in service. The shaft had first been quenched and tempered to a hardness of Rockwell C 19 to 26, then selectively hardened on the journals to a surface hardness of Rockwell C 40 to 46.

Investigation. The fractured shaft was examined for chemical composition and hardness, both of which were found to be within prescribed limits.

The fracture surface (Fig. 11a) shows a complex type of fatigue failure initiated from subsurface inclusions in the zone of transition between the induction hardened surface and the softer core. A concentration of inclusions near the fracture origin is shown in Fig. 11(b).

Conclusion. The failure was caused by fatigue cracks that initiated in an area having an excessive amount of inclusions that were located in a transition zone — which itself is a region of high stress.

Fatigue cracks propagate at right angles to maximum tensile stress; thus, a change in the direction of cracking (or the crack-plane angle) indicates a change in the direction in which stresses were applied. For instance, when a landing wheel is removed from an aircraft to change a tire, it may not be reinstalled on

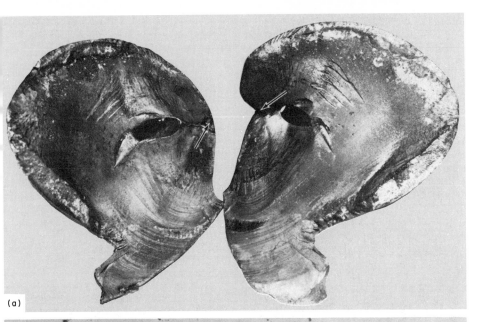

the same side of the aircraft, and changes in direction of wheel rotation cause changes in the crack-plane angle. In the next example, fatigue failure originated at a material defect, and macroscopic features on the fracture surface indicated changes in the crack-plane angle.

Example 6. Fatigue Cracking That Originated at a Material Defect in a Forged Aluminum Alloy Aircraft Wheel Half (Fig. 12)

A commercial-aircraft wheel half was removed from service because a crack was discovered in the area of the grease-dam radius during a routine inspection. The wheel half, shown in Fig. 12, was machined from an aluminum alloy 2014 forging that had been heat treated to the T6 temper. Neither the total number of landings nor the roll mileage was reported, but about 300 days had elapsed between the date of manufacture and the date the wheel was removed from service.

Investigation. The portion of the hub that contained the crack was broken open to reveal the fracture surface. The area in which the crack occurred and a view of the fracture surface are shown in detail A in Fig. 12.

Visual examination of the fracture surface revealed five distinct elliptical beach marks that are characteristic of fatigue failure. The outer boundary of each ellipse (see points 1, 2, 3, 4 and 5 in view B-B in Fig. 12) was a point of crack arrestment, indicating a change in crack-plane angle, which resulted from a change in the direction of wheel rotation. The total length of the crack lies between points 5 in Fig. 12, view B-B. Point O marks the origin of the crack, which was at a prior material imperfection. The type of imperfection was not initially identified but was possibly an undissolved grain refiner or an area of unhealed porosity, both of which are common in aluminum alloys.

The crack apparently was exposed at the inner surface of the wheel half early in the propagation cycle but at the outer surface late in the cycle. Because the inner surface was not readily accessible for inspection, detection was delayed. Propagation of the fatigue crack to the outer surface of the wheel half may have been retarded because the surface had been shot peened during the manufacturing procedure.

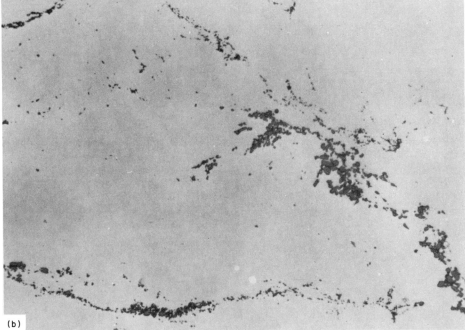

Fig. 11. (a) Mating surfaces of a fatigue fracture in a 1050 steel crankshaft. Fracture initiated at subsurface inclusions (arrows). (b) Micrograph (at 100×) showing concentration of inclusions near the fracture origin. (Example 5)

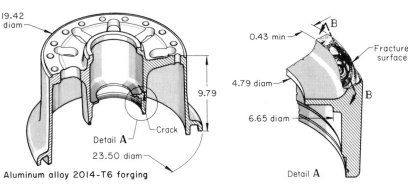

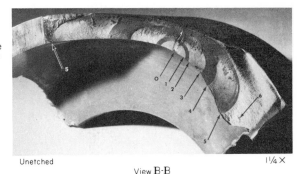

Detail A shows the area in which the crack occurred, and a view of the fracture surface revealed when the hub was broken open to examine the crack. View B-B, a macrograph of the fracture surface, shows the origin of the fatigue crack (at O), major points of crack arrestment (1 to 5), and total crack length (between 5's); arrow at 6 points to an undissolved grain refiner.

Fig. 12. Aircraft wheel half of aluminum alloy 2014-T6 that was removed from service because it developed a fatigue crack at a defect in the material (Example 6)

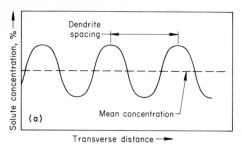

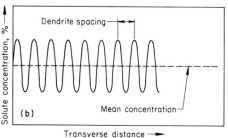

Fig. 13. Schematic diagrams illustrating the transverse distribution of a solute in an ingot (a) immediately after solidification, and (b) after some degree of working in forging. Note the difference in dendrite spacing.

A flat, shiny area (see arrow at 6 in Fig. 12, view B-B) was observed in the fracture surface intentionally produced when the hub was broken open. A micrograph made of a section through this flat, shiny area showed that the area was stringerlike in appearance. Prior experience indicated that such shiny areas were likely to be scattered throughout the forging.

The stringerlike area was analyzed by electron microprobe. The results of the analysis showed that the area contained relatively large amounts of manganese oxide, iron oxide and titanium oxide, medium amounts of copper oxide and aluminum oxide, and traces of chromium oxide, silicon oxide and magnesium oxide. The electron microprobe analysis (mainly, the presence of the titanium oxide) indicated that the shiny, stringerlike area in the fracture surface was an undissolved grain refiner.

Conclusions. The result of the investigation showed that the wheel half failed by fatigue. The fatigue crack originated at a material imperfection, and progressed in more than one plane because changes in the direction of wheel rotation changed the direction of the applied stresses.

Because the standard inspection techniques used in the machining plant were unable to detect subsurface imperfections in the as-received forging, it was recommended that the specifications be rewritten to require sound forgings.

Failures Related to Segregation

Segregation originates during solidification of the ingot. One of the functions of forging is to break up the cast grain structure and to promote homogeneity. Therefore, a minimum amount of cross-sectional reduction is usually required from the cast ingot to the billet. However, although this working can alleviate some of the inhomogeneity, it cannot eliminate it entirely if the ingot is badly segregated.

Figure 13(a) schematically shows the transverse distribution of a solute that might typically exist in an ingot immediately after solidification. Figure 13(b) shows the transverse distribution of the solute in an ingot after some degree of working in forging. The differential in solute concentration (amplitude) remains essentially undiminished; however, the peaks are brought closer together. The reason for this is that the dendrite axes are generally richer in alloying elements and leaner in impurities, such as the sulfur and phosphorus in steel, than the interdendritic regions. Consequently, the dendrite axes are stronger and, upon forging, do not deform and flow as readily as the matrix in which they are incorporated. Initial working causes matrix flow that tends to reorient the dendrites in the direction of flow. With increased working, the dendrites deform and fracture, thus becoming more and more elongated. The elongated dendrite axes, together with the interdendritic spaces, form a quasi-composite structure. Also included in this composite are both ductile and brittle inclusions as well as oxides and gases.

The over-all effect is that the forging contains regions that exhibit varying compositions on a microscale and, therefore, varying chemical and mechanical properties. The homogeneity of the forging is generally better in the longitudinal direction than in the transverse direction.

Segregation, with its attendant discrepancy in mechanical properties, can manifest itself in forging failures, as shown in the following example (Ref 18).

Example 7. Fracture of a D5 Tool Steel Forging Die Caused by Segregation (Fig. 14)

A cross-recessed die of D5 tool steel fractured in service. The die face was subjected to shear and tensile stresses as a result of the forging pressures from the material being worked. A view of the fractured die is shown in Fig. 14(a).

Investigation. A longitudinal section was taken through the die to include one arm of

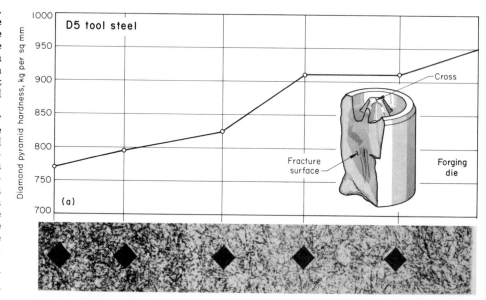

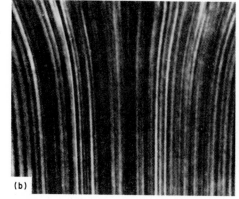

Fig. 14. (a) Hardness traverse correlated with the segregated microstructure of a cross-recessed forging die of D5 tool steel (inset) that failed in service because of segregation. (b) Macrograph of a section through one arm of the cross on the recessed die face, showing a severely segregated (banded) structure; etched in 5% nital. (c) Micrograph, at 200×, of the segregated area; etched in 5% nital. (Example 7; Ref 18)

the cross on the recessed die face. The specimen was polished and examined in the unetched condition. Examination revealed the presence of numerous slag stringers.

The polished specimen was then etched with 5% nital. A marked banded structure was evident, even macroscopically, as shown in Fig. 14(b). Microscopic examination revealed that the pattern was due to severe segregation banding (Fig. 14c).

Hardness measurements were then conducted across the face of the specimen in locations corresponding to the banded and nonbanded regions. These results, presented in Fig. 14(a), show that the segregated region is considerably harder than the neighboring material. The reason is that the increased carbon content of the segregated region, together with its higher alloy content, makes the region more responsive to what would have been normal heat treatment for this grade of tool steel.

The high-hardness material also is subject to microcracking upon quenching; microcracks can act as nuclei for subsequent fatigue cracks. Examination of the fracture surface revealed that the fracture originated near the high-stress region of the die face; however, no indications of fatigue marks were found either on a macroscale or a microscale.

Conclusion. Failure of the die was the result of fracture that originated in an area of abnormally high hardness. Although fatigue marks were not observed, the fact that the fracture did not occur in a single cycle but required several cycles to cause failure defines the failure as low-cycle fatigue.

Failures Related to Microstructure

The principal factors affecting the properties of metals are the alloying elements and the microstructure. The ability of many metals to have their properties controlled and changed at will by heat treatment can also introduce problems for the engineer. Small deviations from optimum processing procedures in alloying and heat treating can produce large discrepancies in the final mechanical properties of forgings. Discrepancies result from insufficient or excessive alloy composition, and incorrect microstructure for a particular application. Both alloy concentration and heat treatment have a pronounced effect on the resulting microstructure.

Incorrect Microstructure. Steel that is heat treated to form tempered martensitic microstructures is considered to possess the best combination of mechanical properties (Ref 19). This combination includes tensile strength, ductility and toughness. Normally, the higher the tempering temperature of a martensitic structure, the greater its ductility and notch toughness. Correspondingly, the hardness, tensile strength, and ductile-to-brittle transition temperature decrease as tempering temperatures increase.

In pressure-vessel technology, for example, the trend is toward achieving

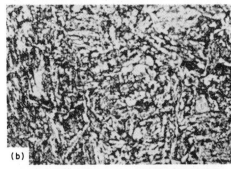

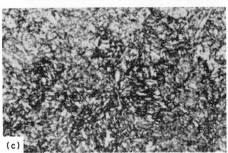

Fig. 15. (a) Fracture surface of an alloy steel lifting-fork arm; origin of fracture is indicated by the arrow. (b) Micrograph, at 200×, showing coarse, bainitic structure of fork arm. (c) Micrograph, at 200×, showing tempered-martensite structure that resulted from revised heat treatment. (Example 8; Ref 21)

higher operating pressures. This increased pressure can be accommodated by increasing the strength of available alloys. In extending the usable strength range of available alloys, heat treatment and the resulting microstructure are considered of prime importance. However, a major difficulty encountered with large forgings, and with small forgings with intricate shapes, is uniform quenching. Whenever the quenching rates vary significantly within a part due to size and shape, the resulting total microstructure can consist of a combination of microstructures that will ultimately contribute to weakening of the metal.

A study of the influence of microstructure on mechanical properties in low-

alloy steel forgings (Ref 20) considered the structures of martensite, upper bainite and lower bainite in both the tempered and the untempered conditions. The microstructure that exhibited the best combination of strength and toughness for the steel involved in the study (4340 steel modified with vanadium) was tempered martensite. Furthermore, it was reported that the yield strength and toughness of the bainitic structures decreased with increasing transformation temperature.

In the following example (Ref 21), lack of ductility and toughness due to an incorrect microstructure caused failure in a lifting-fork arm.

Example 8. Fracture of an Alloy Steel Lifting-Fork Arm Due to Microstructural Deficiency Incurred by Incorrect Forging and Heat Treatment (Fig. 15)

One forged alloy steel arm of a lifting fork with an approximate cross section of 150 by 240 mm (5.92 by 9.45 in.) fractured after only a short service life on a lift truck.

Investigation. The fracture surface had the appearance of a fracture originating from a surface crack (Fig. 15a). A large number of these surface cracks became visible after paint was removed from the surface of the arm. The cracks penetrated the metal to a maximum depth of about 3 mm (0.118 in.) and appeared to have originated during the forging of the fork. Paint that had penetrated into the cracks confirmed this conclusion. Forging at too low a temperature could have caused these cracks.

Results of a chemical analysis showed the steel to be EN-25 (nominal composition: 0.30% C, 0.65% Cr, 2.55% Ni, 0.55% Mo). The steel is suitable for this type of application and can be heat treated satisfactorily even in relatively large components.

Metallographic examination revealed a rather coarse bainitic structure as shown in Fig. 15(b), which indicated low resistance of the steel to shock loading. Shock loads are predictable in the daily operation of a fork-lift vehicle. Charpy V-notch impact tests on specimens at room temperature indicated an energy absorption of only 1.75 kgm/cm² (10.2 ft-lb), confirming the suspected low shock resistance.

The investigators then attempted to improve the impact toughness of this material by a suitable heat treatment consisting of quenching in oil from 860 C (1580 F) followed by tempering at 650 C (1200 F). The treatment resulted in a considerably finer microstructure of tempered martensite, as shown in Fig. 15(c). The improvement of Charpy V-notch energy absorption was confirmed by impact tests that yielded values of 11.87 kgm/cm² (69 ft-lb) — nearly seven times the original energy absorption.

Conclusion. The primary cause of the failure was the brittleness (lack of impact toughness) of the steel. The coarse bainitic microstructure was inadequate for the service application. The microstructure resulted from either improper heat treatment or no heat treatment after the forging operation. The surface cracks in the lifting-fork arm acted as starter notches (stress raisers), assisting in the initiation of fracture.

Retained Austenite. Undesirable microstructures in steels result when the transformation of austenite is incomplete. In correctly hardened steels containing more than 0.55% C, some austenite is usually retained after the quench, particularly when nickel, manganese and chromium are present. With these elements present, austenite may be retained even when carbon is low (Ref 22). Austenite retention is a result of the effect of lowering M_s and thus M_f. Upon reheating to a suitable temperature, retained austenite will transform generally in accord with the isothermal transformation pattern for the specific steel. In some instances, refrigeration will cause some of the retained austenite to transform, and because of the volume increase that accompanies transformation, cracks will occasionally form.

In general, when the amount of retained austenite is small, no appreciable effect on properties is noticed, although the elastic limit and yield strength may be lowered slightly. For larger amounts of retained austenite, ranging from about 10 to 20%, transformation to lower bainite during tempering either causes no change or, in some instances, results in a slight improvement in strength, ductility and impact properties. Tempering at higher temperatures, causing formation of upper bainite or pearlite, has deleterious effects.

The next example describes an investigation that confirms the undesirability of retained austenite in hardened steel.

Example 9. Fracture of a Hardened 52100 Steel Ball Due to a Microstructural Deficiency (Fig. 16)

Swaging mandrels for high-strength, thick-wall tube applications were traditionally designed as truncated cones, and manufactured from tungsten carbide (WC). The inherent high hardness of tungsten carbide was necessary because during the swaging operation, the mandrel is pushed through low-alloy steel cylinders that have yield strengths of about 170,000 psi. The bore of the cylinder is permanently enlarged by this process. However, the operation sets up large stresses in the mandrel.

The use of tungsten carbide as mandrel material was considered expensive, so a less expensive material, 52100 steel, was substituted. Also, the truncated-cone design was replaced with a ball design, the new mandrel resembling a bearing ball 4 in. in diameter. The substitute steel is relatively hard (approximately Rockwell C 55), has good wear resistance, and is easily obtained in the desired form from manufacturers of ball bearings.

During the first pass of its initial run, the ball mandrel fractured into two main segments and a few smaller fragments. Also, a number of cracks extended throughout the two larger segments. Several cracks can be seen as black lines in Fig. 16.

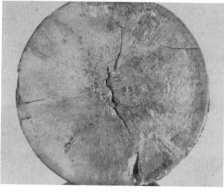

Fig. 16. Fracture surface of a 4-in.-diam 52100 steel ball used for swaging thick-wall tubing. The ball failed because the microstructure contained large amounts of retained austenite. (Example 9)

Investigation. Because the failed ball was cracked and fragmented, it was only possible to conduct metallography, chemical analysis, and a hardness survey on the remaining portions of the mandrel. Composition of the steel was determined to be within the prescribed limits for 52100.

Results of the hardness traverse (from edge to center) indicated that the ball was considerably harder at the outer edge (³⁄₆₄ in. from the surface, Rockwell C 62; ⅛ in. deep, Rockwell C 53.5), with the hardness decreasing to approximately Rockwell C 36 to 39 at the center.

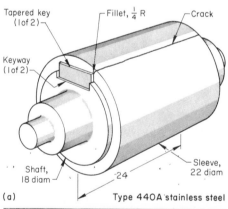

(a)

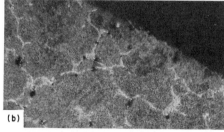

(b)

(a) Roll assembly, consisting of a type 440A stainless steel sleeve shrink-fitted over a 4340 steel shaft and secured by tapered keys. The sleeve cracked from keyway to keyway.

(b) Micrograph, at 150×, of a transverse section through the sleeve, showing a continuous network of massive carbide particles at grain boundaries. (Specimen was etched with a mixture of 10 parts HNO₃, 10 parts acetic acid and 15 parts HCl.)

Fig. 17. Roll assembly on which the stainless steel sleeve cracked because of improper microstructure (Example 10)

The microstructure verified the hardness data, showing the ball to have a martensitic structure with a fine carbide dispersion in the vicinity of the surface and changing after about ⅛-in. depth to a tempered martensitic structure with large amounts of retained austenite. A Knoop microhardness check using a 10-gram load showed average hardness values of 478 Knoop for the areas of high austenite content, and 539 Knoop for the regions of tempered martensite.

Conclusion. The steel contained about 40 to 50% retained austenite, and was considerably softer than ball-bearing steel in general. Also, the condition was aggravated by the fact that the shell of the ball was very hard (Rockwell C 62), while the inside was relatively soft (Rockwell C 36).

From the evidence, it was apparent that the steel in its present condition was inadequate for the swaging application. The complex stresses induced in the ball during swaging were compounded by the fact that a triaxial-stress state develops at the case-core interface of the composite structure. Ebert, Krotine and Troiano (Ref 23) state that a tough core is essential, because at the interface the properties of the core material dominate those of the case. It was concluded, therefore, that the deficient microstructure of the 52100 steel was a major contributor to the failure of the mandrel.

In high-carbon steels, particularly those containing more-than-normal amounts of manganese, the transformation to martensite is usually not complete because of the low M_s temperature; instead, some unstable austenite remains (Ref 24). Even after some of this residual austenite is induced by refrigeration to form martensite, a small proportion persists. Therefore, in a ball of this diameter (4 in.) if through-hardening cannot be practically achieved, the selection of another material may be necessary. A ball of 18% Ni maraging steel, grade 300, probably would be suitable for the application. It can be processed to a yield strength of approximately 300,000 psi and would be uniformly hardened through a cross section. Subsequently, the embrittling effect of multiaxial stresses at a case-core interface is also eliminated.

Continuous second-phase networks in a steel matrix are also considered as microstructural deficiencies that can contribute to failures. The example that follows illustrates such a condition.

Example 10. Brittle Fracture of a Type 440A Stainless Steel Roll-Assembly Sleeve Due to Improper Microstructure (Fig. 17)

A roll manufacturer had successfully used the following procedure to make roll assemblies for many years: A sleeve, or hoop, forged from type 440A stainless steel was shrink fitted over a 4340 steel shaft (Fig. 17a). Tapered keys were inserted into keyways on the ends of the sleeve-shaft interface to additionally secure the sleeve, as shown in Fig. 17(a). A roll assembly of this design was crated and shipped by air. Upon arrival, the sleeve was found to have cracked longitudinally from keyway to keyway.

Examination. The sleeve was torch cut on the opposite side of the crack to expose the fracture. Examination of the fracture surface revealed that the fracture originated in a fillet of the notch formed by the keyway. The radius of the fillet was generous (¼ in.) and should not have posed a problem, particularly in view of its long history of successful use. Further, there were no aberrations (such as tool marks) found on the root of the fillet that might account for crack initiation at that location.

Examination of the fracture· surface by electron microscopy indicated that the fracture was brittle in nature with considerable evidence of intergranular fracture.

Estimates of the residual stress were made on the basis of the interferences resulting from the shrink-fitting operation. Similar calculations were made considering the stress resulting from differential expansion and contraction due to thermal differences occurring during transit by air. These stresses could not by themselves cause cracking.

A transverse specimen was polished and examined metallographically. The results revealed that although the surface of the forged sleeve exhibited a microstructure with carbide particles dispersed in a martensite matrix, the interior of the forging, beginning at a depth of 1 in. below the surface, exhibited a continuous network of massive carbide particles, as shown in Fig. 17(b).

Conclusion. Superficial working of the metal (probably insufficient hot working) produced a microstructure wherein the carbide particles were not broken up and distributed evenly throughout the structure. Instead, the grains were totally surrounded with brittle carbide particles. This permitted the formation of a crack at a fillet in the keyway. Once the crack had initiated, crack growth was rapid.

Failures Related to Forging Defects

A successfully forged part is the result of a series of operations designed to develop the final shape required and simultaneously achieve grain refinement, internal soundness, and improved mechanical properties.

Initial working of a steel ingot, usually referred to as cogging, removes flutes, ripples or corrugations that were formed on the ingot by the mold contour, to prevent cracking of the ingot surface during solidification and cooling (Ref 25). Light drafts (small reductions) are taken all over the ingot until the surface irregularities are smoothed. Heavier drafts are then taken and working continues, ultimately converting the cross section from that of the original ingot into the desired final shape.

During the forging operations, several types of defects may be created or perpetuated. Among these are pipe, laps, folds, seams, cracks, tears and forged-in scale. Pipe is a solidification-shrinkage defect carried through from the ingot stage and is detected as a small round cavity located near the center of an end

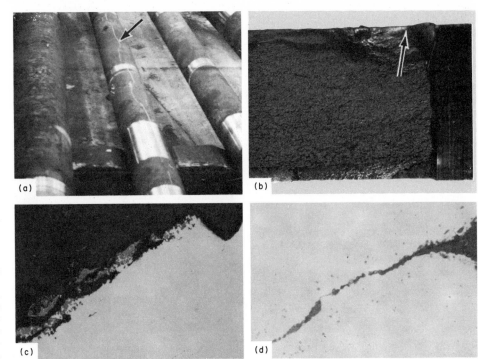

(a) Over-all view of gun tubes; cracked tube is second from left (arrow indicates crack). (b) Macrograph of a section cut for examination; arrow shows suspected area of fracture initiation. (c) Micrograph of an unetched specimen, at 50×, showing nonmetallic inclusions (light gray) along fracture surface. (d) Portion of area in (c), at 500×; note agglomerated appearance of nonmetallics, which were identified as iron oxides.

Fig. 18. Alloy steel gun tubes that developed cracks in the wall during autofrettage, from scale worked into forging laps and seams (Example 11)

surface (see discussion under "Ingot Pipe", on page 291 in this article). Laps, folds, seams, cracks and tears are produced during forging.

Forged-in scale is one of the most prevalent surface defects. The scale is formed in a previous heating operation and has not been eliminated before or during forging. The example that follows describes a pressure vessel that failed from forged-in scale.

Example 11. Cracking of an Alloy Steel Gun Tube During Autofrettage, Because of Scale Worked Into Forging Laps and Seams (Fig. 18)

Gun tubes are subjected to autofrettage to induce a state of residual compressive stress at the inner surface; the chief result of this process is increased fatigue life. During autofrettage of a 105-mm M68 gun tube forged from vacuum-degassed alloy steel, a crack developed through the wall. The cracked region is indicated by an arrow in Fig. 18(a). Although the failure originated approximately 6 ft from the breech end, it was caused to propagate about 12 ft farther by the internal autofrettage mandrel when it was extracted from the muzzle end.

Investigation. Mechanical properties, composition and microstructure were checked. Mechanical properties were as follows: yield strength (0.1% offset), 170,000 psi; tensile strength, 184,000 psi; elongation, 12%; reduction in area, 40%; Charpy V-notch impact strength (−40 F), 23 ft-lb. The strength, ductility and toughness indicated no significant deviations from the manufacturer's reported values, and met

the specified requirements. Composition of the steel (0.31% C, 0.60% Mn, 0.010% P, 0.010% S, 0.24% Si, 2.06% Ni, 0.98% Cr, 0.47% Mo, 0.11% V) also was within specifications.

Metallographic specimens were prepared from the area of the tube containing a suspected crack origin. This region is denoted by an arrow in Fig. 18(b). The specimens were taken from sections perpendicular and parallel to the long axis of the forging. Metallography revealed the tempered-martensite structure normally obtained in this steel after quenching and tempering.

The fracture profile parallel to the longitudinal axis of the tube is shown in Fig. 18(c). This edge, which is adjacent to the outer surface, displays a somewhat continuous light-gray network of nonmetallic inclusions. Figure 18(d) shows a portion of Fig. 18(c) at a higher magnification, and illustrates the agglomerated appearance of the included material. Subsequent electron-microprobe analysis identified the included material as mainly iron oxide.

Conclusion. Iron oxide of this magnitude is highly abnormal in vacuum-degassed steels. Included matter of this nature (exogenous) most likely resulted from oxide scale worked into laps or seams during forging. Therefore, it is not surprising that failure occurred during autofrettage when the mandrel approached the section containing the laps or seams. Since the inclusions were sizable, hard and extremely irregular, this region would effect substantial stress concentration. Consequently, the fracture toughness of the steel was exceeded and failure through the wall resulted.

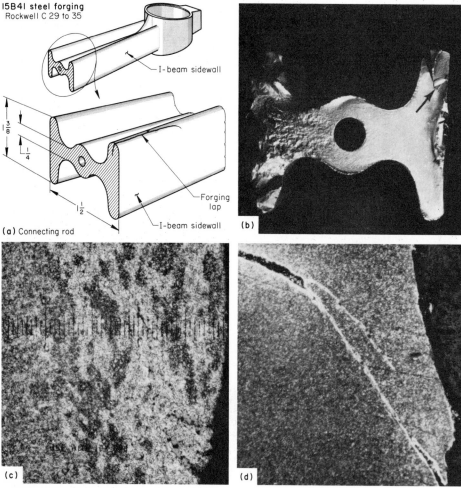

15B41 steel forging
Rockwell C 29 to 35

I-beam sidewall

$\frac{3}{8}$
$\frac{1}{4}$
$1\frac{1}{2}$

(a) Connecting rod

Forging lap

I-beam sidewall

(b)

(c)

(d)

Laps and folds are forging defects that can initiate failures, as illustrated in the following three examples.

Example 12. Fatigue Fracture That Initiated at a Forging Lap in a 15B41 Steel Connecting Rod for a Truck Engine (Fig. 19)

A connecting rod from a truck engine failed after being in service for 45,300 miles. The rod, shown in Fig. 19(a), was forged from 15B41 steel and heat treated to a hardness of Rockwell C 29 to 35. The connecting rod was sent to a laboratory for examination. A piece of the I-beam sidewall about 2½ in. long was missing when the connecting rod arrived at the laboratory.

Investigation. The sidewall and web areas of the I-beam section of the connecting rod were inspected for surface defects by fluorescent magnetic-particle testing. An indication of a defect was found extending along the edge of a sidewall for approximately 1½ in. and ¼ in. deep, starting at, and perpendicular to, the fracture surface. The defect was identified as a forging lap (see Fig. 19a).

Visual examination of the fracture surface (see Fig. 19b) revealed beach marks typical of fatigue failure. The origin was along the forging lap in the sidewall of the I-beam section and was approximately ³⁄₁₆ in. below the forged surface. The fatigue indications extended slightly beyond a lubrication hole drilled longitudinally through the web. The remaining portion of the fracture surface was severely mutilated, but an area in the web contained indications of brittle fracture. The missing portion of the sidewall appeared to be the result of an extension of the forging lap.

Metallographic examination of the metal in the rod disclosed an acceptable tempered martensitic microstructure with a hardness of Rockwell C 30 to 31. A micrograph of a section taken perpendicular to the lap and parallel to the web (see Fig. 19c) showed that the metal was severely decarburized for a depth of 0.010 in. from the lap surface

(a) Connecting rod, and a detail of the I-beam portion showing the forging lap in one sidewall. (b) Fracture surface, at 1½×, showing origin of the fatigue fracture (at arrow). (c) Micrograph, at 100×, of a nital-etched section taken perpendicular to the forging lap and parallel to the I-beam web. Oxides (black)

and decarburization (light) are present along the forging lap; surface of the lap is at right.

(d) Micrograph, at 37½×, of a nital-etched section taken near the intersection of the two branches of the forging lap — one branch is on a 45° angle, the other is vertical (edge at right). Both oxides and decarburization are evident.

Fig. 19. Truck-engine connecting rod, forged from 15B41 steel, that failed in service from fatigue initiated at a forging lap (Example 12)

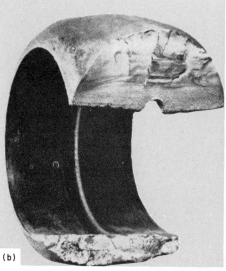

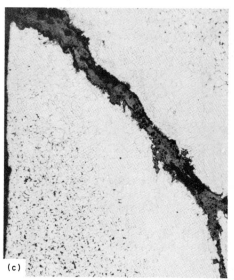

(a) Reassembled rod end showing locations of fractures and crack. At A is a fatigue fracture; at B, a secondary tensile fracture; crack is at C. (b) Fracture surfaces of the broken-off shell; fatigue fracture is at top, tensile fracture (fibrous) is at bottom. (c) Micrograph, at 50×, of the scale-filled forging fold (etched in 2% nital). Note decarburization (white areas) flanking the fold.

Fig. 20. Steel connecting-rod end that fractured and cracked in service because of a forging fold (Example 13; Ref 26)

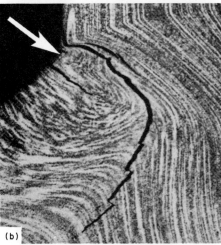

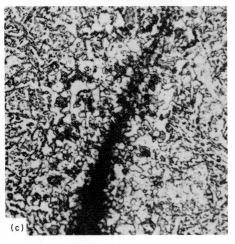

(a) Longitudinal section through socket spanner head, showing region of crack (at arrow). (b) Etched section (2% nital) of cracked region at 20×; arrow indicates forging folds that initiated the crack. (c) Crack at 500×, showing oxides (black) and some decarburization (light); 2% nital etch.

Fig. 21. Steel socket spanner head that cracked in service because of forging folds (Example 14; Ref 27)

and partially decarburized for a depth of 0.020 in. Oxides were scattered for a depth of 0.020 in. from the lap surface.

Figure 19(d) is a micrograph of a section taken near the intersection of the two branches of the forging lap. Oxides and decarburization are clearly visible along the lap surface. One branch of the lap was on a 45° angle, the other was vertical.

Conclusions. The rod failed in fatigue with the origin along the lap and located approximately $3/16$ in. below the forged surface. The presence of oxides may have been a partial cause for the defect. To correct the problem, the forgings should be more carefully inspected by fluorescent magnetic-particle testing before machining.

Example 13. Carbon Steel Connecting Rod That Fractured Because of a Forging Fold (Fig. 20)

A motorboat-engine connecting rod, forged from carbon steel, fractured in two places, and also cracked, at the small end during service. The locations of the fracture surfaces and of the crack are shown as A, B and C in Fig. 20(a), a view of the reassembled rod end. The fracture at A was caused by fatigue resulting from operating stresses; the fracture at B is a secondary tensile fracture. At C, the transition on the other side of the rod is cracked symmetrically to the fatigue fracture. Figure 20(b) shows the fracture surfaces, with the fatigue fracture at top and the tensile fracture at bottom.

Investigation. Magnetic-particle inspection revealed indications of cracking at the transition area, between the rod and the small end; six other connecting rods inspected from the same batch also had these indications.

Metallographic examination of one of the connecting rods selected by the magnetic-particle tests revealed deep folds in the flash zone. As shown in Fig. 20(c), these folds are filled with scale and flanked by a decarburized zone. The microstructure of the remaining material reflected correct annealing practice. Also, because the flash zone was ground after forging, no decarburization can be detected outside the fold zone.

Conclusion. The connecting rods were rendered susceptible to fatigue-crack initiation and propagation by the notch effect of coarse folds formed during the forging operation. (Ref 26)

Example 14. Cracking of a Steel Socket Spanner Head Because of Forging Folds (Fig. 21)

A head of a socket spanner made of heat treated 0.40% C, 0.34% Cr steel cracked in service. One half of the head, longitudinally sectioned, is shown in Fig. 21(a) in the as-received condition.

Investigation. During the preparation of the component for microscopic examination, the pronounced fibrous structure became evident as soon as it was etched with 2% nital. Folds in the material originating from the shaping process could be seen at the point marked with an arrow in Fig. 21(a). The micrograph in Fig. 21(b) shows that cracks run along these folds oriented according to the fiber. One exception is the longest crack, of which only the first third follows the direction of the fiber, the re-

mainder running transversely and showing the typical features of a hardening crack.

The fissures, with the exception of the hardening crack, were partly filled with oxide and showed signs of decarburization at the edges (Fig. 21c). From this it could be assumed that parts of the external skin had been forced into the folds during forging.

Conclusion. Even though there was some indication of chemical segregation, the folds made during forging initiated the main crack. Furthermore, even if the steel had been more homogeneous, hardening cracks would probably have been promoted by the coarse fissures at the fold zones (Ref 27)

Seams can be difficult to detect because they may appear as scratches on the forging or because a machining process may obliterate them. When the constraint exerted by the bulk of material is removed from the neighborhood of a seam, there is a strong likelihood that the seam will open, rendering the forged part inoperative.

The example that follows describes a failure in a small part that was caused by a forging seam.

Example 15. Prongs on Stainless Steel Forceps That Split and Fractured Due to Forging Seams (Fig. 22)

The pointed ends on several stainless steel forceps like the one shown in Fig. 22(a) split (Fig. 22b) or completely fractured where split portions broke off (Fig. 22c). All the forceps were delivered in the

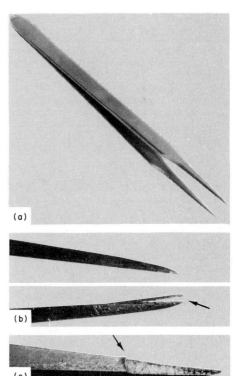

Fig. 22. (a) Forged stainless steel forceps, about $4\frac{1}{2}$ in. long, that split or fractured at prong tips because of forging seams. (b) Prongs showing a split tip (arrow). (c) Prong on which a split tip broke off (at arrow). (Example 15)

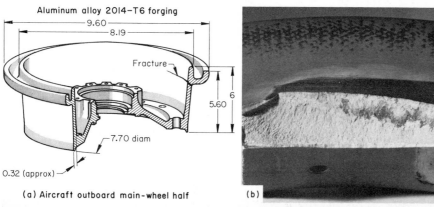

Aluminum alloy 2014-T6 forging
9.60
8.19
Fracture
6
5.60
7.70 diam
0.32 (approx)

(a) Aircraft outboard main-wheel half

(b)

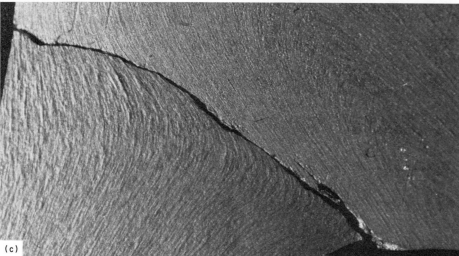

(c)

(a) Sectioned wheel half showing location of fracture. (b) Fracture surface showing what was judged to be the result of aluminum oxidation, indicated by dark-gray patches on light-gray fracture area. (c) Macrograph of a section through the crack and the disrupted grain flow (sodium hydroxide etch; about 8½×).

Fig. 23. One of two aluminum alloy aircraft wheel halves that cracked in service from defects during forging (Example 16)

same lot. The pointed ends of the forceps are used for probing and gripping very small objects and must be true, sound and sharp.

Investigation. Analysis showed the failures to be the result of seams in the steel that were not joined during hot working.

Conclusion. Closer inspection of the product at all stages is necessary. Inspection at the mill will minimize discrepancies at the source, and inspection of the finished product will help detect obscure seams.

Abnormal grain flow is often associated with subsurface defects in forgings that can lead to fracture. The two examples that follow describe forged aluminum alloy aircraft wheels that failed in service because of subsurface defects; both wheels exhibited abnormal grain flow.

Example 16. Cracks in Forged Aluminum Alloy Aircraft Wheel Halves That Originated From Forging Defects (Fig. 23)

Two outboard main-wheel halves from a commercial aircraft were removed from service because of failure. One wheel half was in service for 54 days and had made 130 landings (about 650 roll miles) when crack indications were discovered during

eddy-current testing. The flange on the second wheel half failed, after only 31 landings, when about 18 in. of the flange broke off as the aircraft was taxiing. A sectioned wheel half is shown in Fig. 23(a). Both wheel halves were made from aluminum alloy 2014-T6 forgings. Stains on the fracture surfaces were used to determine when cracking was initiated.

Investigation of Cracked Wheel Half. After cursory examination of the wheel half removed from service because of cracking, it was concluded that the reported crack was superficial, and the following rework was authorized:

1 Liquid-penetrant inspect entire wheel half.
2 Polish surface at known crack indication. Etch and liquid-penetrant inspect as needed to ensure that the crack indication is removed.
3 Chemically treat repaired area in preparation for painting, then paint.

In initial liquid-penetrant inspection, the area containing the crack indication did not bleed out. However, after light surface polishing (step 2) the crack became apparent.

The wheel half was then forwarded to the laboratory for failure examination. The portion containing the crack was saw cut from the wheel half and broken open. No evidence of crack propagation by fatigue

was visible, but, as shown in Fig. 23(b), the fracture surface was marked by a slight gray discoloration that was judged to be the result of aluminum oxidation. Examination of the fracture surface revealed that the crack was associated with disrupted and transverse grain flow. Figure 23(c) is an enlarged section through the crack and shows the abnormal grain flow.

Investigation of Broken Wheel Half. Examination of the fracture surface on the wheel half with the broken flange revealed that fracture was initiated by a crack about 7½ in. long. Surface detail indicated disrupted and transverse grain flow, which was verified by deep etching in aqueous 20% sodium hydroxide. Grain flow at the crack plane changed abruptly from longitudinal to transverse, similar to the pattern shown in Fig. 23(c). The surface showed definite chromic acid stains and evidence of rapid fatigue propagation prior to final failure.

Conclusion. Failure on both wheel halves was by fatigue caused by a forging defect resulting from abnormal transverse grain flow. The crack in the first wheel half occurred during service and the surfaces became oxidized. Because the fracture surface of the second wheel half had chromic acid stains, it was obvious that the forging defect was open to the surface during anodizing.

The forging defects may have been the result of any of the following factors, singly or in combination:

1 The forging blank contained more than the optimum volume of metal in the flange area.
2 The forging blank contained less than the optimum volume of metal in the flange area, resulting in an underfill condition.
3 Forging-die design was inefficient.
4 The forging operation was unduly fast for the specific design.
5 Some metal was removed from the surface during the forging process to eliminate a specific surface defect, resulting in an underfill condition in the flange area.

After the forging vendor was notified of the defects, the frequency of failure decreased markedly. However, forgings with this defect were still occasionally found at incoming inspection.

Example 17. Fatigue Fracture of a Forged Aluminum Alloy Aircraft Wheel Half That Was Initiated at a Subsurface Defect (Fig. 24)

The flange on an outboard main-wheel half on a commercial aircraft fractured during takeoff. The wheel half, shown in Fig. 24, was made from an aluminum alloy 2014-T6 forging. The failure was discovered later during a routine enroute check. The flange section that broke away was recovered at the airfield from which the plane took off and thus was available for examination.

Failure occurred after 37 landings, or about 185 roll miles. Routine inspection of the wheel half prior to takeoff did not disclose evidence of incipient failure. However, a thorough inspection of the surface after failure revealed an unusual grain-flow pattern at numerous points along the crack.

Investigation. Examination of the fracture surfaces revealed that a forging defect was present in the wall of the wheel half. The paint was stripped from the fracture area, and the wheel surfaces were examined. The anodized coating showed distinct twin-parallel and end-grain patterns between which the fracture occurred (see section A-A in Fig. 24). This type of grain pattern has been observed in other wheels that had forging defects.

Macroscopic examination of the fracture surfaces indicated that the forging defect was not open to either side of the wall, and thus the crack was not detected during routine inspection. As shown in view B-B in Fig. 24, the periphery of the defect was the site of several small fatigue cracks that eventually progressed through the remaining wall. Rapid fatigue then progressed circumferentially to a length of about 6 in. before final fracture occurred. The original forging defect was about 2 in. long.

Sections through the fracture plane were prepared for metallographic examination, using Keller's reagent. The microstructure was judged normal for aluminum alloy 2014-T6. The work metal had a hardness of Rockwell B 82 to 83, which surpassed the minimum hardness of Rockwell B 78 required for aluminum alloy 2014-T6. An abrupt change in the direction of grain flow across the fracture plane indicated that the wall had buckled during forging.

Conclusion. The results of the investigation showed that the wheel half failed in the flange by fatigue as the result of a rather large subsurface forging defect.

Failures Related to Postforging Processes

A forging may be properly designed and fabricated from sound material and yet fail from a defect created by improper processing or handling subsequent to forging. The range of the defects can vary from engraved identification marks, which can nucleate fatigue cracks, to undesirable microstructure resulting from variations in the time-and-temperature schedules for heat treatment, to hydrogen embrittlement resulting from surface-finishing operations such as electroplating. Table 1 lists some of the defects that may result from various postforging processes.

Failures Related to Heat Treatment

Improper heat treatment can result in failure to attain the desired microstructure in the metal and, therefore, the desired levels of mechanical or physical properties. Such deficiencies can cause failures in service.

Overheating. As alloys are heated above their recrystallization temperatures, grain growth occurs. As the temperature increases, so does grain growth, becoming quite rapid and resulting in large grains, often accompanied by many undesirable characteristics. The impairment that usually accompanies large grains is caused not only by the size of the grains, but also by the more continuous films that are formed on larger grains

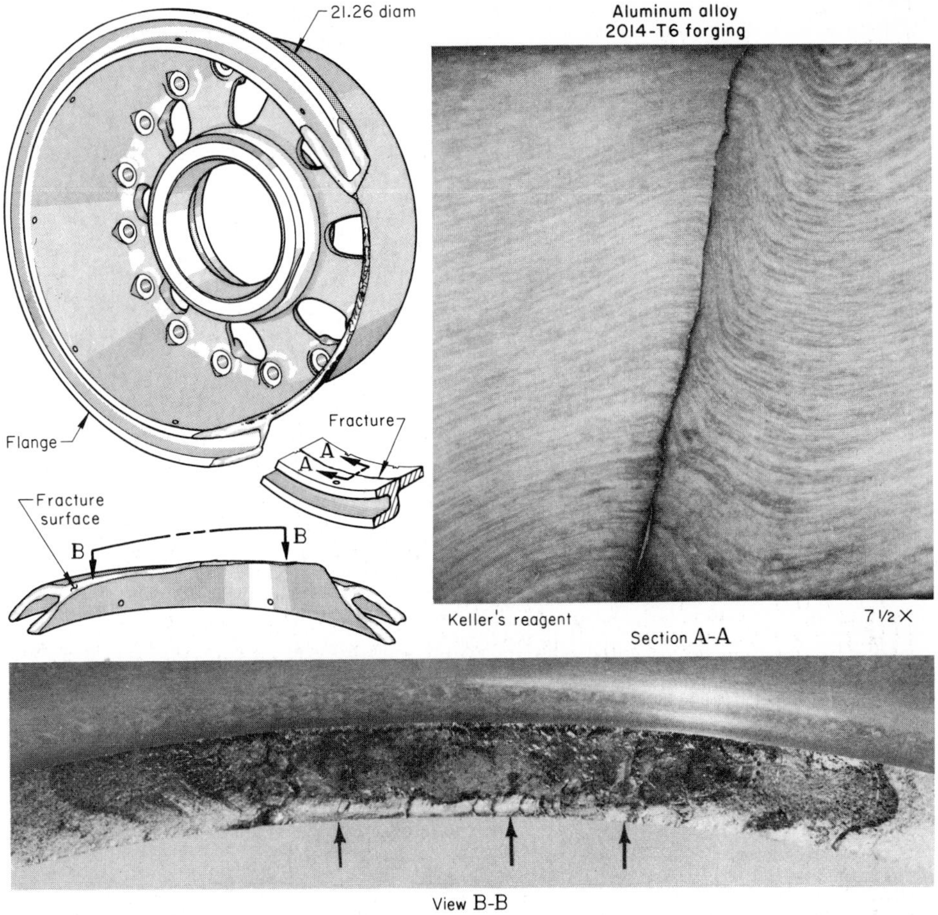

Fig. 24. Aluminum alloy aircraft outboard main-wheel half, and flange portion that broke off during takeoff because of a large subsurface forging defect in the flange. Section A-A is a view of the crack that occurred between the twin-parallel and end-grain patterns. View B-B shows the fracture surface, with arrows indicating sites of several small fatigue cracks. (Example 17)

by grain-boundary impurities such as preferential precipitates and evolved gases. Finer grains, on the other hand, present a greater amount of total grain-boundary area over which the impurities may be distributed.

The detrimental effects of overheating depend on the temperature and the time of exposure as well as on the alloy. For example, a short exposure of a high speed tool steel to temperatures around 1250 C (2282 F) is required to dissolve the carbides, but prolonged heating at that

Table 1. Defects That May Result From Various Postforging Processes

Electroplating: Hydrogen embrittlement; galvanic corrosion
Heat treatment: Grain enlargement; burning of grain boundaries; brittle structure; carburization; decarburization; quench cracks
Electrolytic cleaning: Pitting
Surface hardening, nitriding, carburizing, anodic hard coating: Excessive case thickness; microcracks; embrittled material at stress raisers
Machining: Tool marks; grinding cracks
Welding: Weld-metal defects; cracks caused by hydrogen embrittlement; inclusions; improper structure

temperature will cause grain growth and loss of mechanical properties.

The damage caused by overheating is particularly significant in the high-carbon and medium-carbon steels, in which both strength and ductility are affected.

One of the most conspicuous indications that a metal has been overheated is the coarse-grained fracture surface that results. Usually, examination with a stereoscopic microscope will show the characteristic faceted surface of an intergranular fracture.

Microscopically, the large grain size resulting from overheating is quite evident, and can be measured and compared to a similar metal with a normal grain size. In addition to large grain size, fine oxide particles are often found dispersed throughout the grains, particularly near the surface. These oxides result from internal oxidation and are particularly evident in overheated copper and bronze forgings (see Fig. 25a).

A Widmanstätten structure is often associated with coarse grains in an overheated steel forging. According to Mehl (Ref 28), two conditions are required for the presence of Widmanstätten structure — namely, a controlled rate of cooling,

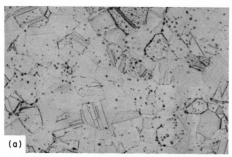

(a) Oxides (black particles) in a copper 102 (oxygen-free copper) forging heated to 1023 C (1875 F). (b) Burning (black outlines) at grain boundaries of a copper 110 (electrolytic tough pitch copper) forging heated to 1066 C (1950 F).

Fig. 25. Micrographs showing effects of (a) overheating and (b) burning, on microstructures of copper forgings

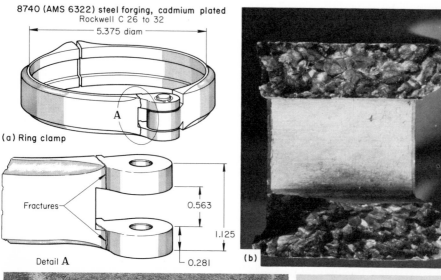

8740 (AMS 6322) steel forging, cadmium plated
Rockwell C 26 to 32

(a) Ring clamp

Detail A

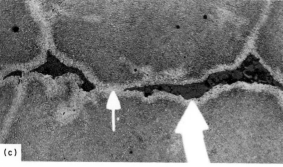

(b)

(a) View of assembled clamp, and detail showing locations of fractures. (b) Fracture surfaces, at about 2×, showing brittle, intergranular nature of fracture. (c) Section through fracture surface (2% nital etch; 100×) showing incipient melting (large arrow) and decarburization at grain boundaries (small arrow). (d) Area adjoining the fractures after being stripped of cadmium plate (5% nital etch; 1½×), showing coarse grains (between arrows).

Fig. 26. Aircraft ring clamp, of cadmium-plated 8740 (AMS 6322) steel, that failed because of burning during forging (Example 18)

neither extremely fast nor extremely slow, and a large grain size.

Burning is a term applied when a metal is grossly overheated and permanent irreversible damage to the metal occurs as a result of the intergranular penetration of oxidizing gas, or occurs by incipient melting. The micrograph in Fig. 25(b) shows burning at the grain boundaries in a specimen of copper 110 (electrolytic tough pitch copper) heated to 1066 C (1950 F). Copper oxide migrated to grain boundaries, forming a continuous network that severely reduces strength and ductility.

In steels, burning may manifest itself with the formation of extremely large grains and incipient melting at the grain boundaries. Melting is particularly evident where segregation has occurred with the marked rejection of low-melting phases in the interdendritic regions and at the grain boundaries.

Burning cannot be readily detected by visual examination. However, a metallographic examination of the structure shows the enlarged grains and the pronounced grain-boundary network.

The most obvious cause of burning is use of a furnace with too high a temperature. Occasionally, burning will occur in adequately controlled furnaces simply because the flame is allowed to impinge upon the metal surface, causing localized overheating. Another source of overheating, though less common, can be the conversion of mechanical energy into heat. If there are segregated areas near the center of the billet, and if the initial forging temperature is close to the melting point of the segregated regions, the additional heat supplied by the transformation of work into heat can cause localized burning during the forging operation.

Burned material cannot be salvaged and should be scrapped, because the metallurgical changes that have occurred are irreversible.

Failure of an aircraft-engine component because of burning is described in the example that follows.

Example 18. Brittle Fracture of an Alloy Steel Clamp Because of Burning During Forging (Fig. 26)

The ring clamp shown in Fig. 26(a) was used for attaching ducts to an aircraft engine. After three hours in service, the clamp became loose. When the clamp was removed from the engine, the hinge tabs on one clamp half were found to be broken. The clamp half had been machined from an 8740 (AMS 6322) steel forging, and was cadmium plated.

Investigation. Visual examination of the clamp half revealed that it had fractured through the hinge tabs, as shown in Fig. 26(a). The appearance of the fracture surface indicated a brittle intergranular fracture (Fig. 26b). Microscopic examination of a section through the fracture surface revealed burning (incipient melting) and decarburization at the grain boundaries (Fig. 26c), which indicates gross overheating of the metal.

Macroscopic inspection of the area adjoining the fractures, after it had been stripped of cadmium plate and swab etched with 5% nital, confirmed that the burning had been confined to the tab end of the clamp half, as shown in Fig. 26(d). This end of the clamp had been hot upset to provide material for the hinge tabs.

The metallurgical quality of the clamp, remote from the burned area, was satisfactory with respect to hardness, microstructure and chemical composition for this grade steel. The thickness of the hinge tabs was within blueprint requirements.

Conclusions. Both hinge tabs on the clamp half fractured in a brittle manner as the result of gross overheating, or burning, during forging. The mechanical properties of the metal, especially toughness and ductility, were greatly reduced by burning.

Evidence that burning was confined to the hinge end of the clamp indicated that the metal was overheated prior to or during the upset forging operation.

Recommendations. The forging vendor should be notified of the burned condition on the end of the clamp.

The clamps should be macroetched before cadmium plating, to detect overheating. The clamps in stock should be inspected to ensure that the metal has not been weakened by overheating during the upset forging operation.

Quench cracks are often the cause of failure in steel forgings. These cracks may be obvious and prompt the removal of a component from production, or they may be obscured during working and be present in the shipped component. Quench cracks in steel often result from stresses produced by the volume increase accompanying the austenite-to-martensite transformation. When a steel forging is quenched, martensite is formed at the outer surfaces first. As cooling continues, the inner austenite transforms, increasing volume and placing the surface material in tension. The resulting untempered martensite is hard and brittle, which renders the forging susceptible to cracking because of localized stresses that exceed the tensile strength of the steel.

This susceptibility to cracking is increased by the presence of stress raisers such as sharp fillets, tool marks or other notches, massive inclusions or voids. Quench cracks in forgings may also occur near the trim line of a closed-die forging where some localized burning may have occurred. Other factors that affect quench cracking are the hardenability of the steel, the rate of cooling, and elapsed time between quenching and tempering. In general, an increase in any of these factors increases the likelihood of quench cracking.

Quench cracks have several recognizable features. Macroscopically, they are usually straight and extend from the surface (often initiating from a fillet or tool mark) toward the center of the component. The margins of the crack may have scale present if the part was tempered after quenching. The cracks are open to the surface and may be detected by magnetic-particle, ultrasonic or eddy-current inspection. Microscopically, quench cracks are invariably intergranular and may be free of decarburization.

The example that follows describes a typical failure that resulted from a quench crack.

Example 19. Fracture of an Alloy Steel Tube Forging Resulting From a Quench Crack (Fig. 27)

One of the processing steps for tube forgings of 4337 steel was autofrettage. In this process, the tubes, heat treated to a yield strength (0.1% offset) of 170,000 psi, were subjected to internal hydraulic pressure sufficient to induce permanent (plastic) deformation, the purpose being to create a residual compressive stress on the inner wall of the tube. Such compressive stress improves the fatigue life of the tube, which is repeatedly subjected to internal pressures in service.

Occasionally, a tube forging fractured during the autofrettage process at pressures

Fig. 27. (a) *Tube forged from 4337 steel that fractured at a quench crack (at arrow) during autofrettage.* (b) *Fractograph, at about 1.1×, of a section through the tube, showing the quench crack (dark-gray area), which originated at a machining gouge on the inner wall of the tube.* (Example 19)

far below those required to cause yielding of the tube. An external view of a fractured forging is shown in Fig. 27(a).

The fractured forging was sectioned and split for examination. The cause of fracture was found to be the presence of a quench crack that extended during the hydraulic pressurization; this crack is indicated by the arrow in Fig. 22(a). The fracture surface and the relatively smooth appearance of the quench crack are shown in Fig. 27(b). The quench crack originated at a machining gouge that was present on the inside wall of the tube. The machining gouge intensified the local stresses during bore quenching and caused the crack.

Temper Embrittlement. Certain steels, particularly the chromium-nickel grades, show a severe decrease in impact strength when tempered at a temperature in the range of approximately 350 to 575 C (660 to 1065 F). The exact range depends largely on the composition of the steel. The degree of segregation and certain variables related to making the steel also influence this range. This embrittlement, which is called temper embrittlement, is believed to result from the precipitation of a complex phase at prior austenite grain boundaries; however, this is not always observable when examining a specimen known to be embrittled.

Temper embrittlement increases the ductile-to-brittle transition temperature and reduces the energy required for brittle fracture. Brittle characteristics are not easily identified by conventional tensile testing, and are more pronounced at high strain rates and low test temperatures. It has also been shown (Ref 30) that temper embrittlement significantly increases the growth rates of both fatigue cracks and stress-corrosion cracks.

When the fracture surfaces of temper-embrittled metal are examined under a microscope, the appearance is always that of an intergranular fracture with the crack path along the prior austenite grain boundaries.

The effect of alloying elements and impurities on temper embrittlement has been investigated thoroughly. The presence of increased amounts of phosphorus, antimony, arsenic and tin generally increase susceptibility to temper embrittle-

ment. It has been demonstrated that, although temper embrittlement depends on the interaction of the major alloying elements, the effect of minor elements was more severe in a chromium-nickel steel than in either a chromium steel or a nickel steel (Ref 31). Embrittlement depends both on the composition of the metal and on the thermal treatment, including the rate of cooling.

For information on several types of embrittlement, including temper embrittlement, that commonly occur in structural alloys, see the discussion beginning on page 78 in the article on Ductile and Brittle Fractures in this volume.

Carburization and Decarburization. Although surface treatment by carburization is commonly employed to improve the wear resistance and over-all strength characteristics of many forged steel components, particularly axles, the accidental alteration of the surface structure during heat treatment can produce disastrous results. Heating a metal surface that is contaminated with oil or carbon, or heating in a carbon-rich atmosphere can produce a surface with a high carbon content. The mechanical properties of a carburized surface layer are different from those of the core and cracking problems can arise because a carburized surface was not considered in the original design. For example, components subject to severe impact are rarely carburized, because the hardened surface layers generally possess low toughness.

Even when carburizing is intentional, care must be taken to control the processing variables, because the depth of case (hardened zone) is often vital to good performance. If the case is excessive, the component may fracture in a brittle manner. If the case is inadequate, it may crush under load.

Fatigue failures may initiate from microcracks in the carburized case or from stresses at the case-core interface, and then propagate during cyclic loading.

The opposite condition (decarburization) can occur by heating in an oxidizing atmosphere. Here the result is a surface layer with a lower carbon content than that of the core. Either carburization or

(a) Gear showing irregular wear on teeth. (b) Microstructure on the periphery of a gear tooth on the unworn side, showing coarse martensite with large amounts of retained austenite (white constituent). (c) Spalled teeth of a pinion. (d) Intergranular cracking at tip of a pinion tooth.

Fig. 28. Gear and pinion forged from 1.60% Mn – 5% Cr alloy steel that failed in service because of improper carburization (Example 20; Ref 29)

decarburization can be the cause of service problems, as described in the example that follows (Ref 29).

Example 20. Gear and Pinion Failures Due to Improper Carburization (Fig. 28)

A gear manufacturer experienced service problems with various gears and pinions that had worn prematurely or had fractured. All gears and pinions were forged from 1.60% Mn – 5% Cr steel and were case hardened by pack carburizing.

Gear Failure. One of the gears showed severe wear on the side of the teeth that came into contact with the opposing gear during engagement (Fig. 28a). This contact point is where high shock loads had to be accommodated at large differences in peripheral speed. The microstructure at the periphery of a worn tooth at its unworn side, shown in Fig. 28(b), consisted of coarse acicular martensite with a large percentage of retained austenite. Parts with such a structure usually have a relatively low wear resistance because of low hardness. They are also very sensitive to shock because of their large grain size.

It was concluded that the high wear rate was caused by spalling of the coarse-grained surface layer. The underlying cause of the wear was overheating during the carburization.

Pinion Failures. The teeth of the pinion in Fig. 28(c) exhibited severe spalling; the fracture surfaces at spalled regions were coarse-grained and lustrous. The microstructure at the surface consisted of coarse acicular martensite with retained austenite, similar to that shown in Fig. 28(b). Also, a coarse network of precipitated carbide par-

ticles showed that the carburization of the case had appreciably exceeded the most favorable carbon content, resulting in increased sensitivity to shock. This structure indicates that the pinions were overheated during carburizing and that the carbon content of the case was excessive.

Another pinion showed wear on one side of the teeth, similar to the wear on the gear teeth shown in Fig. 28(a). Cracks followed coarse prior austenite grain boundaries in regions along tips of teeth (see Fig. 28d).

Examination of the fracture surfaces of the pinions, together with examination of the microstructures, showed that the failures resulted from overheating combined with excessive case carbon content. These factors resulted in a large grain size with a brittle grain-boundary network. The overall effect is that the steel had low resistance to shock loading, wear and surface fatigue.

Failures Related to Hydrogen Damage

Many of the metals used in forgings are susceptible to embrittlement by hydrogen. The embrittling hydrogen originates from various sources. A major source of hydrogen in steels is the reaction of water vapor at high temperatures with the liquid metal during casting. The water vapor may come from the scrap used to charge the furnace, the slag ingredients in the charge, or the refractory materials lining the furnace. The hydrogen that results can then be trapped during solidification. Hydrogen may also

develop during acid pickling or plating operations. Exposure in service to process fluids bearing hydrogen, as in catalytic cracking, can also cause embrittlement. Similarly, hydrogen may be generated as a corrosion product in certain environments and thereby become available to cause embrittlement.

The metals most susceptible to hydrogen embrittlement are those with body-centered-cubic (bcc) crystal structures, such as steel and the refractory metals, and those with hexagonal, close-packed (hcp) crystal structures, such as titanium and zirconium.

Hydrogen Damage in Steel. Hydrogen entrapment is the most common cause of embrittlement in body-centered-cubic metals, such as steel. Hydrogen damage in steels may be evident as flakes or as general embrittlement. Flakes are small internal fissures, occurring in the interior of a forging parallel to the forging direction. These flakes may be detected by ultrasonic inspection or destructively by etching of transverse sections.

On a fracture surface, these flakes appear as bright, highly reflective areas (see Fig. 29a). Fractographic examination shows that the flakes contain some flat areas combined with other areas that appear to be contoured grain boundaries (see Fig. 29b). According to Phillips and Kerlins (Ref 32), the striations visible in the electron micrograph (Fig. 29b) are characteristic of hydrogen flakes.

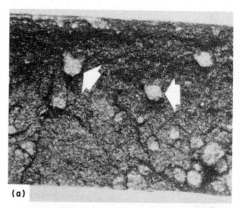

(a)

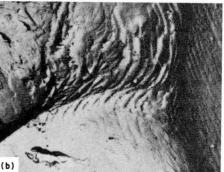

(b)

Fig. 29. (a) Macroscopic appearance of hydrogen flakes (arrows) in a 4340 steel forging at 1×. (b) Electron fractograph of contoured boundary and striations in a hydrogen flake; 6000× (Ref 32)

Hydrogen embrittlement in steel also manifests itself as a decrease in tensile strength and ductility when the steel is tested under static loads at low strain rates. Tetelman (Ref 33) states that impact tests do not indicate the presence of hydrogen embrittlement. Fractographic examinations indicate that the visible features vary. Microcracks begin internally (often near inclusions or other interfaces) and propagate intergranularly for an indeterminate distance, or they may originate from electroplated surfaces, as shown in Fig. 30. The regions between the adjacent microcracks fracture in a ductile manner, presenting evidence of microvoid coalescence (dimpling). When the effective cross section has been sufficiently reduced, final fracture occurs as the result of overstress.

It is possible that part of what has been reported in the literature as the stress-corrosion failure of high-strength steel has often been the result of hydrogen embrittlement resulting from hydrogen generated as a corrosion product. Based on fractographic examination, the differences between the two mechanisms are very subtle (Ref 34), which often makes it difficult to distinguish between them. For a detailed discussion of these mechanisms, see the articles that begin on pages 205 and 230 in this volume.

The example that follows demonstrates the adverse effect of hydrogen on an alloy steel component.

Example 21. Fracture of a Cadmium-Plated 4140 Steel Accumulator Ring Due to Hydrogen Embrittlement (Fig. 31)

Fracture of an accumulator ring forged from 4140 steel was discovered during inspection and disassembly of a hydraulic-accumulator system stored at a depot. The ring had broken into five small and two large segments.

The small segments of the broken ring displayed very flat fracture surfaces with no apparent yielding, but the two large segments did show evidence of bending (yielding) near the fractures. In addition, some segments contained fine radial cracks (see arrow on segment shown in Fig. 31a).

Investigation. Optical microscopy on polished-and-etched specimens cut from the ring revealed the microstructure to be very fine-grained tempered martensite, typical of quenched-and-tempered low-alloy steel.

Hardness testing of the broken ring yielded a range of Rockwell C 43 to 48. This hardness ranged above the required Rockwell C 40 to 45, but this small variation from requirements was not regarded as sufficient to have caused the fracture.

Inspection of fracture-surface replicas by electron microscopy disclosed the fracture mode to be predominantly intergranular (Fig. 31b). Also observed were many hairline indications on the fracture facets and some partly formed dimples. All these features are indicative of the cracking associated with hydrogen embrittlement.

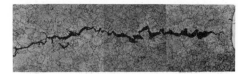

Fig. 30. Intergranular cracks originating from an electroplated coating (Ref 33)

Chemical analysis showed that all elements were within the specified limits for 4140 steel. Hydrogen-gas analysis of four specimens yielded the following hydrogen contents (in ppm): specimen 1, 0.15 ± 0.03; specimen 2, 0.23 ± 0.03; specimen 3, 2.29 ± 0.07; specimen 4, 0.29 ± 0.04. Although three values are low, specimen 3 exhibited a hydrogen content in the range of those generally associated with hydrogen embrittlement (>1 ppm). Also, these data indicate a localized hydrogen concentration rather than a uniform distribution throughout the ring.

Conclusion. Results of the examination point to a brittle fracture mechanism, as evidenced by the intergranular nature of the fracture path. Also, the hydrogen content of one tested specimen indicates that a localized embrittlement of grain boundaries by hydrogen is a very strong possibility. The fine cracks in some of the intact segments most likely existed where the fractures occurred. Since these fractures were clean (that is, showed no corrosion products, discoloration, or obvious contamination), the hydrogen most likely resulted from a processing operation. The processing history for the fractured component was reviewed for potentially detrimental operations.

The review of processing revealed that the components required cadmium plating, after which they were scheduled for stress relieving at 260 C (500 F) for 3 hr. An investigation showed that there was a strong

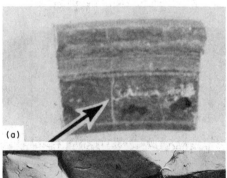

(a) Ring segment showing a fine crack (at arrow). (b) Electron fractograph, at 7800×, showing predominantly intergranular fracture.

Fig. 31. Hydrogen-embrittlement fracture in a cadmium-plated 4140 steel forged accumulator ring (Example 21)

possibility that one batch of rings did not receive the required stress-relieving treatment. The conclusion, therefore, is that the hydrogen penetration occurred during the plating operation, and was not relieved subsequently as required. The slightly higher-than-specified hardness may have helped to promote embrittlement but was not considered significant.

Hydrogen Damage in Nonferrous Alloys. Alloys other than the iron-base alloys can also be adversely affected by hydrogen. Titanium and zirconium alloys have a hexagonal, close-packed (hcp) crystal structure, and both exhibit a marked propensity toward hydrogen embrittlement through the formation of stable hydrides.

Hydrogen is also known to exert a damaging effect on the body-centered-cubic (bcc) refractory metals (tungsten, tantalum and columbium). The evidence indicates that hydrogen exists in a supersaturated solution and that stable hydrides are not present. The effect of hydrogen content on the ductility of tantalum and columbium as measured by reduction in area is shown in Fig. 32. These curves show that even low hydrogen content can be detrimental. Hydrogen in the refractory metals promotes brittle, cleavage fractures.

Failures Related to Service

Many forging failures occur that are not necessarily a result of a deficiency in material or design, but because consideration was not given to the service environment to which the forgings would be subjected. For example, degradation by corrosion or wear may occur in service, and seriously impair the function of a forging either by altering its performance or by initiating defects that can cause failure.

Corrosion is the degradation of metal by chemical or electrochemical dissolution that occurs as a result of the interaction of the metal with its environment. Occasionally, a component with a history of satisfactory performance in one environment will fail when subjected to another environment. The failure may be due to general corrosion, although this is not likely because the general effects of a specific environment are reasonably well known and can be anticipated. The damage that does occur is usually the result of localized attack resulting from crevice corrosion, pitting, corrosion of highly worked or segregated regions, or stress-corrosion cracking.

Intergranular Attack. In certain instances, the grain boundaries in a forging are more susceptible to corrosive attack than the grain interior. The preferential dissolution suffered by these areas may be related to several factors, depending on the particular circumstances.

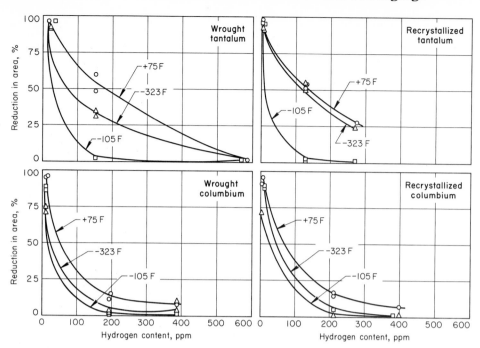

Fig. 32. Effect of hydrogen content on the ductility of wrought and recrystallized tantalum and columbium, as measured by reduction in area at the temperatures shown

Table 2. Effect of Thermal Treatments on Strength, Electrical Conductivity, and Exfoliation Ratings of Aluminum Alloy 7075-T6 Forgings Made From Three Different Materials (Example 22; Ref 35)

Thermal treatment	Longitudinal strength, ksi		Electrical conductivity, % IACS	Exfoliation rating
	Yield	Tensile		
Material I — Extruded Stock				
(5.67 Zn, 2.40 Mg, 1.58 Cu, 0.18-0.30 Cr, 0.05 Mn, 0.1-0.2 Si, 0.1-0.3 Fe, 0.05 Ni, rem Al)				
As-received (T6)	79.4	88.3	32.9	Severe
Re-solution treat, age to T6	81.3	89.1	34.0	Medium
Convert as-received T6 to T7x1	78.7	85.2	36.0	Severe
Re-solution treat, age to T6; convert to T7x1 ..	78.4	84.3	37.8	Severe
Convert as-received T6 to T76	74.7	81.3	36.7	Mild
Re-solution treat, age to T76 ...	73.9	80.3	39.0	Mild
Re-solution treat, age to T6; convert to T76 ...	73.8	80.2	38.5	Slight
Re-solution treat, age to T6; convert to T7x2 ...	74.4	80.9	38.3	Slight
Convert as-received T6 to T7x2	69.0	77.5	40.0	Immune
Convert as-received T6 to T73	64.8	73.2	42.9	Immune
Re-solution treat, age to T73	70.3	77.3	40.5	Immune
Re-solution treat, age to T6; convert to T73	65.8	74.0	40.5	Immune
Material II — Extruded Stock				
(5.67 Zn, 2.47 Mg, 1.47 Cu, 0.18-0.30 Cr, 0.05 Mn, 0.1-0.2 Si, 0.1-0.3 Fe, 0.05 Ni, rem Al)				
As-received (T6)	80.5	87.9	33.0	Medium
Re-solution treat, age to T6	79.0	88.0	32.5	Medium
Convert as-received T6 to T76	71.3	80.1	38.3	Medium
Re-solution treat, age to T76	72.5	80.7	38.9	Medium
Re-solution treat, age to T73	73.1	81.7	38.3	Slight
Convert as-received T6 to T73	67.1	75.8	40.4	Immune
Material III — Rolled Stock				
(5.67 Zn, 2.44 Mg, 1.56 Cu, 0.18-0.30 Cr, 0.05 Mn, 0.1-0.2 Si, 0.1-0.3 Fe, 0.05 Ni, rem Al)				
As-received (T6)	75.6	85.3	32.5	Medium
As-forged, solution treat and age to T6	72.4	83.2	31.4	Slight
As-received (T6) converted to T76	72.7	80.4	35.5	Medium
As-forged, solution treat and age to T6, convert to T76	71.4	78.9	36.7	Medium
As-forged, solution treat and age to T76	69.5	77.6	37.8	Medium
As-forged, solution treat and age to T73	70.6	78.9	38.0	Slight
As-forged, solution treat and age to T6, convert to T73	66.7	75.6	39.2	Immune
As-received (T6) converted to T73	66.5	74.2	40.2	Immune

The primary cause of intergranular attack is an inhomogeneous condition at the grain boundary, which may be the result of a segregation mechanism or of intergranular precipitation. These conditions may also be modified by enhanced diffusion effects operating within the grain boundary or by the selective absorption of certain solutes such as hydrogen.

The over-all effect of this preferential dissolution is that great damage to the structure can occur with only slight corrosive damage occurring to the grain bodies. Because dissolution is confined to such small regions, the actual weight losses are small, penetration rates are high, and destruction can be quite rapid.

Exfoliation is a special form of intergranular attack, which primarily affects aluminum and magnesium alloys. It is markedly directional and is characterized by attack of the elongated grains on a plane parallel to the rolled, extruded or forged surface. This results in a characteristic delamination or stratification of the surface structure. A demonstration of exfoliation of an aluminum alloy, and a discussion of the factors that affect this type of degradation, are presented in the example that follows (Ref 35).

Example 22. Failure of an Aluminum Alloy 7075-T6 Forging Due to Exfoliation (Fig. 33; Table 2)

The lower receiver of the M16 rifle is an anodized forging of aluminum alloy 7075-T6. Degradation of these receivers was observed after three years of service in a hot, humid atmosphere. The affected areas were those in frequent contact with the hands. One of the failed receivers is shown in Fig. 33(a).

Investigation. Because there was no question that the material failed as a result of exfoliation corrosion, the investigation centered around the study of thermal treatments that would increase the exfoliation resistance and still develop the required 65,000-psi yield strength.

Several factors relating to the processing were investigated, using forgings made from three different starting materials (referred to here as materials I, II and III). Specifically, the factors investigated were the grain structures developed by thermomechanical treatments, thermal treatment, and the quenching rate subsequent to the solution heat treatments.

Effect of Grain Structure. A section through a forging fabricated from material I (extruded stock) in the as-received (T6) temper is shown in Fig. 33(b). The metal had an interior structure composed of highly deformed elongated grains (micrograph A in Fig. 33), and a thin, partly recrystallized grain structure at the surface (micrograph B in Fig. 33). The yield strength of the as-received (T6) forging was about 80,000 psi; exfoliation was found to be severe.

Material II was also extruded stock, forged in the as-received (T6) temper. However, the observed microstructure of material II (see Fig. 33c) is somewhat different from that of material I. On one side (right side in Fig. 33c) there is a completely recrystallized surface layer about 0.125 in. wide; on the other side, the layer is only a few grain diameters in width. The surface grains are elongated vertically (micrograph C in Fig. 33), and the structure in the interior of this forging (micrograph D in Fig. 33) is similar to that observed with material I. The yield strength of material II also was similar to that of material I (approximately 80,000 psi), but exfoliation of material II was rated as intermediate.

A third forging, fabricated from rolled stock (material III) had a microstructure (see Fig. 33d) quite different from that of either material I or material II. For the material III forging, the structure on both surfaces was composed of recrystallized grains with no directionality. The microstructure changed from highly deformed grains at the center (micrograph E in Fig. 33) to large equiaxed grains near and at the surface (micrographs F and G in Fig. 33). The yield strength of this material in the T6 temper was 75,600 psi, and the exfoliation resistance was intermediate. Laboratory reheat treatment further enhanced the improvement in exfoliation resistance of the material III forging when all materials were re-treated to the T6 temper.

Thermal Treatment. Table 2 shows the compositions and mechanical properties of materials I, II and III, and the exfoliation resistance of forgings from the three materials that was obtained with various thermal treatments.

In general, forgings in the T6 temper had the highest strength but also had the lowest resistance to exfoliation. Thermal softening of the as-received T6 forgings as induced by the intermediate tempers was accompanied by a slight increase in exfoliation resistance. With two exceptions, all forgings heat treated to the T73 temper were immune to exfoliation and had a minimum longitudinal yield strength of 65,000 psi. All forgings

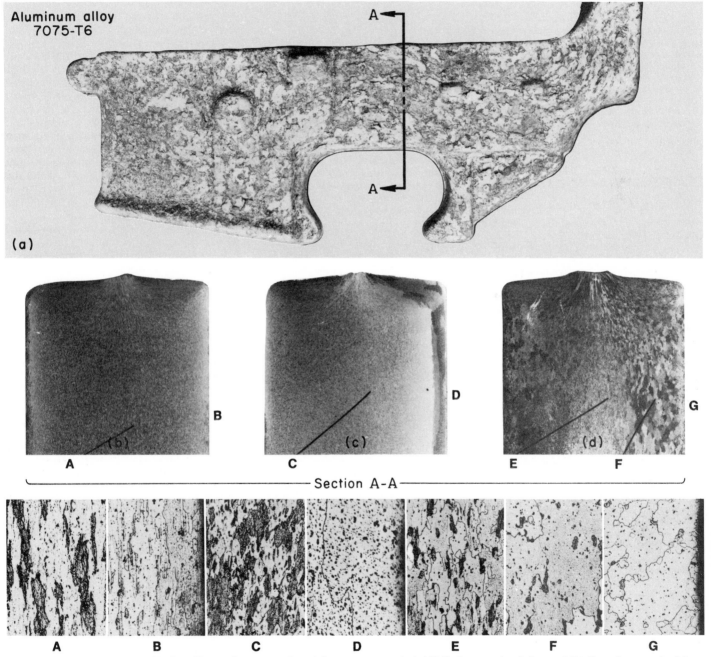

(a) Rifle receiver, at 0.7×. Similar rifle receivers were forged from three different materials to investigate the effects of processing on resistance to exfoliation; see Table 2 for compositions of the materials (identified there as materials I, II and III) and results of thermal treatments. In section A-A, (b), (c) and (d) are sections, etched in concentrated Keller's reagent and shown at 2×, through as-received forgings made of materials I, II and III, respectively; letters A through G indicate locations of specimens, etched in Keller's reagent, shown in the correspondingly lettered micrographs at bottom. These micrographs, at 80×, compare the grain structures of the three materials.

Fig. 33. Forged aluminum alloy 7075-T6 receiver from an M16 rifle that failed by exfoliation corrosion (Example 22; Ref 35)

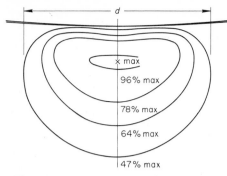

Fig. 34. *Location of maximum stress for elastic contact of a sphere and a flat object relative to the surface of the flat object* (Ref 37)

with an electrical conductivity of at least 40.0% IACS were immune to exfoliation.

Quench Rate. The data below, obtained by quenching in water at four different temperatures, show that susceptibility to exfoliation increased markedly as the temperature of the quenching medium increased:

Quench-water temperature	Yield strength (0.2% offset), ksi	Electrical conductivity, % IACS	Exfoliation rating
24 C (75 F)	81.4	33.0	Mild
66 C (150 F)	81.3	34.0	Medium
79 C (175 F)	76.4	33.9	Severe
82 C (180 F)	74.4	34.1	Severe

Conclusions. The results of the study show that differences in grain structure of the forgings, as induced by differences in thermal-mechanical history of the forged material, can have a significant effect on susceptibility to exfoliation corrosion. This factor, which heretofore was considered to be relatively minor, appears to be very important for material in the T6 temper. It was observed that forgings fabricated from rolled stock, identically treated to T6, had a higher resistance to exfoliation than forgings from extruded stock. The increased resistance to exfoliation observed on forgings from rolled stock is attributable to a more favorable randomized grain structure induced by the rolling process. Thus, for optimizing exfoliation corrosion resistance of high-strength forgings, rolled bar stock should be preferred to extruded bar stock.

Regarding thermal treatment, the results show conclusively that large changes in strength and exfoliation characteristics of 7075 forgings can be induced by changes in temperature or time of thermal treatment.

With regard to the effect of quenching rate on exfoliation characteristics, a cold-water quench $\leq$24 C (75 F) would appear to be far superior to an elevated-temperature quench to minimize exfoliation of 7075 forgings in the T6 temper. Under conditions where the temperature of water approaches 82 C (180 F), exfoliation could become very severe.

Wear is a major mechanism in the degradation of equipment with moving components. If the wear occurs at a predictable and steady rate, the useful life of the component can readily be established and provisions made for its replacement. If, however, the wear mecha-

nism is such that the wear rate is not steady or predictable, or results in catastrophic failure, the consequences obviously are more serious.

Pitting, in a wear situation, is the result of surface (rolling-contact) fatigue under high contact stresses. One major difference between the more conventional fatigue and surface fatigue is that no apparent endurance limit exists in surface fatigue; that is, there seems to be no stress level below which the material remains unaffected by surface-fatigue damage. Another difference is that test data are subject to wider scatter than that obtained in conventional fatigue tests. Consequently, on the basis of test results, it is exceedingly difficult to design a highly stressed bearing component with the positive knowledge that surface fatigue has been eliminated.

Pitting caused by surface fatigue is discussed in detail on page 151 in the article on Wear Failures, and on pages 425 to 430 in the article on Failures of Rolling-Element Bearings.

Cracks may originate at a subsurface location when the maximum contact (Hertzian) stresses are coincident with an inclusion site. Maximum contact stresses occur slightly below the surface (see Fig. 34). Vacuum arc remelting, vacuum induction melting, electroslag melting and electron beam refining have resulted in materials with significantly reduced inclusion counts. In these materials, the importance of inclusions relative to crack initiation has been minimized so that studies have been directed more toward the effects of segregation, retained austenite, and the role of banded or fibered structures on crack initiation.

The type of surface movement (that is, rolling versus sliding) also helps to determine whether the crack will originate at the surface or subsurface. With pure rolling, the maximum shear stress occurs below the surface. When a sliding component is added, however, the maximum shear stresses may occur at the surface.

Pits are generally triangular or fan-shaped in appearance, with the apex of the triangle pointing in the direction of

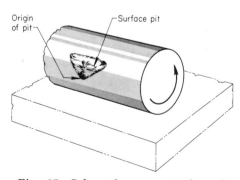

Fig. 35. *Schematic representation of shape and orientation of a surface pit in a rotating component with respect to the direction of rotation*

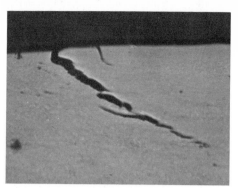

Fig. 36. *Micrograph, at 150×, of a cross section of a pitted area at the surface of a steel forging. Note the gradual incline of the pit to the surface, near top of micrograph.* (Ref 36)

rotation of the surface in which they appear, as shown schematically in Fig. 35. A micrograph of an actual surface pit in the initial stages of development is shown in Fig. 36; note the gradual incline to the surface near the origin.

Electron-microscope techniques have been utilized in fractography to study pitting (and spalling) under conditions of rolling-contact fatigue. These studies show that the fracture surface of the leading edge of a pit is comprised primarily of equiaxed and elongated cavities typical of ductile fracture by the growth and coalescence of microvoids. This area extends approximately one-third the distance to the trailing edge. The remainder of the surface exhibits parabolic tongues. Syniuta and Corrow (Ref 36) suggest that the initial crack results from fatigue at the leading edge and, upon some extension, the crack becomes fast-growing and completes the fracture. This change from fatigue extension to fast growth is believed to result in the change in fracture appearance from the leading-edge area to the trailing-edge area.

Spalling results when several pits join or when a crack runs parallel to the surface for some distance rather than running into it (subsurface). Consequently, spalling defects are typically large. Spalling from cracks is often associated with surface-hardened parts and occurs near the core-case interface. Spalling occurs because the shear strength of the subsurface material is inadequate to withstand the shear stress to which it is subjected. Spalling may often be prevented by increasing the case depth or the core hardness.

Fretting, often called fretting corrosion, occurs as the result of a slight oscillatory motion between two mating surfaces under load, and manifests itself as pits in the surface surrounded by oxidation debris. An example of fretting damage is shown in Fig. 37.

The relative motion required to produce fretting damage may be quite small. Displacements of 10^{-6} in. are sufficient

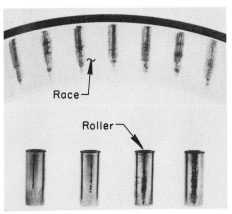

Fig. 37. Fretting damage on rollers and inner race of a bearing assembly (Ref 38)

to cause damage, but the amplitudes of displacement usually seen in service are in the order of a few thousandths of an inch. Figure 38 shows the effect of cyclic displacement on total weight loss for a low-carbon steel.

The total amount of fretting damage increases with increasing number of cycles of oscillation. The increase is essentially linear except for the initial stage of fretting, when very little abrasive material is available to cause damage. Frequency effects are observed but are usually small. Uhlig (Ref 39) indicates that the wear rate is higher at low frequencies but decreases to a constant value as frequency increases.

Although fretting damage alone is sufficient to cause malfunction in many close-tolerance components, the problem is made even more serious because fatigue fractures frequently are initiated from fretting pits.

For additional discussion of fretting and fretting mechanisms, the reader is referred to the article on Fretting Failures, which begins on page 154 in this volume.

Erosion may result from cavitation or from the impingement of liquid or solid particles on a surface. Cavitation erosion and liquid impingement are discussed in the article on Liquid-Erosion Failures beginning on page 160 in this volume. Erosion by solid particles (abrasive erosion) is discussed on page 140 in the article on Wear Failures.

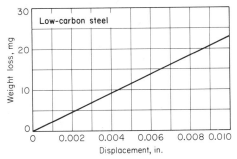

Fig. 38. Effect of cyclic displacement on total weight loss resulting from fretting, for a low-carbon steel (Ref 39)

Erosion can be prevented or minimized by changing the material to one that is more erosion resistant or by modifying the design so as to decrease erosion severity. However, it is impossible to make absolute statements regarding the selection of materials for erosive application without testing, except to state that materials that possess good corrosion resistance to the environment in question and have high hardness will, in general, perform satisfactorily. Tests should always be performed to verify the selection.

Design changes made to reduce turbulence or to reduce velocities, such as removing protuberances or increasing tube diameters, are beneficial. So are modifications such as increased radii on elbows and streamlined baffles, which reduce impingement severity.

Erosion-corrosion is exemplified by an increase in corrosion rate caused by relative motion between a metal surface and a corroding environment.

The good corrosion resistance of many metals is due to an insoluble film that is created and maintained on the metal surface. Although increases in velocity of relative motion between the metal and its environment may occasionally decrease the rate of corrosion because of kinetic factors, the general effect of increasing velocity is that film maintenance is impaired; corrosion rates increase as the surface film is destroyed. Erosion-corrosion presents a distinct appearance. The metal surface usually exhibits severe weight loss, with many hollowed-out regions; the over-all surface presents a carved appearance.

Figure 39 shows progressive thinning caused by erosion-corrosion in the wall of a 1030 steel tube. Progressive thinning of the wall occurred until the hoop stress generated by the internal pressure exceeded the yield strength of the material and the wall ruptured.

Failures Related to Mechanical Damage

Frequently, failure of a component may occur that is obviously the result of a specific failure mechanism such as fatigue, but no abnormality in materials or design may become apparent during the investigations. A search of the records and history of the component may show that the component suffered mechanical damage during the course of service or during handling.

Marks produced by electric engraving tools may produce transformation of the base metal, embrittlement and subsequent fatigue-crack initiation and fracture.

Surface abrasion of cold drawn wire during the handling of the coils may produce fatigue fracture in springs fabricated from the wire.

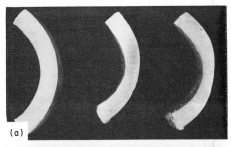

Fig. 39. (a) Progressive thinning (left to right) in the wall of a 1030 steel tube, caused by erosion-corrosion, which resulted in a rupture due to internal pressure. (b) Portion of the tube wall, showing longitudinal rupture.

Impact to an axle during service can result in distortion that can alter the performance of the axle, result in bearing damage and, sometimes, cause fatigue fracture. A fatigue fracture caused by impact during service is discussed in the example that follows.

Example 23. Fatigue Fracture of a 4340 Steel Steering Knuckle Caused by Deformation (Fig. 40)

A steering knuckle used on an earthmover failed in service. The component fractured into a flange portion and a shaft portion. The flange was approximately 11 in. in diameter and had 12 evenly spaced $\frac{5}{8}$-in.-diam boltholes around its diameter. The shaft was hollow, approximately $4\frac{1}{8}$-in. OD with a wall thickness of approximately $\frac{11}{16}$ in. The steering knuckle was made of 4340 steel and heat treated to a hardness of about 415 Bhn (yield strength of about 155,000 psi).

Investigation. The fracture was examined through a stereoscopic microscope. The fracture surface on the flange side of the fracture is shown in Fig. 40. Examination of the fracture surface revealed the presence of numerous beach marks, emanating from several fracture origins.

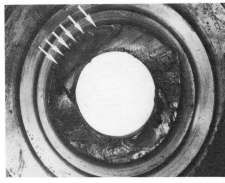

Fig. 40. Fracture surface of a 4340 steel steering-knuckle flange that failed in service by fatigue. Arrows indicate fracture origins. (Example 23)

The fracture originated in the fillet at the junction between the flange and the shaft portions. This is an unexpected location because of the large radius of the fillet, which minimizes stress concentration. Had the fillet been sharp, the stress concentrations would have been high and the fatigue fracture more likely. In addition, the fillet was shot peened, which further reduced tensile stresses. Both of these factors (the large radius and the shot peened surface) indicated that the manufacturer had used good design practice.

Examination of the fracture surface also verified that the component was subjected to a low stress concentration at the origin and to moderate loading. These factors were established by the location of the zone of final fracture. Microstructural examination revealed no unusual discontinuities or inclusions that might act as stress raisers.

Service history of the earthmover indicated that the vehicle had been involved in a field accident six months before the steering knuckle failed. Several components, including portions of the frame, had been damaged and replaced as a result of this accident, but there was no observed damage to the steering.

Conclusions. The failure was due to a fatigue fracture. No evidence of a defective design was observed; on the contrary, the generous radius of the fillet and the shot peened surface are indicative of good design practice. In addition, there was no evidence of an improper microstructure, high inclusion count or other stress-raising condition that might account for fatigue-crack initiation. From the service history, it was concluded that the fracture was the result of the prior accident, the most likely explanation being that the shaft was bent in the accident and continued use caused a crack to initiate and propagate to fracture.

Summary

The more important aspects of forging failures and their analysis have been discussed and illustrated in this article. To include every type of forging failure would be impossible; however, the following tabulation illustrates the variety and frequency of failures that commonly occur in industrial plants:

Service or operational failures	36%
Failures caused by faulty design	34%
Failures resulting from shop and mill practice	17%
Failures due to metallurgical aspects	13%

This information is a result of a review of some 470 failures in a single plant over several years (Ref 40). In the highest category, service or operational failures, overload or overstress for various reasons were predominant, with 28% of the total number of failures reviewed; wear and corrosion were next within this category. In the design-related failure category, sharp corners and sharp fillets alone accounted for 12% of the total number of failures reviewed; misapplication of materials, or simply using the wrong type of steel for the design, was responsible for approximately 8%. Shop and mill practices resulting in failure included such items as improper grinding, welding stress, defective welds, faulty lubrication, and misalignment. The final category, metallurgical aspects, entailed improper heat treatment, quench cracks, forging defects and residual stress.

Although these percentages apply strictly to a particular plant, they also show a good correspondence with the preponderance of forging failures.

It is evident that forging failures usually can be attributed to more than one mechanism or cause. Very often, though, one of these mechanisms controls the failure process. In this circumstance, the failure analyst must isolate and define the particular problem. It is only when this identification has been accomplished that complete corrective measures can be instituted.

References

1. M. Baeyertz, "Nonmetallic Inclusions in Steel", American Society for Metals, Metals Park, Ohio, 1947, p 1
2. V. N. Whittacker, *Nondestructive Testing*, Oct 1971, p 320
3. G. E. Dieter, Jr., "Mechanical Metallurgy", McGraw-Hill, Inc., New York, 1961, p 151
4. A. T. English, *J Metals*, Vol 17, No. 4 (Apr. 1965), p 395
5. V. J. Colangelo, *Trans AIME*, Vol 233 (1965), p 319
6. J. T. Ransom and R. F. Mehl, *Proc ASTM*, Vol 52 (1952), p 779
7. B. M. Kapadia, A. T. English and W. A. Backofen, *Trans Am Soc Metals*, Vol 55 (1962), p 389
8. F. A. Heiser and R. W. Hertzberg, *J Basic Eng*, Vol 93, No. 2 (Feb 1971), p 211
9. V. Packard, "The Wastemakers", David McKay Co., Inc., New York, 1960, p 53
10. D. J. Wulpi, *Metal Prog*, Dec 1965, p 66
11. F. K. Naumann and F. Spies, *Prakt Metallog*, Vol 7, 1969, p 447-456
12. G. E. Dieter, Jr., "Mechanical Metallurgy", McGraw-Hill, Inc., New York, 1961, p 151
13. V. J. Colangelo and F. A. Heiser, "Analysis of Metallurgical Failures", John Wiley and Sons, New York, 1974
14. P. A. Thornton, *J Mater Sci*, Vol 6 (1971), p 347
15. D. V. Edmonds and C. J. Beevers, *J Mater Sci*, Vol 3 (1968), p 457
16. R. Kiessling, "Nonmetallic Inclusions in Steel", Part III, ISI Publication No. 115, The Iron and Steel Institute, London, 1968, p 88
17. F. K. Naumann and F. Spies, *Prakt Metallog*, Vol 10 (1973), p 532
18. E. Kauczor, *Prakt Metallog*, Vol 8 (July 1971), p 443-446
19. D. J. Wulpi, *Metal Prog*, Dec 1965, p 70
20. C. T. Nolan, T. V. Brassard and R. F. DeFries, *Metals Eng Quart*, May 1973, p 30-34
21. G. Paul, *Prakt Metallog*, Vol 8 (1971), p 254
22. E. C. Bain and H. W. Paxton, "Alloying Elements in Steel", American Society for Metals, Metals Park, Ohio, 1961, p 124
23. L. J. Ebert, F. T. Krotine and A. R. Troiano, *Metal Prog*, Sept 1966, p 61
24. E. C. Bain and H. W. Paxton, "Alloying Elements in Steel", American Society for Metals, Metals Park, Ohio, 1961, p 188
25. H. E. McGannon, "The Making, Shaping and Treating of Steel", U. S. Steel, 1964, p 999
26. E. Kauczor, *Prakt Metallog*, Vol 9 (1972), p 298
27. E. Kauczor, *Prakt Metallog*, Vol 11 (1974), p 36
28. R. F. Mehl and C. S. Barrett, Studies Upon the Widmanstätten Structure, Part 1, AIME Technical Publication No. 353 (1930)
29. F. K. Naumann and F. Spies, *Prakt Metallog*, Vol 11 (1974), p 40-44
30. V. J. Colangelo, Effect of Temper Embrittlement on Fatigue and SCC Growth Rates, ASM Westec Conference, 1973 (unpublished paper)
31. J. R. Low, D. F. Stein, A. M. Turkalo and R. D. LaForce, *Trans AIME*, Vol 242 (1968), p 14-24
32. A. Phillips and V. Kerlins, *Metal Prog*, May 1969, p 81-85
33. A. S. Tetelman, Ph.D. Thesis, Yale University
34. B. V. Whiteson, A. Phillips, R. A. Rawe and V. Kerlins, Special Fractographic Techniques for Failure Analysis, Annual Meeting of ASTM, Boston, June 1967
35. J. V. Rinnovatore, K. F. Lukens and J. D. Corrie, *Corrosion*, Vol 29, No. 9 (Sept 1973), p 364-372
36. W. D. Syniuta and C. J. Corrow, *Wear*, Vol 15 (1970), p 187-199
37. E. Rabinowitz, "Friction and Wear of Materials", Wiley, 1965, p 193
38. R. L. Widner and J. O. Wolfe, *Metal Prog*, Apr 1968, p 79-86
39. H. H. Uhlig, I. M. Feng, W. D. Tierney and A. McClellan, Fundamental Investigation of Fretting Corrosion, NACA Technical Note No. 3029, Dec 1953
40. "Republic Alloy Steels", Republic Steel Corp., 1968, p 352

Failures of Iron and Steel Castings

*By the ASM Committee on Casting-Performance Analysis**

ALTHOUGH unfavorable foundry practice can result in a variety of casting imperfections that are detrimental in service and that may contribute to failure, many of the common causes of failure of iron and steel castings are not foundry-related. These include improper design, selection of an alloy that is not suited for the application, faulty machining or welding, improper assembly, abusive use, and a range of environmental service factors, some of which may not have been anticipated when the casting was placed in service. In addition, some failures cannot be fully accounted for because of lack of substantiating data.

This article emphasizes failure analysis, rather than failure statistics. Although many of the common causes of casting failure are considered here, particularly those related to foundry practice, it is recognized that many of the causes not related to foundry practice have received less adequate treatment here because of lack of data.

Imperfections That Can Occur in Iron and Steel Castings

This section presents definitions of the imperfections and discontinuities that can occur in iron and steel castings and that may be the basis for rejection during inspection. Some of these imperfections, if undetected, can serve as initiation points of casting failures during service. The effects of these imperfections on casting performance depend largely on their severity and location.

buckle. An indentation in a sand casting resulting from expansion of the sand.

cold shot. A small globule of metal that has solidified prematurely and that is embedded in, but not entirely fused with, the surface of the casting.

cold shut. A discontinuity on, or immediately beneath, the surface of a casting, caused by the meeting of two streams of liquid metal that failed to merge. A cold shut may have the appearance of a crack or *seam* with smooth rounded edges.

gas porosity. Voids caused by entrapped gas, such as air or steam, or by the expulsion of dissolved gases during solidification.

hot crack. A crack or fracture caused by internal stresses that develop after solidification and during cooling from an elevated temperature (above 650 C, or 1200 F, for gray iron). A hot crack is less visible (less open) than a *hot tear* and usually exhibits less evidence of oxidation and decarburization.

hot tear. A crack or fracture formed prior to completion of solidification because of hindered contraction. A hot tear frequently is open to the surface of the casting and thus exposed to the atmosphere. This may result in oxidation, decarburization or other metal-atmosphere reactions at the tear surface.

inclusions. Nonmetallic materials in a solid metallic matrix. In castings, common inclusions include particles of refractory, slag, deoxidation products, or oxides of the casting metal.

mechanical (cold) crack. A crack or fracture resulting from rough handling or from thermal shock, such as may occur at shakeout or during heat treatment.

metal penetration. An imperfection on the surface of a casting caused by the penetration of molten metal into voids between refractory particles of the mold — usually the result of excessive pouring temperatures or overly coarse refractory.

misrun. A casting not fully formed because of solidification of metal before the mold is filled.

off-dimension casting. A casting of the wrong size, or containing an error in shape, as a result of a dimensional error in the pattern, incorrect design of the pattern and the mold equipment, mismatch between cope and drag, or shifting of a core during pouring.

rattail. In a sand casting, a minor *buckle* occurring as a small irregular line on the surface.

sand hole. A pit in the surface of a sand casting resulting from a deposit of loose sand on the surface of the mold.

scab. An imperfection consisting of a flat volume of metal joined to a casting through a small area. Usually a scab is set in a depression in the casting and is separated from the metal of the casting proper by a thin layer of sand.

seam. An unfused fold or lap on a cast surface that appears as a crack. See also *cold shut.*

shrinkage porosity. Voids resulting from solidification shrinkage. The growth of dendrites during the freezing process may isolate local regions, preventing complete feeding from the risers. Shrinkage cavities or depressions are the result of shrinkage porosity.

stress cracks. Cracks that result from high residual stresses after the casting has cooled to below 650 C (1200 F). Stress cracks may form at room temperature several days after casting.

Composition and Properties. Although improper chemical composition and mechanical properties are not ordinarily considered to be casting "imperfections", they may result in unsatisfactory performance in service. Improper microstructure and deviations from specified hardness or mechanical-property requirements may result in inadequate load-bearing capacity, brittle behavior, or poor wear resistance — deficiencies that may contribute to premature failure.

Procedures Employed in Failure Analysis

In general, the procedures, techniques and precautions in failure analysis described in the article that begins on page 10 may be applied to castings without modification. Other useful information on failure-analysis procedures is available in Volume 9 of this Handbook.

One step in specimen preparation that may require special consideration for castings is macroetching. Deep etching to bring out with greater contrast such aspects of structure as "ingotism" should be avoided. Etching deeply will reveal no additional features, and the acid may produce a type of pitting attack that creates an illusion of internal porosity. Polishing and light macroetching will adequately reveal the characteristics of the cast structure without producing false indications of porosity.

*A. H. RAUCH, *Chairman*, Senior Scientist, Materials Research, Deere & Co.; THOMAS E. BARKER, Director of Metallurgy, National Castings Div., Midland-Ross Corp.; CHARLES O. CAMBRIDGE, Plant Metallurgist, Kokomo Transmission Plant, Chrysler Corp.

ERNEST D. COBERLY, JR., Foundry Metallurgist, Ross Aluminum Foundries; W. J. DOELKER, Manager, Metallurgical Engineering and Quality Control, Metal Molding Operations Div., National Cash Register Corp.; HENRY T. HADLEY, Supervisor – Metallurgy, Materials and Welding Engineering, Pacific Car & Foundry Co.; THEODORE R.

NEWMAN, Chief Metallurgist, Nalco Chemical Co.; GEORGE OTTO, Supervisor – Process Engineering, Maytag Co.; JOHN A. RICHTER, Consulting Engineer, formerly with Engineering Support Service Project, Pan American World Airways, Inc.; WOODROW A. SCHILLING, Chief Chemist, Kohler Co.; LARRY J. VANDE WALLE, Materials Engineer, Engineering Research, International Harvester Co.

RAY E. WARNOCK, Project Metallurgist, Gas Turbine Components Group, Howmet Corp.; SAMUEL L. WILLIAMS, Metallurgist, Rock Island Arsenal, Department of the Army.

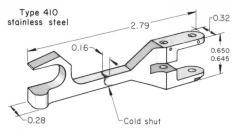

Fig. 1. Cast type 410 stainless steel fuel-control lever that fractured at a cold shut (Example 1)

Effect of Surface Discontinuities

Unless a surface discontinuity is of critical size or is located at a portion of the casting surface that is subjected to major stress, it is unlikely to decrease the service life of the casting. This section describes several types of surface discontinuities, some of which usually contribute only to poor appearance of castings.

The most damaging types of surface discontinuities are those that are linear in nature, those that generate notch-type stress raisers, and combinations of both. Among these are hot tears, cold cracks, and shrinkage porosity that extends to the casting surface; and surface porosity, inclusions, cold shuts and seams. Discontinuities such as misruns, cold shots, scabs and buckles are among those that contribute only to poor casting appearance and that rarely initiate failure.

Cold shuts and seams are discontinuities that are formed in all types of castings. In general, they are caused by pouring metal at too low a temperature or running it over too long a distance. Cold shuts and seams are similar, varying chiefly in severity; seams are less pronounced. Cold shuts and seams occur when two streams of molten metal meet but do not completely merge, and may serve as sites of stress concentration (notches) that can originate fatigue cracks. A failure caused by a cold shut is described in the following example.

Example 1. Fracture of a Cast Type 410 Stainless Steel Lever Because of a Cold Shut (Fig. 1)

The lever shown in Fig. 1 was a component of the main fuel-control linkage of an aircraft engine. After a service life of less than 50 hr, the lever fractured in flight. The lever had been machined from a casting made of type 410 stainless steel and then surface hardened by nitriding.

Investigation. Examination revealed that the lever had broken at a cold shut (see Fig. 1), which extended through about 95% of the cross section of the lever arm. The remaining 5% of the cross section appeared to be sound metal.

Specifications for both the casting and the finished lever required radiographic inspection. This inspection method will reveal internal voids such as gas porosity or shrinkage porosity, but will not detect a crack or a cold shut unless the plane of the imperfection is nearly in line with and parallel to the x-ray beam and unless there is a finite opening; a cold shut that has its faces in contact cannot be revealed by radiography.

Conclusion. The lever broke at a cold shut extending through approximately 95% of the cross section. The normally applied load constituted an overload of the remainder of the lever.

Corrective Measure. Magnetic-particle inspection was added to the inspection procedures for this cast lever. Because cold shuts extend to the surface of a casting, magnetic-particle inspection is a relatively reliable method of detecting them in ferromagnetic materials.

Misruns and Cold Shots. Misruns usually do not result in rejection of castings, unless good surface appearance is of primary importance. If a misrun is not severe, it should offer little difficulty in service provided it is not in a highly stressed region of the casting. Cold shots are the result of turbulence and occur when metal splatters during pouring, adheres to the mold wall, and fails to fuse with the metal that engulfs it as the mold is filled. Cold shots thus are globules embedded in the casting and normally produce no ill effect except for appearance. Under certain conditions, however, the interface between the cold shot and the casting can serve as a corrosion cell that leads to pitting and the initiation of fatigue cracks.

Hot tears and hot cracks sometimes are produced in external surfaces, such as in the fillet of a flange or a rib, when over-all contraction of the casting is hindered by the mold. Normally, hot tears and hot cracks should be discovered during inspection. Steel castings should either be repaired by welding or be rejected, depending on the size and location of the discontinuity and the weldability of the alloy. If hot tears and hot cracks escape detection and are present in castings put in service, they may propagate into larger cracks. Fracture of a casting originating at a hot tear is described in the example that follows.

Example 2. Fatigue Fracture of a Sand Cast Medium-Carbon Steel Axle Housing That Originated at a Hot Tear (Fig. 2)

A sand cast medium-carbon steel (0.25% C, 1.00% Mn, 0.40% Cr, 0.35% Mo) heavy-duty axle housing, which had been quenched and tempered to about Rockwell C 30, fractured after almost 5000 hr of service.

Investigation. The fracture surface of the axle housing is shown in Fig. 2. Study of the casting revealed that the fracture had been initiated by a hot tear (region at A in Fig. 2) about 4 in. long, which had completely penetrated the 1-in.-thick wall; this tear formed during solidification of

Fig. 2. Fracture surface (at about 0.4×) of a sand cast medium-carbon steel heavy-duty axle housing. Failure originated at a hot tear (at A), which propagated in fatigue (at B's) until final fracture occurred by overload. (Example 2)

the casting. The mass of a feeder-riser system located near the tear retarded cooling in this region, creating a hot spot.

Because this tear formed at a high temperature and was open to the surface, it was subject to oxidation, as indicated by the dark scale in the area at A in Fig. 2. Exposure to air also resulted in decarburization below the oxide scale and penetration of oxide along secondary cracks.

Both the size of the hot tear and the long service life of the housing indicated that the service stresses in the region of the tear had been relatively low. Stress concentrations at the tip of the tear, however, were sufficient to initiate the formation of two fatigue cracks (note the beach marks visible in regions B in Fig. 2). Ultimately, the effective thickness of the housing wall was reduced sufficiently for the applied load to cause final fracture. In this instance, the hot tear was located at an area of low stress, and the casting served a satisfactory life. However, had the local stress been high, even a very small discontinuity could have generated an early fracture.

Conclusions. Fracture of the axle housing originated at a hot tear that formed during solidification by hindered contraction and was enlarged in service by fatigue.

Corrective Measure. Changing the feeder location eliminated the hot spot, and thus the occurrence of hot tearing.

Mechanical (cold) cracks may be generated by rough treatment or by thermal shock in cooling, either at shakeout or during heat treatment. These cracks may be very difficult to detect without the aid of nondestructive testing. Magnetic-particle or liquid-penetrant inspection should reveal them clearly. Depending on the value and weldability of the casting, mechanical cracks should be removed and repair welded, unless they are so large as to warrant scrapping of the casting. Removal by grinding, chipping or other methods must be complete, or the remaining portion of the crack will be a stress raiser beneath the weld. Magnetic-particle or liquid-penetrant inspection after grinding is effective in determining if a crack has been removed completely.

Fracture of a highway-truck equalizer beam that propagated from a mechanical crack originating at a casting imperfection is described in the next example.

Example 3. Fracture of Cast Low-Alloy Steel Equalizer Beams, Which Propagated From Mechanical Cracks That Originated at Casting Imperfections (Fig. 3)

Two sand cast low-alloy steel equalizer beams designed to distribute the load to the axles of a highway truck broke after an unreported length of service. Normal service life would have been about 500,000 miles of truck operation. The cast equalizer beams were made according to ASTM A148, grade 105-85, which specifies that all castings be heat treated (either annealed, normalized, normalized and tempered, or quenched and tempered, usually at the option of the foundry).

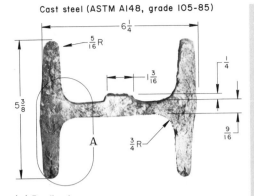

Cast steel (ASTM A148, grade 105-85)

(a) Equalizer beam

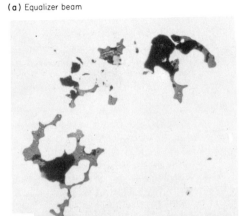

(b)

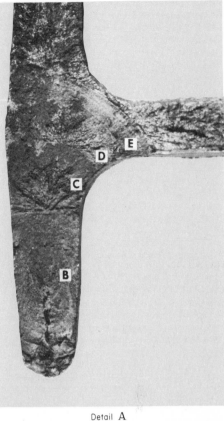

Detail A

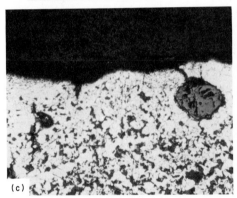

(c)

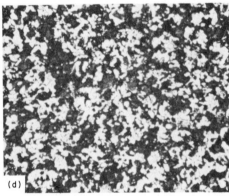

(d)

(a) Fracture surface; detail A shows increments (at B, C, D and E) in which crack propagation sequentially occurred. (b) Micrograph (at 65×) of an unetched specimen, showing internal shrinkage porosity and entrapped oxides. (c) Micrograph (at 65×) of a specimen etched in 1% nital, showing internal tensile crack and cold shut adjacent to fracture surface; note faint evidence of dendritic segregation at lower left. (d) Micrograph (at 65×) showing nonhomogenized microstructure consisting of transformation products and ferrite.

Fig. 3. Highway-truck equalizer beam, sand cast from low-alloy steel, that fractured because of mechanical cracking (Example 3)

Investigation. Figure 3(a) shows a fracture surface of one of the beams. Internal shrinkage porosity and evidence of a cold shut were found near the tip of one flange, as shown in detail A in Fig. 3. Decarburization of the fracture surface indicates that the initial crack (at B in detail A in Fig. 3) was formed prior to heat treatment — most likely as a mechanical crack resulting from rough handling during shakeout. The crack originated in a region of internal shrinkage porosity and entrapped oxides.

The appearance of the fracture surface suggests that propagation of the crack occurred in a sequence of four large increments (marked B, C, D and E in detail A in Fig. 3). The detectable difference in darkening of these fracture segments indicates that they existed in turn for sufficient lengths of time to undergo different cumulative amounts of surface oxidation. This behavior is indicative of infrequent but high loads. The fracture segment marked E in detail A in Fig. 3 shows a band of fatigue beach marks that nearly penetrated the fillet between the upper portion of the left flange and the web of the beam. At this stage, final fracture occurred, either because the remaining section of the beam was unable to sustain the applied load, or as the result of a high load such as those that caused earlier crack advances.

Examination of the fracture surface of the second beam showed that only two incre-

ments of crack propagation occurred before
final fracture and that there was no fatigue
cracking. Failure in the second beam occurred after far less crack penetration than
in the companion beam, indicating that a
high load, rather than a uniformly applied
load, caused final fracture.

Both beams exhibited evidence of internal
shrinkage porosity and entrapped oxides; a
typical condition is shown in the micrograph
in Fig. 3(b). Areas of decarburization were
found on the fracture surfaces of both
beams. Internal cracking and cold shuts such
as those shown in Fig. 3(c) were evident
adjacent to the fracture surfaces.

The microstructure of the beams consisted of transformation products and
ferrite, as shown in Fig. 3(d). The microconstituents exhibited some evidence of
dendritic segregation.

Chemical analysis of the two beams,
which were cast from separate heats of steel,
showed close agreement in composition. The
average composition was 0.32% C, 0.93%
Mn, 0.014% P, 0.023% S, 0.46% Si, less than
0.05%Ni, 0.95% Cr, 0.25% Mo.

A tensile specimen and a Charpy V-notch
test bar were machined from one flange of
each beam. The properties of the two beams
were in close agreement. Average values
were: tensile strength, 103,250 psi; yield
strength (0.2% offset), 55,250 psi; elongation in 2 in., 20%; reduction in area, 48%;
and room-temperature impact strength, 24
ft-lb. These properties indicated that the
steel was too soft for the application —
probably due to improper heat treatment.

Conclusions. Fracture of the equalizer
beams resulted from growth of mechanical
cracks in one flange that were formed before
the castings were heat treated. The pattern
of crack growth suggested a service condition involving many relatively low applied
stresses and occasional high loads.

Recommendations. Three changes in
processing were recommended:

1 Better gating and risering in the foundry
  to achieve sounder castings
2 Better shakeout practice to avoid mechanical damage, and better inspection to detect
  imperfections
3 Normalizing and tempering to achieve
  better mechanical properties.

Pits and Sand Holes. Dirt or sand inclusions in the surface of a casting generally are removed in cleaning. The
resulting cavities affect appearance but,
in general, are unlikely to affect performance in service unless they are large
and are in a critical area.

Scabs, buckles, rattails and pulldowns
are surface discontinuities that result
from local expansion of a sand mold. A
scab is a thin, flat layer of metal formed
behind a thin layer of sand and held in
place by a thin ligament of metal. When
the scab is removed (readily done by
chipping), an indentation called a buckle
is exposed. Rattails are minor buckles in
the form of small, irregular lines on the
casting surface. A pulldown is a buckle
in the cope portion of the casting. All
these discontinuities affect casting appearance but usually have no influence
on service life.

Effect of Internal Discontinuities

Three general types of internal discontinuities are shrinkage porosity, gas
porosity, and inclusions. Because the
major stresses in castings normally are
at or near the surface, internal discontinuities, unless severe, are less likely
than surface discontinuities to be direct
causes of fracture, although they may
contribute to it. The extension of a fracture through a discontinuity is not sufficient evidence that the discontinuity
caused failure. Overload will cause fracture along easy crack paths, which often
include internal discontinuities.

Shrinkage Porosity

Shrinkage cavities, whether large or
small, result from variations in solidification rate (and thus contraction rate).
If such variations are not compensated
for by adequate feeding, shrinkage of
the casting will produce finely dispersed
porosity, or localized internal voids.

Shrinkage porosity can result from use
of an insufficient number of pouring
gates, inadequate gate cross section, excessive pouring temperature or inadequate feeding.

Unless the casting is of simple design,
the use of only one pouring gate often will
result in shrinkage in the vicinity of the
gate. Shrinkage may be caused by too
much metal passing over one area in the
mold, which results in localized overheating of the mold wall and a slowdown in
the solidification rate of the metal in that
area of the casting. This type of shrinkage usually can be eliminated by the use
of two or more gates. The use of only
one gate may be satisfactory when a
lower pouring temperature can be used.
A lower pouring temperature results in
an improvement in the surface appearance of the casting.

Shrinkage often is aggravated by high
pouring temperatures. If the casting will
not run with a moderate pouring temperature, it may be because of back pressure due to inadequate venting, use of
low-permeability molding material, or
inadequate gating. Correction of one or
more of these factors will allow the pouring temperature to be lowered, and will
alleviate the shrinkage difficulty.

In some instances, surface shrinkage
cavities may be caused by inadequate
feeding at the junction of a thin section
and a thick section where risering is insufficient to feed the shrinkage occurring
in the thick section. The shape, location
and size of risers govern the degree to
which they will feed the casting. Small
errors in designing the risers often cause
great differences in the results.

Gating often can affect the efficiency of
a riser. A riser must contain hot metal,
and the metal must remain liquid until

after the casting has been adequately
fed and has solidified. Where possible, it
is generally good practice to gate through
a riser into the casting, causing the riser
to be the last portion of the mold to be
filled. Risers that are located on the side
of a casting opposite the gates usually
are ineffective (or less effective), because
they will contain the coldest metal in the
mold and will be unable to feed the casting adequately.

Chills are an effective tool in controlling shrinkage. One of the functions of a
chill is to equalize the rates of solidification of a thick section and an adjacent
thin section, thus minimizing the likelihood of shrinkage. Chills also are useful in promoting directional solidification
so that a riser can act more effectively.

Depending on casting shape and size,
variations in section thickness, and types
of junctions between component members, dendritic growth during solidification may generate arms that isolate local
internal regions, thus preventing complete feeding by the risers. Usually, the
microscopic voids that may form between
the arms do not significantly reduce density or adversely affect mechanical
properties.

Sometimes, even a small amount of
shrinkage porosity formed near the surface can lead to failure. Consider, for example, a Y-shape casting with a small
included angle. If a small fillet is used
between the arms of the casting, there
will be a thin, sharp wedge of sand at the
junction, which will be heated to a high
temperature by the contacting molten
metal. This wedge of hot sand then will
act as a thermal insulator, retarding
solidification of the metal around it. As a
result, a region will be isolated from the
risers by solid metal and a shrinkage
cavity will form just under the skin of the
Y-junction. This cavity may remain undetected and become a site for crack
initiation or corrosion penetration in
service. Use of a larger-radius fillet could
eliminate this problem.

In the following example, a large region of shrinkage porosity at one corner
of a cast low-alloy steel connector was
the origin of a tensile fracture.

**Example 4. Tensile Fracture That Originated
at Shrinkage Porosity in a Cast Low-
Alloy Steel Connector (Fig. 4)**

A sand cast steel eye connector (see Fig.
4a) used to link together two 120,000-lb-
capacity floating-bridge pontoons broke
prematurely in service. The pontoons were
coupled by upper and lower eye and clevis
connectors that were pinned together.

The eye connector was 3½ by 5 in. in
cross section and was cast from low-alloy
steel conforming to ASTM A148, grade 150-
125. Expected life of such connectors was
5000 or more full-load cycles.

Investigation. Examination of the fracture
surface established that the crack had originated along the lower surface (O in Fig.

4b), initially penetrating a region of shrinkage porosity (A in Fig. 4b) that extended over the lower right quarter of the fracture surface. Cracking then propagated in tension through sound metal (B in Fig. 4b) and terminated in a shear lip at the top of the eye (C in Fig. 4b). The stress configuration that produced the fracture approximated simple static tension.

Conclusion. Fracture of the eye connector occurred by tensile overload because of shrinkage porosity in the lower surface of

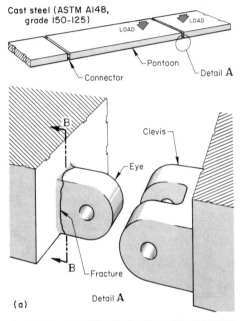

(a)

View B-B

(b)

(a) Schematic illustration of pontoon bridge, and enlarged view of eye and clevis connectors showing location of fracture in eye connector. (b) A fracture surface of the eye connector. Fracture origin is at O, region containing shrinkage porosity is at A, region of sound metal is at B, and the shear lip is at C.

Fig. 4. Sand cast low-alloy steel eye connector from a floating-bridge pontoon, which broke under static tensile loading (Example 4)

the casting. The design of the connector was adequate, because normal service life was more than 5000 load cycles.

Corrective Measure. Subsequent castings were inspected radiographically to ensure sound metal.

The example that follows describes an instance in which carburized-and-hardened sand cast low-alloy steel jaws that were highly stressed in service fractured because of shrinkage porosity, and because of low ductility of case and core.

Example 5. Brittle Fracture of Cast Low-Alloy Steel Jaws Because of Shrinkage Porosity and Low Ductility of Case and Core (Fig. 5)

Eight pairs of specially designed sand cast low-alloy steel jaws that had fractured were submitted for laboratory examination. The jaws were employed to stretch the wire used in prestressed concrete beams. The wire was gripped at one end of the stretching machine between stationary, semicylindrical jaws and at the other end between movable, wedge-shape jaws that were fitted in a block in a manner that forced them together as tension was applied to the wire. Two pairs of movable jaws are shown in Fig. 5(a), and two pairs of stationary jaws are shown in Fig. 5(b).

Investigation. It was found that all the fractures were brittle and exhibited very little evidence of deformation. Two of the jaws contained surface cracks (not distinguishable in Fig. 5), but these cracks did not appear to be related to the main fractures. Figure 5(c) and (d) exhibit fracture surfaces of two individual movable jaws (from different pairs).

Little is known about the possible variations of stress that may have existed in this application. For instance, the fit of the jaws in the block may have been imperfect, or there may have been too large an opening in the block, allowing the tips of the jaws to emerge without support. In such circumstances, the section of wire within the jaws might not have been in axial alignment with the wire under tension, which would have resulted in one jaw being subjected to a side thrust at the tip.

All surfaces of the jaws had been case carburized and heat treated to a hardness of Rockwell C 62 to 64 in the case and Rockwell C 36 to 39 in the core. Metallographic examination of a specimen prepared from a jaw established that: (*a*) the surface had been case carburized to a depth of $\frac{1}{32}$ to $\frac{1}{16}$ in.; (*b*) the case structure was martensite containing small spheroidal carbides but no carbide network; (*c*) the structure of the core consisted of martensite plus some ferrite and bainite; and (*d*) the fracture was related to shrinkage porosity, indicating that the jaws were made from defective castings.

Chemical analysis of the core showed that the composition corresponded to 3310 steel except for low manganese, slightly high chromium, and lower silicon than would normally be expected in a cast steel.

The hardness range of the core conforms to data in end-quench hardenability curves for 3310 steel. It represents, in fact, essentially the maximum hardness values attain-

able and as such indicates that tempering probably was limited to about 149 C (300 F). In view of the hardenability of the core, and assuming that the tapered slot in the block had a hardened surface, the low tempering temperature employed may have contributed to the brittleness.

Conclusion. Failure of the jaws was attributed primarily to the presence of internal microshrinkage, although the brittleness of case and core probably contributed to failure.

Recommendations. The procedure used for casting the jaws should be revised to eliminate the internal shrinkage porosity. Tempering at a slightly higher temperature to reduce surface and core hardness would be desirable. Finally, the fit of the jaws in the block should be checked to ensure proper alignment and loading.

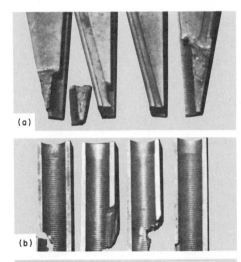

(a)

(b)

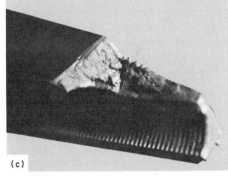

(c)

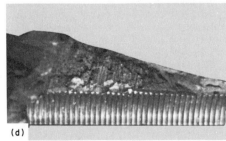

(d)

The jaws, sand cast from low-alloy steel, were used to stretch wire for prestressed concrete beams. (a) Two pairs of movable jaws, at about 0.7×. (b) Two pairs of stationary jaws, at about 0.7×. (c) and (d) Fracture surfaces of two movable jaws, at about 2×.

Fig. 5. Wire-stretching jaws that broke because of shrinkage porosity and low ductility of case and core (Example 5)

Gas Porosity

Formation of cavities resulting from the presence of gas is influenced by many factors, including melting practice, pouring practice, and type of mold to be used. Usually, the gas causing the porosity is steam or air.

Steam bubbles result from exposure of any liquid metal to moisture. Moisture in the air, in gases of combustion, in furnace and ladle linings, and in mold materials provides sources of steam bubbles. Whatever the source, the entrained water is released as steam bubbles on freezing of the molten metal, resulting in porosity in the castings that varies with the manner in which the water was entrained. If the water content in a molding sand is too high or if water exists as condensate on the mold surface, porosity will form at the surface of the casting. If a slight amount of moisture is entrained in the melting furnace, it may be dissipated during cooling in the ladle and the castings may be free of porosity. If a ladle lining is inadequately dried, the entire heat can be ruined by gross gas evolution during freezing in the molds, which causes all the risers to puff and overrun, creating large cavities throughout the casting.

Air bubbles, as a cause of casting porosity, are less detrimental than steam bubbles. Air bubbles usually arise when the conditions of pouring and the nature of the ingate passages combine to produce a turbulent flow that sucks air into the mold cavity. Sometimes the amount of air in the cavity is low enough for all of it to be carried to the topmost riser, causing no porosity in the casting proper. In most instances, smoother pouring and a more streamlined ingate system will minimize air bubbles.

Pinholes resulting from insufficiently dried sand molds may lower the endurance limit of steel castings, or they may cause only poor surface appearance, but if the number of pinholes is high, the castings may corrode in service. Internal gas cavities may reduce the effective cross section appreciably and therefore impair load-carrying ability. In general, however, internal gas cavities have smooth surfaces and do not act as stress concentrators. All but the very smallest cavities can be revealed readily by radiography, and an assessment of quality can be made in terms of the intended service. A measurement of casting density will serve a similar purpose.

Inclusions

Particles of refractory, slag, sand, oxides and other compounds of the casting metal can affect service life of the casting. Some of these, such as refractory and sand, are introduced inadvertently and can be minimized by proper mainte-

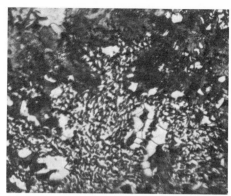

The white islands are free ferrite in a field consisting of type D graphite in a ferrite matrix; the microstructure also contained a dendritic network of pearlite.

Fig. 6. Section through the worn tip of a gray iron cam lobe (2% nital etch; 235×)

nance of linings and by good housekeeping. The presence of slag can be controlled by careful pouring and the use of more effective skimming techniques. Oxides of the casting metal are formed largely during melting and can be avoided by thorough deoxidation. Some elements (chromium in some steels, for example) will oxidize preferentially on the surface of the pouring stream. Skillful skimming is the only means of preventing this oxidized metal from entering the mold.

Other compounds, such as phosphides and sulfides, are detrimental to mechanical properties unless kept to a minimum. Globular manganese sulfides are beneficial as replacements of iron sulfides, which can form films at grain-boundary junctions.

Although it is desirable to minimize inclusions in cast structures, for most applications the cost of preparing castings that are essentially inclusion-free is prohibitive.

Effect of Microstructure

Aspects of microstructure that may be detrimental to the performance of iron and steel castings in service include: embrittling intergranular networks; graphite flakes of unfavorable shape, size or distribution (in gray iron); surface-structure gradients such as accidental carburization or decarburization; and generally unsatisfactory microstructures resulting from improper material selection, improper composition for section size (in gray and ductile irons), or incorrect heat treatment.

On occasion, a generally acceptable microstructure may not perform satisfactorily because of some particular aspect. Figure 6 is a micrograph of a section through the tip of a gray iron cam lobe that sustained rapid lubricated wear because of an excessive amount of ferrite. The microstructure contained a dendritic

network of pearlite, and islands of free ferrite in a field consisting of type D graphite in a ferrite matrix. The large amount of free ferrite present was detrimental to wear resistance although the cam surface was well lubricated. A lower silicon content and a slightly higher chromium content would reduce the amount of free ferrite and suppress the formation of type D graphite in the gray iron.

Intergranular Networks. Grain-boundary networks of either proeutectoid ferrite (in hypoeutectic alloys) or iron carbide (in hypereutectic alloys) sometimes are encountered in as-cast ferrous castings that have been cooled through the austenite temperature range at a slow rate. Such networks impart low ductility and low toughness to castings and constitute paths of weakness because of either the low strength of the ferrite or the brittleness of the carbides. The presence of such networks is indicated by low impact energy in a Charpy V-notch test and can be detected by metallographic examination. A normalizing treatment will eliminate both types of networks provided austenitizing has been done at the proper temperature. The casting then can be tempered to the desired hardness or, if higher strength is desired, can be quenched from just above the critical temperature and tempered appropriately.

In other circumstances, instead of networks, the grain boundaries may contain a film that also has a severe effect on ductility and toughness. In some instances, the presence of a film may be suspected although not conclusively proven, as in the following example, in which carbon steel castings were treated with higher-than-normal amounts of boron or aluminum, or both.

Example 6. "Rock Candy" Fractures in Steel Castings Attributed to Alloying Additions (Fig. 7)

Studies on means of conserving strategic alloys during World War II revealed that the addition of boron to wrought carbon and alloy steels containing very low levels of such critical-supply alloying elements as nickel, chromium and molybdenum provided a significant degree of hardenability. To be effective, however, the boron had to be "free" (not combined with oxygen or nitrogen, for example). Thus, the addition of an adequate quantity of aluminum, titanium or zirconium was necessary to deoxidize the steel and thus protect the boron from oxidation. Because this was a low-cost means of providing good hardenability, the use of boron in steel castings also was begun. Optimum hardenability was found to be associated with a boron content of 0.003 to 0.006%. In a few circumstances, however, anomalous brittle behavior has been encountered with large steel castings containing boron, which, when fractured, exhibited an extremely coarse-grained, or "rock candy", appearance. The fracture of a yoke that was sand cast from a carbon-manganese-boron steel was investigated to determine the effect of the boron. The steel contained approximately 0.35% C, 1.10% Mn, and somewhat more than 0.006% B.

Investigation. The fracture surface, as shown in Fig. 7(a), exhibits the following features: (a) a rim about 1/4 in. deep that shows extremely large intergranular, or "rock candy", fracture, as well as cleavage across some of the large grains; and (b) an interior consisting of somewhat smaller intergranular fracture and including some areas that exhibit dendritic fracture typical of shrinkage areas in castings.

The microstructure of the circled area in Fig. 7(a) contained extensive grain-boundary precipitation and some very large grains. As shown in Fig. 7(b), the precipitated phase, which may contain some boron but more likely is aluminum nitride, outlines a large prior austenite grain (as-cast grain size). The fracture path follows closely, although not precisely, the grain boundaries outlined by the precipitate.

Conclusions. It was not certain whether the boron contributed to fracture, but, because the aluminum content was necessarily high in order to protect the boron addition, it was considered more likely that fracture was the result of aluminum nitride embrittlement. The aluminum content in the casting was 0.072%, and the nitrogen content 0.002%, which would suggest the likelihood of aluminum nitride embrittlement.

Corrective Measure. Because of the high aluminum content required to protect the boron addition, boron-containing alloys were abandoned in favor of more conventional alloys.

Graphite. The size, shape, orientation and distribution of graphite in castings of gray iron, ductile iron, and malleable iron determine the mechanical properties of the castings. For any given gray iron composition, the rate of cooling from the freezing temperature to below about 650 C (1200 F) determines the ratio of combined carbon to graphitic carbon contents; this ratio controls the hardness and strength of the iron. For this reason, the effect of section size is considerably greater for gray iron castings than it is for castings made of more homogeneous ferrous metals, for which the rate of cooling does not affect the form of the carbon content on a macroscopic scale.

The normal or usual microstructure of gray iron is a matrix of pearlite with graphite flakes dispersed throughout. Too-rapid cooling (with respect to carbon and silicon contents) produces "mottled iron", consisting of a pearlite matrix with both primary cementite (iron carbide) and graphite. Very slow cooling of irons that contain larger percentages of silicon and carbon is likely to produce considerable ferrite as well as pearlite throughout the matrix, together with coarse graphite flakes. Under some conditions, very fine graphite (type D) may be formed near casting surfaces or in thin sections. Frequently, such graphite is surrounded by a ferrite matrix; hence, soft areas result.

(a)

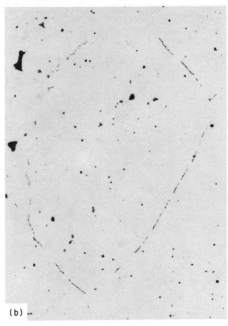

(b)

Fig. 7. Fractograph (a), at about 1×, of the surface of a "rock candy" fracture in a sand cast carbon-manganese-boron steel yoke. The microstructure of the area in the circle is shown unetched and at a magnification of 50× in (b), where an extremely large prior austenite grain is outlined by the grain-boundary precipitate. (Example 6)

The shape of graphite particles influences ductility of both ductile iron and malleable iron. If the control of the shape of graphite nodules in ductile iron is inadequate in the foundry, the casting may fail to perform its intended function, as did the gun recoil pistons discussed in the example that follows.

Example 7. Fracture of Ductile Iron Pistons for a Gun Recoil Mechanism as Affected by Type of Graphite (Fig. 8)

The gun mount used for two types of self-propelled artillery (175-mm guns and 8-in. howitzers) involved a recoil cylinder and a sand cast ductile iron piston containing orifices through which oil was forced to absorb the recoil energy of the gun. A rod attached to the gun tube engaged a thread inside the small end of the piston. The piston was stressed in tension by oil pressure on the flange at the large end, opposing the direction of motion of the rod. Several pistons that had cracked or fractured in service were submitted for analysis.

Investigation. In Fig. 8(a) and (b) are two views of a piston, showing the orifices specially designed to control oil flow and the pattern of cracks that developed. A composite of the fractures found in several pistons is displayed in Fig. 8(c), in which the piston surface has been "developed" as a flat plan view. Orifices A and B correspond to those shown in Fig. 8(a) and (b), respectively; orifices A′ and B′ are 180° from orifices A and B. The vertical fracture (at arrow) in Fig. 8(a) is unusual in origin and direction of propagation; most of the fractures originated at the upper right-hand corners of the large orifices (A and A′ in Fig. 8c), and propagated in an approximately horizontal direction. Some of these nearly horizontal cracks intersected the small slotlike orifices (B and B′ in Fig. 8c); others propagated around the piston to the opposite large orifice, joining it at the left side of the narrow opening at top left.

The surface of one of the horizontal fractures, which has a blotchy, "mottled" appearance, is shown in Fig. 8(d). The pattern this surface displays was created by the graphite present; there was relatively little of the massive, hypereutectic carbide that, by definition, is present in iron with a mottled structure. The arrow in Fig. 8(d) points to a location that exhibits characteristics of a fatigue zone.

The uppermost fracture in Fig. 8(a) is met by the more or less vertical break at virtually a right angle. This signifies that the upper fracture took place earlier (see Fig. 1, and related discussion, on page 12 in the article on General Practice in Failure Analysis, in this volume).

Because some of the pistons exhibited regions with an appearance suggestive of fatigue (as in Fig. 8d), scanning-electron-microscope (SEM) fractographs were prepared in the hope that fatigue striations might be found and that perhaps the number of cycles to failure could be estimated. These fractographs showed configurations similar in appearance to fatigue striations, but it was concluded that they were pearlite lamellae because the spacings agreed with pearlite dimensions observed in light-microscope micrographs. SEM views of the area of final fracture revealed dimples in some regions and features resembling cleavage facets in others. However, what appeared to be facets may have been interfaces of pearlite lamellae oriented nearly parallel to the direction of crack propagation.

The castings were made according to the specifications of MIL-I-11466, grade D7003, which requires minimum properties of 100-

ksi tensile strength, 70-ksi yield strength and 3% elongation in 2 in.; these properties usually are acquired by heat treatment (normalizing for these castings). The specification stipulated that the graphite must be substantially nodular and required a metallographic test for each lot of castings. There was no requirement concerning the matrix. Of 17 pistons that were sectioned for testing (two or more test specimens per piston), 11 averaged 118-ksi tensile strength but the remaining six averaged only 77.6 ksi; 13 met the yield-strength requirement, averaging 80 ksi, whereas four did not, averaging 57.9 ksi; in elongation, nine pistons were satisfactory, averaging 4.7%, whereas eight averaged only 2.1%.

Examination of the microstructures of these 17 pistons, and those of additional pistons, revealed that 77% of those that failed did not contain the required nodular graphite. The range in nodularity was suffi-

cient for establishment of a microstructure-rating system in which quality of graphite was ranked from 1 (nodular) to 16 (vermicular with essentially no nodules). Structures containing graphite ranked 2, 8, 13 and 16 are shown, respectively, in Fig. 8(e), (f), (g) and (h). The micrograph in Fig. 8(h), which shows the structure of the piston with the mottled surface in Fig. 8(d), exhibits massive carbides, but not enough to form a mottled structure in the usual sense of the word. For this application, graphite ranked from 1 to 7 was considered acceptable; graphite ranked from 8 to 12, borderline; and graphite ranked from 13 to 16, rejectable.

The degree of nodularity of the graphite was correlated with the results obtained in ultrasonic testing in order to appraise the quality of pistons that had already been installed. It was found that vermicular graphite damped the back-reflection signal

to a significantly greater degree than did nodular graphite. Comparison of the results obtained in the ultrasonic tests and in the metallographic examinations yielded a correlation coefficient of 0.84 — an indication of a high degree of correlation.

Smooth-bar rotating-beam tests (R. R. Moore) were performed on specimens prepared from pistons specifically selected for a comparison of fatigue-test behavior and graphite structure.

For specimens with rank 1 graphite tested at 30 ksi, the number of cycles to failure was about 10 times that for specimens with rank 12 graphite, and 18 times that for specimens with rank 16 graphite. When tests were performed at 45 ksi, the disparity was not so great, but the order of decreasing fatigue life was the same as at 30 ksi. These findings indicated that low fatigue strength due to vermicular graphite had caused the service fractures.

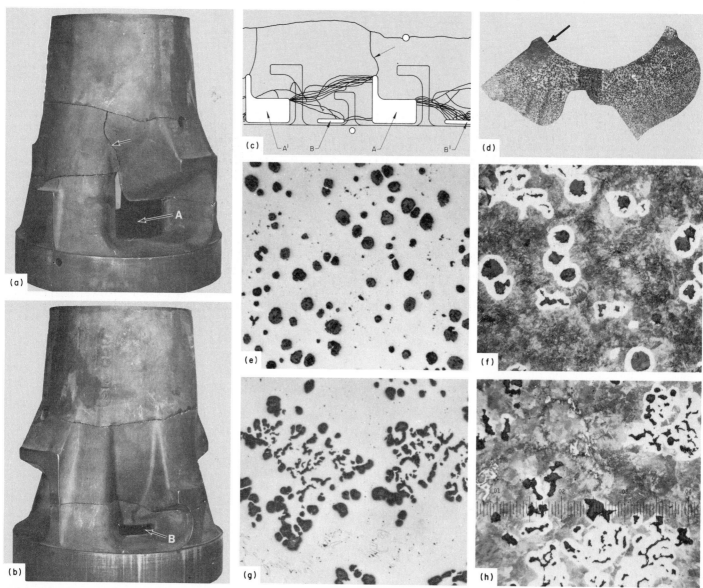

(a) and (b) Two different views of piston, at about 0.35×, showing fractures; A and B indicate orifices (see text). (c) Flat plan view showing composite pattern of fractures in several pistons. (d) Fracture surface, at about 0.25×, showing mottled structure caused by vermicular graphite; arrow points to a fatigue zone. (e) to (h) Micrographs showing graphite with nodularity of: (e) rank 2, at 50×; (f) rank 8, at about 60×; (g) rank 13, at 50×; and (h) rank 16, at about 65×. Specimens in (e) and (g) were unetched; specimens in (f) and (h) were etched in 2% nital.

Fig. 8. Piston for a gun recoil mechanism, sand cast from ductile iron conforming to MIL-I-11466, grade D7003, that fractured in fatigue because of vermicularity of graphite (Example 7)

These tests did not simulate service, because they involved reversed bending whereas gun recoil loadings were primarily in tension. Fatigue tests in simple tensile loading were conducted on new, complete pistons containing nodular graphite. Four tests at a tensile stress corresponding to the gun recoil load produced fatigue fractures at 20,000 to 35,000 cycles. All of these fractures, unlike most of those observed in service, occurred at the base of the threads in the top of the piston, which is the region of the upper crack in Fig. 8(a) and (b). The section through the threads had been calculated during design as the location of maximum stress under simple tension. Because nearly all service fatigue cracks did not occur at the threads but initiated from the oil orifices, cracking may be attributed to (a) slight misalignment that caused bending in addition to tension; and (b) the force of the oil on the surfaces immediately above and below the large orifices, increasing the stresses at the corners of these orifices. These tests showed that life of the pistons was about 20,000 recoil loadings, instead of an indefinite service life as had been anticipated.

Conclusions. Fracture of the pistons occurred under high dynamic axial tension modified by superimposed bending loads from oil pressure and/or normal alignment tolerance. Most of the service fractures occurred in pistons containing vermicular graphite instead of the specified nodular graphite. Brittleness caused by massive carbides may have shortened the service lives of a few pistons.

Corrective Measures. Ultrasonic testing was adopted for inspection of pistons already in the field to identify and reject those containing vermicular graphite. Metallographic control standards were applied to production of new pistons to ensure structures containing substantially nodular graphite and no massive carbides.

Carburization and Decarburization. A carburized layer may form on the surface of a steel casting if furnace combustion gases are adjusted too far on the reducing side during heat treatment, thus producing an atmosphere that contains too much carbon monoxide. Such a carburized layer is nonuniform and results in surface hard spots that may be brittle.

Loss of carbon from the surface of a steel casting can occur during heat treatment if the furnace atmosphere is oxidizing. A decarburized surface will be soft and low in strength and thus may lack the fatigue resistance characteristic of the specified carbon level. Both carburization and decarburization are best revealed by careful hardness testing and metallographic inspection.

Meticulous control of furnace atmosphere is needed to prevent unintentional carburization and decarburization. With heat treating equipment that is properly instrumented, such control is not difficult.

In shell mold castings of gray iron, the high thermal conductivity of the mold produces an initial chill of the iron surface. Subsequent annealing of the surface

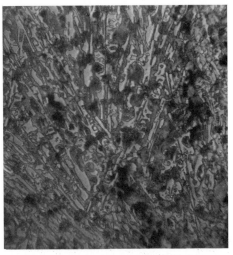

Light-gray areas are carbides; black spots, graphite; matrix, unresolved pearlite. Specimen hardness, Rockwell C 40. (2% nital etch; 180×)

Fig. 9. Mottled structure in a specimen taken from a gray iron oil pan

by the heat of the casting results in a skin that is almost 100% ferrite; such a skin has poor wear properties and should be removed by machining for applications requiring wear resistance.

Effect of Improper Composition

Castings of improper chemical composition can result from specification of material that is unsuitable for the application. Induction hardened teeth on a sprocket cast of low-alloy steel wore at a high rate because of a surface hardness of Rockwell C 50 to 51; Rockwell C 55 min had been specified. Analysis revealed that the alloy content of the steel was adequate for the desired hardenability but that the carbon content (0.29%) was too low. The specified carbon content was increased to 0.45% min in order to achieve the required hardness.

Castings of unsuitable composition can result also from off-composition heats. Improper melting or foundry practice

can cause variations in composition that adversely affect mechanical properties. For instance, in drilling of mounting holes in gray iron oil pans, resistance to the drill was encountered. It was found that the resistance had been caused by the presence of carbides in the metal due to a mottled rather than a normal gray iron structure (see Fig. 9). Analysis revealed that the iron contained only 1.70% Si, whereas the intended level of about 2.30% would have provided the desired graphite-flake structure.

In the following example, a weldment consisting of two low-alloy steel castings broke in the heat-affected zone because the carbon content was higher than specified. Welding was done without preheating or postheating, which resulted in a brittle heat-affected zone.

Example 8. Brittle Fracture of a Roadarm Weldment of Two Low-Alloy Steel Castings, Because of an Excessive Carbon-Equivalent Content (Fig. 10)

A roadarm for a tracked vehicle failed during preproduction vehicle testing. The arm was a weldment of two cored sand castings of steel conforming to ASTM A148, grade 120-95. A maximum carbon content of 0.32% was specified. The welding procedure called for degreasing and gas metal-arc (MIG) welding; neither preheating nor postheating was specified. The filler metal was E70S-6 continuous consumable wire, which was bare except for a copper coating to protect it from atmospheric oxidation while on the reel.

Investigation. Analysis of the two castings revealed that the carbon content was higher than specified, ranging from 0.40 to 0.44%. Except for the carbon content, composition of the castings corresponded to that of a high-manganese 8640 steel. The fracture occurred in the heat-affected zone (see Fig. 10), where quenching by the surrounding metal had produced a hardness of Rockwell C 55.

Some roadarms of similar carbon content, and welded by the same procedure, had not failed; it was determined that this was because they had been tempered during a hot-straightening operation. Rather than attempt to identify and segregate tempered and untempered roadarms, all production arms were tempered, including those already installed. A split induction coil was used to encompass the region of the weld and the adjacent hardened heat-affected zone, thus avoiding the need to dismantle the arm, which would have been required for furnace heat treatment. As a result of tempering, there were no additional failures.

Analysis of these castings revealed a composition unfavorable for welding, particularly without preheating or postheating. The carbon equivalent for an average carbon content of 0.42% was 0.87% using the formula for low-alloy steel and 1.10% using the formula for carbon steel. These values, which are so high that they lie off the graph frequently used to relate weldability to carbon content (see Fig. 3 on page 188 in Volume 6 of this Handbook), indicate that preheating and postheating are mandatory.

Fig. 10. Section, at about 0.8×, through weld in a roadarm (a weldment of low-alloy steel sand castings), which fractured in the heat-affected zone because of high carbon-equivalent content. Fracture surface is at arrow. (Example 8)

Conclusions. Brittle fracture of the road-arm was caused by a combination of too high a carbon equivalent in the castings and the lack of preheating and postheating during the welding procedure, which resulted in heat-affected zones that were extremely hard and brittle.

Corrective Measures. Steps were taken to ensure that future roadarm castings would meet the specified carbon-equivalent content; a preheat was added to the welding procedure, and tempering after welding was specified for all roadarms.

In the following example, gray iron was used in a large oil-pump gear in an intermittently operated compressor subjected to sudden starts and stops. The breakage of gear teeth that occurred indicated that gray iron had insufficient ductility for the application.

Example 9. Fracture of Teeth in a Gray Iron Oil-Pump Gear Because Ductility Was Inadequate for Shock Loading in Service (Fig. 11)

The two oil-pump gears shown in Fig. 11 broke after four months of service in a gas compressor that operated at 1000 rpm and provided a discharge pressure of 1050 psi. The compressor ran intermittently, with sudden starts and stops. The large gear was sand cast from class 40 gray iron with a tensile strength of 42,000 psi at 207 Bhn. The smaller gear was sand cast from ASTM A536, grade 100-70-03, ductile iron with a tensile strength of 101,000 psi at 241 Bhn.

Investigation. Visual examination of the larger gear revealed that several teeth had cracked and fractured at the root and many other teeth were crushed and pitted at the tip. The smaller gear displayed one area in which a segment of the rim had broken away. The remainder of the teeth on this gear showed relatively little wear in light of the battered condition of the larger gear with which it meshed.

Metallographic examination disclosed that both gears had normal microstructures. The ductile iron consisted of a pearlitic matrix containing well-shaped nodules of graphite generally surrounded by ferrite envelopes. The gray iron exhibited a pearlitic matrix containing type A graphite flakes. There were no metallurgical causes of failure other than the inherent brittleness of gray iron. Also, there was no evidence of machining imperfections that could have contributed to the fractures.

Conclusions. Brittle fracture of the teeth of the gray iron gear resulted from high impact loading that arose from the sudden starts and stops of the compressor. During subsequent rotation, fragments broken from the gray iron gear caused damage to the mating ductile iron gear. Excessive beam loading and the lack of ductility in the gray iron gear teeth were the primary causes of fracture.

Corrective Measures. Both gears were subsequently cast from ASTM A536, grade 100-70-03, ductile iron and were normalized at 927 C (1700 F), air cooled, reheated to 871 C (1600 F) and oil quenched. The larger gear was tempered to 200 to 240 Bhn, and the smaller gear was tempered to 240 to 280 Bhn. These hardness levels provided the

Ductile iron, grade 100-70-03
Diametral pitch, 8; pitch diameter, 6.5 in.; face width, 0.75 in.; bore diameter, 0.875 in.

(a)

Gray iron, class 40
Diametral pitch, 8; pitch diameter, 8.0 in.; face width, 1.25 in.; bore diameter, 4.43 in.

(b)

Fig. 11. Oil-pump gears, sand cast from (a) ASTM A536, grade 100-70-03, ductile iron, and (b) class 40 gray iron, that fractured because gray iron was an improper material for the large gear (Example 9)

desired resistance to shock and wear yet retained high strength and good ductility. No further gear failures occurred following these changes.

The following example describes failure of a cast austenitic manganese steel chain link used in a transfer mechanism for hot blooms. This material was unsuitable for the application, which involved repeated heating.

Example 10. Brittle Fracture of a Cast Austenitic Manganese Steel Chain Link Because the Material Was Unsuitable for the Operating Temperatures (Fig. 12)

The chain link shown in Fig. 12(a), part of a mechanism for transferring hot or cold steel blooms in and out of a reheating furnace, broke after approximately four months of service. The link was sand cast from 2% Cr austenitic manganese steel and was subjected to repeated heating to temperatures of 455 to 595 C (about 850 to 1100 F).

Investigation. Chemical analysis revealed that the link had been cast from 13% Mn austenitic manganese steel to which 1.5 to 2.0% chromium was added to improve wear resistance by forming chromium carbides.

Examination with a hand magnet indicated that the entire link was magnetically responsive. When properly heat treated, austenitic manganese steel is a tough nonmagnetic alloy; however, compositional changes that occur at the surface during heating may produce a magnetic skin.

Further examination of the magnetic properties of the link was performed with the aid of a Tinsley thickness gage, which normally is used for measuring thickness of nonmagnetic coatings on ferritic steel surfaces. With this instrument, a completely nonmagnetic substance is given a rating of 10 and a magnetic material such as plain carbon steel is assigned a rating of 0. Speci-

mens cut from the link were tested for magnetism after various heat treatments, with the following results:

Condition(a)	Tinsley reading	Degree of magnetism
As received:		
Web	4.5	Partial
Flange	4.65	Partial
2000 F, WQ	10.0	Nonmagnetic
2000 F, AC	10.0	Nonmagnetic
2000 F, WQ; 4 hr at 850 F	9.0-9.6	Trace at edges
2000 F, FC	8.0	Partial
2000 F, FC; 68 hr at 900 F	4.8	Partial
2000 F, AC; 68 hr at 900 F	4.75	Partial

(a) WQ = water quenched; AC = air cooled; FC = furnace cooled. 2000 F = 1093 C; 850 F = 454 C; 900 F = 482 C.

Figure 12(b) is a macrograph of a polished and nital-etched specimen from the link as received at the laboratory and shows dendritic segregation and microshrinkage pores (dark spots at upper left).

Micrographs of specimens from the as-received link are shown in Fig. 12(c) and (d). These micrographs display a segregated structure of complex carbides (black needlelike phase), $(FeMn)_3C$ carbide (white-on-white area) and pearlite (gray areas) in an austenite matrix, which accounts for the macrostructure shown in Fig. 12(b). The segregation follows the grain boundaries, but the appearance is modified by dark oxide patches left by the nital etch. (The dark oxide can be removed continuously during etching by alternating hydrochloric acid in alcohol with the nital; see page 840 in Volume 1 of this Handbook.)

The effects of the repeated heating of the link on the characteristics of the precipitated carbides can be observed by comparing the micrographs in Fig. 12(c) and (d) with that in Fig. 12(e), which shows the normal microstructure of as-cast standard austenitic manganese steel (nominal composition: 1.15% C, 12.8% Mn, 0.50% Si), displaying pearlite and/or martensite with carbide precipitation at grain boundaries and along crystallographic planes.

The microstructure of a specimen from the chain link that was austenitized for 20 min at 1093 C (2000 F) and air cooled is shown in Fig. 12(f). In this small specimen, the cooling rate from the austenitizing temperature was sufficient to retain the austenitic structure. The globular carbides did not dissolve at this temperature. The effect of reheating this structure to 482 C (900 F) for 68 hr is illustrated by the micrograph in Fig. 12(g), which shows carbides, and austenite decomposed to pearlite, in an austenite matrix. Many patches of fine pearlite formed both along the grain boundaries and within the grains. Note the similarity of the microstructure in Fig. 12(g) to that in Fig. 12(d).

Hardness tests performed on the link adjacent to the fracture surface yielded values of 415 Bhn for the web section and 363 Bhn for the flange; many fine cracks were found in the hardness indentations, which attested to a brittle condition. These hardness values were in distinct contrast to the normal level of 180 to 200 Bhn expected in as-quenched austenitic manganese steel.

One question arising from the data on magnetism and from the results of metallographic analysis was whether the broken link had been properly heat treated before installation in service and magnetized as the result of service temperatures, or whether it had inadvertently been shipped from the foundry as-cast and thus partly magnetic. This question was resolved by the pronounced dendritic segregation observed in the microstructure shown in Fig. 12(c). The presence of the dendritic pattern indicates that the link was not heat treated after casting, because austenitizing followed by rapid cooling would have served to homogenize the microstructure and to largely eliminate the dendritic pattern.

Although quantitative data are lacking concerning the mechanical-property changes that result from tempering of austenitic manganese steel, metallographic data do exist that predict when embrittlement may be expected during reheating at various temperatures. Figure 12(h) is a graph of time at temperature needed to embrittle austenitic manganese steel after an initial heat treatment of 2 hr at 1093 C (2000 F) followed by water quenching. The data used to plot this curve are based on the first evidences of transformation products visible under the microscope.

Conclusions. The chain link failed in a brittle manner because the austenitic manganese steel from which it was cast became embrittled after being reheated in the temperature range of 455 to 595 C (about 850 to 1100 F) for prolonged periods of time. The alloy was not suitable for this application because of its metallurgical instability under service conditions.

The chain links had not been austenitized after casting. This was not as significant a factor in the failure as reheating above 427 C (800 F).

The two deoxidizers most commonly used to produce inherently fine-grained steel are aluminum and vanadium. Unless the grain size of a steel is inherently fine, the amount of grain refinement that can be obtained by adjusting the austenitizing temperature is severely limited. A coarse grain size results in inferior impact strength and fatigue strength, as described for a sand cast 4150 steel gear in the example that follows.

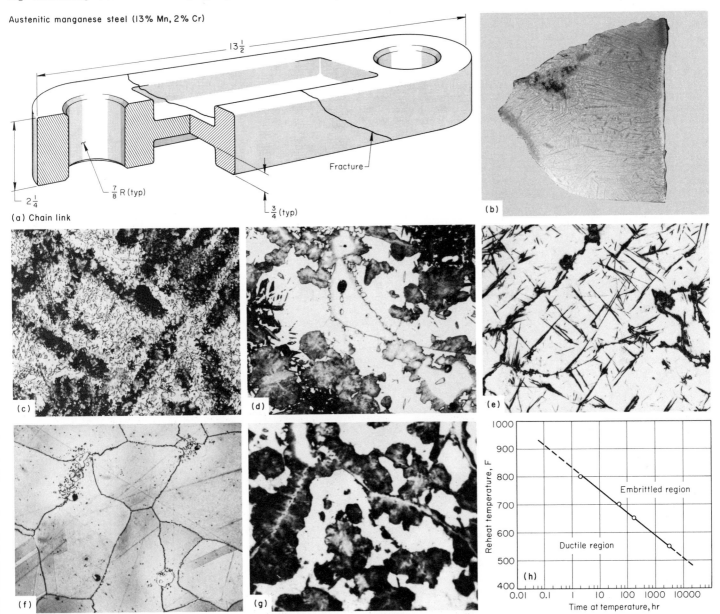

(a) Chain link, showing location of fracture. (b) Macrograph, at 1.85×, of a nital-etched specimen from an as-received chain link. (c) and (d) Micrographs, at 100 and 600×, respectively, of a nital-etched specimen from an as-received chain link. (e) Normal microstructure of as-cast standard austenitic manganese steel, shown at 100×. (f) Micrograph, at 315×, of a nital-etched specimen that had been austenitized 20 min at 1093 C (2000 F) and air cooled. (g) Micrograph, at 1000×, of the specimen in (f) after annealing 68 hr at 482 C (900 F). (h) Chart showing time at temperature needed to embrittle austenitic manganese steel after heat casting for 2 hr at 1093 C (2000 F) and water quenching.

Fig. 12. Reheating-furnace chain link, sand cast from austenitic manganese steel, that failed by brittle fracture because material was not stable at operating temperatures (Example 10)

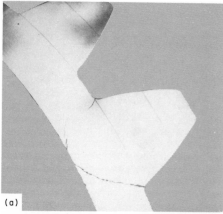

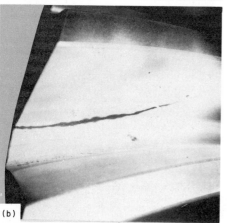

Fig. 13. (a) *End view of two teeth of a sand cast 4150 steel gear, showing fatigue cracks that originated at machining marks; the material was weak because of coarse grain size.* (b) *Crack that extended approximately 11 in. from root fillet into tooth flank.* (Example 11)

Example 11. Fatigue Fracture of a Cast 4150 Steel Edger-Mill Main Drive Gear Because of Coarse Grain Size (Fig. 13)

A sand cast 4150 steel spiral gear was removed from the main drive of a 36-in. edger mill after cracks were discovered in the roots of teeth. The gear was part of the original equipment of the mill, but the length of service was not known.

Investigation. An end view of two teeth of the gear, showing a crack from one root that had penetrated through the section wall at one point and turned upward toward the next root, is shown in Fig. 13(a). Small cracks also had initiated in the fillets of the next two roots. The first crack had grown for a distance of about 11 in. along the first root (see Fig. 13b). These cracks were believed to be fatigue cracks, but they had not been opened up to expose the fracture surfaces for study. The gear showed heavier wear and some spalling at one end of the teeth, indicating probable misalignment. A rough surface was present in the root fillets.

The composition of the casting corresponded approximately to that of 4150 low-alloy steel.

A metallographic specimen revealed a uniform, equiaxed structure of fine pearlite created by normalizing and then tempering at about 538 C (1000 F). ASTM grain size

was 2 to 3, which was deemed coarser than desirable for optimum properties.

Conclusions. Failure by fatigue was attributed primarily to coarse grain size. (Coarse-grained steels are inherently inferior to fine-grained steels in impact and fatigue strength.) Other factors contributing to failure included uneven loading due to misalignment, and the stress-raising effects of tool marks in the root fillets.

Recommendations. Steelmaking practice should be modified to include suitable additions of aluminum to ensure fine-grained castings. Further improvements could be attained by (a) substituting oil quenching and tempering for normalizing and tempering, (b) removing all tool marks from the root fillets of the gear teeth, (c) shot peening root fillets to provide residual compressive stresses in these critical areas, and (d) maintaining alignment to prevent uneven loading.

Effect of Improper Heat Treatment

Incorrect heat treatment can produce structures that are unable to withstand the demands of service. For example, high-temperature (760 C, or 1400 F) "stress relief" of an austenitic Fe-Cr-Ni casting may sensitize it, producing both grain-boundary carbide precipitation and sigma phase that can unfavorably alter its corrosion resistance and severely lower its ductility.

Different heat treatments of cast carbon-molybdenum steel can yield similar values of hardness and tensile strength yet widely different values of impact strength. This is demonstrated by the data in Table 2 on page 124 in Volume 1 of this Handbook. For instance, in one comparison in that table, one heat of 0.22C-0.12Mo steel was annealed at 927 C (1700 F) for 12 hr and then furnace cooled, and another heat was normalized at 927 C (1700 F) for 8 hr, air cooled, and tempered 2 hr at 671 C (1240 F). The two heats had tensile strengths of 68.8

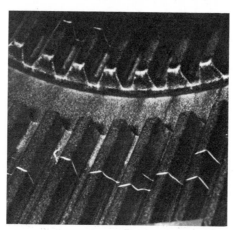

Fig. 14. *Internal teeth in a sand cast ASTM A148, class 105-85, low-alloy steel geared winch drum that cracked transversely during induction hardening. The cracks were judged not detrimental to service life.*

and 72.0 ksi and hardnesses of 138 and 141 Bhn, yet the Charpy V-notch impact strength of the annealed heat was 30 to 34 ft-lb whereas impact strength of the normalized-and-tempered heat was 61 to 64 ft-lb. Obviously, a check of hardness would not give any indication of which heat treatment had been used, but an examination of microstructure would.

Induction hardening of the internal teeth in a geared winch drum produced transverse cracking, as shown in Fig. 14. Because of their orientation, the cracks did not propagate during service and thus were judged not detrimental to service life. The drum was sand cast from low-alloy steel to meet the mechanical-property requirements of ASTM A148, class 105-85. The teeth were machined and then induction hardened to Rockwell C 45 min with a penetration of 1/16 in. min. The gear shown in Fig. 14, and others exhibiting similar cracks, were tested. Required service life was 20 hr at full load. The tests were halted after 42 hr (2×10^5 load cycles); no changes in the cracks had occurred. These data permitted establishment of an acceptance criterion for cracks that normally would have been cause for rejection of the castings.

The teeth were induction hardened one tooth at a time. The expansion stresses created by heating an individual tooth may have been sufficient to crack the adjacent hardened tooth if there were underlying defects. Hardening of the tooth contours by case carburizing with subsequent quenching and tempering might avoid this problem.

In the following example, probable omission of a specified heat treatment contributed to the brittle fracture of a cast steel part. The part also exhibited a large as-cast grain size, and its design incorporated a stress raiser.

Example 12. Brittle Fracture of a Truck-Mounted Posthole-Digger Part Sand Cast From 4130 Steel (Fig. 15)

The sand cast centerpost or anchorage of the derrick of a truck-mounted posthole digger failed in service, fracturing along the fillet between the base flange and the vertical cylindrical wall, as shown schematically in Fig. 15(a). The length of service was not reported. The material specified was cast 4130 steel, heat treated to minimum yield strength of 120,000 psi and minimum tensile strength of 140,000 psi; specified hardness was Rockwell C 30. The post, 9¾ in. long, served as the main support and pivot point of the derrick and all attachments carried by it. The base flange was bolted to the bed of the truck body, and the top was threaded to receive a gear with an internal thread. This gear, when screwed tightly in place and engaged by a worm, made it possible to rotate the derrick.

Investigation. A portion of the fracture surface is shown in Fig. 15(b), displaying an extremely coarse grain size typical of the entire surface. No evidence of foundry defects or of earlier cracks was found. Chevron marks near the inside surface indicate that the fracture propagated in this area from left to right, but no special significance can be attached to this fact.

Metallographic specimens cut from the region of the fracture confirmed the very large prior austenite grain size, which conformed to ASTM macro-grain size number M-4. High magnification revealed the microstructure to be as cast.

Spectrographic analysis of the material in the post revealed the following composition: 0.35% C, 0.85% Mn, 0.42% Si, 0.48% Ni, 1.10% Cr, 0.32% Mo. The percentages of the alloying elements are slightly higher than specified for 4130 steel; the nickel, which is not specified for 4130, imparts deeper hardenability to the casting.

Tensile specimens prepared from the broken centerpost had a yield strength of 112,000 psi and tensile strengths of 115,000 to 123,000 psi; the material had a hardness of Rockwell C 25 to 28. All mechanical properties were below the specified values.

The contour of the fillet between the post wall and the flange contained an undercut (shown as "Original design" in section A-A in Fig. 15) that both reduced the thickness of the wall and served as a source of stress concentration because of the small radius at the root of the undercut.

Conclusion. Failure occurred by brittle fracture at the junction of the body and the flange because of the large grain size and as-cast microstructure of the material, and because of the small undercut that acted as a stress concentrator. It was considered likely that the failed casting had not received the specified heat treatment.

Corrective Measures. The method of making the centerpost was changed from static to centrifugal casting, and the casting was heat treated to a tempered-martensite structure. This procedure reduced grain size and increased toughness.

The undercut at the junction of the body and the flange was changed to a 1-in.-radius fillet, as shown in the "Improved design" view in section A-A in Fig. 15. This greatly reduced the stress concentration at the corner and contributed to increased service life. Centerposts of the original design were replaced on all derricks by centerposts of the improved design, and no additional failures have been reported in more than five years.

Incomplete surface hardening of the pinion discussed in the next example resulted in fatigue fracture of gear teeth.

Example 13. Fatigue Fracture of a Cast Chromium-Molybdenum Steel Pinion Because of Incomplete Hardening of Tooth Surfaces (Fig. 16)

A sand cast countershaft pinion on a continuous reversible car puller for a blast furnace broke after one month of service; normal expected life was 12 months. Although operating conditions during the month in question were reported as normal, overloading did occur. The pinion was specified to be made of 1045 steel and to be heat treated to a hardness of 245 Bhn.

Investigation. The pinion steel was analyzed and found to have the following composition: 0.32% C, 0.70% Mn, 0.01% P,

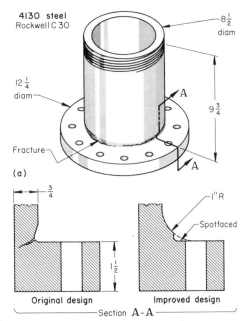

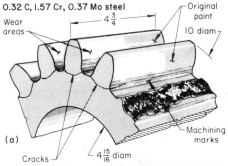

(a) Centerpost, showing location of fracture at a fillet between the cylinder wall and the base flange. Section A-A shows original design (with undercut) and improved design (with 1-in. radius) of fillet. (b) Fracture surface, showing coarse, crystalline grains, and chevron marks.

Fig. 15. Sand cast 4130 steel centerpost, for a truck-mounted posthole digger, that fractured at an undercut fillet because of improper heat treatment (Example 12)

0.023% S, 0.54% Si, 1.57% Cr, and 0.37% Mo, which was considered to be a satisfactory alternative to 1045 steel. The pinion was annealed prior to flame or induction hardening of the teeth, which resulted in a surface hardness of 363 Bhn and a core hardness of 197 Bhn.

A portion of the broken pinion, with one tooth missing, is shown in Fig. 16(a); the missing tooth failed by fatigue fracture through the tooth root. The fracture surface contained beach marks typical of fatigue-crack propagation. Magnetic-particle inspection revealed similar cracks at the bases of the adjacent teeth. Tool marks were found along the roots of these teeth.

A heavy wear pattern was visible on one end of the flank of the pressure side of the teeth, whereas at the other end the original paint was undisturbed. This indicated misalignment of the pinion and therefore abnormally heavy loading at the end from which the fatigue cracks originated.

A section through a broken tooth, etched to reveal the macrostructure, is shown in Fig. 16(b). The surface hardening did not extend to the tooth root, leaving this highly stressed area with a low-strength annealed structure. Microscopic examination of the

hardened surface area confirmed that it had a quenched-and-tempered structure.

Conclusions. The pinion teeth fractured by fatigue because of the low strength of the tooth-root regions, which resulted from incomplete surface hardening of the tooth surfaces. Contributing factors to the fracture included uneven loading because of misalignment and stress concentrations in the tooth roots caused by tool marks.

Corrective Measures. Greater strength was provided by oil quenching and tempering replacement pinions to a hardness of 255 to 302 Bhn. Machining of tooth roots was revised to eliminate all tool marks. Surface hardening was applied to all tooth surfaces, including the roots. Proper alignment of the pinion was ensured by carefully checking the meshing of the teeth at start-up.

Effect of Stress Concentrations

The presence of significant residual internal stresses in a casting may be detrimental. Residual stresses generally result from local plastic deformation imposed by thermal gradients created during processing. These gradients may be caused by local cooling when the casting

(a) Schematic illustration of the pinion, which was sand cast from a chromium-molybdenum steel. (b) Macrograph, at 2½×, of a nital-etched section through a broken tooth, showing surface hardening on sides and top of tooth.

Fig. 16. Countershaft pinion that fractured in fatigue at roots of teeth because of incomplete hardening of tooth surfaces (Example 13)

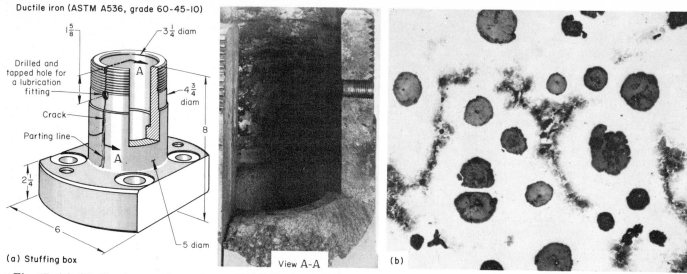

Fig. 17. (a) *Stuffing box, sand cast from ASTM A536, grade 60-45-10, ductile iron, that fractured by fatigue because material was of inadequate strength.* (b) *Micrograph (at 100×) of a nital-etched specimen, showing structure consisting of graphite nodules in a ferrite matrix, with remnants of a network of pearlite.* (Example 14)

is very hot (in the mold or during shake-out, or in quenching from heat treatment) or by local heating (such as in repair or assembly welding). The effect is plastic stretching (or compression) of the weakest (hottest) portion of the casting. By the time the temperature has equalized, the stretched or compressed region is too long or too short to match the size of the other portions of the casting. The result is a sizable residual internal stress that may be compressive or tensile. The behavior in service then depends on whether these internal residual stresses are added to or subtracted from the applied service loads.

Casting Design. The shape of a casting can contribute to residual stresses if it entails sections of markedly different thickness, which can undergo different cooling rates in the mold. This effect can be minimized if the thinner sections are well insulated so that they cool at a slower rate. The use of chills to accelerate cooling of heavy sections can be helpful also. Stress relief can diminish internal stresses if the cast alloy is amenable to such treatment.

Other aspects of design that affect the load-bearing ability of a casting, or its capacity to resist externally applied stress, are fillet radii (whether the fillets serve as stress raisers) and adequacy of thickness of sections.

Foundry Practice. The procedures used in the foundry can influence the creation of residual stresses in castings. Very high pouring temperatures will retard cooling rates of thick sections but may not affect significantly the cooling of thin sections. Shakeout at too high a temperature will accelerate cooling of thin sections. Stress relief, if performed properly, can alleviate residual stresses.

Machining of castings can introduce stress raisers; tool marks, notches, and

sharp edges such as those around drilled holes are among the most common stress raisers produced during machining. The effects of machining, however, apply to wrought products as well and are not peculiar to castings.

Fracture of a ductile iron casting that originated in fatigue at the intersection of a small-diameter lubrication hole and a bored inner surface is described in the next example.

Example 14. Fatigue Fracture of a Ductile Iron Stuffing Box That Originated at the Inner End of a Lubrication Hole (Fig. 17)

The stuffing box shown in Fig. 17(a), which was sand cast from ASTM A536, grade 60-45-10, ductile iron, began leaking water after two weeks of service. The machine was operating at 326 rpm with a discharge water pressure of 3100 psi. The stuffing box was removed from the machine after a crack was discovered in the sidewall.

Investigation. The vertical portion of the crack (see Fig. 17a) passed through a tapped $\frac{5}{16}$-in.-diam lubrication-fitting hole that was centered on the parting line of the casting (also shown in Fig. 17a). The direction of the crack changed abruptly to nearly horizontal at an internal shoulder about $3\frac{7}{8}$ in. below the top of the externally threaded end (see view A-A in Fig. 17). A second nearly horizontal crack (faintly visible in view A-A) at the bottom of the vertical crack extended to the right and slanted slightly downward from the parting line for at least $\frac{3}{4}$ in. This second crack was very tightly closed.

The surface of the fracture was closely examined, and indications of fatigue beach marks were found. As is normal for fatigue of cast iron, these indications were faint. Originally, the beach marks may have been slightly more distinct, but if so, they were partly eroded away by water leaking through the crack at high velocity.

A metallographic specimen cut from the casting displayed a structure consisting of well-rounded graphite nodules in a ferrite

matrix that also contained remnants of a network of pearlite (see Fig. 17b). Evidently, the heat treatment of the stuffing box had not been fully effective in eliminating the pearlite. The mechanical properties, however, were acceptable: 76,500-psi tensile strength, 57,000-psi yield strength, and 12% elongation in 2 in. at 179 Bhn.

Examination of the fracture surface suggested that the crack had been initiated at the inner edge of the lubrication hole and had propagated toward both the threaded and flange ends of the casting. An appreciable residual stress concentration must have been present and caused propagation of the crack, because the operating pressure (3100 psi), combined with the inside radius ($1\frac{5}{8}$ in.) and the section thickness at the roots of the external threads ($\frac{5}{8}$ in.), indicated a hoop stress of only about 10,000 psi. The residual stress may have been caused when a fitting was screwed tightly into the lubrication hole, and it may have been concentrated by notches at the inner end of the hole that were created when the drill broke through the sidewall to the stuffing box.

Conclusion. The stuffing box failed by fatigue cracking that originated at the intersection of the casting bore and the lubrication hole.

Corrective Measure. The material for the stuffing box, ASTM A536 ductile iron, was changed from grade 60-45-10 to grade 86-60-03. This change eliminated subsequent failures except those that occurred in extremely corrosive applications.

Heat Treatment. The methods and types of heat treatment applied to castings (or any other type of part) constitute sources of internal residual stresses. For example, carburized-and-hardened surface layers are sources of compressive stresses that generally are limited to the carburized zone. However, if the core material is of sufficient hardenability, the preferred pattern may be upset — as is described for carburized-and-hardened low-alloy steel supports in the example that follows.

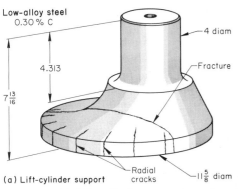

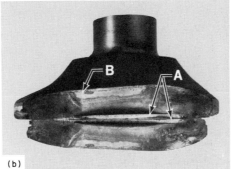

Fig. 18. (a) Lift-cylinder support, sand cast from low-alloy 0.30% C steel, that fractured because of residual surface tensile stresses. (b) Surface of crack opened in laboratory: A is the unfractured lip; B indicates indistinct local fatigue beach marks. (c) Back surface of support; arrowheads indicate small cracks. (Example 15)

Example 15. Fracture of Cast Steel Supports Because of High Residual Tensile Stresses (Fig. 18)

During reworking of frame assemblies for heavy construction equipment, several sand cast lift-cylinder supports similar to the one shown in Fig. 18(a) were found to contain severe cracks around the base. These supports, according to specification, were to be made to a chemical composition that would provide properties similar to those of wrought 8620 steel. Before being welded to the frame, the castings were carburized and hardened, with the periphery of the flange stopped off to prevent carburization. The cracks were not apparent before the frame assemblies were reworked.

Investigation. The surface of the crack in a support that was opened at the laboratory is shown in Fig. 18(b). A light-gray lip (A in Fig. 18b) along the back surface of the support was the only portion that the crack did not penetrate. The crack had begun to curl under and progress parallel to the back face, which indicated that it had propagated from the front surface of the flange. (Indistinct fatigue beach marks on the fracture surface are indicated by B in Fig. 18b.) The coloration of the fracture surface did not indicate time of failure; all coloration was believed to have been produced during removal of the failed support from the frame.

The radial cracks were similar in pattern and orientation to typical quench cracks. Processing history of the support was such that it was impossible to verify quench cracking. It was possible, but unlikely, that these radial cracks had developed during welding of the support to the frame.

The short radial cracks emanating from the edge of the support flange could have propagated across the flange section as the result of bending stresses induced when the frame was rewelded. On removal of the frame, residual stresses could have caused movement within the frame, thus concentrating stresses at the support.

Examination of the back face of the support revealed several large cracks in the surface and a fine pattern of shallow cracks across the entire surface, as indicated by the arrows in Fig. 18(c). Etching verified the presence of grinding burns, which indicated that the cracks on the back face may have developed during grinding. Some of the larger cracks in the center of the back face (away from an edge) had a separation

of 0.010 to 0.040 in., indicating that high tensile stresses were present on this surface.

A spectrographic analysis of material taken from the core of the flange indicated a composition of 0.30% C, 1.27% Mn, 0.68% Si, 0.56% Ni, 0.46% Cr, and 0.31% Mo. Both the carbon content and the alloy content were high compared with specifications for the wrought alloy. The hardenability of the casting material was substantially higher than that of wrought 8620 steel, and was considered too high for the carburizing heat treatment that was performed.

Examination of a cross section of the fractured flange (see Fig. 18b) verified that the surface of the major crack was not carburized; therefore, the crack did not exist in the casting before heat treatment. Examination of an etched specimen indicated that the flange was stopped off for about 1½ in. from the circumference. Both the front and back surfaces of the flange were carburized except in the stopped-off areas.

Microhardness traverses of the cross section indicated that the core hardness of the support flange was Rockwell C 42 to 48, which was much higher than specified. The carburized case depth was about 0.050 in.

Conclusions. The major cracking of the support occurred during quenching of the castings after heat treatment, during welding of the support to the frame or during rewelding of the frame assembly, primarily as the result of high residual tensile stresses present in the back surface of the support flange. The hardenability of the casting alloy was considered too high for the carburizing heat treatment that was performed. The result was a brittle core structure in the flange and development of residual tensile stresses in the back surface of the support flange on quenching.

Recommendations. The core of the support flange should have a maximum hardness of Rockwell C 35. Specimens from the carburized-and-hardened cast steel supports should be checked to verify the core hardness before installation.

All carburized-and-hardened supports should be tempered at 149 C (300 F) for a minimum of 2 hr immediately after hardening to reduce residual tensile stresses.

Welding Procedures. Welding is a major cause of internal stress in metal parts because of the magnitude of the temperature gradients from the weld bead to the unaffected sections. Frequently, the weld

is stronger than the base metal, and the greatest stress exists in the heat-affected zone adjacent to the weld. Thorough preheating to minimize the total thermal gradient often is highly desirable, and stress relief following welding may be even more important.

Service Conditions That Contribute to Failure

The most common cause of failure of machine parts is fatigue under cyclic stress loading, either alone or in combination with corrosion. If the fatigue strength of the part has been reduced by a surface discontinuity such as a crack, a tool mark, or a decarburized layer, the failure is attributable to the condition of the casting and not to the service conditions. But if the stress intensity is unduly high, failure of a flawless casting can result and should be attributed to service. Ways of recognizing fatigue fractures are reviewed on pages 95 to 125 in this volume, and in Volume 9.

Failures in which fatigue was a contributing factor have been cited in previous examples in this article. The fatigue fracture described in the following example was the result of misalignment of a large gear.

Example 16. Fatigue Fracture of a Cast ASTM A148, Grade 105-85, Steel Ball-Mill Gear as a Result of Misalignment (Fig. 19)

Tooth breakage was encountered on a sand cast 13½-ft-diam, 25-in.-wide double-helical bull gear in a large ball-mill drive at a mining site. The gear is shown in Fig. 19(a). The material was a plain 0.52% C high-strength steel conforming to the requirements of ASTM A148, grade 105-85. The length of service was not reported.

Two teeth that had broken from the gear at the roots were examined to determine the cause of failure.

Investigation. Visual examination of the tooth flanks revealed severe plastic flow, pitting, scoring, and abrasive wear, as shown in Fig. 19(b). The plastic flow was high on the teeth, indicating improper gear center distance or poor alignment with the pinion. Tool marks observed near the roots of the

0.52% C high-strength steel
(ASTM A148, class 105-85)
223 Bhn

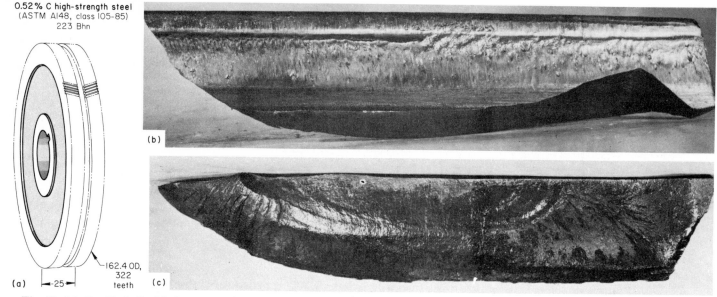

(a) ←25→ 162.4 OD, 322 teeth

(b) (c)

Fig. 19. (a) Double-helical bull gear, sand cast from 0.52% C high-strength steel and used in a large ball-mill drive at a mining site, that fractured by fatigue because of misalignment. (b) Flank of one of the gear teeth, showing wear and tool marks. (c) Fracture surface, exhibiting fatigue beach marks that originated at tool marks. (Example 16)

teeth and in the fillets were evident stress raisers. The fracture surface of one tooth is shown in Fig. 19(c). The fracture surface of both teeth exhibited beach marks typical of fatigue-crack propagation. These cracks developed in bending on the tension side of the teeth, originating at machining marks in the roots.

Study of the microstructure showed heavy cold work at contact surfaces of teeth, corroborating the evidence of flow visible on the external surfaces. Elsewhere, the microstructure was characteristic of that produced by a normalizing heat treatment, consisting of a uniform matrix of fine pearlite with a network of ferrite at the prior austenite grain boundaries.

Chemical composition and microstructure of the metal were satisfactory for the application. Hardness was 223 Bhn.

Conclusions. The gear teeth failed in bending fatigue that originated at machining marks at the roots on the pressure side of the teeth. Meshing of the teeth high on the contact surfaces developed high bending stresses at the tooth roots.

Thermal fatigue is produced by service conditions that repeatedly heat and cool a portion of a casting, thus causing that portion to expand and contract. When the thermal gradients produced in the casting are steep, the large stresses generated by the expansion or contraction can produce failure by fatigue.

Overload. Another cause of service failure is overload, applied either slowly or by impact. Volume 9 of this Handbook presents many examples of the appearance of such fractures (see pages 27 to 29, 36 to 40, 46 to 48, 66 to 68, 73 to 74, 79 to 82, and the Atlas of Fractographs). Overload played a contributing role in the failures described in Examples 3, 4 and 9 in this article. Failures that were direct results of overload are described in the two examples that follow.

Example 17. Fatigue Fracture of a Cast Steel Axle Housing Because of Overload and Rough Terrain (Fig. 20)

A fractured steel sand casting that was part of a rear-axle housing from an off-the-road oil-rig truck was submitted for laboratory analysis of the failure. It was reported that the axle had been subjected to overload prior to failure. There had been a considerable history of successful service of these castings without failure.

Investigation. A view of the fracture surface is shown in Fig. 20. The crack was initiated at the location marked O and propagated for approximately two-thirds of the total fracture surface as a fatigue crack (region A in Fig. 20). The remainder of the fracture (region B in Fig. 20) was produced by a single overload. No evidence of surface defects was detected at the site of the crack origin.

Chemical analysis of the housing established a composition of 0.23% C, 1.20% Mn, and 0.11% V, which was close to the specification. Mechanical properties of the casting were as follows: yield strength, 50,000 psi; tensile strength, 76,000 psi; elongation in 2 in., 31%; reduction in area, 51.9%; hardness, 163 to 167 Bhn. The hardness met the specification satisfactorily (163 Bhn min), but the strength was below specifica-

tion (53,000-psi min yield strength, 85,000-psi min tensile strength); the ductility was acceptable (22% min elongation; 35% min reduction in area). The specification was not consistent in that 163 Bhn corresponds to approximately 79,000-psi tensile strength, and 85,000-psi tensile strength corresponds to a hardness of about 174 Bhn. Because Brinell hardness generally was used as a quality-control check, it is probable that many castings meeting the hardness specification were accepted for this service and were considered to be of acceptable strength.

Corrosion products on the fracture surface indicated that the rate of growth of the crack had been very slow and that the casting had withstood the usual service stresses for a long time despite the presence of the fatigue crack. No material defect was found that could have caused the original crack or hastened its subsequent growth; therefore, operation of the truck over rough terrain must have brought about a condition of shock loading, resulting in excessive stress that initiated the crack.

Conclusion. Fatigue fracture of the rear-axle housing was the result of overstress and cyclic loading when the truck was traveling over rough terrain. This was considered to have been a unique failure, and, because axles of this design had performed satisfactorily, no corrective action was taken.

Fig. 20. Fracture surface of a sand cast steel rear-axle housing, for an off-the-road oil-rig truck, that fractured by fatigue due to overload. Fracture origin is at O, fatigue region is at A, and final-fracture region is at B. (Example 17)

Example 18. Brittle Fracture of a Gray Iron Nut Due to Overload Caused by Misalignment in Assembly (Fig. 21)

The sand cast gray iron flanged nut shown in Fig. 21 was used to adjust the upper roll on a 10-ft pyramid-type plate-bending machine. The flange broke away from the body of the nut during service.

Investigation. Visual examination of the flange disclosed that the fracture was circumferential, extending diagonally from the threaded interior to the fillet where the flange joined the body of the nut (see section B-B in Fig. 21); the fracture surface intersected the threads about 1 in. from the flange face. There were also four radial cracks in the flange, one of which (No. 4 in view A-A in Fig. 21) passed through the flange completely. None of the cracks entered the body of the nut.

Metallographic examination of a nital-etched specimen taken from the flange (see Fig. 21b) revealed a matrix of coarse pearlite. Graphite flakes were distributed and oriented randomly but were undesirably large. Several types of inclusions were observed, including sulfides, oxides, phosphides and silicates. A large inclusion, believed to be manganese sulfide, was found along a prior austenite grain boundary located on the surface of crack 2 at an inside corner. Sizable areas of iron sulfide were identified in the surface of crack 4. No evidence of ductility was found in any of the fracture surfaces, a condition to be expected in this material.

Discussion. The coarseness of the graphite flakes and the presence of sizable inclusions constituted features of microstructure that were not entirely satisfactory yet did not appear severe enough to have caused failure of so massive a nut. Because gray iron has little ductility and is susceptible to fracture by shock loads in bending, the roughly symmetrical array of radial cracks leading from the main fracture face suggested that the flange had been subjected to bending.

The evidence indicated that the nut had been seated improperly against the roll holder (a result of careless installation, not of improper contours of the nut), which created a bending load at a point between cracks 1 and 4. Redistribution of the load could occur only through crack initiation, because of the low ductility of the material. This behavior may have been encouraged by inclusions near the surface, which served as stress raisers. After cracks 1 and 4 had started, the load shifted, and stresses were built up on the opposite side of the flange such that cracks 2 and 3 were initiated.

Conclusions. Brittle fracture of the flange from the body was the result of overload caused by misalignment between the flange and roll holder. The microstructure contained graphite flakes of excessive size and inclusions in critical areas; however, these metallurgical imperfections did not appear to have had significant effects on the fracture.

Recommendations. The flange surface should be carefully and properly aligned with the roll holder to achieve uniform distribution of the load. A more ductile type of metal, such as steel or ductile iron, would be more suitable for this application and would require less-exact alignment.

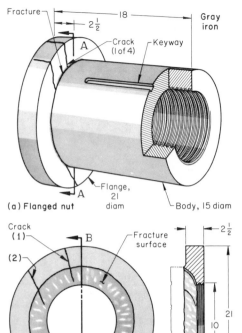

(a) Flanged nut

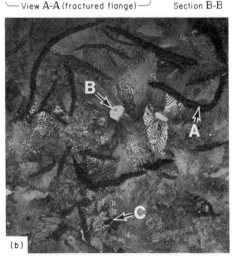

(b)

(a) Flanged nut, which was used to adjust a plate-bending roll, and a view of the flange that fractured from the body. (b) Micrograph, at 150×, of a nital-etched specimen from the flange, showing coarse pearlite matrix, large graphite flakes (at A), manganese sulfide inclusions (at B) and silicate inclusions (at C).

Fig. 21. Sand cast gray iron flanged nut that failed by brittle fracture due to overload (Example 18)

Thermal-Stress Overload. The most common interpretation of the term "overload" involves mechanically applied stress. There is, however, another source of overload that perhaps is even more destructive and that is provided by hindered thermal expansion or contraction. If a thermal change demands a specific change of dimension, there is no property of an alloy that can resist it.

During cooling, for instance, a casting will contract unharmed, pulling the resisting obstacles toward each other, or will plastically deform, or will tear. Brittle fracture resulting from thermal-stress overload is described in the example that follows. In this instance, not only were heat checks produced on a surface cooled rapidly from a high temperature, but also fracture occurred in a section restrained from contracting.

Example 19. Brittle Fracture of a Ductile Iron Brake Drum by Thermal-Contraction Overload (Fig. 22)

A 23-in.-diam heavy-duty brake drum that was a component of a cable-wound winch broke into two pieces during a shutdown period. Other drums had failed in a similar fashion. Average service life of these drums was two weeks; none had failed by wear. The drums were sand cast from ductile iron, because this material had been successful in a similar application; this brake drum, however, was of a relatively new design.

The winch was used to move large loads, which were carried by gears and clutch plates during haul-in and by the brake drum during haul-out. The arrangement of the parts is shown in Fig. 22(a). The brake drum was aligned by and bolted to both the clutch mount and the disk that in turn was bolted to the cable drum. Both the disk and the clutch mount fitted radially against the inside edge of the web of the brake drum with a clearance of 0.0025 to 0.0075 in.

During haul-in, the brake drum idled freely. During haul-out, the cable on the cable drum drove the brake drum and resistance was provided by brake bands (not shown in Fig. 22a) applied to the outside surface of the brake drum. According to the operator, the friction during heavy service was sufficient to heat the brake drum, clutch mount and disk to a red color.

Investigation. The severity of the friction on the surface of the brake drum is illustrated by the heat checks shown in Fig. 22(b). The heat checks completely penetrated the rim of the drum, as shown by regions A in Fig. 22(c). The final-fracture area (B in Fig. 22c) comprised the entire web and part of the rim. The regions of the fracture surface produced by heat checks were oxidized. Final fracture was the result of a single tensile overload.

Measurements of the two fragments of the drum revealed that the diameter of the drum had expanded along the plane of the fracture, indicating the release of internal stress. Cracks found between the inside surface and the boltholes also indicated the existence of internal stress, but these cracks were considered of secondary importance. Along the inside surface of the web, a ridge of heavy oxidation was observed, located between the areas of contact with the clutch mount and the disk. This oxide confirmed the observation of red color during haul-out, indicating a service temperature of at least 650 C (1200 F).

Examination of the assembly indicated that the brake drum would cool faster than its mounts and therefore would contract onto them. The contraction of the inside surface of the web as the drum cooled from about 650 C (1200 F) would be 0.013 in. per hundred degrees Fahrenheit, and the maximum clearance (0.0075 in.) would be closed tightly within less than the first hundred

degrees Fahrenheit of temperature decrease. Therefore, cooling of the brake drum would generate thermal tensile stresses of such a magnitude that the thickness of the rim remaining after heat checking would be in-

sufficient to withstand the stresses, and the result would be fracture.

Conclusion. Brittle fracture of the brake drum occurred as a result of thermal contraction of the drum web against the clutch mount and the disk.

Corrective Measures. The inside diameter of the drum web was enlarged sufficiently to allow for clearance between the web and the clutch mount and disk at a temperature differential of up to 555 C (1000 F). Aluminum spacers were used for alignment during assembly but melted when heated in service, and thus caused no interference. With the adoption of this procedure, brake drums failed by wear only.

Graphitic Corrosion. Gray iron is susceptible to a form of attack known as graphitic corrosion when immersed in soft waters, salt waters, mine waters or very dilute acids, or when buried underground in some soils, particularly those containing sulfates. Corrosion eats away the matrix of the iron, lowering mechanical strength and leaving behind a soft black graphitic residue on the surface. If the residue is permitted to remain on the corroded surface, it serves as a protective coating and effects an appreciable reduction in corrosion rate. In other instances, such as in the example that follows, erosion washes away the graphitic residue, and the process of corrosion is permitted to continue.

Example 20. Failure of a Gray Iron Pump Bowl Because of Graphitic Corrosion From Exposure to Well Water (Fig. 23)

Deterioration of the vanes and a wearing away of the area surrounding the main-shaft bearing housing of the pump bowl for a submersible water pump used in a well field (see Fig. 23a) were noticed during maintenance inspection. The bowl was sand cast from gray iron and had been in service approximately 45 months. An inspection of the pump after 24 months of service did not disclose that a serious condition existed, although some wear was noticed.

Several pumps of the same design and material, but of different sizes, were operating in the well field.

Investigation. Visual examination of the vanes and the area surrounding the main-shaft bearing housing revealed a dark corrosion product that was soft, porous and of low mechanical strength. Also, there were areas in which severe erosion had occurred, as shown in Fig. 23(a).

Macrographs of sections through the pump shell and a vane are shown in Fig. 23(b) and (c). The darker areas on both photographs represent graphitic residue and corrosion products that were not removed by erosion.

Chemical analysis of the pump material confirmed that it was gray iron.

Conclusion. Exposure of the pump bowl to the well water resulted in graphitic corrosion, which generated a soft, porous graphitic residue impregnated with insoluble corrosion products. Failure of the pump bowl, however, resulted from the continuous erosion of the residue by the action of the water within the pump.

(a) Schematic illustration of the clutch – brake-drum assembly. (b) Heat checks on a surface of the brake drum. (c) A fracture surface of the brake drum, showing regions affected by heat checking (at A's) and final-fracture region (at B).

Fig. 22. Sand cast ductile iron brake drum, from a cable-wound winch, that fractured as a result of overload caused by thermal contraction (Example 19)

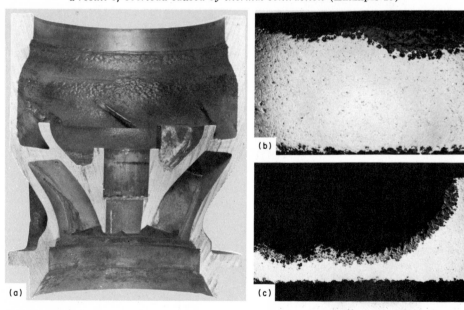

Fig. 23. (a) *Section through a sand cast gray iron pump bowl that failed by graphitic corrosion plus erosion of the graphitic residue by the action of water within the pump.* (b) *and* (c) *Macrographs at 7× of sections through corroded areas in the pump shell and a pump vane, respectively, showing remaining graphitic residue.* (Example 20)

Failures of Weldments

*By the ASM Committee on Failure Analysis of Weldments**

WELDMENT FAILURES may be divided into two classes: those rejected during inspection and mechanical testing, and those discovered in service through inability of the weld to continue to perform its designed function. Failures in service may arise from fracture, wear, corrosion or deformation. In this article, major attention is directed toward analysis of service failures.

Causes for rejection in inspection may be either features visible on the weldment surface, or subsurface features that are found by nondestructive-testing methods of inspection.

Surface features that are causes for rejection include:

Excessive mismatch at the weld joint
Excessive bead convexity and bead reinforcement
Excessive bead concavity and undersized welds
Sharp undercut and overlap at weld toe
Cracks: hot or cold, longitudinal or transverse, crater and at weld toe
Gas porosity
Incomplete fusion
Arc strike
Spatter.

Subsurface features that are causes for rejection include:

Underbead cracks
Gas porosity
Inclusions: slag, oxides, or tungsten metal
Incomplete fusion
Inadequate penetration.

Failure to meet strength requirements is another cause for rejection of weldments. For details of test methods for welds, see the Standards of the American Welding Society, particularly AWS B4.0-74, "Standard Methods for Mechanical Testing of Welds". For a general treatment of evaluation methods for weldments, see Ref 1.

Reasons for Failure. Poor workmanship on the part of the operator because of inadequate training and improper selection of filler-metal composition ac-

counts for numerous arc-weld failures. Other reasons include:

Inappropriate joint design for a successful weld
Improper weld size
Unfavorable heat input
Improper preweld and postweld heating
Improper fit-up
Alloy segregation and embrittlement
Unfavorable cooling rate in heat-affected zone
High residual stresses
Environmental conditions not contemplated in the design of the weld. These comprise accidental overload, continual loads higher than intended, abnormal temperatures, and marine or other corrosive atmospheres.

For a discussion of resistance-weld failures, see page 360 in this article.

Analysis Procedures

The initial task of the failure analyst is to seek out and compile as complete a history as possible of the failed weldment and its preparation. The success in arriving at a correct determination of the cause of failure will be greatly influenced by the amount of information that can be obtained as early as possible. There are no set rules as to the sequence in which the details are sought, but it is important to secure all oral reports of the failure as promptly as possible while the event is still fresh in the minds of the observers. The following is a suggested check list of items of information that will be useful later in analysis:

1 Determine when, where and how the failure occurred. Interview all operators involved. How was the part treated after failure? Was it protected? Was the fracture handled? Did the failure involve any fire, which could have altered the microstructure of the weld or of the base metal?
2 Establish the service history — loads, atmospheric exposure, length of service. Was an accident involved? Have there been other similar failures?

3 Obtain drawings of the joint design, calculations of service stress, estimation of service life. What were the specified and actual base metal and filler metal? Obtain, if possible, the actual chemical composition, heat treatment and mechanical properties of the base metal, and the actual chemical composition of the filler metal.
4 Ascertain the cleaning and fit-up procedures specified and those actually used. Obtain details of the welding procedure, specified and used, and any repairs made. Was postweld heating provided?
5 Establish how the weldment was finished and what tests were performed. For how long was the weldment stored and under what conditions? When was it shipped for installation? How promptly was it installed? Request copies of inspection procedures and inspection reports.

For additional discussion of failure-analysis procedures, the reader is referred to the article beginning on page 10 in this volume.

Examination Procedures. After the background information relating to the failed weldment has been secured, the analyst is ready to undertake the study of the failed part itself. The study should begin with visual examination of the weldment and fracture-surface features, accompanied by preparation of sketches and photographs (both general and closeups) to provide a complete record. This should be followed by careful examination under a low-power (5 to 30 diameters) stereomicroscope. These procedures should be followed for all failures, regardless of whether the failure is a fracture or is caused by wear, corrosion or deformation.

The analyst should determine whether the failure was located in the weld, in the heat-affected zone, or in the base metal, and whether the weld was of proper size, shape and soundness. The subsequent steps to be taken in identifying the exact cause of the failure will be greatly influ-

*STEWART M. DePOY, *Chairman*, Manager, Metallurgical and Quality Systems, Jeffrey Mining Machinery Div., Dresser Industries, Inc.; NICK F. BRATKOVICH (retired), formerly Section Chief, Joining Processes, Materials Laboratory, Detroit Diesel Allison Div., General Motors Corp.; CRAIG D. CLAUSER, Metallurgical Engineer, Materials Engineering Laboratories, Steam Turbine Div., Westinghouse Electric Corp.

MATTHEW J. DONACHIE, JR., Senior Materials Project Engineer, Materials Engineering and Research Laboratories, Pratt & Whitney Aircraft Div., United Aircraft Corp.; JOHN D. EYESTONE, Senior Staff Engineer, Metals Joining Engineering, Western Electric Co., Inc.; GEORGE A. HENDRY, Metallurgy and Welding Section, Materials and

Processes Dept., Grumman Aerospace Corp.; CLARENCE E. JACKSON, Department of Welding Engineering, Ohio State University; RALPH KEIDEL, Director of Plant Engineering, Young Radiator Co. (formerly Chief Engineer, Pressed Steel Tank Co., Inc.); T. L. OBERLE, Program Manager, Research Dept., Caterpillar Tractor Co.; KENNETH F. PACKER, President, Packer Engineering Associates, Inc.

R. QUATTRONE, Chief, Metallurgy Branch, Construction Engineering Laboratory, Department of the Army; WILLIAM A. SVEKRIC, Vice President, Materials Joining Consultants Div., Col-X Corp.; P. R. WHITE, Supervisor, Metals Applications and Properties Group, Bell Laboratories; HUGH BAKER, *Secretary*, Senior Editor, Metals Handbook, American Society for Metals.

enced by the outcome of these early observations.

If the failure is not a fracture, it may be necessary to follow low-power microscopic examination with examination at higher magnification. If so, this should be undertaken before chemical analysis of the weldment surface alters the surface characteristics. Examination of the weldment surface at high magnification should reveal whether there has been selective attack of the part by corrosion, erosion or other failure mechanism and may provide clues as to its nature.

The macroscopic and microscopic features that can aid in identification of a failure mechanism are described in the article on General Practice in Failure Analysis, which begins on page 10, and in the articles on failures from various mechanisms and related environmental factors, which begin on page 57.

If the failure is a fracture, much can be learned concerning the location of fracture origins, the mechanisms and directions of crack propagation, and the types of loading that were involved, by replica or direct examination in a scanning electron microscope. (See also two articles in Volume 9 of this Handbook: "Discontinuities Leading to Fracture That Are Revealed by Fractography" and "Use of Fractography for Failure Analysis".)

Once the macroscopic and microscopic examinations are completed, analysis of the material and of the weldment surface may be undertaken by wet chemistry, by electron microprobe, or by spectrometry using x-ray diffraction or using Auger electron or ion-scattering spectrometers.

Metallographic Sectioning. When all study of the fracture surface is complete, sectioning may then be performed to reveal the microstructure of each zone of the weldment in relation to that expected for the welding procedure reported and the composition of base and filler metals. Sectioning also will permit appraisals of inclusion distributions and contours, disclosure of whether the fracture and any secondary cracks were consistently transgranular or intergranular, and observation as to whether the weld fusion was incomplete or the penetration was adequate. Such a microscopic examination of a distorted but unfractured weldment would also be appropriate as a means of discovering if the distortion was caused by loading at an unscheduled high temperature. Microhardness-test traverses of the weld zones would yield valuable corroborative data as to whether the microstructure was uniform or not.

Nondestructive Testing. Certain nondestructive tests must be used with caution so as to not alter or create confusing evidence. For instance, liquid-penetrant tests are very effective in revealing fine cracks, but if the failure resulted from

stress-corrosion cracking, the use of a penetrant might provide false clues — for example, by introducing a corrodent into the crack system. The correct procedure is to delay application of the penetrant until after completion of the pertinent chemical analyses.

Magnetic-particle testing can also create problems. In one instance, welds were being made successfully on a steel containing more than 0.35% C, but because the normal borderline weldability of this material made it susceptible to cracking, a magnetic-particle test was done to check for cracks. No cracks were found, but a few weeks later the weldments were returned because of cracks at minute hard "burned" spots that were caused by the prods used to make electrical contact for the magnetic-particle tests. Magnetic-particle tests conducted with a magnetic field induced by a "yoke" that does not pass current through the part will avoid this difficulty.

Analysis of Information. The final stage in analysis of a weldment failure is to compare and integrate all of the information that has been gathered. Before this final stage, it is particularly important to avoid arriving at a decision concerning the cause of failure. This is because nearly all welds contain discontinuities of one type or another that at initial investigation might be considered to be a contributing factor to the failure. Therefore, it is important for the analyst to keep in mind that many welds containing discontinuities may have given satisfactory performance over long service lives that were unaffected by such discontinuities.

The techniques of fractography (see Volume 9 of this Handbook) can be used to identify the origin or origins of fracture and the paths that the propagating crack followed. The crack origin should reveal whether a stress concentrator might have contributed to failure. The metallographic specimens should disclose the existence of any nonuniformity in microstructure, such as decarburized layers, carburized skin, alloy segregation, martensite in the heat-affected zone, and inadequate weld penetration. Any one of these items might prove to be the critical contributing factor in a particular instance, but generally the two most important items of information are the location of the origin and the characteristics of the fracture surface. From these two items may be deduced how the fracture began and how it propagated, whether it was generated by a single overload or by repetitive stresses, whether the loading was in tension, torsion, bending, shear or some combination, whether fracture was ductile by microvoid coalescence or by tearing, or was brittle by cleavage or by intergranular separation. However, all of the

other data are necessary to make sure that a more obscure cause of failure is not missed.

The outcome of the failure analysis usually should be a recommendation that will avoid any repetition. Such recommendations generally consist of an "eliminate the cause" procedure, which of necessity will differ as the cause differs. The procedure may consist of the use of a better weld contour, a more favorable filler metal, a more appropriate heat input, a different cooling rate for the heat-affected zone, a more accurate fit-up, a higher-quality base metal, or different service conditions.

Failure Origins in Arc Welds

Some discontinuities that can serve as origins of failures of arc welded parts are found only in welds made by a particular process, but most discontinuities may be produced by any of the welding processes. These latter types of discontinuities are discussed below, and the types found only in a specific process are described later in this article. For information on process variables for control of weld quality, see the articles on specific welding processes in Volume 6 of this Handbook.

The discontinuities found in arc welds vary considerably in their importance as failure origins. In moderate amounts, slag inclusions, porosity, groove overfill or underfill, or similar discontinuities, will not reduce the fatigue strength of the weld sufficiently to warrant their classification as potential causes of fracture originating in a weld. In fact, fatigue cracks that initiate at the toe of a weld will propagate around areas of gas porosity or slag inclusions as often as through them.

However, such features as hot cracks, cold cracks and lamellar tears are much more serious, because they will affect fatigue strength to a degree that cannot be compensated for in design. Hot cracks and lamellar tears normally occur so soon after welding that they can be detected by nondestructive testing and eliminated from finished weldments. However, cold cracks resulting from a supersaturation of hydrogen may not grow to a detectable size until as much as a week after welding operations are completed.

Porosity produced in arc welds can be grouped into three types: isolated, linear and cluster. Isolated porosity is caused by a phenomenon similar to boiling when the arc power is too far above the ideal level. Linear or cluster porosity can result from interaction of components of the shielding gas (such as oxygen, hydrogen or carbon dioxide) with the weld puddle to evolve a gas (such as hydrogen sulfide). Cluster porosity also will be formed when the cover of shielding gas is inadequate or when the welding is done on wet base metal.

Rust, if present on the base-metal surface, is a source of moisture. This moisture either will be dissolved as steam vapor by the molten puddle of weld metal or will be partly dissociated by the arc and dissolved as hydrogen. Where there is a possibility of porosity or embrittlement from rust, it can be avoided simply by removing the rust layer before attempting to weld.

Oxidation of shielded arc welds occurs only when there has been improper or inadequate shielding. Titanium, for example, is sufficiently reactive to require shielding of both the face and the root sides of the weld, as well as of the tungsten electrode (if gas tungsten-arc welded) to prevent oxygen and nitrogen contamination and embrittlement of both the weld and the heat-affected zone. Such additional shielding is not mandatory for the root side of steel or aluminum welds, but it does improve the quality of the weld.

Formation of Compounds. Another effect of the shielding material may be the formation of compounds (such as oxides or nitrides) in the molten puddle from reaction with minute impurities, such as oxygen or nitrogen, in shielding gas. Such compounds have been shown to lower the toughness of the weld compared to that of welds made with pure inert gas. For welding of steel, however, it is impractical to attempt much gas metal-arc welding without deliberate use of a small amount of oxygen for arc stability. This explains in great part why, in steel, gas tungsten-arc welds possess toughness that is superior to gas metal-arc welds.

Hot cracks in welds may be caused by joint design and the restraint imposed on the weld. However, hot cracks are commonly caused by the presence of low-melting constituents that extend the temperature range of low hot strength and low ductility to temperatures below that of the alloy. In steels these constituents are compounds such as phosphides and sulfides and elements such as copper, which segregate at grain boundaries and which cause grain-boundary tearing under thermal-contraction stresses. Another type of hot crack is a crater crack. The material in the crater region is basically richer in solutes than the remainder of the weld, because of the directional nature of weld-metal solidification, and is very prone to cracking. The best method of control is to use welding materials with minimum contents of residual elements (such as phosphorus, sulfur and copper in steel), thus eliminating the possibility of segregation. If this is not feasible, the next best procedure is to avoid the slow cooling rates that favor segregation between the

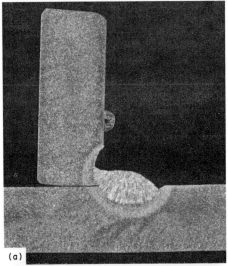

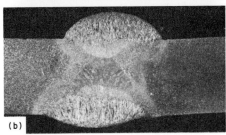

Fig. 1. Two types of poor contours in arc welds: (a) fillet weld, showing two forms of undercut plus weld splatter and uneven leg length; (b) butt weld, showing a very high, sharp crown

liquidus and solidus temperatures and accelerate cooling until the crater has solidified.

In wrought heat treatable aluminum alloys, the relation between working and weld direction will influence cracking. Welds made in the short transverse direction often develop grain-boundary microcracks in the heat-affected zone.

Cold cracks form in welds after solidification is complete. In steel, cold cracks depend on the presence of a tensile stress, a susceptible microstructure, and dissolved hydrogen (Ref 2). The stress may arise from restraint by other components of a weldment or from the simple thermal stresses created by welding in a butt, groove or T-joint. The susceptibility of the microstructure to cold cracking relates actually to the solubility for hydrogen and the possibility of supersaturation. Austenite, which has a high solubility for hydrogen, is least susceptible to cold cracking, and martensite, which has a low solubility for hydrogen, is most susceptible, because the rapid cooling necessary for the austenite-to-martensite transformation traps the hydrogen in a state of supersaturation in martensite. The presence of hydrogen in a gas metal-arc weld is generally due to moisture that is introduced in the shielding gas, dissociated by the arc to form elemental hydrogen and dissolved by the

molten weld puddle and by the adjacent region in the heat-affected zone (which is austenite in a steel weld). In the supersaturated state, the hydrogen diffuses to regions of high stress where it can initiate a crack. Continued diffusion of the hydrogen to the region of stress concentration at the crack tip extends the crack. This behavior means that hydrogen-induced cold cracking is time dependent (that is, time for hydrogen diffusion is needed) and the appearance of detectable cracks can be delayed until long after the weld has passed inspection. The remedy is to eliminate as far as possible the sources of hydrogen — water, oils, greases, and rust that contains hydrates. Preweld and postweld heating will help the hydrogen escape by diffusion and will reduce the level of the tensile stress that may be present.

Poor weld contours include: overlaps, which result when the weld puddle is too cold for fusion, or when the puddle is too hot and solidifies after protruding beyond the toe or root of the weld; undercutting, from too high a welding current or too slow a welding speed (see Fig. 1a); and a bead with a very high, sharp crown from too low a current or too fast a travel (see Fig. 1b). In addition to proper control of amperage and temperature of the bead, the use of a weave type of bead is helpful in contour control.

Embrittlement. Preweld and postweld heating are used for relief of internal stress and elimination of hydrogen. However, temperatures to which parts are heated should be selected with care; carbon steels and many alloy steels undergo a decrease in notch toughness when heated in certain critical temperature ranges. For a discussion of this and other embrittlement phenomena, see pages 78 to 82 in the article on Ductile and Brittle Fractures in this volume.

Inadequate joint penetration and incomplete fusion in arc welds usually result from improper fit-up or groove design or from use of an inadequate welding current. The presence of inadequate penetration and incomplete fusion can be critical because, in addition to reducing the effective cross-sectional area, it provides discontinuities that can be almost as sharp as cracks, and even display crack-extended tips. In welding some alloys, inadequate penetration and incomplete fusion may result from an oxide layer on the weld sidewall.

Arc strikes and flame gouges can cause considerable damage to many metals, and care must be taken to avoid them. Arc strikes can result from accidental contact between the workpiece and the electrode or electrode holder. Also, loosely connected ground cables can cause arc strikes. Careless handling of a cutting torch can result in flame gouging of a part.

(a) Nital-etched metallographic section, at 35×, through the crater of an arc strike, showing porosity and shrinkage cracks below the crater surface. (b) Photograph, at 5×, of fatigue fracture (in profile at top), in which the fracture initiated in the center of the arc strike (at arrow).

Fig. 2. Typical damage to type 410 stainless steel caused by accidental arc strikes

In hardenable alloys, arc strikes and flame gouges cause segregations of carbon and transformations to untempered martensite because of the rapid rate of melting and solidification.

The melting, rehardening and generation of solidification defects (hot cracks and porosity) can result in stress concentrations that may initiate cracks and possible failure by fatigue. Figure 2(a) is a micrograph of a section through an arc strike that displays porosity and shrinkage cracks. Figure 2(b) shows a fatigue fracture that had its origin in an arc strike. In another instance, a welder was making a flame cut on a steel section and allowed the flame to come in contact with an adjacent part. The result was a ½-in.-deep gouge in the part, which eventually led to its fracture.

Shielded Metal-Arc Welding. The condition of the covering of the electrode is important to the quality of shielded metal-arc welds. There are two general types of covering; one has a cellulose-type binder, which contains hydrogen, and the other has a cellulose-free covering that contains almost no hydrogen. The first type of electrode covering is used for welds on noncritical structures in which hydrogen in moderate amounts is acceptable. The second type of electrode covering is used for welds on structures for which even small amounts of hydrogen are not tolerable.

Electrode coverings, however, are hygroscopic and pick up moisture from the atmosphere, particularly if the relative humidity is high. This can occur even in cellulose-free coverings, especially if the electrodes are exposed to the air for more than 2 to 4 hr. Moisture or other hydrogen compounds in the covering are dissociated by the arc temperature, and the resulting atomic hydrogen is readily dissolved in the weld puddle. Water vapor also may be directly dissolved by the molten steel with very little dissociation. The solubility for hydrogen and for water vapor in the steel decreases abruptly and drastically (as much as 4 to 1 for hydrogen) when the molten phase freezes (Ref 3). A further decrease in solubility for hydrogen occurs when the austenite transforms to either ferrite

or martensite, depending on the alloy content and the cooling rate. During freezing, the hydrogen may escape by diffusion or formation of bubbles but a portion will remain in the austenite in a supersaturated state. The dissolved water will largely be ejected as bubbles during the freezing process, which may form a "picture frame" of wormholes if the quantity of dissolved water and the rate of freezing are both moderate. If much vapor has been dissolved, the metal will puff seriously, leaving an extremely porous structure.

The hydrogen in the austenite may escape by diffusion, if time permits. However, if the weld metal and the heat-affected zone (which also will have been invaded by diffusing hydrogen) transform to martensite, the abrupt drop in hydrogen solubility accompanying the phase change can induce significant internal stress. This stress state can generate cracks that are dangerous, because they do not form immediately but form

after a period of time that is sufficient to make them undetectable until well after final inspection.

An illustration of the embrittling effect of hydrogen derived from electrode coverings is given in fractographs 3485 to 3488 on page 144 in Volume 9 of this Handbook; here, the characteristics of impact fractures of welds are related to the compositions of the electrodes used. A more quantitative relationship is given in the table that accompanies Fig. 3, which summarizes data from a series of weld-cracking test specimens prepared from 1-in.-thick, 3.5% Ni steel plates cut with circular grooves, as shown in Fig. 3. In these weld-cracking tests, shielded metal-arc welding was performed semiautomatically on a turntable, producing a 270° weld bead at 175 amp, 26 volts, and a travel speed of 6 in. per minute with a ³⁄₁₆-in.-diam electrode.

The weld in specimen A in Fig. 3 was made with a low-hydrogen covered electrode (E6015) from a sealed container

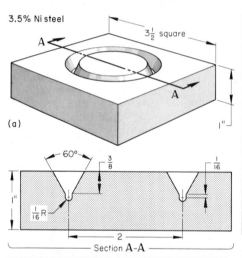

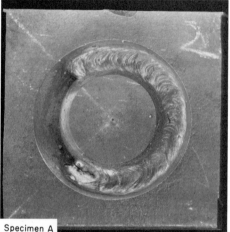

Fig. 3. Drawing showing specifications of circular-groove specimens used in weld-cracking tests, and photographs of three specimens of 3.5% Ni steel plate that were shielded metal-arc welded with low-hydrogen covered electrodes (E6015) that were exposed to welding-room air for different lengths of time before welding. Test results are given in the accompanying table, above.

Test specimen	Exposure of electrode to air, hr	Moisture content of covering, wt %	Length of crack in test weld, in.
A	0	0.25	0.50
B	168 (7 days)	0.56	1.50
C	744 (1 month)	0.70	4.50

that was opened immediately before the test weld was made. Two rods were taken from the package at the same time, the covering of the two rods was stripped, and the moisture content of the coverings was determined by heating them for 1 hr at 1400 C (2552 F). The temperature of the welding room was 24 C (75 F), and the relative humidity during the several tests was 35 to 40%. Other rods, used for the test welds in specimens B and C in Fig. 3, were exposed to the welding-room air for 168 hr (7 days) and for 744 hr (1 month), respectively. The crack lengths in the three welds were correlated with determinations of moisture content, as shown in the table with Fig. 3. Although the electrode coverings were of the low-hydrogen type, the moisture content increased with additional time of exposure to room air and the welds exhibited increases in lengths of cracking.

Hydrogen damage to weld deposits (either as porosity or as embrittlement) can be avoided simply by preventing any exposure of the weldment to hydrogen. For shielded metal-arc welding, this means baking the electrodes to remove all entrapped moisture and storing in holding ovens to prevent moisture from re-entering the covering from the air. Normally, such ovens should be controlled between 121 and 177 C (250 and 350 F). Some electrodes may require initial baking to as high as 427 C (800 F) before storing, but care should be taken to avoid breaking down the covering by heating to excessive temperatures.

Flux-Cored Arc Welding. A specific problem with flux-cored arc welding is the solid slag layer covering the deposit, which in some circumstances firmly adheres to the deposited metal. This slag must be removed between welding passes or it will be entrapped in the weld. However, with certain flux-cored electrodes two-pass horizontal fillet welds can be made without removal of the slag.

Submerged-Arc Welding. Factors that contribute to the formation of discontinuities in other arc welding processes generally also prevail for the submerged-arc process. However, in submerged-arc welding, flux is separate from the welding rod, and the quantity of the flux layer can affect results. For instance, if the flux layer is too deep, it will produce a "ropey" reinforcement, whereas too shallow a layer contributes to the formation of porosity and gas pockets. Also, a flux layer that is too narrow causes a narrow reinforcement.

Gas Tungsten-Arc Welding. A characteristic problem in gas tungsten-arc welding is the pickup of tungsten particles from the electrode caused by physical contact of the electrode with the weld puddle. Contact is difficult to avoid, because of the short arc length generally used, and only highly skilled welders can

judge the correct distance and avoid generating tungsten inclusions. Tungsten inclusions are extremely brittle and fracture readily under stress, and thus can act as failure origins. Tungsten inclusions also may be caused by excessively high welding currents, incorrectly sized or shaped electrodes, and oxygen contamination of the shielding gas. Tungsten particles are easily detected in radiographs.

Plasma-arc welding is closely related to gas tungsten-arc welding. A principal difference between these two welding processes is the "keyhole" effect produced by the constricted arc column of a plasma-arc weld. This effect is created by displacement of molten metal by the forceful plasma jet, permitting the arc column to pass completely through the workpiece. If the welding current should be turned off abruptly at the end of a welding pass, the keyhole would not close and a hole or a large region of subsurface porosity would remain. This is no problem, however, if the weld can be terminated on a runoff tab.

Plasma-arc welding was used in the sealing of the circumferential joints of a high-performance pressure vessel made of modified type 410 stainless steel. The plasma arc completely penetrated through the 0.3-in.-thick joint, which did not require the special edge preparation that would have been necessary if gas tungsten-arc welding had been used, and permitted completion of the joints with fewer weld passes. To avoid introducing porosity in the weld-joint overlap region, it was necessary to program a careful "slope-down" control to reduce the welding current and the orifice-gas flow gradually at the end of the weld, thereby achieving a smooth transition from the deep, keyhole mode of penetration to shallow penetration. Figure 4 is a macrograph of a longitudinal section through a plasma-arc weld, showing the surface irregularity and subsurface porosity that may result when the welding current and orifice-gas flow are not properly reduced through the overlap region.

Failures in Arc Welded Low-Carbon Steel

Low-carbon steels are generally quite ductile, and therefore the existence of porosity and slag inclusions within shielded metal-arc welds is usually not critical. Many welds in low-carbon steel are made successfully using E6010 electrodes, which are known to produce porous weld deposits.

At low temperatures, however, the tolerance of low-carbon steels for weld discontinuities is critically affected by the microstructure. For instance, fine-grained pearlite formed by normalizing is much more tolerant of weld discontinuities than is coarse pearlite formed by furnace cooling. The existence of a coarse pearlitic structure was the basis for failure experienced by the welded Liberty ships of World War II, which split at welds while still at dockside. The fracture origins in the Liberty ships were at weld discontinuities, and the crack propagation was through furnace-cooled plate. The cracking was minimized by specifying normalized plate. (Example 1 on page 338 describes another instance of low-temperature fracture of a weld.)

Embrittlement of low-carbon steel is not common, but the decrease in ductility due to strain aging is a form of embrittlement that the welder should be aware of. For this reason, proper care should be taken in applying peening to low-carbon steel weld deposits.

Inclusions. The presence of flattened inclusions, such as silicates or manganese sulfides, in rolled carbon steel plate can cause difficulties, particularly in welding T-joints. The cooling stresses may cause rupture by decohesion between the inclusions and the steel matrix, giving a fracture with a laminated appearance, as shown in Fig. 5(a). The nature of fracture through the coarse-grained reaustenitized structure of the heat-affected zone is shown in profile in Fig. 5(b). The fine details of the fracture can be seen in the SEM fractograph in Fig. 5(c), which displays the dimpled rupture of

Fig. 4. Macrograph, at 6×, of a longitudinal section through a plasma-arc weld made with improperly programed reduction of welding current and orifice-gas flow, which resulted in surface irregularity and subsurface porosity

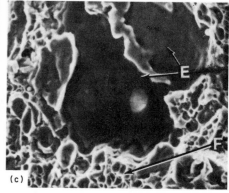

(a) Fractograph of lamellar tear, at about 0.3×, showing separation that has followed flattened inclusions. (b) Macrograph, at about 8×, of section through fracture (at top), which occurred in the coarse-grained reaustenitized region, A, of the heat-affected zone. The fine-grained reaustenitized region is at B, and the partly reaustenitized region of ferrite and refined pearlite is at C. At D is an unaffected region of ferrite and pearlite. (c) SEM fractograph, at 1300×, showing inclusion platelets (at E) and dimples (at F).

Fig. 5. Lamellar tear beneath a T-joint weld that joined two low-carbon steel plates

the low-carbon steel matrix and the exposed surface of silicate and sulfide platelets.

Hot cracking in gas tungsten-arc welds of low-carbon steel depends primarily on the steel composition, the degree of joint restraint, the cooling rate, the amount of heat-energy input, and the type of solidification structure. Susceptibility to cracking increases with increase in carbon content and with decrease in the manganese-to-sulfur ratio. Steels with carbon contents up to 0.25% normally are weldable by the gas tungsten-arc process without hot cracking.

A very rigid joint restraint concentrates the thermal contraction in the weld deposit and thereby induces hot cracks. Rapid cooling and a high heat input both favor formation of hot cracks. The formation of a columnar structure during solidification of the weld is more likely to promote hot cracking than if an equiaxed structure is formed.

Examples. The following six examples discuss failures of low-carbon steel arc welds and the corrective measures recommended or taken.

Example 1. Brittle Fracture of a Carbon Steel Soybean-Oil Storage Tank, Caused by High Service Stresses

A riveted 0.25% C steel oil-storage tank located in Oklahoma was dismantled, the edges of the plates were beveled for welding, and the plates were reassembled in Minnesota by shielded metal-arc welding to form a tank for storage of soybean oil. The reconstructed tank, 60 ft in diameter and 40 ft high, was set on a rather yielding subsoil base, with minimum density requirements. There was gravel fill over the subsoil with no compaction. After storage of soybean oil for a year, the tank was cleaned to remove the heavy semisolid residues. For ease of access, a rectangular opening was cut in the side of the tank large enough to admit a front-end loader. After the tank was cleaned, a frame of heavy angle iron was prepared for the opening. One leg of the angle iron was fillet welded to the tank at a 90° angle to the tank surface along each edge

of the opening, projecting outward; the other leg was drilled to permit bolting a ¾-in.-thick steel plate to it as an external closure that could be removed for periodic cleaning.

During the following year, the tank was filled to a record height. In mid-January the temperature dropped to −31 C (−23 F), accompanied by winds of 29 miles per hour. During this cold period, the tank split on both sides of the opening. The primary origin of the failure was at the upper left corner of the opening, from which the crack rapidly propagated in a brittle-type fracture vertically to the roof of the tank and then turned to follow either side of the roof in a ductile manner, allowing the roof to fall in and the sides to spread out.

Investigation. In addition to the primary origin, the fractures were found to have two secondary origins — at the upper right and lower right corners of the opening. All three origins were located at the toes of the fillet welds attaching the angle-iron frame to the tank wall. The direction of crack propagation was clearly indicated by chevron marks in each instance.

The welding of the frame was done in the fall and early winter, using the shielded metal-arc process with E6010 electrodes. Use of this type of electrode would suggest that weld porosity or hydrogen embrittlement, or both, probably were present. At the subzero temperatures existing at the time of failure, the steel was certainly below its ductile-to-brittle transition temperature. These combined circumstances thus provided a decidedly brittle condition.

The record level to which the tank was filled imposed a high stress on the tank walls, which was accentuated at the corners by the rectangular shape of the opening. Calculated values of the stress at the welds were found to approach the yield strength of the steel. It was therefore not surprising that once the fracture initiated, it propagated at a speed that simulated an explosion.

Conclusions. The tank failed by brittle fracture because very high service stresses were applied to a steel at well below its transition temperature. Fracture was initiated by stress concentrations at the sharp corners of the opening and at the toes of the fillet welds that attached the angle-iron frame to the wall of the tank. The choice of

E6010 electrodes also contributed to a brittle condition in the fillet weld.

Recommendations. Several steps essential to avoid a repetition of such a failure are as follows:

1 For greater suitability to the climate, the steel plate should have a low carbon content and a high manganese-to-sulfur ratio, and should be in a normalized condition.
2 Low-hydrogen electrodes should be used.
3 All corners of the opening should be generously radiused, to avoid stress concentrations at the toes of the welds.
4 Postweld heating would be advisable.
5 Radiographic and penetrant inspection tests should be done.

Example 2. Observatory Column of ASTM A36 Steel That Cracked Because of High Residual Stresses and Stress Raisers in the Welds (Fig. 6)

During construction of a revolving skytower observatory, an 8-ft-diam cylindrical column developed serious circumferential cracks overnight at the 46-ft level where two 40-ft sections were joined by a girth weld. The winds were reported as varying from 4½ to 12 miles per hour during that night, with directions that began from the south but veered to the north between 1 and 4 a.m. The temperatures recorded at a nearby weather station ranged from 12 C (53 F) to 7 C (45 F) between 10 p.m. and 4 a.m. that night.

The column was shop fabricated in 40-ft-long sections of ¾-in.-thick steel plate conforming to specifications for ASTM A36 steel. At the time of the fracture, the foundation had been poured, a 6-ft-high base section installed, and assembly of five 40-ft sections had been partly completed, reaching an over-all height of approximately 200 ft. The design of the section-to-section weld joint is shown in Fig. 6(a). This called for a bevel on the edge of the upper cylinder and an external backing band to facilitate full penetration of the girth weld. The band was to be circumferentially fillet welded at each edge to the outer surface of the cylinders.

Investigation. Figure 6(b) shows the outside surface of the north side of the column that contains the backing band, a vertical pair of guide rails, assorted welded braces, and steadying guy wires. At A and B in Fig. 6(b) are two openings where samples were cut out for examination. The portion of the section-to-section joint beneath the guide rails had not yet been welded, and the backing band does not extend over this section. A similar unwelded portion was found beneath a pair of guide rails diametrically opposite to those shown in Fig. 6(b). The inside of the north side of the column is shown in Fig. 6(c). The unwelded portion is clearly visible at the ½-in. gap between the upper and lower sections of the column wall. The I-beam at near right is a vertical internal stiffener attached to the column wall by intermittent fillet welds. Two short lengths of angle beam that span the joint were welded to the walls of the column. Three cuts, two triangular and one rectangular, were made in this region to remove samples for investigation.

Study of the samples established that there were two crack origins, one in or adjacent to the weld at each end of the unwelded portion shown in Fig. 6(b) and (c). Cutout sample C (see Fig. 6c) contained the fracture origin to the right of the unwelded portion; the continuation of the crack to the right is shown in Fig. 6(c). The crack origin to the left of the unwelded portion was contained in cutout sample D; an I-beam hides the continuation of that crack to the left. The complete extent of cracking in the column wall was as follows. The crack on the west side continued to nearly the southwest side of the column, propagating at about 4 in. above the girth weld. The crack on the east side of the column propagated in the weld to about the northeast side of the column and then emerged to grow in the upper wall at a slight angle to the weld to reach again a distance of about 4 in. above the girth weld. This crack halted at a welded angle on the east side of the column. A 4-in.-long crack was found on the south side of the column that had initiated in the girth weld at the east end of the unwelded section beneath the guide rails. This crack appeared to be about to emerge from the weld into the column wall, but was not opened up for study.

Much of the length of the long cracks displayed chevron marks, which suggested that most of the crack propagation had been fairly rapid. The fact that the cracks halted instead of continuing for the full circumference of the column suggests that there was longitudinal tension across the girth weld on the north side of the column that did not exist at anywhere near the same magnitude on the south side of the column.

Hardness measurements on the column wall outside the weld zone gave an average of Rockwell B 85. This is approximately equivalent to a tensile strength of 80,000 psi or the upper limit required by ASTM A36. Four Charpy V-notch impact test specimens were prepared from one of the cutout samples and tested, with the following results:

Test specimen	Testing temperature		Impact strength, ft-lb
	C	F	
1	24	76	40
2	16	60	34
3	7	45	14
4	0	32	12

These data show that by 4 a.m. on the night of failure, the column steel had cooled below its ductile-to-brittle transition temperature.

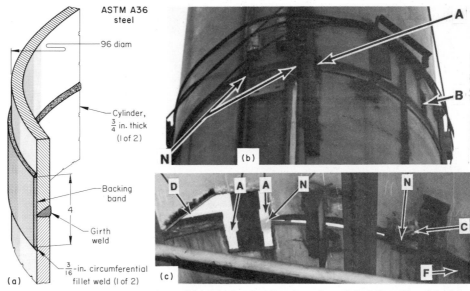

(a) Design of section-to-section weld joint, showing the circumferential girth weld and backing band joined by two continuous, full-penetration, ³⁄₁₆-in.-fillet welds. (b) Outside surface of the north side of the column, showing sites of cutout samples A and B and unwelded portion at N. (c) Inner surface of the north side of the column, showing locations of cutout samples A, C and D, unwelded portion N, and crack F.

Fig. 6. Cylindrical column of arc welded ASTM A36 steel for a sky-tower observatory that cracked during construction because of high residual stresses and stress raisers in the welds (Example 2)

Examination of the girth welds at the 46-ft level revealed that many did not completely fill the groove. Many contained porosity, and areas of weld-bead cracking were seen at the fractures on the north side of the column near the two origins. The backing band had not yet been fillet welded along its upper edge.

Discussion. The exact details of securing fit-up of the two column sections are not recorded. However, the fact that the backing band was fillet welded along its bottom edge but not its top suggests that the backing band may have been applied before the upper section was hoisted in place, and thus used as a positioning ring. There were at least ten short angle beams spanning the joint, which were fillet welded on both sides to the column walls. These apparently were welded in place after the upper section had been set precisely vertical and served as anchors until the girth weld could be applied. How much of the joint had a gap as large as that seen at the unwelded portion in Fig. 6(c) cannot be determined, but the two sections must have been in contact in some areas. However, there was a large gap on the north side of the column, which was maintained by the rigidity of the angle-beam anchors. This combination of rigid restraint and a large amount of weld metal contracting from its solidification temperature showed that there were high residual stresses across the weld. The additional unfavorable factor was the termination of the girth welds, which in effect provided notches that were stress raisers.

Conclusions. Crack initiation was caused by high residual stress from undue restraint during girth welding, combined with the presence of notches formed by the termination of the incomplete welds. Continuation of the cracks in the portion of the base metal that was well removed from the girth weld was attributed to the brittle condition of the

steel when cooled by the night air and acted on by the critical notch created by the crack emerging from the weld bead. The wind was not thought to have significantly contributed to the stresses causing failure.

Recommendations. For a structure of this sort, in which the safety of human life would be at stake, a steel with a much lower ductile-to-brittle transition temperature is essential. The other necessary steps include better control of the girth welding conditions, such as: more accurate fit-up, to provide a uniform gap; preweld and postweld heating, to minimize thermal stresses; welding at a slower rate (with perhaps less metal laid down per pass) combined with careful peening, to reduce internal stress; perhaps the choice of a more favorable electrode, to avoid porosity; careful termination of all welds interrupted by a shift change, to avoid formation of notches; and completion of all welds before other sections of the column are erected.

Example 3. Fatigue Fracture of a 1040 Steel Shaft for an Amusement Ride Because of Undercuts in Welds (Fig. 7)

An amusement ride in a shopping center failed when a component in the ride parted, permitting it to fly apart. The ride consisted of a central shaft supporting a "spider" of three arms, each of which was equipped with a 1040 steel secondary shaft about which a circular platform rotated. Each platform carried six seats, each seat being capable of holding up to three persons. The whole assembly could be tilted to an angle of 30° from horizontal. The main shaft rotated at about 12 rpm and the platforms at a speed of 20 rpm.

The accident occurred when one of the secondary shafts on the amusement ride broke, allowing the platform it supported to spin off the "spider". The point of fracture was adjacent to a weld that attached

Fig. 7. Fractograph, at about 0.4×, of a 1040 steel shaft for an amusement ride in which fatigue fracture originated at weld undercuts, showing two sets of beach marks and a triangular final-fracture zone (Example 3)

the shaft to a ⅝-in.-thick plate, which in turn bore the platform-support arms.

Investigation. The fracture surface of the shaft was found to possess the beach marks characteristic of fatigue fracture, as shown in Fig. 7. It was apparent that the fillet weld had undercut the shaft slightly, creating points of stress concentration that served as nuclei for the fatigue cracks. Crack propagation occurred from two directions, penetrating all of the shaft section except the roughly triangular region (see Fig. 7) that was the zone of final, fast fracture.

The shaft at the location of the fracture was 4¼ in. in diameter, whereas at the bearing raceway, 2½ in. below the weld-

ment, it was 3⅞ in. in diameter. This indicated that cross-sectional area was not the determining factor in the stress level, but rather that the weld contained appreciable residual stress mainly from the restraint and chilling effect exerted by the heavy plate and shaft on the weld as it underwent thermal contraction.

A section through the fracture region revealed a small secondary crack (which did not contribute to fracture but which arose from the same causes) and clearly defined heat-affected zones. The structure confirmed a report from the manufacturer that there had been no postweld heat treatment.

Conclusions. The shaft fractured in fatigue from the combination of residual stresses generated in welding and centrifugal stresses from operation that were accentuated by areas of stress concentration at the undercuts. Without the excessive residual stress, the shaft dimensions appeared ample for the service load.

Recommendations. The fillet weld should be applied with more care to avoid undercutting. The residual stresses should be minimized by preweld and postweld heat application.

Example 4. Fracture of Steel Supplementary Axle-Support Channels for a Highway Trailer, Caused by Restricting Welds (Fig. 8)

A supplementary axle, which was used as an extension to a highway-trailer tractor to increase its load-bearing capacity, failed in service. The rolled steel channel extensions that secured the axle assembly to the tractor main-frame I-beams fractured transversely, with the crack in each instance initiating at a weld that joined the edge of the lower flange to the support-bracket casting. The cracks propagated through the

flange on each side until the effective cross-sectional area had been reduced sufficiently to bring about sudden and complete fracture of the remaining web and upper flange.

Investigation. Figure 8(a) and (b) show the mating fracture surfaces of the left channel. In Fig. 8(b) is the fracture origin in the weld along the toe of the lower flange of the channel extension that attached it rigidly to the support-bracket casting. At left in Fig. 8(a) is the cross I-beam of the supplementary axle assembly; nesting in the channel extension is a support plate, which was bolted through the channel to the support-bracket casting and welded to the I-beam at its web and flanges. The fracture surface in general appears smooth with little evidence of deformation and little visible detail, suggesting that the fracture was brittle. The fracture of the right channel exhibited the same characteristics.

A vertical transverse section through the flange and the weld attaching the channel to the support-bracket casting was prepared for metallographic examination. Figure 8(c) shows the weld, the heat-affected zone, and the flange cross section at low magnification. Of particular note is the light-shaded layer at about midway between the top and bottom surfaces of the flange. This was a region of carbon segregation where chemical analysis showed the steel to contain 0.34% C and 1.16% Mn. Near the surfaces the composition was 0.23% C and 1.06% Mn. As a result of this variance, the microstructure in the light-shaded layer showed much more pearlite than the lower-carbon regions near the surfaces. The residual-element contents of the steel were low: 0.05% Si, 0.05% Ni, 0.05% Cr, and 0.05% Mo.

The higher carbon content of the segregated central layer had its most marked effect in the heat-affected zone of the weld at the toe of the flange, producing a band of very hard martensite in contrast to the lower-carbon, pearlitic microstructure of unaffected areas of the flange. The hardness in the heat-affected zone measured Rockwell C 60 in the carbon-segregated layer and about Rockwell C 53 elsewhere. In regions not influenced by the weld and outside the central segregation, the hardness was between Rockwell C 10 and 20.

The rigid attachment of the channel to the support-bracket casting provided a stress concentration at the weld by creating a steep gradient in section modulus at that point. The natural swaying of the load carried by the trailer imposed high bending-moment stresses on the channels of the supplementary axle assembly, raising the stress concentration at the weld to above the yield strength of the material. Had the heat-affected zone been ductile, fracture might have been delayed by yielding, but the hard and brittle midsection layer was susceptible to cracking under these conditions. Once the crack was formed, its growth became rapid.

Conclusions. Fatigue fracture was caused by a combination of high bending stresses in the bottom flanges of the channels due to the heavy load being carried, concentration of stresses due to the rapid change in section modulus of the channel at its point of attachment to the support-bracket casting, and brittleness of the high-hardness heat-affected zone of the weld associated with the

(a) Photograph of the forward left side of the assembly, showing fracture surface of channel extension. Also visible are the cross I-beam, the supporting plate, and the support-bracket casting. (b) Photograph toward the rear, show-ing mating fracture surface and the fracture origin. (c) Macrograph of the channel flange, at 8×, showing weld metal, heat-affected zone, and non-heat-affected zone. (Polished, and etched in 3% nital.)

Fig. 8. Steel supplementary axle assembly for a highway trailer that broke in service because of restricting welds (Example 4)

abnormally high carbon content in the central part of the channel.

Recommendations. Welding of channel edges is generally viewed as contributing to harmful gradients in section moduli, and should be avoided in future assemblies. The segregation of carbon appears to be such an unlikely occurrence that use of inspection steps to avoid it seems unwarranted.

Example 5. Fatigue Cracking of Carbon Steel Headers for Superheated Water Because of Notches at Welds (Fig. 9)

A system of carbon steel headers, handling superheated water of 188 C (370 F) at 300 psi for automobile-tire curing presses, within about four months developed a number of leaks after two to three years of leak-free service. All the leaks were in shielded metal-arc butt welds joining 8-in.-diam 90° elbows and pipe to 8-in.-diam welding-neck flanges. A flange-elbow-flange assembly and a flange-pipe assembly that had leaked were removed for examination.

Investigation. Magnetic-particle tests confirmed the existence of the cracks in the welds through which leaking had occurred and revealed the presence of other cracks that had not yet penetrated to the weld surface. X-ray inspection was conducted with the source at the centerline of each flange and the film wrapped around the weld bead on the outside. The film showed the cracks indicated by the magnetic-particle inspection as well as additional, incipient cracks and regions of incomplete weld penetration that could not be correlated with the major crack locations.

The butt welds were sectioned, with some cuts being made through regions of pronounced magnetic-particle indication and others at regions where no indications were found. The polished-and-etched surfaces of two such sections from the flange-pipe weld are shown in Fig. 9(a) and (b).

It was immediately apparent on sectioning that, although the outside diameter of the flanges matched those of the elbows and pipe (nominal 8⅝ in.), there was a considerable difference in the inside diameters. Actually, only the elbows had been of schedule 80 wall (7.625-in. nominal ID), as called for in the specification for flanges, elbows and pipe. The welding flanges that were used had been bored to 7.975-in. ID (for use with schedule 40 pipe) and the pipe had been of schedule 100, with a 7.437-in. nominal ID. The result was a disparity in inside diameter of about 0.350 in. between flange and elbow and about 0.538 in. between flange and pipe. This was the reason for depositing an internal fillet weld, which created a stress-concentrating notch at the toe of the weld against the flange inner surface.

The welding procedure had been as follows. The edges were prepared by machining a ¼-in.-deep groove with a 75° included angle at the outside surface. The initial weld deposit was a root pass applied from the outside. Second and third passes were laid on top of this, the latter depositing a wide weave-type bead. Finally, an attempt was made to reconcile the difference in wall thickness by depositing a fillet-weld bead on the inside. In some instances, penetration was deep enough so that the fillet weld merged with the root pass of the exterior

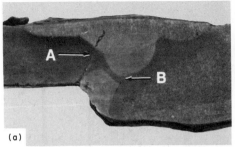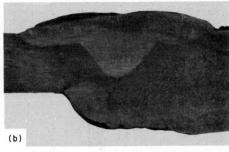

(a) Macrograph of section through butt welded joint showing crack (at A) that originated at toe of weld on inner surface, incomplete weld penetration (at B), and difference in thickness of flange (at left) and pipe. (Etched in 2% nital; about 1.7×.) (b) Macrograph of section through same weld as in (a), but showing no crack indications. (Etched in 2% nital; about 1.7×.)

Fig. 9. Flange-to-pipe assembly of a carbon steel header, used for handling superheated water, that cracked by fatigue because of notches at welds (Example 5)

weld. In others, as in Fig. 9(a) and (b), this did not occur; as a result, a short span existed where there was incomplete penetration, and the original edges of the flange and elbow were still visible in contact. Such a region of incomplete penetration is normally considered a site for stress concentration, but it can be seen in Fig. 9(a) and (b) that there was no crack growth at this point. All the major cracks found in either elbow or pipe welds originated at the toe of the fillet weld in the inner surface of the flange (see Fig. 9a). As is illustrated in Fig. 9(b), some fillet-weld toes did not produce such cracks.

A hardness survey was taken of each weld joint. The results showed that the weld beads and the heat-affected zones were similar in hardness to the base metal and that there was no evidence of hard spots. Tensile and bend-test properties of the welds were not determined, because the stress-concentrating notches present at the toes of the fillet welds would have rendered any test results meaningless. However, the welds were sound, fine-grained, and free from slag inclusions and porosity.

Chemical analysis of the five components of the two assemblies confirmed that these headers conformed to the requirements of the applicable specifications (flanges and elbow of ASTM A105, grade II, and pipe of ASTM A106, grade B; similarly numbered ASME SA specifications also apply).

A powdery, green deposit found in the interior of an iron-body gate valve of the system was determined by chemical analysis to consist of a trivalent chromium oxide or salt plus iron oxide or salt and 22% combined water. No organic matter was detected and no copper was found.

Conclusions. The failures of the butt welds were the result of fatigue cracks caused by cyclic thermal stresses that initiated at stress-concentrating notches at the toes of the interior fillet welds on the surfaces of the flanges. Several of these penetrated to the exterior surface and caused leaks, but others existed that were still in an incipient growth stage.

Incomplete penetration existed in some of the welds, but no evidence was found of cracks originating from these sites and they were not a factor in the failures.

The powdery, green deposit was attributed to reduction of some of the chromate used as a corrosion inhibitor in the superheated water. It was not regarded as a contributing cause of the failures.

Recommendations. It was concluded that all other joints of the system possessing the same mismatch in wall thickness (and thus in all probability the same stress raiser at the toe of the interior fillet weld) could be expected to fail by the same mechanism. Repair of such joints was not considered feasible, and it was recommended that they be replaced. Ultrasonic testing should be used to identify the joints by detecting the differences between the wall thicknesses of the flange and the pipe, and of the flange and the elbow. Special attention to accuracy of fit-up in the replacement joints was also recommended to achieve smooth notch-free contours on the interior surfaces.

Example 6. Cracking of a Weld That Joined the Head to the Shell of a Steam Preheater, Because of Poor Root Penetration (Fig. 10)

A weld that attached the head to the shell of a preheater containing steam at 200 psi and used in the manufacture of paper cracked in service. The length of service was not reported. A section of the failed preheater, plus a section of a proposed new design, were selected for examination.

Investigation. The preheater was approximately 3 ft in diameter and about 4 ft long. The original joint (Fig. 10a) contained a ¼-by-2-in. backing ring that had been tack welded to the inside surface of the shell in a position to project about ⅝ in. beyond the fully beveled top edge of the shell. The ring served the dual purpose of backing up the weld and positioning the head; the projecting edge of the ring fitted against a ⅜-in.-wide, ⅛-in.-deep undercut on the inner corner of the rim of the head. The internal 90° angle in this undercut was sharp, with almost no fillet. A bevel from the lower edge of the undercut to the outside of the head completed the groove for the circumferential attachment weld.

The head was joined to the shell by arc welding, in three passes. In all sections that were taken through the welded joint and examined, the fusion was found to range from poor to none at the root of the weld and at the backing ring. The weld did not penetrate to the undercut rim of the head, and in some locations the weld bead was standing free (not fused with the backing ring). In all sections of the joint examined, there was a crack beginning at the sharp, internal 90° angle of the undercut and extending toward the outer surface of the head. This crack

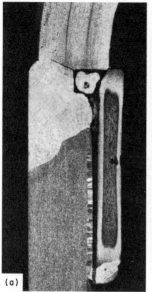

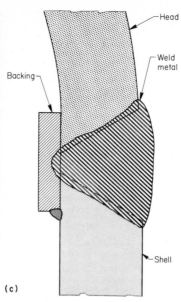

(a)   (b)   (c)

(a) and (b). Macrographs of sections taken through the head-to-shell joint, etched in hot 50% HCl and shown at actual size. The section shown in macrograph (a) is the original design, which used a backing ring; the section shown in macrograph (b) is the first replacement design. (c) A section that shows the final joint design, which achieved full root penetration.

Fig. 10. Weld attaching the head to the shell of a steam preheater that cracked because of poor root penetration in original and first replacement joint designs (Example 6)

had to penetrate only 50% of the full thickness of the head before final fracture occurred.

The first proposed replacement design (Fig. 10b) was more or less the reverse of the failed joint. A deep offset had been machined in the exterior of the rim of the head, reducing the wall thickness by 65%. The outer portion of the offset had been beveled to receive the weld deposit; below the offset, a horizontal step, about 0.10 in. deep, had been cut to align the head against the square-cut shell edge. Below the step was a long taper almost to the inner surface of the head.

A number of sections through the proposed replacement joint showed incomplete root penetration of the weld, and in one section a crack was discovered extending from the outer edge of the positioning step through the root-pass weld bead.

Conclusions. Cracking occurred in the heat-affected zone in the head of the original design, originating in the sharp corner of the undercut, which was an inherent stress raiser. In the first replacement design, beveling of the head and shell was insufficient to permit full root-weld penetration, thus creating an inherent stress raiser. In both designs, the stress raisers would not have been present had full root-weld penetration been obtained.

Corrective Measures. To ensure full root penetration, the joint design shown in Fig.

10(c) was adopted. This joint retained the full thickness of both the head and the shell, and, with the gap between the root edges, made it possible to obtain full root penetration, thereby reducing any notch effect to a minimum.

A suggested alternative that would avoid the possibility of crevice corrosion was the use of a single-V-groove joint without a backing ring, with welding being done from the outside in two or more passes, making sure that the root pass attained full penetration.

Failures in Arc Welded Hardenable Carbon Steel

Welding of medium-carbon and high-carbon steels is limited mainly by the hardenability that these steels possess. Cooling rates must be more carefully adjusted, postweld heating is essential in some instances, and the presence of notches must be guarded against.

Welds in these steels are subject to severe underbead cracking as a result of hydrogen embrittlement; an example is illustrated in Fig. 11. Here, the base metal was 1045 steel and the weld deposit was made by the shielded metal-arc process using ⅛-in. E6010 electrodes

(not a low-hydrogen type). The cellulose covering of the E6010 electrodes emitted hydrocarbons, which were first volatilized and then dissociated by the welding arc. The hydrogen was dissolved in the weld puddle, and portions of it diffused into the heat-affected zone. The heat of welding raised the temperature of this adjacent metal to the austenitic temperature range, and when this metal was quickly cooled by the underlying mass of metal, the abrupt change in hydrogen solubility induced a condition of supersaturation of the hydrogen that had been absorbed from the weld. This created a condition of internal stress, which generated the crack seen in the heat-affected zone in Fig. 11.

The best way to prevent hydrogen embrittlement is to avoid the absorption of hydrogen by using a low-hydrogen type of electrode, such as E7015. If such electrodes are not available and the weld must be made before they can be secured, the alternative is to preheat the weld area so that cooling is controlled at a slow rate to give the absorbed hydrogen time to diffuse out without reaching a state of supersaturation.

Additional problems in welding hardenable carbon steels are illustrated in the two following examples.

Example 7. Failure of a Welded Throttle-Arm Assembly Because of Thread-Root Cracks in the Heat-Affected Zone of the Weld (Fig. 12)

A throttle arm of an aircraft engine fractured and caused loss of engine control. The broken part consisted of a ¼-in.-diam medium-carbon steel rod with a ¼–20 thread to fit a knurled brass nut that was inserted into the throttle knob.

Investigation. The threaded rod had been welded to the throttle-linkage bar by an assembly-weld deposit that had been made on the rod adjacent to the threaded portion. Examination of the threads revealed the presence of thick oxide scale at and near the fracture, and extending three threads back from the fracture. The fracture surface exhibited a coarse-grained brittle texture with an initiating crack at a thread root. The crack was coated with black iron oxide typical of scale formed at high temperature. The brass nut, which had been in contact with the three threads adjacent to the fracture, showed no sign of corrosion or oxidation on its mating threads.

The thread roots in the rod contained many intergranular microcracks, as illus-

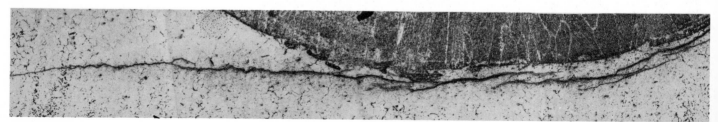

Fig. 11. Underbead crack, resulting from hydrogen embrittlement, in the heat-affected zone of a shielded metal-arc weld in 1045 steel that was made with ⅛-in. E6010 electrodes at 100 amp, 26 volts, and at a 10-in.-per-minute rate of travel. (Etched in 2% nital; 30×.)

ated in Fig. 12(a). A grain-boundary network of ferrite is also visible in Fig. 12(a)
nd at the tip of the thread next to the
racture, shown in Fig. 12(b). Also shown
Fig. 12(b) is a Widmanstätten structure
f ferrite, which is often found in the heat-
ffected zone of welded medium-carbon
teel. The microhardness of the cross section
f the rod, measured by Knoop and diamond
yramid indenters and converted to Rock-
ell C, was 27 to 31. In the tooth-tip area,
he hardness values as converted were
Rockwell B 95 to 100 (about Rockwell C 16
23).

Conclusions. The throttle-arm failed by
rittle fracture because of the presence of
racks at the thread roots that were within
he heat-affected zone of the adjacent weld
eposit. The heat of welding had generated
coarse-grained structure with a weak
rain-boundary network of ferrite that had
ot been corrected by postweld heat treat-
ent. The combination of the cracks and
his unfavorable microstructure provided
weakened condition that resulted in cata-
trophic, brittle fracture under normal ap-
lied loads.

Corrective Measure. The design was altered
o eliminate the weld adjacent to the
hreaded portion of the rod.

**Example 8. Failure of a Repair Weld on a
1080 Steel Crankshaft Because of
Inclusions and Porosity**

The 1080 steel crankshaft of a large-ca-
pacity double-action stamping press broke
n service and was repair welded. Shortly
fter the crankshaft was returned to service,
he repair weld fractured. To determine
what corrective action could be taken, the
repair-weld fracture was examined ultrasonically.

Investigation. Ultrasonic testing revealed
many internal reflectors, thus indicating the
presence of slag inclusions and porosity.
The reflectors were so numerous that the
ultrasonic waves could not penetrate to the
far side of the 18-in.-diam journal. The slag
inclusions and porosity were present because
the repair weld had to be made in a very
cramped position and the slag was difficult
to remove.

A low-carbon steel flux-cored filler metal
was used in repair welding the crankshaft,
without any preweld or postweld heating.
This resulted in the formation of martensite
in the heat-affected zone.

Conclusions. The repair weld failed by
brittle fracture, which was attributed to the
combination of weld porosity with many slag
inclusions and to the formation of brittle
martensite in the heat-affected zone. It was
decided that a second repair weld was worth
trying if all possible precautions were taken
to avoid causes of cracking.

Corrective Measure. A repair weld was
made using an E312 stainless steel electrode,
which provides a weld deposit that contains
considerable ferrite to prevent hot cracking.
Before welding, the crankshaft was preheated to a temperature above that at which
martensite would form. After completion,
the weld was covered with an asbestos
blanket and heating was continued for 24
hr; during the next 24 hr, the temperature
was slowly lowered. The result was a crack-
free weld.

(a) Micrograph, at 200×, showing intergranular cracks that originated in the thread root. Note
grain-boundary network of ferrite. (b) Micrograph, at 100×, showing Widmanstätten structure at
thread tip. (Both specimens were etched in 2% nital.)

*Fig. 12. Coarse-grained microstructure in heat-affected zone formed by assembly-weld
deposit in threaded portion of a broken throttle-arm rod of medium-carbon steel*
(Example 7)

Failures in
Arc Welded Alloy Steel

The high hardenability that characterizes most alloy steels often presents difficulties in welding. The formation of untempered martensite in the heat-affected
zones is compounded by the coarse grain
size created in the weld-bead side of the
heat-affected zone, with the over-all result being a region with a severe loss in
toughness. This condition may contribute to immediate cracking and lead
to fatigue fracture, corrosion-fatigue
cracking, or impact (brittle) fracture at
low temperatures. Welding may also produce alloy segregation, which can lead to
hot cracking, or the presence of hard and
soft spots, which can be failure-initiation
sites. Alloy segregation also can cause
formation of galvanic cells in segregated
areas; this can generate pitting corrosion,
introducing stress raisers that sometimes
lead to final fatigue fracture.

Welds in alloy steels must be stress relieved, and during the stress-relieving
treatment the steels are susceptible to
"blue brittleness". The fracture of an
embrittled weld usually is intergranular
and is recognizable as such at high SEM
or TEM magnification. But whether the
fracture is brittle or ductile, the origin in
alloy steels may be very small and considerable microscopy may be required to
locate it.

The formation of martensite in the
heat-affected zone can be avoided by use
of preheating, interpass heating, and
postheating, which will maintain the
zone at a temperature that will ensure
transformation to lower bainite rather
than to martensite. The specific temperature may be chosen from the available
isothermal transformation diagrams for
the alloy steel in question. This proce-

dure minimizes cracking and provides
greatly increased toughness and ductility
(Ref 4).

Repair welding sometimes produces
side effects that limit its use. In one instance, a number of improperly machined parts of D-6ac steel, heat treated
to a tensile strength of 220,000 to 240,000
psi, were to be repair welded. Tests
showed that the ultimate tensile strength
of gas tungsten-arc welded joints was
only slightly less than that of the base
metal. The fatigue strength of the welds,
however, proved to be considerably
lower than the fatigue strength of the
base metal, with sizable scatter of data
points; fatigue cracking was initiated in
general at microporosity sites in otherwise acceptable welds. Because the fatigue strength of the parts was a critical
requirement, repair welding had to be
abandoned.

Weld cracking is not limited to the
welding process, but also may be encountered in subsequent heat treatment.
In one instance, cracking occurred in
welded 4340 steel box assemblies for aircraft seats during quenching from the
austenitizing temperature. The intended
minimum tensile strength was 180,000
psi. Cracks attributed to nonuniform
cooling were found at interfaces between
weld metal and base metal in thick-section areas. Nonuniform cooling had occurred in the enclosed box assembly,
which was a 1/4-in.-thick trapezoidal
plate welded around its edges to a hol-
lowed support fitting. The fact that
there were only three 1/4-in.-diam holes
in the box did not permit adequate flow
of the quenching medium to the box interior, which was necessary for uniform
cooling. The resultant stresses caused
cracks that initiated at the notches provided by fillet-weld toes.

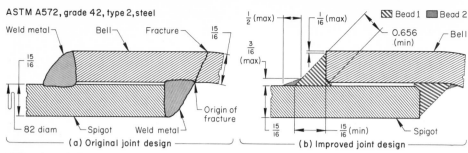

ASTM A572, grade 42, type 2, steel

(a) Original joint design

(b) Improved joint design

Fig. 13. (a) *Double-welded bell-and-spigot joint used in an aqueduct of ASTM A572, grade 42, type 2, steel pipe that cracked because of poor welding technique and poor choice of metal.* (b) *Improved design, showing modifications of weld beads.* (Example 9; Ref 5)

Other instances of failures experienced in arc welded alloy steels and their subsequent diagnoses are described in the six examples that follow.

Example 9. Failure of Welds in an ASTM A572 Steel Aqueduct Because of Poor Welding Techniques (Fig. 13)*

An 82-in.-ID steel aqueduct fractured circumferentially at two points 500 ft apart in a section above ground. A year later, another fracture occurred in a buried section four miles away. Both pipes fractured during January at similar temperatures and pressures. The pipe had a $\frac{15}{16}$-in. wall thickness, and the hydrostatic head was 1085 ft. The air temperature was about −13 C (+9 F), the water temperature about 0.6 C (33 F) and the steel temperature about −4 C (+25 F). The fractures occurred at bell-and-spigot slip joints (see Fig. 13a) that, at the two initial fractures, had been fillet welded both inside and out; at the third break the joints had been fillet welded only on the inside. The pipe had been shop fabricated of ASTM A572, grade 42, type 2, steel in 40-ft lengths and then shop welded into 80-ft lengths. Field assembly was with the bell-and-spigot joints.

Investigation. All three fractures occurred at a bell section and initiated at the toe of the inside fillet weld (see Fig. 13a). The welds in the first two fractures had been made in the field, whereas the third weld that failed had been made in the shop. Also, both of the original inside welds at the early fractures had been gouged out to permit relocation of the pipe to maintain the supporting ring girder legs in a vertical position. The joints had then been rewelded in the inside. This had not been done in the third, later weld that failed.

Charpy V-notch impact tests on the steel used for this pipeline revealed a ductile-to-brittle transition temperature that was unfavorably high — approximately 10 C (50 F). At the temperatures existing at the time of the failures, the impact strength of the steel was about 10 ft-lb, which is dangerously brittle.

Inspection of the interior field welds showed that instead of using continuous circumferential stringer beads, the welder had used a "wash-pass" technique, depositing a heavy bead from toe to crown. This permitted faster welding but gave inconsis-

tent penetration and a considerable number of slag inclusions and imperfections such as deep valleys, grooves and undercuts at the toe of the weld, which served as notches and stress raisers.

Examination of the third fracture at the shop weld disclosed that areas in the heat-affected zone and at the toe of the weld had hardness levels as high as Rockwell C 34. When test welds were made on metal preheated to 93 C (200 F) before welding, the hardness of the heat-affected zone was Rockwell C 22.

Conclusions. Brittle fracture of the aqueduct pipe was attributed to a combination of stress concentrations at the toes of the fillet welds due to poor welding technique, including shop welds made without preheat, and a brittle condition of the steel at winter temperatures caused by a high ductile-to-brittle transition temperature.

Corrective Measures. The following changes were made to eliminate welding and material problems:

1 Any area to be welded was preheated to at least 66 C (150 F).
2 In any weld having an undercut or abrupt transition to the base metal at the toe, an

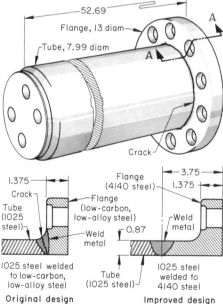

Fig. 14. *Tube post of 1025 steel for a carrier vehicle that failed in fatigue because of improper design and choice of flange metal* (Example 10)

Section A-A

additional weld bead was deposited at the toe, as shown in Fig. 13(b).
3 Tensile loadings of above-ground sections were reduced by the installation of expansion joints.
4 Where the pipe was buried and pipe temperatures varied considerably, butt welds were used.
5 All ASTM A572 steel plate used was rolled from fully killed ingots made with a grain-refining practice and normalized after rolling, which provided a ductile-to-brittle transition temperature of about −32 C (−25 F).

Example 10. Fatigue Cracking of Welded 1025 Steel Tubular Posts in a Carrier Vehicle Because of the Presence of Inclusions That Acted as Stress Raisers (Fig. 14)

Two tubular steel posts in a carrier vehicle failed by cracking at the radius of the flange (see Fig. 14) after five weeks of service. The posts were two of four that supported the chassis of the vehicle high above the wheels so that the vehicle could straddle a stack of steel or lumber for pickup and transport. Over a period of about four years, 47 other posts had failed in nine vehicles. The latest failures occurred in posts of an improved design (see Fig. 14) that had been used in an attempt to halt the pattern of cracking.

The original design involved a flat flange of low-carbon, low-alloy steel that was fillet welded to a 1025 steel tube with a wall thickness of $\frac{7}{8}$ in. The fillet weld was machined to a smooth radius, but the region was highly stressed and fatigue accounted for the numerous failures of posts.

In an effort to improve the strength of the joint, the improved design was adopted. The improvement was in the flange, which was machined from a 4-in.-thick plate of normalized low-carbon, low-alloy steel so that the welded joint would be about 2 in. away from the flange fillet. However, after the brief service of five weeks, the two posts showed the same fatigue cracks in the fillet as the original design.

Investigation. Chemical analysis of the flange metal showed that it met specification requirements. Examination of a metallographic specimen from the fracture area revealed a banded structure in the direction of rolling and aluminum oxide stringers at the fillet surface, which undoubtedly served as stress raisers, in the direction of crack extension.

Conclusions. The failures in the flanges of improved design were attributed to fatigue cracks initiating at the aluminum oxide inclusions in the flange fillet. It was concluded that a higher-strength flange was necessary.

Corrective Measures. The design of the flange with the weld about 2 in. from the fillet was retained but the metal was changed to a forging of 4140 steel, oil quenched and tempered to a hardness of 241 to 285 Bhn. Preheating to 370 C (700 F) before and during welding with 4130 steel wire was specified. The weld was subjected to magnetic-particle inspection and was then stress relieved at 593 C (1100 F), followed by final machining.

No further failures of posts were reported as having occurred in four years of service following the changes.

*Abstracted from Ref 5, with permission of the publisher.

Example 11. Fatigue Fracture of a Rebuilt 4130 Steel Exciter Shaft, Which Was Accelerated by Weld-Deposit Cracks (Fig. 15)

The shaft of an exciter that was used with a diesel-driven electric generator broke at a fillet after 10 hr of service following resurfacing of the shaft by welding. The exciter, which turned at 1750 rpm, was top mounted (instead of floor mounted) on the same base as the main generator, which operated at 450 rpm. Therefore, the vibrations from the main generator also caused vibrations in the exciter unit.

The shaft had previously been installed in an exciter for another diesel-generator unit, where it had experienced turning of a pulley on the shaft. The shaft was polished, the pulley was bored out, and a bushing was inserted, but after indeterminate service, the pulley turning recurred. At this time, the shaft was removed for resurfacing. After belt grinding, the keyway was filled in and the surface of the shaft was built up by gas metal-arc welding using a low-carbon steel filler wire (0.04% C, 1.15% Mn, 0.50% Si) and a shielding gas containing 75% argon and 25% carbon dioxide. Preheating and postheating were not used, nor was the rebuilt surface nondestructive tested for cracks. The shaft was remachined to size, and a new keyway was cut in a different location. The shaft was placed in stock (length of time not reported) until used to replace another exciter shaft, which had been removed for maintenance. At the rated operational speed, the rebuilt shaft had been subjected to just over one million revolutions before failure.

Investigation. Visual inspection established that there were no nicks or toolmarks and no evidence of corrosion in the general area of the fracture, which was located at a fillet where the diameter of the shaft was reduced from 2.1 in. to 1.9 in. The fracture surface contained a dull "off-center" region of final ductile fracture surrounded by regions of fatigue that had been subjected to appreciable rubbing. The fracture appeared to be typical of rotary-bending fatigue under conditions of a low nominal stress with a severe stress concentration. It appeared that the fatigue cracks initiated in the surface-weld layer. Liquid-penetrant inspection of the entire shaft revealed an abundance of weld porosity and one shallow surface crack about ½ in. from the fracture, but no detectable deep cracks.

A polished-and-etched cross section of the shaft taken near the fracture surface is shown in Fig. 15(a) in which the surface-weld layer and the ⅜-in.-thick heat-affected zone (indicated at A and B, respectively, in Fig. 15a) are quite apparent. The thickness of the weld layer varies from ¹⁄₁₆ in. to none at all. The weld deposit in the original keyway (shown at left in Fig. 15a) displays a lack of fusion at the bottom corner (indicated by C in Fig. 15b). Immediately below the filled-in original keyway are two small cracks (indicated at D in Fig. 15b) that were beneath the surface and thus were not reached by the liquid penetrant. The top crack was entirely in the resurfacing weld; the lower crack appeared to be mostly in the resurfacing weld but with a small "tail" in the heat-affected zone.

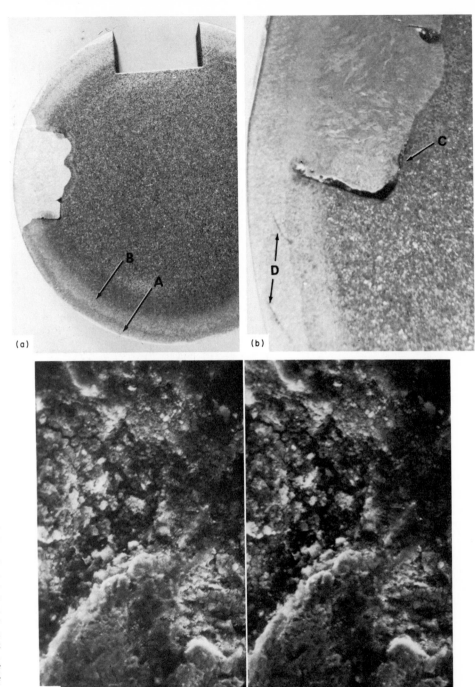

(a) Macrograph of a section through exciter shaft near fracture site; original keyway is at left, recut keyway at top. Resurfacing weld deposit is at A, and heat-affected zone at B. (Nital etch; 2×.) (b) Macrograph, at 8×, of a section near the filled-in original keyway, showing incomplete fusion, C, at the bottom of the keyway and subsurface cracks at D. (c) Stereo pair of SEM fractographs, at 1750×, of the weld-deposit surface near the fracture, showing a very granular appearance. A deep, wide hot crack progresses from upper to lower left.

Fig. 15. Resurfaced exciter shaft of 4130 steel that fractured by fatigue that was accelerated by weld-deposit cracks (Example 11)

The microstructure of the base metal was a normal mixture of ferrite and pearlite, except for having a coarse grain size (ASTM No. 3). Analysis showed the metal to be 4130 steel. The weld metal was finer grained, largely pearlite with only a small quantity of ferrite. This could have resulted only from appreciable diffusion of carbon from the heat-affected zone into the weld, because the filler metal should produce a structure of ferrite. The average hardness of the base metal taken from 44 readings was Rockwell B 88.5; two readings in the filled-in keyway were Rockwell B 89 and 94, perhaps reflecting either the higher proportion of pearlite or an insufficient number of measurements. There was, however, no hardness value in the base metal higher than Rockwell B 90.5.

A scanning-electron-microscope (SEM) examination of the weld surface near the fracture surface showed a granular appear-

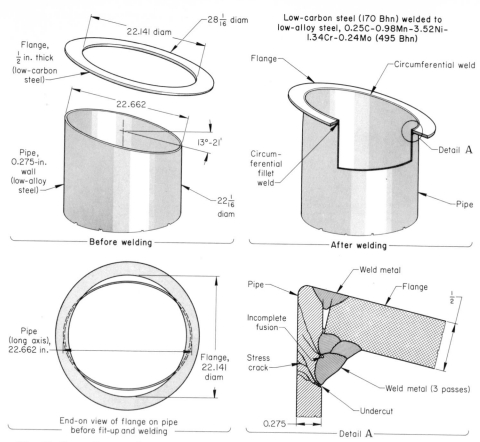

Fig. 16. *Low-alloy steel conveyor pipe that cracked at fillet welds securing a carbon steel flange because of poor fit-up* (Example 14)

ance (Fig. 15c). The deep hot crack that progresses from upper to lower left in Fig. 15(c) is significant, because although this crack did not initiate the fracture, it is believed that a similar one did. In SEM fractographs of the fracture surface, pearlite lamellae were visible in the weld area and rub marks in the shaft interior.

Discussion. In considering the bending stresses that might have caused the failure, it should be realized that the subbase of the diesel-generator set was mounted on springs, which would reduce vertical vibrations much more than if mounted on a firm base. Vibrations were present, however, because the bolts connecting the exciter base-plate to its support plate often fractured. The pulley of the exciter was driven by a matched set of seven V-belts, but the amount of tension used could not have been a significant source of vibrations because the area of fast fracture was small compared to the area of fatigue, indicating a condition of low nominal stress. Mutual misalignment of the two pulleys would not appear to have been a source of vibration unless the misalignment was quite large. Because both pulleys were supported in cantilever fashion at the end of the respective shafts, the possibility of vibration causing some degree of shaft whip could have been a significant factor in the failure.

Conclusions. Fatigue fracture of the shaft resulted from stresses that were created by vibration acting on a crack or cracks formed in the weld deposit because of the lack of preheating and postheating. The cracks in the weld deposit provided severe stress concentrations, so that the fatigue cracks almost

completely penetrated the shaft before fast fracture occurred.

Recommendations. Rebuilding of exciter shafts should be discontinued, and the support plate of the exciter should be braced to reduce the amount of transmitted vibration. Also, the fillet in the exciter shaft should be carefully machined to provide an adequate radius.

Example 12. Hydrogen Sulfide Stress-Corrosion Cracking of Welds in 2.25Cr-0.5Mo Pressure Vessels

After operating satisfactorily for about a year, the outer insulation on a series of large pressure vessels was discovered to be leaking. The vessels were used for hydrogenation and desulfurization of petroleum crude oils at a pressure of about 3000 psi at 315 C (600 F) or higher. The incoming hydrogen was conducted along the interior surface of the pressure vessel to maintain the wall temperature of the vessel below about 232 C (450 F). The vessels were approximately 10 ft in diameter, and the walls ranged from 4 to 9 in. in thickness.

The vessels were fabricated of quenched and tempered plates of 2.25Cr-0.5Mo steel, rolled and welded vertically with electroslag welding. The welds in these sections were quenched and tempered before assembly girth welding with the submerged-arc process. The girth welds were then stress relieved to a final hardness of Rockwell C 28 to 32.

Investigation. The outer insulation was stripped, which exposed perforations through the vessel walls. Examination of the vessel interiors revealed numerous cracks in

the welds, some of which were transverse to the weld but did not penetrate the heat-affected zone on either side.

Initially, it was concluded either that delayed hydrogen embrittlement resulted from the welding process, or that failure resulted from hydrogen sulfide attack. Tests showed that sulfur-bearing hydrogen was capable of cracking 2.25Cr-0.5Mo steel at hardnesses of Rockwell C 28 to 32 in an atmosphere that is essentially moisture-free.

Before these pressure vessels failed, valves, valve fittings, and welded nipples in the system had experienced hydrogen sulfide stress-corrosion cracking.

An effort was made to halt the stress-corrosion cracking by stress relieving the pressure vessels in place, and decreasing their hardness to Rockwell C 22, because it was believed that no stress-corrosion cracking induced by hydrogen sulfide would occur below this hardness. The stress relief was not effective in preventing further cracking.

Conclusions. The vessels failed by stress-corrosion cracking resulting from attack by hydrogen sulfide. Reducing the hardness of 2.25Cr-0.5Mo steel to less than Rockwell C 22 does not prevent stress-corrosion cracking in a hydrogen sulfide atmosphere when the service stress is high — as it was with these vessels. Also, the pre-existing cracks would produce stress concentrations that in turn would cause further crack growth under the high service stress, regardless of the hardness of the steel. Thus, the second stress-relief treatment would not be expected to halt the stress-corrosion cracking and a different corrective action must be devised.

Example 13. Failure in Stainless Steel Welds Joining Low-Carbon Steel Handles to Type 502 Stainless Steel Covers, Because of Martensite Zone in the Welds

Handles welded to the top cover plate of a chemical-plant downcomer broke at the welds when the handles were used to lift the cover. The handles were fabricated of ¾-in.-diam low-carbon steel rod; the cover was of type 502 stainless steel (0.10 max C, 5 Cr, 0.5 Mo) plate. The attachment welds were made with type 347 stainless steel filler metal to form a fillet between the handle and the cover.

Investigation. A metallographic specimen was prepared to show a cross section through the handle, the fillet weld and the cover. The structure was found to contain a zone of brittle martensite in the portion of the weld adjacent to the low-carbon steel handle; fracture had occurred in this zone.

Sufficient heat had been generated during welding to fuse an excessive amount of the carbon steel and thereby dilute the weld deposit locally to create a layer of low-alloy steel between the handle and the weld metal. This low-alloy zone had sufficient hardenability to form martensite when mass quenched by heat transfer to the cover.

Conclusions. Failure was due to brittle fracture. A brittle martensite layer in the weld was the result of using too large a welding rod and too much heat input. The high heat input resulted in excessive melting of the low-carbon steel handle, which diluted the austenitic stainless steel filler metal and formed martensitic steel in a local zone in the weld.

Corrective Measures. Because it was impractical to preheat and postheat the type 502 stainless steel cover plate, the ¾-in.-diam low-carbon steel handle was welded to a ½-by-4-by-6-in. low-carbon steel plate, using mild steel electrodes. This plate was then welded to the type 502 stainless steel plate with type 310 stainless steel electrodes. This design produced a large weld section over which the load was distributed.

Example 14. Fracture of a Low-Alloy Steel Chip-Conveyor Pipe at a Flange Weld as a Result of Poor Fit-Up (Fig. 16)

A pipe in a chip conveyor cracked at the toe of an exterior fillet weld connecting a flange to the pipe.

The chip conveyor consisted of several "spool sections". Each section was made up of a length of 22⅛-in.-OD, 21½-in.-ID low-alloy steel pipe and two 28⁵⁄₁₆-in.-OD, 22⁵⁹⁄₆₄-in.-ID flanges of ½-in.-thick low-carbon steel, which were welded to the two ends of the pipe. The wall thickness of the pipe was 0.275 in. The composition specified for the pipe steel was 0.25% C, 0.98% Mn, 3.52% Ni, 1.34% Cr and 0.24% Mo, which approximates a 9300 steel with high molybdenum. The hardness of the pipe was reported as 495 Bhn, and of the flange as 170 Bhn. The flanges were joined to the pipe by shielded metal-arc welding, using E7018 electrodes.

Investigation. It was found that one end of the pipe had been cut before assembly at an angle of 76° 39′ to its axis, which presented an ellipse (see Fig. 16) over which the flange was forced to fit by hydraulic pressure. A 90° angle would have given a radial clearance between the pipe and flange of about ⁵⁄₆₄ in., but the long outside diameter of the elliptical pipe was 22.662 in. compared to the inside diameter of the flange of 22.141 in., which placed both components in a condition of severe stress.

A schematic illustration of a section cut through the weld in the area of maximum interference is shown in detail A in Fig. 16. Underbead cracking began at the toe on the pipe wall of the first fillet-weld pass at a point where there was incomplete fusion and inadequate penetration of the third and final pass. Several cracks initiated at the toe of the third pass on the pipe wall, where there was a slight undercut.

Conclusions. The conveyor pipe failed by brittle fracture, which was attributed to the stresses induced in forcing the circular flange over the elliptical section of the pipe. The toe of the weld and the adjacent undercut were stress raisers that determined the point of major crack origin. Under residual stress, the internal point of incomplete fusion also initiated additional cracks.

Recommendation. A proper fit between an elliptical flange and pipe end would eliminate the cracking.

Failures in Arc Welded Stainless Steel

The difficulties encountered in welding stainless steels arise from reactions of the microconstituents of the steels to welding temperatures, or from interactions (such as alloy dilution) between the steels and dissimilar alloys.

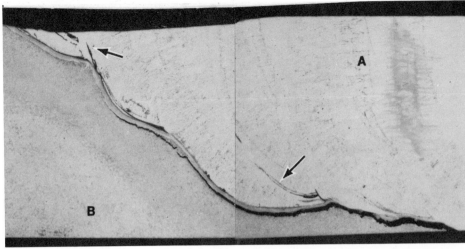

Fig. 17. Stress-rupture crack at the interface of a weld bead, A, made with ER308 stainless steel filler metal, and the heat-affected zone, B, in a 2.25Cr-1Mo low-alloy steel pipe. Arrows indicate propagation of stress-rupture cracks into the weld metal.

Sometimes, it is necessary to weld a stainless steel part to a low-alloy steel part using a stainless steel filler metal. If excessive heat is introduced by the arc, the weld metal can be diluted by excessive melting of the low-alloy steel. At the same time, the heat of welding causes marked grain growth in the heat-affected zone of the low-alloy steel. The result can be regions of intermediate alloy content, too low to be austenitic but high enough to transform to martensite unless the temperature is lowered very carefully. The carbon that diffuses to the stainless steel weld can precipitate as grain-boundary carbide particles. These changes result in the creation of a metallurgical notch that is susceptible to stress-rupture cracking at elevated temperature if sufficient stress is applied. Figure 17 shows a stress-rupture crack at the interface of a stainless steel weld bead and a heat-affected zone in a low-alloy steel pipe welded with ER308 stainless steel filler metal.

To eliminate dilution, it is necessary to use a low heat input during the first weld pass. This can be done with a small-diameter electrode at a low current and a somewhat higher electrode voltage. Also, instead of type 308 stainless steel filler metal, types 309 and 312 can be used — both of which provide a higher alloy level to compensate for possible alloy dilution. (For more information on selection and use of filler metals in welding of stainless steel to carbon or low-alloy steel, see page 274 in Volume 6.)

Martensitic Steels. Welding of type 410 stainless steel in the field can cause stress-corrosion cracking at a later date if it is not feasible to give the heat-affected zone of the weld a satisfactory postweld heat treatment. If type 410 stainless steel is tempered above 500 C (932 F), there should be almost no susceptibility to stress-corrosion cracking, but if this steel is untempered, or is tempered at a temperature lower than 500 C (932 F), it will be susceptible to stress-corrosion cracking when exposed to chlorides and other environments. Figure 18(a) is a micrograph that shows intergranular stress-corrosion cracks in

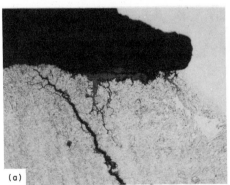

(a) Micrograph of a section through the heat-affected zone that was not tempered after welding, showing an intergranular stress-corrosion crack. The weld deposit is at upper right.

(Electrolytically etched in HCl-methanol; 140×). (b) Fractograph, at 3×, of a fatigue crack initiated by an intergranular underbead crack (at arrow). Note beach marks in fatigue region.

Fig. 18. Cracks in heat-affected zones of type 410 stainless steel beneath weld deposits of ER308 stainless steel

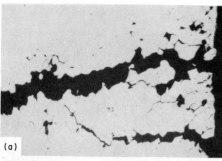

(a) Light micrograph, at 85×, showing intergranular nature of the corrosion, which follows the chromium-depleted regions adjacent to the grains. (b) SEM photograph, at 725×, showing individual grains that have been isolated by dissolution of grain-boundary material.

Fig. 19. Corrosive attack in the sensitized heat-affected zone of a weld in type 304 stainless steel that occurred during an acidified copper sulfate (Strauss) test

the heat-affected zone of an ER308 stainless steel weld deposit on type 410 stainless steel that was not tempered following welding. The hardness was Rockwell C 40 to 45 in the heat-affected zone adjacent to this weld, whereas it should have been approximately Rockwell C 20 for good resistance to stress-corrosion cracking.

Underbead cracks in martensitic stainless steels may be caused by quenching stresses or, with some welding processes, stresses generated by supersaturation of hydrogen. Once they have been formed, such cracks frequently serve as nuclei for fatigue-crack propagation, as shown in Fig. 18(b). Here, the tip of a type 410 stainless steel tool was welded with an ER308 electrode. A crack that formed in the heat-affected zone was shown by examination in a scanning electron microscope to be entirely intergranular.

Austenitic Steels. In austenitic grades of stainless steel, such as type 304, the corrosion resistance of the heat-affected zone of a weld may be seriously reduced by the precipitation of particles of chromium carbide along the grain boundaries, which results in sensitization. The depletion in chromium of the region adjacent to the grain boundaries (because

of the quantity precipitated as carbide) reduces the corrosion resistance of the matrix. The existence of the sensitized condition can be demonstrated by subjecting a specimen of the material to the acidified copper sulfate (Strauss) test. If the material is sensitized, the attack will be completely along the grain boundaries, frequently leaving individual grains entirely detached. The nature of this attack is shown in Fig. 19. If size of the part permits, complete solution heat treatment and quenching after welding will redissolve the chromium carbides and restore corrosion resistance. This cannot be accomplished by localized heating.

Examples. The ten examples that follow describe weld failures that occurred in various grades of stainless steel.

Example 15. Intergranular Fracture of Type 414 Stainless Steel Studs in Weld Heat-Affected Zones That Were Martensitic (Fig. 20)

Several fractures occurred in flange studs used for remote handling of radioactive equipment. The studs, of quenched and tempered type 414 stainless steel, fractured in the heat-affected zones produced in the studs during the circumferential welding that joined the studs to the flanges, as shown in Fig. 20. The weld deposits were of type 347 stainless steel and the flanges were type 304 stainless steel.

Investigation. Metallographic examination of the failed studs revealed that the heat-affected zones contained regions of white martensite and that intergranular cracks, which initiated at the stud surfaces during welding, propagated in the manner indicated in Fig. 20 to complete separation under subsequent loading. Microscopic examination showed that these cracks extended into the stud about $\frac{3}{16}$ in., and about 100° around the circumference. The welding heat had reausetenitized a portion of the heat-affected zone of the stud. When the welding heat was removed, this portion was quenched by the heat-sink effect of the surrounding mass of cooler metal in the re-

Type 414 stainless steel welded to type 304 stainless steel; ER347 stainless steel filler metal

Flange (type 304 stainless steel) — Fracture contour — Weld metal — Stud (type 414 stainless steel)

Fig. 20. Type 414 stainless steel stud, welded to type 304 stainless steel flange, that fractured in service because of intergranular postweld cracking in a martensitic region in the heat-affected zone (Example 15)

mainder of the stud and in the flange to produce martensite. The stresses imposed by the thermal gradients and the phase changes were sufficient to generate the cracks. High-temperature preheat and post-heat treatments would have retarded the cooling rate and prevented the formation of martensite, but preheating and postheating were not considered practical for this application. The studs fractured under service loads as a result of intergranular cracks in the heat-affected zone that reduced the effective cross section and introduced severe stress raisers.

Conclusions. Rapid heating and cooling during attachment welding produced a martensitic structure in the heat-affected zone of the stud, which cracked circumferentially from the combination of thermal-gradient and phase-change stresses.

Recommendations. Joining the studs to the flanges by welding should be discontinued. They should be attached by screw threads, using a key and keyway to prevent turning in service.

Example 16. Failure of a Welded Type 321 Stainless Steel Fuel-Nozzle-Support Assembly Due to Cracking in the Heat-Affected Zone (Fig. 21)

An aircraft fuel-nozzle-support assembly exhibited cracks along the periphery of a fusion weld that attached a support arm to a fairing in a joint that approximated a T-shape in cross section. The base metal was type 321 stainless steel. The exterior appearance of the fusion weld and of some of the fairing surface is shown in Fig. 21 (a).

Investigation. Examination of a section removed perpendicular to the cracks in the weld visible in Fig. 21 (a) showed a good-quality weld penetrating to the support arm beneath, but it revealed notch configurations at the inner mating surfaces at each edge of the fairing, as shown at arrows 2 and 3 in Fig. 21 (b). These configurations were the result of welding a poor fit-up of the support arm to the fairing. The crack adjacent to the weld in the lower section of the fairing is shown at arrow 1 in Fig. 21 (b).

Fractures that originated at the cracks were examined by stereomicroscope and were found to contain fatigue marks that indicated crack propagation from multiple origins at the inner surface of the weld edge. Microscopic enlargement of the weld-edge cracks, like those at arrow 1 in Fig. 21 (b), disclosed that the rupture progressed along the margin of the weld with some incursions into the heat-affected zone and others, to a lesser degree, into the weld bead.

Conclusions. Fatigue cracking was initiated at stress concentrations created by the notches at the inner surfaces between the support arm and the fairing, enhanced by poor fit-up in preparation for welding.

Example 17. Hot Cracks in a Repair Weld of a Type 321 Stainless Steel Fuel-Nozzle-Support Assembly (Fig. 22)

The fuel-nozzle-support assembly discussed in Example 16 also showed transverse indications after fluorescent liquid-penetrant inspection of a repair-welded area at a fillet on the front side of the support neck adjacent to the mounting flange. Visual examination disclosed that the

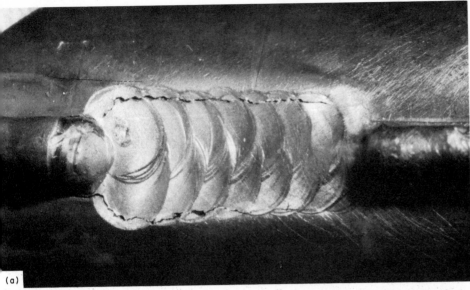

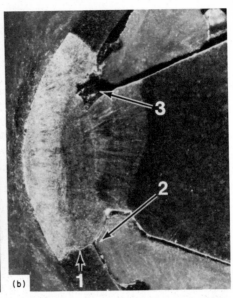

(a) Photograph of the weld, at about 5×, showing fatigue cracks along both edges. The support arm, welded to the fairing at a T-shape joint, is directly beneath the weld contours. (b) Macrograph of a section through the fairing, weld and support arm, showing a crack at the junction of the weld and fairing (arrow 1) and interior notches at arrows 2 and 3. (Electrolytically etched in 10% oxalic acid; about 7×.)

Fig. 21. Cracks that occurred at the margin of a weld that joined a fairing to a support arm of a type 321 stainless steel fuel-nozzle-support assembly (Example 16)

fluorescent-penetrant indications were due to an irregular crack, as shown in Fig. 22(a).

Investigation. The crack through the neck was sectioned; examination showed that the crack had extended through the repair weld (see Fig. 22b) as previously assumed by visual examination. It was evident that the crack had followed an intergranular path. The crack was opened up, and binocular-microscope examination of the fracture surface showed that, to a depth of ⅛ in., the surface contained dendrites with discolored oxide films, which were typical of exposure to air when very hot. Several additional subsurface cracks, typical of hot tears, were observed in and near the weld. In making the repair weld, there had been too much local heat input, perhaps with too large a welding electrode, and probably an excessive deposition rate. The result was localized thermal contraction (which was not shared with abutting colder sections), with the outcome being hot tearing at a temperature at which the weld deposit yielded to the contraction stresses by cracking rather than by plastic flow.

Conclusions. The cracking of the repair weld was attributed to unfavorable welding practice that accentuated thermal contraction stresses and caused hot tearing.

Recommended procedure was to use a small-diameter welding electrode, a lower heat input, and deposition in shallow layers that could be effectively peened between passes to minimize internal stress.

Example 18. Fatigue Fracture of a Type 347 Stainless Steel Fuel Line at a Butt Weld

A weld in a fuel-line tube broke after 159 hr of engine testing. The 0.25-in.-OD, 0.028-in.-wall tube and the end adapters were all of type 347 stainless steel. The butt joints between tube and end adapters were made by automatic gas tungsten-arc (orbital arc) welding, utilizing a very thin outer surface lip on the adapters to ensure concentric alignment with the tube. This

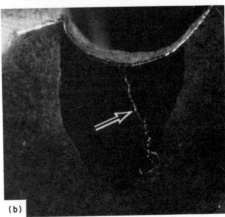

(a) Photograph, at about 6×, showing the crack in the fillet on the front side of the support neck. (b) Macrograph of a section through the support neck; arrow indicates the crack, which was found to be intergranular. (Electrolytically etched in 10% oxalic acid; 7×.)

Fig. 22. Crack that occurred in the repair-welded area of a type 321 stainless steel fuel-nozzle-support assembly because of incorrect welding procedure (Example 17)

outer lip was fused during welding, eliminating any need for filler metal. This procedure has been successful in preparing weld beads with good penetration and smooth root and weld-face contours, particularly when more than one weld pass has been used.

Investigation. It was found that the tube had failed in the heat-affected zone, the crack propagating circumferentially about 180° parallel to the weld before turning approximately 90° to penetrate the weld transversely, parallel to the tube axis. It then turned 90° in the other direction to resume circumferential growth parallel to the weld in the heat-affected zone of the adapter.

Examination of a plastic replica of the fracture surface in a transmission electron microscope established that the crack origin was at the outer surface of the tube. The crack growth was by fatigue; closely spaced fatigue striations were found near the origin, and more widely spaced striations near the inner surface.

A section through the tube revealed a transgranular fracture of a normal microstructure. The quality of the weld and the chemical composition of the tube both conformed to the specifications. However, the fuel-line assembly, which was rigidly supported at both end adapters, had vibrated excessively in service. The service condition thus confirmed the findings of fatigue fracture obtained from study of the fracture-surface replica.

Whether the weld determined the site of the fracture is not wholly clear, because the mode of vibration of the tube is not accurately known. Although the microstructure was found normal in an examination at 500 diameters, it would seem probable that the heat-affected zone would suffer some slight loss of properties either by formation of a few very fine precipitate particles or by a minute amount of phase transformation or both.

Conclusion. The fuel-line fracture was caused by fatigue induced by severe vibration in service.

Corrective Measure. Additional tube clamps were provided to damp the critical vibrational stresses. No further fuel-line fractures were encountered.

Example 19. Fatigue Failure of a Type 347 Stainless Steel Inlet Header Because of Poor Welding Technique and Unfavorable Weld-Joint Design (Fig. 23)

While undergoing vibration testing, a type 347 stainless steel inlet header for a fuel-to-air heat exchanger cracked in the header tube adjacent to the weld bead between the tube and header duct, as shown in Fig. 23.

Investigation. The weld was relatively massive, which was apparently necessary to fill large clearances between the mating parts. Collapse of the base metal in several areas adjacent to the weld indicated that there was damage from excessive heat.

Liquid-penetrant inspection of the weld between the header tube and the header duct revealed a 1⅛-in.-long crack in the weld on the tube side. Several weld-bead undercuts were visible, and the crack appeared to propagate through each of these small defects.

The header was sectioned to open the crack and expose the fracture surface for examination. As shown in the "Original design" view in section A-A in Fig. 23, the tube and duct were initially welded together (weld 1). Then a doubler collar, ⅝ in. wide and of the same material and thickness as the duct, was welded to the duct along the outer edge of the collar (weld 2). A third weld joined the inner edge of the collar to the header tube, thus creating an area of twice the normal header thickness adjacent to the joint. This third weld, throughout much of the collar circumference, penetrated the original tube-to-duct weld (weld 1), but in the area of the fracture there was a gap between the two sheets of stainless steel and the third weld was separate (see weld 3).

Examination of the underside of the joint showed incomplete fusion of the weld between the tube and duct. Distortion of the base metal adjacent to the weld also was visible from this side.

Examination of the surface of the opened crack revealed the origin of the crack at a weld undercut at the toe of weld 3. The crack then progressed through the heat-affected zone of the base metal.

Conclusions. The crack in the header tube was the result of a stress concentration at the toe of the weld joining the doubler collar to the tube. The stress concentration was caused by undercutting from poor welding technique and an unfavorable joint design that did not permit a good fit-up.

Corrective Measures. The doubler collar was made so that it could be placed in intimate contact with the header duct, as shown in the "Improved design" view in section A-A in Fig. 23. The two sheets were beveled, where necessary, to form a V-groove joint with the tube. Two weld passes in the V-groove were used to join the two sheets to the tube. This procedure resulted in a smaller, controlled, homogeneous weld joint with less distortion.

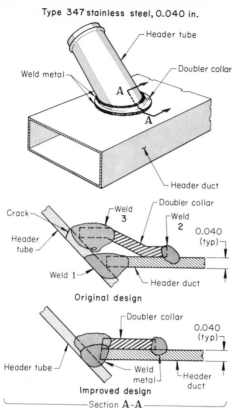

Fig. 23. *Type 347 stainless steel inlet header for fuel-to-air heat exchanger that cracked because of a combination of poor welding technique and an unfavorable joint design* (Example 19)

Example 20. Corrosion Failure of 19-9 DL Stainless Steel in Sensitized Heat-Affected Zone of Assembly Weld

Two aircraft-engine tailpipes of 19-9 DL stainless steel (AISI 651) developed cracks along longitudinal gas tungsten-arc butt welds after being in service for more than 1000 hr. A crack 17 in. long occurred in one tailpipe. The second tailpipe cracked longitudinally in a similar manner to the first and then fractured circumferentially, which resulted in the loss of the aft section of the tailpipe. The gas temperatures during the major portion of the service life were approximately 400 to 550 C (750 to 1020 F), but the metal temperatures probably were lower.

Investigation. Binocular-microscope examination of the cracks in both tailpipes revealed granular, completely brittle-appearing surfaces that were confined to the heat-affected zones of the welds. The crack surfaces were severely discolored, apparently from gaseous "blow-by" following failure. There also were additional longitudinal cracks in the heat-affected zones, where partial weld separation had occurred, and transverse cracks formed by bending during failure.

Microscopic examination of sections transverse to the weld cracks showed severe intergranular corrosion, primarily in the heat-affected zone. The corrosion had been intense enough to cause grain detachment and, in some regions, complete grain dissolution. There was no evidence suggesting that manufacturing procedures prior to

welding could have contributed to the failure. A resistance seam weld remote from the gas tungsten-arc weld showed only superficial (0.0008 to 0.001 in. deep) and sporadic surface attack. The 19-9 DL stainless steel skin remote from the gas tungsten-arc weld had a satisfactory microstructure and chemical composition, and was of the specified thickness.

The fractures gave every appearance of having been caused by loss of corrosion resistance due to sensitization. This condition could have been induced by the temperatures attained during gas tungsten-arc welding.

To determine the degree of sensitization present in the heat-affected zones of the tailpipes, specimens were subjected to 72-hr immersion in boiling, acidified copper sulfate (Strauss test). These specimens showed separation of the gas tungsten-arc weld from the base metal with complete dissolution of the heat-affected zone. A specimen from the resistance seam weld remote from the gas tungsten-arc weld showed only scattered superficial surface attack (as deep as 0.0023 in.). Specimens from the base metal completely remote from any weld showed slight attack that varied from 0.0007 to 0.0019 in. deep. These results decisively demonstrated the presence of sensitization in the heat-affected zone of the gas tungsten-arc weld.

Conclusions. The aircraft-engine tailpipe failures were due to intergranular corrosion in service of the sensitized structure of the heat-affected zones produced during gas tungsten-arc welding.

Recommendations. All gas tungsten-arc welded tailpipes should be postweld annealed by re-solution treatment to redissolve all particles of carbide in the heat-affected zone. Also, it was suggested that resistance seam welding be used, because there would be no corrosion problem with the faster cooling rate characteristic of this technique.

Example 21. Embrittlement of 21Cr-6Ni-9Mn Stainless Steel by Liquid Copper From a Welding Fixture (Fig. 24)

Parts of 21Cr-6Ni-9Mn stainless steel that had been forged at about 815 C (1500 F) were gas tungsten-arc welded. During postweld inspection, cracks were found in the heat-affected zones of the welds. These cracks were small and somewhat perpendicular to the weld. Welding had been done using a copper fixture that contacted the steel in the area of the heat-affected zone on each side of the weld but did not extend under the tungsten arc.

Investigation. Sections of the parts were taken parallel to the weld and perpendicular to the cracks. In SEM examination, the cracks appeared to be intergranular (Fig. 24a) and extended to a depth of approximately 0.05 in. The crack appearance suggested that the surface temperature of the heat-affected zone could have melted a film of copper on the fixture surface and that this could have penetrated the stainless steel in the presence of tensile thermal-contraction stresses. A Cu K_α x-ray fluorescent scan of the crack revealed a heavy copper concentration within the crack as well as on the external surface of the heat-affected zone (Fig. 24b). Residual stresses in the weld away from the cracks were measured at

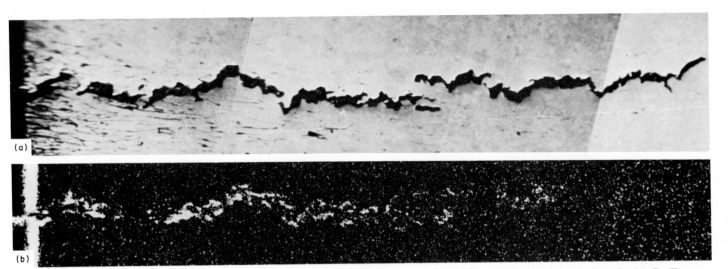

(a) SEM micrograph, at 165×, of section cut parallel to weld and perpendicular to crack, showing intergranular nature of crack. (b) Cu Kα x-ray fluorescence scanning micrograph, at 165×, of crack, showing copper concentrations at surface (at left) and along crack contours.

Fig. 24. Heat-affected zone of a weld in 21Cr-6Ni-9Mn stainless steel part, showing evidence of cracking caused by liquid-copper penetration (Example 21)

50,000 psi in tension, which were considered adequate to cause cracking in the presence of liquid copper.

Conclusions. The cracks in the 21Cr-6Ni-9Mn weldments were a form of liquid-metal embrittlement caused by contact with superficially melted copper from the fixture and subsequent grain-boundary attack of the stainless steel in an area under residual tensile stress.

Corrective Measure. The copper for the fixtures was replaced by aluminum. No further cracking was encountered.

Example 22. Corrosive Attack of Type 316L Stainless Steel Welds in Hot Brine (Fig. 25)

Type 316L stainless steel pipes carrying brine at 121 C (250 F) and at a pH of about 7, failed by perforation at or near circumferential butt-weld seams (see Fig. 25a).

Investigation. The failure was examined optically and radiographically in the field. Specimens were removed and examined metallographically and with a scanning electron microscope in the laboratory. The examinations revealed a combination of failure mechanisms. The weld itself had been perforated by pitting corrosion. Preferential attack of the cast structure of the weld is shown in Fig. 25(b). The high chromium interdendritic region was the last to dissolve. The adjacent base metal had stress-corrosion cracks that extended through the pipe wall. The transgranular nature of the cracking is shown in Fig. 25(c).

Discussion. The pitting corrosion reaction between type 316L stainless steel and the environment in which it was used is typical of the factors that determine whether the surface of a chromium-nickel alloy will be activated or passivated by a solution. The amount of oxygen that is locally present in the brine is particularly critical. A neutral hot chloride solution may locally activate the alloy, causing continuous pitting. Once the reaction has started, ferric chloride can be produced which has an autoacceleration action. This apparently was the main cause of the pitting attack of the seam weld in the pipes. Once the surface has been activated, the metal around the pit becomes cathodic and penetration within the pit is rapid, because the area of effective cathode is very large compared to that of the anodic pit.

In addition to the pitting corrosion of the weld itself, the base metal adjacent to the weld suffered stress-corrosion cracking. The stress that produced these cracks was the result of residual stresses from weld shrinkage. The source of corrodent that caused the cracking was not positively identified. Increased oxygen content of the brine could result in cracking. Another possibility is the action of the pitting corrosion product as the stress-corroding medium.

Conclusions. The pitting failure of the welds was attributed to localized attack of an activated surface, in which anodic pits corroded rapidly. Additionally, stress-corrosion cracking driven by residual welding stresses occurred in the base metal adjacent to the welds.

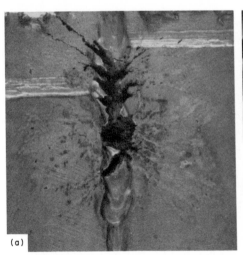
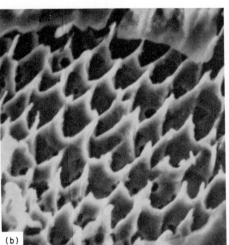
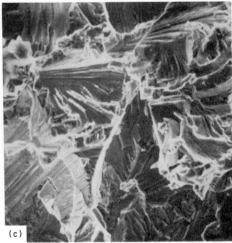

(a) Photograph, at 1×, of interior surface of pipe, showing perforation at the weld seam caused by pits and stress-corrosion cracks. (b) SEM micrograph, at 2000×, of corrosion pits in the weld, showing penetration between high-chromium interdendritic boundaries. (c) SEM micrograph, at 500×, showing transgranular facets of a stress-corrosion crack that formed in the base metal after extended exposure to a chloride-containing environment at a temperature of 121 C (250 F).

Fig. 25. Type 316L stainless steel pipe that fractured by localized attack in welds during exposure to hot brine (Example 22)

Recommendations. The utilization of highly stressed austenitic stainless steels in high-chloride environments having a temperature above 66 C (150 F) should be discouraged. Solution annealing or shot peening to reduce residual stresses may be advisable. If heat treatment is not feasible after welding, the substitution of a more corrosion-resistant alloy, such as Incoloy 800 or 825, may be necessary.

Example 23. Cracking of Type 316L Stainless Steel Pipe at a Weld Defect (Fig. 26)

A leach-heater feedline carrying 50% acetic acid at 55 C (130 F) and at 600 psi developed a small leak after only a short time in service. The pipe had a 3-in. OD and a ³⁄₁₆-in. wall thickness, and was specified to be made of type 316L stainless steel in conformity with ASTM A312. An 8-in.-long section containing the leak was sent to the laboratory to determine the cause of failure.

Investigation. Visual examination of the pipe revealed that it was welded and that there was a small crack on the outer surface along the edge of the weld. No other defects were found on the outside surface. After a white, powdery deposit was removed from the inner surface, a large weld defect (approximately ½ in. in diameter) was found. This defect, shown in Fig. 26(a), was directly opposite the crack observed on the outer surface. There was no evidence of corrosion on the inner surface of the pipe.

Figure 26(b) is a macrograph of a section through the pipe at the crack, which revealed the crack fully penetrating the wall at the upper side of the weld and a sharp line of lack of fusion at the lower side. Figure 26(c) is a macrograph of a section taken through the weld defect beyond the cracked area. The top of the macrograph shows that the weld metal extends for less than half the wall thickness, but that there is a thin heat-affected zone across the full wall thickness. At the lower part of the weld, there is a sharp line indicating incomplete fusion next to a large globule of weld metal, which was an attempt to repair a previous defect. There was no evidence of stress-corrosion cracking in or around the weld defect. A macrograph of a section through the weld remote from the defect (Fig. 26d) indicates that the weld was sound but that filler metal had been used during the welding operation.

ASTM A312 dictates that the pipe shall be made by a seamless or automatic welding process, with no addition of filler metal in the welding operation. Although it was obvious that the pipe had not been manufactured according to the specification, the failure was not caused by using filler metal, but was caused because the welding technique was poor and the final inspection was not thorough enough.

Conclusions. The pipe failed because of a stress concentration that generated a crack at a large weld defect that escaped final inspection. There was no evidence of stress-corrosion cracking.

Recommendation. Welding without a filler metal should be done, because this operation is performed in welding lines equipped for continuous weld inspection, which is thorough enough to detect defects such as the one that caused this failure.

Example 24. Crevice-Corrosion Failure of Type 309S (Cb) Stainless Steel Evaporator Tubes Because of Defective Seam Welds (Fig. 27)

Several tubes in a tube bundle in an evaporator used to concentrate an acid nitrate solution failed by leakage. The feed to the evaporator contained about 6% nitrate, and the discharge about 60% nitrate. The tube bundle was comprised of 751 type 309S (Cb) stainless steel drawn-and-welded tubes 1 in. in outside diameter, 0.109 in. in wall thickness, and about 14 ft long. The tubes were expanded and welded into two type 304L stainless steel tube sheets 2½ in. thick.

Investigation. The leaks were located at the seam welds. Sectioning of a defective tube revealed shallow, longitudinal cracks in the seam weld. Metallographic examination showed that crevice corrosion had attacked

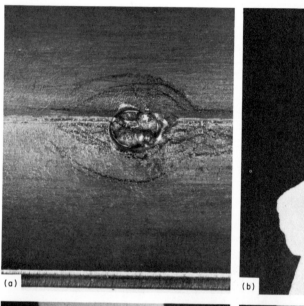

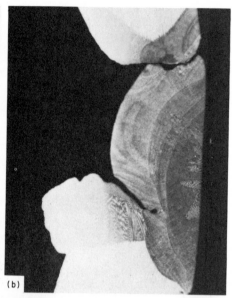

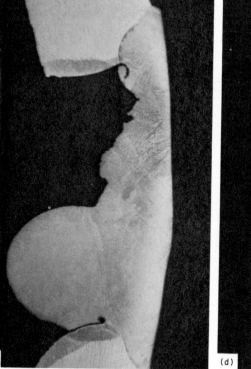

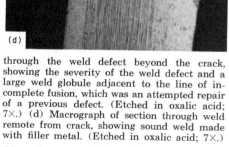

(a) Photograph, at ¾×, of the inside surface of the pipe, showing the weld defect. No evidence of corrosion was observed. (b) Macrograph of a section through the crack on the outside surface of the pipe, showing the crack penetrating the weld metal to meet a line of incomplete fusion on the inside surface. (Etched in oxalic acid; 7×.) (c) Macrograph of a section through the weld defect beyond the crack, showing the severity of the weld defect and a large weld globule adjacent to the line of incomplete fusion, which was an attempted repair of a previous defect. (Etched in oxalic acid; 7×.) (d) Macrograph of section through weld remote from crack, showing sound weld made with filler metal. (Etched in oxalic acid; 7×.)

Fig. 26. Large weld defect that caused cracking of a type 316L stainless steel pipe (Example 23)

he weld cracks on the inner surface of the
ube, ultimately penetrating the full thick-
ess of the weld. In some areas, the pene-
ration also was longitudinal, extending the
avities axially within the weld and below
he inner surface to regions where no trace
f surface cracks existed (Fig. 27).

Conclusions. The tubes failed by crevice
orrosion. The failed tubes were defective
s-received, and the establishment of con-
entration cells within the longitudinal
racks in the seam welds led to ultimate corrosive penetration of the wall. There was
no evidence of crevice corrosion or any
localized penetration of tubes that had
sound welds.

Recommendation. The leaking type 309S
(Cb) welded tubes should be replaced with
seamless tubes of type 304L stainless steel to
minimize the areas requiring welding and to
provide maximum weldability for the tube-
sheet joints.

Failures in Arc Welded Heat-Resisting Alloys

The arc welding of heat-resisting alloys has many aspects in common with
the arc welding of stainless steels. The
nickel-base and cobalt-base superalloys,
and highly alloyed iron-base metals, can
be welded by all arc-welding processes;
specific procedures vary with composition and strengthening mechanism. Joint
design, edge preparation, fit-up, cleanness of base metal and filler metal, shielding, and welding technique all have an
effect on weld quality and must be carefully controlled to prevent porosity,
cracks, fissures, undercuts, incomplete
fusion and other weld imperfections.

In the welding of a nickel-base alloy,
poor welding practice resulted in weld-
component mismatch, weld undercutting
and unfused weld interfaces, as described
in the following example.

**Example 25. Fatigue Fracture of an Alloy 718
Gas-Turbine Inner-Combustion-Chamber
Case Assembly Because of Unfused
Weld Metal and Undercuts (Fig. 28)**

The case and stiffener of an inner-combustion-chamber case assembly failed by
completely fracturing circumferentially
around the edge of a groove arc weld joining
the case and stiffener to the flange (Fig.
28a). The assembly consisted of a cylindrical stiffener inserted into a cylindrical
case and both welded to a flange. The case,
stiffener, flange and weld deposit were all of
nickel-base alloy 718. It was observed that
a manual arc weld repair had been made
along almost the entire circumference of the
original weld.

Investigation. Microscopic examination of
the fracture site revealed unfused weld-
metal surfaces and severe reductions
(undercuts) in thickness of the stiffener in
many areas. The thickness of the case had
also been undercut in several areas. Fatigue
cracks had originated at multiple sites along
the weld interfaces of the case and stiffener.
Also, the groove weld contained areas of mismatch that were greater than those allowed
by the specifications.

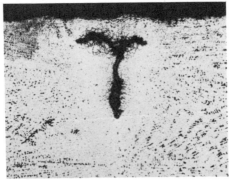

*Fig. 27. Micrograph, at 60×, of a section
through a type 309S (Cb) stainless steel
evaporator tube containing a defective
seam weld in which the cavity shown
resulted from crevice corrosion and extended longitudinally below the inner
surface of the weld (Example 24)*

Metallographic specimens from sections
of the fracture site showed the double weld
beads that were caused by a repair weld and
also indicated that many of the interfaces
were unfused, as evidenced by films of oxide
dross (Fig. 28b).

Conclusions. Failure was by fatigue from
multiple origins caused by welding defects.
The combined effects of undercutting the
case wall, weld mismatch and unfused weld
interfaces contributed to high stress concentrations that generated the fatigue cracks.
Ultimate failure was by tensile overload of
the sections partly separated by the fatigue
cracks.

Recommendation. Correct fit-up of the
case, stiffener and flange is essential, and
more skillful welding techniques should be
used, to avoid undercutting and unfused
interfaces.

Failures in Arc Welded Aluminum Alloys

Almost all arc welding of aluminum
alloys is done by either the gas metal-arc
or the gas tungsten-arc process. Recom-

mended procedures for arc welding of
aluminum alloys are described on pages
296 to 336 in Volume 6 of this Handbook.
(See also Ref 6 and 7 for additional information on the welding of aluminum
alloys.)

Aluminum alloys of the 1xxx, 3xxx,
5xxx and 6xxx series are easily welded.
Those of the 2xxx and 4xxx series require
more care, which may include the use of
special techniques to reduce ductility.
In a few aluminum alloys, such as 7075,
7079 and 7178, welding results in heat-
affected zones that are sufficiently brittle to warrant the recommendation that
these grades usually not be welded. Aluminum alloys 7005 and 7039, however,
were developed specifically for welding
and are not subject to this problem.

The response of an aluminum alloy to
the heat input of welding varies, depending on whether or not the alloy is heat
treatable and thus can be strengthened
by precipitation hardening. In non-heat-
treatable alloys (such as the 1xxx, 3xxx,
4xxx and 5xxx series, and several alloys
in the 7xxx and 8xxx series), the strength
and hardness in the fusion and heat-
affected zones will approximate the
values typical of the annealed condition
— that is, a weld in an annealed non-
heat-treatable alloy will not alter the
base-metal properties. If, however, the
alloy has been strain hardened, the weld
will soften an area within approximately
1 in. from the weld centerline, returning
this area to the annealed condition.
The original hardness and strength may
be restored by re-strain hardening, if
feasible.

If welding conditions are kept constant
or stable, results of the welding operation
are also consistent and reproducible. For
instance, in junctions of plates of aluminum alloys 5456-H321 and 6061-T6
that were repair welded six times, the

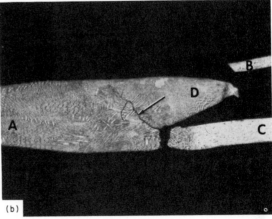

(a) Photograph, at ½×, of the exterior surface of the assembly, showing the circumferential
fracture of the case (at arrow). (b) Macrograph, at 10×, of a section through the fracture, showing
the weld, A, that originally joined the flange to the case, B, and stiffener, C. The external repair
weld, D, had only partial fusion with the earlier bead. Arrow points to a film of oxide dross at
the interface. (Etchant: 2% chromic acid plus HCl.)

*Fig. 28. Alloy 718 inner-combustion-chamber-case assembly that fractured by fatigue in
the weld joining the flange to the case and stiffener (Example 25)*

tensile properties across the welds were not significantly affected by the number of times the plates were rewelded, nor was the width of the heat-affected zone significantly increased, and the effect of the heat of welding consistently extended no more than $1\frac{1}{2}$ in. from the weld centerline (Ref 8).

Defects that may occur in gas metal-arc and gas tungsten-arc welds of aluminum alloys include gas porosity, inadequate joint penetration, cracks, undercuts and inclusions. Distortion may occur also, especially if the weldment is a subassembly of a large structure.

Gas Porosity. The occurrence of gas porosity in aluminum alloy welds is almost always caused by entrapment of hydrogen gas. Solidification shrinkage is not a significant contributor to weld porosity. Hydrogen has high solubility in molten aluminum but very low solubility in solid aluminum (a small fraction of its solubility in solid steel or solid titanium). Hydrogen dissolved in the weld puddle during welding is released during solidification. The high freezing rate associated with gas metal-arc welding, for example, can prevent the evolved hydrogen from rising to the surface of the weld puddle, with the result that porosity occurs. Hydrogen from an extremely limited source can cause a significant amount of porosity.

Hydrogen sources are the water, grease, oil or other hydrocarbons that may contaminate the base-metal surfaces, the ambient atmosphere, the shielding gas or the electrode or filler wire. The causes of hydrogen in the weld include poor quality of electrode or filler wire; dirty filler material because of careless storage, unsatisfactory cleaning of base-metal surfaces, or contamination of welding room by paint spray or oil drips; water condensate on base metal; water leakage into the gas shield through poor torch seals; leakage of moist air into the shielding gas through defective hoses; and use of a shielding gas with a high dew point.

Gas porosity is usually well distributed in overhead-position welds, is frequently found along the top edge of welds made in the horizontal position, and is least likely to be encountered in welds made in the vertical-up position. Linear porosity is most often found in welds where the root-pass penetration is inadequate. Aligned or layered porosity exerts a much greater effect on mechanical properties than does uniformly distributed porosity. Microporosity, too fine to be detected by radiographic procedures, typically occurs in layers along the weld fusion line and at weld-pass interfaces. This type of porosity lowers mechanical properties appreciably.

A study of the effect of porosity on the tensile properties of aluminum alloy

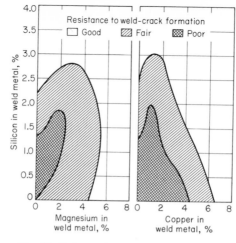

Fig. 29. Schematic representation of the different degrees of resistance to weld-crack formation provided by various combinations of alloy content in Al-Mg-Si (6xxx) and Al-Cu-Si (2xxx) alloys (Redrawn from Ref 10; see also Ref 11)

welded panels $\frac{3}{8}$ and 1 in. thick has made the following deductions possible, based on welds in which gas bubbles were formed by the deliberate introduction of hydrogen (Ref 9):

1 Yield strength was little affected, even by as much as 30% porosity.
2 Tensile strength was mainly determined by the choice of alloy. However, porosity generally reduced tensile strength because of the loss in effective cross-sectional area.
3 Elongation was also affected by the choice of alloy, but in general was markedly diminished by porosity in a roughly linear fashion. At 20% total porosity in the tensile-test fracture, the median strain averaged about 60% of that for sound material.
4 Most macroporosity was in the cover passes, and removal of the reinforcement frequently removed some of the severest porosity. Up to 5% microporosity could be present without any macroporosity; however, at 5% macroporosity, the microporosity in the fracture could be as much as 40%. Radiography was successful in detecting macroporosity but gave no indication of microporosity.

Incomplete fusion and inadequate penetration are usually the result of too low a welding current, poor welding techniques, or poor preparation of the base-metal surface. Specific causes may include inadequate wire brushing between weld passes, poor fit-up in preparing the joint, unfavorable torch angle for the travel speed and current being used, joint design that does not afford proper torch accessibility, and unsuitable angle of impingement between the base metal and the welding arc.

Incomplete fusion occurs if the refractory aluminum oxide film on the base metal or the surface of the previous pass is not completely removed by the scour-

ing action of the arc. If the edges being welded fit too tightly together, the arc may be unable to remove the film. Incomplete weld-to-base-metal fusion and interpass fusion in multiple-pass welds in thick plates is of special concern, because this may be difficult for the welder to detect while welding and is always difficult to detect in finished welds. Such incomplete fusion occurs most often in horizontal- and overhead-position welding, because of the need to use a smaller puddle and therefore less current for these positions. Occluded aluminum oxide is so thin (0.2 micro-in.) that it is difficult to detect with nondestructive-testing procedures. Inadequate root-pass penetration, however, can be discovered by visual, liquid-penetrant, or radiographic inspection.

Weld Cracks. Cold cracking usually is not encountered in aluminum alloy welds except when a bead has been laid down that is too small to resist the cooling stresses. However, both crater cracks and longitudinal hot cracks can occur in aluminum alloy welds if the welding technique is not favorable.

Crater cracks, formed in the residual puddle after the arc has been broken, are potential sources of failure, because although frequently small, they usually exist at the end of the weld where stress concentration is greatest. Their occurrence may be minimized by breaking and restarting the arc several times to feed the shrinkage pipe, or by terminating welding on runoff tabs that are cut away later. If crater cracks are found, they should be chipped out and the area rewelded, because it is very difficult to melt out a crater crack.

Longitudinal hot cracking during welding often is called hot-short cracking, because sensitivity to weld cracking is strongly related to the composition of the weld metal. In most aluminum alloy systems, there is a range of compositions in which maximum crack sensitivity exists. To avoid longitudinal hot cracking, it is necessary to select a filler metal that will provide a satisfactory final weld composition. Figure 29 schematically illustrates the effects of various combinations of magnesium and silicon and of copper and silicon in the weld metal on the relative cracking resistances of several 6xxx and 2xxx series aluminum alloys. Cracking resistance is affected by the heat input during welding. The heat input determines what fraction of the weld is derived from the base metal, and this approaches 50% only at very high heat input. The type of groove (square versus V) also influences the amount of melting of the base metal.

Studies of welds in 5xxx and 6xxx series alloys have shown that susceptibilities to cracking were lowered when aluminum-magnesium filler alloys containing up to 5.5% magnesium were used (Ref 12). Minor alloying elements (titanium and zirconium particularly) are employed as grain-refining agents in filler metal to further reduce the crack sensitivity of welds. Alternatively, minor alloying constituents may accentuate hot shortness by forming low-melting phases at the grain boundaries. Increased copper in 7xxx series alloys, for example, produces this effect, contributing to hot shortness under the thermal stresses present during weld solidification. In some circumstances when the stress on a weld bead is low, cracks may not form immediately but may open up under the heat and stress from a subsequent weld overlay.

Of the various grades of aluminum alloys, the 5xxx series has a very low crack sensitivity. However, under particularly unfavorable conditions and with abusive welding practices, three particular types of weld cracks (aggravated hot-short cracking, cracking of previously deposited welds, and weld shrinkage cracks) have occurred in aluminum alloy 5083 plate welded with aluminum alloy 5183 filler metal.

Aggravated hot-short cracking can occur as a result of applied tensile forces across the solidifying weld metal, producing the type of defects seen in Fig. 30. These cracks may be caused by restraining fixtures, by the mass of the connected aluminum alloy members, or by release of stored energy in formed parts. A revision of the fixturing, of the welding conditions or of the welding sequence on the assembly usually eliminates this problem.

Cracking of previously deposited welds is generally traced to the buildup of residual tensile stresses that finally causes fracture. This type of failure has been observed in large fillet welds and in multiple-pass welds in thick aluminum alloy 5083 plate. This can be avoided by changing the welding conditions or welding sequence.

Weld shrinkage cracks are actually weld shrinkage pores that are similar in shape to cracks and are usually associated with oxide inclusions. This type of defect is uncommon, but has occurred in welds made by inexperienced operators who used excessive welding current, which formed extremely large, deep weld puddles.

Undercuts (grooves in the base metal along the edge of a weld) are serious defects in aluminum alloys because they reduce the cross-sectional area of the welded zone and consequently its load-bearing capacity. Undercuts result from use of unfavorable welding conditions, such as excessive welding current, insufficient arc-travel speed or improper electrode-holder angle, or from dirt or oxidation on the work-metal surface.

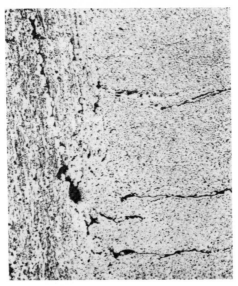

Fig. 30. Micrograph of hot-short cracks in a gas metal-arc weld of aluminum alloy 5083 plate (Etched; 100×)

Inclusions. Aluminum alloys contain particles of the intermetallic compounds and second phases that make it possible for desirable increases in strength and hardness by precipitation (in heat treatable alloys) or by solution strengthening and strain hardening (in non-heat-treatable alloys). These microconstituent particles, however, are integral parts of the alloys and therefore are not considered as extraneous inclusions.

There are two types of extraneous inclusions in aluminum alloys — metallic and nonmetallic. Metallic inclusions consist principally of particles of tungsten and copper. In gas tungsten-arc welding, the use of excessive current for a specific electrode size will cause melting and deposition of tungsten in the weld. Transfer of tungsten is also caused by starting the weld with a cold electrode, by dipping the electrode in the weld puddle, or by touching the electrode with the filler rode. When present as fine, uniformly scattered particles, tungsten has little effect on mechanical properties of the weld. Many codes, however, require that the welds be essentially free of such inclusions.

Copper inclusions may be found in gas metal-arc welds if the electrode suffers burn-back to the contact tube. Such inclusions produce a brittle weld and can be a serious corrosion hazard; therefore they should be removed from the weld deposit.

A third type of metallic inclusion can be caused by wire-brush bristles that become caught in the weld groove in preweld cleaning or in cleaning between weld passes.

Both tungsten and copper inclusions can be identified visually, and x-ray inspection will detect tungsten particles because of their high density.

Nonmetallic inclusions in welds of aluminum alloys are seldom derived from the base metal. Almost always they are caused by deficiencies in the welding procedures, principally by inadequate protection from the ambient atmosphere because of insufficient quantity or purity of the shielding gas.

Distortion of aluminum alloy welds stems from elastic and plastic (permanent) deformation of the base metal by thermal-contraction stresses in both the longitudinal and transverse directions. It can be controlled somewhat by favorable adjustment of joint design, joint fit-up, welding conditions and welding sequence, but it cannot be eliminated without resort to postweld cold flow, as in stretcher straightening or weld planishing.

Elastic distortion is caused by residual stresses in the vicinity of the weld that are less than the minimum yield strength of the alloy in the heat-affected zone. These stresses do not affect the static or impact strength of aluminum alloys but may have an adverse effect on fatigue strength, may cause secondary distortion in assemblies machined after welding, and may be detrimental to stress-corrosion-cracking resistance of certain alloys when welded after tempering. In non-heat-treatable alloys, the residual welding stresses can be reduced to a low level by a thermal treatment with little sacrifice of the original work-hardened strength.

In the assembly of large structures, distortion in welded subassemblies can cause serious mismatch in final assembly, and a force fit of mismatched sections introduces new problems in local damage and new residual stresses. The problems can be minimized by adjusting dimensions, welding procedures and welding sequences to anticipate the direction and magnitude of possible distortion.

Examples. The two examples that follow describe failures that occurred in aluminum alloy welds — the first by grain-boundary eutectic melting during preheating, and the second because of almost total lack of joint penetration.

Example 26. Intergranular Cracking in an Aluminum Alloy 2219-T62 Air Bottle Because of Torch Overheating Prior to Welding (Fig. 31)

An air bottle, machined from a solid block of aluminum alloy 2219-T852, displayed liquid-penetrant crack indications after assembly welding (see Fig. 31a). The air bottle was machined to rough shape, which consisted of a 0.15-in.-wall cylindrical cup with a ¾-in.-wall integral boss on one side, and was annealed at 413 C (775 F). The lip of the cup was then hot spun to a dome shape, the metal being preheated and maintained at 204 C (400 F) with a torch, and was subsequently liquid-penetrant inspected. After a second anneal, a port fitting for the dome opening was attached by four

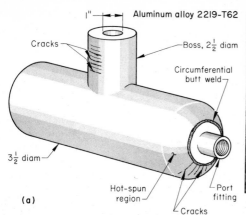

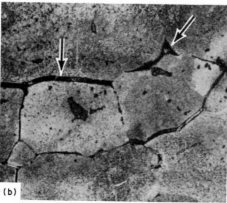

(a) Machined air bottle showing hot-spun region, circumferential butt weld made in assembly, and location of crack indications. (b) Micrograph showing longitudinal intergranular crack and triangular void (at arrows) typical of those at the failed areas of the boss and tank. (Etched in Keller's reagent; 250×.) (c) Fractograph, at 10×, of the fracture surface of one of the tank-wall cracks, showing typical glossy surfaces.

Fig. 31. Air bottle, of aluminum alloy 2219-T62, that failed by intergranular cracking because of overheating prior to assembly welding (Example 26)

tack welds. The assembly was torch preheated to 121 to 149 C (250 to 300 F), using a contact pyrometer to check the temperature. Presumably this included heating of the boss, which constituted a massive heat sink. The port fitting was then welded in place. Final full heat treatment to the T62 temper was followed by machining, pressure testing, and radiographic and liquid-penetrant inspection.

Investigation. The crack indications were found only on one side of the boss and on the lower portion of the hot-spun dome region, as indicated in Fig. 31(a). Sections were cut from both the boss and the tank wall for metallographic examination of the crack indications. Other tank-wall cracks were broken open and studied fractographically.

The metallographic specimens revealed triangular voids and severe intergranular cracks that progressed longitudinally (see Fig. 31b). The cracks that were opened up displayed very few fracture features but did display glossy surfaces (Fig. 31c) that are typical of melted and resolidified material.

At regions away from the crack indications, the material was found to be metallurgically satisfactory with a hardness of Rockwell B 69 to 70, electrical conductivity of 32 to 33% IACS, and a chemical composition conforming to aluminum alloy 2219.

It was apparent, therefore, that at some stage the assembly had been overheated locally, because the proof of melting was restricted to localized regions.

A review of the production procedures indicated that preheating for welding was the only operation where local overheating of both the boss and dome could have occurred. Also, a substantial undercut was found on the inside of the weld, suggesting a higher-than-normal adjacent base-metal temperature at the time of welding. The conclusion was that the torch heating caused local grain-boundary melting.

Conclusions. The localized cracks in the air bottle were the outcome of grain-boundary eutectic melting caused by local torch overheating used in preparation for assembly welding of a port fitting.

Corrective Measure. A change in design was scheduled to semiautomatic welding without the use of preheating for the joining of the port fitting for the dome opening.

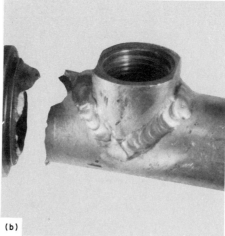

(a) Fracture of gas tungsten-arc weld joining threaded boss to oil-line elbow, showing lack of weld penetration through the surface of the V-notch and cracks at both sides of the apex of the V-notch. (b) Fracture near the brazed flange (at left) after repair welding of the boss V-joint.

Fig. 32. Fractures in aircraft-engine oil-line elbows of aluminum alloy 6061-T6 because of poor welding practice (Example 27)

Example 27. Failure of an Aluminum Alloy 6061-T6 Oil-Line Subassembly Because of Poor Welding (Fig. 32)

Several elbow subassemblies comprising segments of oil-line assemblies that recycled aircraft-engine oil from pump to filter broke in service. The components of the subassemblies were made of aluminum alloy 6061-T6. The expected service life of each subassembly was the same as that of the aircraft, but actual life was between six months and one year.

Two subassemblies were returned to the laboratory for determination of cause of failure. In one (Fig. 32a), the threaded boss had separated from the elbow at the weld made with the gas tungsten-arc process using aluminum alloy 4043 filler metal. In the second, the failure was by fracture of the elbow near the flange, as shown in Fig. 32(b).

Investigation. The fracture through the weld, shown in Fig. 32(a), reveals clearly that penetration of the elbow wall section was entirely lacking. The result was a continuous notch beneath the weld, which provided a stress concentration that overloaded the inadequate weld during normal service stresses. The load on the assembly also caused cracking at the apex on each side of the V-notch in the tube that had been cut to receive the threaded boss. The specifications required that the subassembly be heat treated to the T6 temper after welding; hardness readings of 102 Bhn (normal for T6) taken near the weld confirmed that this had been done. Examination of the weld fracture surface showed evidence of both fatigue and overstressing, but no sign of corrosion.

Study of the second elbow (Fig. 32b) revealed that the welded joint attaching the threaded boss had also failed but had been rewelded by the user and returned to service. The second failure, shown in Fig. 32(b), then occurred in the tube near the flange. The tube hardness near the fracture was less than 53 Bhn, representing a condition harder than fully annealed (30 Bhn) but softer than a T4 temper (65 Bhn). The flange had been attached to the elbow by torch brazing, using BAlSi-3 filler metal (aluminum alloy 4145) and AWS type 1 brazing flux. The manufacturing procedure stipulated that following the brazing of the flange the V-notch be cut, the threaded boss be welded in place, and the subassembly be solution treated and aged to the T6 temper. However, the rewelding of the threaded boss joint undoubtedly over-aged the elbow, reducing its strength to below that of the weld. The fracture showed evidence of fatigue and overstress, suggesting that the service loading had been excessive for the softened tube with failure occurring in the weakest region. No evidence of corrosion was found.

Conclusions. The separation of the threaded boss from the elbow was due to poor welding procedure that failed to achieve penetration of the elbow. The crack propagation was accelerated by fatigue caused by cyclic service stresses.

The fracture of the second elbow near the flange was caused by over-aging during repair welding of the boss weld, with consequent loss of strength in the tube. Had the elbow been re-heat-treated following the repair welding, it is likely that the tube would not have fractured.

Corrective Measures. Satisfactory weld penetration at the threaded boss joint was achieved by improved training of the welders plus more careful inspection. Repair welding was prohibited, to avoid any recurrence of over-aging from the welding heat. As additional support for the oil line was installed to reduce vibration and minimize fatigue of the elbow.

Failures in Arc Welded Titanium and Titanium Alloys

Commercially pure titanium and most titanium alloys can be arc welded satisfactorily by a wide range of welding processes. Unalloyed titanium and all the alpha titanium alloys, being substantially single-phase materials, may be welded with little effect on the microstructure. For this reason, the mechanical properties of a correctly welded joint of these alloys are equal to those of the base metal and have good ductility.

The two-phase microstructures of the alpha-beta titanium alloys respond to thermal treatment and consequently can be altered by welding. The result is extreme brittleness in some alloys that renders them nonweldable. The most commonly used alpha-beta titanium alloys that respond well to welding include Ti-6Al-4V, Ti-3Al-2.5Sn and Ti-6Al-6V-2Sn.

Most beta titanium alloys can be successfully welded. These, however, require particular care if heat treatment is to be employed to strengthen the welds. Aging of certain beta titanium alloy welds (such as Ti-3Al-13V-11Cr alloy) renders the welds susceptible to embrittlement.

Titanium is a highly reactive metal, combining readily at elevated temperatures with carbon, hydrogen, nitrogen and oxygen to form interstitial solid so-

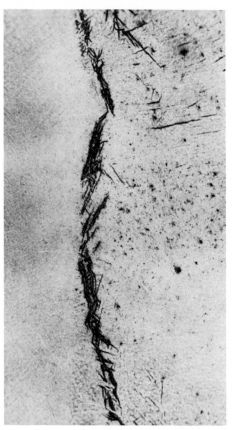

Fig. 33. Gas tungsten-arc weld of pressure-vessel wall that had been stress relieved 1 hr at 538 C (1000 F), showing a band of titanium hydride needles at the interface between unalloyed titanium filler metal at left and the heat-affected zone of titanium alloy Ti-6Al-4V forging at right. (Etched in Kroll's reagent; 100×.)

lutions. If these contaminate the fusion and heat-affected zones of a weld, embrittlement, cracking and weld failure can result. To guard against this, the parts to be welded must first be carefully cleaned to remove scale, oxide, oil, grease, dust, fingermarks, and grinding-wheel grit and binders before welding begins. A solution of 25 to 30% nitric acid plus 2 to 3% hydrofluoric acid in water will remove scale. Acetone or alcohol will effectively degrease the surface; however, chlorinated solvents should never be used, because chloride residues from their use cause stress-corrosion cracking in and around weld zones. During welding, a protective gas shield can be used, such as an inert atmosphere to encompass the arc, the weld puddle and the heat-affected zone during weld deposition. This is readily accomplished during automatic open-air welding with secondary and backup shielding-gas inlets that ensure a complete gas blanket for the operation. Manual welding is done either in an atmosphere-controlled chamber or, when this is not feasible, inside a plastic bag; auxiliary gas shielding is both awkward and unreliable for

open-air manual welding unless containment of some type is employed.

The factors that cause failure of titanium or titanium alloy welds may be metallurgical or mechanical, or a combination of both. Basically, the metallurgical origin is the presence of a phase or combination of phases that possess a very limited capacity to tolerate strain within a critical temperature range. The critical phase or phase mixture will be influenced by the composition of the alloy, the thermal and mechanical processing the alloy has received, the welding conditions used, and the weld shape, which affects the temperature distribution in the adjacent metal. The extent to which either the metallurgical structure or the imposed stresses contribute to a failure can vary considerably.

Mechanical origins include the occurrence of thermal and restraint stresses that, as affected by the presence of weld defects and within this critical temperature range, produce strain in excess of the tolerance of the microstructure. The majority of weld failures in titanium alloys, however, arise from residual stresses in the welded joint from normal weld shrinkage or from weldment restraint. If these residual stresses are multiaxial and exist in areas of limited ductility because of contamination by carbon, oxygen, hydrogen or nitrogen, the result may be cracking immediately after welding or later under applied service loads. Abuse in service is another common source of mechanical origins for failures of weldments made of titanium alloys.

An example of a failure caused by a combination of contamination and stress is the fracture of a heat treated Ti-6Al-4V alloy pressure vessel containing helium (Ref 13); this vessel parted at the weld fusion line of hemispheres with a wall thickness of 0.4 in. The joining was done by multiple-pass automatic gas tungsten-arc welding in an atmosphere-controlled chamber with inadvertent use of unalloyed titanium filler metal. Although the filler metal and the Ti-6Al-4V alloy base metal each contained less than 100 ppm of hydrogen, a band of concentrated titanium hydride, representing a segregated level of 600 to 1600 ppm H_2, was found at the interface between the weld and the heat-affected zone, as shown in Fig. 33. The vessel had previously survived proof testing to pressures well above the service pressure, and so the use of low-strength unalloyed titanium in the weld did not appear to be a direct cause of failure. Rather, the fracture, which was of the brittle-cleavage type, appeared to have resulted from hydride precipitation during service. The unusual aspect of the weld was the almost complete lack of dilution; at the interface between the weld and the heat-affected

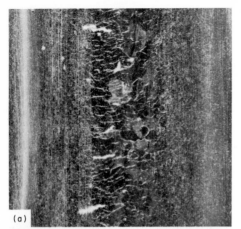

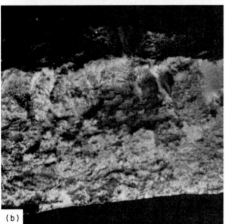

(a) Interior surface of the weld, at 3×, illuminated with ultraviolet light, which reveals fluorescent-liquid-penetrant indications of transverse cracks in the fusion and heat-affected zones. (b) Fractograph, at about 5×, showing fracture origin (dark region at top) formed by welding stresses on the contaminated weld metal. Light region below the origin is the rupture that occurred during the proof test.

Fig. 34. Center girth weld of a titanium alloy Ti-6Al-4V pressure vessel that failed during proof testing because of weld embrittlement that resulted from oxygen contamination (Example 28)

zone, the composition changed from essentially pure titanium to the Ti-6Al-4V alloy.

The use of unalloyed filler metal in welding Ti-6Al-4V alloy is common practice, being employed quite satisfactorily in fabricating many thin-wall pressure vessels. There is usually, however, a significant amount of weld dilution resulting in an appreciable content of aluminum and vanadium in the weld deposit. There have been no failures attributed to hydride formation in these welds.

Failures of arc welded titanium alloy parts caused by a combination of contamination and stress are discussed in the following two examples.

Example 28. Fracture of Welds in a Ti-6Al-4V Alloy Pressure Vessel Because of Atmospheric Contamination (Fig. 34)

A Ti-6Al-4V alloy pressure vessel failed during a proof-pressure test, fracturing along the center girth weld. The pressure vessel, about 4 ft in diameter and 10 ft long, consisted of a dome section, two cylindrical segments and an aft-adapter section. The girth-weld joint was prepared as a 90° single-V-groove joint with a 0.040-in. root face; the wall thickness of the vessel was 0.175 in. The parts were solution treated and aged prior to welding. The girth joints were welded with the automatic gas tungsten-arc process, utilizing an auxiliary trailing shield attached to the welding torch to provide inert-gas shielding for the exterior surface of the weld. A segmented backup ring with a gas channel was used inside the vessel to shield the weld root during weld deposition. The vessel was stress relieved 4 hr at 538 C (1000 F) after welding. This welding procedure had been satisfactory for the open-air welding of large titanium vessels.

Investigation. Preliminary examination of the failed weld revealed that a distinct discoloration existed on the heat-affected zone, suggesting the possibility of atmospheric contamination during welding. The dis-

coloration seemed concentrated at the interface line of the segmented backup ring. A fluorescent liquid penetrant applied to the interior weld surface revealed many small transverse cracks in the fusion and heat-affected zones, as indicated in Fig. 34(a).

The fracture origin was at a surface crack, similar to those in Fig. 34(a), which penetrated through approximately one-quarter of the weld, as shown by the dark, discolored region at the top of the fracture surface in Fig. 34(b). Many of the small transverse cracks in other regions were also considered to be the result of crack initiation that occurred in contaminated areas of the girth weld during proof testing.

Conclusions. The pressure vessel failed due to contamination of the fusion zone by oxygen, which resulted when the gas shielding the root face of the weld was diluted by air that leaked into the gas channel. Thermal stresses, which were inherent in the temperature gradients created by welding, cracked the embrittled weld in various locations, exposing the crack surfaces to oxidation before cooling. One of these cracks (Fig. 34b) provided a critical notch that caused a stress concentration so severe that failure of the vessel wall during the proof test was inevitable.

Corrective Measures. A sealing system at the split-line region of the segmented backup ring was provided, and a fine-mesh stainless steel screen diffuser was incorporated in the channel section of the backup ring, to prevent air from leaking in. A titanium alloy color chart was furnished to permit correlation of weld-zone discoloration with the degree of atmospheric contamination that may have occurred during a particular welding procedure.

Example 29. Cracking in a Gas-Turbine Fan-Duct Assembly of Ti-5Al-2.5Sn Alloy Because of Contamination of a Repair Weld (Fig. 35)

An outer fan-duct assembly of titanium alloy Ti-5Al-2.5Sn (AMS 4910) for a gas-turbine fan section cracked 3 in. circumferentially through a repair weld in an arc weld in the front flange-duct segment, as

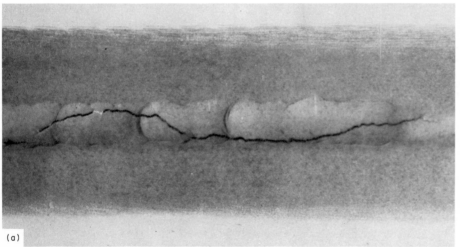

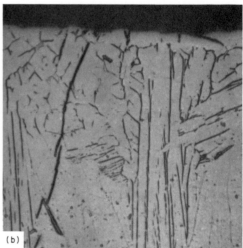

(a) Photograph, at 1.5×, of the circumferential 3-in. crack in the repair weld in the arc weld. (b) Micrograph, at 500×, of a longitudinal section through the repair weld, showing an oxide-rich alpha-case surface layer that contributed to the cracking.

Fig. 35. Gas-turbine fan duct, made of titanium alloy Ti-5Al-2.5Sn, that cracked because of contamination of a repair weld in an arc weld in the front flange-duct segment (Example 29)

shown in Fig. 35(a). The flange was also made of titanium alloy Ti-5Al-2.5Sn but with the designation AMS 4926.

Investigation. Examination of the crack with a binocular microscope revealed no evidence of fatigue. A "blue etch-anodize" inspection (see *Metal Progress,* Aug 1971, p 92-95) showed the presence of an alpha case along the edges of the repair weld. The alpha case, a brittle oxide-enriched layer, forms when welds are inadequately shielded from the atmosphere during deposition. The presence of the layer was confirmed by metallographic examination of longitudinal sections transverse to the weld and the crack (Fig. 35b). The brittleness of this layer (Rockwell C 48 to 52 versus 29 to 33 for the base metal) caused transgranular cracks to form and propagate in tension under the thermal stresses created by the repair-weld heat input.

Conclusions. The crack resulted from contamination and embrittlement of a repair weld that had had inadequate gas shielding. Thermal stresses cracked the oxide-rich layer that formed.

Corrective Measures. The gas-shielding accessories of the welding torch were overhauled to ensure that leak-in or entrainment of air was eliminated. Also, the purity of the shielding-gas supplies was rechecked to make certain that these had not become contaminated.

Cracks in titanium alloy parts also can be caused by the thermal stresses produced by welds that are not contaminated. For example, a bracket-brace assembly of Ti-5Al-2.5Sn (AMS 4966) welded with unalloyed titanium filler metal (AMS 4951) cracked in a corner formed between a weld (see Fig. 36) and the bracket. The crack propagated diagonally across the assembly to a second weld and thence to a nearby slot. Microscopic examination of the fracture surface revealed that the crack propagation was by fatigue under cyclic loading. The origin of the crack, however, was attributed to thermal stresses induced by welding and concentrated by the sharpness of the radius at the corner.

Failure Origins in Electroslag Welds

Electroslag welding is most commonly used for joining relatively thick sections of low-carbon steels, but it also can be used to weld medium-carbon steels such as 1045 and 1050, and to a lesser extent for welding high-strength structural steels, high-strength alloy steels such as D-6ac, stainless steels and nickel alloys.

Because an arc is used to start the welding in the electroslag process and is used until a pool of molten flux (slag) has been formed that is deep enough to quench the arc, the discontinuities typical of arc welds are usually present in the initial deposit. These possible defects, however, can be isolated from the welded joint by the use of a "starting lug" that can be cut away later, leaving only

Fig. 36. Bracket-brace assembly of titanium alloy Ti-6Al-2.5Sn that failed by fatigue fracture, which originated at a weld (at arrow) from concentrated thermal stresses

metal deposited by electrical resistance heating of the molten flux. This heat serves to melt both the filler metal and the surface of the base metal that are in contact. Once the metal has been deposited by resistance heating of the flux, welding must be continuous until the joint has been completely formed if welding defects are to be avoided. A halt at any intermediate stage in completing the joint weld will probably result in a region containing porosity, nonmetallic inclusions, cracks and undercuts when welding is restarted. In welds completed without interruption, discontinuities can be detected visually or by nondestructive testing. (For detailed information on the electroslag welding process, see the article that begins on page 383 in Volume 6 of this Handbook.)

Inclusions. Slag inclusions derived from the flux pool may be found at the weld interface. These inclusions can best be avoided by making certain that the guide tube for the electrode wire is centered between the base-metal surfaces and between the dams.

Other inclusions may result from melting of nonmetallic laminations in the steel being welded. These are detectable by radiography. They can be avoided by inspection of the faying surfaces of the steel to be welded, using magnetic-particle or liquid-penetrant techniques. When located, the laminations should be gouged out to a depth greater than the expected weld penetration, and the cavities filled by repair welds using low-hydrogen electrodes.

Porosity. Because electroslag welding is basically a low-hydrogen process, gas porosity usually is not encountered. However, if gas porosity should be de-

tected and if the flux used is of the composite or bonded type, the flux should be prebaked.

Electroslag welding establishes directional solidification in the welds, which is favorable for the production of welds that are free of shrinkage porosity.

Incomplete fusion or inadequate penetration can lead to a major failure of the weld by cracking from thermal contraction stresses on cooling. This is usually overcome by using a predetermined butt-joint gap or by increasing the depth of the flux pool.

Poor Weld Contour. The weld-face contours are formed by the copper dams or shoes that bridge the gap between the plates being welded. If the clamping pressure on the shoes is too great, the resulting flexure will cause an improper weld contour. In some circumstances, the weld face may contain some undercutting. Undercutting is easily detected by visual, magnetic-particle or liquid-penetrant inspection and can be repaired by grinding or by arc welding plus grinding.

Cold Cracks in Base Metal. In thick plates, microfissures may be produced by forming operations close to or below the nil-ductility temperature. If such microfissures lie close to or in the heat-affected zone of an electroslag weld, they will grow to macrofissures that can be detected by visual inspection or by examination using magnetic-particle, liquid-penetrant or radiographic methods.

Failure Origins in Electrogas Welds

Many aspects of electrogas welding resemble electroslag welding, but there are certain distinct differences. (The electrogas technique is described in detail in the article beginning on page 395 in Volume 6 of this Handbook.) Discontinuities and defects that may be encountered in electrogas welds are described below.

Inclusions. Because a flux is not employed in electrogas welding (except in flux-cored electrodes), this possible source of inclusions frequently is absent in electrogas welds. Nonmetallic inclusions introduced by base-metal laminations are sometimes found by radiographic examination. The detection and removal of such laminations are discussed under "Inclusions" in the preceding section on electroslag welding in this article. The depth of gouging necessary to remove base-metal laminations in preparation for electrogas welding is greater than for electroslag welding, because of the deeper penetration achieved by the electrogas process.

Porosity. Gas porosity almost always is the result of an inadequate volume of shielding gas or because air was aspirated in the flow of shielding gas. A large gas flow and an increased height of gas coverage should correct this condition.

Highly directional solidification exists in electrogas welding to the same degree as in the electroslag process. Thus, the welds should be free of shrinkage porosity.

Incomplete fusion or inadequate penetration will sometimes cause gross cracking during cooling as the result of thermal contraction stresses. The usual remedial procedure is to reduce the gap between the plates being welded, increase the welding current, or decrease the oscillation speed, thereby deepening the molten-metal pool.

Poor Weld Contour. The causes and correction of poor weld contour in electrogas welding are the same as for electroslag welding (see preceding page in this article).

Hot Cracks in Weld Metal. If hot cracks are formed in the weld, they will be observed almost immediately as the weld cools and the weld dams move up. Such defects usually mean rejection of the weldment. Their occurrence can be related to the alloy content of the electrode filler metal and can be eliminated by selection of the proper combination of filler metal and shielding gas.

A filler metal should be similar to the base metal in composition, tensile strength, and elongation. Selection of the shielding gas depends somewhat on the composition of the base metal.

Cold Cracks in Base Metal. The occurrence of cold cracks in the base metal is the same as for electroslag welding (see preceding page in this article).

Failures in Resistance Welds

The general term resistance welding includes resistance spot welding, resistance seam welding, and projection welding, which are all closely related. Flash welding (a resistance butt welding process) is dealt with separately in this article, predominantly because the extensive arcing and plastic upsetting that characterize this process make it appreciably different from conventional resistance welding processes. The techniques and equipment that are appropriate for resistance welding are described in several articles on pages 401 to 484 in Volume 6 of this Handbook.

The qualities of resistance welds are affected by many variables, including the properties of the material to be welded, the surface smoothness and cleanness, the electrode size and shape, and the welding-machine settings that determine welding time, pressure and current. Successful welding depends on consistent weld properties, which in turn require uniform welding conditions. Experience has shown that a change in any single variable of more than 10% is sufficient to

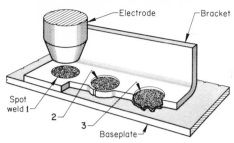

Fig. 37. Schematic representation of failure of spot welds to join a bracket to a baseplate because of inadequate welding current density that was caused by extension of the electrode beyond the edge of the bracket flange

make the weld unacceptable. Unacceptability may represent failure to meet a specified property limit, such as a minimum tensile or impact strength, or it may indicate actual fracture of the weld. Some possible causes of resistance weld failures are described below.

Inclusions. The sources of inclusions in a resistance weld include the surfaces of the parts being joined and their internal structures. Surface contaminants that may cause inclusions are dirt, rust, scale, certain types of coatings, and sometimes oil and grease. These may be between the surfaces to be joined or may be between a part and the electrode contacting the part. Whether or not the inclusions cause failure depends on their quantity, size, location within the weld microstructure and such properties as melting point or softening range. An inclusion that is likely to become fluid enough at the nugget-fusion temperature to penetrate a grain boundary would be particularly damaging.

Porosity. Some inclusions may cause weld porosity, which is generally considered undesirable but is totally unacceptable if certain size limitations are exceeded. Other inclusions may generate blowholes, usually a cause for immediate rejection. Improper machine settings, particularly those causing excessive current and insufficient pressure, can cause porosity or blowholes. These defects at the weld surface can cause part rejection, but moderate porosity near the center of the weld nugget usually is acceptable.

Inadequate Penetration. Except in aircraft-quality spot welding, limits of nugget penetration in welded parts are commonly not specified. Even for aircraft quality the range may be from 20 to 80%. Inadequate penetration results from too low a current density in the weld, perhaps from a malfunction or improper setting of the machine or other cause, such as mushroomed electrodes, partial shunt of welding current through adjacent welds, excess pressure or improper material.

The effect of inadequate current density was observed when a bench-type resistance spot welder was being used to

join two crossed wires by direct-current welding for an electronic assembly. The measured weld strength was 9 lb. After maintenance on the weld head, the cables to the electrodes were accidentally reversed and the subsequent welds showed a strength of 3 to 4½ lb. This was due to the effect of polarity in welding dissimilar metals with direct current. This effect can also be observed in very short-time welds (1 to 2 cycles) made with alternating current.

In another instance in which inadequate current density prevented satisfactory welding of a crossed-wire junction, a tinned-copper wire was to be welded to a nickel wire. The welding operation, in which power input was 25 watt-sec, was unsuccessful in producing a weld. Checking the wires for cleanness with emery paper revealed a copper color beneath the surfaces of both wires, and a hand magnet showed that both wires were nonmagnetic. Another tinned-copper wire had been accidentally substituted for the nickel wire; a power input of 65 watt-sec would have been necessary to weld together the two copper wires.

Insufficient current density resulted in inadequate joint penetration when three spot welds were made in attaching a small angle to a sheet; both the angle and the sheet were of cold rolled steel ¹⁄₁₆ in. thick. The spot welds were made ½ in. apart. However, welds 2 and 3 were often weak. AWS C1.1-66, Recommended Practices for Resistance Welding, provides a recommended minimum spacing of 1 in. between welds. Suspecting shunting as the cause of the weak welds, tests were performed, which showed that weld 1 was always good while welds 2 and 3, when made in that order, were both weak, because part of their current passed through the earlier made welds. Conversely, it was shown that if weld 3 was made after weld 1, they were both strong, whereas if weld 2 was made last, it was extremely weak. It was decided to eliminate weld 2 and use two welds 1 in. apart, which would minimize shunting, ensure adequate current density and provide two strong welds consistently.

Poor weld shape encompasses a variety of defects that may result from part configurations causing undersized nuggets that can lead to failure. Examples of these conditions include poor fits, inadequate flange width or contacting overlap, edge bulges, and cracks, burnthroughs, and distortion. In many such instances, the defects are often the result of carelessness on the part of the machine operator. Less frequently, the fault may be the result of an improper design, such as the insufficient flange width of the bracket shown in Fig. 37.

The bracket shown in Fig. 37 had been difficult to spot weld to the baseplate. The size of the welding electrode was determined by the bracket thickness, which required that the electrode be of a specific size that definitely related to the electrode-face diameter and to the electrode-shank diameter. The narrowing flange caused the electrode used to extend over the edge of the bracket, producing a bulge and crack at spot weld 2 and an unsound weld at position 3 because of metal expulsion. The operator could have selected a smaller-diameter electrode, but then the spot welds, although sound, would have been smaller and perhaps unable to carry the load on the bracket. The correct solution is either to redesign the bracket with a wider flange or to emboss the flange with projections to concentrate the current flow at proper distances from the flange edge.

Poor weld surfaces that can cause weld failure, usually because of unsatisfactory nugget formation, are often the result of poor machine operations or adjustments that lead to weld spatter, blowholes, electrode pickup or excessive indentation.

Cracks. Welds containing cracks usually result from overheating, improper loading during the welding cycle, or the use of welding programs that are unfavorable for crack-sensitive metals. Hot cracks are uncommon in resistance welding because the time at high temperature is so brief. Cold cracks may occur because the weld metal froze under insufficient pressure and therefore was forced to undergo thermal contraction relative to the surrounding matrix that demanded more deformation than the metal could tolerate. Such cracks weaken the weld considerably if they are at the weld rim but are innocuous if at the weld center. These cracks may be avoided by proper pressure control, especially by application of forging pressure at the end of the weld cycle.

Unfavorable fabrication procedures or inadequate bend radii sometimes cause cracks that propagate in parts to induce failures that can be confused with weld-crack failures. There is a clear need to determine the true crack origin before assigning the cause of failure in such circumstances. Water quenching during resistance seam welding can lead to quench cracks from martensite transformation and contraction stresses.

Inadequate Weld Properties. Conditions that affect nugget formation include surface coatings, preweld cleaning, electrode overlap, spot-weld-to-edge distance, sheet thickness, and wall thickness of embossed projections. Any variation in properties that influences the electrical resistance between the parts will influence the weld quality.

Intermittent weld failures can result from variations in surface conditions that are not machine controlled. Examples include the presence of rust or of die-casting flash or mold-release compound in layers of varying thickness. Careful surface cleaning and inspection before welding are the only preventatives.

Parts made of hardenable alloys may be hardened by the high heat and rapid quench of a typical resistance welding cycle. Such parts will be brittle and the welds can easily be broken unless they are tempered, either as an added portion of the weld cycle or in a separate operation outside the welding machine.

Examples. The next three examples describe failures of resistance welds. The first two involve spot welds in aluminum alloys (alclad 2024-T62, and 2024-T8511 joined to 6061-T62) that had weld nuggets of inadequate size because of problems in fit-up; in both instances, poor fit-up between the structural members prevented development of the proper welding current at the required location. In the third example, a seam weld in titanium alloy Ti-6Al-4V failed in fatigue because expulsion of weld metal created stress raisers along the edges of the weld.

Example 30. Failure of Resistance Spot Welds in an Alclad Aluminum Alloy 2024-T62 Aircraft Drop Tank Because of Poor Fit-Up

A series of resistance spot welds joining Z-shape and C-shape members of an aircraft drop-tank structure failed during ejection testing. The members were fabricated of alclad aluminum alloy 2024-T62. The back surface of the C-shape members showed severe electrode-indentation marks off to one side of the spot weld, suggesting improper electrode contact.

Investigation. Visual examination of the weld fractures showed that the weld nuggets varied considerably in size, some being very small and three exhibiting a heat-affected zone but no weld. Metallographic examination of sections through the spot welds indicated normal metallurgical structure with no sign of embrittlement. Three welds showed lack of penetration (the cladding being intact at the joint interface), and most of the welds were irregular in size and shape. Of 28 welds, only nine had acceptable nugget diameters and fusion-zone widths.

The weld deficiencies were traced to problems in forming and fit-up of the C-shape members and to difficulties in alignment and positioning of the weld tooling. In particular, the marks on the backs of the C-shape members were due to curvature of the faying surface that interfered with electrode contact at the correct point. It was evident that the lack of precise electrode alignment created an unfavorably long current path, reducing the heat input at the weld and the size of the nugget.

Conclusions. The failure of the resistance spot welds was attributed to poor weld quality caused by unfavorable fit-up and lack of proper weld-tool positioning.

Recommendation. The problem could be solved by better forming procedures to provide an accurate fit-up that would not interfere with electrode alignment.

Example 31. Failure of Resistance Spot Welds Joining Aluminum Alloy 2024-T8511 Stiffeners to the 6061-T62 Skin of an Aircraft Drop Tank, Because of Poor Fit-Up

Resistance spot welds joining aluminum alloy 2024-T8511 stiffeners to the aluminum alloy 6061-T62 skin of an aircraft drop tank failed during slosh and vibration testing.

Investigation. Visual examination of the fracture surfaces showed that the failure was by tensile or bending overload, which was subsequently confirmed by TEM investigation. Measurements of the diameter of fractured spot welds established that all welds were below specification size, which indicated that the joints had lower-than-required strength. Review of the assembly procedures revealed that there had been poor fit-up between the stiffeners and the tank skin, which probably caused shunting of the welding current and resulted in weak, undersize weld nuggets.

Conclusions. The spot welds failed because of undersize nuggets that were the result of shunting caused by poor fit-up.

Corrective Measures. The forming procedures were revised to achieve a precise fit between the stiffener and the tank wall. Also, an increase in welding current was suggested.

Example 32. Crack in a Resistance Seam Weld in a Titanium Alloy Ti-6Al-4V Stator Vane Because of Metal Expulsion That Caused Fatigue

A fluorescent-liquid-penetrant inspection of an experimental stator vane of a first-stage axial compressor revealed the presence of a longitudinal crack over 2 in. long at the edge of a resistance seam weld. The vane was made of titanium alloy Ti-6Al-4V (AMS 4911).

Investigation. The crack was opened by fracturing the vane. The crack surface displayed fatigue beach marks emanating from multiple origins at the inside surface of the vane at the seam-weld interface. Both the leading-edge and trailing-edge seam welds exhibited weld-metal expulsions up to 0.14 in. in length. Metallographic examination of transverse sections taken through the main fatigue origin and at other random points confirmed that metal expulsion from the resistance welds was generally present. The surface imperfections created by the metal expulsion provided points of stress concentration that lowered the fatigue strength and led to failure in experimental testing.

Conclusions. The stator vane failed by a fatigue crack that initiated at internal surface discontinuities caused by metal expulsion from the resistance seam weld used in fabricating the vane.

Recommendations. Expulsion of metal from seam welds should be eliminated by a slight reduction in welding current to reduce the temperature or by an increase in the electrode force, or both.

Failure Origins in Flash Welds

Flash welding is a variation of resistance welding, in which arcing (flashing) is employed to supply the major portion of the initial heat for the formation of a butt weld. The techniques of flash welding are described in the article that begins on page 485 in Volume 6 of this Handbook. A general discussion of the causes and prevention of defects in flash welds is presented on pages 504 to 505 in that article. Some characteristics of flash welds that may lead to failure are described below.

Poor Surface Conditions. Preweld cleaning of the workpieces at the die-contact area is important to ensure proper current flow and prevent local overheating of the workpiece surface. No surface coating (plated metal, conversion coating or anodized coating) should be present before welding, because it will result in weld-area contamination or die burns. Oxides and foreign particles can cause small pits in the surface as they overheat and burn into the workpiece.

Inclusions. During the flashing action, craters are formed that contain molten metal and possibly oxides. If the energy input that produces the flashing is properly controlled, these oxides should be expelled with the flashing molten-metal particles that give the process its name. When the upsetting force is then applied, most of the impurities not expelled by the flashing will be expelled with plastic upset metal. Any nonmetallics that are not expelled usually remain at the fusion line with little apparent depth back into the base metal on either side. Most static and fatigue failures that occur in flash welds originate at such discontinuities. These discontinuities normally have little effect on static strength, but can measurably produce fatigue life. Excessive energy input and insufficient upsetting force or travel speed are the most common causes of such inclusions.

An example of failure of a flash welded joint attributed to the presence of nonmetallic inclusions is the fracture surface of an aircraft arresting-hook stinger shown in Fig. 38. This stinger, which was fabricated of 300M steel with a tensile strength of 280,000 to 305,000 psi, was one of several that failed at flash welded joints during proof loading. The light-colored radial lines visible in the fracture surface in Fig. 38 are nonmetallic impurities that penetrated the fusion line and that were not completely expelled during the upsetting action following flashing. Further occurrence of these inclusions, which were identified as manganese silicate stringers, was eliminated by changing the protective atmosphere from natural gas to propane, to provide a greater deoxidizing potential, and by increasing the upset pressure and reducing the rate of energy input.

Porosity. Insufficient upsetting force or travel may leave porous areas of cast metal in the weld. Excessive electrical energy input can also lead to porosity by the formation of large craters by the expulsion of molten metal. Where large-

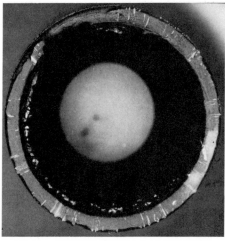

Fig. 38. Fracture surface, at ½×, of a failed flash welded joint in an arresting-hook stinger of 300M steel, showing light-colored radial manganese silicate inclusions

diameter pieces are to be joined, one end face should be slightly chamfered so as to start the flashing at the center of the cross section. This helps to avoid trapping of particles in the weld.

Incomplete Fusion. Inadequate heating will result in incomplete fusion, but it may also result from an upsetting travel that is so slow that the metal does not become sufficiently plastic to forge properly during upsetting. Another cause of inadequate heating can be the shunting of electrical current around the closed side of a ring to be flash welded; sufficient current may be by-passed to make flashing difficult, even resulting in a melt-through of the closed side of the ring.

Poor Weld Contours. Whenever heating is not uniform over the intended joint, an unfavorable temperature gradient is established, which contributes to misalignment after welding. If parts are not properly aligned by the dies, they may slip past each other during upsetting, creating a lap instead of a proper weld. Workpieces of different cross sections that have not been adjusted in design to achieve a good heat balance (such as tubes of different diameters or wall thickness) may slide (telescope) over each other and create a poor-quality weld.

The internal flash and upset metal formed in flash welding of tubes or pipe are normally not removed (often, they cannot be), which leaves a reinforcement with two sharp notches adjacent to the fusion line. These notches act as stress raisers that, under cyclic loading, will reduce the fatigue strength. They also restrict fluid flow and can serve as concentration-cell sites for corrosion.

Hot Cracks. Alloys that possess low ductility over a temperature range below the melting point may be susceptible to hot cracking. Such "hot short" alloys are

more difficult to flash weld, but usually can be welded if the most favorable welding conditions are selected. Tension obviously should be avoided, and because the rim of the upset metal is in circumferential tension as upsetting progresses, it may be essential to keep the upsetting force to the minimum acceptable. In such an operation, some cracks are likely to form that are shallow enough to allow complete removal when the upset metal is machined away. Precise coordination of current cessation and upsetting travel are important, and the joint should be under moderate compression during cooling.

Cold Cracks. Insufficient heat during upsetting or excessive upsetting travel causes colder metal to be forced into the weld zone. The metal will crack transversely to the weld line in the upset zone. This effect is also encountered in the flash welding of hardenable steels, because of the mass quench provided by the remainder of the workpiece. The use of a slow cooling rate, and heat treatment following welding, will alleviate transformation stresses that could cause cracking under service loads.

Failure Origins in Upset Butt Welds

Upset resistance butt welding is similar to flash welding but is less widely used. Advantages of resistance butt welding are (a) there is little weld spatter, because there is no flashing; (b) less metal is used in the weld upset; and (c) the upset is usually smooth and symmetrical, although it may be pronounced. Upset butt welding is used in joining small ferrous and nonferrous strips, wires, tubes and pipes end to end.

Because there is no flashing of abutting workpieces, joint preparation for upset butt welding is more critical than for flash welding. Shearing to provide clean, flat, parallel ends is the usual procedure for small parts and wires. Beveled or other special shapes (such as spherical) are used to restrict the area of initial contact in butt welding larger parts, especially if they have oxidized ends. Wires are sometimes pinch cut in wedge shapes and the opposing ends rotated 90°.

Unlike a flash weld, for which the proper upset slope is 45° to 80°, the slope of the burr of an upset butt weld is normally 80° to 90°, quite thin, and often split into two, three, or even four petal-shaped segments (see Fig. 39); the burr diameter should be at least twice the wire diameter. A split burr with a diameter three to four times the wire diameter is a better burr. The burr can be easily removed by hand or by cutting pliers.

Causes and suggested remedies or preventive measures for several problems that may be encountered in upset butt welding are listed in Table 27.6, page

27.31, Section Two, Chapter 27 of The AWS Welding Handbook, 6th Edition.

In the example that follows, two problems in upset butt welding hardenable high-carbon steel wire made it necessary to alter procedure and design to meet requirements.

Example 33. Failures of Upset Butt Welds in Hardenable High-Carbon Steel Wire Because of Martensite Formation and Poor Wire-End Preparation (Fig. 40)

Extra-high-strength zinc-coated 1080 steel welded wire, 0.080 ± 0.003 in. in diameter, was wound into seven-wire cable strands 0.240 ± 0.006 in. in diameter for use in self-supporting aerial cables and guy wires. The wires and cable strands failed to meet tensile, elongation and wrap tests, with wires fracturing near welds at 2.5 to 3.5% elongation and through the welded joints in wrap tests. The property requirements, a modification of ASTM A475, included: (a) 6650-lb minimum tensile strength for the strand, with or without a weld in one wire, one joint allowed per 150 ft; (b) 1000-lb minimum tensile strength for the wire; (c) 4% minimum elongation in 24 in. for a strand without welds, 3.5% for a strand with one weld; and (d) no fracture of an individual wire with or without a weld when wrapped in a close helix of at least five turns at a rate not exceeding 15 turns per minute around a ⁵⁄₁₆-in.-diam cylindrical mandrel.

The welded wire was annealed by resistance heating with a 3-kva transformer and control separate from the welding transformer. The wire was clamped in annealing jaws that were 36 in. apart (outside the upset jaws), and the automatic cycle included six pulses of 3 sec on and 5 sec off. The wire ends had a chisel shape, produced by the use of sidecutters, as shown in Fig. 40(a).

Investigation. Tests of wire and weld properties gave the following values:

Wire condition	Tensile strength, lb	Elongation in 24 in., %
Unwelded, as received .	1115-1125	4.5
Welded:		
As welded	250	0
Heat treated	454-496	4.0-9.5
Heated at		
80% voltage	494	3.0
Heated at		
88% voltage	510	0.5-1.5

Tests of the heat treatment temperatures showed that the wire exceeded 774 C (1425 F) at a point 12 in. from the weld area. Metallographic examination revealed that there was martensite present in the weld area even after the heat treatment. The wrap test was being poorly applied, with the wire and mandrel gripped together in a vise and wrapping done with pliers; this subjected the wire to variations in magnitude and type of load as well as of speed of wrap. The weld burrs were excessive, cracked and poorly formed, as shown in Fig. 40(a).

At this stage, the manufacturer changed the specified steel from 1080 to 1055 and increased the minimum tensile strength for individual wires (unwelded) from 1000 to 1150 lb. Although this single-wire strength was more stringent, it meant that the 6650-lb

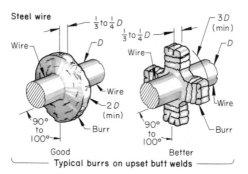

Fig. 39. Upset butt welded steel wires, showing typical acceptable burrs on the butt welds

strand-strength requirement could be met even if one wire broke prematurely. Tests were undertaken to determine the appropriate postweld heat treatment, using a resistance heating setup employing a 7.5-kva transformer equipped with digital time controls from 1.0 to 9.9 sec and digital heat control from 10 to 99%. Heat-sensitive crayons and a hot-wire pyrometer were used to measure wire temperature. The effects of heat treatment time and temperature on room-temperature tensile strength and elongation were as follows:

Wire condition	Tensile strength, lb	Elongation in 10 in., %
Unwelded (as received) ..	1160	5.0
Welded:		
As welded	250	0
Resistance heated (a):		
3-5 sec at 1100 F	785-980	1.0-2.0
6.2-6.5 sec at 1100 F ..	640-665	1.8-2.0
7-8 sec at 1200 F	525-555	3.0-8.0
7.7-8.2 sec at 1300 F ..	514-540	9.0-12.5
7.9-8.4 sec at 1300 F..	548-555	5.5-11.5
8.5-9.3 sec at 1400 F ..	540-546	9.0-12.5
9.3-9.5 sec at 1400 F ..	520	9.2-9.8
9.7-9.8 sec at 1450 F ..	520-530	8.5-12.5

(a) 1055 steel heated for adequate time at 1120-1240 F should undergo stress relief; at 1240-1340 F, spheroidization; at 1340-1410 F, transformation to austenite; and at 1410-1475 F, full annealing.

The outcome of the tests was that the welds were brittle unless they were heated at high enough temperatures to undergo transformation to austenite. Although the heat treatment at 1400 F (760 C) did not eliminate all martensite, it did produce enough ductility so that the weld could satisfactorily pass the wrap test.

Conclusions. The test failures of the 1080 steel wire butt welded joints were due to martensite produced in cooling from the welding operation that was not tempered adequately in postweld heat treatment and to poor wire-end preparation for welding that produced poorly formed weld burrs. The heat treatment of the 1055 steel welds that produced transformation to austenite was successful in minimizing the martensite content sufficiently for the welds to pass the wrap test.

Corrective Measures. The postweld heat treatment was standardized on the 1400 F (760 C) transformation treatment to obtain consistent tensile strengths of about 540 lb and elongations above 8%. In addition, the shape of the wire ends, which was a chisel shape produced by the use of sidecutters, was abandoned in favor of flat, filed ends

(see Fig. 40b), to make the weld heating more uniform and improve the alignment. The jaw spacing was reduced to half of the initial opening, which further improved the alignment, reduced the amount of upset (thereby improving the shape of the burr), and decreased the time at weld heat. The wrap test was improved by adopting a hand-cranked device that made it possible to conduct the wrapping about the mandrel at a uniform speed and load. Under these conditions the welded joints withstood the tensile and wrap tests.

Failure Origins in Friction Welds

Welding by the direct conversion of mechanical energy to thermal energy at the interface of the workpieces without heat from other sources is called friction welding. A detailed description of friction welding is given on pages 507 to 518 in Volume 6 of this Handbook. The types of defects that may lead to failure of friction welds are described below.

Center Defects. A small unwelded area that can occur in friction (inertia) welding at the center of the interface of the workpieces is called a center defect. It can range from 0.010 to 0.250 in. in diameter, depending on the size of the workpiece. Center defects are more common in low-carbon and medium-carbon steels than in high-carbon or strong alloy steels. Their cause is insufficient friction at the center of the interface, giving rise to heat generation that is inadequate to achieve a complete weld. An increase in peripheral velocity or a decrease in axial pressure will avoid creation of a

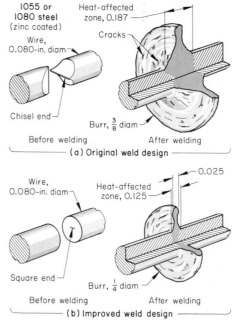

Fig. 40. Wire-end preparation for upset butt welding that was changed from (a) chisel end to (b) square end to eliminate test failures in welded zinc-coated 1080 or 1055 steel wire (Example 33)

center defect. Another remedy is to provide either a center projection or a slight chamfer to one of the workpieces.

Restraint Cracks. A type of crack that is most commonly encountered in friction welding a bar to a larger bar or plate is called a restraint crack. This type of crack, which is usually observed in medium-carbon, high-carbon and alloy steels, occurs during cooling and is caused by thermal stresses, particularly if the heat-affected zone is thicker at the center than at the periphery. Decreasing the peripheral velocity or increasing the axial pressure to gain a thinner heat-affected zone at the center will eliminate this type of crack, but care must be exercised to avoid overcompensation, which would create a center defect.

Weld-Interface Carbides. Carbide particles may be present in a friction weld interface in tool steels or heat-resisting alloys. In both metals, the particles impair weld strength. If a friction weld of tool steel is fractured, circumferential shiny spots will be seen in the weld interface. The formation of these spots is attributed to the lack of adequate time and temperature of the process to take the carbide particles into solution. In welding of heat-resisting alloys, precipitation of carbide particles at the interface at welding temperature can be prevented by increasing the amount of upset.

Poor Weld Cleanup. If the exterior surface of a friction weld does not clean up completely in machining to final diameter, it is the result of hot tearing at or near the surface. In ferrous metals, this usually happens when welding two alloys of different forgeability. The best procedure to avoid this is to increase the section size of the workpiece that has the

better forgeability. If the workpieces must be of the same size, an increase in surface velocity and in axial pressure will be helpful. For instance, in welding of a low-alloy steel engine-valve stem to a heat-resisting alloy head (using the flywheel method) a stepped pressure cycle has proved useful. The second pressure is applied at the end of the weld cycle to stop the flywheel rapidly, thereby eliminating the hot tearing.

In friction welding of nonferrous alloys, poor weld cleanup is usually because of hot tearing at the back edge of the heat-affected zone, especially in copper alloys. This is because the maximum torque generated as the surface velocity approaches zero becomes too much for the metal to resist. An increase in speed will help avoid this condition. For aluminum alloys, an increase in speed plus an increase in axial pressure will normally eliminate such hot tearing.

Hot-Shortness Cracks. Brittleness in the hot-forging temperature range requires special precautions if friction welds free of hot-shortness cracks are to be made in a hot short metal. The welding conditions must be adjusted to keep the weld temperature to a minimum, using high axial pressures and very low surface velocities.

Trapped oxide occurs occasionally. Oxide entrapment is usually caused by a concave initial weld interface or a remnant of a hole for a machine center in one or both workpieces. As welding starts, the pieces will behave like tubes, with flash flowing inward toward the axis. In normal circumstances, the trapped air will not be able to escape and will remain either under pressure as gas pores or combined with the metal as

oxide and nitride. If pieces with machine-center holes must be used, the cavities should be large enough so that the air is not compressed more than 90%. Concave surfaces should be avoided.

Porosity. If cast workpieces that contain shrinkage or gas porosity at or near the weld interface are friction welded, the porosity will normally be evident in the final interface. These defects will usually be gray or black but will differ in appearance from center defects, which have a metallic appearance. Porosity cannot be eliminated, but careful inspection of the workpieces will reveal the defect.

Failure Origins in Electron Beam Welds

Electron beam welding (vacuum and nonvacuum) is used to weld essentially any metal that can be arc welded, and the weld quality in most metals is either equivalent to or better than that achieved in the best gas tungsten-arc or plasma-arc welding. The advantages of vacuum electron beam welding include the capability of making deeper, narrower and less tapered welds with less total heat input than is possible with arc welding, and a superior control of depth of penetration and other weld dimensions and properties. The vacuum and nonvacuum electron beam welding processes are discussed in detail on pages 519 to 564 in Volume 6 of this Handbook. Defects that may cause difficulties in electron beam welds are described below.

Inclusions are minimal in vacuum electron beam welds, because of the protection from oxidation and because many impurities are vaporized at high temperature and very low pressure. If foreign metal is inadvertently positioned in the path of the electron beam, it will be added to the melt in a dispersed form. If this occurs, that portion of the weld should be gouged out and rewelded.

Porosity. Electron beam welds are particularly susceptible to the formation of porosity resulting from the release of gases dissolved or trapped in the base metal, or from impurities remaining on the metal surface because of inadequate cleaning. To a limited extent, welding conditions such as the power input can influence the degree of porosity created. In the welding of carbon steels, for example, aluminum-killed or silicon-killed grades should be selected to minimize internal porosity. The porosity that can occur in an electron beam weld in a rimmed low-carbon steel is illustrated in Fig. 41(a). The material was 1010 steel welded at a speed of 60 in. per min at 150 kva with a current of 4.3 ma.

An unusual variety of porosity called "massive voids" is sometimes found in electron beam welded joints that are thicker than 1 in. These cavities are simi-

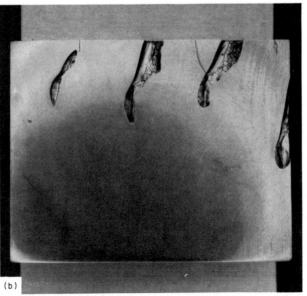

Fig. 41. Gas porosity in electron beam welds of low-carbon steel and titanium alloy. (a) Micrograph, at 30×, of a specimen etched in 5% nital, showing gas porosity in a weld in rimmed 1010 low-carbon steel. (b) Macrograph, at 1.2×, showing massive voids in weld centerline of 2-in.-thick titanium alloy Ti-6Al-4V.

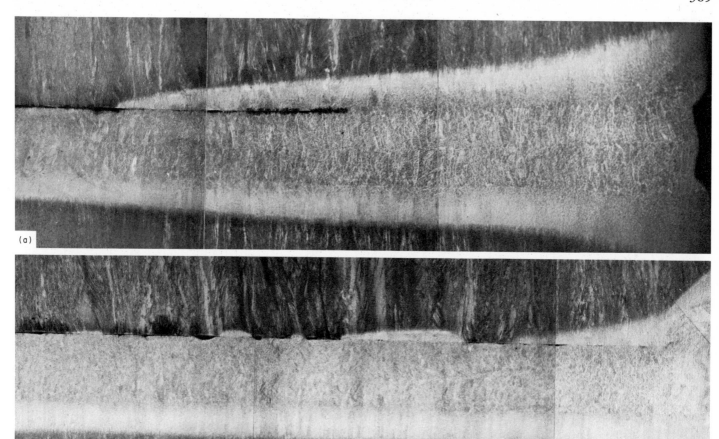

Fig. 42. Macrographs, at about 13×, of sections through electron beam welds in titanium alloy Ti-6Al-4V, showing two types of "missed seam" defects: (a) angular misalignment and (b) position misalignment. Tops of welds are at right.

lar to wormhole porosity in steel and may result from gas evolution from the base metal during welding, or from the presence of an inverted V-shape gap in the joint prior to final welding. This inverted V-shape (joint edges in contact at weld-face surface, separated by perhaps 0.03 in. at root surface) may be caused by poor fit-up or may be produced when partial-penetration tack welds or locking passes are used before full-penetration passes in 2-in.-thick material. The appearance of massive voids in a centerline section of an electron beam weld in 2-in.-thick titanium alloy Ti-6Al-4V is shown in Fig. 41(b). These defects are readily detected by x-ray inspection. Corrective measures to avoid their occurrence include more careful check of joint fit-up and the procedures cited above for general porosity.

Incomplete fusion and inadequate penetration are caused either by insufficient power input or by misalignment between the electron beam and the seam. Such a defect may be eliminated by re-welding the area with increased power or a more accurate alignment. Two types of "missed seam" defects are shown in Fig. 42, one being an angular misalignment (Fig. 42a) and the other a beam parallel to the seam but with its position displaced sufficiently to one side to miss the seam (Fig. 42b).

A different type of incomplete-fusion defect, called spiking, is often associated with the irregularly shaped melting pattern at the root of a partial-penetration electron beam weld. Labels such as "cold shuts", "root porosity" and "necklace porosity" have been used for defects of this type. They are typically conical in shape and appear similar to linear porosity when examined radiographically in a direction parallel to the electron orientation. They thus have the characteristics of solidification and shrinkage defects in the weld root at the tips of a portion of the spikes. An illustration of spiking that occurred in a 3-in.-thick

Fig. 43. Macrograph, at 1.6×, showing a spiking defect in a centerline section at the root of a partial-penetration electron beam weld in 3-in.-thick titanium alloy Ti-6Al-4V plate

titanium alloy Ti-6Al-4V plate is shown in Fig. 43. A sound weld existed to a depth of 2.15 in. below the weld face.

The peak-to-valley depths can vary over a wide range, depending on the welding conditions employed; sometimes these depths can amount to 25% of the depth of penetration.

The primary procedure for preventing spiking is to defocus the beam so that beam crossover is near the surface instead of being buried 1½ in. deep in the metal. Also helpful is a reduction in travel speed, to aid fusion of the root spike. Usually, the depth of a partial-penetration pass in titanium alloys cannot exceed 1⅜ in. without the occurrence of some spiking, although the exact depth is a function of the capability of the equipment.

The example that follows describes a fatigue failure of an electron beam weld that initiated at an area of incomplete fusion.

Example 34. Fatigue Fracture of an Electron Beam Weld in the Web of a 9310 Steel Gear Because of Incomplete Fusion (Fig. 44)

A 9310 steel gear was found to be defective after an unstated period of engine service. A linear crack approximately 1 in. long was discovered by routine magnetic-particle inspection of an electron beam

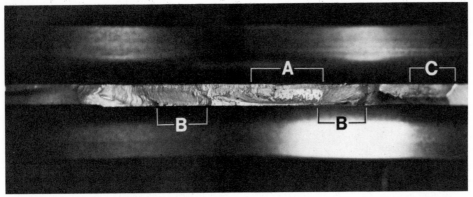

Fig. 44. Fracture surface, at 2×, of an electron beam weld in web of a 9310 steel gear; weld fractured by fatigue because of incomplete fusion. At A is incomplete-fusion zone where primary fracture originated; zones at B's show fatigue beach marks; area at C exhibits bending-fatigue patterns. Root of weld is at bottom surface. (Example 34)

welded joint that attached a hollow stub shaft to the web of the gear. The shaft had a step 0.10 in. wide and 2 in. in diameter, which was about ¾ in. larger than the outside diameter of the shaft. Thus, the joint in the web was circumferential, about 2 in. in diameter and with a butt-joint thickness of 0.10 in. The assembly procedure permitted a variation in diameter between an interference of 0.001 in. and a clearance of 0.002 in. In setting up the welding procedure, it had been necessary to apply a cosmetic weld pass on top of the initial full-penetration weld. Gears were welded by this method over a period of several years with no other known service failure. Magnetic-particle and radiographic inspection were employed on a routine basis.

Investigation. The crack in the gear web was opened and the fracture surface, which is shown in Fig. 44, was examined. One zone of the welded joint showed incomplete fusion; this zone is shown at A in Fig. 44. Surrounding the incomplete-fusion zone were two zones containing fatigue beach marks (at B's in Fig. 44), which indicated that the incomplete-fusion zone was the site at which primary fracture originated. Secondary fatigue patterns that originated on both surfaces of the gear web were evident in several small areas; one of these areas is at C in Fig. 44. These were interpreted as indicating bending fatigue.

The composition, microstructure and hardness of the gear were as specified. The design was adequate because it was known that the service stresses in the weld joint region were low.

Review of the conditions of failure suggested that this particular gear assembly contained an interference fit prior to welding. The possible causes of the incomplete-fusion defect include: (a) localized magnetic deflection of the electron beam, (b) a momentary "arc-out" of the electron beam, and (c) eccentricity in the small weld diameter. Failure to detect the defect in final inspection in the shop probably occurred because interference fits may not be revealed by radiography and because the cosmetic weld pass may have covered the weld face sufficiently to have prevented detection by magnetic-particle inspection.

Conclusions. The failure was attributed to fatigue originating at the local unfused interface of the electron beam weld, which had

been the result of a deviation in the welding procedure.

Careful examination of the possible causes of failure gave no evidence that a recurrence of the defect had ever occurred. Thus there appeared to be no basis on which to recommend a change in design, material or welding procedure.

Poor Weld Contours. Poor contours of the face of the weld in electron beam welds may be improved by using cosmetic weld passes (see page 521 in Volume 6 of this Handbook). Relatively poor root-surface contours are inherent in the process at the beam exit, especially as base-metal thickness is increased. Thin sections (less than 0.15 in. thick) may be welded by partial penetration of the thickness, which entirely avoids the rough root side at the beam exit of a full-penetration weld.

Hot Cracks. Craters and crater cracks are typically produced in weld-stop areas

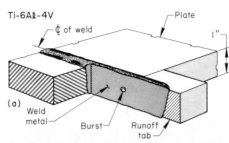

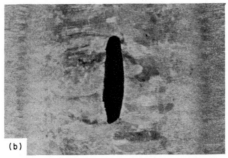

Fig. 45. (a) Shape, location and appearance of a burst in an electron beam butt weld. (b) Macrograph, at 20×, of a cross-section of a burst in a weld in a titanium alloy Ti-6Al-4V plate.

on full-penetration passes. Use of runoff tabs or procedures for slope-down and pull-out of the beam are helpful in solving this problem.

Hot cracks in the weld may mean that the base-metal alloy is not weldable (because of its metallurgical structure) or that a foreign metal has contaminated the melt. The use of filler metal (skin stock) to provide weld metal that is less brittle than the base metal (or metals) can prevent cracking; this is especially helpful in joining dissimilar metals if a filler metal is chosen that has a composition that is compatible with both members of the joint.

In welding some materials, such as the heat treatable aluminum alloys, the grain direction of the base metal relative to the weld can affect the susceptibility to cracking and should be critically reviewed when planning welding. Welds made or stressed in the short-transverse direction, for instance, often show a tendency to develop grain-boundary microcracks in the heat-affected zone.

Bursts. A disc-shaped solidification defect that occurs at the electron beam weld centerline is called a burst. It is usually found near a change in mass — for instance, near corners or near adjacent lugs or stiffeners. Figure 45(a) shows the shape, location and appearance of a burst and Fig. 45(b) shows the defect in the last part of the weld to freeze (that is, the portion at centerline and near the end).

A typical burst in a 1-in.-thick joint has a length (in the weld direction) of 0.050 to 0.125 in., a height (in the direction of the joint thickness) that is comparable to the length, and a thickness (maximum dimension transverse to weld direction) of approximately 0.010 to 0.015 in. Occasionally, burst lengths to 1 in. have occurred. Bursts can be prevented by reducing the travel speed as the beam nears the change in mass, or by welding on the runoff tabs to reduce the change in mass.

Failure Origins in Laser Beam Welds

Laser beam welding is used principally in the electronics industry. Welds are used to join wire to wire, wire to sheet, tube to sheet, and for stud welding. Principles, applications, equipment, cutting and safety practices of laser beam welding are discussed on pages 55.4 to 55.20 in Section 3B, Chapter 55 of the AWS Welding Handbook, 6th Edition. Several defects that may cause difficulties in laser beam welding are described below.

Inclusions. Because the laser equipment itself does not contact the workpieces, the presence of any inclusions that could affect the quality of a laser beam weld would be due to foreign materials either on the surface or within the structure of the metals being joined. In most instances, any foreign substances on the workpiece surfaces are vaporized by the high heat of welding. Careful selection, cleaning and preparation of materials are the best means of minimizing failures from inclusions of any type.

Porosity. Because the power levels delivered by laser beams are difficult to measure accurately, weld pulse-time schedules must be very carefully developed to avoid the formation of voids and porosity. If energy is delivered too rapidly, there will not be time for heat conduction to the interior of the joint and vaporization may occur. For the same reason, variations in pulse time and energy can be a cause of porosity. Cleanness of workpiece surfaces and avoidance of low-boiling alloy constituents, such as zinc, are important in minimizing voids.

Inadequate Penetration. Generally, the penetration that can be achieved with a laser beam increases with the square root of the available pulse time and of the thermal diffusivity of the metal being welded. But at the same time, high surface reflectivity may be a cause of reduced energy input and inadequate penetration. Simply raising the energy level to compensate for high reflectivity may exceed the intensity limits and produce vaporization and holes. One technique to overcome this difficulty is to apply a suitable thin absorptive coating (such as an anodize or black oxide) that will decrease the surface reflection without affecting the metallurgy of the weld. Sometimes, metal surfaces can be roughened to obtain lower reflectivity. An ideal technique when the workpiece shape permits, however, is to arrange the surfaces to be joined so that the weld is in a crevice or hole that can act as a black body, which is a perfect absorber. Here, the high reflectivity is actually an advantage, guaranteeing that melting will occur only at the intended area.

The example that follows illustrates the effect of inadequate penetration on the strength of a laser beam attachment weld.

Example 35. Failure of a Laser Beam Attachment Weld Because of Inadequate Penetration in Joint Between Hastelloy X Cooling Components for a Jet Turbine Blade (Fig. 46)

Airfoil-shape impingement cooling tubes were fabricated of 0.010-in.-thick Hastelloy X sheet stock and then were pulsed laser beam butt welded to cast Hastelloy X base plugs. Each weldment was then inserted through the base of a hollow cast turbine blade for a jet engine. The weldments were finally secured to the bases of the turbine blades by a brazing operation. At operating speed, the centrifugal force exerted on the welded joint was 30,000 psi at a temperature of approximately 595 C (1100 F). One of the laser beam attachment welds broke after a 28-hr engine test run.

Investigation. Exposure of the fracture surface for study under the electron microscope revealed that the joint had broken in stress rupture, the fracture surface indicating a ductile tensile fracture. A metallographic section taken through an unfailed area of the weld disclosed that penetration at the weld root had been clearly inadequate, creating a sharp notch that was a severe stress raiser (see Fig. 46a). A second section, through the fracture, shows in

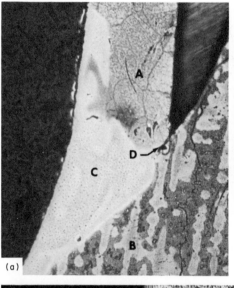
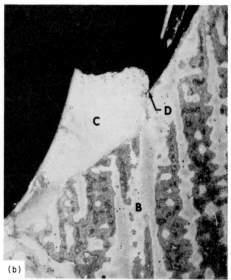
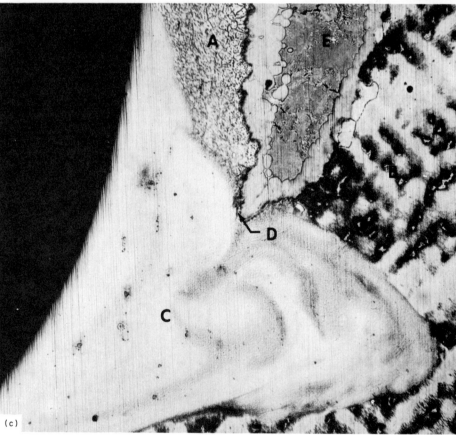

(a) Unfailed portion of weld, C, joining cooling tube, A, to base plug, B; notch caused by inadequate penetration is at D. Magnification, 100×. (b) Profile of stress-rupture fracture following upper margin of fusion zone of weld, C. The sharp notch between the tube wall and the base plug, B, where the crack started, is shown at D. Magnification, 100×. (c) Laser beam weldment that has been back brazed. The tube wall is at A, the base plug at B, the laser weld at C, the initial notch at the weld root at D, and the brazing alloy at E. Magnification, 170×.

Fig. 46. Micrographs of sections through a fractured laser beam attachment weld joining a Hastelloy X cooling tube to a cast Hastelloy X base plug. The weld fractured by stress rupture from tensile overload, which resulted from stress concentrations at a notch left by inadequate joint penetration. (Example 35)

Fig. 46(b) that the fracture initiated at the sharp notch and propagated outward through the cooling-tube wall, following the edge of the weld fusion zone.

Although the turbine blades were 100% radiographically inspected prior to engine assembly, the sharp root notch (D in Fig. 46a) was not detected, possibly because of less-than-optimum orientation of the x-ray beam. After the failure occurred, several other tubes were radiographed with improved orientation of the x-ray beam, which revealed the presence of discontinuities at similar locations.

Conclusions. Failure was caused by tensile overload from stress concentration at the root of the laser beam weld, which was caused by the sharp notch created by the lack of full weld penetration.

Corrective Measures. Careful radiographic inspection of all cooling-tube weldments was made mandatory, with rejection stipulated for any joints containing subsurface weld-root notches. In addition, all turbine blades containing cooling-tube weldments were reprocessed by back-brazing in vacuum at 985 C (1800 F) using a small hairpin preform of an 82Au-18Ni alloy. This preform could easily be preplaced through the small cooling holes in the base of the turbine blade and was chosen for its excellent oxidation resistance and strength at the 595 C (1100 F) service temperature. The bond between the back braze, the cooling tube, the weld and the base plug is shown in Fig. 46(c) in the region of the weld root. The turbine blades that had been back brazed were reinstalled in the engine and withstood the full 150-hr model test run without incident.

The back-brazing operation was incorporated into the procedure to fill any notches that might be undetected, as well as to provide a small internal fillet, thus reducing the stress concentration.

Poor Weld Shape. The most favorable joint configuration for laser beam welding is probably the lap joint, although sound welds also can be made with other types of joints. In any configuration, the important factors are process variations, because these have a definite influence on weld quality. At the desired laser energy output, for example, a 10% change in output produces a 4% change in weld strength. Focusing distance is likewise important to weld strength. For a 2-in. focal length, variations in position of up to ±0.05 in. will still produce acceptable welds. Even though no separation between wires in a lap joint is recommended, some degree of separation can be tolerated.

Poor welds may also be caused by variations in alignment of the axis of the joint with respect to the axis of the laser beam; weld failures may thus be attributed to the use of fixtures that were

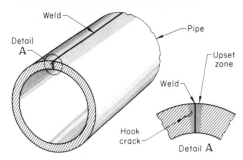

Fig. 47. Schematic representation of a hook crack in a pipe caused by pipe-wall delamination after high-frequency welding. "Hook" has turned outward to follow direction of metal flow in outer portion of upset at weld zone.

inadequate to position and hold the workpieces with the necessary precision.

A further factor influencing weld shape and weld strength is the environment in which the laser functions. The laser beam will be modified by any condition that will absorb radiant energy, such as smoke, weld spatter, water vapor or condensates on the ruby, lens or mirror surfaces of the equipment. Clean deionized cooling water through the optical cavity, dry nitrogen gas flow through the laser chamber, an exhaust fan for the welding chamber, and regular replacement of the glass slide over the objective lens all represent desirable procedures to maintain constant laser beam input energy to the weld joint.

Base-Metal Cracking. When laser beam energy is put into the weld at too high a rate the surface may not only suffer from vaporization, but also base-metal cracking may occur from thermal shock. This relates to the limitations of thickness that can be welded, which in turn depend on the thermal properties of the metal, its vaporization characteristics and reflectivity. Generally, longer pulse times are needed to weld the lower thermal conductivity metals and higher pulse-energy densities are necessary in welding high-reflectivity and high-melting-point alloys. The need for precisely developed weld schedules and controls is therefore apparent.

Failure Origins in High-Frequency Induction Welds

Pipes for high-pressure service, pipes for well casings, and structural beams have been welded by the high-frequency induction process. This process is described in Section 3A, Chapter 45 of the AWS Welding Handbook, 6th Edition.

"Hook cracks" are a type of discontinuity associated with these welds. They are difficult to detect and require extremely careful inspection for assurance that they are not present.

Delamination of the pipe wall just outside of the narrow weld zone can be the cause of hook cracks. The slight upset of the metal at the weld acts to turn the ends of these usually very small subsurface cracks in the direction of the metal flow, as shown in Fig. 47. Because the metal flow of the upset is toward both surfaces, the "hook" of the hook crack may turn toward either the outside or the inside surface depending on which is closer to the delamination, and in which direction the greatest amount of upset occurs. Generally, upset is greater toward the outer surface, thus causing hooking to turn outward.

Use of the cleanest steel available and the lowest possible heat input will greatly reduce the possibility of hook cracks.

References

1. J. J. Vagi, R. P. Meister and M. D. Randall, "Weldment Evaluation Methods", DMIC Report 244, Defense Metals Information Center, Battelle Memorial Institute, Columbus, Ohio, Aug 1968
2. F. Coe, "Welding Steels Without Hydrogen Cracking", British Welding Institute, 1973
3. D. J. Carney, Gases in Liquid Iron and Steel, p 69-118 in "Gases in Metals", American Society for Metals, Metals Park, Ohio, 1953
4. M. A. Pugacz, G. J. Siegel and J. O. Mack, The Effect of Postheat in Welding Medium-Alloy Steels, *Welding J Res Supp,* Oct 1944
5. R. V. Phillips and S. M. Marynick, Brittle Fracture of Steel Pipeline Analyzed, Civil Engineering, American Society of Civil Engineers, July 1972, p 70-74
6. "Aluminum Welder's Training Manual and Exercises", The Aluminum Association, New York, 1972; and "AWS Welding Handbook", American Welding Society, New York, Section 4, Chapter 69
7. Aluminum Welding Seminar Technical Papers, The Aluminum Association, 1973
8. F. G. Nelson, Effects of Repeated Repair Welding of Two Aluminum Alloys, *Welding J,* Apr 1961
9. F. V. Lawrence, Jr., and W. H. Munse, Effects of Porosity on the Tensile Properties of 5083 and 6061 Aluminum Alloy Weldments, Welding Research Council Bulletin No. 181, Feb 1973
10. P. H. Jennings, A. E. R. Singer and W. I. Pumphery, Hot-Shortness of Some High-Purity Alloys in the Systems Al-Cu-Si and Al-Mg-Si, *J Inst Metals,* Vol 74, 1948, p 235 and 238
11. H. E. Adkins, Selection of Aluminum Alloys and Filler Alloys for Welding, Paper No. 3 in Aluminum Welding Seminar Technical Papers, The Aluminum Association, 1973
12. J. D. Dowd, Weld Cracking in Aluminum Alloys, *Welding Res Supp,* Oct 1952
13. D. N. Williams, B. G. Koehl and R. A. Mueller, Hydrogen Segregation in Ti-6Al-4V Weldments Made With Unalloyed Titanium Filler Metal, *Welding J Res Supp,* May 1970, p 207s-212s

Failures of Brazed Joints

By the ASM Committee on Failure Analysis of Weldments*

BRAZING is used to join a wide variety of ferrous and nonferrous metals. Joining is effected by heating the base metal to a suitable temperature and by using a filler metal having a liquidus above 427 C (800 F) and below the solidus of the base metal. The filler metal is distributed between closely fitted surfaces of the joint by capillary action. Procedures for brazing steels, cast irons, stainless steels, aluminum alloys, and copper and copper alloys are described on pages 593 to 702 in Volume 6 of this Handbook.

Regardless of brazing method (furnace, torch, induction, resistance or dip), the basic causes of failures of brazed joints are similar from one metal or combination of metals to another. However, the severity of a particular failure problem will vary with the metal or metals being brazed, because of differences in brazeability. Low-carbon steels, and copper and copper alloys (except the high-leaded brasses), generally are conceded to be the metals most easily brazed, whereas stainless steels and heat-resisting alloys are among the metals most difficult to braze. As brazeability decreases, the likelihood of inferior brazed joints increases. For instance, in brazing some metals, such as stainless steels and some heat-resisting alloys, alloy penetration can result in cracking due to liquid-metal embrittlement (see Example 4 in this article).

Conditions that most often lead to brazed joints of poor quality are discussed in the paragraphs that follow.

Inclusions at the surface of the base metal, such as oxides, sulfides or nitrides, are particularly harmful because they interfere with the flow of filler metal and can result in imperfect bonds and thus in low-strength joints. During the brazing operation itself, flux inclusions can form. Generally, flux inclusions result from improper application of heat, although they also can be caused by application of too much flux or by excessively loose fit-up.

Porosity. Improper cleaning of the metal surfaces before brazing is the most common cause of porosity in brazed joints. Porosity also may result from vaporization of lower-melting constituents of the filler metal or from incomplete flow of the filler metal. Microporosity may result from shrinkage of the filler

*See page 333 for committee list.

metal, just as in castings. Rapid cooling is the usual cause.

Incomplete brazing, in which the joint surfaces are not completely covered with filler metal and bonded, can result from any one, and frequently more than one, of several causes. Among these causes are (*a*) unsatisfactory cleaning that prevents good flow of the filler metal by reducing wettability of the surfaces; (*b*) insufficient heat, and therefore inadequate filler-metal fluidity; (*c*) loss of protection by shielding gas or flux, resulting in oxidation, and thus impaired fluidity, of filler metal; and (*d*) improper fit-up; too large a gap reduces capillary action.

Flow of filler metal also is impeded by surface contaminants; these contaminants may include lubricants such as oil, graphite, molybdenum disulfide and lead, which are applied during machining and forming. Nonmetallic materials such as ceramics, or metals that are not compatible with the base metal, also can cause low joint strength.

Excessive alloying of the brazing filler metal with the base metal will cause liquid-metal erosion and flow of the base-metal surface. Also, brittle phosphides and intermetallics may form at the interface, resulting in a poor bond. For instance, significant amounts of arsenic and phosphorus in the filler metal should be avoided when brazing carbon and low-alloy steels, because these alloying elements form brittle compounds in the brazed joint.

The properties of brazed joints in copper alloys can be degraded if low-melting elements such as lead, tellurium and sulfur, which are added to improve machinability, make the alloys susceptible to hot cracking. The susceptibility of leaded brasses to hot cracking varies directly with lead content. Brazing results are poor at a lead content of 3%; alloys containing more than 5% lead should not be brazed.

Interface Corrosion. Ferritic and martensitic stainless steels that contain little or no nickel are susceptible to interface corrosion in plain water or in moist atmospheres when brazed with nickel-free silver alloy filler metals, using a liquid or paste flux. Filler metal containing nickel will help to prevent interface corrosion. However, for complete protection, special brazing alloys containing nickel and tin should be used and brazing should be done in a protective atmosphere without flux. Some

austenitic stainless steels brazed with BAg-1 filler metal and then hydrostatically tested with tap water may be susceptible to interface corrosion unless carefully dried after testing. Brazing with BAg-3 filler metal can produce a joint more resistant to corrosion. Hydrostatic testing with a fluid less corrosive than tap water also reduces the possibility of interface corrosion.

Examples

The first three of the five examples that follow deal with failures of brazed joints in stainless steel, two because of poor bonding and the third by stress-corrosion cracking. The fourth example describes failure of a heat-resisting alloy because of metal penetration, and the fifth example describes failure of a brazed joint in a copper pipe caused by use of an unsuitable brazing alloy.

Example 1. Fracture of a Brazed Joint in a Type 321 Stainless Steel Radar Coolant-System Assembly Because of Poor Bonding Due to Inadequate Cleaning (Fig. 1)

A radar coolant-system assembly, made of type 321 stainless steel and fabricated by torch brazing with AWS BAg-1 filler metal and AWS type 3A flux, broke at the brazed joint when subjected to mild handling prior to installation after being in storage for about 2½ years. Before being put in storage, the assembly had withstood a 150-psi pressure test using tap water. All surfaces were to have been passivated according to MIL-S-5002 before assembly, but no other cleaning techniques were stipulated.

Investigation. The failed braze had joined a convolute bellows to a cup on the end of a tube elbow (see Fig. 1a). Visual examination revealed that the filler metal had not tinned all of the mating surfaces and that the surface of the braze metal was not bright and shiny; no fresh fractures were visible. The surfaces of the joint were covered with what appeared to be residues of (*a*) oxidation products from the filler metal and (*b*) flux. Spectrographic analysis of the oxide residue indicated that it contained major amounts (more than 10%) of silver and copper and minor amounts (0.5 to 10%) of cadmium and zinc, which confirmed that it had been derived from the filler metal. The residue conjectured to be flux, however, contained a major amount of zinc and a minor amount of cadmium, which are unlikely as constituents of flux except in trace amounts. Also, the boron content (0.01 to 0.5%) was too low for a material composed of boric acid, borates, fluoborates and fluorides. The presence of boron in the resi-

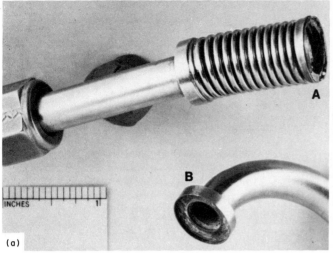

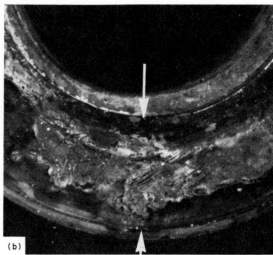

(a) Portions of the broken coolant-system assembly; bellows is at A, cup at B. (b) Fractograph, at 24×, showing residual brazing alloy at the bottom of the cup. No brazing alloy was found on the sides of the cup. The surface of the braze appeared oxidized and contaminated. Location of section shown in (c) is indicated by the arrows. (c) Micrograph, at 350×, of a section through residual brazing alloy and cup, from location between arrows in fractograph (b). Braze metal (C) appears to be mechanically bonded to oxide layer (D) on surface of cup (E).

Fig. 1. Segments of a type 321 stainless steel radar coolant-system assembly that broke at a brazed joint between a bellows and a cup because of inadequate bonding between the brazing alloy and the stainless steel (Example 1)

due, however, indicated that a flux had been used on the faying surfaces.

Examination of the broken joint at the cup (see Fig. 1b and c) revealed that much of the filler metal had flowed into the cup but had not formed a metallurgical bond. Instead, the filler metal had been mechanically bonded to an oxide layer on the stainless steel surface. It was evident that the flux had not protected the steel surface from oxidation during torch heating, because the oxide layer was about 0.0003 in. thick and thus could not have been only the normal passivated film, which is too thin to measure.

During examination of this joint, another such assembly broke at the brazed joint when the bellows was subjected to slight deflection. Visual examination disclosed a lack of bonding in the second joint also. Through consultation with other laboratories, it was learned that sound brazed joints in type 321 stainless steel are difficult to produce because of a tough, tenacious oxide film that is formed by the heat of brazing and that is believed to be impervious to brazing fluxes. This film is attributed to preferential oxidation of the titanium present in this steel.

The lack of metallurgical bonding explained the joint failure, but appeared to be in contradiction to the success of the 150-psi water-pressure test prior to storage. However, the end thrust, which was only about 34 lb, may have been absorbed by a fixture; no information is available on how the assembly was supported for testing.

Conclusions. The joint failed because of a lack of metallurgical bonding between the brazing alloy and the stainless steel due to an oxide film on the steel, produced during brazing, that the flux did not clean away.

Recommendations. Type 347 stainless steel was recommended for the components of the coolant-system assembly instead of type 321, because of the better brazeability of type 347. Also recommended was deflection testing at several orientations during final inspection of the brazed joints. Other rec-

ommendations were use of type 3B instead of 3A flux, to achieve better flow of filler metal, and use of a larger torch tip, to allow wider distribution of heat in the joint area.

Example 2. Stress-Corrosion Cracking of a Brazed Joint in a Type 321 Stainless Steel Pressure-Tube Assembly (Fig. 2)

A pressure-tube assembly of type 321 stainless steel (AMS 5570), which contained a reinforcing liner attached by brazing, leaked air during a pressure test. Fluores-

Fig. 2. Micrograph, at 80×, of a section through the cracked wall of a type 321 stainless steel pressure tube (A), showing the branched, transgranular nature of the crack. The crack origin (B) was at the inner surface of the tube, next to the braze (C) joining the tube to the reinforcing liner (D), also of type 321 stainless steel. (Example 2)

cent-liquid-penetrant inspection revealed a circumferential crack extending approximately 180° around the tube parallel to, and at a distance of 0.10 in. from, the fillet of the brazed joint.

Investigation. The tube was deliberately fractured to expose a portion of the crack surface, which was found to be relatively smooth, with discolorations and multiple crack origins at the inside surface. A longitudinal metallographic section that was taken through another portion of the crack (see Fig. 2) showed that the crack was branched and transgranular, that it had originated adjacent to the braze joining the tube and the reinforcing liner, and that it had propagated through the wall of the tube to its outer surface.

Residues on the inner surface of the tube were identified by chemical analysis as fluorides from the brazing flux. Because it was known that the tube end had been swaged prior to brazing without an intervening stress-relief treatment, because the residual fluorides represented a potential for corrosion, and because of the nature of the crack, it was deduced that the failure had resulted from stress-corrosion cracking.

Conclusions. Brazing-flux residues provided fluoride attack in a region of the pressure-tube assembly where residual swaging stresses existed, producing failure by stress-corrosion cracking.

Recommendations. The tube should be stress relieved after swaging but before brazing, and the joint should be thoroughly cleaned of all residual fluorides immediately after brazing.

Example 3. Fatigue Fracture of a Type 347 Stainless Steel Pressure-Probe Housing Originating at Voids in a Brazed Joint (Fig. 3)

A rectangular segment broke from the type 347 stainless steel housing of a pressure-probe assembly used in experimental instrumentation. The pressure probe and the housing had been joined by brazing with AMS 4772D filler metal.

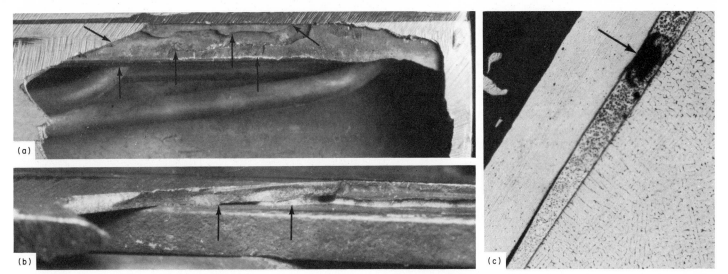

(a) Photograph, at 5¼×, of opening produced in housing by detachment of a segment at time of fracture. Large region delineated by arrows is devoid of braze metal. (b) Fractograph, at 10½×, showing marks of fatigue-crack propagation from multiple origins (two are indicated by arrows) on inside surface of housing. (c) Micrograph, at 50×, of a specimen taken from an area remote from the fracture and etched in aqueous FeCl₃, showing large voids (at arrow), and joint separation (at lower left), resulting from poor bonding between housing and braze metal.

Fig. 3. Type 347 stainless steel pressure-probe housing that failed by fatigue fracture because of voids in a brazed joint (Example 3)

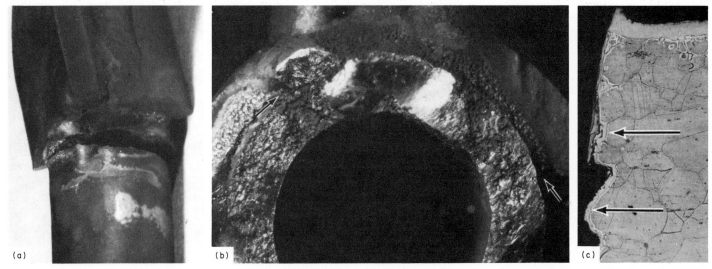

(a) Macrograph, at 4×, showing fracture at the edge of the brazed joint between the tube and the sleeve. (b) Fractograph, at 12×, showing granular, discolored region of fracture origin (between arrows). (c) Micrograph, at 100×, of a longitudinal section (etched with Kalling's reagent) through granular region of fracture, showing penetration of molten braze metal (at arrows) along grain boundaries.

Fig. 4. Waspaloy (AMS 5586) spray-manifold tube that failed by fatigue fracture because of embrittlement by penetration of molten braze metal (Example 4)

Investigation. Visual examination of the upper portion of the opening produced by detachment of the segment (Fig. 3a) revealed that a large region of the joint between the pressure probe and the housing was devoid of braze metal at the fracture. Further study of the fracture surfaces revealed fatigue marks emanating from multiple crack origins on the inside surface of the housing at the brazed joint (see Fig. 3b). Sections taken at the fracture and well away from it (see Fig. 3c) showed large, irregular voids and some trapped flux in the braze metal, plus separation between the housing and the braze, which indicated a poor metallurgical bond.

Conclusions. The failure of the pressure-probe housing was attributed to fatigue cracking that originated at multiple origins at the interface between the housing and the braze metal in areas where there were large, irregular voids in the braze metal and separation of the joint because of poor bonding.

Example 4. Fatigue Fracture of a Waspaloy Spray-Manifold Assembly Because of Embrittlement by Penetration of Molten Braze Metal (Fig. 4)

The inner ring of a spray-manifold assembly fabricated from Waspaloy (AMS 5586) fractured transversely through the manifold tubing at the edge of a brazed joint between the tube and a support sleeve (see Fig. 4a). The assembly was brazed with AWS BAu-4 filler metal (AMS 4787).

Investigation. Microscopic examination of the fracture surface revealed fatigue beach marks that had propagated from the extremities of a granular, gold-tinted surface region (between arrows in Fig. 4b) adjacent to the tube-to-sleeve brazed joint and extending circumferentially in the tube wall

for approximately 110°. Figure 4(c) is a micrograph of a section through the granular portion of the fracture, displaying evidence that, during the brazing operation, molten braze metal (arrows) penetrated along the grain boundaries, embrittling the tube. This penetration provided a continuous intergranular layer that reduced the strength of the tube locally to that of the braze metal. From the profile of the initial fracture (at left in Fig. 4c), it is evident that the fatigue crack began as an intergranular separation and subsequently became transgranular.

The original inner-ring sleeve halves had been removed by melting the braze metal with a torch, and then new, longer sleeves were brazed to the inner ring.

Conclusions. Failure of the tube was caused by excessive alloying between the braze metal and the Waspaloy, producing

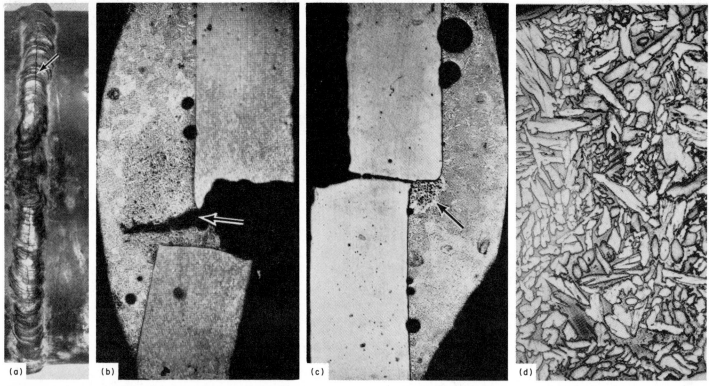

(a) View of crack (arrow) in braze welded joint, which extended around one-third of pipe circumference. (b) Macrograph, at 10×, of a section through the joint, showing a crack partly penetrating the braze metal (arrow), and dezincification surrounding crack. (c) Macrograph, at 10×, of a section from side of pipe opposite that in (b), where pipe ends were more closely butted, showing a much smaller region of dezincification (arrow). (d) Micrograph, at 150×, showing attacked zone (at right) and unattacked zone (at left) of the braze-metal structure.

Fig. 5. Copper water main that failed because of dezincification and cracking in a braze welded joint (Example 5)

a grain-boundary network of braze metal in the tube and consequent embrittlement that rendered the penetrated region vulnerable to fatigue cracking.

Fatigue stresses acting in combination with additional heating and possible over-tempering of the tube during torch debrazing and subsequent rebrazing may have contributed to failure.

Recommendation. Reduction of the temperature to which the components of the joint were heated, either in torch debrazing or in rebrazing, would make the tube less susceptible to penetration by molten braze metal (liquid-metal embrittlement).

Example 5. Failure of a Copper Water Main Because of Dezincification and Cracking of a Braze Welded Joint (Fig. 5)*

A braze welded joint between lengths of 4-in.-OD by 0.092-in.-wall copper pipe failed by cracking around more than one-third of

*Source: Some Examples of Dezincification of Brass, p 20-25 in *Technical Report*, Vol IV, March 1962, British Engine, Boiler & Electrical Insurance Co., Ltd., Manchester, England

the pipe circumference, as shown in Fig. 5(a). The pipe had served as part of a cold-water main. The filler metal used for braze welding was 60-40 alpha-beta brass corresponding approximately to AWS RBCuZn-A.

Investigation. Metallographic sections from a region of the joint other than the cracked section shown in Fig. 5(a) revealed that water had caused dezincification of the filler metal, originating at the inner surface of the pipe, and that the consequent loss in mechanical strength had led to penetration of the corroded area by cracks, as illustrated in Fig. 5(b). The attack had been on the beta-phase matrix, and removal of the zinc had left a porous copper structure, as shown at right in Fig. 5(d). That dezincification caused a loss in joint strength is indicated by the distortion of the specimen shown in Fig. 5(b). This distortion occurred during sectioning because of the weakened condition of the structure.

Figure 5(c) shows a section from the side of the pipe opposite that in Fig. 5(b), at a point where the pipe ends were closely butted (and, thus, where no filler metal had

penetrated between the pipe ends). Here, penetration of the joint by water was more difficult, and it can be seen that much less dezincification occurred.

Attack of a braze welded joint by water is not unusual for such a high-zinc filler metal as 60-40 alpha-beta brass, and use of a lower-zinc alloy would have been more favorable. Another aspect of the joint that was less than ideal was the shape of the pipe ends. Use of a V-groove butt joint would have permitted penetration of filler metal between, and thus fusion of, the pipe ends. Actually, the filler metal had simply been run around the external surface of the pipe, without penetrating the joint.

Conclusion. Failure of the braze welded joint resulted from a loss in mechanical strength due to dezincification of the beta phase of the alpha-beta brass structure by water.

Recommendation. Substitution of a copper-phosphorus or copper-silver-phosphorus filler metal (such as AWS BCuP-1 or BCuP-4, for instance) was recommended, to provide a braze welded joint much more resistant to dezincification.

ANALYSIS AND PREVENTION OF SERVICE FAILURES: MANUFACTURED COMPONENTS AND ASSEMBLIES

CONTENTS

Failures of Shafts

By the ASM Committee on Failures of Shafts*

A SHAFT is a metal bar — usually cylindrical in shape and solid, but sometimes hollow — that is used to support rotating components or to transmit power or motion by rotary or axial movement. In addition to failures in shafts, this article also discusses failures in connecting rods, which translate rotary motion to linear motion (and vice versa), and in piston rods, which translate the action of fluid power to linear motion.

Shafts operate under a broad range of service conditions, including dust-laden or corrosive atmospheres, other types of corrosive environments, and temperatures that vary from extremely low, as in arctic or cryogenic environments, to extremely high, as in gas turbines.

Shafts may be subjected to a variety of loads — in general, tension, compression, bending, or torsion, or combinations of these. In addition, shafts are sometimes subjected to vibratory stresses.

Apart from wear by bearings, which can be a major contributor to shaft failure (see discussion in the section "Wear", page 379 in this article), the most common cause of shaft failure is metal fatigue. Fatigue is a "weakest link" phenomenon; hence, failures start at the most vulnerable point in a dynamically stressed area — typically, a stress raiser,

which may be either mechanical or metallurgical in nature, and sometimes a combination of the two. Mechanical stress raisers include such features as small fillets, sharp corners, grooves, splines, keyways, nicks, and press or shrink fits. Shafts often break at edges of press-fitted or shrink-fitted members, where high degrees of stress concentration exist. Such stress concentration effectively reduces fatigue resistance, especially when coupled with fretting. Metallurgical stress raisers may be quench cracks, corrosion pits, gross nonmetallic inclusions, brittle second-phase particles, weld defects, or arc pits.

Occasionally, ordinary brittle fractures are encountered, particularly in low-temperature environments, or as a result of impact or a rapidly applied overload. Brittle fracture may thus be attributable to inappropriate choice of material because of incomplete knowledge of operating conditions and environment or failure to recognize their significance, but it may also be the result of abuse or misuse of the product under service conditions for which it was not intended.

Surface treatments can cause hydrogen to be dissolved in high-strength steels and may cause shafts to become embrittled even at room temperature. Electro-

plated metals, for instance, have caused failures of high-strength steel shafts. Baking treatments applied immediately after plating are used to ensure removal of hydrogen.

Ductile fracture of shafts usually is caused by accidental overload and is relatively rare in normal operation. Creep, a form of distortion at elevated temperatures, can lead to stress rupture, and also can cause shafts having close tolerances to fail because of excessive changes in critical dimensions.

Fracture Origins

Fractures of shafts originate at points of stress concentration either inherent in design or introduced during fabrication. Design features that concentrate stress include ends of keyways, edges of press-fitted members, fillets at shoulders, and edges of oil holes. Stress concentrators produced during fabrication include grinding damage, machining marks or nicks, and quench cracks resulting from heat treating operations.

Frequently, stress concentrators are introduced during forging of shafts; these include surface discontinuities such as laps, seams, pits and cold shuts, and subsurface imperfections such as bursts.

*HERMAN D. GREENBERG, *Chairman*, Manager, Advanced Manufacturing Development, Manufacturing Development Laboratory, Westinghouse Electric Corp.; LEOPOLD ALBERTIN, Application Metallurgy, Research and Development Center, Westinghouse Electric Corp.; EDWARD L. AUL, Chief Metallurgist, Dresser Clark Div., Dresser Industries, Inc.

S. R. CALLAWAY, Chief Materials Engineer, Electro-Motive Div., General Motors Corp.; F. ERIC KRUEGER, Forensic Engineer, Chemistry Section, The Centre of Forensic Sciences, Ontario Ministry of the Solicitor General; SAUL H. LOWE, Head, Industrial Laboratory, Norfolk

Naval Shipyard; DANIEL F. MCGRATH, Manager of Metallurgy, Heppenstall Co.; J. E. STEINER, Research Consultant, Research Laboratory, U. S. Steel Corp.; JOHN W. SULLIVAN, Metallurgical Supervisor, Experimental and Specifications Dept., Bethlehem Plant, Bethlehem Steel Corp.; RICHARD WALTEIN, Supervisor, Fracture Investigations Group, Hamilton Standard Div., United Aircraft Corp.

DAVID E. WERSTLER, Plant Metallurgist, Forge Div., Earle M. Jorgensen Co.; DONALD J. WULPI, Head, Engineering Metallurgical Laboratory, Motor Truck Div., International Harvester Co.; NOBLE C. YORK, Plant Metallurgist, Chassis Plant, Ford Motor Co.

Subsurface stress concentrators can be introduced during solidification of ingots from which forged shafts are made. Generally, these stress concentrators are internal discontinuities such as pipe, segregation, porosity, shrinkage, and nonmetallic inclusions.

Fractures also result from bearing misalignment, either introduced at assembly or caused by deflection of supporting members in service, from mismatch of mating parts, and from careless handling in which the shaft is nicked, gouged or scratched.

To a lesser degree, shafts can fracture from misapplication of material. Such fractures result from use of materials having (a) high ductile-to-brittle transition temperatures; (b) low resistance to hydrogen embrittlement, temper embrittlement, or caustic embrittlement; or (c) chemical compositions or mechanical properties other than those specified. In some instances, fractures originate in regions of decarburization or excessive carburization, where mechanical properties are different because of variations in chemical composition.

Examination of Failed Shafts

In examining a failed shaft it is generally desirable to gather as much background information as possible about the shaft. This information should include design parameters, operating environment, manufacturing procedures, and service history. Detailed knowledge of these factors often can be helpful in guiding the direction of failure investigation and corrective action.

Design Parameters. The failure analyst should have copies of the detail and assembly drawings, and material and testing specifications that involve the shaft. Potential stress raisers or points of stress concentration, such as splines, keyways, cross holes and changes in shaft diameter, should be noted. The type of material, mechanical properties, heat treatment, test locations, nondestructive examination used, and other processing requirements also should be noted.

Special processing or finishing treatments, such as shot peening, fillet rolling, burnishing, plating, metal spraying and painting, can have an influence on performance, and the analyst should be aware of such treatments.

Mechanical Conditions. How a shaft is supported or assembled in its working mechanism and the relationship between the failed part and its associated members can be valuable information. The number and location of bearings or supports, and how their alignment may be affected by deflections or distortions that can occur as a result of mechanical loads, shock, vibrations, or thermal gradients, should be considered.

The method of connecting the driving or driven member to the shaft, such as press fitting, welding, or use of a threaded connection, a set screw or a keyway, can influence failure. Also important is if power is transmitted to or taken from the shaft by gears, splines, belts, chains or torque converters.

Manufacturing records may indicate when the part was made, and the material supplier, heat or lot number. Inspection records may provide the inspection history of the part and indicate any questionable areas.

Service History. Checking the service records of an assembly should reveal when the parts were installed, serviced, overhauled and inspected. These records also should show whether service or maintenance operations were conducted in accordance with the manufacturer's recommendations. Often, talking with operators or maintenance personnel reveals pertinent unrecorded information.

Initial Examination. The entire assembly that was involved in the failure should be made available for examination. Samples of oil, grease and loose debris should be carefully removed from all components, identified, and stored for future reference. Then, the components can be cleaned with a solvent that will not remove or obliterate any rust, oxidation, burnishing marks or other pertinent evidence.

Surfaces of all areas that may have been involved in, or that may have contributed to, the failure should be examined, noting scuff marks, burnished areas, abnormal surface blemishes and wear. These marks should be associated with some abnormal service condition, if possible.

The fractured part should be examined to establish the general area or location of failure, noting the proximity to any possible stress concentrations found when examining the part drawings.

Fracture surfaces should be examined visually to determine if there are indications of one or more fracture mechanisms and if there is an apparent crack origin. Surfaces of the component adjacent to the fracture surface should be examined for secondary cracks, pits or imperfections. Photographs should be taken to record the condition of the shaft before physical evidence is destroyed by subsequent examinations.

Sometimes, nondestructive methods of inspection (such as ultrasonic inspection) can provide useful information. Such methods may reveal other cracks that have not progressed to rupture; these frequently have fracture surfaces that are not as badly damaged as the primary fracture and that can be diagnosed more readily.

Also, some machines may have other shafts similar to the one that failed; these shafts may have the same service history as the failed shaft, and examination of them may reveal cracks that can provide useful information. Whenever possible, the analyst also should request shafts that are from machines in service but that have not failed.

Macroscopic Examination (*from less than actual size to not more than 50 diameters*). Many characteristic marks on fracture surfaces, though visually identifiable, can better be distinguished with macroscopic examination. A magnifying glass or binocular microscope can be used to study the unique vestigial marks left on tensile-fracture surfaces in the form of fibrous, radial and shear-lip zones from which the relative amounts of ductility and toughness possessed by the metal can be appraised. In the study of fatigue fractures, macroscopic examination of such features as beach marks, striations, ratchet marks, fast-fracture zones, and crack-initiation sites yields information relative to the kinds and magnitude of the stresses that caused failure.

Microscopic Examination (*50 to 2000 diameters*). Metallographic sections taken through fractures are used to classify fracture paths (transgranular or intergranular), to establish the mode of fracture (shear, cleavage), and to locate and identify crack-initiation sites. Plating before mounting can be used to preserve the edge or edges of the fracture surface. In addition, metallographic examination can reveal microstructure near the fracture surface; the grain size of the material; and the presence of undue segregation, inclusions, alloy concentrations, brittle grain-boundary phases, decarburization, and fabricating imperfections.

SEM and TEM Examination (*scanning electron microscopy and transmission electron microscopy at magnifications from 50 to 15,000+ diameters*). The optical metallograph is limited for fracture studies by its restricted depth of field (the SEM has a depth of field about 300 times that of the light microscope). Because of this, the electron microscope is more suited for fractographic work. With it, fractures may be classified by fracture path, fracture mechanism, and fracture features. There are two fracture paths: transgranular (or transcrystalline) and intergranular (or intercrystalline).

The fracture mechanisms and related microscopic features of transgranular fracture are: microvoid coalescence (dimples, associated with ductile fracture), tearing (tear ridges), cleavage (river patterns, feather marks, Wallner lines and cleavage tongues, all associated with brittle fracture), and fatigue (striations and tire tracks).

The fracture mechanism of intergranular fracture is grain-boundary separation. The causes are presence of grain-boundary phases; alloy-depleted boundaries; and environmental or mechanical factors such as stress-corrosion cracking, hydrogen damage, heat damage, and triaxial stress states.

For additional information on microscopic examination by TEM and SEM, the reader is referred to Volume 9 of this Handbook. Volume 9 also contains information on examination of fracture surfaces by light microscopy.

Physical testing and chemical analysis occasionally pinpoint the cause of a failure as wrong material, improper heat treatment, or in-service changes in properties. Hardness testing and spectrographic analysis are easy to perform and should be done as a matter of course. Impact tests, tensile tests, and other special mechanical tests may be performed if manufacturing procedures are in doubt or if other paths are not fruitful.

Stress Systems Acting on Shafts

The stress systems acting on a shaft must be understood clearly before the cause of a fracture in that shaft can be determined. Also, both ductile and brittle behavior under static loading or single overload, and the characteristic fracture surfaces produced by these types of behavior, must be clearly understood for proper analysis of shaft fractures.

Simplified, two-dimensional free-body diagrams showing the orientations of the normal-stress and shear-stress systems at any internal point in a shaft loaded in pure tension, torsion and compression are shown in Fig. 1. Also, the single-overload-fracture behavior of both ductile and brittle materials is illustrated with the diagram for each type of load.

A free-body stress system may be considered as a square of infinitely small dimensions. Tensile and compressive stresses act perpendicular to each other and to the sides of the square to stretch and squeeze the sides, respectively. The shear, or sliding, stresses act on the diagonals of the square, 45° to the normal stresses. The third-dimension radial stresses are ignored in this description.

The effects of the shear and normal stresses on ductile and brittle materials under the three types of loads illustrated in Fig. 1 and under bending load are discussed below.

Tension. Under tension loading, the tensile stresses (σ_1) are longitudinal, whereas the compressive-stress components (σ_3) are transverse to the shaft axis. The maximum-shear-stress components (τ_{max}) are at 45° to the shaft axis (see Fig. 1a).

In a ductile material, shear stresses developed by tensile loading cause considerable deformation (elongation and necking) prior to fracture, which origi-

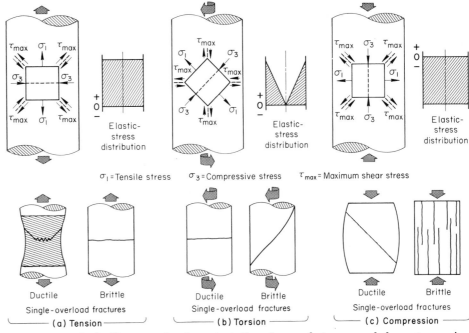

Fig. 1. Free-body diagrams showing orientation of normal stresses and shear stresses in a shaft under simple tension, torsion and compression loading, and the single-overload-fracture behavior of ductile and brittle materials. See text for discussion.

nates near the center of the shaft and propagates toward the surface, ending with a conical shear lip usually about 45° to the shaft axis.

In a brittle material, a fracture from a single tensile overload is roughly perpendicular to the direction of tensile stress, but involves little permanent deformation. The fracture surface usually is rough and crystalline in appearance.

The elastic-stress distribution in pure tension loading, in the absence of a stress concentration, is uniform across the section. Thus, fracture can originate at any point within the highly stressed volume. (For macrographs and fractographs of typical tensile fractures, see pages 136 and 381 in Volume 9 of this Handbook.)

Torsion. The stress system rotates 45° counterclockwise when a shaft is loaded in torsion, as shown in Fig. 1(b). Both the tensile and compressive stresses are 45° to the shaft axis and remain mutually perpendicular. One shear-stress component is parallel with the shaft axis; the other is perpendicular to the shaft axis.

In a ductile material loaded to failure in torsion, shear stresses cause considerable deformation prior to fracture. This deformation, however, usually is not obvious, because the shape of the shaft has not been changed. If a shaft loaded in torsion is assumed to consist of an infinite number of infinitely thin disks that slip slightly with respect to each other under the torsional stress, visualization of deformation is simplified. Torsional single-overload fracture of a ductile material usually occurs on the transverse plane, perpendicular to the axis of the shaft. In pure torsion, the

final-fracture region is at the center of the shaft; the presence of slight bending will cause it to be off-center.

A brittle material in pure torsion will fracture perpendicular to the tensile-stress component, which is 45° to the shaft axis. The resulting fracture surfaces usually have the shape of a spiral.

The elastic-stress distribution in pure torsion is maximum at the surface and zero at the center of the shaft. Thus, in pure torsion, fracture normally originates at the surface, which is the region of highest stress. (For photographs and fractographs of typical torsion fractures, see pages 305 and 387 in Volume 9 of this Handbook.)

Compression. When a shaft is loaded in axial compression (see Fig. 1c), the stress system rotates so that the compressive stress (σ_3) is axial and the tensile stress (σ_1) is transverse. The shear stresses (τ_{max}) are 45° to the shaft axis, as they are during axial tension loading.

In a ductile material overloaded in compression, shear stresses cause considerable deformation but usually do not result in fracture. The shaft is shortened and bulges under the influence of shear stress. A brittle material loaded in pure compression, if it does not buckle, will fracture perpendicular to the maximum tensile-stress component. Because the tensile stress is transverse, the direction of brittle fracture is parallel to the shaft axis.

The elastic-stress distribution in pure compression loading, in the absence of a stress concentration, is uniform across the section. If fracture occurs, it likely will be in the longitudinal direction because compression loading increases the shaft diameter and stretches the metal at the circumference.

Bending. When a shaft is stressed in bending, the convex surface is stressed in tension and has an elastic-stress distribution similar to that shown in Fig. 1(a), and the concave surface is stressed in compression and has an elastic-stress distribution similar to that shown in Fig. 1(c). Approximately midway between the convex and concave surfaces is a neutral axis, where all stresses are zero.

Fatigue Failures

Fatigue in shafts generally can be classified into three basic subdivisions: bending fatigue, torsional fatigue, and axial fatigue. Bending fatigue can result from these types of bending loads: unidirectional (one-way), reversed (two-way), and rotating. In unidirectional bending, the stress at any point fluctuates. Fluctuating stress refers to a change in magnitude without changing algebraic sign. In reversed bending and rotating bending, the stress at any point alternates. Alternating stress refers to cycling between two stresses of opposite algebraic sign — that is, tension (plus) to compression (minus) or compression to tension — that usually are of equal magnitude. Torsional fatigue can result from application of a fluctuating or an alternating twisting moment, or torque. Axial fatigue can result from application of alternating (tension-and-compression) loading or fluctuating (tension-tension) loading.

For a more complete discussion of fatigue failures, see the article that begins on page 95 in this volume.

Unidirectional-Bending Fatigue. The axial location of the origin of a fatigue crack in a stationary cylindrical bar or shaft subjected to a fluctuating unidirectional bending moment evenly distributed along the length will be determined by some minor stress raiser such as a surface discontinuity. Beach marks (also called clamshell, conchoidal and crack-arrest marks) of the form shown in Fig. 2(a) and (b) are indicative of a fatigue crack having a single origin at the point indicated by the arrow. The crack front, which formed the beach marks, is symmetrical with respect to the origin and retains a concave form throughout. Both the single origin and the smallness of the final-fracture zone in Fig. 2(a) suggest that the nominal stress was low. The larger final-fracture zone in Fig. 2(b) suggests a higher nominal stress. Figure 2(c) shows a typical fatigue crack originating as several individual cracks that ultimately merged to form a single crack front. Such multiple origins usually are indicative of high nominal stress. Note the presence of ridges (ratchet marks) between crack origins.

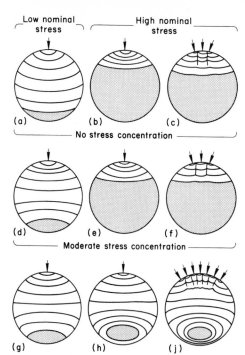

Fig. 2. Fatigue marks, typical for a uniformly loaded shaft subjected to unidirectional bending, produced from single origins at low and high nominal stresses and from multiple origins at high nominal stresses. Arrows indicate crack origins; final-fracture zones are shaded.

Figure 2(d), (e) and (f) show typical fatigue beach marks resulting when a change in section in a uniformly loaded shaft provides a moderate stress concentration. With a low nominal stress, the crack front changes from concave to convex prior to rupture, as shown in Fig. 2(d). At higher nominal stresses, the crack front flattens and may not become convex prior to final fracture, as shown in Fig. 2(e) and (f).

A change in section in a uniformly loaded shaft that produces a severe stress concentration will lead to a pattern of beach marks such as that shown in Fig. 2(g), (h) or (j). An example of a severe stress concentration is a small-radius fillet at the junction of a shoulder and a smaller-diameter portion of a shaft or at the bottom of a keyway. Such a fillet usually results in the contour of the fracture surface being convex with respect to the smaller-section side. The crack-front pattern shown in Fig. 2(g) was produced by a low nominal stress. The crack front in Fig. 2(h) developed more rapidly because of a higher stress in the peripheral zone. Multiple crack origins, high nominal stress and unidirectional bending produced the beach-mark pattern shown in Fig. 2(j).

The following example describes a shaft that failed as the result of unidirectional-bending stresses. The crack originated at a single origin at a sharp change in section.

Example 1. Unidirectional-Bending Fatigue Failure of an A6 Tool Steel Shaft, Initiated at a Nonmetallic Inclusion at a Sharp Change in Section (Fig. 3)

The shaft shown in Fig. 3 was part of a clamping device on a tooling assembly used for bending 2¼-in.-OD tubing on a 3⅜-in. radius. The assembly contained two of these shafts; the shafts failed simultaneously and were sent to the laboratory for examination. The maximum clamping force on the assembly was 120,000 lb. The material specified for the shafts was a free-machining grade of A6 tool steel.

The shafts were subjected to a tensile stress imposed by the clamping force and a bending stress resulting from the nature of the operation. Unidirectional-bending stresses were imposed on one shaft when a right-hand bend was made in the tubing and on the other shaft when a left-hand bend was made. Approximately 45 right-hand and 45 left-hand bends were made per hour on the machine; the total number of bends made before the shafts failed was not known. The tensile stress on the shafts also was cyclic, because the clamping force was removed after each bend was made.

Investigation. Analysis of the steel, using wet chemical and spectrographic techniques, showed that the composition was within specifications. The average hardness of the steel was Rockwell C 48. A 0.505-in.-diam tensile specimen removed from the center of one of the shafts failed in a brittle manner at a tensile stress of 228,000 psi.

The microstructure of the steel was fine, dispersed, tempered martensite with elongated stringers of manganese sulfide. Also present were spheroidized white particles that were identified as high-alloy complex carbides (M_6C) corresponding to the double carbides Fe_4Mo_2C and Fe_4Cr_2C.

Microscopic examination of the edge of the fracture surface, at 100 and 1000 diameters, revealed some nonmetallic oxide-sulfide segregation.

Visual examination of the fracture surface revealed both a smooth area and a coarse, granular area (see view B in Fig. 3). The dull, smooth area is typical of fatigue fracture and resulted from a rubbing action that occurred as the crack was opened and closed by the bending stress. Beach marks on the smooth area of the fracture surface also indicated fatigue fracture. The coarse, bright, crystalline-appearing area is the final-fracture zone. The smooth-textured fatigue zone is relatively large compared with the crystalline-textured final-fracture zone, which indicates that the shaft was subjected to a low overstress and little or no stress concentration. The single-side, concave final-fracture surface suggests that a one-way bending load was involved.

The fatigue crack was initiated in a 0.010-in.-radius fillet at a change in section (see "Original design" in section A-A in Fig. 3). Cracking was nucleated by a nonmetallic inclusion that intersected the surface at a critical location in the fillet.

Conclusions. The shafts fractured in fatigue as the result of a low-overstress, high-cycle, unidirectional bending load. The small radius of the fillet at the change in section resulted in a stress concentration which, acting in combination with the oxide-

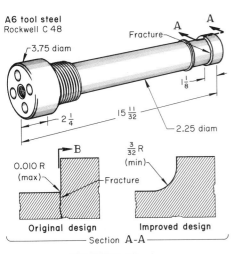

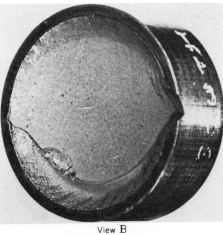

Fig. 3. Tube-bending-machine shaft made of A6 tool steel that failed by fatigue fracture; original and improved designs for fillet in failure region; and view of fracture surface, showing regions of fatigue-crack propagation and final fracture (Example 1)

sulfide inclusion that intersected the surface of the fillet, initiated a crack.

Corrective Measure. New shafts were made with a ³⁄₃₂-in.-radius fillet at the critical change in section (see "Improved design" in section A-A in Fig. 3). The larger-radius fillet minimized stress concentration in this region and prevented recurrence of failure.

Reversed-Bending Fatigue. Where the applied bending moment is reversing (alternating), all points in the shaft are subjected alternately to tension stress and compression stress; while the points on one side of the plane of bending are in tension, the points on the opposite side are in compression. If the bending moment is of the same magnitude in either direction, two cracks of approximately equal length usually develop from origins diametrically opposite each other and often in the same transverse plane. If the bending moment is greater in one direction than in the other, the two cracks will differ in length.

Typical fatigue marks on the fracture surface of a stationary (nonrotating)

shaft subjected to a reversing bending moment evenly distributed along its length are shown in Fig. 4. The crack origins (at arrows) are shown diametrically opposite each other, but sometimes they are slightly displaced by minor stress raisers. The pattern shown in Fig. 4(a) is typical of that for a single-diameter shaft with no stress concentration. The bending moment is equal in both directions.

A large-radius fillet at a change in shaft diameter imposes a moderate stress concentration. The pattern on the surface of a fracture through such a fillet is shown in Fig. 4(b). A small-radius fillet at a change in diameter results in a severe stress concentration. The typical pattern on the surface of a fracture through a small-radius fillet is shown in Fig. 4(c).

Under the above loading conditions, each crack is subjected alternately to tensile and compressive stresses, with the result that the surfaces of the crack are forced into contact with one another during the compression cycle, and rubbing occurs. Sometimes, rubbing may be sufficient to obliterate many of the characteristic marks, and the crack surfaces may become dull or polished.

Rotary-Bending Fatigue. The essential difference between a stationary shaft and a rotating shaft subjected to the same bending moment is that in a stationary shaft the tensile stress is confined to a portion of the periphery only. In a rotating shaft, every point on the periphery sustains a tensile stress, then a compressive stress, once every revolution.

Another important difference introduced by rotation is asymmetrical development of the crack front from a single origin. There is a marked tendency of the crack front to extend preferentially in a direction opposite to that of rotation. The crack front usually swings around about 15° or more, as shown in Fig. 5(a) and (c). A third difference arising from rotation is in the distribution of the origins of a multiple-origin crack.

In a nonrotating shaft subjected to unidirectional bending, the origins are located in the region of the maximum-tension zone (see Fig. 2). In a nonrotating shaft subjected to reversed bending, the origins are diametrically opposite each other (see Fig. 4). In rotary bending, however, every point on the shaft periphery is subjected to a tensile stress at each revolution, and therefore a crack may be initiated at any point on the periphery, as shown in Fig. 5(b) and (d).

The crack surfaces are pressed together during the compressive component of the stress cycle, and mutual rubbing occurs. A common result of final fracture is that slight movement of one side of the crack relative to the other side frequently causes severe damage to the fracture surfaces and tends to obliterate many marks. However, although the high spots on one

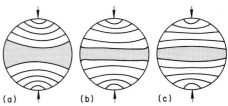

Fig. 4. Typical fatigue marks on the fracture surface of a uniformly loaded nonrotating shaft subjected to reversed-bending stresses and having (a) no stress concentration, (b) moderate stress concentration, and (c) severe stress concentration. Arrows indicate crack origins; shaded areas are final-fracture zones.

surface abrade the high spots on the other, the marks in the hollows are retained. Because the hollows are mirror images of the damaged high spots on the opposing surface, they provide useful evidence, and thus it is desirable to examine both parts of a cracked or fractured shaft.

The similarity in macroscopic appearance of fractures in shafts resulting from rotary-bending fatigue and from torsional shear frequently results in misinterpretation. The fracture surface shown in Fig. 6(a) was the result of fatigue, as evidenced by the ratchet marks around the periphery and the pronounced beach marks. Under the low magnification of the fractograph shown in Fig. 6(b), beach marks are not visible, because they were obliterated by rubbing. However, the presence of ratchet marks around the periphery is an indication of rotary-bending fatigue. The metal smearing apparent on the fracture surface shown in Fig. 6(c) is an indication of torsional shear and would preclude this fracture's being mistaken for a fatigue fracture.

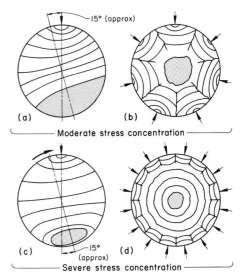

Fig. 5. Typical fatigue marks on the fracture surface of a uniformly loaded rotating shaft produced from single and multiple origins (at arrows), having moderate and severe stress concentrations; shaded areas are final-fracture zones. Shaft rotation is clockwise.

The fracture shown in Fig. 6(d) exhibits a superficial similarity to a fatigue fracture. However, it is evident that this fracture was the result of torsional shear, because the entire fracture surface has a smooth texture and no well-defined final-fracture area.

In splined shafts, fracture resulting from torsional shear frequently is accompanied by deformation of the splines not engaged by the mating part. This deformation is shown in Fig. 6(d) and in Fig. 2 on page 36 in Volume 9 of this Handbook. Occasionally, however, the portion of the shaft not engaged by the mating part is unavailable for examination. When macroscopic examination affords only inconclusive evidence, use of an electron microscope may reveal fatigue striations or shear dimples.

Torsional Fatigue. Fatigue cracks arising from torsional stresses show the same beach marks and ridges as those produced by bending stresses. Longitudinal stress raisers are comparatively harmless under bending stresses, but are as important as circumferential stress raisers under torsional loading. This sensitivity of shafts loaded in torsion to longitudinal stress raisers is of considerable practical importance, because inclusions in the shaft material are almost always parallel to the axis of rotation. It is not unusual for a torsional-fatigue crack to originate at a longitudinal inclusion, a surface mark, or a spline or keyway corner and then to branch at about 45°.

When a stress raiser such as a circumferential groove is present, different states of stresses exist around the stress raiser, and the tensile stress is increased to as much as four times the shear stress. Therefore, the tensile stress on the 45° plane will exceed the tensile strength of the steel before the shear stress reaches the shear strength of the steel. Fracture occurs normal to the 45° tensile plane, producing a conical or star-shape fracture surface, as in the following example.

Example 2. Torsional-Fatigue Fracture of a Large 4340 Steel Shaft That Was Subject to Cyclic Loading and Frequent Overloads (Fig. 7)

The 4340 steel shaft shown in Fig. 7(a), which was the driving member of a large rotor subject to cyclic loading and frequent overloads, broke after three weeks of operation. The shaft was also part of a gear train that reduced the rotational speed of the driven member. The driving shaft contained a shear groove at which the shaft should break if a sudden high overload occurred, thus preventing damage to an expensive gear mechanism. The rotor was subjected to severe chatter, which was an abnormal condition resulting from a series of continuous small overloads at a frequency of about three per second.

Investigation. Examination disclosed that the shaft had broken at the shear groove and that the fracture surface contained a star-shape pattern, as shown in Fig. 7(b). Figure 7(c) shows the fracture surface with the pieces fitted back in place. The pieces were all nearly the same size and shape, and there were indications of fatigue, cleavage and shear failure in approximately the same location on each piece.

The cracks were oriented at approximately 45° to the axis of the shaft, which indicated that final fracture was caused by a tensile stress normal to the 45° plane and not by the longitudinal or transverse shear stress that had been expected to cause an overload failure.

Examination of the surfaces of one of the pieces of the broken shaft revealed small longitudinal and transverse shear cracks at the smallest diameter of the shear groove. Also, slight plastic flow had occurred in the metal adjacent to these cracks. Cracking occurred at many points in the groove in the shaft before several of the cracks grew to a critical size.

No surface irregularities were present in the shear groove at any of the shear cracks. The structure of the metal was normal, with a uniform hardness of Rockwell C 30 to 30.5 across the section, indicating a strength normal for quenched and tempered 4340 steel shafts. A hot-acid etch showed the steel to be free from pipe, segregation, or abnormal irregularities.

Conclusion. The basic failure mechanism was fracture by torsional fatigue, which started at numerous surface shear cracks, both longitudinal and transverse, that developed in the periphery of the root of the shear groove. These shear cracks resulted from high peak loads caused by chatter. Stress concentrations developed in the regions of maximum shear, and fatigue cracks propagated in a direction perpendicular to the maximum tensile stress, thus forming the star pattern at 45° to the longitudinal axis of the shaft.

The shear groove in the shaft, designed to prevent damage to the gear train, had performed its function, but at a lower overload level than intended.

Corrective Measures. The fatigue strength of the shaft was increased by shot peening the shear groove, and chatter in the machine was minimized.

The relative extent of development of two torsional-fatigue cracks mutually at right angles can indicate the magnitude of the torque reversals that have been applied. If the cracks are of approximately the same length, the indications are that the torque reversals have been of equal magnitude, but only if the cracks are in a comparatively early stage of development. Beyond this stage, one crack usually takes the lead and such inferences are no longer justified. If the shaft transmits a unidirectional torque but two

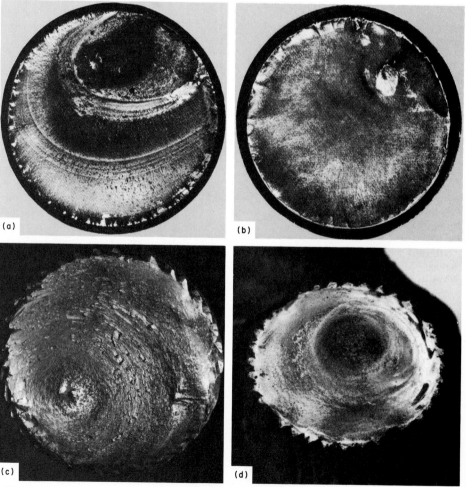

(a)   (b)   (c)   (d)

Fig. 6. Fracture surfaces of shafts that failed by fatigue (a) *and* (b), *and by torsional shear* (c) *and* (d). *See text for discussion.*

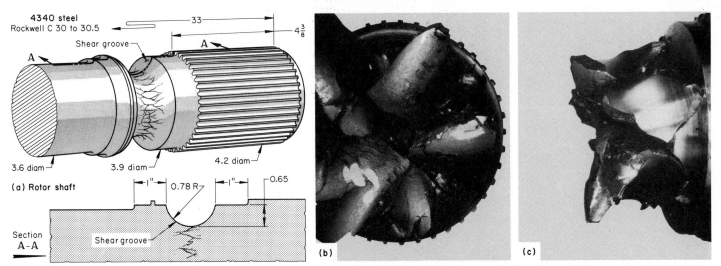

Fig. 7. (a) *Rotor shaft made of 4340 steel, with shear groove designed to protect gear mechanism from sudden overload, that fractured by torsional fatigue. (b) Star-shape pattern on a fracture surface of the shaft. (c) Longitudinal and transverse shear cracks on the surface of the shear groove, which resulted from high peak loads caused by chatter. (Example 2)*

cracks develop mutually at right angles, it can be presumed that the torque was of a reversing character. If a bending stress is applied to a shaft that is transmitting torque, the angle at which any fatigue crack develops will be modified. Therefore, if the angle differs significantly from 45° to the shaft axis, the presence of a bending stress is indicated.

Contact Fatigue

Contact fatigue occurs when components roll, or roll and slide, against each other under high contact pressure and cyclic loading. Spalling occurs after many repetitions of loading and is the result of metal fatigue from the imposed cyclic contact stresses, which are at a maximum value beneath the contact surface. Factors that govern contact fatigue are contact stress, material properties and metallurgical, physical and chemical characteristics of the contacting surfaces, including the oil film that lubricates the surfaces.

The significant stress in rolling-contact fatigue is the maximum alternating shear stress that undergoes a reversal in direction during rolling. In pure rolling, this stress occurs on a plane slightly below the surface and can lead to the initiation of subsurface fatigue cracks. As these cracks propagate under the repeated loads, they reach the surface and produce spalling.

When sliding is imposed on rolling, the tangential forces and thermal gradient caused by friction alter the magnitude and distribution of stresses in and below the contact area. The alternating shear stress is increased in magnitude and is moved nearer to the surface by friction resulting from the sliding action.

Forged, hardened steel rolls are prone to surface spalling. The factors that must be considered in spalling of rolls are

(a) the forces existing between work rolls and backup rolls, (b) the forces generated between the rolls and the material being rolled, and (c) the load distribution across the rolls as a function of elastic deformation; all of these factors interact while the rolls are rotating.

Generally, spalling in a roll is attributed to initiation of a subsurface fatigue crack of undetermined origin, or is a result of surface-induced microscopic cracking. However, spalling cannot be attributed to a single primary cause. Spalling may originate below the surface as a result of localized stress concentration, which causes plastic flow or fracture at the point of maximum reversed shear.

The incidence of spalling can be reduced by removal of the cold worked surface produced during operation before it becomes a source of contact-fatigue cracking and the resultant spalling. A cold worked surface layer can reach the depth normally associated with the maximum reversed shear stress. Also, redressing removes small surface cracks that are potential initiators of spalling. For instance, forcing of lubricating liquids into surface cracks under very high rolling pressures can cause these cracks to propagate.

For additional information, see the section on contact fatigue in the article on Fatigue Failures, and the section on failure by rolling-contact fatigue in the article on Failures of Rolling-Element Bearings, in this volume.

Wear

Wear of metal parts commonly is classified into either of two categories: abrasive wear or adhesive wear.

Abrasive wear — undesired removal of material by a cutting mechanism — can reduce the size and destroy the proper shape of a shaft. The shaft may then

either fail by another means, such as by fracture, or cease to perform its designed function.

Foreign particles such as sand, dirt and other debris in the lubricant can cause wear of a shaft.

Vibration, sand and metallic particles in a fuel pump caused abrasive-wear failure of the shaft described in the following example. Wear occurred in the splines on the shaft and in the impeller.

Example 3. Wear Failure of a Fuel-Pump Drive Shaft Because of the Presence of Sand, Metallic Particles and Vibration (Fig. 8)

The fuel pump in a turbine-powered aircraft failed, resulting in damage to the aircraft. The pump, shown in Fig. 8(a) and (b), was sent to the laboratory for examination and to determine the cause of failure.

This particular model of fuel pump had a history of wear failures and had been redesigned to incorporate a shaft of case-hardened steel (composition not reported). Vibration was common during operation but generally was not excessive for the aircraft.

Investigation. The pump and the filter chamber were dry and free of any debris or contamination, except for some accumulated deposit on the filter cartridge, when the pump was disassembled in the laboratory. The drive-shaft splines that engaged the impeller were almost completely destroyed down to the roots (see detail A in Fig. 8). Extensive damage to the splines was apparent because on subsequent reassembly the shaft could be rotated without rotating the impeller.

The pressure side of each spline tooth in the impeller also exhibited some damage. Relatively smooth cavities and undercutting of the flank on the pressure side of the spline teeth indicated that the damage had not been caused by wear from metallic contact between the splines, but by an erosion or abrasion mechanism.

Hardness readings taken at several axial locations on the drive shaft showed a reasonably uniform hardness of approximately

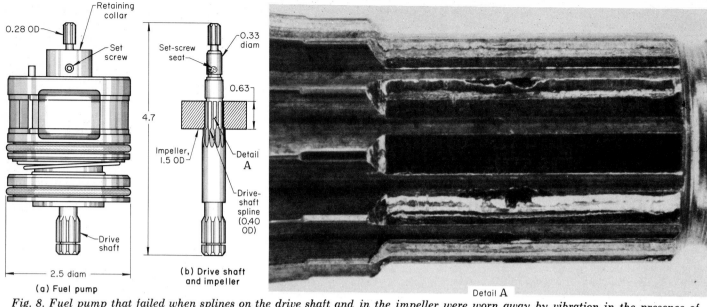

Fig. 8. Fuel pump that failed when splines on the drive shaft and in the impeller were worn away by vibration in the presence of sand and metallic particles; and enlarged view of failure area, showing worn splines (Example 3)

570 dph. The impeller and the retaining ring each had a hardness of approximately 780 dph, and the parts surrounding the impeller (including the vanes) exhibited a hardness of approximately 630 dph. The microstructure of the metal in the impeller exhibited scattered porosity and carbide particles and appeared to be a sintered powder metallurgy compact.

Metallographic examination of a section through the damaged splines and of a section through the adjacent undamaged part of the same splines disclosed no material defects. The microstructure indicated that the shaft had been satisfactorily heat treated by quenching and tempering, but there was no evidence of case hardening on the spline surfaces, a treatment commonly given to shafts of this type.

The worn surfaces of the splines showed evidence of cold work at the edges. Also, there was a relatively smooth worn area at the center of each tooth that appeared to be free of cold work and that appeared to have been caused by an abrasive action. The damaged side of each spline appeared as an undulating outline with some undercutting rather than a jagged or deformed shape.

The residue on the filter cartridge was brown in color and, when viewed under a low-power microscope, particles of sand, paint or plastic, fibers from the cartridge, brass and steel could be identified. Application of a magnet to the sample showed that it contained a large amount of iron.

Chemical analysis indicated that the deposit contained about 20% sand, 30% iron and 30% organic material (paint, plastic and filter fibers). The reddish-brown color of the deposit suggested that some of the iron present was an oxide (rust), but this was not confirmed.

Discussion. Vibration in the fuel pump could be expected to initiate damage, particularly when combined with an abrasive action. Under these conditions, fretting or abrasive wear can be expected on sliding-contact surfaces that are not sufficiently abrasion resistant. The residue from the

filter contained significant quantities of sand and iron; the iron probably originated from the damaged shaft.

The examination indicated that the splines on the drive shaft had been damaged by abrasion, which could have been caused by the combined effect of vibration and abrasives such as sand and the metal particles removed from the splines.

The same action also would damage the internal splines of the impeller — but to a lesser extent, because of its greater hardness and thus greater abrasion resistance. However, the internal splines exhibited significant damage, which appeared to have been produced by erosion. Thus, the internal splines suffered slight abrasive damage and somewhat more damage by erosion.

Fig. 9. (a) End of shaft that was severely damaged by wire wooling. (b) Micrograph (at 50×) of an unetched section through loose material found in grooves worn in shaft by wire wooling.

Conclusions. Failure of the shaft was the result of excessive wear on the splines caused by vibration and the abrasive action of sand and metal particles.

Recommendations. To increase resistance to wear and abrasion, the surfaces of the spline teeth should be case hardened. Although the drive shaft exhibited reasonably high strength, its resistance to wear and abrasion was inadequate for the conditions to which it was exposed.

Wire Wooling. Abrasive-wear failure of shafts by wire wooling has been observed under certain circumstances where contact occurs between the shaft and a stationary part, resulting in removal, by machining, of fine wire shavings that resemble steel wool. This type of failure has been found on turbine and turbine-generator shafts made of 3Cr-0.5Mo steels, on 12% chromium stainless steels, on 18Cr-8Ni stainless steels, and on non-chromium steels in the presence of certain chloride-containing oils. Wire wooling also has been observed on thrust bearings and on centrifugal compressor shafts.

The end of a 5.25-in.-diam shaft that was worn by wire wooling is shown in Fig. 9(a). The surface that was worn was in contact with a labyrinth seal and was not a bearing surface. The shaft had operated for about 3½ years before the damage was discovered. Although records were not available, the machine was known to have been opened at least once during that time, but damage under the seal had not been noticed. Figure 9(b) shows a micrograph of a section through the material found in the circumferential grooves in the shaft. The material was loose in the grooves; some was almost identical in appearance with steel wool, whereas other pieces were coarser and more like slivers.

Although the mechanisms of wire wooling are not clearly understood, it is known that wire wooling requires contact between a shaft (or shaft sleeve) and a labyrinth (or bearing), either directly or through buildup of deposits. If the deposit or the stationary part contains hard particles, fine slivers can be cut or spun off the shaft surface. As fine slivers or pieces come off, if the resultant friction and heat are sufficient, additional hard particles may be formed by reaction between the iron and/or chromium and the oil or gas present. Sometimes scabs or solid chunks of laminated or compacted slivers and other deposits are formed (see Fig. 9b). Bearings or labyrinths of babbitt or copper alloys have been associated with this type of failure. Contact-area atmospheres, in addition to bearing oils, have contained air and methyl chloride.

Methods for prevention of wire wooling include: (a) changing the shaft material, (b) using a softer bearing or labyrinth material, (c) changing to a different oil, (d) eliminating the deposits and (e) providing greater clearance.

Adhesive wear, often identified by the presence of scoring, scuffing, galling or seizing, is the result of microscopic welding at the interface between two mutually soluble metals. It frequently occurs on shafts where there is slight movement between the shaft and a mating part such as a gear, a wheel or a pulley.

Adhesive wear has a characteristic torn appearance, because the surfaces actually weld together and then, by continued motion, are torn apart, creating a series of fractures on both surfaces. This indicates that metal-to-metal contact took place between clean, uncontaminated mating surfaces.

Because excessive frictional heat is generated, adhesive wear often can be identified by a change in the microstructure of the metal. For instance, steel may be tempered or rehardened locally by the frictional heat generated.

Influence of Bearings. If acceptable wear resistance is not obtained by optimizing selection of shaft material and heat treatment, consideration should be given to the sliding (sleeve) bearing material and its compatibility with the shaft. Very often, the high-wear area of a shaft may be chromium plated, or be covered with a sleeve that can be discarded and replaced when worn (rather than throwing away an expensive shaft or replacing the bearings). There are risks attendant to the use of these methods, and steps should be taken to avoid or offset their effects.

Brittle Fracture of Shafts

Brittle fractures (which result from cleavage) are associated with the inability of certain materials to deform plastically in the presence of stress at the root of a sharp notch, particularly at low temperatures. Brittle fractures are characterized by sudden fracturing at extremely high rates of crack propagation, perhaps 6000 ft per second or more, with little evidence of distortion in the region of fracture initiation. This type of fracture is characterized by marks known as herringbone or chevron patterns on the fracture surface. The chevrons point toward the origin of the fracture.

Additional information on brittle fractures can be found in the article on Ductile and Brittle Fractures, which begins on page 61 in this volume.

Ductile Fracture of Shafts

Ductile fractures (which result from microvoid coalescence) exhibit evidence of distortion (plastic flow) at the fracture surface similar to that observed in ordinary tensile-test or torsion-test specimens. When a shaft is fractured by a single application of a load greater than the strength of the shaft, usually there is considerable plastic deformation prior to fracture. This deformation often is readily apparent on visual inspection of a shaft that fractured in tension, but often is not obvious when the shaft fractured in torsion. This ability of a material to deform plastically is a property known as ductility. The appearance of the fracture surface of a shaft that failed in a ductile manner also is a function of shaft shape, the type of stress to which the shaft was subjected, rate of loading and, for many alloys, temperature. In general, ductility is decreased by (a) increasing the strength of the metal by cold work or heat treatment; (b) the presence of notches, fillets, holes, scratches, inclusions and porosity in a notch-sensitive material; (c) increasing the rate of loading; and (d) for many alloys, decreasing the temperature.

Ductile fracture of shafts occurs infrequently in normal service. However, ductile fractures may occur if service requirements are underestimated, if the materials used are not as strong as had been assumed, or if the shaft is subjected to a single overload such as in an accident. Fabricating errors such as using the wrong material or using material in the wrong heat treated condition (for instance, annealed instead of quenched and tempered) can result in ductile fractures. (For typical ductile fractures, see Volume 9 of this Handbook.)

Distortion of Shafts

Distortion of a shaft can make the shaft incapable of serving its intended function. Permanent distortion simply means that the applied stress has exceeded the yield strength (but not the tensile strength) of the material. If it is not feasible to modify the design of the shaft, the yield strength of the shaft material must be increased to withstand the applied stress. Yield strength may be increased either by using a stronger material or by heat treating the original material to a higher strength.

Corrosion of Shafts

Most shafts are not subject to severe reduction in life from general corrosion or chemical attack. Corrosion may occur as general surface pitting, may uniformly remove metal from the surface or may uniformly cover the surface with scale or other corrosion products.

Corrosion pits have a relatively minor effect on the load-carrying capacity of a shaft, but they do act as points of stress concentration at which fatigue cracks can originate.

A corrosive environment will greatly accelerate metal fatigue; even exposure of a metal to air results in a shorter fatigue life than that obtained under vacuum. Steel shafts exposed to salt water may fail prematurely by fatigue even if they are thoroughly cleaned periodically. Aerated salt solutions usually attack metal surfaces at the weakest points, such as scratches, cut edges, and points of high strain. To minimize corrosion fatigue, it is necessary to select a material that is resistant to corrosion in the service environment, or to provide the shaft with a protective coating.

Most large shafts and piston rods are not subject to corrosion attack. However, because ship-propeller shafts are exposed to salt water, they are roll burnished, which produces residual surface compressive stresses and inhibits fatigue cracks from originating at corrosion pits. Also, rotating parts such as centrifugal compressor impellers and gas-turbine disks and blades often experience corrosion. Centrifugal compressors frequently handle gases that contain moisture and small amounts of a corrosive gas or liquid. If corrosion attack occurs, a scale is often formed that may be left intact and increased by more corrosion, eroded off by entrained liquids (or solids), or slung off from the rotating shaft.

Stress-corrosion cracking (SCC) occurs as a result of corrosion and stress at the tip of a growing crack. Stress-corrosion cracking often is accompanied or preceded by surface pitting, but general corrosion often is absent, and rapid, overall corrosion does not accompany stress-corrosion cracking.

The stress level necessary for stress-corrosion cracking is below the stress level required for fracture without corrosion. The critical stress may be well below the yield strength of the material, depending on the material and the corrosive conditions. Evidence of corrosion, although not always easy to find, should be present on the surface of a stress-corrosion-cracking fracture up to the start of final rupture.

All of the common materials used in shafts may undergo stress-corrosion cracking under suitable conditions. Factors that influence stress-corrosion cracking, either directly or indirectly, include microstructure; yield strength; hardness; corrodent(s); concentration of corrodent(s); amounts and nature of water, pH, and applied and residual stresses; degree of cold working; and chemical composition of the base metal. (For additional discussion, see the article on Stress-Corrosion Cracking, which begins on page 205 in this volume.)

Corrosion fatigue results when corrosion and an alternating stress — neither of which is severe enough to cause failure by itself — occur simultaneously and thus can cause failure. Once such a condition exists, shaft life will probably be days or weeks, rather than years. Corrosion-fatigue cracking is usually transgranular; branching of the main cracks occurs, although usually not as much as in stress-corrosion cracking. Corrosion products generally are present in the cracks, both at the tips and in regions nearer the origins.

The article on Corrosion-Fatigue Failures, which begins on page 240 in this volume, contains more detailed information on the effect of combined corrosion and fluctuating stress.

Fretting of Shafts

Fretting on a shaft can be a source of serious damage. Production of a reddish-brown powder is characteristic of fretting corrosion on steel. Typical locations for fretting are at splined or keyed hubs, components that are press fitted or shrink fitted to a shaft, and clamped joints. Shot peening, glass-bead peening, and surface rolling are methods that are used to prevent fatigue fracture of shafts because of fretting of joints.

Fretting is discussed in detail in the article on Fretting Failures, which begins on page 154 in this volume.

Creep and Stress Rupture of Shafts

Creep, by definition, is time-dependent strain occurring under stress imposed at elevated temperature, provided that the operational load does not exceed the yield strength of the metal. If creep continues until fracture occurs, the part is said to have failed by stress rupture.

Some high-temperature applications such as gas turbines and jet aircraft engines may require materials to operate

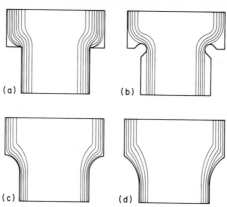

Fig. 10. Effect of size of fillet radius on stress concentration at a change in shaft diameter. See text for discussion.

under extreme conditions of temperature and stress with only a limited amount of deformation by creep. In other high-temperature applications, the permissible deformation is high and may not even be limited as long as rupture does not occur during the intended life of the part. For this type of service, stress-rupture data, rather than long-term creep data, are used for design.

Common Stress Raisers in Shafts

Most service failures in shafts are attributable largely to some condition that causes an intensification of stress. In local regions, the stress value is raised above a value at which the material is capable of withstanding the number of loading cycles that corresponds to a satisfactory service life. Only one small area needs to be repeatedly stressed above the fatigue strength of the material for a crack to be initiated. An apparently insignificant imperfection such as a small surface irregularity may severely reduce the fatigue strength of a shaft if the stress level at the imperfection is high. The most vulnerable zone in torsional and bending fatigue is the shaft surface; an abrupt change of surface configuration may have a damaging effect, depending on the orientation of the discontinuity to the direction of stress.

All but the simplest shafts contain oil holes, keyways, or changes in shaft diameter. The transition from one diameter to another, the location and finish of an oil hole, and the type and shape of a keyway exert a marked influence on the magnitude of the resulting stress-concentration and fatigue-notch factors, which often range in numerical value from 1.0 to 5.0 and sometimes attain values of 10.0 or higher.

Types of Stress Raisers. The majority of stress raisers can be placed into one of the following general groups:

1 Nonuniformities in the shape of the shaft, such as steps at changes in di-

ameter, broad integral collars, holes, abrupt corners, keyways, grooves, threads, splines and press-fitted or shrink-fitted attachments
2 Surface discontinuities arising from fabrication practices or service damage, such as seams, nicks, notches, machining marks, identification marks, forging laps and seams, pitting and corrosion
3 Internal discontinuities such as porosity, shrinkage, gross nonmetallic inclusions, cracks and voids.

Most shaft failures are initiated at primary (group 1) stress-raisers, but secondary (group 2 or group 3) stress raisers may contribute to a failure. For instance, a change in shaft diameter can result in stress intensification at the transition zone; if there is a surface irregularity or other discontinuity in this zone, the stress is sharply increased around the discontinuity.

Influence of Changes in Shaft Diameter

A change in shaft diameter concentrates the stresses at the change in diameter and in the smaller-diameter portion.

The effects of an abrupt change and three gradual changes in section on stress concentration are shown schematically in Fig. 10. The sharp corner at the intersection of the shoulder and shaft in Fig. 10(a) concentrates the stresses at the corner as they pass from the large to the small diameter. The large-radius fillet shown in Fig. 10(d) permits the stresses to flow with a minimum of restriction. However, the fillet must be tangent with the smaller-diameter section; otherwise, a sharp intersection will result, overcoming the beneficial effect of the large-radius fillet.

In the following example, fracture of the large-diameter main shaft in a coal pulverizer originated in a small-radius fillet at the shoulder between two different diameters of the shaft. Increasing the size of the radius reduced the incidence of failure.

Example 4. Fatigue Fracture of a 6150 Steel Main Shaft in a Ball-and-Race-Type Coal Pulverizer (Fig. 11)

Unusual noises were noted by the operator of a ball-and-race-type coal pulverizer (shown schematically in Fig. 11a), and the unit was taken out of service to investigate the cause. The pulverizer had been in service for ten years.

The lower grinding ring of the pulverizer was attached to the outer main shaft, as shown in Fig. 11(a). The upper grinding ring was suspended by springs from a spider that was attached to the main shaft. The weight of the upper grinding ring and the load imposed by the springs resulted in a total force of 18,000 lb on the pulverizer balls.

The shaft was made of 6150 steel normalized to a hardness of about 285 Bhn.

Investigation. Visual examination of the shaft revealed a circumferential crack in the main shaft just below the upper radial bearing at an abrupt change in shaft diameter.

The shaft was set up in a lathe to machine out the crack for repair welding, and the smaller (7-in.-diam) end was found to be slightly eccentric with the remainder of the shaft. The crack did not disappear after a ¼-in.-deep cut, and the crack was opened by striking the small end of the shaft. The shaft broke about ½ in. from the crack.

Examination of the fracture surface (see Fig. 11b) revealed a previous fracture, almost perpendicular to the axis of the shaft, that resulted from torsional loading acting along a plane of maximum shear.

Although the shaft operated at the relatively low speed of 82 rpm, the weight of the upper portion of the shaft, the spider, and the upper ring caused the shaft to repair itself by friction welding in a band about 1 in. wide beginning at the periphery of the shaft. Thus, friction welding was confined to a small part of the 7-in.-diam cross section. The center region of the fracture surface (see Fig. 11b) contained swirls of metal softened by frictional heat as a result of rotation of the lower part of the shaft. Welding of the plasticized outer ring of metal on the shaft and solidification of the swirls probably occurred while the pulverizer was shut down.

Examination of the machined surface revealed light lines parallel to the visible crack. These light lines generally followed bands containing large grains. The lines were thought to be fatigue cracks.

The hardness of the shaft in the friction welded area was Rockwell C 38 to 49, and inward from the weld area the hardness was Rockwell C 31 to 33.

Conclusion. The second fracture of the shaft was by fatigue, which resulted from an eccentric condition after the shaft was friction welded and from the inherent vibrations within the machine. Shafts in other coal pulverizers at the same plant fractured in the same region after similar service lives.

Corrective Measures. The shaft was repaired by welding a new, 8-in.-diam section to the older, longer section and machining to the required diameters. The fatigue cracks in the longer section were machined away before repair welding. Liquid penetrant inspection was performed to ensure soundness of the metal in the older section. The repaired shaft was machined to provide a taper between the two diameters, rather than reproduce the sharp change in diameter in the original design. The taper section was carefully blended with the smaller diameter so that there were no sharp corners.

The repaired coal-pulverizer shaft operated satisfactorily for more than five years. As shafts in other units failed, they were repaired by the same technique.

The pushrod described in the following example was fabricated from two different alloy steels by inertia welding. A hole was drilled in the end of one piece to reduce the surface area to be inertia welded. High stress concentration oc-curred at the intersection of the tapered surface produced by the drill point and the surface of the hole.

Example 5. Bending-Fatigue Fracture of an Inertia Welded Alloy Steel Pushrod Originating at a Sharp Internal Corner and a Decarburized Surface (Fig. 12)

The pushrod shown in Fig. 12 fractured two weeks after it was installed in a mud pump operating at 160 rpm with a discharge pressure of 2100 psi. The pushrod was made by joining two pieces of bar stock by inertia welding. Each piece was rough bored or drilled to produce a wall thickness of about ½ in. at the surfaces to be inertia welded. The flange portion was made of 94B17 steel, and the shaft was made of 8620 steel. After welding, the rod was machined, carburized and hardened to Rockwell C 60, then the shaft was chromium plated to within ½ in. of the flange.

Investigation. Visual examination of the pushrod disclosed that fracture had occurred in the shaft portion at the intersection of the ½-in.-thick wall and the tapered surface at the bottom of the hole. This intersection was about ½ in. from the weld.

The fracture surface contained indications that a fatigue crack had initiated at the inner surface and progressed around the entire inner circumference, forming a narrow plateau, before propagating outward to final fracture.

Operation of the pushrod after it had fractured obliterated some detail of the fatigue pattern on the fracture surface, but it still was evident that one-way bending

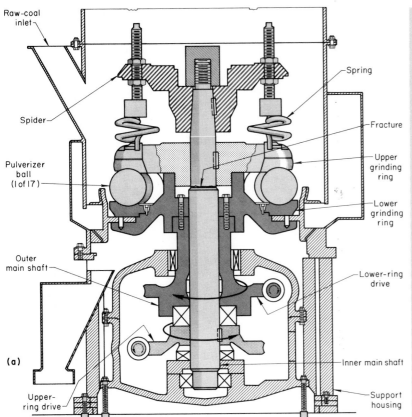

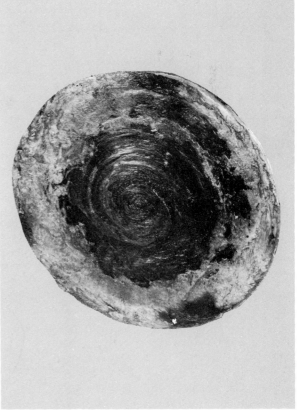

Fig. 11. (a) *Section through coal pulverizer, showing the inner main shaft that fractured, repaired itself by friction welding and fractured a second time.* (b) *Photograph of the friction welded surface.* (Example 4)

stresses had influenced cracking. The amount of coarse texture on the fracture surface indicated that fatigue cracking had occurred for a short time.

Detail A in Fig. 12 shows a macrograph of a section through the weld and fracture region. A heavily decarburized layer was found on the inner surface of the flange portion but was not detectable in the shaft portion. The inner surface had a poor finish and there was a sharp corner at the intersection of the sidewall and bottom of the hole. The weld flash protruded from the inner wall, producing a small-radius fillet at the wall surface. Except for the metal extrusion, the weld zone was almost undetectable.

A metallographic specimen taken from near the fracture surface showed that the microstructure of the metal at the inner surface contained acicular ferrite and bainite, indicative of decarburization (see Fig. 12b). The microstructure of the metal

approximately 1/16 in. from the inner surface contained low-carbon martensite and bainite (see Fig. 12c).

Hardness of the flange was equivalent to Rockwell C 27 at the bottom of the hole and Rockwell C 37 on the inner-wall surface. The shaft had a hardness equivalent to Rockwell C 22 at the bottom of the hole and Rockwell C 27 at the inner-wall surface.

Sample parts having shapes and dimensions similar to those of the fractured pushrod were joined by inertia welding and then sectioned so that the weld area and inner surfaces could be examined. The sample weldment was neither heat treated nor machined. Sharp corners and rough surfaces were found that were similar to those on the fractured part (see detail A in Fig. 12). The cut surface was ground smooth and etched, which revealed the heat-affected zone of the weld but no indications of abnormal oxidation or decarburization of the inner surfaces.

Conclusion. The pushrod failed in fatigue primarily from one-way bending stresses. Cracking was initiated in a sharp, rough corner at the intersection of the sidewall and the bottom of a drilled hole that acted as a stress raiser. The stress raiser created by the abrupt section change was accentuated by the roughness of the drilled surface and by the decarburized layer. Decarburization occurred during heat treatment and was caused by the atmosphere trapped in the cavity formed by friction welding.

Corrective Measures. The design of the pushrod was changed to a one-piece forging. To produce a high-quality welded pushrod, it would be necessary to provide radii at the corners of the drilled holes, finish machine the inner surface, and drill a hole in the flange end of the rod to permit circulation of atmosphere during heat treatment.

Press-Fitted Members. Gears, pulleys, wheels, impellers and similar components often are assembled on shafts by means of press fitting or shrink fitting, which can result in stress raisers under bending stress. Typical stress flow lines in a plain shaft at a press-fitted member are shown in Fig. 13(a). Enlarging the shaft at the press-fitted component and using a large-radius fillet would produce a stress distribution such as that schematically shown in Fig. 13(b). A small-radius fillet at the shoulder would result in a stress pattern similar to that shown in Fig. 10(a).

An investigation was conducted to study the influence of absolute specimen dimensions on the fatigue strength of specimens with press-fitted bushings. The tests were carried out on specimens of St 35 carbon steel (0.18% max C, 0.40% min Mn, 0.35% max Si, 0.05% max P, and 0.05% max S; ultimate tensile strength, 57 kg per square millimeter) and high-quality 38 CrNiMo alloy steel with ultimate tensile strength of 74 kg per square millimeter (similar to AISI 9840). Specimen blanks were cut from the surfaces of large forgings that were to be used for propeller shafts. Two groups of specimens were tested: (a) smooth cylindrical specimens 5, 12, 27 and 50 mm in diameter, with gage portions equal in length to four specimen diameters and shoulder radii equal to one diameter; and (b) smooth cylindrical specimens 5, 12, 27 and 50 mm in diameter with press-fitted bushings. The outside diameter and length of each bushing were equal to two specimen diameters, and thus the bushings were similar in size to actual machine parts of this kind. The bushings were made of normalized (195 Bhn) St 34 steel (0.15% max C, 0.08% max P, and 0.06% max S) and a brass alloy of unreported composition. Press fitting was done to class 2 tolerances.

The specimens were tested in rotary bending at a constant frequency of 50 cps. The test base (in air) was 10⁷ cycles

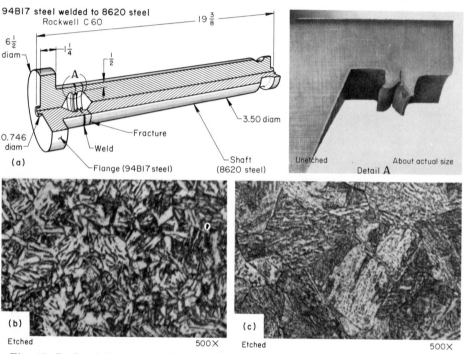

Fig. 12. *Pushrod that fractured in bending fatigue after being fabricated by inertia welding; and micrographs showing structure of decarburized inner surface and sound metal below the decarburized layer (Example 5)*

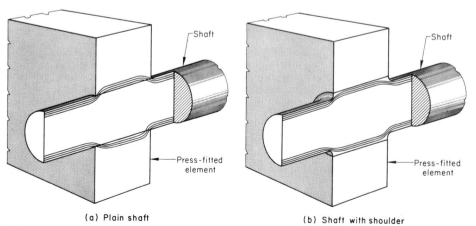

(a) Plain shaft   (b) Shaft with shoulder

Fig. 13. *Schematic illustration of stress distribution in two types of rotating shafts with press-fitted elements under a bending load*

for specimens without bushings and 5×10^7 cycles for specimens with bushings. The results, which are given in Table 1, showed that the fatigue limit of steel specimens was sharply reduced by the presence of press-fitted bushings and that the magnitude of this reduction increased with increasing steel strength.

The endurance of specimens with press-fitted bushings depends on specimen diameter to a greater extent than does the endurance of specimens without bushings. The effect of specimen diameter on the fatigue strength of both plain carbon steel and alloy steel specimens with press-fitted bushings was more pronounced when the bushings were made of steel than when they were made of brass.

The main cause of the reduction in the fatigue strength of the specimens with bushings was friction between the bushing and the shaft, which resulted from the cyclic loads in rotary bending, and the resulting wear of the shaft. The wear, which depends on the frictional force (that is, on the distribution of specific pressure), should vary (as did the pressure) along the shaft surface. When a shaft with a press-fitted bushing is bent, the maximum pressure should be near the bushing edge, at a point whose location will vary depending on the fit.

Friction produces wear of the shaft, leads to wear-induced surface roughness, and causes a local temperature increase, all of which promote nucleation and growth of cracks. Friction also leads to the destruction of oxide films, which passivate and strengthen metal parts, and activates metal surfaces as a result of plastic deformation. These factors facilitate chemical reaction between the metal surfaces and the working environment; the resulting damage is known as fretting.

The fatigue strength of specimens up to 20 mm in diameter was reduced more by the brass bushings than by the steel bushings. Conversely, the fatigue strength of specimens greater than 20 mm in diameter was reduced less by the brass bushings than by the steel bushings. The steel bushings, which are harder and more rigid than brass bushings, exhibited (when in contact with steel) a higher friction coefficient, and produced more intense wear, than the brass bushings. Other factors being equal, the environment had a more damaging effect on small-diameter specimens; the fatigue strength of large-diameter specimens was influenced predominantly by stress raisers produced as a result of friction-induced wear.

Longitudinal grooves in shafts, such as keyways and splines, are the origins of many service failures of shafts subjected to torsional stress. Most of these failures result from fatigue fracture where a small crack has initiated at a sharp corner be-

cause of stress concentrations. The crack gradually enlarges as cycles of service stress are repeated until the remaining section breaks. A sharp corner in a keyway can cause the local stress to be as much as ten times the average nominal stress.

Failures of this kind can be avoided by using a half-round keyway, which permits the use of a round key, or by using a generous fillet radius in the keyway. Good results are obtained by the use of fillets having radii equal to approximately one-half the depth of the keyway. A half-round keyway produces a local stress of only twice the average stress, thus providing greater load-carrying ability than that permitted by a square keyway. Many shafts with square keyways do not fracture in service because stresses are low or because fillets with generous radii are used.

In an assembly in which a keyed member was loosely fitted to a shaft, nearly all the alternating torque was transmitted through the key, resulting in initiation of cracks at the bottom edge of the keyway of the shaft and producing a peeling type of fracture (see Fig. 14a). Occasionally, peeling progresses entirely around the shaft and results in a sharp-edged shell like that in Fig. 14(b). Peel-

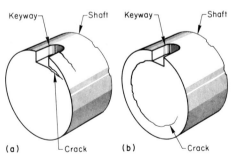

Fig. 14. Peeling-type cracks in shafts, originating at keyways

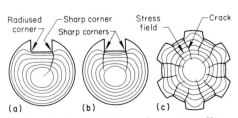

Fig. 15. Stress fields, and corresponding torsional-fatigue cracks, in shafts with keyways or splines

ing-type fractures also are illustrated by fractograph 4811 on page 382, and by photograph 4882 on page 402, in Volume 9 of this Handbook.

Stress fields, and corresponding torsional-fatigue cracks, in shafts with keyways or splines are shown in Fig. 15. In Fig. 15(a), the fillet in one corner of the keyway was radiused and the fillet in the other corner was sharp, which resulted in a single crack; note that this crack progresses approximately normal to the original stress field. In Fig. 15(b), both fillets in the keyway corners were sharp, which resulted in two cracks that did not follow the original stress field, a condition which is the result of the cross effect of cracks on the stress field.

A splined shaft subjected to alternating torsion can crack along the bottom edges of the splines, as shown in Fig. 15(c). This is another instance of a highly localized stress field strongly influencing crack development.

Peeling that originated at the corner of a shaft keyway is described in the following example.

Example 6. Fatigue Cracking of 4340 Steel Compressor Shafts Because of Cyclic Stresses Induced by Gear-Type Couplings (Fig. 16)

A plant utilized high-horsepower electric motors to drive large compressors required for a manufacturing process. Eight compressors had shafts made of 4340 steel quenched and tempered to a hardness of Rockwell C 35 to 39, and gear-type couplings. The compressors operated for short periods at power levels up to 5000 hp and for longer periods at slightly above 4000 hp. The design of the shaft and the keyways is shown in Fig. 16(a). Two keys, spaced 180° apart, were expected to transmit the load so that an interference fit between shaft and coupling would not be required, thus simplifying maintenance.

After only a few months of operation at above 4000 hp, six of the eight compressor shafts were found to be cracked in a keyway, and one of the six had fractured.

Investigation. Visual examination of the fractured shaft disclosed cracks propagating from one of the keyways. Cracks that originated in the keyway corner and propagated to the surface are shown in Fig. 16(a). Examination of a cross section of a shaft revealed that the crack propagated from the keyway corner circumferentially around the shaft but remained near the surface, as shown by the arrow in section

Table 1. Fatigue Strength of Steel Specimens Without Bushings, With Steel Bushings, and With Brass Bushings

| Specimen diameter, mm | Fatigue strength, kg per sq mm, of specimens of: | | | | | |
| | St 35 carbon steel | | | 38 CrNiMo alloy steel | | |
	Without bushings	With steel bushings	With brass bushings	Without bushings	With steel bushings	With brass bushings
5	27.0	16.0	15.0	32.5	20.0	15.0
12	26.0	16.0	14.5	32.0	17.0	15.5
27	22.5	12.5(a)	12.5	30.0	12.5	15.0
50	20.5	10.5	11.0	30.0	10.5	12.5

(a) 20-mm-diam specimen

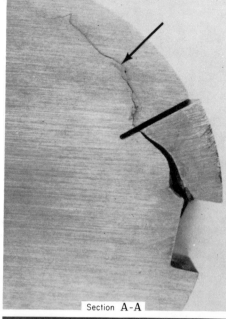

4340 steel
Rockwell C 35 to 39

$\frac{15}{16}$
$\frac{1}{8}$
$4\frac{3}{4}$
$\frac{1}{8}$

A

Crack

A

Keyway
(1 of 2)

$4\frac{3}{8}$—12 UN—2A

5.420 diam

(a) Compressor shaft

Keyway — $\frac{1}{8}$R

(b)

Section A-A

(c)

Fig. 16. Compressor shaft made of 4340 steel that fractured because of peeling-type fatigue cracking; and photographs showing crack path, failure origin, and beach marks on fracture surfaces of shaft and key (Example 6)

A-A in Fig. 16. This type of cracking occurs when there is slippage between a shaft and a coupling.

Fretting was found on the shaft surface both in and near the keyways. Upset keys were found, indicating that slippage had occurred. Fretting was noted on the non-loaded side of the keys, which suggested that appreciable chattering had occurred. The fretting greatly reduced the fatigue limit of the shaft metal and resulted in initiation of fatigue cracks.

Examination of the fractured shaft revealed beach marks around the 1/8-in.-radius keyway corner (arrow in Fig. 16b). These beach marks indicated that fatigue cracking had initiated at the corner radius and propagated across the shaft. As shown in Fig. 16(c), similar fatigue marks were observed on the key that fractured, radiating from one corner (at arrow). Propagation of fatigue cracks was the result of repetitive impact loading.

Chemical analysis confirmed that the shafts were made of 4340 steel. Hardness traverses indicated that the shaft metal was within an acceptable hardness range.

High cyclic bending stresses were caused by misalignment between the electric motor and compressor and were transmitted to the shaft through the geared coupling. Measurements on shafts using a flexible disk-type coupling indicated cyclic bending stresses of less than 1000 psi.

Conclusions. The shafts failed by fatigue cracking that initiated at the corner radii of the keyways.

The cyclic stresses that caused fretting and fatigue cracking in the keyways were the result of bending stresses from motor-to-compressor misalignment and were transmitted to the shaft through the gear-type coupling.

Corrective Measures. Flexible-disk-type couplings capable of transmitting the required horsepower were installed on the

shafts. After three years of operation at 3000 to 4000 hp with the new couplings, no failures of shafts or keys had been reported.

Size and mass of shafts have considerable influence on residual stresses, load distribution, and mechanical properties. Mechanical properties and residual stresses in quenched-and-tempered shafts are greatly influenced by both mass and diameter, which affect the cooling rate during heat treatment. The difference between surface and internal properties becomes greater where the metal does not harden throughout the section because its critical diameter is exceeded.

Influence of Fabricating Practices

Surface discontinuities produced during manufacture of a shaft and during assembly of the shaft into a machine can become points of stress concentration and thus contribute to shaft failure. Operations or conditions that produce this type of stress raiser include:

1 Manufacturing operations that introduce stress raisers such as tool marks and scratches
2 Manufacturing operations that introduce high tensile stresses in the surface, such as improper grinding, repair welding, electromachining and arc burns
3 Processes that introduce metal weakening, such as forging flow lines that are not parallel with the surface, hydrogen embrittlement from plating, or decarburization from heat treatment.

Fatigue strength may be increased by imparting high compressive residual stresses to the surface of the shaft. This can be accomplished by surface rolling or burnishing, shot peening, tumbling, coining or induction hardening.

Improper Machining. There are many ways in which improper machining can lead to shaft failures, and unless they are recognized, correction of service-failure problems can be difficult. The metal on the surface of a machined part can be cold worked and highly stressed to an appreciable depth (approximately 0.020 to 0.030 in.). Occasionally the heat generated in machining — particularly in grinding — is sufficient to heat a thin layer of the steel above the transformation temperature and thus cause martensitic hardening at the surface on cooling. Stresses resulting from thermal expansion and contraction of the locally heated metal may even be great enough to cause cracking of the surface layer (grinding cracks). A rough-machining operation can produce surface cracks and sharp corners, which concentrate stresses.

Scratches or surface notches produced during hot trimming or snag grinding of flash can be points of initiation of fatigue cracks, as in the following example.

Example 7. Fatigue Fracture of a 4140 Steel Forged Crankshaft Resulting From Stress Raisers That Were Created During Hot Trimming (Fig. 17)

Textile-machine crankshafts like that shown in Fig. 17 usually were forged from 1035 steel, but because of service conditions, the material was changed to 4140 steel. The forgings were made from 2⁵⁄₃₂-in.-diam bar stock by the following sequence of operations: cut bars to length, bend hot, upset, hot trim flash, hot press, inspect visually and ship.

The crankshafts were failing by transverse fracture of one cheek after one to three years of service. The expected life was 20 years of continuous service (24 hr per day, 365 days per year).

One complete forging that had fractured (No. 1 in this example), and a section containing the fractured cheek on the shorter shaft of another forging (No. 2), were sent to the laboratory so that the cause of failure could be determined.

Investigation. Visual examination of the fracture surfaces of both crankshafts revealed indications of fatigue failure; however, the origins were not readily visible, as can be seen in Fig. 17(b). The surfaces had a clean, fine-grain structure, but the edges were peened — evidently the result of damage after fracture. No significant evidence of brittle fracture was present on either of the forgings.

The surfaces of the throws at the parting line contained rough grooves from hot trimming of the flash and from snag grinding, as shown in Fig. 17(c) and (d). Forging No. 2 contained the most severe of such markings.

Longitudinal and transverse sections were prepared and etched with hydrochloric acid at a temperature of 71 to 77 C (160 to 170 F). The steel was of good quality and contained the normal amount of nonmetallic inclusions but no segregation or pipe.

Examination of an as-polished specimen revealed no intergranular oxidation. Etching the specimen with a 10% sulfuric acid and 10% nitric acid solution revealed no evidence of burning or overheating of the steel.

An area containing shallow surface folds was found on the outer face of one cheek of the throw on forging No. 1 (see Fig. 17e). As shown in Fig. 17(f), the metal around one of the folds contained some ferrite, and the forged surface was slightly decarburized. Also, a fatigue crack had initiated in the fold and was propagating across the cheek. Examination of a section through the fracture surface disclosed cold working of the surface, which could have been the result of a rather extended period of fatigue cracking.

Chemical analysis of the two forgings found the metal to be 4140 steel, as specified. The hardness of the two forgings at the subsurface, midradius and core ranged from Rockwell C 19 to 22. The specified hardness of the machined forging was unknown.

Tensile strength of the forgings ranged from 114,500 to 118,500 psi, and yield strength at 0.2% offset was 84,000 to 90,000 psi. Elongation in 1.5 in. was 20.6 to 22%, and reduction in area was 56.2 to 59.4%. These properties were representative of

4140 steel quenched and tempered to a hardness of Rockwell C 20 to 22. The general microstructure of the forgings was tempered bainite; the grain size was ASTM No. 6 to 8.

Conclusions. Fatigue cracking resulted in the transverse fracture of one cheek in each of the two crankshafts submitted for examination. In crankshaft No. 1, fatigue cracks were initiated at a shallow hot work defect. A rough surface resulting from hot trimming or snag grinding of the forging flash was the point of initiation of fatigue cracks in crankshaft No. 2.

Corrective Measures. Before being machined, the forgings were normalized, hardened and tempered to Rockwell C 28 to 32 to increase fatigue strength. The quenching

procedure was changed to produce a more complete martensite transformation and to increase the ratio of yield strength to tensile strength.

The surfaces were inspected by the magnetic-particle method, and shallow folds, notches or extremely rough surfaces were removed by grinding carefully.

Identification Marks. Excessive stresses may be introduced in shafts by stamped identification marks that indicate manufacturing date or lot number, steel heat number, size, or part number. The location of such a mark, and the method by which it is made, can be important. Identification marks should not be placed in

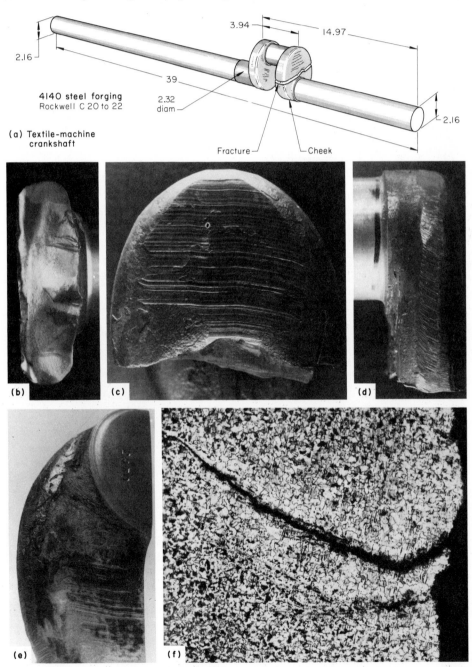

Fig. 17. (a) Textile-machine crankshaft, made from a 4140 steel forging, that fractured in fatigue that originated at machining marks and forging defects. (b) Fracture surface. (c) Hot trim marks. (d) Snag grinding marks. (e) Hot folds. (f) Section (2% nital etch, 100×) through a hot fold. (Example 7)

areas of high bending or torsional stresses. For shafts, this often requires that they be located either on the end face or on an adjoining collar, but surface-finish requirements on the end of the shaft cannot be ignored if thrust loads are taken at that location. Stamping of marks with straight-line portions is the most likely to cause cracks, although characters with rounded contours also can cause cracking, as shown in Fig. 18. Stamping of metal shaft surfaces should be avoided because it is impossible to predict on which surface stamp marks will cause cracking in service. (See also the section on Identification Marking on page 119 in the article on Fatigue Failures.)

Marking of a part by electroetching also should be done in a region of low stress to avoid the possibility of producing a zone of untempered martensite that would serve as a stress raiser, as in the example that follows.

Example 8. Fatigue Fracture of a 4337 Steel Articulated Rod Originating at an Electroetched Numeral (Fig. 19)

The articulated rod in an aircraft engine fractured after being in operation for 138 hr since the engine had been overhauled; total operating time was unknown. The rod was made from a 4337 steel (AMS 6412) forging and was quenched and tempered to Rockwell C 36 to 40.

Investigation. Visual examination disclosed that the rod had broken into two pieces, approximately 2½ in. from the center of the piston-pin-bushing bore. The fracture had nucleated at an electroetched numeral 5 on one of the flange surfaces (at B in Fig. 19a). Around the nucleus was a series of concentric beach marks (A and C in Fig. 19a) that extended almost the full width of the flange and about one-half the width of the web.

Metallographic examination of a polished-and-etched section through the fracture origin revealed a notch (at E in Fig. 19b) that was caused by arc erosion during electroetching.

The microstructure of the metal at the origin consisted of a remelted zone (D in Fig. 19b) and a layer of untempered martensite 0.015 in. deep (F in Fig. 19b). Small cracks were observed in the remelt area and were the result of thermal stresses caused by the high temperatures developed during electroetching.

The hardness of the untempered martensite was Rockwell C 56, and hardness of the tempered-martensite core was Rockwell C 40. The hardness of the rod (Rockwell C 40), and the microstructure of the tempered martensite remote from the electroetched area, indicated that the material had been properly heat treated.

Conclusions. Fatigue fracture of the rod was caused by a metallurgical notch that resulted from electroetching of an identification number on the flange.

Corrective Measure. Marking of the articulated rods by electroetching was discontinued because of the detrimental effect of electroetching such highly stressed parts.

Fig. 18. *Cracks in a shaft radiating from deep identification marks made with steel stamps. Cracking occurred during heat treatment of the shaft.*

Residual Surface Stresses. Most machining operations produce notches and also may cause residual tensile stresses on the surface of the workpiece. Grinding can cause local high-temperature heating followed by very rapid cooling as the surface of the workpiece leaves the grinding-wheel-contact area. Grinding cracks can result and these cracks can provide points of fatigue-crack initiation. However, grinding under properly controlled conditions provides a surface with a minimal amount of residual stress.

Grinding cracks are sometimes visible in oblique light but are often so tight that they are impossible to see. They can be detected readily by magnetic-particle inspection, by fluorescent-liquid-penetrant inspection, or by etching in cold dilute nitric acid. If grinding cracks are not de-

tected before the shaft is put in service, the cracks may enlarge such that the shaft can fail by fatigue or brittle fracture. Grinding cracks often show a characteristic pattern; light grinding cracks occur as parallel cracks at 90° to the direction of grinding, whereas heavy grinding cracks have a rectangular network pattern.

Residual surface stresses also are produced by electrical discharge machining (EDM). The cutting effect is produced by a succession of sparks between the electrode and the workpiece. Each spark heats a small volume of metal to a temperature well above its melting point. Most of the molten metal is removed from the part by the action of the spark and the surrounding liquid dielectric, but a thin white surface layer remains on the workpiece and resolidifies as it is quenched by the surrounding mass of metal. The thickness of the white (untempered martensite) layer varies from 0.0002 in. on finishing cuts to 0.003 in. on roughing cuts.

Beneath the quenched surface layer is another layer of steel that is gradiently heated during electrical discharge machining; thus, if the workpiece originally was in the hardened condition, the gradiently heated layer is gradiently tempered. The lowest tempered hardness is adjacent to the quenched layer and the hardness gradually rises in subsequent layers until

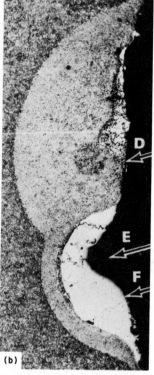

Fig. 19. (a) *Fracture surface of an articulated rod made from a 4337 steel forging, showing fracture origin (B) at an electroetched numeral, and beach marks (A and C). (b) Micrograph (at 100×) of a section, etched in 2% nital, through fracture origin, showing remelted zone (D), notch produced by electroetching (E), and untempered martensite (F). (Example 8)*

the original base hardness is reached. The tempered layer is similar metallurgically to the heat-affected zone in welding and is impossible to avoid. Electrical discharge machining often produces an as-quenched martensitic layer of base metal that was not molten, but only heated above the critical temperature to a depth about the same as the white layer. Frequently this layer cannot be distinguished as separate from the re-melted white layer. The gradiently tempered zone, when hardened steel is cut by EDM, varies in depth from about 0.002 in. for finishing cuts up to 0.030 in. for roughing cuts.

The following example describes fracture of a hardened tool steel mandrel in which a hole had been drilled by electrical discharge machining.

Example 9. Fatigue Fracture of an A2 Tool Steel Rolling-Tool Mandrel That Was Initiated at Cracks Formed by Electrical Discharge Machining of a Hole (Fig. 20)

The mandrel shown in Fig. 20 was part of a rolling tool used for mechanically joining two tubes before they were installed in a nuclear reactor. The operation consisted of expanding the end of a zirconium tube into a stainless steel cylinder having an inside diameter slightly larger than the outside diameter of the zirconium tube.

Difficulty was experienced in withdrawing the tool, and a ¼-in.-diam hole was drilled by electrical discharge machining (EDM) through the square end of the hardened mandrel.

The mandrel, which fractured after making five rolled joints, was made of A2 tool steel. The tapered end was hardened to Rockwell C 60 to 61, and the remainder of the mandrel to Rockwell C 50 to 55.

Visual Examination. Fracture had occurred at approximately 45° through the ¼-in.-diam hole in the square end and progressed into the threaded section to form a pyramid-shape fragment, as shown in de-

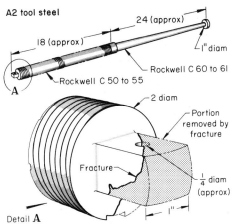
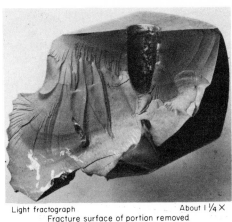

Fig. 20. An A2 tool steel mandrel, for a tube-expanding tool, in which fracture originated at ¼-in.-diam hole in square end that was drilled by electrical discharge machining; and fractograph showing crack pattern on fracture surface that originated at the hole (Example 9)

tail A in Fig. 20. The fracture surfaces exhibited brittle fracture characteristics but with clearly defined beach marks. The fracture pattern was characteristic of a torsional fatigue fracture.

The fracture originated on both sides and near the top of the hole in the square end, as shown in the fractograph in Fig. 20. (Note poor surface finish of hole.) Examination at approximately 10 diameters revealed that the rough surface was the result of the metal having been melted.

Metallographic examination (at a magnification of 250 diameters) of specimens taken through the fracture origin revealed that melting had occurred around the hole, resulting in an irregular zone of untempered martensite with cracks radiating from the surface of the hole. The core material away from the hole exhibited a microstructure of fine tempered martensite containing some carbide particles.

The martensitic zones around the hole had a hardness of Rockwell C 68 to 70; the core structure had a hardness of Rockwell C 60 to 61.

Conclusion. Failure of the mandrel was the result of torsional fatigue initiated by

cracks formed by the electrical discharge machining process used to drill the hole in the square end.

Propagation of the crack was accelerated by the hardness of the material, which was considered exceptionally high for this application.

Corrective Measures. The hole through the square end of the mandrel was incorporated into the design of the tool and was drilled and reamed before heat treatment.

The specified hardness of the threaded portion and square end of the mandrel was changed to Rockwell C 45 to 50, from the original hardness of Rockwell C 50 to 55. The specified hardness of the tapered end remained at Rockwell C 60 to 61.

Damage During Assembly. Operations performed during assembly sometimes can introduce misalignment, which can be detrimental to the performance of shafts. Proper alignment of components such as bearings, seals, couplings, pedestals and foundation has an influence on vibration and hence on the fatigue performance of shafts.

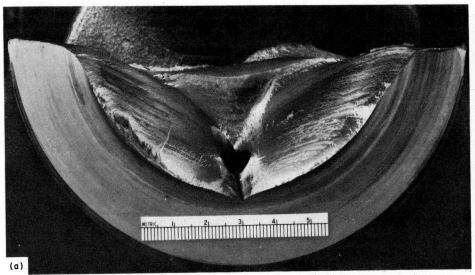

Fig. 21. (a) Fatigue marks on the fracture surface of a diesel-engine crankshaft that broke because of misalignment. (b) Micrograph, at 500×, of a nital-etched section through the fracture origin, showing a small crack (at arrow) and some inclusions.

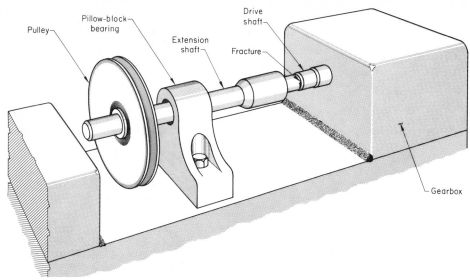

Fig. 22. Shaft assembly in which height of pillow-block bearing caused misalignment of extension shaft with drive shaft, resulting in bending-fatigue fracture

Misalignment, or even a change in alignment within tolerance limits, in conjunction with a stress raiser such as a deep scratch or a large nonmetallic inclusion, may initiate a fatigue crack. Figure 21(a) shows the fracture surface of a crankshaft for a diesel engine that had been operating for several years. The engine was overhauled, and the bearing journals were chromium plated. The crankshaft failed after the engine had operated only a few hundred hours.

No scratches or tool marks were found at the fracture origin. Metallographic examination of a section through the fracture surface revealed a very fine crack parallel to the fracture surface and a line of inclusions, as seen in Fig. 21(b).

Misalignment of the extension shaft with the drive shaft of the assembly shown in Fig. 22 resulted in bending-fatigue fracture of the shaft at a change in shaft diameter. The drive shaft protruded from a gearbox that was mounted rigidly on the base of the machine, but the extension shaft was supported in a pillow-block bearing. Tightening the pillow block deflected the extension shaft downward such as to impart significant bending stress to the drive shaft.

Heat Treatment. The mechanical properties of the material in most shafts are developed through heat treatment or cold drawing. For quenched-and-tempered shafts less than 3 in. in diameter, a predominantly martensitic microstructure tempered to a hardness of 235 Bhn or higher is typical.

Where the properties of the shaft material throughout its entire cross section are important, use of the lowest austenitizing temperature consistent with the strength required usually is good practice. The higher the fracture toughness of a shaft (high K_{Ic}) the larger the crack needed to cause fracture.

For most shafts, where surface stresses are high and crack initiation is of concern, surface decarburization can be a major problem.

For very large shafts, rotational speeds are often high enough that internal centrifugal stresses are of major concern. For such shafts, heat treatments are designed to give optimum strength and toughness uniformly across the full section.

Where parts have been tempered to a hardness level below which brittle fracture would occur, nitriding can be used to produce a compressively stressed hardened case that will improve the fatigue limit, as in the following example.

Example 10. Fatigue Fracture of an 8640 Steel Shaft From a Fuel-Injection-Pump Governor Because of Insufficient Fatigue Strength (Fig. 23)

The shaft shown in Fig. 23 was from a fuel-injection-pump governor that controlled the speed of a diesel engine used in trucks and tractors. Shafts in newly installed governors began breaking after having been in operation for only a few days.

Specifications required the shaft to be made of 8640 steel heat treated to a hardness of Rockwell C 32 to 36.

The shaft had a cross hole and a groove that were part of a force-feed lubricating system for a sleeve that moved longitudinally on the shaft to control the amount of fuel delivered to the engine.

The shaft rotated at relatively high speed and was subjected to shock loading; therefore, the mechanism that drove the shaft included a slip clutch designed to eliminate transmission of shock to the governor shaft.

Investigation. Visual examination of the broken shaft showed that fracture had initiated in the sharp corner at the bottom of the ⅛-in.-diam longitudinal hole, as shown in section B-B in Fig. 23. Beach marks were observed on the fracture surfaces. The shafts had been made of the prescribed metal and heat treated as specified.

Further investigation disclosed that, in an effort to reduce costs, the slip clutch had been eliminated from the drive mechanism, thus removing the cushioning effect that had been provided for the governor shaft. Restoration of the original design in a short time was not feasible.

Shafts were taken from stock and fatigue tested in a rotating-beam machine in a manner that would concentrate the stress at the circumferential groove. By this procedure, the fatigue limit for the shaft (survival for ten million cycles) was found to be about 70,000 psi. This fatigue limit was insufficient for the application because shafts were fracturing after operating a few hours to a few days.

To improve the fatigue life of the shafts, finished shafts were taken from stock and nitrided for 10 hr at 515 C (960 F). The nitrided shafts were then fatigue tested. Results of the tests indicated that the nitriding treatment had increased the fatigue limit from a minimum of 70,000 psi to a minimum of 110,000 psi. Tests showed this strength to be satisfactory for the application.

Conclusions. Fatigue fracture of the shaft was the result of increased vibration and shock loading after the slip clutch had been eliminated from the drive mechanism. The increased vibration produced stresses that exceeded the fatigue strength of the metal in the shaft.

Corrective Measures and Results. The shafts were nitrided and the portion of the surface covered by the sleeve was lightly buffed after nitriding. No further changes were made in the manufacture of these parts. No failures occurred during several months of operation, and the use of nitrided shafts became standard practice. Nitriding the shafts was more economical than restoring the slip clutch.

In the following example, it was recommended that fatigue life be increased by heat treating a shaft to produce a quenched-and-tempered structure in the steel. Shot peening of the fillet at a shoulder between two shaft diameters also was recommended as a means of increasing service life.

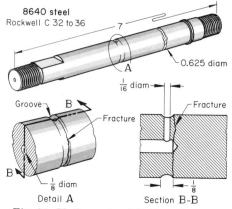

Fig. 23. Shaft, made of 8640 steel, for a fuel-injection-pump governor that fractured by fatigue through a lubrication hole. Fatigue life of the shaft was increased by nitriding the critical surface.
(Example 10)

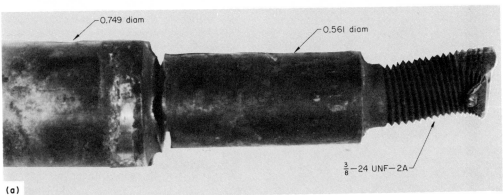

Fig. 24. (a) *Fan shaft, of 1040 steel, that fractured in reversed-bending fatigue.* (b) *View of fracture surface showing diametrically opposed origins, at arrows.* (Example 11)

Example 11. Fracture of a 1040 Steel Fan Shaft Resulting From Use of an Improper Material, Which Had Low Fatigue Strength (Fig. 24)

The fan drive support shaft shown in Fig. 24 fractured after 2240 miles of service (minimum expected life, 4000 miles). Specifications required that the shaft be made of cold drawn 1040 to 1045 steel with a minimum yield strength of 85,000 psi.

The fractured shaft was sent to the laboratory to determine if failure had resulted from inherent stress raisers in the design or from nonconformance to specifications.

Investigation. Visual examination of the shaft revealed that the fracture had been initiated near the fillet at an abrupt change in shaft diameter. Examination of the fracture surface disclosed that cracks had originated at two locations approximately 180° apart on the outer surface of the shaft (arrows in Fig. 24b) and propagated toward the center. Final fracture occurred near the center of the shaft. The fracture surface exhibited features typical of reversed-bending fatigue, as shown in Fig. 24(b). Analysis of the material in the shaft showed that it conformed with the composition of 1040 steel.

The mechanical properties of a tensile specimen machined from the center of the shaft were: tensile strength, 91,500 psi; yield strength, 53,500 psi; and elongation, 27%. The yield strength was much lower than the specified minimum of 85,000 psi. Hardness of the shaft was 179 Bhn.

Metallographic examination disclosed that the microstructure was predominantly ferrite and pearlite, indicating that the material was in either the hot worked or normalized condition. The grain size was ASTM 6 to 7, which is a fine-grain structure. No nonmetallic stringers or segregation were visible.

Severe rusting, which may have occurred after fracture, was found on the fracture surfaces of the shaft.

Conclusions. The shaft failed in reversed-bending fatigue. Fracture was initiated near a fillet at an abrupt change in shaft diameter, which is considered a region of maximum stress.

The metal did not conform to specifications; it was either hot rolled or normalized, and had a yield strength of only 53,500 psi.

Recommendations. The development of a quenched-and-tempered microstructure

would result in an improvement of the fatigue strength of the shaft. A 40% increase in the fatigue limit could be effected by quenching and tempering the steel to a hardness of Rockwell C 30 to 37 (286 to 344 Bhn) after machining.

Shot peening the fillet after machining would provide residual compressive stresses at the surface, which would inhibit the formation of fatigue cracks and additionally increase the fatigue limit.

Influence of Metallurgical Factors

The fatigue properties of a material primarily depend on microstructure, inclusion content, hardness, tensile strength, distribution of residual stresses, and severity of the stress concentrators that are present.

Internal discontinuities, such as porosity, large inclusions, laminations, forging bursts, flakes, and centerline pipe, will act as stress concentrators under certain conditions and may originate fatigue fracture.

In order to understand the effect of discontinuities, it is necessary to realize that fracture can originate at any location — surface or interior — where the stress first exceeds material strength. The stress gradient must be considered in torsion and bending because the stress is maximum at the surface but zero at the center or neutral axis. In tension, however, the stress is essentially uniform across the section.

If discontinuities such as those noted above occur in a region highly stressed in tension by bending or torsional loading, fatigue cracking may be initiated. However, if the discontinuities are in a low-stress region, such as near a neutral axis, they will be less harmful. Similarly, a shaft stressed by repeated high tensile loading must be free from serious imperfections for there is no neutral axis; any imperfection can be a stress concentrator and can be the origin of fatigue cracking if the stress is high with respect to the strength.

Nonmetallic inclusions oriented parallel to the principal stress do not exert as

great an effect upon fatigue resistance as those that are 90° to the principal stress, as in the following example.

Example 12. Fatigue Cracking of a 4337 Steel Master Connecting Rod for an Aircraft Engine Because of Nonmetallic Inclusions in the Forging (Fig. 25)

Routine inspection of a reciprocating aircraft engine revealed cracks in the master connecting rod. Cracks were observed in the channel-shape section consisting of the knuckle-pin flanges and the bearing-bore wall.

The rods were forged from 4337 (AMS 6412) steel and heat treated to a specified hardness of Rockwell C 36 to 40.

Investigation. Visual examination revealed H-shape cracks in the wall between the knuckle-pin flanges, as shown in Fig. 25(a). The cracks originated as circumferential cracks and then propagated transversely into the bearing-bore wall. Magnetic-particle and x-ray inspection prior to sectioning did not detect any inclusions in the master rod.

Macroscopic examination of one of the fracture surfaces revealed three inclusions lying approximately parallel to the grain direction, and fatigue beach marks around two of the inclusions; the inclusions and beach marks are shown in Fig. 25(b).

Microscopic examination of a section through the fracture origin showed large nonmetallic inclusions that consisted of heavy concentrations of aluminum oxide (Al_2O_3). These inclusions were of the type generally associated with ingot segregation patterns.

The hardness of the rods, Rockwell C 36 to 40, and the microstructure of the metal were satisfactory for the application.

A preliminary stress analysis indicated that the stresses in the area of cracking, under normal operating conditions, were relatively low compared with other areas of the rod, such as in the shank and the knuckle-pin straps.

Conclusions. The rod failed in fatigue in the bore wall between the knuckle-pin flanges. Fatigue was initiated by the stress-raising effect of large nonmetallic inclusions. The nonmetallic inclusions were not detected by routine magnetic-particle or x-ray inspection because of their orientation.

Recommendations. The forging vendors were notified that nonmetallic inclusions of a size in excess of that expected in aircraft-

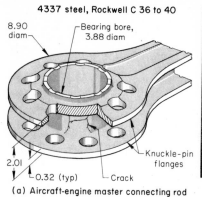

4337 steel, Rockwell C 36 to 40

8.90 diam — Bearing bore, 3.88 diam

2.01
0.32 (typ) — Crack
Knuckle-pin flanges

(a) Aircraft-engine master connecting rod

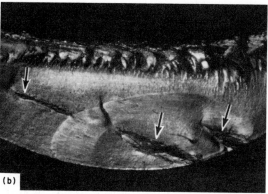

(b)

Fig. 25. (a) *Master connecting rod, made from a 4337 steel forging, for a reciprocating aircraft engine that failed by fatigue cracking in the bore section between the flanges.* (b) *Fractograph showing inclusions (at arrows) and fatigue beach marks.* (Example 12)

quality steel were found in the master connecting rods.

Forging techniques that provided increased working of the material between the knuckle-pin flanges to break up the large nonmetallic inclusions were not successful.

A nondestructive-testing procedure for detection of large nonmetallic inclusions was established.

Fatigue testing of large diesel-engine crankshafts indicated that torsional fatigue strength was essentially unaffected by the presence of nonmetallic inclusions in the cylindrical and fillet portions of the crankpin. However, a fatigue crack usually originates at the most severe flaw in a highly stressed region, such as a sharp notch, a seam or a large brittle nonmetallic inclusion. Nonmetallic inclusions were found in the webs at the main-bearing journals of the crankshaft described in the next example.

Example 13. Fatigue Cracking of a 1040 Steel Crankshaft Because of Excessive Segregation of Nonmetallic Inclusions (Fig. 26)

The crankshaft in a reciprocating engine had been in operation for less than one year when the engine was shut down for repairs. Examination of the engine components disclosed that the crankshaft had suffered fairly severe cracking. The crankshaft was sent to the laboratory for a complete examination.

Investigation. The journals of the main and crankpin bearings were inspected by the magnetic-particle method. At least four of the main-bearing journals had 3 to 6 indications of discontinuities 1/16 to 3/8 in. long. Another main-bearing journal had approximately 20 similar but generally shorter indications. One main-bearing journal had a crack along the fillet and almost entirely through the web, as shown in Fig. 26. Another main-bearing journal had a 1/2-in.-long crack in the fillet. Several of the crankpin journals had cracks 4 to 5 in. long, primarily in the fillets.

A metallographic section was taken through the No. 4 main-bearing journal at the primary crack. The surface was macroetched, which disclosed numerous large, coarse segregates identified as sulfide inclusions, as shown in Fig. 26.

Macroscopic examination of the crack surface disclosed indications of fatigue cracking with low-stress, high-cycle characteristics. Sulfide inclusions were present in the region where cracking originated.

The crankshaft was made from a 1040 steel forging. The mechanical properties of the metal met the specifications.

Conclusion. The crankshaft failed in fatigue at the main-bearing and crankpin-bearing journals because of excessive segregation of sulfide inclusions, which acted as stress raisers at which fatigue cracks initiated.

Corrective Measure. Ultrasonic inspection was used in addition to magnetic-particle inspection to detect discontinuities.

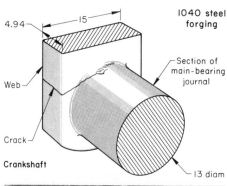

4.94 — 15 — 1040 steel forging

Web
Section of main-bearing journal
Crack
Crankshaft
13 diam

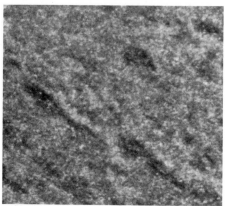

Fig. 26. *Section of main-bearing journal of a 1040 steel forged crankshaft that failed in fatigue with cracks originating at coarse sulfide inclusions; and macrograph (at 4×) of a 5%-nital-etched section showing the segregated inclusions (dark areas)* (Example 13)

Surface Discontinuities. During primary and secondary mill operations, a variety of surface imperfections often result from hot plastic working of material when lapping, folding or turbulent flow is experienced. The resultant surface discontinuities are called laps, seams and cold shuts. Similar discontinuities also are produced in cold working operations, such as fillet and thread rolling. Other surface imperfections develop from embedding of foreign material under high pressures during the working process; for example, oxides, slivers, or chips of the base material are occasionally rolled or forged into the surface.

Most of these discontinuities are present in the metal prior to final processing and are open to the surface. Standard nondestructive testing procedures such as liquid-penetrant and magnetic-particle inspection will readily reveal the presence of most surface discontinuities. If not detected, discontinuities may serve as sites for corrosion or crack initiation during fabrication, in addition to their deleterious effect on fatigue strength.

Because fatigue-crack initiation is the controlling factor in the life of most small shafts, freedom from surface imperfections becomes progressively more important in more severe applications. Similarly, internal imperfections, especially those that are near the surface, will grow under cyclic loading and result in cracking when critical size is attained. Service life can be significantly shortened when such imperfections cause premature crack initiation in shafts designed on the basis of conventional fatigue-life considerations. Surface or subsurface imperfections can cause brittle fracture of a shaft after a very short service life when the shaft is operating below the ductile-to-brittle transition temperature. When the operating temperature is above the transition temperature, or when the imperfection is small relative to the critical flaw size, especially when the cyclic-loading stress range is not large, service life may not be affected.

In the following example, a seam in a small-diameter shaft escaped detection. A spline tooth on the shaft in the region of the seam broke off after being induction hardened.

Example 14. Brittle Fracture of Splines on 1151 Steel Rotor Shafts After Induction Hardening, Because of Seam in Material (Fig. 27)

Splined rotor shafts like that shown in Fig. 27 were used on small electric motors. It was found that one spline was missing from each of several shafts before the motors were put into service. The shafts were made of 1151 steel, and the surfaces of the splines were induction hardened to Rockwell C 58 to 62. Several shafts were sent to the laboratory for examination to determine the cause of failure.

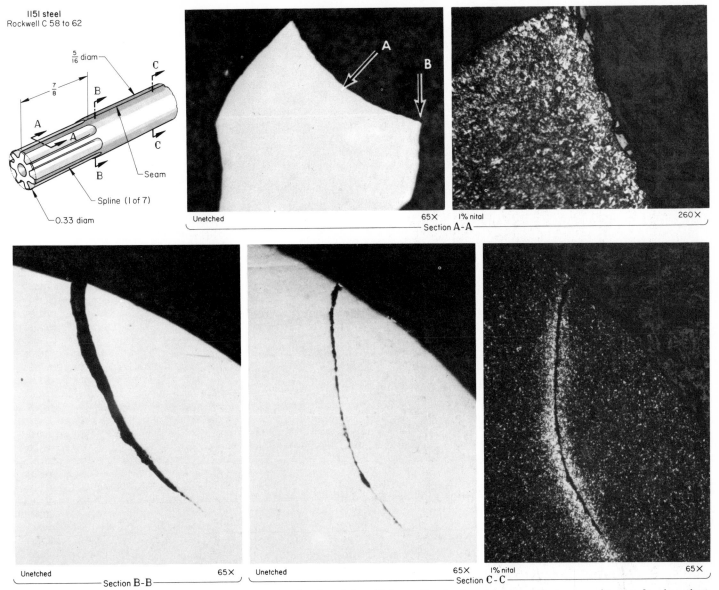

Fig. 27. Rotor shaft, made of 1151 steel and induction hardened, in which a spline fractured because of a seam; micrographs of section through broken spline, showing shape of fracture (A), root of seam (B), and decarburized surface; and micrographs of section through seam, showing regions where metal was affected and not affected by induction heating (Example 14)

Visual Examination. The shafts were examined both visually and with the aid of a stereoscopic microscope. This examination revealed apparent peeling of splines on the induction hardened end of each rotor shaft. Only one tooth on each shaft had broken off. Examination of the fracture surfaces revealed that they were dark in color, which indicated that cracking had occurred before or during oil quenching after induction heating.

The shafts were inspected by the fluorescent liquid-penetrant method for surface cracks or imperfections. This inspection revealed a longitudinal discontinuity extending from the fracture surface of the tooth through the heat-affected zone at the end of the spline and into the unheated portion of the shaft, as shown in Fig. 27. This defect exhibited the characteristic directionality of a seam.

Metallographic Examination. Specimens were removed at three locations along each of the fractured shafts and prepared for metallographic examination.

A micrograph (at a magnification of 65 diameters) of an unetched section through a fractured tooth (left part of section A-A in Fig. 27) showed that the fracture surface (A in Fig. 27) was concave and had an appearance characteristic of a seam. The tooth separated from the shaft when a crack originated at the root of the seam (B in Fig. 27) and propagated at 90° to the seam toward the root fillet. Etching the specimen in 1% nital and examining it at a magnification of 260 diameters disclosed partial decarburization of the surface (see right part of section A-A in Fig. 27). The microstructure of the metal in this region of the shaft was characteristic of a free-machining medium-carbon steel.

Examination (at a magnification of 65 diameters) of an unetched section through the region at the end of the splines that was affected by induction heating (section B-B in Fig. 27) showed that the defect had been opened as the result of thermal stresses produced during the induction hardening process. The curvature of the surface at

the defect was similar to that on the fractured tooth.

Examination (at a magnification of 65 diameters) of an unetched section through the shaft in an area unaffected by induction heating (left part of section C-C in Fig. 27) disclosed the presence of a crack extending to a depth of approximately 0.025 in. The root of the crack contained oxides typical of those found in seams. Etching the specimen in 1% nital and examining it at a magnification of 65 diameters revealed partial decarburization along the crack surfaces similar to that found on the fracture surface of the tooth (see right part of section C-C in Fig. 27). The curvature of the crack surface was similar to that observed in the heat-affected zone and on the fracture surface of the spline tooth.

Decarburization of the crack surfaces and oxides in the root of the crack indicated that the seam had been present before the shaft was heat treated, and are characteristics of seams produced during manufacture of steel billets, bars, rods and wires.

The average hardness across the tooth surface was Rockwell C 60, which was within the specified range.

Conclusions. The shafts failed by brittle fracture because of deep seams produced during processing of the steel. The seams acted as stress raisers during the induction hardening process.

Recommendations. Specifications should require that the shaft material be free of seams and other surface imperfections.

Grain size, composition and microstructure of a shaft material largely define the strength and toughness of that material and thus performance of a shaft of that material. Generally, a fine-grained low-temperature transformation product (martensite or bainite) is desirable. However, where elevated temperatures are involved, a coarse grain size may be preferred. Grain size, composition and microstructure affect material toughness at any given strength level; only when these factors combine to produce low toughness do they contribute to brittle fracture of a shaft.

Toughness and transition temperature generally are more important in large-diameter shafts than in small-diameter shafts. The life of a small-diameter shaft usually is determined both by the time required for a fatigue crack to initiate and by the rate of crack propagation. Large-diameter shafts are more likely to contain flaws of critical size. Thus, the life of a large-diameter shaft often is determined solely by the rate of propagation of cracks originating at pre-existing flaws. For large-diameter shafts with high internal stresses, the minimum level of toughness that can be expected in the shaft at minimum operating temperature must be known in order to determine the maximum size of flaw that can be tolerated. The combination of a high ductile-to-brittle transition temperature and surface flaws produced during machining resulted in failure of the 1040 steel splined shaft described in Example 10 on page 114 in the article on Fatigue Failures, in this volume.

Temper embrittlement of certain shaft steels, especially the Ni-Cr, Ni-Cr-Mo, and Ni-Cr-Mo-V steels used in larger rotor shafts, results from prolonged exposure at temperatures of 350 to 575 C (660 to 1070 F), or from slow cooling after exposure above this temperature range. In most instances a short exposure time within, or rapid cooling through, this temperature range will minimize temper embrittlement. However, when heat treating thick sections this procedure may not be possible, and temper embrittlement may occur. Fortunately, temper embrittlement can be reversed by retempering above the temperature range of 350 to 575 C (660 to 1070 F) followed by rapid cooling through this range to restore toughness.

(For details of various types of embrittlement, the reader is referred to the section "Embrittlement Failures of Steel Parts" on page 78 in the article on Ductile and Brittle Fractures, in this volume.)

Temper embrittlement decreases impact toughness by increasing the ductile-to-brittle transition temperature and decreases the amount of ductile fracture; thus it is of considerable concern for larger shafts. For steels that exhibit a sensitivity to temper embrittlement, the degree of embrittlement that develops is largely dependent on composition, heat treatment, and service conditions.

With respect to composition, molybdenum in amounts from 0.20 to 0.30% significantly retards temper embrittlement. Greater amounts of molybdenum yield no additional improvement. The effect of molybdenum on suppressing temper embrittlement decreases as the purity of the steel increases. The total content of impurities (sulfur plus phosphorus plus nonferrous elements plus gases), expressed in atom parts per million, ranges in value from about 1500 ppm in steels of conventional purity (corresponding to the usual amounts found in air-arc melted steel), to 1000 ppm in very clean steel (corresponding to vacuum-melted steel), and to about 500 ppm in the extra-clean steels (corresponding to vacuum-melted steel using a very pure charge). Hence, when relatively impure steel is used (with over 1500 ppm impurities and over 0.01% P), the unique role of molybdenum in minimizing temper embrittlement is very important. Molybdenum does not appear to be a necessary alloying element in the production of high-purity steels (under 500 ppm impurities and under 0.001% P), which are not susceptible to temper embrittlement.

Effect of Surface Coatings

Metallic coatings of several types and compositions often are used to protect shaft surfaces from wear and corrosion and to repair worn shafts. The types of coatings include, but are not limited to, electroplating, metal spraying (with or without subsequent fusing), catalytic deposition, and metal overlaying. Typical coating materials are chromium, nickel, iron, alloy steels, aluminum alloys, copper alloys, and Cr-Ni-Fe alloys. Care must be taken in applying these coatings, because harmful residual stresses and/or stress concentrators may be inadvertently left in or produced in the shaft.

Many electroplating processes leave harmful residual stresses in the plating and, therefore, in the adjacent base metal. Chromium, iron and nickel platings generally contain high residual tensile stresses, which reduce the fatigue strength of the base metal of a shaft. Re-sidual tensile stresses reduce the corrosion resistance of both the plating and the base metal. Piston rods and other parts made of high-strength steel and plated with metallic coatings can crack and fracture at unexpectedly low stress levels in simple fatigue.

During acid cleaning and electroplating, hydrogen usually is produced and may be absorbed into the base metal. If the hydrogen is not removed by a subsequent heat treatment, severe embrittlement of the base metal may occur — especially in base metals with hardness above approximately Rockwell C 35. High-strength, highly stressed parts can crack and fracture as a result of hydrogen embrittlement. Failure by hydrogen embrittlement is even more likely to occur if the shaft contains high residual tensile stresses before being plated.

Metal spraying to obtain specific surface properties sometimes is used on shafts and, if proper bonding is obtained, usually is satisfactory. However, spraying of metals that have fairly high coefficients of thermal expansion on large-diameter shafts in heavy thicknesses results in high residual tensile stresses; in the as-sprayed condition, the metal sometimes cracks. If subsequent heating is required to bond the coating to the base metal, high residual stresses and/or thermal cracking of the base metal or coating may occur.

Sprayed metal is mechanically weak and, if overloaded in compression, tends to spread laterally, thus disturbing its adhesion to the underlying base metal. Sprayed metal adheres well to crankshaft main journals but not to crankpin journals, which are more heavily loaded than crankshaft main journals and subject to shock loading. The sprayed metal is entirely dependent on a mechanical keying action for its adherence to the base metal. A shallow V-shape groove such as a shallow, small-pitch thread not only is inadequate but also has an undesirable stress-raising effect. The most satisfactory method of surface preparation is shot or grit blasting, which must be done in a manner so that the surface is roughened and not simply peened. The stress-raising effects of blasting are negligible because of the small size of the indentations. However, adhesion of sprayed metal to a surface prepared by grit blasting may not always be satisfactory under severe loading conditions, such as those to which a crankpin is subjected in service.

The following example of the fracture of a reconditioned crankshaft illustrates both the stress-raising effect of grooving and the inadequacy of grooving as a method of keying a sprayed coating to a surface. Other portions of the same shaft, which were prepared by shot or grit blasting, had a much more adherent coating and no damaging notches.

Example 15. Fatigue Fracture of a Crankshaft That Had Been Reconditioned by Metal Spraying (Fig. 28)*

During a general overhaul of a four-cylinder engine, the crankpin journals and 3-in.-diam main-bearing journals were built up by metal spraying. Four weeks later, the crankshaft broke through the crankpin farthest from the flywheel (driving) end.

Investigation. Examination of the fracture surface revealed that cracking had originated in the fillet at the "inside" surface of the crankpin, as shown at A in Fig. 28(a). The crack had propagated in fatigue perpendicular to the crankpin axis and across approximately 80% of the crankpin before final rupture occurred.

It was found that adhesion of the sprayed metal coating to the fractured crankpin was very poor and that the coating could be detached easily by tapping a chisel inserted between the coating and the pin. Portions of the sprayed coating were removed from all the pins and journals in order that the surface preparation carried out prior to metal spraying could be examined. In each of two pins, a helical groove approximately 1/32 in. wide and 1/32 in. deep, with a pitch of 10 per inch, had been cut in the surface (B in Fig. 28b). The grooving extended over one-half of the pin periphery only; the remaining portion of the surface had been indiscriminately indented with some form of toothed punch, as depicted in Fig. 28(b).

The surfaces of the main journals had not been grooved but appeared to have been roughened by shot or grit blasting before spraying. The sprayed coating was more firmly adherent to these surfaces than to those of the pins. From one pin, a large portion of the sprayed metal, extending the whole width of the crankpin and covering one-third of its circumference, came away in one piece. Examination indicated that the tongues of metal that filled the grooves had broken away from the main layer at the level of the original pin surface. The average thickness of the sprayed layer was 1/32 in. The hardness of the crankpin was only 163 Bhn, indicating that it was readily machinable.

With regard to the sequence of failure, there was a possibility that the crack might have been developing at the time restoration of the shaft was carried out. But careful examination showed that this was most unlikely, because the origin of the crack was situated at the bottom of one of the turned grooves and the crack followed the groove about halfway around the pin periphery. Figure 28(c) is a view of a portion of the crankpin, showing that the crack occurred in the groove. The continuation of the groove beyond the point where the crack changed direction is shown at C in Fig. 28(c). The crack was not located near the region where the fillet was tangent with the shaft surface, as are the majority of such cracks in crankshafts, but developed about 1/8 in. away in the cylindrical region of the pin, which also suggests that its location was determined by the pre-existing machined groove.

*Adapted from "Fatigue Failure of a Metal-Sprayed Crankshaft", British Engine Technical Report, Vol III, 1957, p 125-127

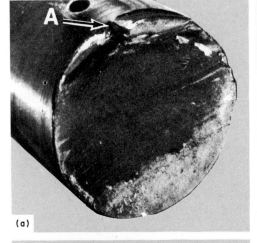

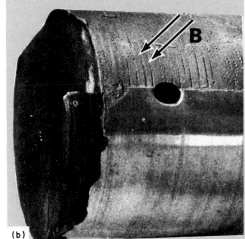

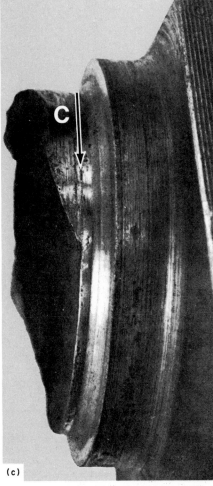

Fig. 28. Crankpin of a crankshaft that fractured in fatigue after the crankpin journals and main-bearing journals were rebuilt by metal spraying. (a) Fracture surface, showing fracture origin, at A. (b) Machined grooves and punch marks, at B, on surface of crankpin. (c) Groove in crankpin, where cracking was initiated. (Example 15)

Conclusions. The shaft failed in fatigue. Cracking originated in a groove that was machined in the crankpin to help retain the sprayed metal.

Recommendations. Surfaces should be prepared for metal spraying by shot or grit blasting in such a manner that they are roughened, not simply peened. Metal spraying generally is satisfactory for rebuilding of the surfaces of main-bearing journals, but not for the surfaces of crankpins that are subject to shock loading.

Shaft Repair by Welding. Repair of shafts made of annealed materials usually can be done without difficulty using well-established welding practices. Generally, these practices include matching of base-metal and filler-metal compositions, proper preparation of the region to be welded, and thermal procedures that include preheating, postheating and stress relieving. The repaired shaft is then heat treated in the conventional manner.

Welding of hardened materials involves compromises and should be avoided whenever possible. For instance, the heat-affected zone usually contains areas with hardness 10 to 20 Rockwell C points lower than that of the base metal, thereby causing stresses in the shaft due to a so-called metallurgical notch. To minimize these stresses, the material should be slowly cooled after welding and then tempered immediately, using a temperature slightly lower than the original tempering temperature.

Weld overlays resulting in a diameter larger than the adjacent shaft diameter should have a tapered transition. This would minimize the stress concentration at an otherwise abrupt change of section that coincided with the heat-affected zone of a weld.

Any subsequent grinding of the weld area to produce the desired dimensions should be done carefully, using a soft grinding wheel and numerous light passes to avoid overheating that would cause grinding cracks.

If a weld or a weld overlay is adjacent to the transition region of a stepped shaft, a large-radius fillet should be used at the change in section. In the following example, fracture was initiated in a sharp fillet at a surface that had received a weld overlay.

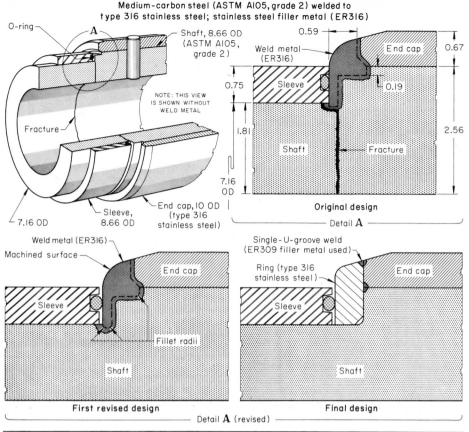

Fig. 29. Stub-shaft assembly for agitator in a polyvinyl chloride reactor, which failed by ductile fracture; and sections through failure area showing original design, first revised design and final design (Example 16)

| | ─── Chemical analysis of steels in shaft assembly ─── | | | | | |
| | ASTM A105, grade 2, steel (shaft) | | Type 316 stainless steel (end cap) | | | Nominal composition of type 316 stainless steel (a) |
Element	Typical	At fusion line	At fusion line	At center of weld	In end cap	
Carbon	0.456	...	0.55	0.054	0.037	0.08(b)
Manganese	0.25	0.18	0.20	0.73	0.53	2.0
Phosphorus	...	...	...	0.010	0.016	0.045
Sulfur	0.017	...	...	0.016	0.022	0.03
Silicon	0.35	0.35	0.25	0.29	0.607	1.00
Nickel	0.10	0.75	10.00	10.16	11.06	10 to 14
Chromium	0.068	2.00	16.00	19.43	19.46	16 to 18(c)
Molybdenum	0.023	0.65	2.00	2.86	2.88	2 to 3
Iron	Rem	Rem	Rem	Rem	Rem	Rem

(a) Maximum content unless range is given. (b) Carbon content is 0.03% max for type 316L stainless steel. (c) Chromium content is 18 to 20% for type 316 stainless steel filler metal.

Example 16. Ductile Fracture of a Forged Steel Shaft at a Change in Section and at a Stainless Steel Weld (Fig. 29)

The stub-shaft assembly shown in Fig. 29, which was part of the agitator shaft in a PVC (polyvinyl chloride) reactor, fractured in service after a nut that retained a loose sleeve around the smaller-diameter section of the shaft had been tightened several times to reduce leakage.

Removal of the stainless steel sleeve revealed that tightening of the retaining nut had forced the end of the sleeve against the machined stainless steel shoulder on the shaft and permanently flattened the O-ring seal.

The shaft was made of ASTM A105, grade 2, steel and the larger-diameter section was covered with a type 316 stainless steel end cap. The cap was secured at each end by welding, using type ER316 stainless

steel filler metal (see detail A, "Original design", in Fig. 29). The radial surface at the change in diameter was a weld overlay, a continuation of the weld metal securing the cap to the shaft. Transverse fracture of the shaft occurred near this abrupt change in shaft diameter.

The stub shaft was removed from the agitator so that a replacement stub shaft could be installed. Both sections of the fractured shaft were sent to the laboratory for analysis.

Replacement of Stub Shaft. A new stub shaft was made by welding a type 316 stainless steel cap to a forged steel shaft that had a chemical content of 0.25% C, 0.25% Mo and 1% Cr, and a tensile strength of 87,000 psi. The grooves machined in the replacement shaft for the weld overlay had radii instead of sharp corners (see detail A, "Original design" and "First revised design", in Fig. 29).

Investigation. Examination revealed that the forged steel shaft had fractured at approximately 90° to the shaft axis, as shown in detail A, "Original design", in Fig. 29. The face of the outboard section of the shaft had a groove approximately 1/4 in. deep by 5/16 in. wide around its circumference. This step followed the shape of the weld metal on the mating piece. The fracture surface along the weld metal contained no forged steel, indicating that the failure was in the weld metal and not in the heat-affected zone of the forged steel shaft. Worn and smeared metal on both mating surfaces indicated that the stub shaft had continued to rotate after it had fractured.

Inspection of the PVC reactor revealed that the drive coupling between the shaft and motor was purposely misaligned 0.050 in. in the vertical direction with the shaft. This misalignment was done to counter the misalignment caused by bow of the concrete slab base, which occurred when the reactor was loaded.

Cracks in the heat-affected zone or cracks in the martensite transition zone at the fusion line were possible, but were not evident from microscopic inspection of the weld area. Presence of the martensite transition zone offered a path of easy crack propagation.

Chemical analyses of the steel shaft and the stainless steel end cap at various locations are given in the table that accompanies Fig. 29. Analyses of metal at the fusion line were made from scrapings and drill shavings that included metal on either side of the fusion line; therefore, the values are average values for the general area rather than actual values for the metal at the fusion line.

The chromium, nickel and molybdenum contents of the weld metal were lower than those of the filler metal whereas the contents of the same elements in the heat-affected zone of the shaft were higher than those of the base metal, indicating that the weld metal had been diluted by the carbon steel shaft.

The stainless steel used for the end cap was similar to type 316 stainless steel except for a higher chromium content. The carbon content of the forged steel used for the shaft was greater than the maximum specified for ASTM A105, grade 2.

Microstructure. The base metal that was not affected by the heat of welding had a typical pearlitic grain structure with white ferrite surrounding each grain. The microstructure changed as the fusion line was approached: the amount of ferrite decreased and the microstructure became martensitic.

The hardness of the metal in the steel shaft near the fusion line was 358 dph. Because a maximum hardness of approximately 520 dph can be obtained with a carbon steel of 0.45 to 0.50% carbon content, the martensite may have been tempered by the welding heat during subsequent weld passes.

Discussion. The sharp corners at the root of the weld, which were shown on the original shaft drawing, were not evident on the shaft, and there was no evidence of a sharp corner on either fracture surface. Therefore, it can be assumed that the fracture was initiated at the surface. (The welding practices employed and penetration of the weld metal may have removed evidence of the sharp corners.)

Some features on the fracture surface were removed by rotation after fracture, which was unfortunate because the surface may have contained indications of whether fracture originated on the surface in the heat-affected zone or at the fusion line of the weld. An initial crack on the surface of the shaft could have been caused by inherent defects in the weld or by tensile stresses resulting from rotation of the misaligned shaft.

Conclusions. The forged steel shaft failed by ductile fracture. The fracture surface was approximately 90° to the axis of the shaft. The fracture was the result of:

1 Reduction of the effective cross-sectional area of the shaft by a crack that followed the fusion line of a circumferential weld that served as an overlay and as a means of securing one end of a stainless steel cap
2 A stress concentration from the notch effect of the crack created at the root of the weld
3 Tensile stresses induced by misalignment of the shaft
4 In addition to the normal torsional and tensile stresses of the shaft, a tensile stress that was applied to this area by the sleeve being forced against the machined surface of the weld when the retaining nut was tightened excessively.

Corrective Measures. The replacement shaft for the immediate failure followed the first revised design shown in detail A in Fig. 29.

Shafts for new agitators were made using the final design in detail A in Fig. 29. Both the end cap and the ring were made of type 316 stainless steel. Welding was done with type ER309 stainless steel filler metal, and the end cap and end ring were preheated to 150 C (about 300 F). The cap was joined to the shaft using a single-U-groove weld, which was machined flush before the stainless steel ring was installed. Another single-U-groove weld was used to join the ring to the end cap. This design eliminated welding at an inside corner, reducing the stress-concentration factor at that area.

Manganese and zinc phosphate are conversion coatings capable of producing stress concentrations on hardened ferrous material. This condition results from failure to follow proper processing procedures, which include control of bath composition, of bath temperature, and of processing time. Sometimes, camshaft lobes and bearings are coated with manganese phosphate to assist when lubrication is marginal and during break-in. If one or more control parameters are not observed, the surface becomes grossly etched and pitted. This intergranular surface attack leads to flaking in service, and ultimately to complete deterioration of the highly stressed lobe surface.

Failures of Sliding Bearings

*By the ASM Committee on Failures of Sliding and Rolling-Element Bearings**

SLIDING BEARINGS operate with relative sliding motion of elements that ideally are separated by a film of lubricant. They include all types of journal or sleeve bearings, which are used to position shafts or moving parts radially; all types of thrust bearings, which in general are used to prevent axial movement of shafts; and bushings used as guides for linear motions of various types.

Some journal bearings completely surround the shafts they support, either as continuous cylinders or as segmented cylinders; others may encompass only a small arc of the shaft circumference. Thrust bearings vary widely in design, ranging from simple flat thrust collars to tapered-land bearings and bearings of great complexity. When loading has both axial and radial components, flange bearings are sometimes used. A flange bearing is, in effect, a combination of a journal bearing and a thrust bearing (single-flange bearing) or of a journal bearing and two thrust bearings (double-flange bearing).

Bearing-Characteristic Number

The bearing-characteristic number is a measure of the operating characteristics of a sliding bearing. There are several bearing-characteristic numbers in use, and each is derived from calculations using values based on operating conditions. The Sommerfeld number, S, is in wide use, and is calculated by:

$$S = (D^2/C^2)(DL/W)\mu N$$
$$= (D^2/C^2)(\mu N/P)$$

where D is diameter of bearing, in.; C is diametral clearance between bearing and shaft, in.; L is length of bearing surface, in.; W is load on bearing, lb; N is rotational speed of shaft, rps; P is pressure on bearing, psi (W/DL); and μ is viscosity of lubricant at operating temperature and pressure, Reyns (lbf-sec/in.²). (Conversion constants are used when viscosity is expressed in units other than Reyns.)

The hydrodynamic film thickness is a function of the Sommerfeld number, and usually increases as the Sommerfeld number increases. The Sommerfeld number varies directly with bearing length, oil viscosity, shaft speed and the third power of the bearing diameter, and inversely with the load on the bearing and the second power of the diametral clearance.

Shaft speed and load are compensating factors; therefore, where the load changes directly with speed, a bearing may operate through wide ranges of shaft speeds and loads provided the viscosity of the oil does not change substantially.

Changes in viscosity due to changes in operating temperature, or use of lubricants having different viscosities, can alter the bearing-characteristic number and thus affect bearing operation.

The diametral clearance of the bearing is in the denominator of an expression in the equation and is squared; thus, a change in clearance can cause a significant change in the function of the bearing. If the diametral clearance increases because of wear or expansion of the bearing, the film thickness is reduced.

*STUART L. RICE, *Chairman*, Engineering Materials Div., Caterpillar Tractor Co.; JAMES W. BUTLER, JR., Vice President, Research and Development, Johnson Bronze Co.; JAMES L. CHEVALIER, Aeronautical Engineer, Technical Management Div., Office of Project Manager, Heavy-Lift Helicopter, Department of the Army.

V. W. COMSTOCK, Head, Service Section, Bearing Engineering Dept., Torrington Co.; A. L. FABENS, President, Truline Bearing Co.; ERWIN M. ICHIYASU, Metallurgist, CCAD, Technical Analysis Div., AMC, Department of the Army; MICHAEL F. McGUIRE, Manager, Material and Process Research, Clevite Engine Parts Div., Gould, Inc.; RICHARD

W. MEEK, Chief Metallurgist, Oilfield Products Div., Dresser Industries, Inc.; W. L. MITCHELL, Senior Materials Engineer, International Business Machines Corp.; CONRAD J. POLK, Leader, Metallurgical Engineering Group, Mobil Research & Development Corp.; HUGH R. ROBERTS, Metallurgical Engineer, Northwest Engineering Co.

CHARLES N. SCOTT, Senior Metallurgical Engineer, Southern Railway System; RALPH W. STEVENSON, Research Metallurgist, Bearing Group, Research and Development, Federal-Mogul Corp.; PETER R. WEIHSMANN, Senior Engineer, Research Center, Reliance Electric Co.; PHILIP D. HARVEY, *Secretary*, Senior Editor, Metals Handbook.

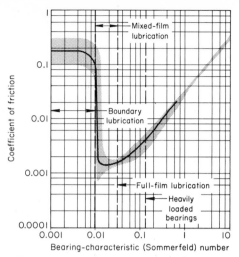

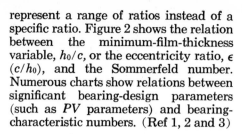

Fig. 1. Approximate relation of coefficient of friction to the bearing-characteristic (Sommerfeld) number, for a range of bearing length-to-diameter ratios. PV (pressure-velocity) parameters apply in the boundary-lubrication region.

The Sommerfeld number can be used to determine if specific operating conditions have a significant effect on the operation of a bearing. For instance, if a bearing is operating under nonstandard conditions, the Sommerfeld number can be calculated for these conditions. This number can be compared with the Sommerfeld number calculated for standard operating conditions by consulting charts such as those in Fig. 1 and 2.

Figure 1 shows the approximate relation between the coefficient of friction in the bearing and the Sommerfeld number for the ratio of bearing length to diameter. The curve is shown as a band to represent a range of ratios instead of a specific ratio. Figure 2 shows the relation between the minimum-film-thickness variable, h_0/c, or the eccentricity ratio, ϵ (c/h_0), and the Sommerfeld number. Numerous charts show relations between significant bearing-design parameters (such as PV parameters) and bearing-characteristic numbers. (Ref 1, 2 and 3)

Bearing Lubrication

Bearing lubricants are of various types, including hydrocarbons, water and oil emulsions, soaps, greases, air, and solid materials such as graphite and molybdenum disulfide.

Optimum conditions of bearing lubrication exist when the sliding surfaces are separated by a film of lubricant thick enough to prevent metal-to-metal contact. This means that the minimum film thickness must be several times greater than the combined surface roughnesses of the bearing components. (Minimum lubricant-film thicknesses are listed in tables in Ref 3; this publication also gives formulas for determining these values under special conditions.)

Films of thicknesses that greatly exceed the combined surface roughness can either be maintained by an externally pressurized oil-supply system (hydrostatic lubrication) or be self-generated by favorable surface configuration, an adequate lubricant viscosity, and a bearing-characteristic number high enough to produce full-film (hydrodynamic) lubrication. The most undesirable conditions of lubrication are promoted by high loads, moderate speeds, extreme temperatures or insufficient lubrication. These factors

can result in dry metallic friction, high-temperature catastrophic wear, and possibly seizure, all of which may be partly alleviated by the presence of natural protective coatings in the form of metallic oxides or other substances on the sliding surfaces. Between the two extremes of dry sliding and a thick lubricant film, two other distinct states of lubrication can be identified: boundary lubrication and thin-film lubrication.

Boundary lubrication and thin-film lubrication are states in which lubricant is present but, because of high loading, low speed, unfavorable configuration of mating surfaces, or insufficiency or low viscosity of lubricant, complete separation of the surfaces is not effected. In thin-film lubrication, surface asperities penetrate the film so that only part of the load is carried by hydrodynamic forces and the remainder by solid-to-solid contacts. Thin-film lubrication is an intermediate state in which the laws of hydrodynamic lubrication are no longer applicable. True boundary lubrication occurs only when contact pressures are high enough and sliding velocities low enough for hydrodynamic effects to be completely absent; the entire load is then carried by an extremely thin, multimolecular layer of boundary lubricant. In addition, the term boundary lubricant is usually extended to cover other types of lubricant that do not function hydrodynamically, such as chemical coatings, surface films, and lamellar solids such as graphite. The approximate limits for boundary lubrication, in relation to the Sommerfeld number, are shown at the left in Fig. 1.

Lubrication of most sliding bearings depends on hydrodynamic action and is influenced primarily by the viscous flow properties of the oil. Oil adheres to both the bearing and rotating shaft surfaces and is dragged into the clearance space — which, because of the eccentricity of the shaft and bearing centers, converges in the direction of motion. Thus, a convergent wedge of oil is generated that builds up sufficient fluid pressure to hold the shaft and bearing surfaces apart and carry the applied load.

The transition from boundary to thin-film to hydrodynamic lubrication is a gradual one, and mixed states of lubrication commonly exist in the wide range of rubbing and sliding conditions that are found in bearings. Part of the total load carried by the bearing is supported by individual load-carrying pools of self-pressurized lubricant, and the remaining part of the load by the very thin contaminating film associated with boundary lubrication. The regions covered by mixed-film lubrication and by full-film (hydrodynamic) lubrication, in relation to the Sommerfeld number, are shown in Fig. 1.

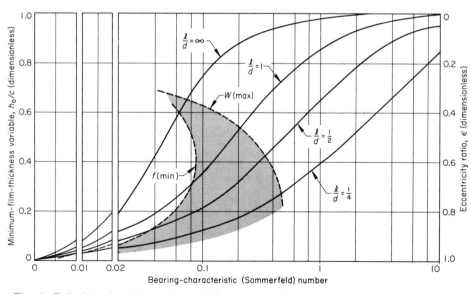

Fig. 2. Relation of minimum-film-thickness variable, h_0/c, and eccentricity ratio, ϵ, to the bearing-characteristic (Sommerfeld) number, for four ratios of bearing length, l, to diameter, d. The left boundary of the shaded zone defines the optimum minimum film thickness, h_0, for minimum friction; the right boundary is the optimum h_0 for maximum load; c is the radial clearance between the shaft and the bearing. See text for discussion of Sommerfeld numbers. (Ref 2)

A change from one state of lubrication to another can occur also at different stages in the cycle of operation of the same mechanism. For instance, in sleeve bearings, which normally are designed to run hydrodynamically, boundary or thin-film conditions may develop during starting, during stopping, and when the shaft passes through zero speed in reversing, and under operating conditions of severe loading or high temperatures.

Figure 3 shows a bearing and shaft with greatly exaggerated clearance. For Fig. 3(a) and (b), assume that this clearance space is kept completely filled with oil and that a steady load is applied to the top of the shaft. When at rest, the shaft settles down and contacts the bearing at the bottom. As the shaft begins to rotate clockwise, it rolls up the right side of the bearing, moving the point of nearest contact to the right, as shown in Fig. 3(a). There is then a thin film of oil between the contact surfaces, and fluid friction is substituted for metal-to-metal contact. The shaft slides and begins to rotate, dragging more oil between the surfaces and forming a thicker film between the shaft and the bearing.

As the speed of rotation increases, the oil drawn under the shaft builds up a pressure that forces the shaft up and to the left until a condition of equilibrium is reached. The net result is that the minimum-clearance point is at the position indicated in Fig. 3(b); the exact position depends on the diameter and length of the bearing, the operating clearance, the speed of rotation, the operating oil viscosity, and the load on the shaft. Increasing the load will cause the shaft to settle lower in the bearing; decreasing the viscosity or decreasing the speed has the same effect. After the shaft reaches the equilibrium position, oil moving toward the minimum-clearance point because of shaft rotation builds up a pressure that reaches a maximum some distance ahead of the point of minimum clearance, and then decreases rapidly beyond that point, reaching a minimum near the location marked A in Fig. 3(b).

The diagram in Fig. 3(b) also can represent a condition of centrifugal loading in which the load rotates with the shaft at shaft speed. Under these conditions, the minimum-clearance point also rotates at shaft speed in the direction of shaft rotation. The viscous lubricant builds up pressure between point A and the approaching minimum-clearance point and is prevented from escaping from this tapered volume by its viscous adherence to the shaft. The net result of this motion and pressure buildup is, for all practical purposes, the same as the pressure buildup in the steady-load condition.

Under certain high-speed conditions, with small imbalances and small unidi-

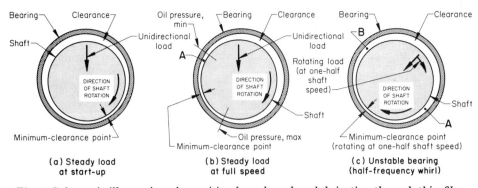

Fig. 3. Schematic illustration of transition from boundary lubrication through thin-film lubrication to hydrodynamic lubrication under a steady load, and conditions under which half-frequency whirl occurs in a bearing with small unbalances and small unidirectional loads. See text for discussion.

rectional loads, the load is not strong enough to hold the shaft in one position and the rotating centrifugal loading on the shaft is not strong enough to hold the shaft in a position with the minimum-clearance point rotating at the speed of the shaft. The shaft may become unstable and orbit within the bearing (see Fig. 3c) at a speed one-half that of the shaft rotational speed, resulting in an instability known as half-frequency whirl. Between point A and the minimum-clearance point in Fig. 3(c), the shaft is drawing oil into the tapered volume at shaft-rotation speed. At the same time, the minimum-clearance point is retreating at one-half that speed. Thus, the net volume of lubricant drawn into this tapered area is one-half of what it normally would be. At the same time, because the minimum-clearance point is retreating, the bearing surface, in effect, is drawing lubricant out of this area, resulting in a negligible buildup of pressure between point A and the minimum-clearance point.

The opposite effect takes place between the minimum-clearance point and point B in Fig. 3(c). In this area, the motion of the minimum-clearance point toward point B would normally build up pressure because of the viscous attraction of the lubricant to the bearing surface. In this area, however, shaft rotation is faster than the motion of the minimum-clearance point, which results in the shaft drawing lubricant out of this area and defeating the buildup of lubricant pressure here as well.

Half-frequency whirl occurs only at high speed — generally in excess of 5000 rpm — and with a large centrifugal load that is well balanced (or has only small imbalances) and has very small unidirectional components. Half-frequency whirl can be eliminated by reducing the load-carrying capability of the bearing. This can be done in either of two ways: by reducing the land area of the bearing or by cutting multiple slots through the bearing surface. (Additional information on instability of sliding bearings is presented in Ref 4 through 9.)

Characteristics of Sliding-Bearing Materials

For proper selection of a sliding-bearing material, the characteristics of the material must match the requirements of the machine.

Material characteristics that affect selection include compatibility, conformability, embeddability, load capacity, strength, fatigue strength, corrosion resistance, and hardness. Only metallic bearing materials are discussed in this article, although nonmetallic materials can be used for some applications.

Compatibility is a measure of the anti-welding and antiscoring characteristics of a bearing material when operated with a given mating material. Some metal-to-metal contact occurs in most journal bearings during starting and stopping and when the machine is idle for an extended period. In metal-to-metal contact, sliding surfaces rub on microscopic high spots, and the friction developed at these points can produce localized welding, causing seizing and scoring.

Conformability is the ability of a bearing metal to compensate for slight misalignment and to conform to variations in the shape of the shaft or the bearing-housing bore. Soft metals with a low modulus of elasticity and good plasticity have good conformability characteristics.

Embeddability is the ability of a bearing metal to embed dirt or foreign particles and thus avoid scoring and wear of the bearing or shaft surfaces by the particles. Good embeddability is usually found in bearing metals with good conformability. (However, although carbon-graphite has a low modulus of elasticity and good conformability, its ability to absorb dirt is poor because of its high hardness.)

Load capacity is a measure of the maximum pressure, in pounds per square inch, that a bearing metal can withstand with low friction and moderate wear. Load capacity depends on the viscosity of the lubricant, the condition of the shaft, and the operating temperature, as well as on the composition of the bearing materials.

Strength. Compressive and shear strengths of bearing materials are important, but tensile-strength and yield-strength values usually are related and are more readily available, and provide a good measure of mechanical-strength characteristics. In general, a low-strength material provides more deflection under load and better conformability than a high-strength material. A material with low shear strength can sustain shearing of small particles with little heat generation and welding.

Fatigue strength is particularly important in applications where the load changes direction, such as in internal-combustion engines. Sufficiently high fatigue strength is necessary in these applications to enable the bearing to operate below its elastic limit without developing cracks or surface pits.

The use of a layer of a soft bearing material (such as babbitt) bonded to a stronger backing material (such as steel, bronze or cast iron) often gives the desirable combination of fatigue strength and compressive strength. In such instances, the fatigue strength of the bond requires particular attention. Layers of bearing material approximately 0.010 in. thick are used in automotive applications; however, some industrial applications use layers $\frac{1}{16}$ to $\frac{1}{8}$ in. thick. Thin layers are desirable where fatigue is a factor.

Corrosion resistance is important where uninhibited industrial lubricating oils, industrial acidic environments or salt water are present. Oxidation products from some lubricating oils can attack and corrode cadmium, lead, zinc and some copper-bearing alloys. Both tin and aluminum usually are unaffected by oxidized oils.

Hardness. The softer the bearing material, the better its antiscoring, conformability and embeddability properties. Higher hardness provides better load capacity and greater wear resistance. In general, the shaft should be harder than the bearing.

Sliding-Bearing Materials

Sliding-bearing surfaces are made of tin-base and lead-base babbitts, copper-lead alloys, bronzes, aluminum alloys, and powder metallurgy materials. These materials are used in both the cast and wrought forms, with or without a backing plate made of a stronger metal such as wrought or cast steel, cast iron, or brass.

Babbitts. There are two types of babbitt in common use: tin-base babbitt with 4 to 8% copper and 4 to 8% antimony (SAE No. 11 and 12; ASTM B23, grades 1, 2, 3 and 11), and lead-base babbitt with a maximum of 10.7% tin, and 9.5 to 17.5% antimony (SAE No. 13 to 16; ASTM B23, grades 7, 8, 13 and 15).

Tin-base and lead-base babbitts generally offer the best surface action between bearing and shaft surfaces. There is a minimum of damage to steel shafts under conditions of boundary lubrication or dirty operation. Babbitts have excellent compatibility and nonscoring characteristics and are outstanding in embedding dirt and conforming to geometric errors in machine construction and operation. Tin-base babbitt is more desirable than lead-base babbitt because it has greater corrosion resistance, is less likely to adhere to the shaft under conditions of poor lubrication, and is easier to bond to a steel backing. Corrosion problems are minimized by using inhibited oils or by minimizing oil operating temperature. Attack of lead-base materials can be minimized by changing the oil frequently, so that it does not become acidic.

Babbitts are inherently weak and are further reduced in strength by high temperatures. Therefore, babbitts usually are bonded to stronger backing materials such as bronze, low-carbon steel, or cast iron. The thickness of a babbitt lining varies with the application, but it generally ranges from a few mils (in automotive engines) to $\frac{1}{8}$ in. or more (for industrial applications).

Copper-lead alloys used as bearing materials contain 20% or more lead, 1.5 to 5.5% silver, 0.5% max tin and 0.10% max zinc. Typical alloys are SAE No. 48, 49, 480 and 481 (CDA alloys 982, 984, 986 and 988, respectively).

The combination of good fatigue strength, high load capacity and good high-temperature performance makes the copper-lead alloys well suited for heavy-duty main and connecting-rod bearings for internal-combustion engines. Corrosion can be a major problem with bare copper-lead alloys under certain conditions. A lead-tin overlay containing 8 to 12% tin is sufficiently corrosion resistant to survive corrosive oil conditions. A nickel or brass dam approximately 50 micro-in. thick is necessary to prevent diffusion of tin into the copper phase of the copper-lead alloy. In the absence of this dam, the overlay soon loses the protective action of the tin.

Bronzes. Bearing bronzes may be grouped into three categories: leaded bronzes, tin bronzes and aluminum bronzes. Strength and elevated-temperature properties generally improve from leaded bronzes to tin bronzes to aluminum bronzes. There is a loss in compatibility, conformability and embeddability as the amount of lead in the bronze decreases. Therefore, it is advisable to use the highest-lead-content (softest) bronze that has the necessary strength and load-carrying capacity for the application.

The leaded bronzes contain from 5 to 25% lead and up to 10% tin; lead provides good compatibility properties in these alloys, and tin gives better strength and fatigue resistance and higher hardness levels than are possible with the simple copper-lead alloys and promotes retention of thin oil films. Substitution of zinc for tin in bronze improves ductility but sacrifices strength and hardness. In castings where strength and hardness are essential, it may be desirable to limit the use of zinc, but where zinc is allowed by specification, sound, clean castings usually result.

The strength of leaded bronze is limited at elevated temperatures by weakening of the lead between the copper-tin grains, and performance is not considered satisfactory above 230 to 260 C (approximately 450 to 500 F) because the lead tends to bleed from the alloy. Leaded bronzes have better bearing characteristics than tin bronzes but lower mechanical and fatigue strengths.

Typical wrought leaded bronzes used as bearing materials are SAE alloys 791 to 794, and 797 and 799. SAE alloy 795 is a wrought bronze bearing material that is hard and strong and has good fatigue resistance. Leaded bronze casting alloys used widely are: SAE 40 (CDA 836), SAE 660 (CDA 932), SAE 66 (CDA 935), SAE 64 (CDA 937), CDA 941 and CDA 943. SAE alloy 660 is the most widely used.

Tin bronzes contain more than 20% tin, with less than 10% lead added to aid machinability. Small amounts of zinc or nickel, or both, are sometimes added for increased strength. Bronzes having intermediate amounts of tin have relatively high tensile strength, excellent fatigue resistance, and the ability to operate at higher temperatures than babbitts. Because of their high hardness and poor conformability, these alloys are used in applications where good alignment and reliable lubrication are possible.

Aluminum bronzes used as bearing materials contain aluminum as the principal alloying element with additions of iron, nickel, silicon and manganese. They have hardnesses that range up to 240 Bhn in some instances, and they have excellent shock resistance. Compatibility characteristics of aluminum bronzes are not as good as those of leaded bronzes. Aluminum bronze bearings are used for applications requiring high strength and good resistance to fatigue and impact, and for high-temperature operation. Typical alloys are CDA 862, 863, 952, 953, 954 and 955.

Aluminum Alloys. Solid cast aluminum alloy bearings sometimes are used in heavily loaded moderate-speed to high-speed applications such as diesel-engine main and connecting-rod bearings, hydraulic pumps, and turbosuperchargers.

Compared with solid aluminum alloy bearings, steel-backed aluminum alloy bearings have two major advantages. If adequately bonded, they operate satisfactorily under high unit loading because of their greater fatigue resistance. Differential expansion in the steel-backed bearings is minimal, permitting closer assembly clearances and helping to maintain tight fit of the bearing in the housing. For either type of bearing, shaft hardness is less important when a babbitt or lead-tin overlay is used. Overlays improve the antiscoring and embeddability characteristics of aluminum alloy bearings.

Some of the aluminum bearing alloys contain about 7% tin and 1% copper with 1 or 2% silicon or magnesium. Typical alloys are 850.0-T5, A850.0-T5 and B850.0-T5 (formerly 750-T5, A750-T5 and B750-T5). The copper is retained in solid solution to provide moderate increases in strength and hardness of the aluminum matrix for improved resistance to scuffing and wear. Antiscoring characteristics of some types of aluminum alloys are improved by additions of tin, lead or cadmium, but the resulting bearing material is relatively weak unless a thin layer is used with a strong backing.

Powder Metallurgy Materials. Self-lubricating sintered powder metallurgy bearings are made from lead bronzes, high-density and low-density bronzes, iron alloys, iron-copper alloys, iron-copper-carbon alloys, and aluminum-tin alloys. In these types of bearings, lubricating oil is stored in voids that comprise 10 to 35% of the volume and feeds through these interconnected voids to the bearing surface.

Trimetal bearings are designed to provide higher strength and fatigue resistance than bearings made only of babbitt. They consist of an overlay of babbitt, ranging from 0.0005 to 0.005 in. thick, on an intermediate layer of copper-lead alloy, bronze, aluminum alloy or silver bonded to a low-carbon steel backing. The intermediate layer increases the strength of the bearing and provides compatibility should the thin babbitt surface be worn through during operation. Some trimetal bearings with a copper alloy intermediate layer have a thin electroplated deposit, such as nickel, on the intermediate layer. The plating acts as a dam to prevent diffusion of tin from the babbitt into the copper alloy. Bearings having silver as the intermediate layer are described in AMS 4815.

Procedure for Failure Analysis

A comprehensive analysis of failure of a sliding bearing can be made by performing the following steps as completely as possible:

1 Obtain complete information regarding the bearing design and conditions of the application (load, speed, lubrication, temperature and other environmental factors). If possible, obtain examples of the earliest stage of damage that can be found.
2 Make a thorough visual inspection of the bearing with the aid of low (3 to 50×) and high (100 to 500×) magnification, and classify the type of damage. Select and photograph the most promising areas associated with the damage for metallographic studies.
3 Do the necessary sectioning and metallographic examination to verify the classification by visual inspection.
4 Use information obtained in step 1 in comparing observed and expected life.

Information about the application in which the bearing under investigation was used is important for at least two

Table 1. Information About Application and Environment for Analysis of Bearing Failures

Machine Identification:

Nameplate data and any other information that will facilitate locating applicable records.

Operating Speed:

The speed or speed range for most of the operating life; also, maximum speed and approximate time at that speed.

Load:

Steady load in horsepower or torque; also, transverse and axial load in pounds, and directions in which mechanical loads are applied. If load varies, estimate time at normal load and at maximum load.

Vibration:

Level and frequency of predominant mode in each of three reference planes (two transverse planes 90° apart and an axial plane) as close as possible to each bearing housing. State if source of vibration appears to be within or outside the failed unit.

Alignment:

Measurements under actual operating conditions; if impractical or impossible to make such measurements, list significant side effects. Note whether or not alignment changed during operation as a result of differential thermal expansion or from dynamic effects.

Bearing Temperatures:

Minimum and maximum bearing temperatures and locations in which temperatures were taken. Describe measuring instruments used and the service conditions at which temperatures referred to prevail. Preferred locations for recording temperatures are within $\frac{1}{16}$ in. of bearing load in sliding bearings.

Corrosive Influences:

Describe known or suspected presence of moisture, acids, strong alkaline atmospheres, galvanic effects, other corrosion sources.

Mechanical Connections:

Describe all mechanically connected equipment and power-transmission method such as direct-coupling type, gears, belts, chains.

Failure Symptoms:

Describe any smoke, rapid increase in temperature, or change in noise level. Note whether or not operating temperature or vibrations increased long before final failure.

Bearing Life:

Actual or estimated life of bearing and other affected machine components.

Maintenance:

Describe all preventive or corrective maintenance prior to failure.

Failure of Similar Units:

Describe known failure history of similar units (or previous failure of same unit).

Lubricant:

Trade name and grade of lubricant used in the failed unit.

Condition of Lubricant:

Color. Note any changes from the original color. A darkened appearance may indicate, although not conclusively, that excessive oxidation or contamination may have occurred. A white-yellowish appearance may indicate the presence of water or entrained air.

Impurity Level. A piece of filter paper formed into a cone shape may be used to separate solids from a lubricant. Washing by successive dilution with solvents such as trichlorethylene followed by drain periods will remove the lubricant, leaving solids on the filter paper.

Type of Solid Matter. Describe size, shape and color of solid matter. Moving a magnet under the filter paper will indicate which particles are influenced by a magnetic field.

Viscosity. Describe degree of thinning or thickening of lubricant. A thinned or thickened oil and soupy or caked grease suggest the need for further investigation. Compare the condition of the lubricant in the failed unit with fresh lubricant corresponding to the equipment-manufacturer's specification, and record observations.

Analysis. Submit samples of used and fresh lubricant to laboratory for chemical analysis.

reasons. First, from such information as load, speed, lubricant type, and temperature, the hydrodynamic-film thickness can be estimated. Film thickness, when combined with a film-thickness – surface-roughness parameter, can provide information on the extent of metallic contact between the bearing and shaft surfaces, which has been related to fatigue life and the occurrence of surface-initiated failures. Second, comparison with previous experience can expedite analysis.

A list of useful types of information about application and environment for analysis of bearing failures is given in Table 1. When using the items on a field report, space should be provided at each item for a check mark or for comments.

Visual Inspection. Information obtained from visual or macroscopic inspection includes:

1 General condition of the bearing
2 Specific condition of damaged regions
3 Classification of the failure mechanism or mode of failure.

During visual inspection, the failure areas are photographed and classified as to possible origin or cause, and it is decided where to cut particular sections for metallographic examination; sectioning should not be rushed into before proper photography and classification are completed.

After sectioning, photographs of the failure area as it originally appeared often are needed for comparison with features observed on the sectioned surfaces. Accidents in cutting or identifying specimens can be less detrimental to a valid failure analysis if good photographs (or sketches) of the failure area are available.

Magnification of at least ten diameters is required to perform a useful visual inspection. A binocular microscope with fluorescent lighting that is capable of providing several magnifications in the range of 5 to 40 diameters is a useful tool. Magnifications up to 500 diameters may be required for examination of surface detail.

Items to be considered when assessing the general condition of a bearing include: (*a*) physical dimensions such as parting-line height, wall thickness, and liner thickness; (*b*) location of discolored and bowed regions on backings; (*c*) material quality; (*d*) evidence of excessive temperature on inner and outer surfaces of the bearing; and (*e*) quality of adhesion of laminated materials.

Specific conditions to be determined include location of embedded foreign material, cracks, blowholes and other imperfections. The bearing should be studied with a microscope to assess fatigue of the overlay or the intermediate layer, and wear, fretting, corrosion or cavitation erosion of the bearing surface. Evidence of metallurgical alteration of the material may also be observed.

Metallographic Examination. Up to this point, analysis of bearing failure is nondestructive. If destructive analysis is required, selection of the metallographic section is based on the location and type of failure or damage.

Examination of the microstructure may reveal whether the material was correctly processed and the effects, if any, of heating during service. Material and processing specifications should be available for comparison with the observed condition of the bearing material.

Specimens taken transverse to cracks or fractures are useful in evaluating localized metallurgical effects. Corrosion in a crack or on a fracture surface may be

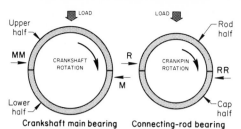

Fig. 4. *Preferred locations from which to remove specimens from sliding bearings to obtain cleanest definition of embedded material. MM and RR are best locations; M and R are next-best.*

an indication that it was a factor in the failure. Oxidation on the surface of a crack may be evidence that the crack was present prior to the most recent application of heat.

The use of brass bearings sometimes results in penetration of copper and other nonferrous alloying elements into steel journals. Metallographic examination of the journal near the origin of the failure will confirm if such penetration was a factor.

Microscopic examination of the bond between the lining and the backing will determine if the bond completely covered the interface, and if not, the cause of unbonding usually can be determined. Common causes of weak bonding are impurities on the backing prior to bonding, lack of flux or use of an improper flux, improper bonding temperature, improper lining material and lack of tinning material.

Other factors that sometimes contribute to failure and that can be confirmed by microscopic analysis include origin of fatigue cracks, origin of metal melted or glazed into parts, maximum service temperature, and galling or score marks that exhibit evidence of direction of motion prior to failure.

At this point, a more detailed laboratory investigation is necessary to accurately pinpoint the cause of such failure. Such investigation includes chemical and metallurgical analysis of the bearing material and chemical analysis of the oil.

Studying Embedded Particles. The running surfaces of all used sliding bearings usually contain varying amounts of embedded foreign particles picked up from dirt suspended in the lubricant. Examination of a surface containing such particles often reveals valuable information concerning the original internal cleanness of the machine as well as conditions of the operational environment.

The most likely place to find the largest and least-damaged embedded particles is at the leading parting-line area of the unloaded (or least-loaded) bearing half. In general, these locations for crankshaft main bearings and connecting-rod bearings are as shown in Fig. 4. Particles that lodge in these

maximum-clearance areas have not passed through the minimum-clearance area for that particular bearing half, and are more likely to represent the true size and condition of the particle.

Vitreous transparent particles of materials like silica (sand) or alumina (from an aluminum oxide grinding wheel) usually appear dark to black when embedded, because the incident light is internally scattered and very little light emerges from the surface. If these particles are pried out of the bearing, their brilliant glasslike nature becomes apparent. Very frequently, a score line, or a repetitive tracking caused by the rolling over and over of a sharp granular particle, can be seen in the bearing surface. Either of these features may end with an embedded particle and the resultant cratering in the surrounding metal. If a needle point is plunged below the surface at this location, the original particle or its fragmented remains can usually be seen as the point is lifted upward.

After embedment, very brittle particles are likely to break up into finer particles as a result of repeated cycling. These finer particles frequently become dislodged and move circumferentially into areas of lesser clearance, and may become re-embedded there; often only a powdery residue remains at the site of initial embedment.

Embedded metallic particles frequently can be identified by specific characteristics associated with the metal. For instance, aluminum alloy chips are usually soft enough to embed in and conform to the bearing in flakelike shapes. Moreover, their distinctive color and microstructure are visible even without etching, and a drop of caustic applied to the aluminum will cause hydrogen-gas evolution readily visible under low magnification. No other common white metal reacts in this manner.

Cast iron chips first embed in the bearing material intact, then are likely to fragment along the weak graphite flakes into clusters of smaller chips. This differentiates cast iron chips from steel chips, which usually remain intact. Drillings, turnings and grinding chips each have their own characteristic shape and size, and known examples can be compared with debris embedded in a bearing.

Identification of embedded particles by sectioning the bearing and metallographically preparing the cut faces has the following disadvantages:

1 It is difficult to cut precisely through any specific particle.
2 Particles embedded in the soft bearing alloy at the extreme polished edge of the specimen are likely to fall out.
3 Unless the embedded particles are quite numerous, the probability of en-

countering very many of them in any random plane of polish is extremely small.

4 The soft surface material may be contaminated with extraneous debris picked up during the various stages of ordinary metallographic preparation, thus confounding the evidence.

Embedded particles can be studied without sectioning by flattening a portion of the bearing surface so that the embedded particles can be polished. This technique works well when the bearing material is a soft metal like lead, which it usually is. The bearing surface is inspected for areas of particular interest with respect to embedded dirt, then a specimen approximately ½ by 1 in. is carefully sawed out, and the inner (bearing) surface is flattened in a hydraulic press between heavy, very smooth, clean, parallel blocks of hardened steel.

After the specimen has been flattened, it can be lightly polished by hand using the final wet metallographic polishing-wheel surface (not rotating) as a hand lap. Inspection under the microscope after this light polishing should give some idea of the nature of the very finest embedded material. Any vitreous abrasive material observed must have been embedded in the bearing during service, because this method of omitting all abrasive papers precludes the trapping of extraneous grit.

It may now be necessary to further polish the specimen by using the rotating wheel. Polarized light, if available, can be used to determine if the embedded material is sand or alumina. Embedded metallic particles often can be identified by shape and color, and can be further characterized by the same methods used for standard metallographic specimens. Frequently it is difficult to fully develop the microstructure of these fine particles by etching, particularly when they have been plastically deformed by severe machining operations, such as grinding. The flattened surface should be polished only a small amount; otherwise, the embedded particles will be pulled out and lost. By examination between successive polishing and etching steps, the maximum information can usually be obtained. A standard metallurgical or binocular microscope with vertical illumination is recommended for this phase of the examination rather than a binocular microscope. Magnification up to 500 diameters may be necessary for positive identification of material. Microprobe analysis also may be useful.

Failure Mechanisms

The mechanisms by which sliding bearings fail include fatigue, wear, fretting, corrosion, corrosion fatigue, and cavitation.

Fatigue. Failure of a sliding bearing by fatigue results when the magnitude and frequency of a cyclic load exceed those which the bearing material is able to withstand. Fatigue may be initiated by stress concentrations at dirt particles, by

(a)

(b)

Fig. 5. Sliding-bearing surfaces that failed by fatigue: (a) wormhole appearance in lead-base babbitt bearing; (b) flaking (between arrows) of overlay in a trimetal bearing

stresses resulting from misassembly of the bearing on a shaft or into a housing, by material weaknesses caused by high temperature or corrosion, or simply by extended service under fluctuating loads.

Few sliding bearings completely escape fatigue during normal operation. Fatigue cracking of bimetal bearings occurs in stages, beginning with hen-track patterns that initiate and propagate perpendicular to the bearing surface. Before reaching the bond line, the cracks turn, run parallel to the bond line, and join. As fatigue progresses, the bearing metal breaks away from the steel backing in a wormhole pattern similar to that shown in Fig. 5(a). This type of failure is a purely mechanical phenomenon and bears no relation to improper lubrication, except when minimal oil film causes higher temperatures, resulting in weakening of the material. The cyclic stresses necessary for such failures result from changes in direction of loading, such as those initiated by the normal power impulses of pistons in an internal-combustion engine.

In trimetal bearings, the most common type of fatigue is that which occurs in the overlay; the cracks turn and run parallel to the nickel dam. When the cracks join, the overlay flakes off, as shown in Fig. 5(b). However, a minor amount of fatigue in the overlay is not regarded as bearing failure because the load-carrying strength of a bearing is contained in its intermediate layer and steel backing. A true fatigue failure involves the intermediate material rather than the sacrificial overlay.

The bearing shown in Fig. 6 failed in a small, centrally located area of a bearing half as a result of a ridge on the shaft journal. This type of fatigue failure is typical in automotive applications and is most prevalent in main bearings that have been in service for a long time or that have oil grooves in the upper shells only. During extended service, both the main journals and the bearings undergo

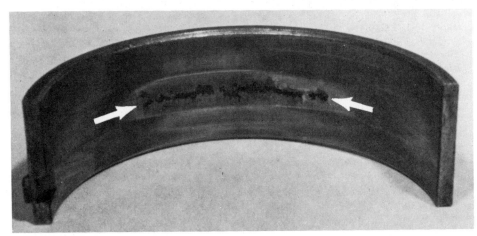

Fig. 6. Sliding-bearing half that failed by fatigue (in zone between arrows) because of a ridge that formed on the shaft journal by wear

Table 2. Maximum Peak Loads for Normal Fatigue Life of Various Bearing Metals Used in Automotive Applications(a)

Bearing metal	Peak load (max), psi
Solid-Metal Bearings	
Aluminum alloy SAE 770-T101 0.162 in. thick	5000
Bimetal Bearings	
Tin babbitt 0.022 in. thick on steel	1200
Lead babbitt 0.022 in. thick on steel	1400
Tin babbitt 0.004 in. thick on steel	2200
Lead babbitt 0.004 in. thick on steel	2400
Cu-Pb 0.022 in. thick on steel	5000
Aluminum alloy SAE 780 0.030 in. thick on steel	6000
Trimetal Bearings	
Pb-Sn 0.001 in. thick on Cu-Pb 0.022 in. thick on steel	7500
Pb-Sn 0.001 in. thick on silver 0.013 in. thick on steel	7500
Pb-Sn 0.001 in. thick on aluminum alloy SAE 780 0.030 in. thick on steel	8000
Pb-Sn-Cu 0.015 in. thick on aluminum alloy SAE 781 0.015 in. thick on steel	10000

(a) Fatigue strength of these bearing metals was determined under laboratory conditions of excellent alignment, excellent oil flow, a high degree of cleanness, ideal clearance, and normal operating temperatures of 82 to 104 C (180 to 220 F). Normal fatigue life of bearings is considered to be 100,000 miles (approximately 2000 hr) in automobile (gasoline) engines, and 250,000 miles (approximately 5000 hr) in truck (diesel) engines.

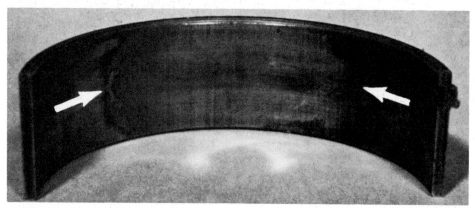

Fig. 7. Sliding bearing exhibiting wear (between arrows) in the area of journal dwell

wear. Journal wear is uniform, except in the small area opposite the oil groove, which does not wear as much. As a result, the journal develops a ridge in the center that serves as a stress-concentration mechanism, causing the load to be distributed over a smaller-than-normal area of the bearing surface. Fatigue failure from this type of origin can be avoided by refinishing the crankshaft journals to eliminate the ridges before replacement bearings are installed.

Maximum peak loads (in psi) for normal fatigue life of bearings used in automotive applications — as established under laboratory conditions for several common solid, bimetal and trimetal bearings — are listed in Table 2. Normal fatigue life for these bearings is considered to be 100,000 miles (approximately 2000 hr) in automobile (gasoline) engines and 250,000 miles (approximately 5000 hr) in truck (diesel) engines.

Wear of sliding bearings usually occurs during machine break-in. Thereafter, wear continues at a much slower rate because surface roughness has been stabilized and the bearing surface has

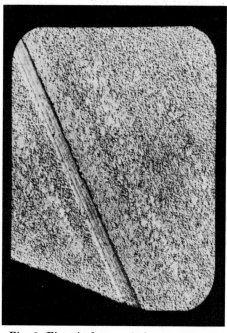

Fig. 8. Electrical wear (microscopic pitting caused by sparking from electric current) on the surface of a thrust bearing from a steam turbine; actual size

conformed to the shaft surface. With proper maintenance, only those dirt particles that are too small to be filtered will abrade the bearing surface. On this basis, bearings have a finite life, but one that usually is acceptably long.

Normal wear can be recognized by two conditions. First, in trimetal bearings, some of the babbitt overlay will have been removed, exposing the nickel dam or the intermediate layer in the primary area of journal dwell, as in Fig. 7. Although one function of the overlay is to embed unfiltered dirt particles, its main purpose is to provide a running-in surface for the bearing. Thus, partial loss of overlay is not considered serious.

The second sign of normal wear is the presence of minor surface scratches caused by foreign material in the lubricant as it passes through the bearing. These are, in general, not serious unless the surface has been deeply penetrated. Often, a shaft with a scratched surface will exhibit a higher temperature rise after continued operation than one without major imperfections.

Wear occurs in hydrodynamic bearings during machine starting and stopping, when the speed is too low to produce sufficient fluid pressure to support the shaft on a lubricant film.

Hydrostatic bearings that are operating properly do not wear, because the bearing surfaces are separated by a film of oil, even during starting and stopping. In gas-lubricated bearings, impact or vibrational loads may cause rubbing that can result in wear.

Boundary-lubricated and solid-lubricated bearings wear much faster than fluid-film bearings.

Electric currents occasionally pass through bearings. In such instances, sparks pass through the oil film and cause microscopic pits in the surfaces of the shaft and bearing. This action results in a continual removal of metal from the bearing surface and is referred to as electrical wear. Electrical wear produces a frosted surface in the loaded zone of the bearing where the oil film is thinnest. Under a microscope the frosted area appears as many small craters. These craters result from the fusing temperature generated by an electrical spark. The surface of a steam-turbine thrust bearing pitted by electric-current flow is shown in Fig. 8. Water droplets in the vapor passing through the low-pressure stages of the turbine caused an electrostatic charge to build up on the rotor buckets; these charges were grounded through the bearing.

Fretting of the outside surface of a bearing (see Fig. 9) occurs as a result of small relative movement between mating surfaces. Movement may occur when there is insufficient press fit between the bearing and housing. Lack of press fit can result when housing bores are oversize, when dirt or burrs are present on mating faces of the housing, when bolts are insufficiently tightened, or when bearing parting lines are filed, reducing the height such that a press-fitting effect is not present.

Another cause of fretting is flexibility in the bearing assembly. If the main bearing cap on a connecting rod is undersize, or if the connecting rod itself is undersize, the rod may deflect under dynamic load, permitting movement between the bearing and the connecting-rod bore.

Fretted areas on a bearing housing can act as stress concentrators and can lead to cracking of the housing. Incomplete contact between the bearing and housing impedes heat transfer and can cause overheating and finally fatigue or hot shortness of the bearing metal (see discussion under "Hot Shortness Failures", on page 409 in this article).

Corrosion in sliding bearings occurs as chemical attack of the bearing alloy by corrosive compounds in the lubricant. These compounds may be contaminants, such as water or antifreeze solutions, or may have developed in the lubricant during operation as a result of oxidation.

A corrosive environment may deplete one or more of the alloying elements in the bearing alloy, such as lead or zinc. Deleading or dezincification results in a weakened structure, which allows fatigue cracking and removal of large sections of the lining material. A brittle and weak oxide film may form on the bearing surface in a corrosive atmosphere. Consequently, a bearing with an oxidized surface is more subject to fatigue cracking than it was prior to oxidation. Figure 10 shows a micrograph of a section through a copper-lead alloy bearing that failed by deleading. Lead had been depleted from the copper-lead alloy to a depth of approximately 0.008 in. from the bearing surface, creating voids (dark areas in Fig. 10) that are depositories for oil sludge. The copper matrix (light areas in the upper part of Fig. 10) that remains is compressed under load because of lack of support from the lead phase.

Corrosion of sliding bearings occurs only infrequently, because lubricant additives have been developed that inhibit oxidation over extended periods and under severe operating conditions. If oil is not changed at regular intervals, however, it eventually will be degraded through formation of corrosive compounds. These compounds include alcohols, aldehydes, ketones and acids. Oxidation may be accelerated by elevated temperatures and by exposure to air, water, or foreign materials in the oil.

Normally, when lubricants become corrosive because of an accumulation of acids and peroxides, lead is removed

Fig. 9. Fretting on the outside surface of steel backing of a sliding bearing

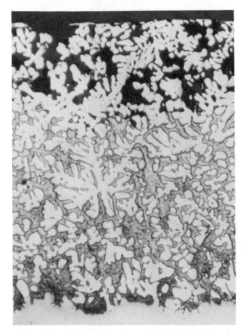

Fig. 10. Micrograph, at 100×, of an unetched section through a copper-lead alloy bearing that failed by deleading. Light area at the upper surface is the copper matrix that remained after alloy was depleted of lead.

from copper-lead bearing alloys. However, if both the copper and the lead are attacked, the presence of metallic sulfides as the corrosion product indicates that sulfur compounds were responsible for the corrosion. The source of the sulfur compounds can be either the fuel or the lubricant. Most likely they form in the lubricant as the result of extended intervals between oil changes and higher-than-normal operating temperatures. Both of these factors are known to promote decomposition of sulfur compounds in additives; the decomposition products then become corrosive. Adherence to the proper machine-maintenance schedule is important under such circumstances. Also, bearing life can be extended by using a more corrosion-resistant design, such as an overlay on a copper alloy bearing surface.

In the following example, both the copper and the lead in a copper-lead bearing alloy were attacked by sulfur compounds.

Example 1. Corrosion of Copper-Lead Alloy Sliding Bearings by Sulfur Compounds

A connecting-rod bearing from a six-cylinder gasoline engine was returned to the factory for examination. The bearing was made of copper-lead alloy SAE 485 bonded to a low-carbon steel backing. The recommended lubricating oil was used in the engine. Length and type of service were not reported.

Investigation. Examination of the bearing halves disclosed that wall thickness at the centerline position of the upper bearing half was 0.006 to 0.007 in. less than the specified 0.0755 in. Regions adjacent to the parting line in both bearing halves, and at the centerline position of the lower bearing half, exhibited material loss to a depth of 0.001 to 0.035 in. The steel backing of the upper bearing half was exposed in a wide region at the centerline.

No dirt or other foreign particles were found on the surface of either bearing half. Shallow pits and a darkened region were observed on the bearing surface. The pits were partly filled, and the darkened region partly covered, with a brittle waxlike substance that was identified as a mixture of copper and lead sulfides.

The sulfides were formed by the action of sulfur acids in the lubricating oil on the copper and lead in the bearing material. Decomposition of sulfur compounds in lubricating oil usually occurs when moisture is present in the oil and when operating temperatures are high. Changing the oil before the sulfur acids accumulate to a harmful level can reduce corrosive attack on the bearing materials.

Loss of liner material occurred across the entire bearing surface but was most severe in the loaded regions. Deterioration of the bearing was not the result of wear by dirt or other foreign particles, but a combination of chemical attack and mechanical wear, which was accelerated because of the easily abraded sulfides on the surface.

Conclusion. A combination of chemical attack by sulfur compounds and mechanical wear caused a reduction in the liner thickness. The copper and lead in the liner alloy had been attacked at nearly equal rates, which is typical of corrosion of Cu-Pb alloys by sulfur compounds. The dark corrosion product that covered the bearing surface was identified as copper and lead sulfides, which wear rapidly. Dirt was absent from the bearing surface and thus was not a factor in bearing wear.

Corrective Measures. Changing the engine oil at or before recommended intervals minimized the effect of chemical attack by decomposed sulfur compounds in the lubricant. (Use of a trimetal bearing with a corrosion-resistant overlay also would give longer bearing life in this application.)

Corrosion fatigue is the interaction of a corrosive environment with an alternating stress field that causes accelerated fatigue-crack initiation and propagation where possibly neither the environment nor the alternating stress acting alone or acting in conjunction with a static stress would produce cracking.

In the following example, a spherical self-aligning bearing made of corrosion-

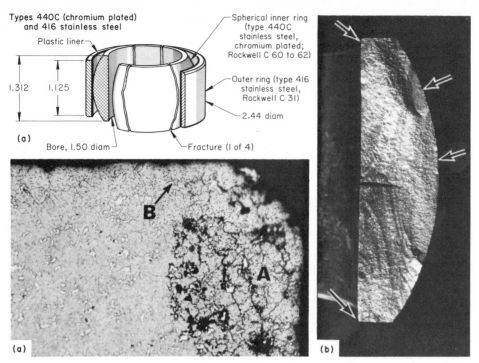

(a) Construction of bearing and location of fractures. (b) View of fracture surface at 2½×, showing multiple fatigue origins (arrows) at edge of bore and on the spherical surface. (c) Micrograph at 250× of a picral-etched section through one of the fatigue origins at the edge of the bore, showing intergranular corrosion, at A, and intergranular attack, at B, on fracture surface.

Fig. 11. Plastic-lined stainless steel spherical bearing for a hydrofoil that fractured by corrosion fatigue (Example 2)

resistant stainless steel with a plastic insert operated under an oscillating, high radial load and conditions where adequate lubrication was difficult. Corrosion fatigue occurred in one of the bearing elements, which was a spherical inner ring made of a stainless steel with good wear resistance but with lower corrosion resistance than that required for the application.

Example 2. Corrosion-Fatigue Failure of a Stainless Steel Bearing in a Marine Environment (Fig. 11)

A front support bearing (Fig. 11a) for the rear foil on a hydrofoil failed after approximately 220 hr of operation and was sent to the laboratory for examination. Failures of the adjacent front support bearing, the rear support bearings and the lower bell-crank bearings were also reported, but these parts were not submitted for investigation.

The bearing consisted of a heat treated stainless steel outer ring (type not specified by vendor) and a chromium-plated type 440C stainless steel truncated spherical inner ring. The bearing liner, bonded to the inner surface of the raceway with epoxy resin, was a proprietary plastic material composed primarily of asbestos fibers and plastic resin on a plain-weave metal-screen backing.

Investigation. The inner ring had fractured transversely at four locations, as shown in Fig. 11(a). In addition, there were numerous secondary transverse cracks that had not propagated completely through the ring. The plastic liner on the inner surface of the outer ring had disappeared, and the

exposed steel surface contained areas of galling and smeared metal where it had been contacted by the inner ring. Magnetic-particle inspection of the outer ring did not reveal any evidence of cracking. The inner ring was severely pitted on all surfaces and contained a considerable amount of corrosion residue.

Examination of the fracture surfaces of the inner ring, which were heavily discolored, showed that fatigue cracking had nucleated at pits along the edges and at the midpoint of the outer surface and at the edges of the bore (see Fig. 11b). Examination of one of the secondary fatigue cracks, after it had been opened in the laboratory, disclosed that parts of the fracture surface were covered with a plastic material containing short fibers. This material was identified as being from the plastic liner. The entire surface of the secondary crack was

Fig. 12. Typical cavitation damage on the surface of a sliding bearing

heavily discolored, including the areas beneath the plastic.

Microscopic examination of a section through the origin of one of the fractures at the edge of the bore (see Fig. 11c) revealed intergranular corrosion as deep as 0.006 in. The fracture, which was mostly transgranular, contained areas of intergranular attack where the corrodent (seawater) had migrated as cracking progressed. The discoloration of the fracture surfaces resulted from the corrosive action of the seawater.

The inner ring, which was confirmed to be of type 440C stainless steel, was satisfactory with respect to hardness (Rockwell C 60 to 62) and microstructure (spheroidized chromium carbides in a matrix of tempered martensite). The plating was identified as chromium, using a chemical spot test; the chromium plating was too thin to measure accurately. The material in the outer ring was identified as type 416 stainless steel with a hardness of Rockwell C 31.

Conclusions. Corrosion fatigue was the cause of failure. The spherical inner ring fractured transversely at four locations (at the edges and center of the outer surface and at the edges of the bore).

The sequence of events that led to failure was as follows: (a) corrosion pitting of the spherical inner ring produced local stress concentrations and resulted in formation of cracks under repeated stressing, and (b) simultaneous cyclic stressing and corrosion in the cracks led to deepening of the cracks and ultimate failure of the inner ring.

Loss of the composite plastic liner in the outer ring occurred as a result of a paring action by the cracks as they opened and closed under load during normal oscillation of the inner ring. Increased stress amplitude because of excessive radial clearance, which resulted from loss of the liner, led to fatigue fracture.

Recommendation. The inner and outer rings both should be made of 17-4 PH stainless steel, which is more resistant to corrosive marine environments than either type 440C or type 416 stainless steel.

Cavitation. Small vapor-filled cavities form in the oil when, under rapid fluctuations, the oil-film pressure in an isolated area drops below the vapor pressure of the oil. If the pressure then increases, or if the cavities travel to an area of higher pressure, the cavities collapse and the surrounding oil impinges on the adjacent bearing metal and erodes the bearing surface (see Fig. 12). For more information on cavitation erosion, see the article that begins on page 160 in this volume.

Cavitation usually occurs in the unloaded area of the bearing, and only superficial degradation takes place. Thus, bearings from which large sections of the overlay have been removed by cavitation erosion may not be severely damaged.

Cavitation erosion is an infrequent occurrence, and there are no reliable methods of predicting it. In certain engines and in other applications, cavitation occurs regardless of what measures are taken to minimize it. The unloaded connecting-rod bearing halves of some

V-8 engines, and bearings for high-speed gears (where the rapid tooth engagement causes fluctuations in loads and oil-film pressure), are some applications in which cavitation frequently occurs.

There are steps that can be taken to reduce the probability of cavitation or to minimize its effects. The cavitation resistance of bearing materials is very much like fatigue resistance in that the harder alloys are damaged much less than the softer ones. Thin layers of bearing material appear to be less susceptible to cavitation damage than thick layers. Also, the nickel dam between the overlay and a bronze alloy layer, although developed to fill another need, is an effective barrier to cavitation erosion of the bronze alloy layer. Increasing oil viscosity and oil pressure often will reduce cavitation. Cavitation increases greatly with contamination of the oil by water or entrained air. These contaminants provide nuclei for the formation of bubbles in the oil; also, water has a low vapor pressure. These properties of the contaminants make cavitation in the oil occur more readily and at higher local pressures.

Effects of Foreign Particles

The most common cause of bearing damage is the presence of foreign particles between the bearing and shaft surfaces. Particles such as grit, shot, steel

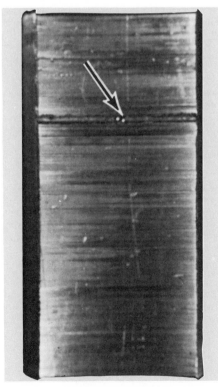

Fig. 13. Foreign particle (at arrow) embedded in the surface of a bronze bearing, which resulted only in light scoring of the shaft, rather than in more extensive shaft wear or in bearing failure

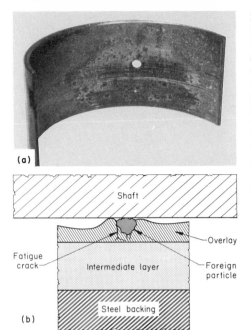

Fig. 14. (a) Trimetal bearing half with foreign particles embedded in soft overlay. (b) Schematic representation showing displacement of metal in overlay by embedded particle.

chips or cast iron chips can be missed in the cleanup of a new machine. Road dirt and sand can enter an engine through the air intake. Fine particles often abrasively wear away the bearing lining and the shaft surface. Particles that are too large to embed in the bearing material cause scoring of the bearing and shaft surfaces. Particles lodged between the steel backing and the housing can cause high spots at which high localized loads and disrupted heat transfer promote fatigue fracture of the bearing-surface material. Excessive embedment of foreign particles disrupts oil films and causes bearing temperature to rise. At high temperatures, fatigue strength decreases, and hot-shortness failures can occur in bearing materials with a low-melting-point constituent such as is found in aluminum-tin bearing alloys.

Figure 13 shows a section of a bronze sliding bearing containing an embedded foreign particle (at arrow) that had lightly scored an intermediate drive shaft in a crawler excavator. The light scoring was detected during replacement of another component in the drive mechanism. The bronze bearing material performed its function of embedding hard foreign particles and thus prevented significant damage to the shaft or bearing. The foreign particle was identified as weld spatter that had entered the splash oiling system.

Foreign particles become embedded in the soft matrices of babbitt, copper-lead and bronze bearing alloys (see Fig. 14a). If the particle is of sufficient size that it is only partly embedded, the bear-

ing alloy is displaced upward and away from the particle, as shown in Fig. 14(b). Clearance between the bearing surface and the shaft is reduced significantly, and the load on the bearing is concentrated on the plateau surrounding the particle. Contact between the shaft surface and the bearing metal around the particle generates flashes of extreme heat, which reduce the fatigue strength of the bearing material. Under repeated stressing and heating from the concentrated load, a small portion of the bearing material cracks by fatigue and breaks away; this material then travels through the bearing as debris.

Frequently, particles circulate in the lubricating oil that are too large to completely embed in the bearing lining (see Fig. 15a). Such particles will be carried by the lubricant to a point where the clearance is less than the size of the particles. At this point, the particles either shatter into smaller pieces (which may or may not embed in the lining) or move around the bearing in the clearance space, scoring the shaft and removing bearing material. The bearing half in Fig. 15(b) was severely scored by metal chips resulting from prior failure of another engine component.

The types of foreign matter most common in bearing-shaft interfaces in office machines are eraser and paper debris. Properties of soft-metal bearings such as embeddability, conformability, and antiseizure are not highly important for prevention or retardation of wear by such debris, because (*a*) erasers commonly contain about 50% glass (by weight); (*b*) good-quality paper often

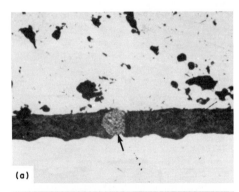

Fig. 15. (a) Micrograph, at 110×, of an unetched specimen, showing a large foreign particle (at arrow) at the interface of the bearing and the shaft. (b) Bearing surface scored by metal chips.

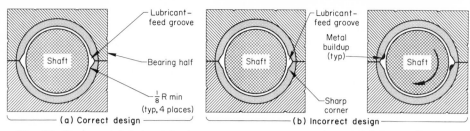

Fig. 16. Design of lubricant-feed groove to prevent scraping of lubricant film from shaft. (a) *Correct design.* (b) *Incorrect design with sharp corner (in view at left), which acts as a site for buildup of wiped metal (in view at right).*

has a clay filler, which produces very small particles of debris; and (*c*) office machines usually operate at high speed and under light loads. Other than by mechanically excluding foreign material from the bearing surface with felt wipers, closer tolerances, or covers, wear caused by eraser and paper debris can be decreased by using hardened sintered-iron bearings. Substitution of hardened sintered-iron bearings for bronze bearings does not eliminate wear, but in many applications it can defer failure beyond design life of bearings.

Effect of Lubrication on Bearing Failure

Adequate lubrication of any sliding bearing deters the effects of such conditions as misalignment, poor surface finish, improper shaft configuration, or presence of foreign particles. But not even the best lubricants can function properly without adequate oil flow. When and where to place grooves in sliding bearings are critical decisions in bearing design. (Grooves in the loaded sections of bearings tend to decrease load-carrying capacity.) Grooves of various cross-sectional shapes are available; cost of manufacture and oil-flow requirements are factors in selection.

Improper design of the lubricant-feed groove can cause destruction of the oil film in the bearing. The corner between the lubricant-feed groove and the inner surface of the bearing must have a small radius (Fig. 16a), instead of a sharp corner (Fig. 16b). A sharp corner can provide a site for buildup of wiped metal (Fig. 16c). A sharp corner or a buildup of wiped metal can scrape the lubricant film from the shaft, which will result in improper oil-film formation and insufficient lubrication.

Inadequate Lubrication. Some of the reasons for inadequate lubrication of sliding bearings are: dry start; insufficient oil-clearance space; low supply of oil; malfunction of oil pump or oil-pressure-relief valve; oil dilution by fuel, antifreeze or coolant water; extended usage of oil; and overheating of the oil-cooling system.

A common cause of failure in bearings is breakdown of the oil film, which results in direct contact between the shaft and bearing surfaces and greatly increases friction. Under such conditions, wear of the bearing surface (and often of the shaft surface also) is excessive. The increased friction may cause seizure, or the heat generated may melt the bearing alloy. The most frequent causes of seizure include overloading, failure of oil supply, or an increase in the coefficient of friction of a bearing material during continued service. The coefficient of friction of the material increases, for example, in copper-lead alloy bearings if the operating conditions cause selective corrosion of the lead, deleading the bearing surface.

Moderate permanent deformation of bearing surfaces is desirable during machine break-in. The soft inner layer of the bearing, such as babbitt, may be wiped by the rubbing action of the contacting surfaces, or may be displaced by localized compression. The rubbing action or surface-contour adjustment because of yielding provides satisfactory seating so that the bearing can operate without complications.

A section of a bearing exhibiting excessive wiping is shown in Fig. 17. A pad of deposited babbitt has displaced the oil film in the region of minimum film thickness. This pad has a characteristic shiny appearance on the bearing surface. When the oil film has been disrupted by the babbitt deposit, mixed-flow or boundary lubrication results, and a sharply increased coefficient of friction accelerates the failure process. The thickness of the pad of babbitt approximates the oil-film thickness.

Fig. 17. Section through a sliding bearing, showing a pad of babbitt deposited in the region of minimum film thickness as a result of excessive wiping

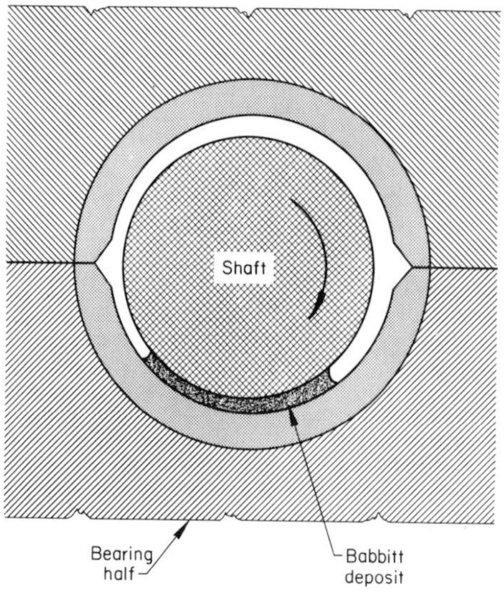

If scoring and wiping continue, the lubricant flow is disrupted and the bearing will eventually seize, as in the following example.

Example 3. Seizure of Trimetal Connecting-Rod Bearings Because of Inadequate Lubrication (Fig. 18)

Forewarning of an impending engine failure was given by a sudden rise in engine temperature and a loss of oil pressure. Failure occurred before the engine could be shut down. The engine had operated for a total of 478 hr.

Investigation. Teardown analysis of the engine-crankshaft assembly revealed failure of the No. 5 cylinder connecting-rod bearing. The bearing had an inside diameter of approximately 2.5 in. and was of trimetal construction. The babbitt layer was 0.0007 in. thick, the intermediate copper-alloy layer was 0.014 in. thick, and the low-carbon steel backing was 0.047 in. thick. Rod bearings in the other cylinders, and all main bearings, were in good condition, and all oil passages were clear. The area surrounding the No. 5 crankpin was blackened as if by overheating, and the crankpin journal appeared to have metal particles welded to and smeared over its surface, as shown at the arrow in Fig. 18(a). Welding occurred mainly on the outer surface of the crankpin journal (that farthest from the main-bearing journal). Examination by x-ray diffraction confirmed that the metal smeared on the crankpin journal was from the bearing.

The connecting rod and the bolts that attached the bearing cap to the rod were broken.

The bearing surface was severely wiped and scored, which indicated intermittent conditions of inadequate lubrication. Both bearing halves exhibited cracks approximately 0.3 in. long across the face of the bearing. Once adherence of bearing material to the crankshaft started, even a continuous flow of lubricant would not have arrested further degradation.

Metallographic examination of a section through the failed bearing disclosed that the structure of the copper-alloy intermediate layer was distorted from the normal dendritic pattern. Distortion was caused by shear stresses. Figure 18(b) shows a laterally oriented shear zone (at A) in the copper-alloy intermediate layer slightly above the bond line (at B) between the intermediate layer and the steel backing.

No cracks started at the inner surface of the bearing and propagated to the fracture zone slightly above the bond line; such a condition would have indicated fatigue fracture.

Conclusion. Seizure occurred at areas of metal-to-metal contact between the bearing and crankshaft surfaces during periods of inadequate lubrication. Fatigue was ruled

out because of the distortion (from shear) in orientation of the metal structure from the normal dendritic pattern in the intermediate layer. Subsurface shear stresses were generated as the frictional forces increased at the bearing – crankshaft-journal interfaces.

Dry Start. In machines that are used intermittently and that stand idle for days or weeks, most damage occurs during start-up, when the oil has drained from the bearing and has been squeezed from between the shaft and bearing surfaces. In such instances, spherical indentations added to the bearing surface act as reservoirs and provide sufficient oil to minimize damage during dry start. These indentations must not be used indiscriminately on highly loaded bearings because they reduce the bearing area (and thus the load-carrying capacity) by as much as 18%. Before a machine is started for the first time, or after an overhaul, the oil lines, oil pump, and filter should be primed with good clean oil so that when the machine is started, oil is instantly fed to the bearings.

Oil dilution by leakage of antifreeze solution into the crankcase can cause the oil to become gummy and to build up on the bearings and other parts. This leads to premature damage of bearings and can even cause seizure.

Suitable maintenance monitoring with a spectrographic oil-analysis program may be utilized to predict and prevent impending bearing failure. In such a program, a sample of oil from the machinery is removed at predetermined intervals to determine its condition and to check for unusually high concentrations of metal worn from the bearing surface.

Effect of Operating Temperatures

Heat is generated in sliding bearings either by shearing of the oil film or by rubbing contact. Frictional heating is a function of bearing load, sliding velocity (rpm times bearing circumference), and coefficient of friction.

In hydrostatic and hydrodynamic bearings, generation of heat results from shearing of the oil film. Shear rate increases with increasing rotational speed and decreasing film thickness. The coefficient of friction is generally below 0.004.

Boundary-lubricated and thin-film-lubricated bearings can operate under lower sliding velocities than can hydrodynamic bearings, but with higher friction. Coefficients of friction are 0.001 to 0.10 for thin-film lubrication and 0.01 to 0.3 for boundary lubrication.

Bearings designed to operate with a free flow of air may become overheated when shields, baffles or insulation restrict air flow. Air flow from fans and other moving or rotating parts may have been incorporated in the original design of the

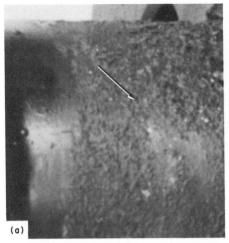
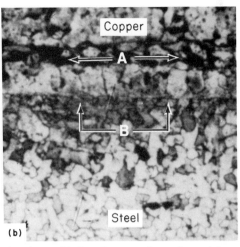

Fig. 18. (a) *Portion of a crankpin journal, showing welded and smeared metal particles (at arrow).* (b) *Micrograph of a section through the trimetal bearing; shear zone in the intermediate copper alloy layer is at A; bond line is at B.* (Example 3)

equipment to maintain heat balance in bearings. Restriction of this air flow can cause overheating.

In combination sleeve and thrust bearings, heat can be transmitted from one portion to the other, which can affect operating conditions. An overload on the sleeve portion can cause a rise in temperature and expansion of the bearing. A change in length of the bearing can increase the axial load on the thrust portion, resulting in failure of both the thrust and sleeve portions of the bearing.

Overheating of a bearing may be induced by abnormal operating conditions. A bearing may be capable of supporting a heavy load at low speed for long periods, a moderate load at high speed for long periods, or a heavy load at high speed for short periods. However, long operation at a high speed and heavy load may result in excessively high temperatures. Rapid acceleration to a high speed may cause severe overheating.

At high speed, lubricant flow and air flow around the bearing normally may result in a steady-state temperature, somewhat lower than the temperature resulting from a rapid change from one speed to another. Thus, the sequence of operations should be considered in investigating a bearing failure.

Short periods of heating and cooling of some bearings can be important. Large-diameter bearings with small clearances may be distorted by small temperature differences. Bearings of this nature may require slow, progressive start-up and slowdown while the temperature reaches a stable and acceptable value. The recommendations of the bearing or machine manufacturer on starting and stopping the machine should be checked against the actual sequence of operations. All parts of the system must be brought to normal operating temperature before the bearing is operated at moderate to high speeds.

Surface finish on the shaft and the clearance between the shaft and the bearing are as important as the condition of the bearing itself. Reworking or replacing a worn shaft may result in substantially different operating conditions than those experienced by the original shaft. A smaller clearance may result in higher operating temperatures; a larger clearance may result in lower load-carrying capacity. An increase in surface roughness of a shaft can result in metal-to-metal contact in a bearing that was designed to operate hydrodynamically. This can result in bearing failure because of high friction and elevated temperatures that would not be encountered with a shaft with a finer surface finish. (See the section on Shaft Design, page 413.)

Hot-Shortness Failures. Many bearing alloys that contain even a small amount of a low-melting-point constituent exhibit low ductility when stressed in tension at a temperature above the melting point of that constituent. At elevated temperatures, the alloy consists of pockets of liquid metal surrounded by a continuous solid matrix. When the matrix is subjected to tensile stresses arising from tension, bending, or torsion (shear), the molten metal in the pockets penetrates rapidly between the grains of the matrix, causing separation of the grains without appreciable plastic deformation of the matrix. At this temperature the alloy is said to be hot short (brittle when hot).

Following are hot-shortness temperatures of some bearing alloys.

Alloy		Hot-shortness temperature	
SAE No.	Composition	F	C
780	Al-6Sn	449	232
...	Al-20Sn	449	232
...	Al-8.5Pb-1.5Sn	700	371
781	Al-4Si-1Cd	700+	371+
49	75Cu-24Pb-1Sn	620	327
794 or 799	72Cu-25Pb-3Sn	620	327

Fig. 19. Surface of a sliding bearing that failed because the bearing material reached a temperature that caused the alloy to be hot short

In a bearing system, the elevated temperatures that initiate hot-shortness failure can result from insufficient oil supply, misalignment, poor shaft geometry, foreign particles, and relative motion between the bearing and its housing. Excessive amounts of foreign particles are the most prevalent cause. Foreign particles circulating with the lubricating oil disrupt the oil film, allowing metal-to-metal contact. As a result, friction is increased, and this in turn causes the temperature to rise. When the hot-shortness temperature of a bearing material is reached, large sections of lining are cleanly removed from the steel backing, as shown in Fig. 19. High temperature alone will not cause hot-shortness failure; tensile stresses, such as those that occur when a shaft seizes in a bearing, must be present also.

Example. The following example describes overheating of trimetal bearings because of insufficient lubrication. Overheating resulted in distortion of the steel backing of these bearings and caused the bearing alloy to be hot short.

Example 4. Failure of Locomotive-Engine Trimetal Bearings by Fatigue and Hot Shortness Because of Inadequate Lubrication (Fig. 20)

The main bearings in a freight-locomotive engine were removed during a change-out program after 630,000 miles of operation. The No. 3 lower main bearing, which exhibited considerable damage, and two other complete sets of lower main bearings with similar operating history, were returned to the laboratory for analysis.

The bearings were of trimetal construction, consisting of leaded bronze (SAE 794; 72% Cu, 25% Pb, 3% Sn) cast onto a low-carbon steel backing and then plated with a lead-tin overlay.

Investigation. On most of the bearings, the overlay was completely worn away except in areas near the parting line, which are indicated by the A's in Fig. 20(a). This is expected in such long-mileage bearings and is the result of abrasion by fine particles in the lubricating oil. The amounts of scoring and particle embedment of the bearing surface were minor.

Some of the bearings had a crack through the steel backing, as shown at B in Fig. 20(b). The crack initiated near the edge of the bearing, propagated almost to the central oil groove, and then progressed along

the groove for a short distance. Pronounced fatigue cracking of the copper-lead bearing material and failure of the bond between the leaded bronze alloy layer and the steel backing, both of which resulted from a hot-shortness condition, were observed in the regions where cracking of the steel backing had occurred. The hot-shortness damage, shown in Fig. 20(c), was indicative of severe overheating. Corrosive deleading of the leaded bronze structure 0.001 to 0.005 in. deep was present in regions where the intermediate layer had been exposed by wearing away of the lead-tin overlay. Deleading is caused by a corrosive environment, frequently the result of dilution of the lubricant by fuel oil. In the undamaged regions, the leaded bronze alloy had a fine as-cast dendritic structure with an interdendritic lead phase.

Examination of the outer surface of the steel backing revealed severe fretting on the edges and bowing, which resulted in poor contact with the housing in the central portion, as shown in Fig. 20(b). The parting-line surfaces also showed evidence of fretting, as indicated by the C's in Fig. 20(c). Loss of fit or contact between the bearing and housing occurred in bearing halves that were in the advanced stages of distress.

Conclusions. The distress exhibited by these bearings was attributable to inadequate lubrication, possibly the result of dilution of the lubricant by fuel. This situation resulted in thin, low-quality films of

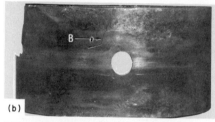

(a) Surface of bearing with overlay worn away; A's indicate unworn areas. (b) Fretting and crack (at B) in steel backing. (c) Hot-shortness damage and bond failure caused by overheating that resulted from lack of sufficient lubrication (fretting of the parting-line edges is indicated by the C's).

Fig. 20. Locomotive-engine trimetal bearings that failed by fatigue and hot shortness because of inadequate lubrication (Example 4)

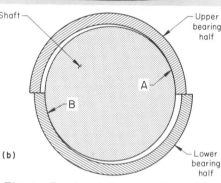

Fig. 21. Bearing halves (a) that failed by fatigue resulting from localized overloading after the bearing cap shifted position (b). Note damaged areas (at A and B) on diametrically opposite sides of the bearing halves where they contacted the shaft as a result of cap shift.

lubricating oil and in subsequent metal-to-metal contact. The heat generated caused a loss in fit and bowing of the bearing halves, which resulted in loss of contact of the central portion of the bearing with the housing bore. Severe fretting, because of poor contact combined with flexure, resulted in cracking of the bearings. The cracks in the steel backing were responsible for the severe fretting and hot-shortness damage evident in some bearing halves.

Effect of Overloading

Sliding bearings may fail by fatigue or wear because of one or more of the following conditions: steady unidirectional overloading, centrifugal overloading, and cyclic loading.

Steady overloading can result from rotors, pulleys or gears having excessive weight, belts being overtightened, or shafts being misaligned, especially when rigid shafts are supported by more than two bearings.

The two bearing halves shown in Fig. 21 are a mating pair that exhibited evidence of fatigue. The bearing cap shifted,

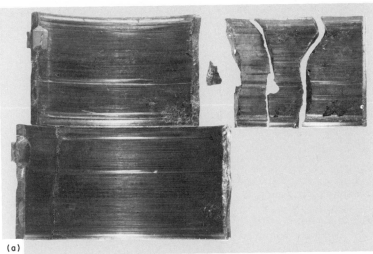

Fig. 22. Trimetal bearing for a diesel-engine connecting rod that failed by fretting and fatigue because of improper assembly. (a) Bearing surface, showing severely scored and heavily worn areas. (b) Outer surface of the steel backing, showing fretted and severely worn areas. (Example 5)

causing the load to be concentrated in areas A and B in Fig. 21(a) and (b). The load was carried over a smaller area of each bearing half than normal, resulting in fatigue failure of the metal. In some instances, severe wear of the bearings results when the bearing cap shifts position. Wear due to cap shift is easily identified because the damaged areas are on diametrically opposite sides of the bearing and nearer the same end of the bearing on each bearing half, as shown in Fig. 21(a).

Centrifugal Loading. Sliding bearings may fail because of excessive centrifugal loading. Such failure generally is indicated by a 360° wear pattern in the bearing sleeve and a local wear area on the shaft. Centrifugal loading may be caused by a rotor that has been bent, worn, chipped, or otherwise damaged such as to produce an out-of-balance condition, or by misalignment or unstable oil pressure.

In general, a sliding bearing can withstand larger centrifugal loads than steady-state loads. In high-speed shafts (particularly, vertical shafts), centrifugal forces may be larger than the forces of gravity or the forces imposed by belts, gears, and other driving mechanisms.

Cyclic loading is a rotating load of varying magnitude, such as occurs in crankpins and crankshafts. The load-supporting characteristics and minimum film thickness in the bearing are critical under cyclic loading. There are two types of cyclic loading: rapid and gradual (rapid loading is one or more applications per revolution). Under rapid loading conditions, the load-carrying capacity under steady-state conditions is quite conservative because of the squeeze-film effect. A squeeze-film condition is said to prevail if the peak load is significantly greater than the average load. Under a more gradual load application, the bearing should be designed con-

sidering the higher load as an alternate steady-state condition.

In either condition of cyclic loading, the oil groove in the bearing should be located outside the maximum-load zone. Cyclic loading of a bearing can assist the flow of lubricant by a natural pumping action. It also can assist in the load-supporting characteristics of the bearing because of the cushioning effect of the lubricant as the film is suddenly subjected to high pressure.

A cyclically loaded bearing may show a 360° wear pattern, but generally wear on the bearing or on the shaft is more pronounced in one direction (circumferential or radial) than in others. Thus, the bearing history and loading type should be known in order to assign a cause for failure.

Wear in one direction (circumferential or radial) usually can be determined visually if the bearing surface has not been destroyed. Scratches produced by wear will begin light and become wider and deeper as the displaced metal is carried farther. If the shaft is stopped or reversed, evidence of the displaced metal can be seen at the end of the scratches.

Effect of Improper Assembly

Improper assembly or fit of mating parts can have a marked influence on the life of a sliding bearing. Improper bearing assembly can result in excessive or insufficient crush, cap shift, misalignment of oil holes, bending or twisting of connecting rods, bending of crankshafts, and distortion of crankcases. These in turn can cause looseness of bearings, misalignment between shafts and bearings, and vibrations and incomplete contact between the bearing and the housing bore. The consequence usually is fatigue from local overloading; seizure, fretting and wiping are less frequent results.

Loose bearings permit excessive flexing and allow foreign particles to be introduced between the bearing backing and the housing bore, resulting in localized high spots and bearing failure. Sufficient crush must be provided to prevent the bearings from loosening at operating temperature when the bearings and housings expand by different amounts at that temperature. Crush is the press-fit allowance necessary to hold the two bearing halves securely in the housing bore and is obtained by machining the parting-line faces of each bearing half to a height slightly above the centerline.

Bolts holding the housing and cap together must have enough strength to compress the bearing until the bearing and cap seat properly while still carrying the operational bearing load. The strength of the housing must be adequate to prevent distortion that would result in insufficient clearance and subsequent bearing failure.

In the following example, looseness and misfit of a bearing resulted in extensive damage to the bearing halves.

Example 5. Fatigue Fracture of a Trimetal Bearing for a Diesel-Engine Connecting Rod Because of Improper Assembly (Fig. 22)

The fractured connecting-rod bearing shown in Fig. 22 was from a diesel engine in a highway truck that had traveled 29,900 miles. Expected life of the bearing was 300,000 miles.

The bearing, of trimetal construction, was made of cast leaded bronze (SAE alloy 49; 75% Cu, 24% Pb, 0.25% Sn) backed with low-carbon steel and plated with a lead-tin overlay. As cast, the bearing material had a fine dendritic structure with an interdendritic lead phase.

Investigation. The bearing was in several pieces when received at the laboratory for examination. The lead-tin overlay had been worn away from the bearing surface, and the leaded bronze had been severely

Fig. 23. Sliding-bearing halves, made of a copper-lead alloy (a) and an aluminum alloy (b), that failed because of edge loading resulting from misalignment

scored and heavily worn, as shown in Fig. 22(a). Indications of extensive fatigue damage were observed in both the leaded bronze and the steel backing. In the undamaged regions, the bond between the lining and the steel was satisfactory.

The lead-tin plating on the outer surface of the steel backing was severely worn, and evidence of fretting was present on the backing (see Fig. 22b). Fretting of the bearing backing indicated looseness in the housing bore, which permitted flexing. Flexing of the bearing caused fatigue cracks in both the intermediate layer and the steel backing, resulting in fracturing.

The steel backing had a hardness of Rockwell B 80, which was satisfactory, and could be bent 180° without cracking, which indicated good ductility. There were no indications that the bearing material had been overheated.

The crankpin had been worn out-of-round approximately 0.001 in. more than the maximum permissible, and its surface was highly lapped and polished.

Conclusions. The bearing failed by fatigue cracking that resulted from fretting and flexing, which indicated looseness and relative motion between the bearing and the housing. Possible causes of bearing looseness were: (a) improper seating of the bearing cap because of dirt or burrs on the contact surface, (b) insufficient tightening of the connecting-rod-cap screws, (c) bottoming of screws in blind tapped holes, (d) an oversize housing bore, and (e) crush that was low initially and that decreased while the bearing was in service.

Recommendation. Establish assembly and inspection procedures so that the above-listed possible causes are eliminated or their effects are minimized.

Misalignment. A shaft in a sleeve bearing must be straight and properly aligned with the bearing. A hydrodynamically lubricated bearing can tolerate shaft misalignment equal to about 50% of the minimum film thickness. This misalignment generally is rather small and often is less than 0.0005 in. within the bearing length. The shaft of a machine

may be misaligned because of deflection or permanent bending or because the bearing was assembled or machined out-of-line.

Misalignment is recognizable by distorted wear patterns on the bearing surfaces. The wear patterns are skewed similar to those shown in Fig. 21(b). Faulty bearing installation is a common cause of misalignment.

The length-to-diameter ratio of a bearing can affect the permissible amount of misalignment between a shaft and a bearing. A long bearing will tolerate less misalignment than a short one. The edge of the bearing should be rounded and contact between the shaft and the edge of the bearing should be avoided, because such contact generates heat, which is destructive to the bearing material. Some bearing materials, such as babbitts, have sufficient plasticity to deform under a small amount of misalignment. However, the bearing material should not be expected to adjust to gross inaccuracies in assembly.

Journal taper, bearing-bore taper, misalignment, excessive shaft deflection, or overhung loads can cause edge loading and subsequent fatigue failure of a bearing. In edge loading, the load is concentrated over a smaller area than normal and the resulting load exceeds the capability of the material. Copper-lead alloy and aluminum alloy bearings that failed because of edge loading are shown in Fig. 23(a) and (b), respectively. Where shaft deflection cannot be avoided and the bearing length is such that edge loading might result, the bearing surface can be tapered provided that the reduced contact area can support the load.

Design of the bearing system under these conditions often involves the fact that a flexing shaft will not contact the entire bearing surface under any particular load. That is, it may contact one area under heavy load and another area under lighter load. This effect may be reduced by increasing the rigidity of the

Fig. 24. Burrs around a hole drilled through the wall of a spherical bearing at a lubrication groove. Burrs contacted the mating surface, resulting in rough operation of the bearing.

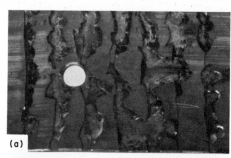

Fig. 25. (a) Fatigue pattern on bearing surface and (b) areas of contact and non-contact on bearing backing, caused by chatter marks in the housing bore

shaft by shortening its length or by increasing its diameter. Reducing shaft deflection may also increase the length of the contact area of the bearing.

Where more than two bearings support a shaft, the possibility of misalignment increases. Slight inaccuracies in fabrication may result in the bearing housing bores being misaligned before the bearings are even assembled. This condition may be corrected if the bearings are bored to size after assembly. However, this type of bearing is difficult to replace with original accuracy unless field equipment is available to rebore the replacement bearings. Also, a machine may be in good alignment when cold, but after the machine has run for a short time, unequal thermal expansion of the supporting structure may induce excessive misalignment.

Fit of mating parts can be affected by poor workmanship. A portion of the outer ring of a spherical (self-aligning) bearing from a link assembly is shown in Fig. 24. Several of these bearings were removed because of roughness in operation. Each bearing contained a hole that was drilled through the bearing wall into an internal lubrication groove. Examination of the bearing surface revealed burrs around the edge of the drilled hole jutting out far enough from the bottom of the groove to contact the mating part. Deburring the hole after drilling eliminated the problem.

Uneven and incomplete contact of the bearing backing with the housing bore resulted in the fatigue pattern on the bearing surface shown in Fig. 25(a). Chatter marks in the surface of the housing bore, which resulted from poor machining, prevented the bearing backing from making full contact with the housing bore. The bearing flexed into the valleys in the chatter pattern each time the load was applied. The areas of contact and noncontact on the bearing backing are shown in Fig. 25(b).

Effect of Subsurface Discontinuities

Sliding-bearing materials occasionally contain subsurface discontinuities that contribute to fatigue failure of the bearing. These discontinuities may be inclusions or porosity.

Inclusions in the bearing material may be the result of incomplete melting of the bearing-material ingredients, improper fluxing during bonding to the steel backing, or use of contaminated scrap metal. Scrap metal may contain oxides, sand and other particles.

The effect of inclusions in the bearing material depends on the number and distribution of inclusions and on the type of service to which the bearing is subjected. The effect is much more severe when the bearings are heavily loaded, and also when many inclusions are scattered throughout the material rather than when a small number are widely separated in the metal.

In examining a failed bearing to determine the probable cause of failure, it is important to distinguish between inclusions in the bearing metal and deeply embedded particles. Although it is possible that one isolated inclusion may appear on the surface of the bearing, it is more probable that if there is one inclusion, many others are spread throughout the bearing material and will show up in microscopic examination of a cross section taken near the origin of fracture.

Porosity in bearing materials may vary from an occasional small hole or cavity to a widespread or even a continuous network of holes or cavities. Porosity may be associated with oxide particles and segregated alloying elements such as lead, or it may be shrinkage porosity resulting from the casting mold or casting technique. The extent of porosity can be determined by fracturing the bearings into several pieces, then macroscopically examining fracture surfaces and microscopically examining a section taken near the fracture origin.

Porosity that is confined to the unloaded portion of a bearing, even though large or widespread, generally will have no effect on operation of the bearing. However, porosity in heavily loaded areas can seriously affect the load capacity and life of the bearing.

A bearing that operates with a hydrodynamic film depends on developing a high lubricant pressure, often of several thousand pounds per square inch. Po-

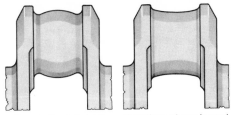

Barrel-shape journal   Hourglass-shape journal

Fig. 26. Barrel-shape and hourglass-shape journals, which can penetrate the oil film and result in bearing failures because of increased loading in localized areas

rosity in a heavily loaded area, even if it is microporosity, may provide passages that release the oil pressure and change the lubrication of the bearing from hydrodynamic to boundary. Under high-speed, heavy-load conditions, this change in lubrication condition can result in premature failure of the bearing from high temperature, rapid wear and overheating of the lubricant and shaft.

A boundary-lubricated bearing depends not only on oil-film pressure, but also on the properties of a low-friction surface. Provided the remaining bearing-surface area is sufficient to support the operating load, porosity in a boundary-lubricated bearing has very little effect on bearing temperature or bearing life.

Effect of Surface Discontinuities

Discontinuities in the surface of a bearing may be tool marks or scratches that were produced in handling or assembly of the bearing, or they may be scratches produced by abrasive particles and other debris carried through the bearing by the lubricant.

In a lightly loaded bearing with either hydrodynamic or boundary lubrication, a surface defect may have little or no effect other than a very slight reduction in load capacity approximately proportional to the amount by which the supporting surface area is reduced by the presence of the defect. In such a bearing, a reduction in load capacity of 2 to 5% often will leave the bearing with an adequate factor of safety and thus not change the life or operation of the bearing.

The load capacity of a heavily loaded boundary-lubricated bearing generally will also be decreased only in proportion to the reduction of effective supporting area. A tool mark, even if it passes through a heavily loaded area, may reduce the bearing surface only 2 to 5%, and not reduce the effectiveness of the bearing, if there is a reasonable factor of safety in the design.

In a heavily loaded hydrodynamic-lubricated bearing having a tool mark or discontinuity of about the same depth as

the film thickness, the supporting high-pressure oil film can escape by flowing through the mark. Even one deep tool mark can reduce the effective support to one-half of that originally designed. This can change the lubrication of the bearing from hydrodynamic to boundary. In effect, the oil pressure does not develop and the shaft contacts the bearing material, increasing friction, temperature, and rate of wear.

Foreign particles embedded in the surface of a bearing can penetrate the lubricating film and scratch the shaft surface. The effects of foreign particles on sliding bearings are discussed in the section starting on page 407 in this article.

Shaft Design

The design of the shaft in a sleeve bearing can affect the operation of the bearing. In addition to adequate strength to support the load, several other factors must be considered to provide a successful long-life bearing.

Surface Finish. The average surface roughness on the portion of the shaft within the bearing must be less than the minimum lubricant-film thickness, permitting the bearing to operate hydrodynamically without metal-to-metal contact. Generally, the average surface roughness on this portion of the shaft should be not more than 20% of the minimum lubricant-film thickness.

The average surface roughness required for a shaft to perform properly in most hydrodynamic sleeve bearings is approximately 20 micro-in. However, some high-performance hydrodynamic bearings require shafts with a surface roughness of 8 micro-in. or finer. With boundary and thin-film bearings, friction and wear can be reduced by using shafts having a surface roughness of approximately 8 micro-in.

Journal Shape. A good surface finish is ineffective if the shape of the journal allows only partial contact with the bearing surface. Barrel-shape and hourglass-shape journals (see Fig. 26) can penetrate the oil film, increasing the load on localized areas. In light-load applications, oil-film thickness usually is great enough to absorb slight irregularities, but high bearing loads and thin oil films require that the shape of shaft journals be closely controlled.

Rebuilding Journal Surfaces. Shafts with worn journals have been salvaged by chromium plating the journals to rebuild them to their original diameter. But chromium plating is subject to cracking and peeling, which can damage babbitt bearing surfaces; therefore, when worn journals are rebuilt by chromium plating, bearings of a more wear-resistant material must be used, as was done in the example that follows.

Example 6. Failure of Babbitt Crankshaft Bearings Because of Cracks in Chromium-Plated Journals

A diesel engine that produced 575 hp at 514 rpm was connected to an electric generator rated at 450 kw. The engine was used during a peak production period in a stone quarry to operate shovels and auxiliary equipment. A crack developed in the crankshaft and was repaired by thermit welding, and the journals were chromium plated to rebuild them to their original diameter; the bearings, which were made of babbitt, were not replaced, and failed soon after the engine was returned to service.

New bearings were installed, the engine was thoroughly cleaned, new oil and oil filters were installed, bearing alignment and clearances were carefully checked, and the bearings were carefully run in. After 150 hr of operation, the bearings were checked and a loss of babbitt and a general failure condition were found.

The bearings had an inside diameter of 8.498 in. and a width of 4 in.

Investigation. Examination of the main and connecting-rod bearings revealed mottled surfaces with little or no wiping of the babbitt. Very little evidence of incipient melting of the babbitt was found, thus eliminating insufficient clearance as a possible cause of bearing failure.

The lubricating oil was checked for water content, acidity and breakdown. Results indicated that the oil was in good condition, and therefore it was not considered a direct contributing factor in the bearing failures.

Because polished hard-chromium plating has poor wettability, breakdown of the lubricating-oil film was considered. However, breakdown of the oil film generally is evidenced by babbitt wiping, which did not occur in this instance. Overloading was not considered a factor, because the engine was operated at only 60% load.

The chromium-plated surfaces were found to contain craze cracking. The edges of the cracks were slightly raised above the adjacent surfaces. These cracks were considered to have been factors contributing to the bearing failures.

The bearings were checked for babbitt bonding and composition; both were found to meet specifications. However, these bearings and the bearings that failed previously showed evidence of fatigue, and the diesel-engine manufacturer had stated this was an engine with critical bearings. (A critical bearing has an area-to-load ratio such that a minor overload would exceed the strength of the bearing material.) In such a case there are two solutions: install bearings with a larger bearing surface, or use a bearing material having greater strength.

Replies from inquiries indicated that aluminum alloy bearings had performed satisfactorily in diesel engines for up to ten years, whereas babbitt bearings lasted only a few months. However, reports on the use of aluminum alloy bearing materials with chromium-plated journal surfaces were conflicting. Some reported that aluminum alloy bearings were not entirely satisfactory; others indicated that aluminum alloy bearings gave excellent results even where there were craze cracks in the chromium plating on journal surfaces.

Conclusions. Fatigue failure of the babbitt bearings was the result of two contributing factors: low fatigue strength in the babbitt, and high-cycle loading imposed by craze cracking in the chromium plating.

Corrective Measures. Nothing was done to crankshaft journals; two of the babbitt bearings were replaced with bearings made from aluminum alloy 750-T101, then inspected after 150 to 200 hr of operation. These two bearings were satisfactory, and all babbitt bearings were replaced with aluminum alloy bearings.

The aluminum alloy bearings operated satisfactorily for more than ten years with the craze-cracked chromium plating; thus, it was not necessary to remachine the journals.

Compatibility. The shaft should be made of a material that is compatible with the bearing material and the lubricant to minimize friction, wear, galling, corrosion, or galvanic attack. Generally, the steels used in shafts are satisfactory in these respects with normal sleeve-bearing materials; however, bearings that involve high temperatures and exotic materials or exotic lubricants should be examined for compatibility.

Expansion and contraction of a shaft with temperature changes should be considered in the design of a sleeve bearing. If a bearing is to operate at both low and high temperatures, the clearance between the shaft and the sleeve bearing may change markedly unless the bearing and shaft materials have similar coefficients of expansion.

Clearance is important in operation of sleeve bearings — particularly, hydrodynamic sleeve bearings. Over wide temperature ranges, clearance may change considerably because of the differences in coefficients of expansion of the bearing and shaft materials. Because the bearing is generally the outer piece and the bearing material has the higher coefficient of expansion, the clearance increases as the temperature rises, resulting in a bearing with a decreasing load capacity. At decreasing temperatures, the bearing would contract more rapidly than a steel shaft. Extreme differences in expansion and contraction can be minimized if the shaft and the bearing are made from the same base material so that they expand and contract at the same rate. A bimetal or trimetal bearing made of a bronze or a tin-aluminum material expands and contracts about the same as a shaft made of steel and thus maintains a relatively uniform clearance throughout a wide temperature range.

Design of Bearing Housings

Insufficient support of a bearing by its housing may result in cracking of a bearing or in a change in the effective shape and clearance of a bearing, preventing the bearing from supporting the load on a film of lubricant. Also, the bearing can move in the housing, resulting in a temperature rise and seizure of the shaft.

The bearing housing or supporting members should support a load without undue stress and strain within the bearing materials. Whenever possible, the support member should be a single piece of metal within the load-support area. The housing must maintain alignment of the bearing with the shaft without motion or flexure that would change the angle or position of the bearing under load.

The bearing housing generally contains a system for supplying lubricant to the bearing, either from an external source through a feed hole in the bearing or from a system consisting of a sump and oil ring that turns with the shaft and brings the lubricant constantly to the bearing surface.

An essential role of a bearing housing is dissipation of heat from the bearing. To perform this function, the housing must be in intimate contact with the bearing backing (80% contact is considered to be a practical minimum).

Design of the bearing housing must consider expansion or contraction of the bearing in operation or at unusual temperatures. Under these circumstances, the housing must hold the bearing securely in proper alignment and prevent the bearing from rotating.

Housing Distortion. Alternating periods of heating and cooling during operation of a machine result in repetitive expansion and contraction of bearing housings, and may cause distortion.

When the crankcase in an internal-combustion engine becomes excessively distorted, extremely high loads are placed on the bearings. Wiping, heat buildup, and fatigue generally result. The center main bearing is usually the most severely distressed, because distortion generally is greatest at the center of the crankcase. Damage usually is confined to the lower halves, and diminishes with increased distance from the point of greatest distortion; often, the end main bearing will not be affected.

In the example that follows, the center main bearing from a diesel engine failed by fatigue. The lower bearing half closed in at the top as a result of heat buildup caused by distortion of the crankcase.

Example 7. Failure of Diesel-Engine Trimetal Bearings Because of a Distorted Crankcase (Fig. 27)

Figure 27 illustrates a set of main bearings from a diesel engine in a highway truck that had traveled 191,000 miles. The bearings were of trimetal construction, consisting of 0.018-in.-thick leaded bronze (SAE alloy 49: 75% Cu, 24% Pb, 0.25% Sn) cast on a 0.139-in.-thick low-carbon steel backing and plated with a lead-tin overlay 0.001 in. thick. As cast, the bearing material had

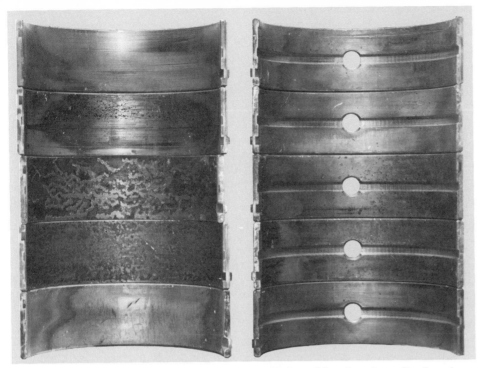

Fig. 27. Lower (left) and upper (right) halves of trimetal bearings for a diesel engine, which failed because of distortion of the crankcase. The center three lower bearing halves sustained greater damage than the two end halves. (Example 7)

a fine dendritic structure with an interdendritic lead phase. The engine lubricating oil was changed at intervals of 16,000 miles. The bearings had an expected life of 300,000 miles.

Investigation. Visual examination revealed heavy wear of the lower bearing halves. There was a medium amount of embedment, mainly of dislodged bronze particles. Closing in, or loss of spread, of the center lower bearing half indicated a high operating temperature. The bearing surfaces contained no evidence of wiping, cavitation or corrosion; however, the bearing material in the lower half of the center bearing and, to a lesser degree, in the lower halves of the two adjacent bearings showed evidence of heavy fatigue damage.

Conclusion. The three center lower bearing halves failed by fatigue. The wear pattern and other distress on the three center lower bearing halves were attributed to a warped crankcase. This is supported by the fact that the center lower bearing half displayed the most fatigue, even though it is not normally the most heavily loaded main bearing. The three center main bearings were not in alignment with the two outboard bearings.

Strip-Type Bearings

Strip-type sliding bearings are rolled to shape from thin strip stock. There are two basic types of strip-type bearings: semicylindrical, wherein the bearing is split in two halves longitudinally; and fully cylindrical.

A strip-type bearing surrounds the shaft completely, and derives most of its mechanical strength from being held tightly by the housing bore.

Grooves used as paths for lubricant are coined into the bearing surface before forming or are milled after forming. When grooves are coined in bronze alloy bearings with high lead content, separations along the lead lines of the alloy may result. Sometimes these separations cause flaking of the material and reduction of the load-carrying capacity.

Life of a strip bearing depends greatly on the surface finish of the shaft. A finish of 8 to 12 micro-in. is preferred. In high-speed or heavily loaded applications, a polished surface is necessary.

Another factor that has an effect on the life of strip bearings is the direction of forming with respect to the rolling direction of the strip. For longest bearing life, the strip stock should be rolled into a full cylindrical bearing or a semicylindrical bearing such that the rolling direction is around the periphery of the bearing. The following example describes strip bearings that failed prematurely because the rolling direction of the strip stock was parallel to the bearing axis.

Example 8. Failure of Phosphor Bronze Strip Bearings That Occurred Because of Low Wear Resistance Due to Grain Orientation in Rolling (Fig. 28)

Four-piece tappet assemblies like that shown in Fig. 28 were used in fuel-injection pumps for diesel engines. The bearings in these tappet assemblies were rolled from strips made of copper alloy 544 (free-cutting phosphor bronze). New engines using these assemblies began failing after a few hours of service, whereas older engines had operated successfully for several years.

Production was stopped until the cause of failure of the engines could be determined and corrected.

Service Conditions and History. The tappet assembly was subjected on the upstroke to a pressure of 2500 psi or higher. The pressure was applied with an impactlike force because of the steep-rise cam. Lubricating oil in the sump was constantly diluted by fuel oil that leaked past the pump plunger, resulting in marginal lubrication. Despite these operating conditions, this unit was expected to have an operating life of several thousand hours without major repair.

Investigation. Fuel-injection pumps that had failed in the field were from the latest production lot and had been subjected to very little service. Initial examinations showed that all failures were similar and revealed evidence that the bearings had been overheated. In all the pumps, the bearing was almost entirely extruded out of the rollers, and the color on the rollers suggested that the temperature had reached at least 260 to 315 C (500 to 600 F). The rollers and the pins were badly scored and battered.

Twenty-five fuel-injection pumps were taken from the production lines and installed on engines in the laboratory in an effort to duplicate the field failures. Over one-half of the pumps tested failed within 5 hr of engine operation; these failures were identical to those encountered in the field. A few pumps ran for 5 to 15 hr. Approximately one-third of the 25 pumps tested showed no signs of failure after 75 to 100 hr of operation.

Steel components from several tappet assemblies that had failed and from several that had not failed were examined for composition and other metallurgical properties. No abnormalities or significant differences were found. Fifty bearings were subjected to thorough examination. Approximately one-half of the bearings were from recent production lots, and the other half were taken from pumps that were known to contain much older bearings. The hardness of all bearings was found to vary from Rockwell B 63 to 78. The bearings were analyzed with a spectrograph; the specified elements (88% Cu, 4% Sn, 4% Pb and 4% Zn) were, for all 50 bearings, within the prescribed ranges, and no more than normal amounts of unspecified elements were observed.

The microstructure of several of the new and old bearings was examined. No significant differences were observed.

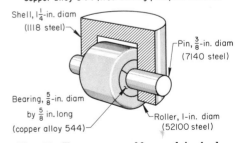

Copper alloy 544 (free-cutting phosphor bronze)

Shell, $1\frac{1}{4}$-in. diam (1118 steel)

Pin, $\frac{3}{8}$-in. diam (7140 steel)

Bearing, $\frac{5}{8}$-in. diam by $\frac{5}{8}$ in. long (copper alloy 544)

Roller, 1-in. diam (52100 steel)

Fig. 28. Tappet assembly used in fuel-injection pumps. The strip-type, phosphor bronze bearing failed because the rolling direction of the strip stock was parallel to the bearing axis. (Example 8)

X-ray diffraction patterns were made on a number of old and new bearings. It was immediately evident from the diffraction patterns that the new bearings were significantly different from the old bearings. The cause of the differences in diffraction patterns was suspected to be a difference in grain orientation. The bearing manufacturer was asked if the procedure for manufacturing the bearings had been changed in any way. It was found that the direction in which the strips were sheared from stock had been changed. Originally, the pieces of strip stock were sheared so that the rolling direction was parallel to the long axis of the strip, placing the grain direction around the periphery of the bearing. For the manufacturer, it cost less to shear the strips cross-wise so that the rolling direction was perpendicular to the long axis of the strip.

Conclusion. The difference in rolling direction and, as a result, the difference in grain direction caused the bearings to fail.

Corrective Action. The manufacturer reinstated the original rolling practice and all bearings on hand were scrapped. Service failures were eliminated, and the reliability of the pumps was again very high.

References

1. A. A. Raimondi and J. Boyd, A Solution for the Finite Journal Bearing and Its Application to Analysis and Designs – III, *Am Soc Lubrication Engrs Trans,* Vol 1, No. 1, Apr 1958

2. J. E. Shigley, "Mechanical Engineering Design", 2nd edition, McGraw-Hill, 1972

3. H. C. Rippel (Ed.), "Cast Bronze Bearing Institute Design Manual", 2nd edition, Cast Bronze Bearing Institute, Cleveland, Sept 1962

4. B. Sternlecht, Rotor-Bearing Dynamics of High-Speed Turbomachinery, SAE Paper 670059, Automotive Engineering Congress, Detroit, Jan 9-13, 1967

5. E. H. Hull, Oil-Whip Resonance, ASME Paper 57-A-169, 1957

6. A. Akers, S. Michaelson and A. Cameron, Stability Contours of a Whirling Finite Journal Bearing, ASME Paper 70-Lub S-3, 1970

7. A. C. Hagg and P. C. Warner, Oil Whip of Flexible Rotors, *ASME Trans,* Oct 1953, p 1339-1344 (ASME Paper 52-A-162)

8. H. Seirg and H. Ezzat, Optimum Design of Hydrodynamic Journal Bearings, ASME paper 68 WA/LUB 3, 1968

9. E. J. Gunter, Dynamic Stability of Rotor Bearing Systems, NASA SP-113

Failures of Rolling-Element Bearings

By the ASM Committee on Failures of Sliding and Rolling-Element Bearings*

ROLLING-ELEMENT bearings employ rolling elements (either balls or rollers) interposed between two raceways, and relative motion is permitted by the rotation of these elements. Bearing raceways that conform closely to the shape of the rolling elements normally are used to house the rolling elements. The rolling elements usually are positioned within the bearing by a retainer, cage or separator; in ball bearings of the filling-slot type and in needle bearings, they occupy the available space, locating themselves by contact with each other.

Ball bearings may be divided into three categories: radial contact, angular contact, and thrust. Radial-contact ball bearings are designed for applications in which loading is primarily radial with only low axial (thrust) loads. Angular-contact bearings are used in applications involving combinations of radial loads and high axial loads, and where precise axial positioning of shafts is required. Thrust bearings are used primarily in applications involving axial loads.

*See page 397 for committee list.

Roller bearings have higher load capacities than ball bearings for a given envelope size and are used in moderate-speed, heavy-duty applications. The principal types of roller bearings are: cylindrical, needle, tapered and spherical.

Following are load conditions for various types of rolling-element bearings:

Type of bearing	Load condition (a)
Deep-groove ball	1, 3
Filling slot	1
Angular contact	1, 2
Cylindrical roller	1
Needle	1
Spherical roller	1, 3
Ball thrust	2
Conical roller	1, 2
Spherical thrust roller	1, 2

(a) Direction of load condition: 1, radial; 2, thrust, one direction; 3, thrust, two directions.

Cylindrical-roller bearings have rollers with approximate length-to-diameter ratios of 1:1 to 3:1. Needle-roller bearings have cylindrical rollers (needles) with greater length-to-diameter ratios (ap-

proximately 4:1 to 8:1). The rolling elements of tapered-roller bearings are truncated cones. Spherical-roller bearings are available with both barrel-shape and hourglass-shape rollers.

Figure 1 shows the principal components of ball and roller bearings.

Bearing Materials

The bearing industry has used 52100 steel as a standard material since 1920. For bearings, this steel is commonly vacuum melted and degassed for maximum cleanness. A commonly accepted tolerable hardness for most bearing components is Rockwell C 58 min, but rolling elements are usually Rockwell C 60 min. At hardness values below these minimums, resistance to pitting is decreased and brinelling of bearing raceways can occur. Because hardness decreases with increasing operating temperature, conventional bearing materials such as 52100 steel can be used only to temperatures of approximately 177 C (350 F). Although bearings made of an intermediate-temperature tool steel such as M50 (0.80% C, 4% Cr, 1% V, 4.25% Mo) are usable to approximately 315 C (600 F), the practical limitation is perhaps 204 to 232 C (400 to 450 F), above which the lubricant breaks down.

Molybdenum high speed tool steels such as M1, M2 and M10 are suitable for use to about 425 C (800 F) in oxidizing environments. M1 and M2 maintain satisfactory hardnesses to about 480 C (900 F), but the oxidation resistance of these steels becomes marginal after long exposure at this temperature. Regardless of operating temperature, bearings require adequate lubrication for satisfactory operation.

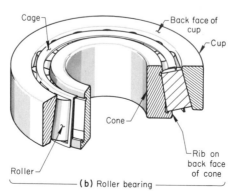

Fig. 1. *Principal components of rolling-element bearings*

For bearings that operate in moderately corrosive environments, type 440 C stainless steel should be considered. Its maximum obtainable hardness is about Rockwell C 62, and it is recommended for use at temperatures to 177 C (350 F). However, the dynamic-load capacity of bearings made of type 440C stainless steel is not expected to be comparable to that of bearings made of 52100 steel, because the carbide structure of 440C is coarser, the hardness in general is lower, and the fracture toughness is about one-half that of 52100 steel.

Roller bearings generally are made of carburized materials with case hardness of Rockwell C 58 to 63 and core hardness of Rockwell C 25 to 40. These materials are limited to operating temperatures of less than 177 C (350 F), but special low-carbon steels that can be carburized operate satisfactorily at temperatures as high as about 315 C (600 F).

Bearing Ratings

Bearing ratings are based on results of laboratory rolling-contact-fatigue tests that have been conducted under conditions as near ideal as possible. Any departure from these near-ideal conditions, such as misalignment, vibration, shock loading, insufficient or inefficient lubrication, extremes of temperature, or contamination, will reduce life expectancy and may cause a type of failure other than by rolling-contact fatigue.

The life of a bearing is expressed as the number of revolutions, or the number of hours at a given speed, that a bearing will complete before failing by subsurface fatigue. Life may vary from bearing to bearing but conforms to a statistically predictable pattern for large numbers of bearings of the same size and type operating under the same service conditions. The L_{10} rating life of a group of such bearings is defined as the number of revolutions (or hours at a given constant speed) at which not more than 10% of the tested bearings will fail. Similarly, the life reached or exceeded by 50% of the tested bearings is called the L_{50} life. The L_{50} life is about five times the L_{10} life. Bearings usually are designed to have an L_{10} rating life of one million revolutions, although specific grades may be designed for a higher minimum-life rating.

The basic load rating for a radial rolling-element bearing is the calculated constant radial load that a group of apparently identical bearings with stationary outer rings can theoretically endure for one million revolutions of the inner ring. The basic load rating is a reference value only. An applied loading as great as the basic load rating results in octahedral shear stresses greater than the strength of the bearing steel, causing local plastic deformation of the rolling surfaces. In order to avoid such plastic deformation, published static-load capacities must not be exceeded in design.

Formulas used by most manufacturers to calculate basic load ratings of rolling-element bearings are given in Anti-Friction Bearing Manufacturers (AFBMA) standards. The basic load rating is modified by factors such as degree of desired reliability, material, lubrication (and the likelihood of operation in the completely elastohydrodynamic domain), alignment, temperature, and presence of vibratory loads. For further information regarding use of these formulas, the AFBMA-ANSI Standards 9 and 11, and literature from bearing manufacturers, should be studied.

Empirical calculations and experimental data point to a predictable relationship between load and bearing life. The bearing life in millions of revolutions equals the ratio, raised to an exponential power, of the basic load rating to the applied load. The value of the exponent depends on the basic type of rolling element. The exponential character of this relationship between basic load and bearing life indicates that, for any given speed, a change in load may have a substantial effect on life in hours.

Examination of Failed Bearings

If a bearing fails to meet its predicted life requirement, the analyst must discover the cause of damage that led to failure and recommend measures that will eliminate or control this damage. The influence of uncontrolled or unknown factors that can overshadow the effect of the controlled variable in tests must be determined.

To analyze damage, the following steps may be taken:

1 Obtain complete information about the application and operating environment. If possible, get samples showing the earliest detectable stages of damage.
2 Visually examine the bearings, and the machine if possible, to determine the general condition of all related parts and the specific condition of the bearing components so that the type of damage can be identified. Photograph the bearing, and the installation, to document the appearance of the damaged area. Such pictures are valuable because the bearing may be sectioned for metallographic examination and thus be destroyed. Parts of this step may be done by an experienced field engineer.
3 Collect samples of lubricant and of debris for analysis.
4 Examine the bearings thoroughly at low magnification (3 to 50 diameters) to classify the type of damage. Significant areas may be photographed.
5 Select representative areas associated with the damage for metallographic study at high magnification (100 diameters or higher) to verify the results of visual examination.
6 Consider available information on load, speed, lubrication, operating temperature, and other environmental factors in comparing actual and expected life.

The analyst needs information about the application so that he can compare it with previous experience to expedite analysis. The following information should be available about the application and environment.

1 Description of the application, including method of mounting the bearing
2 Speed of rotation and whether rotation is constant or intermittent or of variable speed
3 Lubrication: type of system, lubricant, and filtering, if used
4 Temperature of environment, lubricant and bearing components
5 Potential sources of debris
6 Potential sources of electrical current passing through the bearing.

Not all of this information may be needed for every analysis, but it is desirable because the data needed cannot be established until considerable analytical work has been done. Later acquisition of pertinent data frequently is difficult or impossible. Generally, the data come from the field representative or the bearing user, or both. Comments by the field representative or bearing user that should be noted by the analyst include those regarding overheating, excessive noise, frequency of replacement, vibration, looseness, and resistance to shaft rotation.

Before a failed bearing is removed from its housing, the orientation of the outer race with respect to the housing, and that of the inner race with respect to the shaft, should be marked so that any distress pattern noted in subsequent inspection can be related to the conditions that might have produced it. Frequently, such orientation markings can be compared with similar markings applied at the time of original assembly.

For a list of information that is helpful during the analysis of a bearing failure, see Table 1 on page 401 in the article on Failures of Sliding Bearings.

Ball-Path Patterns. Damage to bearings usually results from subjection to loads or conditions other than those for which the bearings were designed. For example, misalignment or improper fit can result in loading that differs considerably, both in magnitude and direction, from that anticipated by the designer. Determination of such abnormal conditions by inspection of the location and distribution of damage on bearing components frequently is helpful. Most types of damage to ball bearings will be located on the path of ball travel. Because each type of loading produces its own characteristic ball path, the condi-

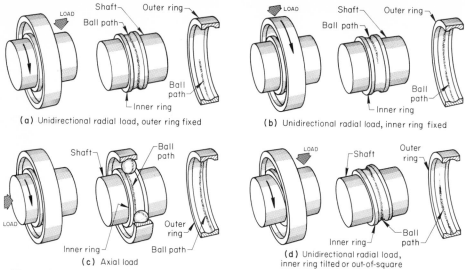

Fig. 2. Ball paths produced on raceways of ball bearings by axial and unidirectional radial loads; small arrows indicate rotating elements. See text for discussion. (Ref 1)

tions of loading under which the damage occurs can be determined from an inspection of this ball path. Similar observations can be made on roller bearings.

Satisfactory operation of a bearing that has functioned under radial loads can easily be recognized. In radial ball bearings that have been properly mounted, operated under good load conditions, kept clean and properly lubricated, the paths of the balls on the highly polished raceways appear as dulled surfaces (similar to lapped surfaces) on which microscopic grinding scratches have been smoothed out. No appreciable amount of material has been removed from the surface of the raceways or balls, as indicated by the fact that there is no measurable decrease in the diameter of the balls, although the entire surface has been dulled.

Other indications of satisfactory operation are uniformity, exact parallelism with the side of the raceway (which indicates correct alignment), and centering of the ball path in the raceway (which indicates that loading of the bearing has been purely radial).

Normally, with unidirectional radial loading and a fixed outer ring (see Fig. 2a), the load is carried on slightly less than half of the outer-ring raceway. The inner ring rotates into the loaded region, thus the ball path on the inner-ring raceway extends around its entire circumference. Ball paths produced by unidirectional radial loading of a fixed-inner-ring bearing are shown in Fig. 2(b). The load is carried by slightly less than half of the inner-ring raceway; the outer ring rotates into the load region and develops a ball path that extends around the entire outer-ring raceway.

The ball paths produced by unidirectional radial loading of a bearing whose fixed outer ring has crept rotationally in its housing are centered in the raceways,

but the path on the outer raceway is longer than that shown in Fig. 2(a) by an amount equal to the length of the arc through which rotational creep has occurred. Usually, any rotational creep that occurs is sufficient to make the ball path around the outer raceway of the bearing continuous.

A radial-type load can be imposed on a bearing by the manner in which the bearing is mounted. Too tight a press fit of the outer ring in its housing, or of the inner ring on its shaft, will result in a uniform ball path around the circumference of each raceway.

The ball paths produced by pure axial (thrust) loading are shown in Fig. 2(c). In an angular-contact bearing, the distance that the paths are displaced from the center of the raceways is greater than for a radial-contact bearing carrying an axial load, because of the greater angle of contact in the radial type. If the axial load is applied continuously, the balls do not have an opportunity to change their axis of rotation, and circumferential banding of the balls results as shown in Fig. 2(c).

If both radial and axial loads act together on a bearing, the path produced will depend on the relative magnitude of each load. If the axial load is large compared with the radial load, the paths will be similar to those produced by pure axial loading. However, if the radial load is greater than the axial load, the path on the inner raceway will be wider than the path on the outer raceway, and the outer-raceway path will be tilted by an amount depending on the relative magnitudes of the radial and axial loads.

Another type of ball path is caused by misalignments such as bearings being out of line, outer rings being tilted or out of square, or inner rings being tilted or out of square. Tilting of the outer ring in its housing causes the ring to become

slightly oval, which results in a squeeze across one diameter and a relief across the diameter at right angles to the first. This results in narrowing of the ball path at the opposite sides of the diameter across which the relief occurs. If the tilt is not great enough to take up all the clearance, there will be no ball path on the upper (nonloaded) half of the outer raceway.

Figure 2(d) shows a bearing whose inner ring was tilted or out of square with respect to the axis of rotation. Again, the amount of tilt and the amount of bearing clearance affect ball-path characteristics. The paths shown are produced when the load is taken by the bottom portion of the bearing — that is, when some clearance still exists at the top of the bearing after tilting. The inner-ring ball path is at an angle in the raceway as shown and becomes narrower at two opposite points on the raceway. This is due to the ovality caused by pressing the ring on the shaft in a tilted manner. If the tilting were great enough to take up all the clearance at the top of the bearing, the path on the outer raceway would extend around the entire circumference.

Failure Types

Failure of rolling-element bearings can occur for a variety of reasons. Accurate determination of the cause of a bearing failure depends to a large extent on the ability of the analyst to recognize, and distinguish among, the various types of failures. In most instances, this recognition will enable the analyst to determine the primary cause of failure and make suitable recommendations for eliminating the cause.

The major factors that, singly or in combination, may lead to premature failure in service include: incorrect fitting, excessive preloading during installation, insufficient or unsuitable lubrication, overloading, impact loading, vibration, excessive operating or environmental temperature, contamination by abrasive matter, ingress of harmful liquids and stray electric currents.

The deleterious effects resulting from the above factors are as follows, though not necessarily in the same related order: flaking or pitting (fatigue), cracks or fractures, rotational creep, smearing, wear, softening, indentation, fluting and corrosion (Ref 2).

Two or more failure mechanisms can be active simultaneously and thus be in competition with one another to terminate the life of the bearing. Also, a mechanism that is active for one period in the life of a bearing can lead to or even be supplemented by another mechanism, which then produces failure. Thus, in some instances a single mechanism will be obvious, whereas in others indications of several mechanisms will be evident, making exact determination of the cause difficult. When more than one mechanism has been active, proper determination depends not only on careful examination of the failed components, but also on analysis of the material, and on the manufacturing, installation and operating history of the bearing.

Before discussing the characteristics of the various types of failure in detail, it is pertinent to mention that a rolling-element bearing does not have an unlimited life — a fundamental fact that does not appear to be generally appreciated. Even if a bearing is run under the recommended conditions of load, speed and lubrication, and is protected against adverse external influences that otherwise would tend to reduce its life, failure will ultimately result by some process such as fatigue, wear or corrosion.

When a bearing is loaded, elastic deformation occurs at the zones of contact between the rolling elements (balls or rollers) and the raceways. Although the stresses involved appear to be compressive only, just below the surface there are high shear stresses and low tensile stresses. Repeated stressing in shear resulting from rotation of the bearing ultimately leads to the initiation of fatigue cracks, and fragments of metal become detached to produce the effect described as pitting or flaking. This type of failure is similar to that found on the flanks of gear teeth. There is evidence that the hydrostatic pressure of the lubricant, when it is forced into cracks that extend to the bearing surface, is a factor in the detachment of small particles to form the characteristic pits.

Experimental data indicate that a rolling-element bearing, considered as a composite whole, does not appear to possess a fatigue limit such as is found with the materials from which it is constructed; that is, a rolling-element bearing has no lowest value of loading below which failure will not occur no matter how many stress cycles are applied.

Following are definitions and descriptions of some common types of bearing failures. Typical characteristics and causes of several of these types of failure are given in Table 1 (on next two pages).

Brinelling, False. Depressions produced when rolling-element bearings are subjected to vibration or to both, while not rotating. The bearing surfaces either are polished or show a characteristic red-brown stain of fretting.

Brinelling, True. Indentations produced by plastic flow when rolling elements are forced against the raceway surfaces by stationary overload or, especially, by impact during mounting. Original surface features, such as machining marks, are usually visible at bottoms of indentations.

Electrical Pitting. A type of pitting produced by passage of electrical current between two surfaces. Microscopic pitting over a large portion of a bearing surface by electric arcing is called electrical wear.

Flaking. An advanced type of pitting resulting from fatigue. Material is removed from the surface in the form of shallow flakes or scalelike particles.

Fluting. A type of pitting in which cavities occur in a regular pattern, forming grooves or flutes. Fluting is caused by fretting or by electric arcing.

Indentations. Surface depressions resulting from deformation without removal of material. True brinelling and impressions formed by pressing of foreign particles into the surface are types of indentations.

Pitting. Any removal of material resulting in the formation of surface cavities.

Rotational Creep of Bearing Rings. Relative motion between a press-fitted inner ring and its mating shaft, or between a press-fitted outer ring and its mating housing, because of excessive initial clearance as a result of fitting errors or of plastic or elastic deformation.

Scuffing. Superficial scratches caused by metal-to-metal contact where a lubricating film is too thin or lacking or where localized friction welding has occurred.

Sliding (Skidding). Excessive slipping of rolling elements caused by improper lubrication, light loading between rolling elements and their raceways, or binding of rolling elements in the retainer.

Smearing. The removal of material from one point on either of the surfaces of two bodies in sliding contact and its redeposition or welding at another point on either or both of the surfaces in the form of a smear.

Softening. The result of heating above the temperature at which the hardened rolling elements, rings and cones were tempered during manufacture.

Spalling. Deterioration of bearing or other highly stressed surfaces by pitting fatigue, producing irregularly shaped, sharp-edged, deep cavities. Spalling may be referred to as a severe form of flaking. It is regarded as the most common type of bearing failure.

Fig. 3. Needle-roller bearing that failed because of wear by abrasive material in the bearing. Note that flats have been worn on the rollers.

Failure by Wear

Rolling-element bearings are designed on the principle of rolling contact rather than sliding contact, but the frictional effects, although low, are not negligible, and lubrication is essential. It is taken for granted that, if a bearing is adequately and correctly lubricated, wear should not occur. In practice, however, the ingress of dirt, hard particles, or corrosive fluids will initiate wear, causing increases in the running clearances of the various parts of the bearing, which may lead to noisy operation and early failure.

Significant amounts of material can be removed from contact surfaces under relatively mild operating conditions if (a) abrasive contaminants are present in the contact area, (b) there is highly inadequate lubrication, or (c) the contact surfaces are subjected to a high rate of sliding. This failure mode is characterized by the presence of wear debris in the lubricant and by evidence of abrasion on the contact surfaces of the raceways and rolling elements. Generally, the surface character is impaired only gradually, and some rolling-element bearings can sustain considerable wear before they become unsuitable for operation. Wear failure can be evaluated by dimensional or weight measurement of the components, by observation of loose wear particles near the contact area, or by spectrographic analysis of the lubricant for wear particles.

Dirt. Ball bearings are particularly sensitive to dirt or foreign matter, which is always more or less abrasive, because of the very high unit pressure between the balls and raceways, and because of the rolling action of the balls, which entraps foreign particles, especially if they are small. Foreign matter may get into the bearing during initial assembly of the machine, during repairs, or by seepage from the atmosphere into the bearing housing during operation of the machine. Dirt also can enter bearings as adulterants in the lubricant.

The character of the damage caused in bearings by different types of foreign matter varies considerably. Foreign matter that is fine, or soft enough to be ground fine by the rolling action of the balls or rollers, will have the same effect as that resulting from the presence of a fine abrasive or lapping material. Both raceways and rolling elements become worn, and the bearings become loose and noisy. The lapping action increases rapidly as the fine steel debris from the bearing surfaces adds more lapping material.

A full-complement (uncaged), drawn-cup needle-roller bearing that failed because of wear by fine abrasive material in the bearing is illustrated in Fig. 3. Wear decreased each roller diameter by

Fig. 4. *Drawn cup for a needle-roller bearing that was damaged by vibration in the presence of dirt and moisture. Roller spacing is indicated by polished indentations.*

more than 0.002 in., and a block of rollers eventually turned in the cup. The flow of lubricant (and abrasive) through the bearing was sufficient to forestall development of heat, although polished flats are much in evidence on the rollers.

Hard particles, usually nonmetallic, of any size that will scratch, cut or lap the surfaces of a bearing must be regarded as abrasive. Some substances that might not normally be considered as hard or even abrasive, like iron oxide powder, are excellent lapping compounds.

Hard, coarse foreign particles of iron, steel or other metals introduced during assembly of the machine produce small depressions considerably different from those produced by overload failure, acid etching or corrosion. Jamming of such hard particles between rolling elements and raceways may cause the inner ring to turn on the shaft or the outer ring to turn in the housing.

Corrosive Fluids. Water, acid or other corrosive fluids, including corrosives formed by deterioration of the lubricant, produce a type of failure that is characterized by a reddish-brown coating and very small etched pits over the entire exposed surfaces of the raceways. Frequently, such etching is not evident on the ball path because the rolling action of the balls pushes the lubricant, loaded with corrosive, away from the ball path. The corrosive oxides formed act as lapping agents that cause wear and produce a dull gray color on the balls and the ball paths, in contrast with the reddish-brown color of the remainder of the surface. A failure traceable to vibration in the presence of dirt and moisture is shown in Fig. 4. General rusting and deep pits can be seen in this drawn cup, as well as polished indentations resulting from abrasive action under vibratory conditions. The roller spacing is indicated by the spacing of the polished indentations.

Some lubricants decompose after extended service without replacement or replenishment, forming acidic by-prod-

Table 1. Characteristics and Causes of Some Common Failures of Rolling-Element Bearings
(Based on a Chart in Ref 3)

Characteristic and/or location	Cause and remarks
Wear	
Dull raceway surfaces	Coarse abrasive matter in bearing
Shiny raceway surfaces	Fine abrasive matter in bearing
Dull indentations in raceway at same spacing as rolling elements	See *Fretting* and *Indentation*.
Wear, together with discoloration	Running without lubricant or with lubricant that has hardened
Wear at points of contact with cage	Inertia forces acting on cage and insufficient lubricant
Wear of ball cage	Inner or outer rings out of square; abrasive matter in bearing
Internal looseness from wear of raceway surfaces and rolling elements	Abrasive matter in bearing because of insufficient or inefficient lubrication, or ineffective filtration of lubricant
Uneven wear in ball path	Vibration in presence of abrasive matter
Shaft wear or wear in bearing or housing bore	Rotational creep because of loose fit
Electrical Pitting	
Small craters uniformly distributed over ball paths	Continuous passage of electric current
Small craters randomly oriented or in bandlike order along ball paths	Intermittent passage of electric current
Fluting	
Ridges with burnt craters	Vibration together with electrical current passing through rotating bearings
Ridges without burnt craters	Vibration together with wear or excessive overload on rotating bearings
Smearing	
Cage material smeared onto the rolling elements	Jamming of rolling elements in cage pockets; too high speed; inefficient lubrication; inertia forces
Smeared peripheral streaks in bore or on periphery of outer ring	Rotational creep from inner ring being loose on shaft or outer ring being loose in housing bore
Smeared peripheral streaks on end face of ring	Rotational creep as above, or sliding under pressure against shoulder or other surface
Axial smear marks on raceway and/or rolling elements of cylindrical and spherical roller bearings	Mounting under load; inner and outer rings forcibly assembled out of square with each other; axial displacement between inner and outer rings while under load
Axial smear marks on spherical raceway of self-aligning bearings	Angular movements of shaft while bearings are stationary under load
Axial smear marks on spherical raceway of self-aligning thrust bearings	Radial movement in unloaded bearings; improper mounting; inefficient lubrication; faulty manufacture of parts adjacent to bearing
Peripheral streaks on raceways, cage pockets or rolling elements	Inefficient lubrication or light loads and high speeds
Spiral streaks on ends of rollers or locating flange	Inefficient lubrication under axial load; running under no load because of large radial clearance
Fretting	
Red or black oxide spots, usually with shiny borders, in bore or on periphery of outer ring	Incomplete contact and slight movement or vibration between ring and its seat
Red oxide on surface where ring contacts shoulder	Slight movement due to shaft flexure
Dull indentations on raceway at same spacing as rolling elements	Vibration in stationary bearing, particularly in presence of abrasive particles; referred to as false brinelling
Corrosion	
Local spots or pits on raceways, same spacing as rolling elements	Moisture or acid in bearing while stationary for extended periods
Spots or pits on surfaces	Corrosive lubricant or free water in lubricant; moisture on unprotected surfaces; corrosive atmosphere

(continued)

Table 1 (continued). Characteristics and Causes of Some Common Failures of Rolling-Element Bearings (Based on a Chart in Ref 3)

Characteristic and/or location	Cause and remarks

Indentation

Shiny indentations on raceway at same spacing as rolling elements	Improper mounting procedure, hammer blows during mounting or excessive load on stationary bearings; referred to as true brinelling
Dull indentations on raceway at same spacing as rolling elements	Vibration in stationary bearing particularly in presence of abrasive particles; referred to as false brinelling
Indentations near filling slot or other isolated area on raceway	Excessive external force when assembling rolling elements
Irregular indentations all over rolling elements	Abrasive products or other foreign matter

Flaking

At isolated areas on raceway	Early stage of fatigue originating at indentations from foreign matter, bruise on raceway, or corrosion
All around one raceway	Progressive fatigue from overload or insufficient clearance because of inner-ring expansion or outer-ring contraction
At diametrically opposite points on radial bearings	Ring oval through distortion by mounting on out-of-round shaft or in out-of-round housing bore
On only one side of raceway surface	Improper mounting or excessive axial load
At one end of roller raceway	Ring misaligned with cylindrical roller bearings
Equally spaced apart as the spacing of rolling elements	Either true brinelling or false brinelling, depending on appearance of surface; see *Indentation*
Oblique flaking on raceway of rotating shaft	Misalignment or deflection of shaft; ring out of square
Oblique flaking on raceway of stationary shaft	Shaft deflection or ring out of square
On rolling element	Forced assembly; overloaded or insufficient lubrication
Eccentric pitting on raceway of thrust bearing	Eccentric mounting or loading

Cracking and Fracturing

Cracks through ring	Fit too tight; nonuniform seating surface; deformation or ovality of housing; rotational creep or fretting
Axial cracks in inner-ring bore or on periphery of outer ring	Rotational creep or fretting
Circumferential cracks in rings	Deformation of housing; nonuniform seating surface; excessive overload
Radial cracks on end face of rings	Smearing resulting from rotational creep
Radial cracks on end face of rotating ring	Fouling or rubbing on housing or shoulder during operation
Fractured flange on ring of roller bearing	Mounting pressure unevenly distributed around flange; hammer blows during mounting
Crack or fracture at root of cage tongues or across cage pocket	In bearings generally: insufficient lubricant; too high speed or inertia forces; smearing; fracture of rolling elements; misalignment
	In thrust bearings: ring mounted eccentrically or out of square; one row of balls not under load

Miscellaneous

Enlargement of inner and outer rings	Operation for prolonged periods at high or low temperature; aging of ring material
Superficial discoloration of material without reduction in hardness	Lubricant affected by temperature rise; film deposited by extreme-pressure (EP) lubricants
Abnormal temperature increase	Low lubricant viscosity; too much lubricant, resulting in churning; insufficient internal clearance; speed too high; excessive load; incipient failure
Pronounced high noise level	Raceways indented by blows during mounting or by vibration when bearings are stationary
Piping or metallic sound	Insufficient internal clearance; inadequate lubrication
Irregular noise	Foreign matter in bearing; incipient flaking or other surface discontinuities on the raceways; acoustical properties of adjacent parts

ucts. In the presence of moisture, bearing surfaces may be badly attacked by what is referred to as black acid etching. Such attack produces numerous stress raisers that, under subsequent heavy service loads, can lead to spalling.

Electrical Pitting. In applications such as electrical equipment and railway cars and locomotives, there is a possibility of electric current passing through the bearings. When the current is broken at the contact surfaces between raceways and rolling elements, arcing or sparking occurs, producing high temperatures and damage at localized points. The over-all damage is proportional to the number and size of localized points.

A peculiar characteristic of the passage of electric current for prolonged periods of time is the fluting that sometimes occurs. It apparently can occur in any type of bearing. Flutes sometimes develop considerable depth, producing noise, vibration and eventual fatigue from local overstressing. The cause of fluting is not definitely known. However, it is believed that arcing takes place on the trailing edges of the rolling elements, resulting in local vaporization of metal and the production of craters and pits. This spark-erosion effect frequently gives rise to rapid vibrations that assist in producing the characteristic fluting effect. In some instances, under high magnification, it is possible to observe the burnt or fused metal associated with individual craters. The effects of the passage of electric current usually are shown on raceways, but occasionally they may be found on rolling elements, particularly if sparking occurred while the bearing was stationary.

If fluting is found in bearings in rotating electrical machinery, it is reasonable to suspect that it resulted from passage of electric current associated with defective insulation or induction effects. Remedial measures to eliminate such stray currents include incorporation of insulation within bearing housings or at bearing pedestals and use of suitable short-circuiting connections between the rings or cones.

Pitting of bearing elements by electrical action causes noisy bearing operation. In the following example, use of an electrically nonconductive grease prevented proper grounding.

Example 1. Pitting Failure of Type 440C Stainless Steel Ball Bearings in an Electric Motor by Static Electric Discharges (Fig. 5)

The electric motor in an office machine was producing intermittent noise. Ball bearings were suspected as the source of the noise and were removed from the motor and sent to the laboratory for examination.

The ball bearings were made of type 440C stainless steel and hardened to Rockwell C 60, and were 1.625 in. OD, 0.750 in.

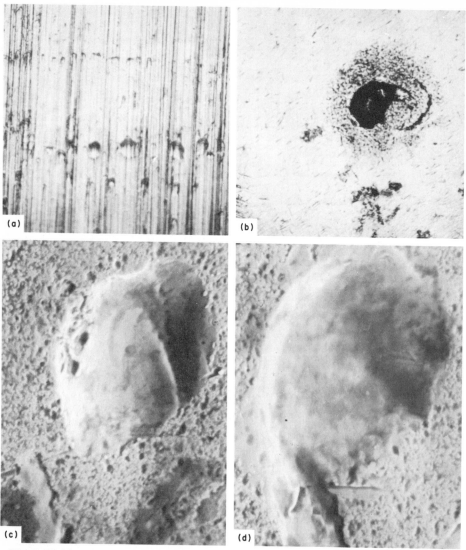

Fig. 5. Weld spots on contact surfaces of a type 440C stainless steel ball bearing, caused by static electrical discharges resulting from use of an electrically nonconductive grease. (a) and (b) Photographs, at 10× and 100×, respectively, of inner-raceway surface. (c) and (d) SEM micrographs, both at 1000×, of ball surfaces. (Example 1)

ID and 0.500 in. wide. Specifications required the bearings to be lubricated with a grease that could conduct electricity. Bearing life was approximately 200 hr.

Investigation. The ball-bearing rings were sectioned for examination in a light microscope. The surfaces of the balls were observed in a scanning electron microscope. A number of spots were found on the inner-ring raceway, as shown in Fig. 5(a). An enlarged view of one spot, Fig. 5(b), shows more clearly an area from which metal was removed and evidence of a heat-affected zone around the area.

Figure 5(c) shows a spot on a ball where metal was removed. The metal in the area around the spot showed evidence of having been melted. Another spot on a ball is shown in Fig. 5(d). This ball was welded to the raceway in the region shown at the top in Fig. 5(d) and was separated from the raceway as it rotated. Melting of the metal and welding were indicated by small round beads found in deep indentations in both the ball and the inner-ring raceway. The metal was melted and joined together for only a brief period of time and then was

pulled apart by the force of rotation of the ball and the inner-ring raceway.

Because welded areas were found on the raceways of both the inner and outer rings, and were randomly spaced and not continuous, it was thought that welding was the result of short electrical discharges between the bearing raceways and balls. The elec-

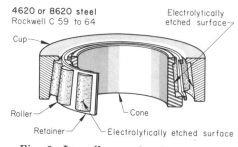

4620 or 8620 steel
Rockwell C 59 to 64

Electrolytically etched surface

Cup

Roller

Retainer

Cone

Electrolytically etched surface

Fig. 6. Low-alloy steel roller bearing, from an improperly grounded electric motor, that was pitted and etched by electrolytic action of stray electric currents in the presence of moisture (Example 2)

trical discharges were suspected to have resulted from use of an electrically nonconductive lubricant in the bearings, which permitted a static charge to be built up and discharged. To confirm this, a motor made by the same manufacturer was obtained from stock for testing. The electrical resistance between the rotor and the motor frame was measured and was found to be 2 to 3 megohms while the motor was running. A set of bearings lubricated with a grease known to conduct electricity were installed in the motor. The resistance between rotor and motor frame with this arrangement was only 0.01 to 0.02 megohms. When not running, the motor had resistance of less than 0.5 ohms (0.0000005 megohms).

As a further check on the electrical conductivity of the lubricant in the failed motor, the resistance across two copper plates was measured using each type of grease as a separator. The result indicated that the grease in the failed bearings was a poor conductor of electricity.

Conclusions. Intermittent electrical discharges across the nonconductive lubricant in the ball bearings resulted in melting and welding of metal at several locations. Because welding was momentary, pits were produced in the ball and ring surfaces.

Remedial Action. The lubricant was replaced by an electrically conductive grease. This permitted proper grounding of the rotor and eliminated welding between balls and raceways.

Stray electric currents and moisture caused electrolytic etching of the rollers and raceways of the bearing described in the following example.

Example 2. Failure of a Low-Alloy Steel Bearing in an Electric Motor Because of Stray Electric Currents (Fig. 6)

The roller bearing shown in Fig. 6 was one of two that were mounted in an electric-motor – gearbox assembly. Rough operation of the bearing was observed and the unit was shut down. The bearing was removed and submitted for laboratory analysis.

The bearing components were made of a low-alloy steel such as 4620 or 8620. The cup, cone and rollers were carburized, hardened and tempered to Rockwell C 59 to 64.

Investigation. Visual examination of the cup, cone and rollers revealed that their contact surfaces were uniformly electrolytically etched. This could have occurred only as a result of an electric current and the presence of an electrolyte, such as moisture, between the cup and roller surfaces of the bearing. The action was similar to anodic etching, as in electroetching of metallographic specimens, only more severe.

Conclusion. Failure of the bearing was the result of electrolytic etching of the contact surfaces by stray currents in the electric motor, which was not properly grounded. The etching was caused by uncontrolled input of current for a long period of time and the presence of ample electrolyte (moisture).

Corrective Measures. The motor was electrically grounded, and the bearing was insulated for protection from stray currents. Both bearings in the assembly were then sealed to keep out moisture.

Cumulative material transfer, a type of failure sometimes called smearing or galling, results from considerable sliding between bearing contact surfaces. It is characterized by the formation of welded junctions between the contact surfaces. This welding usually occurs on a localized microscopic scale and results in removal of material from one or both bearing surfaces by a tearing action. Wear particles may form, which sometimes are work hardened and cause abrasive wear. Usually, however, metal buildup occurs on one or more of the bearing surfaces.

Smearing failures appear to be confined to contact surfaces that have undergone considerable sliding. Smearing generally is a self-aggravating condition and, if allowed to progress, often is followed by a heat-unbalance failure resulting from the high friction between the smeared surfaces. If the operating conditions that lead to smearing are relaxed, the failure may be arrested and there will be some plastic smoothing and possibly wearing away of the transferred material, which may permit continued operation. The transferred metal appears as a bright, fracturelike patch.

One cause of sliding is hardening of grease lubricant due to deterioration or contamination by dirt or other foreign matter. As a result of hardening of grease, rotation of the balls or rollers within the cage may be effectively prevented, and in some instances the bearing can freeze — for example, to such an extent that it will prevent rotation of an electric motor.

Sliding of rollers and subsequent smearing may also occur in a bearing if wear has taken place to a degree sufficient to permit skewing of the rollers so that their axes of rotation are no longer parallel to that of the shaft. Smearing, in a characteristic cycloidal pattern, may frequently be observed on the end faces of rollers as a result of sliding contact between the end faces and their retaining flanges. The possibility of smearing, and not the fatigue properties of the material, limits the amount of axial loading that a roller bearing fitted with flanges on both cones can withstand. A lubrication failure can be the cause of smearing of cage material on the raceways or rolling elements.

Rotational creep, when the term is applied to bearing-failure analysis, refers to an effect whereby relative motion takes place between a press-fitted bearing ring and its shaft or housing. Rotational creep occurs principally on the inner ring and may result from the ring being initially loose on the shaft as a result of fitting errors, or from plastic or elastic deformation due to either abnormal loads or severe imbalance in service. Under rotational-creep conditions, the assembly behaves as a friction gear, with rotation resulting from the very slight difference in the circumferences of the shaft and the inner ring.

Rotational creep also may occur in thrust bearings if the shaft shoulder against which the ring abuts is not perpendicular to the shaft axis. The relative motion that occurs produces heavy score marks and polished regions, both in the bore of the inner ring and on the shaft. The end face of the ring, which is in frictional contact with the shoulder on the shaft, shows a characteristic scuffing effect typified by heavy circumferential score marks and, in severe cases, by short, radial cracks. This effect is similar to local seizure, and it is believed that the cracking arises from thermal stresses induced by intermittent local heating. In some instances, cracks can extend completely through the ring.

Scuffing effects, in addition to those resulting from rotational creep, may occur if a bearing locks solid. Scuff marks may be present on an outer ring, particularly if the bearing rotates as a whole, and generally a high polish is produced on the outer cylindrical surface where it rubs against the housing.

Failure by Fretting

Fretting is variously referred to as fretting corrosion, vibrational false brinelling, friction oxidation and even chafing or wear corrosion. Such damage is common where there is vibration or low-radial-angle oscillation between the bearing elements such that relative slip of the involved bearing-element surfaces takes place. "Corrosion", which is part of two of the expressions for fretting given above, describes the resultant wear product, red iron oxide (Fe_2O_3) — the usual evidence of fretting of opposing steel contact surfaces. However, ordinary red rust ($Fe_2O_3 \cdot H_2O$) looks the same. The by-product of fretting may also be black iron oxide (FeO or Fe_3O_4).

Types of Fretting. Fretting may be of two types. Type 1 is the contact corrosion (fit rust) that takes place between the bore of the bearing and the shaft or between the outside surface of the bearing and the bore of the housing. Type 2 is fretting damage within the bearing contact area. This type of fretting is frequently referred to as false brinelling.

False brinelling is caused by vibrations or oscillations over a few degrees of arc between rolling elements and raceways in a nonrotating bearing. At the contact areas between the rolling elements and raceways, lubricant is squeezed out, resulting in metal-to-metal contact and localized wear. False brinelling does not occur during normal running, but is found in the bearings of machines subjected to vibrations while at rest.

There are several features that permit false brinelling to be distinguished from true brinelling (see "Brinelling" on page 425 in this article). False brinelling is found on those regions of a bearing that are subjected to the heaviest loads (for example, at the 6 o'clock position in a bearing supporting a horizontal shaft; the effect diminishes in a fairly regular manner on either side of this position).

False brinelling, although most often found in machines on stand-by duty subjected to vibration from nearby running machinery, has been found to occur also during transit. Transport by rail or truck is conducive to this form of damage. Even transport by sea does not guarantee immunity, particularly where pronounced vibrations from diesel engines may be present. False brinelling has also been found in the roller-bearing axle boxes of railway cars that have been standing for some time in sidings and that are subjected to vibrations from passing trains.

In many instances, false brinelling remains undetected until the machine is started, at which time noisy running is at once evident. The phenomenon is thought to be a manifestation of fretting. The minute movements initiated by vibration cause wear of the contact surfaces, and the fine particles produced rapidly oxidize and result ultimately in production of characteristic grooves, with the oxide acting as an abrasive.

To prevent false brinelling in bearings of stand-by equipment, it may be necessary to arrange for continuous slow rotation of shafts while nearby machines are running.

For a given angular rotation of a shaft resulting from vibration, slightly greater movements of rolling elements relative to raceways will occur in a bearing with a greater number of elements. These movements may be greater than those at which false brinelling develops. Therefore, where false brinelling is not severe, changing to a bearing with a larger number of rolling elements or to one of the needle-roller type may be sufficient.

When equipment is to be transported, one of the following preventive measures should be adopted: (*a*) dismantle the machine; (*b*) remove the rolling-element bearings and fit temporary wooden packings in their place; or (*c*) employ clamps to lock rotors of electric motors rigidly to the frames and, at the same time, relieve the bearing of the dead-weight load. In other instances, the machinery could be packed so that the axis of the rotating portion is in the vertical plane, thereby preventing damage by stationary indentation.

In the list that follows are some recommendations for reducing fretting in rolling-element bearings:

1 Keep radial play in the bearings at the lowest practical value.

2 Increase the angle of oscillation (if possible) to secure roller or ball overlap such as to drag fresh lubricant into the area. If the surfaces can be separated by lubricant, fretting of the metal cannot occur.

3 Relubricate frequently to purge the red iron oxide debris and reinstate the lubricating film.

4 Use a larger bearing of higher capacity, to reduce contact loads.

5 Increase the hardness of the elements as much as possible. The commercial antifriction bearing already has fully hardened components. For best results, the shaft, if used as an inner raceway, should be hardened to Rockwell C 58 minimum.

6 Use a grease that has been specially formulated to provide maximum feeding of lubricant to areas susceptible to fretting damage. If the bearing is oil lubricated, flood it if possible.

The corrugated surfaces produced by fretting or false brinelling form stress raisers which, under subsequent conditions of rotation, may produce excessive noise and may cause premature spalling by rolling-contact fatigue.

Figure 7 shows a portion of a shaft that served as the inner raceway for a drawn-cup needle-roller bearing. The rollers left deep and clearly defined impressions on the shaft. The damage was identified as fretting, or false brinelling, because of the dull surface with little or no trace of the original surface finish remaining at the bottoms of the indentations, even though the shaft was also brinelled by a very heavy overload.

Failure of a front-wheel bearing in a motor vehicle by fretting is described in the following example.

Example 3. Fretting Failure of Raceways on 52100 Steel Rings of an Automotive Front-Wheel Bearing (Fig. 8)

The front-wheel outer angular-contact ball bearing shown in Fig. 8 generated considerable noise shortly after delivery of the vehicle. The entire bearing assembly was removed and submitted to the laboratory for failure analysis.

The inner and outer rings were made of seamless, cold drawn 52100 steel tubing, the balls were forged from 52100 steel, and the retainer was stamped from 1008 steel strip. The inner ring, outer ring, and balls were austenitized at 845 C (about 1550 F), oil quenched, and tempered to a hardness of Rockwell C 60 to 64.

Investigation. Visual examination of the outer raceway revealed severe fretting and pitting in the ball-contact areas at spacings equivalent to those of the balls in the retainer. The areas were elongated, indicating that only a slight oscillation of the ring or wheel had occurred. Similarly spaced but less severely damaged areas were observed on the inner raceway.

Conclusion. Failure was caused by fretting as the result of vibrations of the vehicle in a stationary position without rotation of the bearing. These vibrations were incurred during transportation of the vehicle. This

Fig. 7. Severe damage from fretting (false brinelling) on the surface of a shaft that served as the inner raceway for a needle-roller bearing

bearing had experienced little if any service but showed conclusive evidence of fretting between the balls and raceway. This condition is sometimes referred to as false brinelling.

Recommendations. Improve methods of securing the vehicle during transportation to eliminate vibrations.

Failure by Corrosion

Corrosion of any or all components of a bearing can result from the ingress of water or other liquids, or from deterioration of the lubricant. The formation of deleterious decomposition products in lubricants is discussed under "Corrosive Fluids" on pages 420 and 421.

General corrosion of the hardened bearing surfaces often takes the form of minute pitting, which leads to noisy operation and provides surface discontinuities at which cracks can originate. Corrosion of bearings can take place during nonoperating periods or even when the bearings are being stored awaiting installation, although corrosion of bearings in

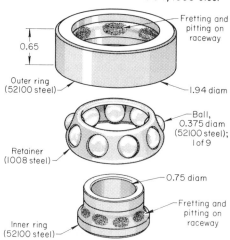

Fig. 8. Automotive front-wheel bearing that failed by fretting of raceways on both the inner and outer 52100 steel rings (Example 3)

storage should not occur if the bearings are properly packaged.

Corrosion damage may not be externally visible and may show itself only by subsequent noisy operation. In this respect, it is generally recommended that the protective lubricant in which the bearings have been packed by the manufacturer not be removed unless, in the case of very small bearings, it is desirable to replace the lubricant by one of lower viscosity. The presence of a small amount of moisture in a lubricant, although perhaps not sufficient to cause general corrosion, may result in a lowering of the fatigue life of a bearing ring.

If a cold bearing is degreased or washed in a cold, volatile solvent, moisture will condense on the cold bearing surfaces. The moisture may not be noticeable, but if the bearing is then dipped in cold oil, or covered with a cold slushing compound, the moisture cannot evaporate and will expend itself in corroding the steel. If the bearing is immersed in hot oil or slushing compound of suitable temperature and allowed to assume the temperature of the bath, the moisture will be driven off and no corrosion should occur. The presence of water or acids in the lubricant of a running bearing will sometimes cause lines of corrosion to develop in the direction the lubricant is squeezed out from between the rolling elements and raceways.

Failure by Plastic Flow

Bearing components such as balls, rollers and rings generally are made of high-strength steels with a hardness of Rockwell C 58 to 64. But even at this hardness, overloading of metal components in rolling contact will cause plastic flow. The geometric relationship of the contact surfaces can be altered by cold flow or by unstable overheating.

Cold Plastic Flow. The primary effect of plastic flow on the operation of a bearing is geometric distortion. The contact surfaces can be damaged by formation of indentations if the bearing is stationary, or by distortion if the bearing is rotating. Plastic flow on a small scale occurs under normal contact loads and operating temperatures. This has been recognized in defining a static capacity for rolling-element bearings. The absence of all plastic flow is not required, but flow must be limited to a tolerable level. Plastic flow in a rolling-element bearing may be evaluated by measuring the distortion of the contact area.

Rolling-element bearings can be damaged by indentations of several forms, each from a different cause: (a) shallow, random marks from rolled-in particles; (b) shallow indentations in the raceways corresponding to regions in contact with rolling elements when the bearing is sta-

Figure caption labels (Fig. 8):
52100 steel at Rockwell C 60 to 64; 1008 steel
0.65
Outer ring (52100 steel)
Fretting and pitting on raceway
1.94 diam
Ball, 0.375 diam (52100 steel); 1 of 9
Retainer (1008 steel)
0.75 diam
Inner ring (52100 steel)
Fretting and pitting on raceway

tionary; and (c) well-defined indentations spaced at a uniform pitch.

The first form of indentation results in rolling-contact fatigue and the second causes bulk damage (damage outside the contact zone; see page 430). The third form of indentation is a type of cold plastic flow. The well-defined indentations spaced at a uniform pitch generally result from balls or rollers having been inadvertently forced into the raceways and often arise from carelessness or use of incorrect procedures in withdrawing or installing rings. In the most common situation, the force that is required to assemble the bearing is applied indirectly through the balls or rollers instead of directly to the ring itself. Careless handling of the machine in transit also can damage bearings, particularly where impact loading has been sustained. Similar, regularly spaced marks may be produced on the raceways of a bearing that has been forcibly assembled with the axis of one ring at a slight angle to the other. These effects (to which the term brinelling is sometimes applied) usually manifest themselves by noisy operation.

Brinelling, sometimes referred to as true brinelling, or as denting, is permanent deformation produced by excessive pressure or impact loading of a stationary bearing. Hollows or dents are produced by plastic flow of metal. Such indentations in raceways will be spaced in correspondence to ball spacing, thus differentiating true brinelling from dents made by debris such as dirt or chips, which usually are spaced randomly. With the aid of a stereoscopic microscope, the final grinding marks made during manufacture of raceways can be seen, still virtually undisturbed, within the dented areas. Improper mounting procedures, such as forcing of a tight-fitting or cocked outer ring into a housing, are common causes of true brinelling. Improper handling, such as dropping or pounding of bearings, also will cause true brinelling. True brinelling can also be caused by vibrations in ultrasonic cleaning, as described in the example that follows.

Example 4. True Brinelling of Ball-Bearing Raceways During Ultrasonic Cleaning

During the early stages of production, randomly selected dictating-machine drive mechanisms, which contained small ball bearings, were found to exhibit unacceptable fluctuations in drive output. This seemed to indicate that the bearing raceways were being true brinelled prior to or during installation of the bearings.

Investigation. The preinstallation practices and the procedures for installing the bearings were carefully studied to determine the cause of failure. New control practices were instigated with no net gain in bearing performance.

One of the preinstallation procedures involved removing the bearing lubricant ap-

Fig. 9. Surface of a shaft, which served as an inner bearing raceway, that failed by spalling initiated at true-brinelling indentations

plied by the bearing manufacturer and relubricating the bearings with another type of lubricant. The bearings were ultrasonically cleaned in trichloroethylene to ensure extreme cleanness. Careful examination of the bearing raceways at a moderate magnification revealed equally spaced indentations resembling true brinelling. Further examination showed that the ultrasonic cleaning technique was improper in that the ultrasonic energy transmitted to the balls brinelled the raceways enough to cause fluctuations in machine output.

Conclusion. The bearing raceways were true brinelled during ultrasonic cleaning.

Corrective Measures. The lubricant was removed from the bearings by solvent-vapor cleaning instead of by ultrasonic cleaning.

Spalling that originated at true-brinelling indentations in the surface of a shaft is shown in Fig. 9. The shaft surface in the failed area served as the inner raceway of a bearing.

Softening is a plastic-flow phenomenon observed in rolling-element bearings with unstable thermal balance resulting

from the generation of more heat in the bearing than is being removed. The maximum permitted temperature in bearings depends on the material but generally is quoted as approximately 120 C (250 F). An increase in operating temperature, if undetected, may result in lubricant failure and seizure of the bearing, or softening of the bearing steel with a reduction in L_{10}. Gross overheating of bearings above the temperature at which the rolling elements and rings were tempered during manufacture will result in rapid softening of these parts with subsequent plastic deformation. Occasionally, if the applied torque is sufficient to overcome the inherent resistance of a seized bearing or, alternatively, to cause the shaft to rotate within the inner ring, the heat generated may result in temperatures approaching a dull red heat, leading to loss of strength in the shaft followed by rapid failure from shear.

Gross destruction of heat-softened components sometimes can be recognized by discoloration and a predominantly plastically deformed appearance. It therefore may be different in appearance from fracture that results from cracking. Often, however, temperature-imbalance failures are so devastating that little is left of the bearing from which to identify a failure source.

Failure by Rolling-Contact Fatigue

Failures caused by rolling-contact fatigue are the result of cyclic stresses developed at or near bearing contact surfaces during operation. These stresses result in progressive deterioration of the material by one or more cumulative damage mechanisms that eventually cause initiation and propagation of fatigue cracks. In some failures, the initial stages are characterized by polished contact surfaces in which small pits are often observed; this damage may be serious enough to preclude further satisfactory bearing operation. Such surface distress, if allowed to continue, also can lead to spalling, in which metal fragments break free from the components, leaving cavities in the contact surfaces. In other instances, subsurface cracks are initiated with little or no observable surface deterioration until the final stages of the process, when cracking and spalling become evident. The mechanisms of rolling-contact fatigue are discussed in more detail on page 123 in the article on Fatigue Failures, and on page 151 in the article on Wear Failures.

Rolling-contact-fatigue failures can be separated into two general categories: surface initiated and subsurface initiated. These two categories may be further subdivided according to the appearance and location of the fatigue spalling, as well as the factors that led to crack initiation. These factors may be related to material, manufacture, mounting, operation, lubrication and care of the bearing. The recognition of the interplay of such factors is achieved through fractography, as illustrated in Volume 9 of this Handbook.

Surface-Initiated Failures. Fatigue cracks may be initiated at or very near the contact surfaces of bearing components as the result of several causes. Geometric stress concentrations, for example, can produce abnormally high stresses in localized regions of bearing raceways because of improper contact configuration, misalignment or distortion. Eventually, such situations can lead to surface deterioration, crack initiation, and spalling, as illustrated in Fig. 10, which shows the damage on the outer raceway of a roller bearing due to surface deterioration and spalling that resulted from overloading of the rollers at one end. Inclusions and other defects seldom are responsible for surface damage, although they sometimes act as sites for crack initiation. In some failures, cracks are formed at the surface, and in others, slightly below it.

Corrosion pits, handling scratches, surface inclusions and surface dents also can cause stress concentrations and lead to surface-initiated rolling-contact-fatigue cracks. Surfaces of fractures (spalls) resulting from such origins usually have an arrowhead type of appearance and point in the direction of load approach. The cracks are open to the surface at the earliest stages of development and thus can be reservoirs for the lubricant. Crack propagation may then be accelerated by hydraulic pressure developed in the cracks during each stress cycle. Corrosive contaminants such as water and organic acids resulting from lubricant deterioration also may expedite crack propagation if they infiltrate the cracks.

Minor surface discontinuities such as peeling usually are associated with inefficient lubrication. Shallow flakes of material are removed from the contact zone, whereas relatively deep cavities are produced by spalling. Micropits may form on the surface and can initiate fatigue cracks. Crack propagation usually is at an acute angle to the contact surface but results in a spall cavity that is parallel to the contact surface, with only shallow penetration.

Damage involving large regions of a bearing surface is indicative of marginal oil-film thickness. Damage limited to areas surrounding surface irregularities such as scratches and other depressions results from localized metal-to-metal contacts; if surface deterioration is allowed to continue, deep spalling will eventually occur.

Fig. 10. Damage from surface deterioration and spalling in the drawn-cup outer raceway of a needle-roller bearing because the rollers were overloaded at one end

In an application in which a portion of the surface of a shaft served as a roller-bearing inner raceway, flaking on the raceway (see Fig. 11) contributed to failure of the shaft. The lubricating oil was very light, and the film was of insufficient thickness to separate the raceway and the rollers. Fine flaking propagated along the ridges of the surface finish and, as the ridges flaked away, the valleys began to flake and surface breakup became general.

A surface that was not flat, resulting from faulty grinding practice, led to deterioration of the thrust-bearing raceway described in the following example.

Example 5. Contact-Fatigue Failure of an 8620 Steel Raceway for a Thrust Bearing Because of Faulty Grinding Practice

The service life of a production gearbox had decreased drastically from that normally encountered. The axial load on a

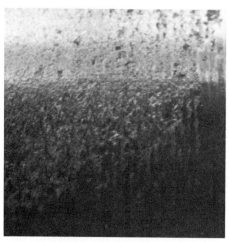

Fig. 11. Fine flaking damage on the surface of a shaft that served as a roller-bearing inner raceway; the flaking originated along the ridges of the surface finish of the shaft.

bevel gear was taken by a thrust-type roller bearing in which a ground surface on the back of the bevel gear served as a raceway. The gear was made of 8620 steel and was carburized and case hardened to Rockwell C 60; case depth was 0.036 in. The OD of the bevel gear was 3⅝ in. The thrust bearing had a 1½-in. ID and a 2³⁄₁₆-in. OD.

Investigation. The gearbox was dismantled, and inspection of the bevel gear disclosed spalling damage on the ground bearing raceway at five equally spaced zones.

The gear was mounted on an arbor and the bearing raceway was checked for run-out. The raceway was found to undulate to the extent of 0.0003 in. TIR. A spalled area was observed at each of the high points.

The outside surface of the gear hub was a 1½-in.-diam raceway for a radial-contact roller bearing. Examination of this surface disclosed a five-lobe contour having a 0.00028-in. (TIR) radial deviation. A chart trace on a rotary profile recorder was made of the two surfaces. The high surfaces on the radial-bearing raceway coincided exactly with the beginning of the spalled area on the thrust-bearing raceway and, therefore, the high points on that raceway.

Magnetic-particle inspection of the thrust-bearing raceway revealed the presence of numerous cracks that resembled grinding cracks. Microscopic examination of a section through the thrust-bearing raceway also disclosed numerous fissures that resembled grinding cracks.

Metallographic examination of a specimen taken from the bevel gear revealed that the microstructure of the case-hardened surface contained sufficient retained austenite to make it difficult to grind the part without cracking it.

The thrust bearing operated under a heavy load, which was intensified by the local support at the five high zones. This high nonuniform loading, in conjunction with grinding cracks, was sufficient to produce spalling.

Conclusion. The thrust-bearing raceway failed in rolling-contact fatigue, which resulted in spalling at five high points. The high points were caused by a faulty grinding procedure. During grinding, the retained austenite transformed to untempered martensite with the resultant change of volume and cracking.

Corrective Measures. The spindle of the grinding machine was reconditioned to eliminate the five equally spaced undulations. Heat treatment of this gear was more carefully controlled to minimize retained austenite. Fatigue life of the bearing returned to normal with these changes.

Flaking is preceded by formation of pits, which appear initially on one of the raceways rather than on the balls or rollers. In the early stage of flaking, isolated pits are formed, but these rapidly join, forming lines or bands of confluent pits and progressively destroying the raceways. The process of destruction is self-accelerating because the pits themselves, and the particles of metal that become embedded in the raceways, cause vibration and noisy running. Impact loading at the edges of the pits produces

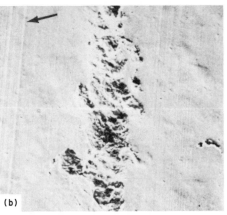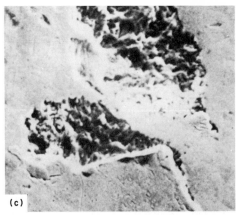

(a)   (b)   (c)

Fig. 12. SEM views of the surface of the outer-ring raceway of a type 440C stainless steel radial-contact ball bearing that failed by rolling-contact fatigue, and of particles found in the lubricant. (a) Lubricant-residue particles that flaked off the raceway; 100×. (b) Flaked surface, at 200×, showing nearness of flaking to edge of raceway (arrow). (c) Flaked surface, at 1000×. (Example 6)

further deterioration. In addition, metallic particles in the lubricant increase the over-all rate of wear.

As a general rule, fatigue flaking first becomes evident in the stationary ring of a bearing. For a horizontal shaft supported by bearings at each end, with the inner rings rotating and the outer rings stationary (see Fig. 2a), loading is radial and the highest stress occurs opposite the point of loading. On each outer (stationary) raceway, there is a specific zone that is subjected to a cycle of maximum stress every time a rolling element passes over it, but because of the rotation of the inner ring, the maximum stress is exerted at a different region of the inner raceway with every cycle. In circumstances where the outer ring revolves and the inner ring is stationary (see Fig. 2b), the converse is true. For the same speed of rotation, a bearing having a fixed inner ring has a lower life expectancy than a bearing in which the inner ring rotates.

The cause of flaking frequently can be determined by its location on a raceway. Ideally, the load in a roller bearing is uniformly distributed across the rollers and raceways. Flaking in a narrow ring in a plane corresponding to one end of the rollers would indicate grossly uneven loading and would suggest that the axes of the two raceways are not parallel. Flaking restricted to one portion of a stationary raceway usually is caused by overloading from a dead weight, excessive belt tension, gear-tooth reaction, or misalignment of driving couplings. Service life can be extended by partially rotating the stationary ring at appropriate intervals, shorter than those at which flaking was found to occur.

Shaft-bearing assemblies required to withstand a significant amount of axial loading usually incorporate angular-contact bearings arranged in opposition and initially adjusted to a certain degree of preload. In this type of application, flaking can be caused by the stresses induced by an increase in preload resulting from

thermal expansion as the operating temperature is increased.

Flaking damage also may be distributed around a raceway at intervals corresponding approximately to the distance between the balls or rollers. In these instances, flaking is initiated at indentations (true-brinelling marks) produced by impact when the bearing is mounted. In the following example, the bearings were preloaded, which contributed to a temperature increase. Also, the raceways were damaged by flaking at true-brinelling marks.

Example 6. Rolling-Contact-Fatigue Failure of Type 440C Stainless Steel Radial-Contact Ball Bearings Because of Excessive Axial Load (Fig. 12)

The radial-contact ball bearings supporting a computer microdrum became noisy and were removed for examination. A sample of the lubricant used with the bearings was sent to the laboratory with four sets of bearings.

Two sizes of bearings were used for the microdrum: 20-mm ID by 42-mm OD by 12 mm wide, and 35-mm ID by 62-mm OD by 14 mm wide. The bearings were made of type 440C stainless steel and hardened to Rockwell C 60 to 62. For accurate positioning of the microdrum, which rotated at 3600 rpm, a spring washer that applied a 50-lb axial load on the smaller bearing was installed in contact with the inner ring.

Investigation. The seals of one set of bearings (one small and one large) were removed so that the inner surfaces of the bearings and seals could be examined. Also, samples of the grease in the bearings were taken for analysis and comparison with the sample submitted with the bearing.

Comparison of infrared spectrophotometer patterns indicated that the two greases were similar but not of the same composition.

The bearings were soaked and washed in a petroleum solvent until they were absolutely clean of grease. The solution was evaporated by heating. The residue contained particles that were attracted to a magnet. These magnetic particles were recleaned and mounted for viewing in a scanning electron microscope. Observation at a

magnification of 100 diameters indicated that the particles had flaked off the outer-raceway surface and were not foreign contaminants (see Fig. 12a).

The surfaces of the inner and outer raceways were examined in a scanning electron microscope. Smearing, true-brinelling marks and evidence of flaking were found off-center on one side of the outer-ring raceway. This pattern is commonly found in a radial ball bearing subjected to an axial load that moves the contact area to one side of the raceway. Views of the flaked surface in the outer-ring raceway are shown in Fig. 12(b) and (c). Surface damage to the inner raceway was less severe.

The true-brinelling marks on the raceways were caused by excessive loading when the bearing was not rotating or during installation. These marks were not prominent and were smeared when the raceway surfaces were flaked.

A new bearing of the smaller size was installed in a test stand with a preload of 50 lb. After 4000 hr of operation, the temperature of the bearing was 44 C (111 F) and the bearing was noisy. Normal operating temperature for these bearings did not exceed 31 C (88 F).

Conclusions. The bearings failed in rolling-contact fatigue, as indicated by flaking in the raceway surface. The 50-lb preload moved the zone of contact between the balls and raceway to one side of the raceway, reducing the normal contact area. Metallic particles found in the lubricant in the bearing were from the outer-ring raceway. Some flaking occurred at the true-brinelling marks in the raceways.

Corrective Action. The preload was reduced to 28 lb, using a different spring washer. This eliminated the noise, reduced the operating temperature to normal and extended bearing life to an acceptable level.

Spalling failure is the result of fatigue and is recognizable by craterlike cavities in the surfaces of raceways or rolling elements. The cavities have sharp edges, generally steep walls, and more or less flat bottoms. Spalling may be obliterated by further destruction of the part or by rolling of surrounding metal into the cavities. Spalling can originate either at or below the contact surface.

Severe spalling damage on the end of a shaft that served as a raceway for a roller bearing is shown in Fig. 13. The spalling did not extend all the way around the shaft, only about 225°. The general pattern of spalling damage indicated good alignment and load distribution. However, failure was premature. Linear marks in the damaged surface indicated that the shaft was of poor-quality material. The raceway surface was underlaid with inclusions, which served as stress concentrators for fracture initiation.

Subsurface-Initiated Fractures. The effects on the shear-stress field below the surface of a bearing raceway as a cylindrical roller travels across the surface are shown schematically, from right to left, in Fig. 14. The roller is shown at position 1 in Fig. 14(a). In the material directly below the roller, the shear stresses along the x, y and z axes are equal to zero and are not shown in the stress diagram below the roller, but the maximum shear stress, τ_{max}, is indicated on planes at 45° to the coordinate axes. The material just to the left of the roller, at position 2, in Fig. 14(a) is subjected to shear stresses, τ_{zy} and τ_{yz}, in the directions of the coordinate axes. In position 3, Fig. 14(a), the shear stresses are zero. In Fig. 14(b), the roller is shown in position 2. The 45° shear stress in the material below the roller is at a maximum, and τ_{zy} and τ_{yz} are zero. The material just to the right and left of position 2 is subjected to stresses τ_{zy} and τ_{yz}, which have finite values.

Figure 14(c) shows the roller in position 3, and τ_{max} is shown as being in the material below the roller. The shear stresses along the major axes at position 2 once again have finite values whereas the stress at position 1 has dropped to zero.

It will be noted, after studying Fig. 14(b), that the shear-stress field reverses itself at position 2. It is this reversal that is believed to be the prime contributor to bearing failure and on which the Lundberg-Palmgren theory (Ref 4) is based. A maximum value for τ_{zy} is reached at approximately the same distance below the surface as is τ_{max}. The absolute value of this maximum, because it extends from $+\tau_{zy}$ to $-\tau_{zy}$, becomes $|2\tau_{zy}|$ and thus is greater than the maximum shear stress, τ_{max}.

The probability of survival of a bearing is assumed to be a function of the stressed volume, alternating shear stress, number of stress repetitions and depth of alternating shear stress. For a discussion of the theoretical relationships involved, see Ref 5. The products of the above assumptions are mathematical relationships that allow life predictions based on geometric properties of the bearing.

Alternating shear stresses reach maximum values at a distance below the sur-

Fig. 13. Spalling damage on the end of a shaft that served as a roller-bearing raceway. The spalling was initiated at subsurface inclusions.

face determined by the load on the bearing as well as by other design factors. Subsurface cracks usually are initiated in regions of surface contact where these alternating shear stresses acting in the material are at a maximum. Pure rolling loads generate maximum shear stresses slightly below the surfaces of the contacting components. With the addition of frictional or sliding forces, maximum shear stresses move closer to the surface. Sliding forces of sufficient magnitude can cause failure to originate at the surface and can significantly reduce bearing life.

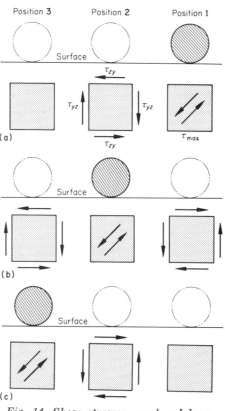

Fig. 14. Shear stresses, produced by a cylindrical roller, below the surface of a bearing raceway (Ref 4)

Subsurface-initiated fatigue cracks usually propagate parallel to the surface and then abruptly to the surface, and are easily distinguishable provided subsequent operation does not destroy the identifying features. As metal flakes out, steep-sided, flat-bottomed pits remain. The following example describes subsurface-initiated failures of balls in a transmission bearing.

Example 7. Failure of Bearing Balls as a Result of Subsurface Shear Stresses (Fig. 15)

The signal light for the magnetic chip detector in an aircraft transmission came on, indicating metal contamination. The aircraft was grounded so that the transmission could be dismantled and inspected.

Teardown inspection revealed failure of a ball bearing in the transmission. The bearing and related components had been properly assembled. The failed bearing was made to class ABEC-5 (Annular Bearing Engineers' Committee) tolerances, had a machined bronze cage piloted by the outer ring, and operated at a maximum speed of 215 rpm with MIL-L-7808 lubricant. Total operating time was 690 hr.

Investigation. The failed bearing contained two balls that were badly flaked but that had not fractured (see Fig. 15a), and three balls that had flaked and fractured essentially in half (see Fig. 15b and c). The fracture surfaces of each of the three fractured balls displayed beach marks, typical of fatigue failure, that formed a dished area progressing toward the center of the ball. The beach marks emanated from steepsided subsurface locations 0.003 in. deep. Pieces of the balls were missing from the origin sites. Both raceways were flaked and highly polished. The inner raceway was the more severely damaged. Macroscopic examination revealed no apparent cause of the bearing failure. No microstructural factors contributing to the failure were discovered. The bearing material and hardness were acceptable.

Conclusion. The bearing failed by fatigue as a result of subsurface shear (Hertzian) stresses. This is substantiated by the fact that flaking and fatigue fracturing of the balls occurred although microstructural features that would contribute to fracture were absent.

Effect of Inclusions. Nonmetallic inclusions in the load-carrying areas of bearing elements can reduce resistance to contact-fatigue fracture. An inclusion is foreign material with properties different from those of the matrix. Nonmetallic inclusions are usually complex compounds formed between the metallic alloying elements and oxygen, nitrogen, silicon, carbon, phosphorus and sulfur. Hard inclusions, such as oxides and carbides, appear to be more detrimental to fatigue life than soft inclusions, such as sulfides. In wrought products, the inclusion formations are usually discontinuous or semicontinuous stringers oriented parallel to the grain flow. Thus the most adverse effects of nonmetallic

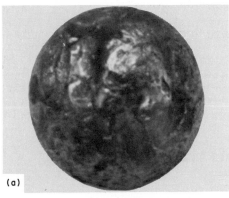

Fig. 15. Flaked (a) *and fractured* (b) *and* (c) *bearing balls that failed in fatigue as the result of subsurface shear stresses. In* (c), *note fatigue beach marks at arrow.* (Example 7)

inclusions occur when the stress direction is perpendicular to the lay of the stringer. Under cyclic or fluctuating load, inclusions locally intensify stresses to a degree depending on the shape, size, hardness and distribution of the inclusions. Initiation and propagation of fatigue cracks then can be expected and will result in a shorter bearing life than predicted. By minimizing the inclusion content in bearing steels, noticeable increases in operating life are achievable.

The following example describes a premature bearing failure that was caused by subsurface nonmetallic inclusions.

Example 8. Fracture of Ball-Bearing Components by Rolling-Contact Fatigue Because of Subsurface Nonmetallic Inclusions (Fig. 16)

The pilot of an aircraft reported illumination of the transmission oil-pressure light and an accompanying drop in pressure on the oil-pressure gage. The aircraft was grounded so that the transmission could be checked.

Investigation. Teardown analysis of the transmission revealed no discrepancies in assembly of the bearings and related components. The oil strainer contained numerous fragments of bronze similar to that used in the bearing cage.

The center bearing of the transmission input-shaft ball-bearing stack had a broken cage and one ball that had been split into several pieces along paths resembling the seams of a baseball. Also, several scored balls, and flaking damage in the raceways of the inner and outer rings, were observed. Total operating time for this bearing stack was 770 hr.

The origin of flaking in the raceway of the rotating inner ring was identified by the following distinguishing features, which are shown in Fig. 16(a). The origin (area in rectangle), oriented axially in the raceway, was dark and discolored and was flanked by areas of pronouncedly different-textured flaking damage — namely, shallow, fine-textured flaking damage extending from the origin in the direction of inner-ring rotation (A), and deep, coarse-textured flaking damage extending from the origin in the direction opposite to the rotation of the inner ring (B). Both areas had a convex texture in relation to the axial origin.

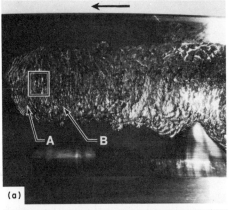

(a) Macrograph, at 3×, of inner-ring raceway, showing fine-textured flaking damage (at A), coarse-textured flaking damage (at B), and origin of flaking (in rectangle). (b) Micrograph, at 440×, of section through inner ring at origin of flaking, showing inclusions (at C's).

Fig. 16. Inner-ring raceway of an aircraft-transmission ball bearing that failed by rolling-contact fatigue because of subsurface nonmetallic inclusions (Example 8)

A section parallel to the axially oriented origin was cut at the origin area. The specimen was ground and polished for metallographic examination. As shown in Fig. 16(b), stringers of nonmetallic inclusions (at C's) were revealed at the origin.

The chemical composition, microstructure and hardness of the bearing elements were checked and found to be acceptable.

Conclusion. Failure of the bearing occurred through a contact-fatigue mechanism (flaking) activated by the presence of subsurface nonmetallic inclusions (stringers).

Microstructural alterations are another type of inhomogeneity sometimes found in bearing materials. Although inclusions and other kinds of discontinuities are initially present in bearing materials, microstructural alterations are formed during actual operation of the bearing. These alterations result from localized plastic deformation caused by the action of subsurface cyclic stresses. When observed in a microscope, microstructural alterations appear as a white-etching constituent — either in a characteristic patchy form known as "butterflies", as shown in Fig. 17, or in the form of narrow parallel bands at an acute angle to a contact surface, as shown in Fig. 18(a) beneath a spall. (Microstructural alterations are shown also in the micrographs on page 61 in Volume 7 of this Handbook.) At present it is uncertain to what extent such alterations affect fatigue life of bearings. Although fatigue cracks have been observed in or very near alterations and sometimes propagate along them, it is not certain that alterations actually cause fatigue-crack initiation. Nevertheless, microstructural alterations are associated with rolling-contact fatigue and

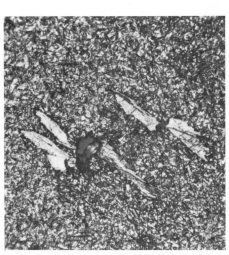

Fig. 17. Stress "butterflies" (microstructural alterations) in a steel bearing ring (4% nital etch; about 425×)

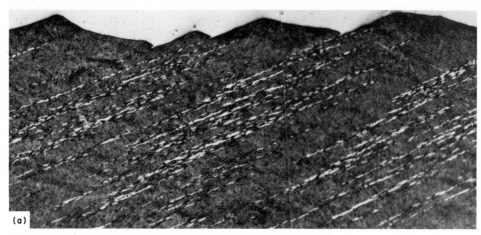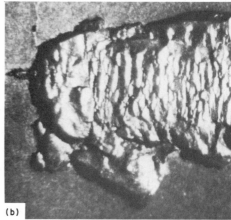

Fig. 18. (a) *Micrograph, at 200×, of picral-etched section through a spalled area on a 52100 steel bearing ring, showing elongated bandlike microstructural alterations. At top is profile of bottom of spalled area. (b) Macrograph, at 7.25×, of part of the spalled area; note parallel ridges that were formed because subsurface cracking partly followed microstructural alterations.*

may yet prove to be responsible for the initiation of cracks in certain instances.

Microstructural alterations create planes of weakness along which cracks can propagate. Figure 18 illustrates a spalled area that was produced by rolling-contact fatigue in which cracks propagated alternately along and between bandlike microstructural alterations inclined at 23° to the surface.

Subcase fatigue also is the result of subsurface-initiated cracking (see facing page) in case-hardened components. Cracks are initiated in or below the lower-carbon portion of the case near the junction of case and core. Once formed, such cracks usually propagate parallel to the case-hardened region until branching cracks propagate to the surface and form spalling cavities. This type of failure is rarely encountered in normal service; rather, it appears under gross-overload conditions, such as may be encountered in accelerated tests. Increasing case depth usually minimizes subcase fatigue.

Failure by Bulk Damage

Bulk-damage failures are the result of damage to bearing components outside the contact zone. Although evidence of material deterioration may be observed on the rolling-contact surfaces, the most severe damage is found at other locations on bearings. Deterioration of the bearing results from one or more causes, including overloading, overheating, bulk fatigue, fretting (type 1 as defined on page 423 in this article), and permanent dimensional changes.

Fractured rings, rollers, balls and cages are examples of bulk-damage failures. Such failures may be the result of overloading the bearing beyond its design limits, but they also can occur because of misalignment, improper mounting, and improper fitting of a ring on a shaft or in a housing. Severe overloading usually is accompanied by permanent

dimensional changes in the bearing as evidenced by distortion of the components. Figure 19 shows a drawn-cup needle-roller bearing that was mounted side-by-side with another in a sleeve, or tire. The bearing failed because of gross overload. The core material, being relatively soft, suffered bulk plastic flow. As the cup increased in width, circumferential stretch cracks developed on the outside surface, and the oil hole became elongated. The cup wall thinned out sufficiently that radial play became excessive and, coupled with noisy operation, resulted in termination of the service life of the bearing.

Cracks and Fractures. Significant cracking in rings and rolling elements takes several forms and results from several causes. Although fracture can result from fatigue, fatigue that leads to fracture differs from the very localized rolling-contact-fatigue cracking that causes pitting, flaking and spalling.

Circumferential cracks that develop in the outer ring of a bearing may be indicative of a lack of uniform support from a housing not truly cylindrical but shaped like a barrel or an hourglass. Under these conditions, flexing can take place under load, leading to the development of fatigue cracks which, in a ball bearing, usually are found at the bottom of the ball raceway. This form of cracking ultimately leads to separation of the ring into two or more pieces. "Crowned" races can be used to compensate for bending in the shaft.

Cracking of inner rings frequently occurs in service. Such cracking generally takes place in an axial direction and may be caused by an abnormally high hoop stress resulting from an excessive interference fit on the shaft. On the other hand, a loose fit can lead to movement between the ring and the shaft, giving rise to radial cracking on the end faces — an effect discussed under "Rotational creep" (see page 423).

Fig. 19. *Drawn-cup needle-roller bearing that failed by gross overload. As the cup increased in width under overload, the oil hole became elongated and circumferential cracks developed in the outer surface.*

Cracking of any component of a bearing can result from gross overloading but also may be associated with other effects such as overheating, wear and flaking. Fatigue cracks sometimes are initiated at surface locations where pitting, flaking and spalling have occurred. In other instances, cracks may start from regions where there is evidence of fretting, which has an adverse effect on fatigue endurance.

Cracks that lead to detachment of small, roughly semicircular pieces from the retaining flanges (back-face ribs) of roller bearings may be caused by excessive loading arising from any of the following: (*a*) incorrect assembly and dismantling procedures, (*b*) general abuse in service, or (*c*) abnormally severe axial impact, which brings the ends of the rollers into heavy contact with the cup or cone back-face rib.

Fracture and cracking of balls and rollers occasionally occur. Balls generally fail by splitting into portions of approximately equal size. Beach marks on the fracture surfaces indicate normal fatigue cracking (that is, not cracking due to rolling-contact fatigue); the cracks often originate in regions of incipient flaking on the outer surface. Splitting of balls is initiated primarily in the area of fiber flow essentially perpendicular to the rolling surface. Fiber orientation arises because balls are manufactured by upsetting slugs of round stock between hemispherical dies.

A similar form of failure is shown by rollers. Most rollers fracture axially into two equal portions, but others, although extensively cracked, remain intact. The region of final fracture is of approximately circular shape and is situated on the central axis of the roller adjacent to one end face. The basic cause of this particular form of cracking is not obvious, but it most likely arises from gross overloading in both the radial and axial directions.

Rollers subjected to considerable end thrust, with one face being forced into heavy contact with one of the flanges of the inner raceway, frequently fail by smearing and wear. Final fracture usually is located adjacent to the smeared end but may be near the opposite end face.

Another form of failure involves fatigue cracking in a diametral plane and also in a helical direction at 45° to the axis of the roller. The pattern of cracking is symmetrical, with a second, helical crack on the remote side of the roller. Usually, cracking in the diametral plane develops first, and the cracks turn when they reach the opposite edge of the roller and proceed in a helical direction. In general, such cracking develops as a result of excessive compressive loads, which produce tensile stresses at right angles to the direction of loading. In addition, torsional stresses are involved, as indicated by the helical cracks. In theory, a roller should not be subjected to torsional stresses, but such stresses can result from misalignment or inherent dimensional discrepancies, particularly if the load on the inner and outer rings is carried by opposite ends of the rollers.

Fretting on the external cylindrical surface of an outer ring is not uncommon, and it is essential to examine all failed bearings for evidence of this effect, because local flaking of a raceway is often found to be associated with it. This form of damage shows itself as black or reddish-brown areas and arises from minute, interfacial movements between surfaces in contact; the resulting attrition produces fine metallic detritus which, being very active, quickly oxidizes to form a characteristic red corrosion product. The affected areas on both the outer ring and the housing will be found to be of identical shape. In a like manner, fretting on the bore of an inner ring may be caused by movement between the ring and the shaft; in such instances, the fatigue strength of the shaft may be adversely affected. (For additional information on fretting, see the section on Failure by Fretting on page 423 in this article.)

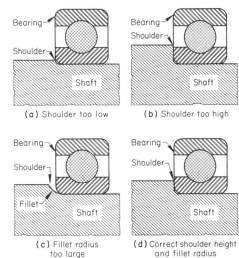

Fig. 20. Incorrect and correct shaft-shoulder heights and fillet radii for mounting rolling-element bearings on shafts; (a), (b) and (c) are incorrect designs; (d) is the correct design. See text for discussion.

Effects of Fabrication Practices

Correct assembly of a rolling-element bearing into a machine, and correct design and fabrication of the machine elements contiguous with the bearing, are essential for satisfactory operation. Satisfactory life and operation of a bearing depend on (a) correct mounting design, (b) accuracy of the machine elements that support the bearing, (c) cleanness of the bearing assembly, and (d) proper mounting on the shaft and in the housing.

Mounting Design. The rotating ring of a rolling-element bearing generally is press fitted onto a shaft or into a housing whereas a sliding fit is maintained on the other ring. Tightness of fit between a bearing ring and a shaft or housing varies with the use to which the bearing will be subjected. The type of fit depends on magnitude and direction of load (radial or axial), and on whether the load will be applied to the inner or the outer ring or whether application of load to both members may occur. Recommended classes of shaft and housing tolerances have been standardized by ANSI and AFBMA.

The standard internal looseness in a bearing is sufficient to allow for recommended tightness of fit between the inner ring and the shaft or between the outer ring and the housing. If tight fits are required in mounting both rings, or if the inner ring will be substantially warmer than the outer ring during operation, the internal clearance in the unmounted bearing must be greater than normal to compensate for press fitting or thermal expansion. A smaller internal clearance than normal is used when radial and axial displacements must be minimized.

Selection of a bearing with inadequate internal clearance for conditions where external heat is conducted through the shaft can result in overheating or noisy operation due to expansion of the inner ring. An oversize shaft or undersize bore results in an excessive press fit and reduces the internal bearing clearance sufficiently to make the bearing tight, causing the bearing to overheat or become noisy.

Rotational creep will occur when the inner ring is loose on the shaft, or the outer ring is loose in the housing. This will result in overheating, excessive wear, and contact erosion, or fretting, between the ring and the shaft or housing.

Shaft Shoulders and Fillets. The height of the shaft shoulder should be about half the thickness of the inner ring at the face. If the shaft shoulder is too low, the corner radius of the inner ring will push up against the shaft shoulder, as shown in Fig. 20(a). Inadequate support of the bearing at the shaft shoulder can result in bending of the shaft or cocking of the bearing, which can cause overheating of the bearing, vibration, hard turning of the shaft and general unsatisfactory operation of the equipment.

A shaft shoulder that is too high (see Fig. 20b) results in rubbing or distortion of the bearing seals. Also, it sometimes is necessary to remove the bearing from the shaft. This operation requires that a puller be placed against the inner ring, and a surface must be left free on which the puller can operate.

A slight corner break should be used on the shaft shoulder and on the bearing seat to avoid raising burrs that would interfere with assembly of the bearing.

Either an undercut or a fillet is used between the bearing-seat surface and the shaft shoulder. An undercut usually is the simplest design at the corner between the shaft seat and the shoulder, provided the weakening effect of the undercut can be tolerated. Frequently, however, a fillet must be used; the shaft fillet radius should be less than the bearing bore corner radius indicated in the bearing catalog for the particular bearing being considered. With too large a fillet radius, the face of the bearing will not seat against the shaft shoulder, as shown in Fig. 20(c), and misalignment of the bearing, bending of the shaft, inadequate support, and improper shaft and bearing location may result.

The proper relationship between the diameter of the shaft and the outside diameter of the inner ring, and the proper relationship of the shaft fillet radius and the corner radius on the inner ring, are shown in Fig. 20(d). Generally, these same conditions apply to the housing shoulder and fillet radius.

Shaft Alignment and Deflection. Alignment of shaft, bearings, bearing seats and

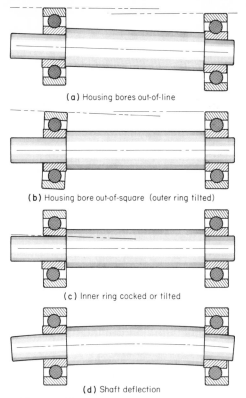

(a) Housing bores out-of-line

(b) Housing bore out-of-square (outer ring tilted)

(c) Inner ring cocked or tilted

(d) Shaft deflection

Fig. 21. Four types of misalignment of rolling-element bearings

the machine itself should be within certain tolerances to provide efficient mechanical operation. Misalignment can originate from any of the four general situations shown in Fig. 21. Carefully calibrated micrometers and dial indicators, with the appropriate mounting and clamping accessories, are employed in evaluating misalignment.

In actual engineering applications, misalignment does not always cause failure. A single-row, deep-groove ball bearing can withstand $1/4°$ angular misalignment without cramping or binding. This is less than $1/16$ in. per foot, and a 1-ft-long shaft out of line by as much as $1/16$ in. is unusual. Figure 21(a) illustrates tilting of inner rings when housing bores are out of line. Much more prevalent is an out-of-square bearing-housing bore (Fig. 21b) or housing shoulder; these can cause tilting of the outer ring. A cocked or tilted inner bearing ring (Fig. 21c) is also common. The same effect is created by out-of-square lockwashers and locknuts holding the bearing inner ring. On a 1-in.-diam shaft, a shoulder being out of square by 0.005 in. corresponds to $1/4°$ misalignment; thus, difficulties with tilted inner and outer bearing rings are not uncommon. Shaft deflection (Fig. 21d) is rarely critical, because many shafts would break before their angularity at the bearing reached $1/4°$. All these conditions should be checked if the ball path on a raceway indicates misalignment; if any of the conditions exist, changes in bearing clearances may be

required or inspection procedures with improved measurement techniques might be necessary.

Misalignment is indicated by a ball path not parallel to the edge of the raceway (see Fig. 2d). When the misaligned path is on the outer raceway, in applications where the inner ring rotates, the bore of the housing is not parallel to the shaft axis, as depicted in Fig. 21(b). If the path on the inner raceway is not parallel with the edge of the raceway, it is generally because (a) the inner ring is cocked on the shaft (Fig. 21c), (b) the shaft shoulder is not square with the bearing seat, or (c) the shaft is bent (Fig. 21d).

Misalignment of either ring of a deep-groove bearing will impose an additional load on the bearing. This additional load, together with the normal load, causes overstressing and overheating, resulting in early failure, as in the next example.

Example 9. Failure of a 52100 Steel Bearing for a Jet Engine Because of Misalignment Between the Bearing and a Shaft (Fig. 22)

An engine on a jet aircraft produced excessive vibration in flight and was immediately shut down.

Dismantling the engine revealed complete failure (fracture) of the cage in one of the two main-shaft ball bearings.

The ball bearings were both of the single-row, deep-groove type with split inner rings, manufactured for use in jet-aircraft engines. The bearings were made of vacuum-melted 52100 steel and were designed to operate at a maximum temperature of 177 C (350 F). The bearings were side by side in the engine.

Investigation. Hardness surveys were conducted on the inner and outer rings of both bearings. Hardness of the inner and outer rings of the bearing having the unfailed cage averaged Rockwell C 58 and 59, respectively, which is consistent with the specified hardness of Rockwell C 58 to 64.

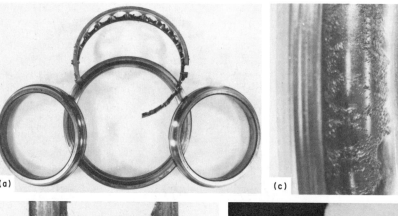

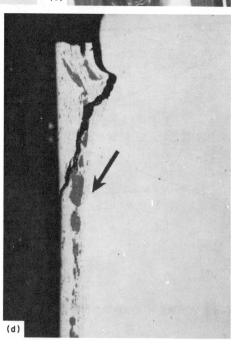

(a) Photograph of bearing components, showing fractured cage. (b) Enlarged view of cage, showing damage caused by scoring, scuffing and plastic deformation around ball pockets, and a circumferential crack (arrow). (c) Segment of ball groove in outer raceway, showing off-center damage from misalignment. (d) Micrograph of section through spalling cavity in inner raceway of unfailed bearing, showing inclusion (arrow) about 0.005 in. below surface.

Fig. 22. Jet-engine ball bearing, of 52100 steel, that failed because of overheating resulting from misalignment (Example 9)

The inner ring of the bearing with the failed cage had a hardness of Rockwell C 55, and the outer ring, Rockwell C 57. At 177 C (350 F), these parts would have a hot hardness of Rockwell C 50, perhaps indicative of overtempering.

All components of both bearings were visually inspected for evidence of excessive heating, structural damage and misalignment. A photograph of the bearing with the fractured cage is shown in Fig. 22(a). Damage caused by severe scoring, scuffing and plastic deformation of the material surrounding the ball pockets of the cage is shown in Fig. 22(b). The cage also was cracked between pockets at several locations around the periphery; one of these cracks is visible (at arrow) between the two pockets at top in Fig. 22(b).

Examination of the outer raceway of the bearing with the failed cage revealed severe damage to approximately 20% of the load-bearing surface. As shown in Fig. 22(c), more damage occurred on one shoulder of the groove than on the other, indicating misalignment of the bearing during at least part of its operation. Further evidence of misalignment was found in the ball pockets of the cage, which were unevenly worn. Such misalignment caused severe stressing of the cage material, resulting in fracture of the cage. Discoloration of the bearing components indicated that the bearing had been heated to temperatures in excess of the design limit. The cause of misalignment is uncertain, but may have been improper mounting of the bearing on the main shaft.

The second bearing exhibited no damage other than several small spalling cavities in the inner-ring raceway. Metallographic examination of a circumferential section through the largest cavity revealed an elongated subsurface inclusion, as indicated by the arrow in Fig. 22(d). This inclusion was in the region of maximum shear stress in the bearing (approximately 0.005 in. below the surface), which indicated that it had initiated the spalling cavity.

Conclusions. Failure of the cage resulted from overheating and excessive stressing of the cage caused by misalignment of the bearing on the main shaft. The bearing that failed was slightly tempered by overheating during operation.

The small spalling cavities found on the inner ring of the backup bearing were caused by an elongated subsurface inclusion located several thousandths of an inch below the surface and in the region of maximum shear stress. These cavities were not large enough to contribute to vibration in the engine at the time it was shut down.

Abuse before or during mounting can cause bearing raceways to become ball dented. Bearings operated in this condition are very noisy. Ball denting, or true brinelling, is caused by excessive pressure exerted on the raceways through the balls when the bearing is not rotating. (See the discussion under "Brinelling" on page 425 in this article.) Denting commonly occurs in small bearings that are pressed into the housing while already mounted on the shaft. If the outer ring is tight or becomes cocked in the housing, and pressure to force it into

position is applied through the inner ring, indentations are produced.

Impact in an axial direction can force the balls against the edge of the groove, causing dents and nicks. Ball dents, or brinelling, can be easily distinguished from dents produced by chips or dirt because ball dents usually are spaced the same distance apart as the balls. Ball dents can be produced in the bottom of a groove if sufficient impact loads are transmitted through the balls in a radial direction.

Mounting bearings on a shaft by applying blows or force to the outer raceway also will cause denting. If the force is sufficient, the raceway may crack. With less force, dents are produced near the center of the raceway, causing rough and noisy operation. As operation continues, pitting followed by flaking will develop at the individual dents. A nick on a ball or a raceway resulting from impact by some sharp object causes noise and vibration, and pitting is likely to follow.

Metal chips and dirt can adhere to and enter bearings that are placed on dirty benches or floors. Such contaminants can cause noise, denting, and locking of one or more of the rolling elements, which ultimately produces failure. Heating bearings with a torch to facilitate mounting or removal is hazardous. A severe temperature gradient is produced that may cause cracking or warping, and excessive heating will lower the hardness, change dimensions and induce early failure.

Punctured and bent bearing shields interfere with bearing performance and eventually cause bearing damage. Shield damage usually results from use of an improper tool in mounting or removing a bearing from a shaft or spindle.

Broken ball retainers in ball bearings may be the result of misalignment during installation. Excessive shaft deflection also can be responsible for broken retainers. A ball-path pattern alternating

from one side of a raceway to the other will be in evidence when a retainer has failed.

When bearings are pressed onto a shaft, the bore must be in perfect alignment with the shaft surface before force is applied. If a misaligned bearing is forced onto a shaft, the inner ring may be distorted or cracked. Forcing a misaligned hardened ring onto a shaft can burr or score the shaft seat. An arbor press is the most satisfactory means of applying the mounting force; use of impact tools should be avoided.

Heat Treatment and Hardness of Bearing Components

The most common through-hardened bearing materials are 52100 low-alloy steel and M50 high speed tool steel. Table 2 gives average hardness, amount of retained austenite, and typical austenite grain size for eight common bearing materials (three heat treatment lots of each material).

Hardness is an important variable in rolling-contact fatigue and can significantly affect bearing life. In general, bearing hardness should be at least Rockwell C 58 for adequate bearing life. Investigations have shown that, within limits, rolling-contact-fatigue life increases as hardness of the bearing components is increased (Ref 8).

Significant differences in hardness between rings and balls can affect bearing life. Experimental results (Ref 9) indicate that balls should be approximately 1 to 2 Rockwell C points harder than rings.

Because bearings operate at elevated temperatures and bearing life is dependent on hardness, the hardness of the bearing material at operating temperature is significant. Data on short-term hot hardness (Ref 10) indicate that there is a significant difference between bearing components of low-alloy steels such as

Table 2. Variations Among Heat Treatment Lots in Average Rockwell C Hardness, Amount of Retained Austenite, and Austenite Grain Size, for Eight Bearing Materials (Ref 7)

Bearing material	Average hardness, Rockwell C	Retained austenite, vol %	Austenite grain size (ASTM E112-63)	Bearing material	Average hardness, Rockwell C	Retained austenite, vol %	Austenite grain size (ASTM E112-63)
52100 steel:				M50 tool steel:			
Lot A	62.5	4.90	13	Lot A	62.6	1.90	10.3
B	62.0	4.10	13	B	62.2	2.90	9
C	62.5	0.80	13	C	62.3	1.50	10
Halmo:				M10 tool steel:			
Lot A	60.8	0.60	8	Lot A	62.2	1.10	9
B	60.8	1.00	8	B	62.0	2.40	6
C	61.1	1.70	8	C	61.8	1.60	6
T1 tool steel:				M1 tool steel:			
Lot A	61.4	7.30	11	Lot A	63.3	2.90	10
B	61.4	5.20	9	B	63.4	3.30	9
C	61.0	9.50	10	C	63.5	1.00	8
M42 tool steel:				M2 tool steel:			
Lot A	61.8	1.00	9	Lot A	63.4	1.70	6
B	61.3	4.40	10	B	63.4	2.40	10
C	61.3	4.90	8	C	63.4	2.30	9

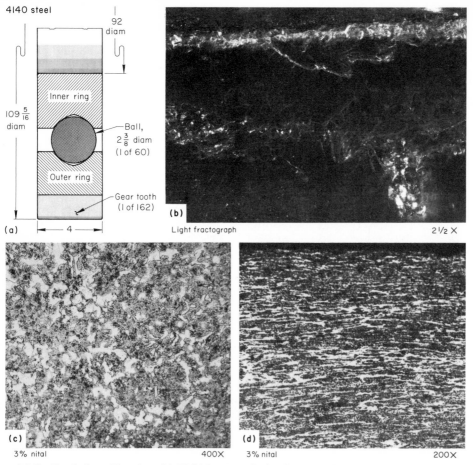

(a) Sectional view of bearing. (b) Light fractograph showing typical damage on outer-ring raceway. (c) Micrograph of section through metal in outer ring adjacent to raceway, showing ferrite, scattered patches of pearlite, and tempered martensite. (d) Micrograph of section through outer ring at raceway, showing grains elongated by metal movement (raceway surface is at top).

Fig. 23. *Large-diameter radar-antenna bearing, of 4140 steel, that failed because of improper heat treatment of outer-ring raceway* (Example 10)

52100 and those of high speed tool steels such as M50 in ability to maintain hardness as temperature increases.

Most bearing alloys fall within the low-alloy or high speed tool steel categories; however, a heat treatment that is optimum for a material in a tool is not necessarily optimum for the material when used in a bearing component. Unfortunately, most heat treatments for these bearing materials are based on the heat treatments that have been developed for the materials as tools.

The large ball bearing described in the following example failed because of improper heat treatment.

Example 10. Failure of a Large 4140 Steel Bearing Because of Improper Heat Treatment of Outer-Ring Raceway (Fig. 23)

A large bearing from a radar antenna was replaced because of deformation, surface cracking, and spalling on the raceway of the outer ring. A sectional view of the bearing is shown in Fig. 23(a).

Specifications required the rings to be made of 4140 steel. The raceway surfaces were to be flame hardened to Rockwell C 55 min, and Rockwell C 50 at ⅛ in. below the

surface. Other surfaces of the rings were to have a hardness of Rockwell C 24 to 28.

The bearing capacity at 1.67 rpm was a radial load of 1,572,000 lb and an axial (thrust) load of 1,012,800 lb.

Samples of the inner and outer rings 6 to 8 in. long were sent to the laboratory for examination.

Investigation. Examination revealed that the raceway of the outer ring was damaged by deformation, surface cracking and spalling, as shown in Fig. 23(b). The raceway of the inner ring exhibited little or no damage.

A wet chemical analysis of the material in the inner and outer rings showed it to be 4140 steel. Molybdenum contents were 0.26% in the inner ring and 0.31% in the outer ring, both slightly above the specified range of 0.15 to 0.25%. However, this deviation is not significant and would not affect strength properties or hardenability.

A cross-sectional specimen about ⅜ in. thick was taken through the center of each sample; after cutting, both surfaces of each specimen were ground smooth. Hardness of the raceway of the outer ring was Rockwell C 29.8 to 11.7. A horizontal traverse through the center of the ring showed a hardness of Rockwell C 26.1 to 18.7. A vertical traverse 1⅝ in. from the outer surface showed a hardness of Rockwell C 25.2 to 18.9. The low hardness values for the outer-

ring raceway indicated that it had not been properly flame hardened. The hardness of the top and outer surfaces of the rings were within specifications.

The hardness traverse of the inner-ring raceway showed a hardness of Rockwell C 46.8 to 54.8, which was below the specified hardness of Rockwell C 55 min.

The specimens were etched in 3% nital to differentiate between hardened and unhardened areas. The inner ring showed a well-developed hardened case at the raceway, whereas the outer ring did not.

Metallographic examination of an etched specimen showed that the structure of the inner ring adjacent to the raceway was a mixture of tempered martensite and some ferrite. This condition suggested that heat treatment was insufficient to make the structure completely austenitic prior to quenching; therefore, the full hardening capability of the steel was not attained. The microstructure of the material away from the hardened surface was a mixture of finely divided pearlite and ferrite, which resulted in the metal being relatively soft.

The microstructure of the material in the outer ring adjacent to the raceway (see Fig. 23c) was a mixture of white ferrite, scattered patches of pearlite and martensite, which showed that the steel had been improperly austenitized, producing very low hardness.

Displacement of metal on the outer raceway is shown in Fig. 23(d). The grain structure had been elongated, indicating metal movement. Rolled-out and embedded metal particles were also found in the surface.

Hardenability of the metal in the outer ring was checked by heating a specimen 1 in. by 1 in. by ¼ in. along one edge with an oxyacetylene torch to 870 to 900 C (about 1600 to 1650 F) and then quenching in water. Hardness in the heated area was Rockwell C 57 to 60, and in the unheated area, Rockwell C 23.

Conclusion. Failure of the raceway surface of the outer ring of the bearing was the result of incomplete austenitization. The steel in the inner-ring raceway had been hardened to slightly below the specified hardness of Rockwell C 55 min, but the outer-ring raceway had a maximum hardness of only Rockwell C 29.8.

The raceway surface in the outer ring was not properly heated by the flame-hardening process; therefore, subsequent quenching and tempering operations (if any) would have had virtually no effect on hardness.

Lubrication of Rolling-Element Bearings*

The functions of lubricants for rolling-element bearings are to: (*a*) provide a thin film of oil between bearing contact surfaces to reduce metal contact; (*b*) prevent excessive heating by acting as a coolant; (*c*) remove wear debris and other foreign substances from the contact sur-

* This section is a condensation of an unpublished article by Dr. Conrad J. Polk, Associate Engineer, Engineering Dept., Mobil Research and Development Corp.

faces; and (d) help seal out dust, dirt, and other environmental contaminants. Experience has shown that reductions in bearing life will occur if a lubricant is ineffective in performing any one of these functions. Lubricants must have the proper physical and chemical characteristics under the conditions of operation. A program of regular inspection and maintenance is necessary to ensure that both the lubricant and its distribution system, as well as other mechanical components, remain in satisfactory condition.

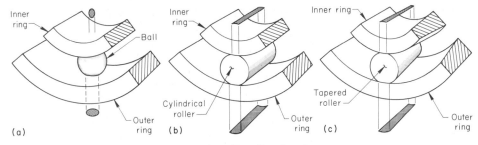

Indicates areas on raceways elastically deformed by rolling elements

Fig. 24. Schematic representation of areas on raceways deformed by (a) a ball, (b) a cylindrical roller, and (c) a tapered roller (Ref 11)

Thin-Film Lubrication. When the proper amount of lubricant is supplied to a bearing, a thin film is formed on the bearing surfaces. During operation, extremely small and randomly distributed surface irregularities penetrate the thin film, causing metal-to-metal contact. The operational life of a bearing is inversely related to the number of such contacts per revolution. Other factors being equal, the fewer the contacts made per cycle, the longer the life of the bearing.

Under load, the area of contact between a ball and its raceway is elliptical in shape, as illustrated in Fig. 24(a). The zone of contact between a cylindrical roller and its raceway is rectangular (Fig. 24b) whereas a tapered roller forms an area that is wider at one end (Fig. 24c). As load is applied, the elements deform elastically, and contact is spread over an increasingly larger area. With a suitable lubricant between the surfaces, such an increase in contact area and the increase in fluid viscosity caused by the load result in the formation of a pressurized (elastohydrodynamic) film that separates the surfaces during operation (Ref 12).

Elastohydrodynamic films are only a few micro-inches in thickness. Film thickness can be increased by increasing the rotational velocity of the bearing, increasing the viscosity of the oil, or improving the conformity of rolling elements to their raceways. Increasing either temperature or load decreases film thickness. Consequently, it is detrimental to bearing life to operate a bearing at too low a speed, too high a load or temperature, or with an oil of insufficient viscosity.

The surface finish of bearing elements is also an important consideration in elastohydrodynamic lubrication. In addition to the periodic dimensional deviations resulting from machining, bearing surfaces contain nonperiodic irregularities, including scratches, debris, and indentations with raised edges. Ordinarily, these features are quite small and have a statistical size distribution; they range in height from a few micro-inches to a few hundredths of a micro-inch or less. However, elastohydrodynamic films are only a few micro-inches in thickness

also, and, for a given film thickness, some of the surface features protrude through the film and contact the opposing surface. Under conditions of insufficient film thickness, the number of contacts per revolution is excessive, and bearing life suffers accordingly.

Temperature. Sources of heat in bearings include (a) frictional contact between component surfaces, (b) hysteresis losses because of cyclic stressing of the metal, and (c) fluid friction caused by displacement and churning of the lubricant. Sources external to the bearing may also contribute to heating, as in hot rolling mills, paper-mill dryers, and jet aircraft engines.

Lubricating oils and greases are available for applications over a wide range of temperatures. As shown in Fig. 25, oils of higher viscosity are better suited for bearing applications in which rotational velocities are low and operating temperatures are high. Oils of lower viscosity are more suitable for bearings operated at higher speeds and lower operating temperatures. Petroleum-base oils and greases are available for both subzero and high-temperature operations. Many lubricants are formulated to function over a wide temperature range. Certain greases, for example, can be used at temperatures from −54 C to 177 C (−65 F to 350 F) (Ref 13). Under certain conditions, greases made with nonsoap thick-

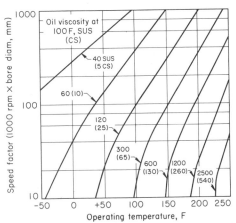

Fig. 25. Viscosities of several lubricants for ball and roller bearings, as related to operating speed and temperature (Ref 6)

eners can operate at temperatures up to 260 C (500 F). If oil-type lubricants are required for continuous high-temperature operation, as in jet-engine applications, specially formulated ester-base fluids may be required.

Contamination. Contaminants that may enter a bearing include dust, dirt, fine metallic particles, water, and acid fumes. Lubricants help to keep such contaminants out of the bearing and restrict the action of those that reach the raceway and rolling-element surfaces. Hydrophobic oil films and antirust additives inhibit the effects of water contamination. Lubricating oils also may be used to flush foreign particles from the contact zone; these particles are removed from the oil by filtration.

Abrasive dust or dirt in a bearing causes wear of bearing components. The resulting increase of internal clearance causes radial and axial play, reduced accuracy and rigidity of shaft positioning, and increased vibration and noise. Furthermore, metallic particles and other hard debris can be embedded in contact surfaces. Repeated impact of rolling elements on these particles causes dents and scratches that deteriorate the surface finish. The resulting raised or sharp edges produce highly localized stress concentrations that can lead to early fatigue failure. Adequate lubrication minimizes the effects of such abrasive particles by establishing films of sufficient thickness to allow easy passage of the contaminants between bearing surfaces.

Rusting can result if condensation occurs in an idle bearing, or if water enters the housing during operation. Rust particles can flake off the components, forming surface pits; also, an abrasive lapping compound may be formed by mixing of the particles with the lubricant. Water contamination also can cause corrosion fatigue, stress-corrosion cracking, galvanic corrosion, and hydrogen embrittlement of high-strength bearing steels (Ref 14). Corrosion from other sources, such as acid fumes, can produce effects similar to those caused by water. Although corrosion inhibitors are included in most lubricant formulations, moisture and other corrosive elements

Table 3. Guides for Choosing Between Grease and Oil Lubrication for Bearings (Ref 6)

Operating condition	Grease	Oil
Temperature	Below 200-250 F (93-121 C)	Above 200-250 F (93-121 C)
Speed factor (bore, mm, × rpm)	Below 200,000-300,000	Above 200,000-300,000
Load	Low to moderate	High, where oil is necessary for cooling
Long periods without attention	Yes	No, rate of leakage and other losses higher
Central oil supply for other machine elements	No	Yes
Dirty conditions	Yes, if proper design seals out contaminants	Yes, if circulated and filtered
Lowest torque	No, soap structure offers resistance	Yes, except excessive amount of oil and churning should be avoided. Use oil mist.

must be excluded from the bearing and the lubricating system.

Housings of open-type bearings are provided with shaft seals to control the flow of lubricant. Outward flow of a lubricant aids in preventing dirt, water, and other contaminants from entering the bearing. Shaft seals may be of the clearance or rubbing-contact type. Seals must be periodically inspected for excessive wear and to evaluate effectiveness in preventing contamination. Sometimes, slingers can be installed on shafts for centrifugal removal of water or other liquids.

In the following example, wear of a labyrinth seal permitted grease lubricant to leak out of several bearings and contaminants to enter them.

Example 11. Failure of Bearings Because of Wear of Labyrinth Seals

A large number of drive-shaft-hanger bearings failed after 300 to 400 hr in service. The bearings normally lasted 600 hr or more. The shaft was made of aluminum alloy 2024-T3 tubing 1 in. in diameter and 0.049 in. in wall thickness. The shafts were supported by labyrinth-sealed, single-row, radial ball bearings of ABEC-1 tolerances. The bearings had spot-welded two-piece retainers and were lubricated with 1.5 ± 0.2 grams of a paste-type mineral-oil lubricant or a grease conforming to MIL-G-81322. The lubricant contained molybdenum disulfide and polytetrafluoroethylene particles having a size of about 5 microns. The grease contained a thickening agent and synthetic hydrocarbons.

Investigation. Examination of the failed bearings revealed that the rings were blackened, deformed and smeared. The balls were embedded in the inner-ring raceway, which had been softened by the elevated temperatures reached during the failure. The retainers were broken and the seals were worn and bent out of shape.

Examination indicated that the following factors contributed to the failures:

1 Insufficient lubrication
2 Contamination of the bearings by gritty particles (dirt)
3 Intrusion of a corrosive agent (water)
4 Corrosion pitting of rings and balls
5 Contact-fatigue mechanisms.

Bearings that had been in service about 300 hr were examined. These bearings exhibited light corrosion pits throughout the rings and balls. However, pitting occurred primarily in the areas of contact between balls and raceways. Areas surrounding these pits contained evidence of contact fatigue. The bearings were blackened by the high temperatures, but the amount of coke residue or burnt lubricant was minimal. The seals exhibited wear, which had permitted penetration of gritty particles, water and other corrosive agents, and leakage of lubricant out of the bearing.

Maintenance reports contained notes regarding grease slinging by these bearings. This was substantiated by the dry condition of the failed bearings.

New bearings were tested under simulated environmental conditions. Half of these bearings had labyrinth seals and were lubricated with the mineral-oil paste; the remainder had a positive rubbing seal and the MIL-G-81322 grease. The bearings with the positive rubbing seals and MIL-G-81322 grease lubricant had 30 to 100% longer life than those with the labyrinth seals and mineral-oil-paste lubricant.

Conclusions. Wear of the labyrinth seals permitted the lubricant to flow out of the bearing and dirt and corrosive agents to enter, resulting in overheating.

Corrective Action. Bearings containing a positive rubbing seal and a MIL-G-81322 grease lubricant were installed. These bearings had satisfactory life.

In certain applications, contamination problems require a change in the method of lubrication. For example, where bath oiling is used and considerable trouble is encountered with dirt, it may be advisable to change to circulation oiling. The lubricant then can be cleaned by passing it through a full-flow filter. Where dust, moist air, or acid fumes are a problem, changing to an oil-mist system may be beneficial. This type of system can maintain clean, dry air under positive pressure in the housings and thus prevent contaminants from entering. In all instances, passages for supply and drainage of oil must be free of dirt and other clogging debris.

Effective Oil and Grease Lubrication. General guides for determining if oil or grease should be used as a lubricant are listed in Table 3. Lubricating oils must be of suitable viscosity for the particular application in order to minimize the frequency of contact between the bearing surfaces, reduce frictional heating from all sources, and protect against wear. Adequate film strength is necessary to resist the wiping action between components, particularly in tapered-roller bearings carrying heavy axial and radial loads. Lubricating oils should have the highest possible resistance to oxidation, to prevent the formation and accumulation of sludge during long periods of operation. Corrosion inhibitors are needed to provide maximum protection when corrosive agents are present.

Greases suitable for bearing applications should be of high quality to last for long periods of service. In addition to the requirements listed for oils, greases should have proper structural stability to resist both softening and stiffening in service, and the appropriate consistency for the method of application. Greases must have the proper slump characteristics at operating temperature, or controlled oil-bleeding properties, for adequate penetration into the small clearances between separators and raceways. Greases used in permanently packed bearings must be exceptionally stable.

Although the housings of some bearings are packed by hand, most have grease fittings. Except when it is necessary to exclude water by complete filling with grease, no housing should be packed so full that the constant churning by the rolling elements causes unnecessary lubricant friction and high operating temperatures. Just as is true for lubricant starvation of bearings, excessive lubrication is detrimental to optimum performance and long bearing life.

References

1. H. N. Kaufman, Classification of Bearing Damage, p 1-7 in "Interpreting Service Damage in Rolling Type Bearings — A Manual on Ball and Roller Bearing Damage", The American Society of Lubrication Engineers, Chicago, Ill., Apr 1958
2. F. R. Hutchings, A Survey of the Causes of Failure of Rolling Bearings, Technical Report Vol VI, British Engine Boiler & Electrical Insurance Co., Ltd., Manchester, England, 1965, p 54-75
3. R. K. Allan, "Rolling Bearings", Sir Isaac Pitman & Sons, Ltd., London, 1945
4. G. Lundberg and A. Palmgren, Dynamic Capacity of Roller Bearings, Acta Polytech, No. 210, 1952
5. A. Mendelsen, "Plasticity: Theory and Applications", Macmillan, New York, 1968
6. D. F. Wilcock and E. R. Booser, "Bearing Design and Application", 1st edition, McGraw-Hill, 1957
7. J. L. Chevalier and E. V. Zaretsky, Effect of Carbide Size, Area, and Density on Rolling-Element Fatigue, NASA TN D-6835, June 1972
8. T. L. Carter, E. V. Zaretsky and W. J. Anderson, Effect of Hardness and Other Mechanical Properties on Rolling-Contact Fatigue Life of Four High-Temperature Bearing Steels, NASA TN D-270, March 1966
9. E. V. Zaretsky, R. J. Parker and W. J. Anderson, Component Hardness Difference and

Their Effect on Bearing Fatigue, *J Lubrication Technol (Trans ASME, Ser F)*, Jan 1967, p 47

10. J. Chevalier, M. Dietrich and E. Zaretsky, Short-Term Hot Hardness Characteristic of Rolling-Element Steels, NASA TN D-6632

11. Anti-Friction Bearings and Their Lubrication, Technical Bulletin No. 3-92-002, Mobil Oil Corp., New York, 1963

12. T. E. Tallian, Rolling Contact Failure Control Through Lubrication, *Proc Inst Mech Engrs (London)*, Vol 182, Pt 3A, 1967-68, p 205

13. Rolling Element Bearings, *Machine Design*, Vol 44, June 22, 1972, p 59-75

14. I. M. Felsen, R. W. McQuaid and J. A. Marzani, Effect of Seawater on the Fatigue Life and Failure Distribution of Flood-Lubricated Angular Contact Ball Bearings, *Am Soc Lubrication Engrs Trans*, Vol 15, 1972, p 8-17

Selected References

H. R. Bear, R. H. Butler, Preliminary Metallographic Studies of Ball Fatigue Under Rolling-Contact Conditions, NACA TN3925, 1957

T. L. Carter, R. H. Butler, H. R. Bear and W. J. Anderson, Investigation of Factors Governing Fatigue Life with the Rolling-Contact Fatigue Spin Rig, *Am Soc Lubrication Engrs Trans*, Vol 1, No. 1, 1958, p 23-32

R. F. Jacobs, Sleeve-Bearing Fatigue, *Machine Design*, Dec 19, 1963, p 134-139

B. W. Kelly, Lubrication of Concentrated Contacts — The Practical Problem, Interdisciplinary Approach to the Lubrication of Concentrated Contacts, NASA symposium held at Rensselaer Polytechnic Institute, Troy, N. Y., July 15-17, 1969

T. W. Morrison, T. Tallian, H. O. Walp and G. W. Baile, The Effect of Material Variables on the Fatigue Life of AISI 52100 Steel Ball Bearings, *Am Soc Lubrication Engrs Trans*, Vol 5, No. 2, Nov 1962, p 347-364

J. C. Shurka, Elastohydrodynamic Lubrication of Roller Bearings, *J Lubrication Technol*, Apr 1970, p 281-291

K. Sugino, K. Miyamoto, M. Nagumo and K. Aoki, Structural Alterations of Bearing Steels under Rolling Contact Fatigue, *Trans Iron Steel Inst (Japan)*, Vol 10, No. 2, 1970, p 98-111

N. M. Wickstrand, Depth of Permanent Indentations in Flat Plates Due to Loaded Cylindrical Rollers, *J Lubrication Technol*, Jan 1970

E. V. Zaretsky, W. J. Anderson, R. J. Parker, Effect of Nine Lubricants on Rolling-Contact Fatigue Life, NASA TN D-1404, Oct 1962

Failures of Mechanical Face Seals

By John W. Abar*

A MECHANICAL face seal is a pressure-tight seal used to prevent leakage of a fluid (liquid, gas or vapor) between a rotating shaft and a housing through which the shaft passes. Sealing is performed by continuous contact between two ultraflat annular sealing faces, which are perpendicular to the axis of the shaft. The component containing one of the faces is attached to the shaft and rotates with it; the component containing the other face is attached to the housing, and thus is stationary (nonrotating). One component is designed to move axially to maintain contact between the two faces at all times; a preload force normally is used to ensure this contact. In addition, secondary seals are used to keep the fluid from escaping between the components containing the primary-seal faces and the respective machine members to which these components are mounted.

Seal Design

Although differing in design details, all mechanical face seals comprise the following elements, which are shown in Fig. 1: primary-seal ring, mating ring, spring-loading device, and secondary seals.

The seal head, which either rotates or is stationary (secured to the housing), consists of the primary-seal ring, secondary seal, spring, and (for rotating heads) mechanical-drive hardware. If the head rotates, the mating ring is stationary, and vice versa.

The seal head is mounted either inside or outside the equipment housing, and, as shown in Fig. 1, incorporates rotating or stationary primary-seal rings,

and inside-mounted or outside-mounted seals — each of which has varying uses and limitations, depending on the particular seal application.

Rotating seal heads most commonly are used with shafts or sleeves that are machined to close tolerances from comparatively high-grade materials. Furthermore, they are used in applications involving relatively low shaft surface speeds (less than 3500 fpm for seal heads that incorporate one spring, and less than 5000 fpm for seals that have multiple-spring preload assemblies).

Stationary seal heads are best used when comparatively high speeds are encountered. A stationary seal head requires less-critical dynamic balancing and is not subject to centrifugal forces. By holding close tolerances on the rotating mating ring, greater dynamic balance can be attained than by having to control all of the tolerances on the seal-head components. In some applications, where operating conditions are simple, stationary seal heads are also considered more practical because of the space available for the seal.

One disadvantage of a stationary seal head is that a small clearance in the bore and a high-grade finish must be maintained. Often, special features such as auxiliary liners, sleeves or adapters must be used to retain the mechanical advantages of this type of seal.

Mating-ring design varies with rotating and stationary seals and the method of mounting (inside or outside). A greater variety of mating-ring designs, all of which can be adapted to an end plate, are available for the rotating seal head. In many instances, the end plate is the stationary mating ring, as in Fig. 6. Where brittle materials such as ceramics

are used, it is desirable that stresses in the mating ring, caused by the secondary sealing element and pressure direction, place the mating ring itself in compression. If an O-ring is used on the inside of the mating-ring member, any swell created by this O-ring places the mating ring in tension. This is relatively dangerous for brittle mating rings that are rotating and are mounted outside the machine housing. Proper choices of elastomers for secondary seals and mating-ring materials and design can overcome swell to a large extent.

Inside-mounted seals are the most common type of mechanical seal. The seal components are mounted entirely within the stuffing box (see views at left in Fig. 1) and cannot be adjusted without dismantling the equipment. The materials are selected to withstand the corrosive nature of the fluid in the stuffing box. They are easily modified to include environmental controls and can be balanced to withstand high stuffing-box pressures. Inside-mounted seals are subject to compressive stresses.

Outside-mounted seals have either the primary-seal ring or the mating ring outside the stuffing box (see views at right in Fig. 1). If an extremely corrosive fluid is to be sealed and has satisfactory face-lubricating properties, an outside-mounted seal provides an economical alternative to the corrosion-resistant materials needed for an inside seal. In an outside-seal arrangement, only the rotating components are exposed to the atmosphere. Some components of outside-mounted seals are subjected to critical tensile stresses because of the direction of pressure. One advantage of outside-mounted seals is that they are more readily inspected for seal-face wear.

*Director of Mechanical Testing, Crane Packing Co.

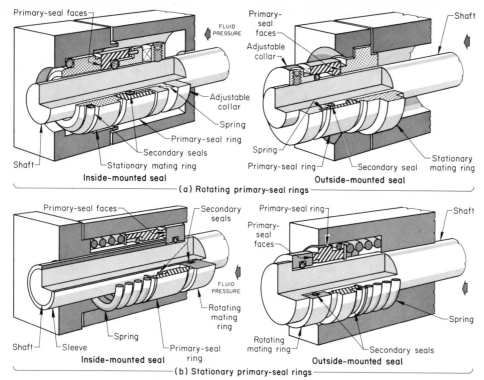

Fig. 1. *Inside-mounted and outside-mounted mechanical face seals incorporating rotating and stationary primary-seal rings*

Balanced Seals. One of the most frequently encountered environmental conditions requiring a slight modification in seal design is pressure. If an inside mechanical seal is required to seal high pressures, provisions must be made to ensure that not all of the pressure on the seal is trying to push the primary-seal ring to the atmospheric side of the stuffing box.

A conventional inside-mounted unbalanced seal is shown at left in Fig. 1(a). Almost all of the stuffing-box pressure is exerting a closing force on the seal ring. Only a very small portion of the seal-ring face is exposed over the top of the mating ring, allowing a proportionately small amount of pressure to act against the seal ring in the opposite direction, in addition to the opening force exerted by the fluid film between the faces. If the closing force becomes great enough, the liquid film between the faces is literally squeezed out. Deprived of lubrication and highly loaded, the faces soon destroy themselves.

In the seal at left in Fig. 1(a) a small amount of the face of the primary-seal ring is exposed to an opening hydraulic force immediately over the mating-ring face. Thus, if the closing pressure on the seal ring is reduced, a greater area of the seal-ring face must be exposed to hydraulic pressure that will act in a direction opposite to the closing force.

A conventional outside-mounted seal that has been balanced is shown at right in Fig. 1(a). The O-ring shaft seal is forced against the collar, leaving an area

under the primary-seal ring exposed to stuffing-box pressure. The closing force exerted by this pressure, acting against the shoulder of the seal ring, slightly exceeds the opening force exerted by the fluid film between the faces, thereby keeping the faces in contact at all times.

Inside-mounted seals that are balanced frequently use a stepped shaft, which permits moving the mating face radially inward without decreasing the width of the face itself. The seal ring remains on the original shaft diameter, which means that the closing force remains unchanged. Because more of the seal-ring face is exposed to hydraulic pressure acting to open the seal, the design is considered to be balanced.

Sealing points in a mechanical face seal are shown in Fig. 2. In a pump or a similar device, the leakage path by which

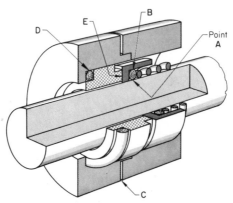

Fig. 2. *Sealing points in a mechanical face seal. See text for discussion.*

liquid can bypass the mating ring along the shaft is blocked by the O-ring shaft packing at A in Fig. 2. Liquid attempting to pass under the primary-seal ring is blocked by the O-ring packing at B. Liquid attempting to pass over the primary-seal ring is blocked from reaching the atmospheric side of the pump by the gland gasket C and the O-ring D. The path of escape remaining is interface E between the rotating primary-seal ring and mating ring. The face of the seal ring and the face of the mating ring are lapped to a flatness that is measured in microinches. These faces remain in contact throughout their entire contact-surface area, thus providing a nearly positive seal. These mechanical seal faces ride on a microscopic film of liquid that is able to migrate between them. When this film reaches the atmosphere, it can be classified as leakage. This leakage is so slight, however, that it will vaporize before it can be visually detected. When liquids that do not readily evaporate, such as wax, are being sealed, minor accumulations may be detectable under the gland, but only after hours of operation.

Materials for Seal Rings

The environment in which mechanical face seals operate has a great influence on the materials used in seal rings. The corrosive properties of the liquid, gas or vapor being contained must be considered so that materials with adequate corrosion resistance are selected. Temperature also is important because the corrosiveness of many liquids, gases and vapors varies from one temperature level to another. Also, certain seal-ring materials are unable to withstand high or low temperatures beyond a certain level. Therefore, materials must be used that are compatible with both the temperature and the fluid.

Lubricity is another important factor. Liquids with lubricating qualities similar to or less than those of water require face materials capable of maintaining satisfactory wear rates without the benefit of good lubrication. In addition, the two face materials must provide compatible wearing surfaces. Table 1 lists combinations of materials used for faces of primary-seal rings and mating rings in applications involving various liquids.

Operating Conditions

In many applications, primary-seal faces (flat and parallel annular mating surfaces of the rotating and stationary components of mechanical seals) are subject to simultaneous wear and corrosion. Therefore, primary-seal faces are more subject to failure than are other components of mechanical face seals such as secondary seals and hardware.

Seal-face wear is governed by the conditions of sliding contact at the seal faces, namely: (*a*) sliding speed, (*b*) contact pressure, (*c*) fluid being contained and (*d*) temperature of fluid. Sliding speed is a function of shaft speed and size. Typical sliding speeds for mechanical seals range from 20 to 6000 ft per minute. Contact pressure is a function of fluid pressure, seal balance and mechanical load. Seal-face contact pressures typically range from 30 to 500 psi. The product of face pressure, *P*, and sliding speed, *V*, is commonly referred to as the *PV* value of seal operation. This *PV* value is empirically related to wear rates of seal-face materials and, consequently, to wear life. Seal power consumption and cooling requirements for removal of frictional heat developed at the seal faces can also be derived from this *PV* relationship. Mechanical seals are capable of operation at *PV* values of 1.25×10^6 psi-fpm.

Most mechanical face seals are designed for a wear life of two years (approximately 18,000 hr) at maximum specified operating conditions. This service life may be considerably shortened or lengthened depending on the severity of the application, duty cycle, seal design, and materials of construction.

Mechanical face seals, in most instances, are lubricated by the fluid being contained. It follows, then, that materials of construction must be compatible with the fluid in terms of resistance to corrosion and chemical attack. Seal designs and materials tolerate, to varying degrees, dissolved and undissolved solids in the fluid and products of fluid decomposition and oxidation.

Fluid temperature is critical in terms of the corrosiveness, lubricating properties, and over-all chemical and physical stability of the fluid. Temperature (independent of or in combination with pressure) is often the limiting factor for elastomers and other materials used as secondary seals. Mechanical seals are capable of operating over an approximate temperature range of −195 to 400 C (−320 to 750 F).

Common Causes of Failure

A mechanical face seal is considered to have failed when leakage past the seal causes excessive loss of fluid from, or excessive reduction of pressure within, the system being sealed. Several of the common causes of seal failure are (*a*) mishandling of seal components, (*b*) incorrect seal assembly, (*c*) improper seal design and materials, (*d*) improper equipment start-up and operational practices, (*e*) fluid contaminants, and (*f*) poor equipment condition. Normal leakage of seals is sometimes misinterpreted as seal failure when it is

Table 1. Combinations of Materials for Faces of Primary-Seal Rings and Mating Rings for Applications Involving Various Liquids(a)

Water and Water Solutions

Carbon-graphite or filled phenolic can be used with any of the following:

6 to 8% Ni cemented tungsten carbide
6 to 8% Co cemented tungsten carbide
85 to 99.9% Al_2O_3 ceramic
17-4 PH stainless steel
Silicon-carbide-coated carbon
Ni-Resist (high-nickel cast iron)
Sintered iron
Sintered bronze
Bronze
Chromium plating
Al_2O_3 coating
Chromium oxide coating
Tungsten carbide coating
Phosphor bronze
Cast iron

Bronze can be used with:
6 to 8% Ni cemented tungsten carbide
6 to 8% Co cemented tungsten carbide

Cemented tungsten carbide can be used with cemented tungsten carbide.

Silicon-carbide-coated carbon can be used with silicon-carbide-coated carbon.

Caustic Solutions

Carbon-graphite or carbon-filled Teflon can be used with any of the following:

Cemented tungsten carbide
Stellite
Stellite hard facing
98 to 99.9% Al_2O_3 ceramic
Silicon-carbide-coated carbon
Boron carbide
Monel

Caustic Solutions (continued)

Cemented tungsten carbide can be used with cemented tungsten carbide.

Silicon-carbide-coated carbon can be used with silicon-carbide-coated carbon.

Acid Solutions

Carbon-graphite or glass-filled Teflon can be used with any of the following:

85 to 99.9% Al_2O_3 ceramic
Stellite
Silicon-carbide-coated carbon
Boron carbide
Hastelloy A, B or C
Binderless cemented tungsten carbide
Carpenter 20 (stainless steel)
17-4 PH stainless steel

Silicon-carbide-coated carbon can be used with silicon-carbide-coated carbon.

Oil and Gasoline

Carbon-graphite, bronze or filled phenolic can be used with any of the following:

Cast iron
Cemented tungsten carbide
85 to 99.9% Al_2O_3 ceramic
Ni-Resist (high-nickel cast iron)
Stellite
Stellite hard facing
Sintered iron
Tool steel
17-4 PH stainless steel
Chromium plate

Cemented tungsten carbide can be used with cemented tungsten carbide.

Silicon-carbide-coated carbon can be used with silicon-carbide-coated carbon.

(a) Coatings cover the entire ring, which is made from a suitable base material where no base material is specifically stated in this table.

---

encountered by inspecting personnel who are uninitiated as to leakage characteristics of the seal in question. It is a common myth that mechanical seals do not leak; actually, all mechanical seals leak. The leakage may range from 0.036 to 60 cu cm per hour, depending on seal size, design, materials of construction and severity of service.

Mishandling of seal components accounts for many premature seal failures. The faces of primary seals are precision finished. In many instances, they are manufactured from fragile materials that very easily can be chipped, cracked, nicked or scratched to the extent of causing immediate seal failures.

Cleanness is also an important handling consideration. Dirt trapped between seal faces or on secondary-seal surfaces also may cause premature failure, or at least cause damage sufficient to reduce seal life. Scratches, nicks and cuts on secondary-seal surfaces or on interfaces between seals and machine members will produce premature if not immediate failure.

Incorrect Seal Assembly. Seal working-height setting is critical for reliable seal performance, particularly where high-load-rate devices (such as wave-washer springs and metal bellows) are employed for mechanical face loading. Improper working-height setting may cause seal-face loads to be too low, which will result in lack of seal-face contact, or to be too high, which will result in jamming and subsequent fracture of seal components.

Misplacement or omission of secondary seals is also a common cause of premature seal failure.

Improper alignment of seal faces with the shaft axis and nonuniform tightening of gland or end-plate fasteners (and the resulting seal-face distortion) will cause seal malfunction.

Improper seal design and materials will produce premature failures. The most common failure mode is chemical attack of primary or secondary seals. Another mode is excessive face wear, which can result when *PV* values of operation are not properly considered during design and materials selection. Failure by extrusion of secondary seals can occur where design limits of pressure or temperature, or both, are exceeded.

Improper equipment start-up and operational practices that adversely affect seal environment — namely, pressure, fluid-flow rate, and temperature — may precipitate immediate seal failure or cause damage sufficient to reduce normal seal life. Mechanical face seals rely on their environment for two primary requirements: (a) lubrication of seal faces, and (b) dissipation of frictional heat developed at the seal faces.

Pump start-up or operation with the pump suction shut off will at best reduce seal cooling, and will more than likely cause the seal to run completely dry unless special equipment for seal-environment control is provided. Fluids having low boiling points or high melting points may require auxiliary cooling or heating, respectively, prior to and during seal operation. Fluids that contain dissolved and undissolved solids, or that are readily decomposed or oxidized, may also require temperature controls.

Fluid contaminants are common causes of early seal failures, especially in start-up of a new plant or system where the fluid is contaminated with construction material such as sand, welding slag or corrosion products. Equipment that has been idle long enough for corrosion products or sediments to build up in the system may also sustain seal damage because of these contaminants.

Poor equipment condition that permits axial and radial shaft movement in excess of the seal-design capability will precipitate either abnormal seal performance or seal failure.

Common Failure Modes

Seal failures can be classified as occurring by three basic modes: (a) chemical attack, (b) mechanical damage, and (c) thermal damage. The following itemization is a detailed breakdown of these failure modes:

Chemical Attack

Seal Faces:
Softening or disintegration of carbon-graphite seal faces
Over-all corrosion of metal faces
Leaching of binders in tungsten carbide and alumina and of the impregnants in carbon-graphite

Secondary Seals:
Over-all corrosion of metal bellows
Stress-corrosion cracking of metal bellows
Excessive volume change of elastomeric bellows, O-rings and other secondary seals
Chemical degradation of elastomeric bellows, O-rings and other secondary seals
Fretting corrosion and/or oxygen-concentration-cell corrosion of hardware and/or interfaces between machine components and secondary seals

Hardware:
Over-all corrosion of springs
Over-all corrosion of drive mechanisms — that is, pins, set screws, drive dents, and drive slots

Table 2. Modes, Causes and Corrections of Mechanical-Face-Seal Failures

Failure mode	Cause	Correction
Primary-Seal Faces		
Over-all corrosion	Improper materials	Upgrade materials.
Intergranular corrosion	Improper materials	Upgrade materials.
	Improper processing	Correct processing, such as welding and heat treating.
Stress-corrosion cracking	Improper material	Upgrade material.
	Improper processing	Correct processing, such as stress relief.
Leaching corrosion	Improper material	Upgrade material.
Seal-face distortion (concavity, convexity, waviness or nonuniform contact)	Excessive fluid pressure on seal	Lower fluid pressure, upgrade material, upgrade design.
	Excessive swell of confined secondary seal	Change secondary-seal materials or design.
	Improper seal assembly, excessive or nonuniform clamping or bolting stresses, or weight or misalignment of suction piping on end-suction overhung-type pumps	Correct assembly.
	Internal stress	Stress relieve and refinish.
	Improper finishing	Refinish.
	Foreign material trapped between faces	Remove foreign material.
	Excessive PV value of seal operation	Reduce PV value, or upgrade design or materials.
	Improper equipment operation resulting in adverse seal environment (for example, insufficient seal lubrication)	Correct environment, such as cooling or fluid flow rate. Upgrade materials or design.
Fracture	Improper handling	Handle parts with care.
	Improper assembly (jamming)	Correct assembly.
	Stress-corrosion cracking	See above, at *Stress-Corrosion Cracking.*
	Excessive thermal stress by: Improper operation such as insufficient seal lubrication	Improve equipment operation or environment. Upgrade design or materials.
	Excessive PV value	Reduce PV value.
	Excessive fluid pressure on seal	Reduce fluid pressure or upgrade design or materials.
	Excessive swell of secondary seal	Upgrade materials, change fluid or lower temperature.
Edge chipping	Excessive fluid pressure on seal	Reduce fluid pressure, upgrade design or materials.
	Excessive shaft runout	Reduce runout or upgrade seal design.
	Excessive shaft deflection	Reduce deflection or upgrade seal design.
	Excessive shaft whip	Reduce shaft whip or upgrade seal design.
	Seal faces out-of-square	Square faces to shaft axis.
	Seal-face vibration	Reduce fluid temperature to 28 C below boiling point.
Severe, uniform adhesive wear	PV value too high	Reduce PV value, upgrade materials, improve seal balance or lubrication.
	Deposition of dissolved solids	Reduce fluid temperature to 28 C below boiling point. Reduce dissolved solids. Upgrade face materials.
	Incorrect assembly (jamming)	Correct assembly.
	Fine abrasives in sealed fluid	Remove abrasives from fluid; upgrade materials.
	Failure of axial holding hardware (jamming)	Correct for axial slippage of set screws or collar.
	Excessive shaft end play	Correct end play.
	Poor environment, such as insufficient seal lubrication or loss of cooling	Correct equipment operation, upgrade face materials or design.
Heavy, nonuniform wear, galling and grooving	Abrasive contaminants	Remove contaminants or upgrade materials.
	PV value too high with one or both faces of metal	Reduce PV value; upgrade materials or design.
Erosion	Abrasive flow into seal face	Remove abrasive from sealed fluid. Shroud seal faces or direct flow away from seal.

Table 2 (Contd). Modes, Causes and Corrections of Mechanical-Face-Seal Failures

Failure mode	Cause	Correction
Primary-Seal Faces (Contd)		
Blistering of carbon-graphite faces	Improper materials	Upgrade seal-face material.
	PV value excessive or cyclic	Reduce PV value and cycling.
	Inadequate seal cooling	Improve seal cooling.
Secondary Seals		
Extrusion	Excessive pressure	Reduce pressure or upgrade design or material.
	Excessive temperature	Reduce temperature or upgrade design or material.
	Excessive swell	Upgrade materials or change seal fluid.
Chemical attack	Improper material	Select proper material.
Cracking	Excessive temperature	Reduce temperature (by cooling), upgrade materials, reduce PV value.
	Chemical attack	Select proper material.
	Ozone attack	Upgrade materials, reduce ozone concentration, reduce stress.
Cuts, tears and splits	Improper handling	Correct handling.
	Poor dispersion	Correct manufacturing.
	Poor knit	Correct manufacturing.
	Inclusion	Correct manufacturing.
	Material overstressed	Lower stress or upgrade materials.
Corrosion of interface	Crevice corrosion	Eliminate crevice; apply corrosion-resistant coating.
	Fretting corrosion	Eliminate vibration caused by out-of-square faces, or excessive deflection, endplay or runout of the shaft. Apply corrosion-resistant coatings. Lubricate interface. Upgrade resistance to corrosion and wear.
Hardware, General		
Over-all corrosion	Improper material	Upgrade material.
Stress-corrosion cracking ..	Improper material	Upgrade material.
	Improper processing	Correct processing, such as stress relief.
Intergranular corrosion	Improper material	Upgrade material.
	Improper processing	Correct processing, such as heat treating and welding.
Hydrogen embrittlement ...	Improper processing	Correct processing.
Fatigue	Excessive stress or vibration	Reduce stress or vibration.
	Seal-face vibration	Reduce fluid temperature to 28 C below boiling point.
Mechanical Drive		
Torsional shear	Excessive torque due to:	
	Improper lubrication	Correct for stoppage of lubricant flow to seal faces. Clean out or install (if needed) bypass flushing line.
	Failure of axial holding device	Check set screws or other means of securing collar for slippage or jamming.
	Excessive fluid pressure	Reduce fluid pressure or redesign (for example, seal balance).
Axial shear	Excessive shaft end play	Correct end play.
	Improper assembly (jammed)	Correct assembly.
	Excessive pressure loading	Reduce pressure or upgrade design.
Wear	Excessive torque	See *Torsional shear*.
	Out-of-square seal faces	Square faces to shaft axis.
	Excessive shaft runout	Reduce runout.
	Excessive shaft deflection	Reduce deflection.
	Excessive shaft end play	Reduce end play.
	Seal-face vibration	Reduce fluid temperature to 28 C below boiling point.
Seal hang-up	Deposition of dissolved solids, or products of corrosion, seal-fluid oxidation or decomposition	Change to nonpusher seal. Upgrade corrosion resistance of material; lower temperature of fluid; quench seal.

Hardware (continued): Intergranular corrosion of drive mechanisms

Stress-corrosion cracking of springs and drive mechanisms

Mechanical Damage

Seal Faces:

Excessive seal-face wear (adhesive and/or abrasive)
Distortion of primary-seal faces
Scratches on primary-seal faces
Fractures of seal faces
Erosion damage
Damage due to misalignment of seals

Secondary Seals:

Cut, torn or nicked elastomeric bellows, O-rings and other secondary seals
Extruded bellows, O-rings, wedges or other secondary seals
Scratched, nicked or chipped plastic secondary seals, hardware and equipment interface surfaces

Hardware:

Seal hang-up (locking, from deposits of corrosion products, dissolved or undissolved solids, or fluid oxidation or decomposition products)
Excessive wear or shear of drive members
Spring failure
Erosion damage
Incorrect diametral clearances

Thermal Damage

Seal Faces:

Blistered carbon-graphite seal faces
Thermal distortion of seal faces
Cracked seal faces of materials such as ceramics or carbides
Heat-checked seal faces

Secondary Seals:

Extrusion of TFE secondary-seal members
Overaged and cracked elastomeric bellows, O-rings and gaskets
Compression set of elastomeric secondary seals.

Table 2 summarizes failure modes, causes, and methods of correction for primary-seal faces, secondary seals, hardware, and mechanical-drive components.

Corrosion of Seal Components

Many corrosion-failure mechanisms, such as over-all corrosion, stress-corrosion cracking and intergranular corrosion, occur in the same fashion in mechanical face seals as they do in other devices and can be analyzed accordingly. This section discusses corrosion-failure mechanisms as they characteristically occur in mechanical face seals. Again, improper material selection is the most common cause of chemical attack or corrosion failure of mechanical seals.

Primary-seal faces are particularly vulnerable to corrosion damage, because they are subject to sliding-contact wear. Primary-seal faces, therefore, must for all practical purposes be chemically inert to their environment. A corrosion rate of 1 mil per year, although acceptable for most hardware items, would be disastrous for seal faces in most applications. Even if corrosion is sufficiently uniform to maintain seal-face flatness, seal-face wear

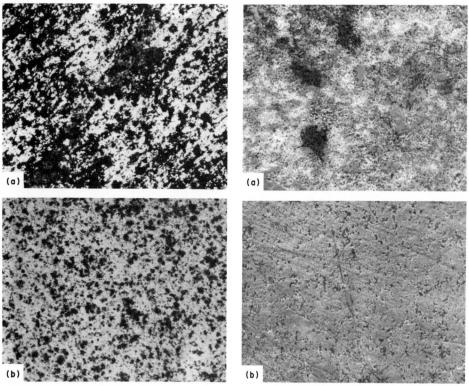

Fig. 3. Micrographs, at 50×, comparing (a) leached and (b) unleached 85% Al₂O₃ ceramic seal faces

Fig. 4. Micrographs, at 550×, comparing (a) leached and (b) unleached 6 to 8% Co cemented tungsten carbide seal faces

Acidic fluids may leach nickel or cobalt binders incorporated in cemented tungsten carbide and produce seal failure by the mechanism described above for alumina ceramics. Figures 3 and 4 compare leached and unleached seal faces of 85% Al₂O₃ ceramic (Fig. 3) and 6 to 8% Co cemented tungsten carbide (Fig. 4). Leaching corrosion will effect a hardness loss of approximately 5 Rockwell A points for both 85% Al₂O₃ ceramics and cemented tungsten carbide.

Corrosion failures of carbon-graphite seal faces generally occur through an over-all corrosion mechanism. Carbon-graphite seal faces are reduced to sludge in severe cases — for example, when contacted by highly oxidizing acids or highly concentrated caustic fluids. At left in Fig. 5 is a carbon-graphite primary-seal ring that failed after six months in concentrated hydrofluoric acid at 50 C (120 F); at right, a new seal ring is shown for comparison. A hardness reduction of 20 Shore scleroscope points is typical for carbon-graphite materials that have undergone chemical attack.

Carbon-graphite seal faces are impregnated to render the otherwise porous material impervious to the fluids being contained. Selective leaching of the impregnant will produce seal failure either by increasing wear rate or by rendering the seal face porous. Leaching of the impregnant will generally reduce the hardness of the carbon-graphite seal face by 5 Shore scleroscope points. It follows then that hardness measurements can be used to assist detection of both over-all corrosion and leaching corrosion of carbon-graphite materials. Pressure testing for porosity can also be used to assist analysis of gross leaching of impregnant.

Secondary Seals. Excessive volume change (either swell or shrinkage) of elastomeric secondary seals will cause seal failures through one or more of the following modes: (a) extrusion caused by swell, (b) loss of secondary-seal interference caused by shrinkage, (c) loss of secondary-seal drive caused by shrinkage on seals that depend on secondary-seal drive, and (d) primary-seal-face distortion and misalignment caused by swell, as illustrated in Fig. 6.

The most direct method of determining failures due to excessive volume change is by measuring the secondary seals and comparing the measured dimensions to those specified on assembly drawings or to dimensions of mating components. Secondary-seal dimensions should be measured in both the free and assembled conditions. Shrinkage should not be confused with compression set. The latter does not involve significant volume change. Complete cross-sectional examination on an optical comparator is a good technique for distinguishing between shrinkage and compression set.

Fig. 5. At left is a carbon-graphite primary-seal ring with face damaged by corrosion; an undamaged ring is shown at right for comparison.

rates will increase to the point of reducing seal wear life. This is particularly true where corrosion products act as fixed or free abrasive contaminants to one or both of the seal faces. Corrosion products may also cause seal hang-up, as discussed under "Seal hang-up" in the section on Mechanical Damage (page 446). Many highly corrosive fluids, such as concentrated nitric acid or oleum, present a trade-off between corrosion and wear resistance in the selection of material for primary-seal faces. This trade-off often results in a maximum seal life of only a few months.

Leaching corrosion of binders incorporated in alumina and tungsten carbide seal faces is a common mechanism of corrosion failure. Except for very-high-alumina ceramic (94% alumina or greater), alumina particles are bonded to one another by a predominantly silica glass binder. Sealed fluids having pH values greater than 10 or contaminated with hydrofluoric acid will leach out the glass binder and, in effect, convert the alumina seal face into a grinding surface. The net result is excessive wear of the mating material. As leaching continues, alumina particles will eventually be dislodged from the parent body and cause abrasive damage to one or both seal faces. The voids resulting from loss of alumina particles, alone or in combination with abrasive damage, will degrade face flatness to the point of causing seal failure.

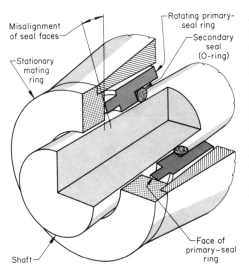

Fig. 6. Distortion of rotating primary-seal ring, and misalignment of seal faces, caused by swell of secondary seal

Extrusion failures are also best observed on an optical comparator. Most failures due to excessive volume change can be prevented by changing to a more fluid-resistant material or by increasing the clearance between mating components. An alternative solution would be to use a seal fluid that produces an acceptable volume change. Primary-seal-face distortion caused by excessive swell of secondary seals is discussed in detail under "Distortion", on the next two pages.

Fretting corrosion and oxygen-concentration-cell corrosion of secondary-seal interface surfaces produce very subtle leakage paths. Fretting-corrosion failures are governed to a large extent by mechanical considerations such as proper material selection, seal-assembly procedures and equipment conditions. Common mechanical contributions to fretting-corrosion failures of secondary seals include (*a*) excessive shaft end play (over 0.004 in.), (*b*) excessive shaft deflection (over 0.003 in.), and (*c*) excessive out-of-squareness of seal face to shaft axis (over 0.003 in. TIR).

The tolerances given in parentheses above are for the most sensitive conditions of pusher-seal design and corrosive environment. (Pusher-type seals are those in which the secondary seal is pushed along the shaft or sleeve to compensate for wear.) Under severe conditions, corrosion-resistant coatings are applied to the interface to prevent fretting corrosion. Nonpusher seals for the most part are not subject to fretting corrosion and are often used as a corrective measure. A pump-shaft sleeve that underwent secondary-seal failure by fretting corrosion at the interface between primary and secondary seals is shown in Fig. 7; fretting occurred at point A.

The auger-shaft seal assembly of an ice dispenser for a beverage-vending machine (see Fig. 8a) sustained an oxygen-concentration-cell (crevice) corrosion failure of the type 303 stainless steel auger shaft where it contacted the elastomeric-bellows secondary seal. Figure 8(b) is a photograph of the corroded shaft. The corrosion allowed leakage of ice water through the secondary seal at the shaft after one year of an expected five-year service life. A polished area (at arrow in Fig. 8b) adjacent to the corroded section was generated by hydrogen emanating from beneath the bellows. A polished or gas-scrubbed surface portion is a good indication for distinguishing between crevice and fretting corrosion of secondary-seal interfaces. The auger shaft in this instance was machined from bar stock having a hardness specification of Rockwell B 70 min, with no passivation surface treatment specified. Failure by this mode necessitated replacement of not only the seal but of the auger shaft as well. Corrective action comprised chromium plating the auger shaft and modifying the bellows to reduce the crevice at point A in Fig. 8(a).

Mechanical Damage

Mechanical damage of primary-seal faces may be from wear or erosion, fracture, distortion or chipping. Damage to

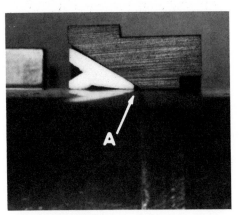

Fig. 7. Fretting corrosion on a pump-shaft sleeve at point of contact with the TFE wedge-type secondary seal

secondary seals may be from poor handling and installation, and from nicks, scratches and cuts. Seal hardware may be subjected to the same types of damage that affect primary-seal faces. Primary-seal faces also may be prevented from engaging properly because of seal hang-up, which results when deposits restrict axial seal-ring movement along a shaft.

Wear of primary-seal faces can be adhesive or abrasive. Adhesive wear is caused primarily by excessive *PV* values or by poor lubrication. Excessive adhesive wear will leave seal faces heavily worn but in relatively good condition with respect to flatness (that is, the faces will have a smooth appearance with a minimum of grooving), except for face combinations with one or both faces made of metal, such as carbon-graphite against cast iron or bronze against cast iron. Advanced or extreme adhesive wear of such combinations will lead to galling, grooving, or ultimate face seizure. Adhesive-wear failures of carbon-graphite – 85% Al_2O_3 ceramic, carbon-graphite – cast iron, and bronze – tool steel seal-face combinations are illustrated in Fig. 9.

Failures due to excessive adhesive wear can be prevented by upgrading seal-face combinations, changing seal balance, or improving seal-fluid lubricating properties through temperature change — or by combinations of these measures. Excessive wear is often caused by improper seal assembly, poor equipment condition or poor operational practices.

Excessive-abrasive-wear failures leave seal faces scuffed or severely grooved. However, abrasive wear caused by very fine abrasive particles such as dissolved solids that precipitate at the seal faces may take on the same appearance as adhesive wear. The distinguishing difference is that in abrasive wear dissolved solids or fine abrasive particles are deposited on the primary-seal faces or surfaces adjacent to them.

Abrasive wear should be distinguished from erosion damage. The latter results in a sculptured appearance with islands

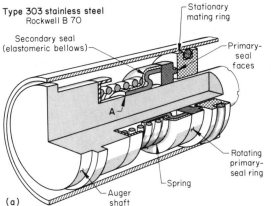

Fig. 8. Type 303 stainless steel auger shaft of a beverage-vending-machine ice dispenser, which failed by crevice corrosion at point A

Carbon-graphite primary-seal ring (top); 85% Al₂O₃ ceramic mating ring (bottom)

Carbon-graphite primary-seal ring (top); cast iron mating ring (bottom)

Bronze primary-seal ring (top); 52100 steel mating ring (bottom)

Fig. 9. Three combinations of primary-seal rings and mating rings that failed by adhesive wear. Arrows point to seal faces.

of original mating surface still exposed. A carbon-graphite seal face that failed by abrasive wear is shown in Fig. 10. Distinction between abrasion and erosion failure is important with respect to preventive courses of action. Abrasion and erosion damage are both caused by abrasive contaminants and can be prevented by elimination of the contaminants or upgrading of seal-face materials. Erosion damage can also be prevented by shrouding the seal faces or by altering the flow of fluid around the seal. Figure 11 compares new and eroded carbon-graphite primary-seal rings, and shows the eroded face on a mating ring of Al₂O₃ ceramic.

Fracture of mechanical seal faces is caused by one or more of the following:

1 Mishandling before or during assembly
2 Improper seal assembly and installation
3 Excessive face torque
4 Excessive hydraulic pressure
5 Excessive swell of confined secondary seals
6 Careless seal removal and disassembly
7 Excessive thermal stresses resulting from thermal shock or gradients.

Many seal-face materials, such as carbon-graphite, ceramics and cemented carbides, are fragile and must be handled with extreme care to avoid scratches, nicks, chips and fractures. Misindexed drive engagement may cause fracture of fragile seal-face materials. Such fractures are generally accompanied by indentations, chips, or nicks created by the configuration of the mating drive element. Jamming of a seal commonly causes fracture of seal faces or hardware members. Fractures caused by excessive torque will

extend through one or more points of drive engagement — that is, slots, dents, grooves or holes — and generally are accompanied by wear or shear at the points of drive engagement. A proper corrective course of action would consist of locating and eliminating the source of excessive torque. Causes of excessive torque include: (a) improper assembly (jamming, causing heavy face loads), (b) failure of axial holding devices such as set screws and thrust bearings, (c) excessive fluid pressure, (d) corrosion at the seal faces, and (e) poor lubrication.

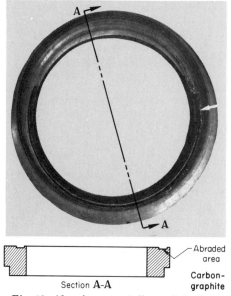

Fig. 10. Abrasive-wear failure of the face of a carbon-graphite primary-seal ring. The arrow indicates a chipped region.

Fractures caused by excessive hydraulic pressure and by swelling of secondary seals of inside-mounted seal assemblies will be similar to jamming-type failures. Most common seal-face materials are considerably weaker in tensile and shear strength than in compression strength. Consequently, failure occurs predominantly by tension or shear unless the particular seal design and application place the material in high compressive loading.

Careless seal removal and disassembly will result in seal-component fractures of the same type as those produced by mishandling and improper installation. These fractures, although generally identifiable, are an unnecessary burden in failure analysis. Care should be taken in handling failed components if they are to be analyzed. Fractures caused by excessive thermally induced stresses are discussed under "Thermal Damage" (see page 446 in this article).

Distortion of seal faces is evidenced by nonuniform contact patterns observed directly on the seal faces. Such patterns can be highlighted by lightly polishing the seal face on a flat polishing plate. Distortion will produce concavity, convexity, waviness, or combinations of waviness with concavity or convexity. The following are the most common causes of seal-face distortion:

1 Improper assembly causing nonuniform or excessive bolting or clamping stresses
2 Improper cooling, which induces nonuniform thermal stresses
3 Fluid pressures above design limits

Fig. 11. Comparison of (a) a new carbon-graphite primary-seal ring with (b) a severely eroded (in area between arrows) seal ring, and (c) the eroded face on the mating ring made of 85% Al₂O₃ ceramic

4 Excessive swell of confined secondary seals
5 Improper processing or finishing, leaving seal faces in a nonflat or nonstable condition
6 Improper seal-face-support surface
7 Entrapment of foreign material between seal faces.

Distortion caused by nonuniform bolting or clamping will leave an intermittent wear pattern (one or more low spots) on the seal faces. Excessive clamping, hydraulic pressure or swell of confined secondary seals will generally cause the seal face to distort in a concave or convex manner. Distortion caused by swell of secondary seals is illustrated in Fig. 6. Predominant OD or ID contact will be obvious on the seal face, provided the seal has operated for a sufficient period of time. The combination of distortion and wear caused by hydraulic pressure on balanced seals operating under relatively high and cyclic pressure conditions is commonly referred to as the wedge-effect failure mechanism. Distortion analysis of the seal face shown in Fig. 12(d) would indicate contact at the ID because of wear on the OD incurred in conditions shown in Fig. 12(b) and (c). Wear of the outer edge is often accompanied by chipping of seal-face edges on seal rings made of brittle materials, and

by mushrooming of edges on seal rings made of ductile materials.

Convex or concave distortions will be accompanied by some degree of waviness. In fact, most seal faces will have a small wavy pattern, generally less than 22 micro-in. TIR. Waviness will become excessive under adverse thermal conditions, excessive PV value (product of face pressure, P, and sliding speed, V), or poor lubrication. Seal-face waviness in excess of 100 micro-in. generally produces excessive seal leakage. Nonflat or nonstable seal-face-support surfaces will induce distortion of primary-seal faces, particularly when seal pressure exceeds 600 psi.

Scratches and chips that result in excessive seal leakage are most frequently caused by poor handling of seal components during manufacture, assembly or installation. Cleanness is critical, in that a very small dirt particle trapped between the seal faces may cause immediate seal leakage through excessive seal-face separation or early damage to the face in the form of chips or scratches. Scratches and nicks will not necessarily produce excessive seal leakage, and often are erroneously cited as a cause of seal failure. Generally speaking, scratches less than 50 micro-in. deep by 0.001 in. wide will not cause excessive leakage,

unless they are radial. Seals leak when scratches are in the radial direction, regardless of scratch depth or width. Poor equipment or operating practices also can result in severe chipping of seal-face edges that is similar in appearance to chipping caused by excessive hydraulic distortion. Edge chipping can be developed by excessive shaft deflection, runout or whip, or by out-of-square seal faces. These conditions will also lead to excessive wear of the drive mechanism. Operation of balanced seals at temperatures in excess of 28 C (50 F) below the boiling point of the sealed fluid will cause face popping (boiling of fluid film between seal faces) and excessive chipping, and in extreme cases, chipping because of face nutation of nonpusher-type seals.

Secondary Seal Failures. Plastic seals possess less elastic self-healing properties than elastomeric secondary seals, and thus are more vulnerable to nicks, scratches and cuts. Poor handling and installation practices and presence of dirt are the most common causes of surface damage to secondary seals. Care should be taken to remove all sharp burrs and edges of steps, keyways and previous set-screw indentations prior to seal installation. Assembly tools and fixtures often are used to facilitate seal installations over sharp shoulders and into counterbores. Nicking, cutting or tearing of elastomeric secondary seals may also be caused by manufacturing defects such as

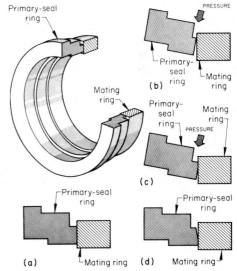

(a) Little or no pressure, no mechanical distortion; faces of primary-seal ring and mating ring are approximately parallel. (b) External pressure; primary-seal ring deflects, with face diverging from face of mating ring. (c) After wear-in with external pressure, nose is worn at outer edge, making faces of primary-seal ring and mating ring parallel. (d) Pressure back to normal; gap admitting fluid is present in outer edge of primary-seal ring, and faces converge.

Fig. 12. Distortion and wear of face of primary-seal ring caused by high and cyclic pressure conditions

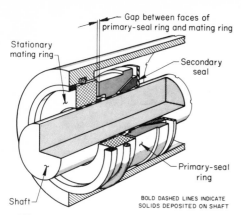

Fig. 13. *Hang-up of secondary-seal element of a pusher-type seal resulting from deposits on shaft*

poor knit, inclusions, poor dispersions or incorrect curing of the seals.

Extrusion failures of secondary seals are caused predominantly by excessive pressure and can be prevented by reducing the pressure or by upgrading the design or materials. Temperature may also contribute to extrusion of thermoplastic materials; for example, materials such as TFE and Viton are more susceptible to extrusion at elevated temperatures. A reduction in temperature may prevent extrusion failures of secondary seals made of these or similar materials.

Excessive swell of confined secondary seals will also induce extrusion failure. Changing to a material more compatible with the sealed fluid is the most direct action to be taken. A change of seal fluid is sometimes mandatory where alternative materials or designs are not applicable.

Excessive drive torque on secondary seals that provide a drive function will cause relative rotational movement and resulting wear or ultimate failure of the

seal from the frictional heat developed during sliding contact. Elimination of excessive torque is the most direct course of action. Upgrading of design or incorporating mechanical drive are alternative courses of action.

Hardware Failures. Wear or fracture of the torsional-drive components is the most common mechanical-damage failure mode of seal hardware. Many of the causes of these failures are common to other failure modes such as edge chipping or torsional-stress fracture of the primary-seal faces and can be corrected accordingly. For review purposes, these causes are: jammed seal assembly, excessive shaft end play, failure of axial holding device, poor seal-face lubrication, excessive seal-fluid pressure, seal face out-of-square with shaft axis, excessive shaft runout, excessive shaft deflection, and seal-face vibration resulting from stick-slip face friction and from equipment vibration.

Seal-face vibration will also produce fatigue failures of metal-bellows secondary seals. Again, keeping the temperature of the sealed fluid 28 C (50 F) below the boiling point will prevent this type of failure.

Seal hang-up caused by buildup of deposited dissolved solids, corrosion, oxidation or decomposition products is illustrated in Fig. 13. Such deposits prevent the secondary-seal element from engaging the primary-seal ring, so that the gap between the primary-seal faces is not closed. The most expedient means of preventing seal hang-up is to employ a nonpusher-type seal. An alternative to this would be to provide a suitable quench. (*Quench*: a neutral fluid that is introduced into a seal chamber or cavity for the purpose of diluting fluid that may have leaked through a seal.) For ex-

ample, a water quench will prevent the deposition of aqueous dissolved solids. A nitrogen quench will prevent the formation of oxidation products. An oil quench or other suitable quench media will prevent the formation of corrosion products. Finally, a suitable coolant quench will prevent thermal decomposition products from forming. Even if the generation of solids is not completely eliminated by the quench, any solids that are produced will for the most part be flushed away, thus preventing their buildup and subsequent seal hang-up.

Thermal Damage

Primary-seal faces operating at relatively high PV values are subject to high thermally induced stresses resulting from the frictional heat developed at their sliding interface. If PV values and corresponding thermal stresses become excessive, fractures will occur. The fracture will be complete or in the form of surface cracks commonly referred to as heat checks. Improper equipment operation that results in thermal shock of the seal, such as inadequate lubrication, insufficient lubrication during equipment startup, or rapid quenching of an operating seal, will also produce thermal-stress failures even though operational PV values are relatively low. Many outside-mounted seals have failed because pumps were washed down with a water hose during operation. Heat-checked 6% Co cemented tungsten carbide and thermal-stress-cracked 85% Al_2O_3 ceramic seal faces are shown in Fig. 14. Complete thermal fractures are often multiple or are accompanied by several surface heat checks. Liquid-penetrant-inspection techniques are effective in detecting thermal-stress cracks.

Although heat checking does not produce catastrophic failures such as complete fractures, the fine surface cracks act as cutting tools against the mating seal-face material, thus severely reducing seal wear life. Corrective measures for thermal-stress fractures include (a) upgrading the thermal-stress resistance of the material, (b) reducing the PV value where excessive, (c) improving seal lubrication or seal cooling (or both), and (d) correcting equipment-operation practices where applicable.

Carbon-graphite primary-seal-face materials are extremely resistant to thermal stress and as such are not readily subject to thermal-stress fracture; however, they are susceptible to blistering failure in contact with oil and under conditions of fluctuating PV values or temperature. Blistering failures of carbon-graphite seal faces are encountered in hydraulic pumps, motors, gear reducers, mixer heads, and air-conditioning and refrigeration compressors. Blistering occurs in

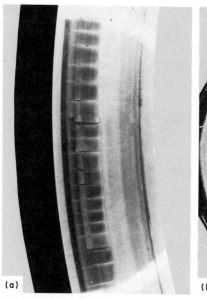

(a)   (b)

Fig. 14. (a) *Heat-checked seal face made of 6% Co cemented tungsten carbide;* (b) *thermal-stress-cracked seal face made of 85% Al_2O_3 ceramic*

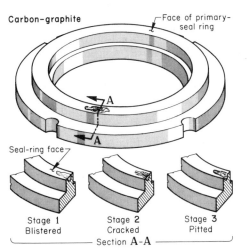

Fig. 15. Three stages of blistering in faces of primary-seal rings made of carbon-graphite material

three stages, as shown in Fig. 15. The first stage produces a round or oval raised area on the carbon-graphite seal-face surface. The small raised surface is generally more polished than the surrounding area because of its more intimate contact with the mating seal surface. As blistering progresses to the second stage, cracks appear in the raised area, generally in a "starburst" pattern. Finally, in the third stage, the cracks progress to the point where particles within the blisters are pulled out, leaving small to massive pits or craters in the seal face.

The first and second stages of blistering will cause excessive seal leakage because of the greater seal-face separation caused by the blisters. If enough pits are produced, the final stage will produce catastrophic failures as typified by that of the carbon-graphite primary-seal ring shown in Fig. 16.

The blister resistance of carbon-graphite varies from grade to grade. Mating materials will also affect the blister resistance of carbon-graphite. For example, a given grade of carbon-graphite will have less blister resistance when mated with tool steel than with an alumina ceramic. Lower and less-cyclic PV values and resulting thermal-energy levels will also reduce or prevent blistering. A final corrective course of action is to improve seal cooling.

Many resin-bonded seal-face materials are subject to extreme thermal-mechanical distortions when PV-related thermal energy becomes excessive, or under improper seal-environment conditions such as insufficient lubrication or cooling. The thermal-mechanical distortion is attested to by extreme seal-face waviness (greater than 200 micro-in.). This waviness generally is in the form of a two-node or saddle-shaped configuration, the nodes being disposed from one another by 180°, as shown in Fig. 17(a).

In extreme cases, multiple-node waviness (see Fig. 17b) may occur. Corrective courses of action for excessive waviness are upgrading of seal-face materials in thermal-mechanical stability, reducing the operational PV value, or improving seal lubrication and cooling. Where recording, stylus-type analytical equipment is not available, lightly polishing the seal face on a flat polishing plate will aid in detecting excessive seal-face waviness.

Thermal damage to secondary seals can be caused by heat from three separate sources acting independently or in combination: (a) frictional heat developed at the primary-seal face, (b) heat soak from the seal environment including the shaft and housing, and (c) relative rotational movement between the secondary seal and the shaft or housing. As discussed in the section "Detailed Failure Analysis" (on next page), thermal damage to elastomeric secondary seals should be distinguished from chemical attack. The source of thermal degradation should also be identified, inasmuch as it may lead to the major cause of seal failure. This is particularly true if the source of heat was relative movement between the secondary seal and the shaft or housing, or excessive friction that developed at the primary-seal face. For example, frictional heat from an excessive PV-value condition may have caused secondary-seal failure prior to ultimate failure of the primary-seal faces. Upgrading the temperature resistance of the secondary seal may prevent the failure of the secondary seal but would not prevent the ultimate failure of the seal face operating at an excessive PV value.

Preliminary Examination

The general procedures for analyzing failures of mechanical face seals are similar to those for analyzing failures of other components. Some special conditions that require investigation are outlined here. Detailed descriptions of failure mechanisms, together with techniques for performing failure analyses,

Fig. 16. Carbon-graphite primary-seal ring that failed because of blistering

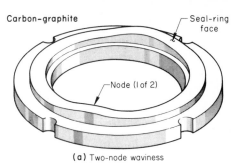

(a) Two-node waviness

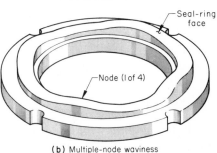

(b) Multiple-node waviness

Fig. 17. Two-node and multiple-node waviness in faces of carbon-graphite primary-seal rings, caused by thermal-mechanical distortions

are presented in the article that begins on page 10 in this volume.

Background Information. Before equipment is dismantled for removal of a failed seal, background information should be compiled for analysis. The following is a list of information needed for good analysis of a seal failure.

1 Service life of the seal — that is, hours of operation and description of duty cycle
2 Fluid sealed (including contaminants)
3 Operating shaft speed
4 Fluid pressure on seal and in system
5 Fluid temperature on seal and in system
6 Fluid flow rate within the seal chamber or stuffing box
7 Condition of equipment with respect to axial and radial shaft vibration
8 Amount and nature of abnormal leakage — that is, is leakage constant or variable and, if variable, is it related to changes in speed, pressure or temperature of operation
9 Possible sources of abnormal leakage. (An assembly drawing of the seal is of great assistance here.) Most mechanical seals have at least three possible sources of abnormal leakage: the primary seal and two secondary seals. Exposed equipment surfaces should be inspected for indications of the source or sources of abnormal leakage. This inspection should be conducted throughout subsequent equipment and seal disassembly. If possible, isolate sources of abnormal leakage while equipment is still operating or through a bench hydrostatic test of the equipment. Extreme care and safety precautions should be taken on all leakage-check operations.
10 Once equipment has been put into a safe condition, make the necessary

marks and measurements to determine the following: (a) seal working height; (b) squareness of seal faces to shaft axis; (c) concentricity of seal faces to shaft axis; (d) shaft end play; and (e) shaft radial runout, whip and deflection.

Equipment Disassembly. During equipment disassembly, care should be taken that no seal surfaces are disturbed. They should not be wiped or cleaned more than is necessary for safely dismantling the equipment. Examination for foreign contaminants, wear debris, small fragments or chips from broken components, and corrosion products should be made before seal components are cleaned for detailed examination. Again, exposed surfaces should be inspected for indications of sources of abnormal leakage. Next, the seal should be checked for hang-up by flexing the seal slightly above and below its installed working height. Once this analysis has been completed, the seal subassembly can be cleaned. Care should be taken not to use wire brushes, sharp tools, or abrasive cleansers that may damage the seal surface or otherwise obscure actual failure mechanisms. Cleaning agents that adversely affect seal materials should be avoided. For example, methyl ethyl ketone will cause excessive swelling of most elastomeric secondary seals. Packaging of failed seal components for shipment to a laboratory or repair center should be done with extreme care. Use of wire-mounted identification tags or bulk-packaging techniques should be avoided.

Pressure testing of seal subassemblies for leakage-source determination prior to disassembly is a valuable step, particularly when a large number of the same type of seals are being examined and when the cost of the test fixture required for the subassembly pressure test can be offset by savings in analysis time.

Detailed Failure Analysis

Unless background information, equipment disassembly, or seal-subassembly pressure testing reveals the source or sources of failure, a detailed analysis should be conducted in accordance with the following procedures for analyzing premature and extended-service failures. Seal-assembly drawings showing the seal materials, design and replacement parts are of great assistance in analysis of damage to mechanical face seals caused by wear and chemical attack.

Premature failures of mechanical face seals should be analyzed according to the following procedure:

1 Examine for defective, misassembled or omitted secondary seals.
2 Examine for misassembled or misindexed drive and face-loading hardware.

3 Examine for loss of drive on seals that rely on secondary-seal interference for drive, such as bellows and static seals.
4 Clean primary-seal faces and examine them for the following:

Nicks and Scratches. Microscopic examination of scratches relative to the face contact pattern will often help determine whether the scratch was generated prior to, during or after seal operation. For example, if the wear pattern is altered by the scratch, the scratch occurred before or during seal operation. If the same scratch extends outside the mating area, it more than likely occurred prior to seal operation. If it does not extend outside the mating area and is spiral in form relative to the shaft axis and in the direction of rotation, it probably occurred during operation and can be attributed to a particle entering or coming from the primary interface. Scratches that interrupt but do not alter the wear pattern were probably produced after seal operation.

Fractures. Microscopic examination of the fracture surface for presence of wear debris is one technique for distinguishing between fractures that occurred prior to or during service and those that occurred during seal removal. If no wear debris is present, fracture occurred during disassembly. Nonuniform discoloration or partial discoloration of the fracture surface indicates partial fracture prior to or during seal operation. Fractures caused by excessive face torque will extend through one or more points of drive engagement.

Nonuniform Contact Pattern. Dirt trapped between the faces, distortion of one or both faces, or improperly finished faces may result in a nonuniform contact pattern. Optical flats and monochromatic lights are of great assistance in detecting seal-face distortion. Stylus-type surface-profiling equipment is also of extreme benefit, particularly when distortion exceeds 44 micro-in. or for analysis of nonreflective faces. Light polishing of seal faces on a flat polishing plate will help detect permanently distorted faces or those that have worn in a distorted position.

Excessive pitting, grooving, spalling, galling, blistering or other thermal damage such as heat checks. (See also the following discussion of extended-life failure.)

5 Clean and examine secondary-seal surfaces for: (a) nicks, scratches, cuts and tears; (b) twisted, extruded or otherwise distorted static seals; (c) score marks that may have been created by relative rotational movement between secondary seals and mating surfaces; (d) excessive volume change or compression set of elastomeric secondary seals; and (e) fretting of sealing surface at secondary seals from mechanical and chemical action at the interface.

Extended-Life Failures. Examination of mechanical seals that failed after a satisfactory life can produce valuable information. The primary-seal faces should be cleaned and the wear surfaces examined for over-all corrosion, leaching, abnormal grooving, erosion damage, and excessive pitting, spalling and galling.

Wear profile should be observed first with the naked eye and then under magnification of 10 diameters. Low-incidence-angle light will highlight wear patterns and other surface irregularities caused by erosion or corrosion. Leaching corrosion can best be observed at magnifications greater than 50 diameters, or on polished cross sections. Also, the face should be examined for thermal damage such as waviness, heat checks, cracks, blisters, deposition of solid materials, and over-all thermal discoloration.

Secondary seals should be examined for extrusion, chemical attack on both seal and interface surfaces, excessive volume change, excessive compression set, and hardening and cracking.

Chemical attack or degradation of elastomeric secondary seals in the form of cracking is often difficult to distinguish from thermal damage. In fact, by strict definition, thermal damage may be considered as a form of chemical attack. Chemical attack is more likely on secondary-seal surfaces exposed to fluid; thermal degradation is more frequently observed on surfaces exposed to atmosphere. If most or all of the damage occurs on secondary-seal surfaces that contact a primary-seal-face member, excessive primary-seal-face frictional heat will more than likely have caused the thermal damage. Comparative analysis of secondary seals from all locations will reveal whether the thermal condition was local to one secondary seal or an over-all excessive-temperature condition. Over-all chemical degradation is indicated by distinct loss of material.

The drive mechanism should be examined for failure or excessive wear, and secondary-seal members employed for drive purposes should be examined for loss of drive.

Indications of Failure

Some conditions that indicate that a mechanical face seal is not functioning properly are itemized in the list that follows, together with causes of the malfunctions and corrective measures:

Seal Spits and Sputters in Operation:

1 Fluid being sealed is vaporizing and flashing across seal faces.
2 Take steps to maintain fluid in a definite liquid condition.
3 Check balance design with seal manufacturer, which requires accurate readings of stuffing-box pressure, temperature and specific gravity of fluid.

Seal Leaks and Ices Gland Ring:

1 Fluid being sealed is vaporizing and flashing across seal faces.
2 Icing may score seal faces, especially those of carbon-graphite mating rings. Seal rings should be replaced, or faces lapped, before starting up after vaporizing condition has been corrected.

Seal Drips Steadily:

1 First, determine location of leakage.
2 Check gland gasket for proper compression.
3 Faces not flat. Gland bolts possibly too tight, causing warpage of gland and mating ring.
4 Shaft packing nicked or pinched during installation.
5 Carbon-graphite mating ring cracked, or face of rings chipped during installation.
6 Seal faces scored from foreign particles between them.
7 Leakage of liquid under shaft sleeve.

Seal Squeals During Operation:

1 Inadequate amount of liquid to lubricate sealing faces (not all dry seals squeal).
2 Bypass flush line may be needed; if one is already in use, it may need to be enlarged to produce more flow.

Carbon Dust Accumulating on Outside of Gland Ring:

1 Inadequate amount of liquid to lubricate sealing faces.
2 Liquid film flashing and evaporating between seal faces, leaving residue that grinds away the carbon-graphite ring.

3 Pressure in the stuffing box is excessively high for the type of seal and the fluid being sealed.

Seal Leaks, Nothing Appears To Be Wrong:

1 Faces not flat. This out-of-flat condition will be evident by the wear pattern on seal faces.
2 Face of carbon-graphite mating ring is distorted from improper or excessive tension on gland-ring bolting. This usually can be determined by the wear pattern of the seal face.
3 Distortion of seal faces. This problem frequently is encountered on end-suction overhung-type pumps. Because of their design and size, pumps of this type will not tolerate weight or misalignment of suction piping on the overhung portion.
4 Possible shaft vibration, caused by misalignment, impeller unbalance, cavitation or bad bearings.

Short Seal Life:

1 Fluid being contained is abrasive, causing excessive seal-face wear. Determine source of abrasives. When abrasives are in suspension in the liquid, bypass flushing, preferably through the gland over the seal faces, will alleviate the

condition by keeping the abrasive particles moving and preventing them from settling out or accumulating in the seal area. When abrasives are forming as the sealed liquid is cooling down and crystallizing or partly solidifying in the seal area, bypass flushing will help introduce maximum fluid to the seal cavity at correct temperature. Additional heat to the seal area also will alleviate this condition.
2 Equipment mechanically out of line.
3 Seal shows signs of running too hot. Recirculation or bypass line may be necessary. Check for possible rubbing of some seal component along the shaft. Throttle bushing in the gland, and clearance between rotating seal member and stuffing-box bore and the bore of the mating ring, are some points to check for this condition.
4 Cool seal area more completely. Be sure that all cooling lines are connected, and that there is unobstructed flow in cooling lines (look for scale formation in cooling jackets and lines).
5 Deterioration of a seal component from corrosion or excessive heat may result from improper choice of seal-ring materials.

Failures of Fluid-Power Cylinders

By Bruce P. Bardes*

A FLUID-POWER cylinder is a device that translates the energy of pressurized fluid into linear force and motion. Although a wide variety of such cylinders have been designed to fill specific needs, each includes a tubular body closed at both ends and a piston-and-rod assembly that extends through one or both ends.

The components of typical fluid-power cylinders are identified in Fig. 1. A light-duty, single-acting (spring-return) pneumatic cylinder and a heavy-duty, double-acting pneumatic or hydraulic cylinder are shown to illustrate common design features and components. Some of the materials frequently specified for the

*Chief Metallurgist, Bimba Manufacturing Co.

major components of a fluid-power cylinder are as follows:

Body. Low-alloy steel, low-carbon steel (sometimes hard chromium plated), aluminum that has been hard anodized, brass, stainless steel.
Heads and Piston. Low-carbon steel bar stock or forging, aluminum alloy bar stock or forging, cast iron, brass bar stock.
Piston Rod. High-strength carbon steel (sometimes case hardened and hard chromium plated), stainless steel.
Piston-Rod Gland or Bearing. Bronze bar stock, porous sintered bronze, filled fluorocarbon plastic.
Seals. Elastomers or leather.
Tie Rods. Low-carbon steel rod.

Pneumatic cylinders generally operate at pressures below 250 psi. Such rela-

tively low pressures are dictated by convenience and by the catastrophic consequences of rupture of any container holding compressed gas. By comparison, many hydraulic cylinders operate at pressures of 1000 psi or higher. Hydraulic cylinders must be designed and constructed to withstand such high internal pressures and the correspondingly high forces exerted through the piston rod and the cylinder mounting. Because the operating liquid is nearly incompressible, a hydraulic cylinder must be capable of withstanding impulse loads on the piston rod and the mounting at any point in its operating cycle. Pressurized gases have much greater compressibility and much lower viscosity than liquids,

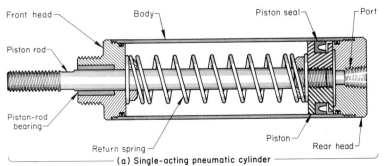

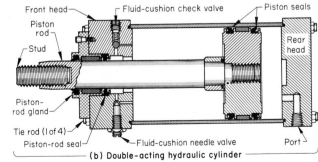

Fig. 1. Typical construction and components of fluid-power cylinders. (a) Small-bore, light-duty, single-acting pneumatic cylinder. (b) Heavy-duty, double-acting pneumatic or hydraulic cylinder.

and thus a gas can fill a cylinder far faster than a liquid can. Consequently, the piston-and-rod assembly in a pneumatic cylinder can be rapidly accelerated by the introduction of pressurized gas and by expansion of the gas already within the cylinder. A pneumatic cylinder must be designed to withstand high operating velocities and impact between the piston and one head at each end of its operating cycle.

In many pneumatic-cylinder applications, particularly for small-bore cylinders (1½ in. in diameter or less), movement and operating speed are more important than force. For hydraulic cylinders, force and position are usually the important considerations.

Devices Related to Fluid-Power Cylinders

Two devices that are related to fluid-power cylinders are shock absorbers and gas springs. The functions of these devices are different from that of a fluid-power cylinder, but construction and some failure modes are similar.

Shock Absorbers. An air-filled shock absorber contains a spring that forces a piston to the end of the cylinder. When the shock absorber is loaded, air trapped inside it is forced through a small orifice to the atmosphere. When the load is removed, air is admitted to the cylinder through a check valve. A liquid-filled shock absorber is sealed to prevent loss of the liquid and has a small orifice in the piston to permit passage of liquid from one side of the piston to the other at a controlled rate.

Gas Springs. A gas spring is a cylinder filled with gas at high pressure in which the gas is permitted to flow past the piston. The device exerts an extending force on the piston rod equal to the area of the piston rod multiplied by the internal pressure. Unlike most springs, the force exerted by a gas spring is nearly independent of position. Loss of fluid from either a liquid-filled shock absorber or a gas spring prevents proper operation.

Causes of Cylinder Failures

Like most manufactured products, fluid-power cylinders usually fail as a result of improper or abusive application, improper installation or maintenance, or defects in workmanship or material. A fluid-power cylinder produces linear force and motion. The location and direction of the force and motion are defined by the axis of the piston rod. If mounting or loading of the cylinder requires force or motion that does not coincide with the axis of the piston rod, parts of the cylinder will be subjected to bending moments for which they may not have been designed. The user of a fluid-power cyl-

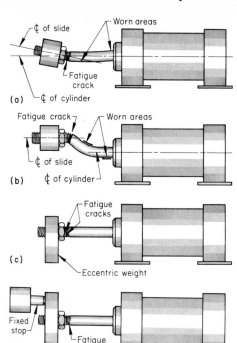

(a) Application of force of cylinder to slide (machine component) not parallel to centerline of cylinder (angular misalignment). (b) Application of force to slide (machine component) parallel to but not coincident with centerline of cylinder (parallel misalignment).
(c) Operation of cylinder with eccentric weight attached to piston rod. (d) Constraint of movement of component attached to piston rod at point not in line with centerline of rod.

Fig. 2. Types of application of force of cylinder that can result in wear and fatigue cracking of piston rod

inder must observe rated pressure limitations. Likewise, the cylinder must be used in an environment compatible with its materials. Clean fluids, and proper lubrication where indicated, are essential to satisfactory operation.

Most applications of fluid-power cylinders require many cycles of operation. Operating stresses are relaxed or reversed during each cycle. Thus, fatigue and corrosion fatigue are common failure mechanisms. Fatigue failures of fluid-power cylinders are caused by the same conditions that cause fatigue failures of other types of components (see the articles on Fatigue Failures, page 95, and Corrosion-Fatigue Failures, page 240, in this volume).

The locations of severe stress concentration in cylinders are the threads on piston rods and tie rods, joints between bodies and heads, and mounting devices. Piston-rod bushings, edges of pistons, and pivot mountings are the metallic components most subject to wear.

A cylinder also may fail as the result of a single accidental application of load. Body dents, bent piston rods, broken mountings, and stretched or broken tie rods are examples of this type of failure. When fracture occurs, it usually shows evidence of some ductility.

Failure of Piston Rods

The one component that most frequently is responsible for failure of fluid-power cylinders is the piston rod, which must transmit the force exerted against the piston by the operating fluid. A piston rod is a slender member that is subject to axial tensile and axial compressive loading, and possibly to bending loading.

A common type of piston-rod failure is breakage in the exposed thread, just at the edge of a nut, a clevis, or whatever is attached to the rod. The failure mechanism usually is fatigue. Fatigue cracking can result when a bending moment is applied to the threaded portion of the rod during some part of each operating cycle and is relaxed or reversed during another part of each cycle. The bending moment can be produced by:

1 Application of the force of the cylinder in a direction not parallel to the centerline of the cylinder (angular misalignment), as shown in Fig. 2(a). Use of a freely rotating clevis at the end of the piston rod could prevent this from causing failure.

2 Constraining the end of the piston rod to move along a line parallel to but not coincident with the centerline of the cylinder (parallel misalignment), as shown in Fig. 2(b).

3 An eccentric weight attached to the rod, as shown in Fig. 2(c). At each end of the stroke, the kinetic energy of the weight is transformed to a bending moment on the rod.

4 Constraint of the motion of the component attached to the rod at a point not in line with the centerline of the rod (see Fig. 2d).

5 Loose or improper cylinder mounting.

Fatigue fracture of a piston rod at the threaded end because of fixed, off-axis attachment is described in the example that follows.

Example 1. Low-Cycle Fatigue Fracture of 1137 or 1141 Steel Tilt-Actuator Piston Rods on Ram-Type Lift Trucks (Fig. 3)

Tilt-actuator piston rods on several ram-type industrial lift trucks that had been in service for ½ to 2 years broke transversely at a threaded area near the point of attachment to the tilting mast. The 10-to-12-ton-capacity lift trucks normally handled coils of steel strip, rod and wire weighing from 3 to 7 tons. Each truck was equipped with two actuator assemblies that tilted the mast and ram; one such assembly is shown schematically in Fig. 3. The actuator piston rods were 18 in. long and were made of cold drawn normalized-and-tempered 1137 or 1141 steel having a specified hardness of 179 to 217 Bhn. Both ends of each rod were roll threaded (1½–12 UNF), and the 2-in.-diam central portion was polished.

Five piston rods broke, after approximately 700 to 2000 hr of operation. Usually, only one of the two rods on a given truck broke, but in a few instances both rods broke at about the same time. Fracture of either of the rods jammed the tilting mechanism, making it inoperative. Fracture of a single rod sometimes caused the load to drop, constituting a potentially serious safety hazard.

Investigation. Each fracture was perpendicular to the axis of the rod and occurred along one of the three innermost threads on the outboard end, as shown in detail A in Fig. 3. The fracture surfaces were fairly flat and, when examined visually and at low magnification, had the characteristic appearance of fatigue-fracture surfaces. A very smooth area extended inward from the fracture origin in a typical curved beachmark pattern and then terminated in a rough region of fast fracture. The maximum depth of penetration of the smooth fatigue region varied from 3/8 to 1 in. across the 1½-in.-diam fracture surface. The remaining portion of the fracture surface had the appearance of brittle fracture.

Composition and hardness of the five broken rods and of one unused replacement rod were checked. Compositions were within specifications for 1137 or 1141 steel. Hardness values fell within the upper portion of the specified range for cold drawn 1137 or 1141 steel (179 to 217 Bhn), except for one broken rod that had a hardness of 241 Bhn.

Metallographic examination of sections taken near the fracture surfaces revealed a normal structure for 1137 or 1141 steel as cold drawn. Irregular patches of fine pearlite were interspersed in a matrix of ferrite, which also contained many sulfide inclusions. Ferrite and pearlite were present in about equal amounts.

Analysis. The location and appearance of the fractures indicated that initial fatigue cracking had resulted from low-frequency cyclic one-way bending stresses. The threads in the fracture region had served as stress raisers. There was no evidence that any other factors had contributed to the failure; no abnormalities in material composition, structure or hardness were detected, and there were no signs of local defects.

The typical maximum cyclic bending moment for the rods was estimated to be 100,000 to 150,000 in.-lb in the failure area. Static tensile loads were about 12,000 lb.

No failure occurred at the 1½-in.-diam threaded inboard end of any of the rods, because the bending force on this end was exerted only on the 2-in.-diam polished section. The bending moment was estimated to be lower on the inboard end of the rod than on the outboard end.

Conclusion. The actuator piston rods broke in low-cycle fatigue under a varying applied cyclic bending moment. Exposed threads in the highly stressed area were stress raisers.

Corrective Measures. The rods were carbonitrided to a case depth of 0.020 to 0.030 in. Carbonitriding was done after final machining and thread rolling, but before grinding and polishing. The bending moment on the outboard end of each rod was reduced by attaching the rod at a higher position on the mast.

An equally effective but more expensive alternative that was considered was the use of 4140 or 8640 alloy steel rods rough machined at a hardness of 180 Bhn, then hardened and tempered to 270 to 310 Bhn.

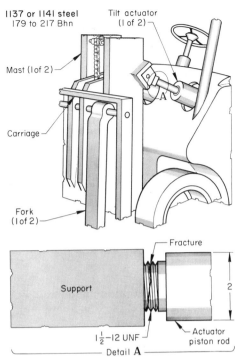

Fig. 3. Lift-truck tilt-actuator assembly that failed by fracture of 1137 or 1141 steel piston rod because of off-axis mounting and operation (Example 1)

The appearance of the fracture surface of a broken piston rod usually is similar to that of a broken threaded fastener or shaft (see the articles on Fatigue Failures, page 95, and Failures of Shafts, page 373, in this volume). The surface exhibits either single or multiple points of initiation, depending on the type of loading and on whether or not the piston rod was free to rotate. Some indication of the type of loading that caused a fatigue fracture of a piston rod may be obtained by examining wear patterns on the rod and on other components of the cylinder. The locations of wear regions for two types of loading are shown in Fig. 2(a) and (b). Prevention of these types of piston-rod failures is achieved by removing the loading conditions that produce the failures. Because it is often difficult to change an application to prevent failure, cylinder manufacturers have adopted a variety of measures to permit cylinders to perform satisfactorily under adverse loading conditions. Most cylinders contain high-strength cold drawn steel piston rods. In some instances, there are tapped holes in the ends of the rods so that the member most subject to fatigue is a replaceable bolt or stud. Other designs eliminate threads on the rods by incorporating a clamped connection between the rod and the component it operates.

Occasionally, a piston rod may fail in fatigue at the joint between the piston and the rod. Although there are many different joint designs, most include a threaded fastening. Fatigue of this joint

usually is caused by bending of the piston relative to the rod. A foreign body between the piston and the head or careless assembly (during manufacture or repair) can produce bending.

Buckling of a piston rod is possible, particularly in long-stroke cylinders, but cylinders usually are designed to minimize buckling. Buckling also may occur because of the application of a load perpendicular to the axis of the cylinder, or as the result of a worn, damaged or lost rod bearing.

Piston rods may be scratched or nicked during manufacture, installation or service. Although such a scratch or nick rarely causes a rod to break, it may cause leakage of fluid from the cylinder, binding between the rod and rod bearing or damage to the rod bearing. Any of these conditions may be considered a cylinder failure.

Failure of Tie Rods

Tie rods are used in many fluid-pressure cylinders to hold the cylinder together during operation. Tie rods must withstand the operating forces of the cylinder and also must be preloaded sufficiently to prevent leakage of fluid between the body and either head of the cylinder.

Failure of tie rods frequently is caused by nonuniform tightening during assembly, repair or installation. An undertightened tie rod permits excessive motion between the two heads; an overtightened tie rod must support more than its normal share of the operating load, plus the load developed through the head motion near any undertightened tie rods. Tie-rod failure also may result from stopping the movement of a large external weight against one head of the cylinder; the tie rods are subjected to the kinetic energy of the external weight at one end of the stroke. The appearance of a broken tie rod is similar to that of a broken shaft, bolt or screw.

Failure of Joints Between Body and Head

In cylinders built without tie rods, the body and the heads are held together by threaded joints, by mechanically formed joints, or by snap rings, and the function of the tie rod is assumed by the body of the cylinder. The joint between the body and head is a vulnerable part of these cylinders. Failure of this joint may be caused by improper assembly, improper installation, or use of the cylinder head to stop the movement of a large weight. Such a failure may occur by fatigue through either a threaded joint or a formed joint, or by distortion of a formed joint, permitting the head to be separated from the body.

Some hydraulic cylinders are machined from forgings, castings or solid billets; thus, the body and one head are one piece. The end of the machined and honed cylinder bore is a vulnerable point, because it must sustain the stresses caused by pressurizing the cylinder and the operating loads of the cylinder — either simultaneously or alternately. The change in cross-sectional size and shape and the variations in local stresses indicate severe strain discontinuities, which are accentuated by sharp internal corners. The example that follows describes failure of a cylinder that had a sharp internal corner.

Example 2. Fatigue Fracture of a Cast Steel Hydraulic Press Cylinder Originating in a Sharp Internal Corner at the Head (Fig. 4)

The hydraulic cylinders on three identical presses failed in a similar manner after approximately ten years of service. On the occasion of the first failure, no detailed examination was made; the cylinder was repaired by welding and returned to service. Shortly afterward, the cylinder on another press began leaking, and an investigation was made.

The fractured cylinder, which was closed by a flat head, is shown in Fig. 4(a). During operation, the cylinder was initially subjected to a pressure of 750 psi, which ultimately rose to 4480 psi. Figure 4(b) shows the appearance of both the internal surface of the head and the fracture surface. The cylinder was a steel casting, and it was apparent that during machining of the internal surfaces a sharp corner had been left at the junction of the head and the body. It was evident that from this stress raiser a smooth fatigue crack had developed around the entire circumference of the cylinder. When this annular crack had extended approximately 1 in. into the cylinder wall, final and sudden failure occurred as a brittle annular fracture 1/8 in. to 1/4 in. wide and more irregular in appearance than the smooth fatigue crack. As indicated in detail A in Fig. 4(a), the crack as it developed followed a curved path into the thicker head portion, which is characteristic of fatigue fracture at sharply filleted changes in section.

Chemical analysis indicated that the material was cast steel with a carbon content of 0.3 to 0.4%. Examination of the microstructure did not reveal any significant inclusions or segregates, which if present might have contributed to the failure. The hardness of the material was 163 Bhn, which is equivalent to a tensile strength of approximately 80,600 psi. Following the second failure, the cylinder of a third machine was examined ultrasonically, and a crack was found in the course of development at the identical location.

In view of the similarity of the three failures, it is evident that they resulted from a common cause. Under internal pressure, the flat head assumed a dished form, which imposed bending stresses at the junction with the cylindrical portion; these stresses were repeated at each cycle of operation of the press. The absence of a significant radius at the junction resulted in stress concen-

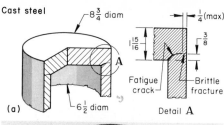

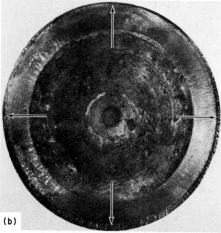

(a) Section through the cylinder, and detail showing location and curvature of the crack. (b) Fracture surface on the head portion; arrows indicate start of final-fracture region.

Fig. 4. Cast steel hydraulic press cylinder that fractured by fatigue originating at a sharp internal corner at intersection between flat head and body (Example 2)

tration, and the magnitude of the stress that developed in this region must have exceeded the fatigue strength of the material.

Calculation of the longitudinal stress in the cylinder at the junction with the flat end showed:

Stress due to pressure	7,580 psi
Additional stress due to bending moment	30,100 psi
Total longitudinal stress	37,680 psi

Assuming that the material had a yield strength of 44,800 psi, a stress-concentration factor of only 1.2 (44,800/37,680) would result in application of a stress of yield-point magnitude at the location where the fatigue crack originated in service. It is assumed that the actual stress-concentration factor exceeded this value.

Conclusions. The cylinders failed in fatigue, which originated at the sharp corner at the intersection of the flat head and the body. The use of the flat head and a sharp internal corner resulted in excessive stresses at the intersection.

Corrective Measure. The flat head of the cylinder was changed to a spherical one, which reduced the value of the maximum stress to that of the hoop stress in the cylinder (15,200 psi), which was an acceptable level.

Failure of Cylinder Bodies

Because the body of a fluid-power cylinder is a pressure vessel, its design is usually very conservative. Consequently, failure of cylinder bodies by either single overload or fatigue is rare, unless the

body was defective or corroded. In most cylinder designs, the tie rods or the joints between the body and the heads are more prone to failure than the body. A scratch on the interior surface, a gross dent in the body, or a nick on either end-sealing surface may prevent proper operation of the cylinder. In the next two examples, corrosion pits and forging laps initiated fatigue failures of forged cylinder bodies.

Example 3. Fatigue Fracture of a Forged Aluminum Alloy 7075-T73 Landing-Gear Cylinder Body, Originating at Corrosion Pits (Fig. 5)

Severe cracks halted a life-cycle impulse test of an uplatch-actuator cylinder for an aircraft nose landing gear. The crack occurred longitudinally in the body of the cylinder, penetrating from the bore of the body through the longitudinal retract pressure-fluid port to the external surface (see Fig. 5a and b). The body was machined from an aluminum alloy 7075-T73 forging. After being machined, it was cleaned and then anodized on all surfaces.

Investigation. The cylinder body was cut to expose a cross section of the crack. The cut surface was ground flat and etched with modified Tucker's reagent to reveal the forged grain flow (see Fig. 5c). It was evident that propagation of the crack had followed the flow lines at the parting line.

The body was then cut lengthwise to expose the fracture surface. Visual examination established that there had been several crack origins on the bore surface and on each side of the retract-port surface. These origins had generated individual longitudinal crack fronts, which grew until they joined to form a single fracture. Several secondary cracks were found in the main fracture, some initiating in the retract-port surface and extending toward the bore, others starting in the bore surface and growing toward the retract port.

Pitting of the retract-port surface of the body as shown in Fig. 5(d) was characteristic of the retract-port and bore surfaces. The pits were predominantly in areas where elongated grains were nearly perpendicular to the machined surface. The presence of the small cracks issuing from the pits indicated that the crack that led to failure in all probability originated from such pits.

The anodized surface layer was protected with metal foil during metallographic mounting and polishing. The anodized layer was measured on the polished surfaces and was found to be 0.0001 to 0.0004 in. thick on the retract port and 0.0002 to 0.0003 in. thick on the bore. On both surfaces it was evident that the pits had been created before anodizing, because the anodized layer conformed to the contour of each pit.

Secondary cracks were found extending from the retract-port surface toward the bore to a depth of about 3/64 in. These cracks also followed the direction of the forging flow and the elongated grains.

Selected areas of the fracture surface were examined by electron microscopy. The fracture mode at the various origins was found to be intergranular. In the immediate vicinity of the origins, however, the surface contained fatigue striations. The spacing of

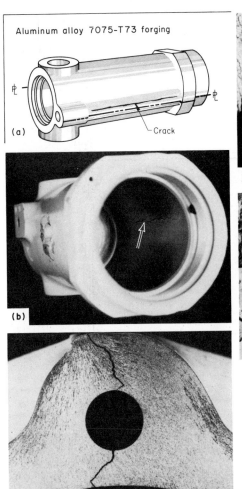

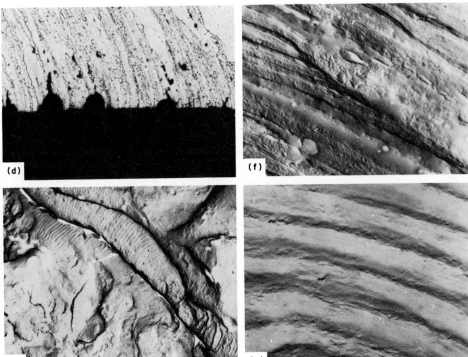

(a) Exterior surface, showing location of longitudinal crack. (b) Interior surface, showing longitudinal crack (at arrow). (c) Section through retract pressure-fluid port, showing cracks following flow lines. (d) Micrograph, at 250×, showing microstructure, pits that penetrated end grains, and fatigue cracks at pits. (e) Electron-microscope fractograph, at 4120×, of an area adjacent to the bore surface, showing fine fatigue striations.
(f) Electron-microscope fractograph, at 4120×, of an area adjacent to the lower surface of the retract pressure-fluid port, showing widely spaced fatigue striations. (g) Electron-microscope fractograph, at 4120×, of an area adjacent to the top surface of the retract port, showing fatigue striations more widely spaced than those in fractographs (e) and (f).

Fig. 5. Forged aluminum alloy 7075-T73 nose-landing-gear uplatch cylinder in which fatigue cracking originated at corrosion pits (Example 3)

the striations varied with location. Figure 5(e) shows fine striations observed in a region adjacent to the bore surface. At the bore side of the retract port, the striations were more widely spaced, as illustrated in Fig. 5(f). The widest striation spacing was found between the retract port and the external surface of the body, as shown in Fig. 5(g). Because the test conditions and the pulsation rate did not vary during the life-cycle tests, the wider striations could have been caused only by a greater rate of crack growth per cycle. This would have resulted from an increase in true stress as growth of the crack reduced the effective wall section. The evidence indicated, therefore, that the earliest cracking was in the bore surface; cracking of the retract-port surface nearest the bore was next; and the final stage of failure began between the reject port and the outside surface of the body.

Measurements of electrical conductivity gave a value of 39.6% IACS for the body material. Hardness of the body averaged Rockwell B 85. These data indicated that the composition and heat treatment matched the specifications for aluminum alloy 7075-T73.

Conclusions. The uplatch-cylinder body failed in fatigue from cracks that originated in small pits on the surfaces of the bore and of the retract pressure-fluid port. The pits that initiated the fatigue cracks were created before anodizing — probably during cleaning after final machining.

Corrective Measures. Control of the pre-anodizing cleaning procedure was revised to eliminate the pitting. Inspection of the surfaces after cleaning was instituted to guard against anodizing actuator bodies with surface pits.

Example 4. Fatigue Fracture of a Forged Aluminum Alloy 7079-T6 Cylinder Body for an Aircraft Flap Actuator, Which Was Initiated at a Forging Lap (Fig. 6)

During final-assembly checkout of an aircraft center leading-edge flap, the cylinder body for the flap actuator was found to have a 6-in.-long longitudinal crack through the body wall in a plane about 90° from the forging parting plane. The cylinder body had been machined from an aluminum alloy 7079-T6 forging. The flap system on the aircraft had been operated five or six times before the failure occurred.

Investigation. The crack in the cylinder body (Fig. 6a) was exposed by saw cuts made from each end of the body to meet the ends of the crack. The crack surface disclosed a forging defect about 2½ in. long at one end. The defect extended inward radially to a depth of 0.15 in. A band of crack-arrest marks about 0.07 in. wide was found at the base of the defect. Inspection of the exterior surface after the paint had been stripped showed a longitudinal pattern of irregular grain flow adjacent to the crack, which is a characteristic forging defect.

Electron-microscope fractographs of the crack surface showed nondescript features in the region of the forging defect. At the base of the defect, a narrow band contained fatigue striations, indicating either that the reported number of actuations was in error or that each actuation induced a very large number of pulse cycles; beyond the zone of fatigue marks, the fracture had the dimpled topography of a rapid-overload failure.

Metallographic inspection of sections taken through the forging-defect area confirmed that a forging lap or seam had existed in the cylinder wall before the crack was formed (Fig. 6b). The lap had failed to weld during forging and was partly open after machining (an anodized layer was found on the surface of the defect near the area shown in Fig. 6b).

A substantial number of nonmetallic inclusions were found in the microstructure, identified by electron-microprobe analysis as iron and magnesium spinel particles. These particles were present in sufficient quantity to have impaired the forgeability of the metal locally.

Hardness readings averaged Rockwell B 88, and electrical-conductivity measurements averaged 30.5% IACS. Both values were satisfactory, indicating that heat treatment had been adequate.

Conclusions. Fracture began at a forging defect and penetrated for a short distance as a fatigue crack, then the remainder of the wall fractured by rapid overload. The forg-

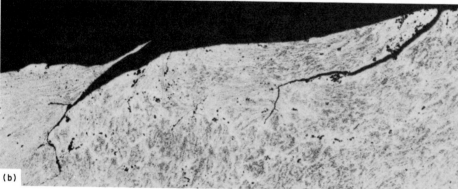

Fig. 6. (a) *Aircraft flap-actuator cylinder body, forged from aluminum alloy 7079-T6, that failed by fatigue fracture (between arrows) originating at a forging lap. (b) Micrograph, at 125×, showing forging laps at fracture surface. (Example 4)*

ing defect was a lap or a seam, apparently the outcome of local poor forgeability resulting from an unfavorable concentration of nonmetallic inclusions.

Corrective Measure. Liquid-penetrant inspection of the cylinder body was incorporated after machining but before anodizing, to reveal the presence of any laps or seams.

Corrosion fatigue occurs by the combined action of cyclic stress and corrosion. In forgings, ends of grains exposed to a corrodent are sites for initiation of corrosion fatigue, as in the following example.

Example 5. Corrosion-Fatigue Failure of a Forged Aluminum Alloy 7079-T6 Hydraulic-Cylinder Body at the Flash Line (Fig. 7)

The hydraulic-cylinder body shown in Fig. 7(a) developed leaks and was removed from service in an aircraft. The service life of the cylinder was not known.

The cylinder body had been machined from a solid aluminum alloy 7079 forging that had been heat treated to the T6 temper. Laboratory reports indicated that other cylinders made from the same type of forging had failed in service or during preflight testing. Operating pressure for the cylinder was 3000 psi.

Investigation. Visual examination of the cylinder body revealed a longitudinal crack near the flash line and extending virtually the entire length of the body. Also noted was mismatch caused by misalignment of the forging dies. The crack was on the side containing the port (see Fig. 7a). The cylinder body was cross-sectioned for a dimensional check and to appraise the amount of die mismatch.

Spectrographic analysis identified the metal as aluminum alloy 7079, and metal-

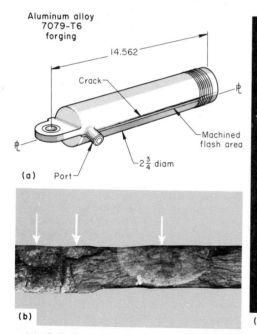

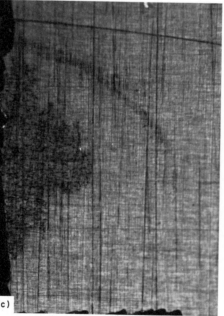

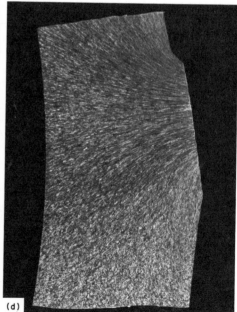

(a) Cylinder body, showing location of crack. (b) Fractograph, at 3½×, showing fatigue marks originating at small corrosion pits (at arrows) on the inner surface of the cylinder body. (c) Macrograph, at 8½×, of an unetched specimen, showing corrosion on the inner surface at the flash line. (d) Macrograph, at 7×, of a specimen etched with a modified Keller's reagent, showing grain orientation at the flash line.

Fig. 7. *Hydraulic-cylinder body, forged from aluminum alloy 7079-T6, that failed by corrosion fatigue at the flash line in a thin area resulting from forging-die mismatch* (Example 5)

lographic analysis showed a typical structure for 7079-T6. Hardness surveys showed an average hardness of Rockwell B 87.6.

The wall thickness, specified as 0.155 in. min, varied from 0.165 to 0.216 in., with the thinnest area near the flash line at the point of mismatch. The outside diameter ranged from $2\frac{23}{32}$ to $2\frac{13}{16}$ in. The inside diameter, specified as 2.376 ± 0.001 in., measured 2.377 to 2.379 in. All measurements were taken on the cylinder body after sectioning.

The cylinder body was opened so that the fracture surface could be examined. As shown in Fig. 7(b), clamshell-shape fatigue patterns were found originating from the inner surface of the body. At each origin were tiny corrosion pits where the anodized coating had worn thin. Corrosion at the flash line on the inner surface is shown in Fig. 7(c). Microscopic examination showed this corrosion to be mostly intergranular. This intergranular corrosion produced pits and cracklike notches that served as nuclei for fatigue cracks.

Figure 7(d) is a section through the flash line at the pitted area of the cylinder body and shows an abrupt change in the grain direction that exposed the short transverse grains at the inner surface. Similarly exposed grains were discovered during previous investigations of failed hydraulic-cylinder bodies. One report described this condition as oxides present in an area on the inside surface of the cylinder body that still contained an area of the original forging surface that had not been cleaned up by the normal machining operation. This postulation appeared unreasonable, because the cylinder body had been machined from a solid forging and had no forging surface on the inside.

Conclusions. The cylinder body failed by corrosion fatigue that originated at corrosion pits on the inner surface. Fracture occurred in the thinnest portion of the cylinder-body wall — the mismatch at the parting line. Direction of flow at the parting line had caused the grain to be nearly perpendicular to the surface rather than parallel to it. The rough manner in which the flash had been removed had created a notch in the cylinder-body wall.

Final failure occurred by brittle fracture when the effective wall thickness was reduced such that it could no longer withstand the load.

Corrective Measures. The forging supplier was asked to minimize forging mismatch and to improve grain direction at the flash line. Although, even with mismatch, the wall thickness of the machined cylinder body met the minimum requirement, an undesirable notch had been created when flash was removed. For this reason, the machine shop was instructed to blend the flash line into the side wall so as to minimize the notch effect. This procedure greatly reduced, but did not completely eliminate, failures.

Other recommendations included (a) increasing the wall thickness of the cylinder body, using the same aluminum alloy (7079-T6) or an alloy of similar strength (such as 7075-T6); and (b) rough machining the body before heat treatment.

Failure of Mountings, Fittings and Springs

Cylinder mountings occasionally fail in service, frequently as a result of careless installation. Excessive torque can strip mounting threads or fracture a threaded member. However, if the mounting is not tight enough, mating surfaces are subjected to wear, and other components of the cylinder may be subjected to unintentional loading. Overloaded mounting brackets may deform or break. Pivot bearings in one head and at the end of the piston rod are subject to wear, particularly if the pivot pins are not parallel with each other and with the axis of rotation of the moving member of the system.

Porous sintered bearings may be worn or crushed by overload or misalignment. Pipe and tube fittings in cylinder ports may be overtightened or may break off in the port. Springs in single-acting cylinders may fail; failures of springs are described in the article beginning on page 487 in this volume.

Failures of Lifting Equipment

By Frank L. Jamieson and Richard A. Wright*

LIFTING EQUIPMENT is used for raising, lowering and transporting materials, parts and equipment, generally within a limited area. The types of metal components used in lifting equipment include gears, shafts, drums and sheaves, brakes and brake wheels, couplings, bearings, wheels, electrical switchgear, chains, steel wire rope, and hooks. This article deals primarily with many of these metal components of lifting equipment in the following three categories:

1 Cranes and bridges, particularly those for outdoor and other low-temperature service
2 Attachments used for direct lifting, such as hooks, chains, wire rope, slings, beams, bales and trunnions; and the members to which they are attached, such as lifting lugs or eyes
3 Built-in members that are the items necessary for the operation of lifting equipment, such as shafts, gears and drums.

*Mr. Jamieson is Laboratory Supervising Metallurgist, and Mr. Wright is Laboratory Project Metallurgist, Metallurgical Laboratory, Steel Company of Canada.

Most of the failures discussed here are related to the more common and critical components of lifting equipment used in steel mills and similar industrial applications, but the problems encountered and the methods of analysis are the same as for lifting equipment used in other industries.

Failure Mechanisms. Failures of lifting equipment commonly result from fatigue, ductile fracture, brittle fracture, and wear. A part may fail from any one of these mechanisms, or from a combination of two or more of them. A member may initially fracture by fatigue, with final fracture being of a ductile or brittle nature. Total brittle fracture of a part is most undesirable, because it is unpredictable and often has catastrophic results. Periodic inspection of a part that is susceptible to brittle fracture is quite often of little purpose. It is preferable for fracture of a component to begin by fatigue rather than suddenly in a brittle manner. Properly timed inspections usually will reveal a slowly propagating crack, and the equipment can be removed from service before failure occurs.

Wear is easily recognized; excessive wear usually can be corrected by changing the material or its processing. However, the complete elimination of wear of lifting equipment may require selection of a material that is subject to brittle fracture — an alternative that may well be unacceptable.

Failure Origins. Failures occur for a number of reasons, which may be related to operation, design, material selection, material quality and manufacturing practices. The largest portion of lifting-equipment failures are of operational origin. Overloading of a lifting mechanism is a common practice and often leads to either ductile or brittle fracture, or to fracture by fatigue from repeated overstressing. With a fatigue type of failure, the member usually will fail at a load well below its specified load limit; thus, a false sense of security exists when dealing with a member that is fracturing by fatigue. Periodic inspection of such parts is therefore very important. Items that show signs of excessive wear or abuse should be removed from service for replacement or repair. Figure 1 shows the end of a steel wire rope that failed in tension because of overloading. Excessive wear on a 5/8-in.-diam 6x37 fiber-core improved plow steel wire rope is described in Example 4 in this article (see page 461). Corrosion failures also are relatively frequent, because of the environments in which lifting equipment is operated.

Section changes, keyways, lubrication holes, rough-machining marks, and threaded sections frequently are points of initiation of cracks. Small fillets, sharp corners, grooves and threads act as stress raisers from which fatigue cracks initiate and fractures propagate. Correct design of a threaded shank on a hook, for instance, and the stress-relieving groove at the base of a threaded shank, are very important to failure prevention. Failures have also occurred where names, numbers and other identification marks are die stamped or imprinted on highly stressed surfaces. For information on the effects of identification marks, see page 119 in the article on Fatigue Failures, and pages 387 and 388 in the article on Failures of Shafts.

Another common cause of lifting-equipment failures is improper material selection. The choice of a material is related to such aspects as its basic quality, composition, over-all mechanical properties, notch toughness, corrosion resistance, weldability and machinability. In most applications, many materials may be satisfactory for a particular part but only a few materials will be optimum.

In hardenable steels, tempered martensite has greater fatigue resistance than mixed structures. From a practical and theoretical aspect, alloy steels are a better material selection than carbon steels because of the deeper-hardening characteristics of alloy steels.

The most encompassing cause of failures of lifting equipment is poor manufacturing, assembly and maintenance practices. Inferior machining, defective welds, residual welding stresses, misalignment, and improper and insufficient lubrication are all common and critical causes of lifting-equipment failures. Metallurgically, the most common cause of failures is improper heat treatment. Quench cracks, forging defects, and residual heat-treat stresses contribute to such failures. The examples in this article illustrate many of these causes.

Investigation of Failures. The investigation of a failure can provide valuable information that can be used for design improvement, material selection, and other factors related to the efficient operation of lifting equipment. Much information may be obtained by visual examination. Close, careful visual inspection always precedes any technique requiring destruction or cutting of a failed part.

Fig. 1. End of a steel wire rope that failed in tension because of overloading. Necking at the ends of the wires indicates ductile fracture; no worn or abraded areas were found at the break.

A frequent error in investigating a failure is automatically to interpret it on the basis of the most commonly known causes indicated from past experience. Although this cannot be avoided entirely, efforts should be made to be alert for possibly other or unique details that may be contributory or related factors, and that may then significantly alter the interpretation. In the investigation of a fatigue failure, the following should be considered: (a) material, (b) design of the entire machine as well as that of the failed part, (c) fabrication practice (machining, welding, forging or casting), (d) heat treatment, (e) types of loading to which the equipment is subjected, and (f) operating environment such as corrosive or high-temperature atmospheres.

Many failures may be the result of a combination of several faults or contributing factors. Correcting one fault may not be sufficient, or may even have a strongly adverse effect in the presence of other uncorrected faults. It is important that an investigator sort out the contributory causes of failure from the associated but immaterial aspects of the failed part to determine the proper corrective measures. The techniques for making failure analyses are given in the article beginning on page 10.

Materials for Lifting Equipment

Recommendations are listed below regarding materials commonly used in the manufacture of lifting equipment for the steel industry; other industries may use different materials as required by the application. The recommendations are general, thus each situation must be considered individually. Transition temperatures of the steels used in the equipment should be considered in all instances, particularly for applications that involve temperatures below 20 C (68 F). For a discussion on ductile-to-brittle

transition, the reader is referred to the article that begins on page 44.

Chains, Chain Hooks, and Fittings. Low-carbon steel chains are in wide use and are generally acceptable. However, to ensure a greater margin of safety, alloy steel chains with a hardness of 302 to 352 Bhn are recommended.

Chain hooks usually are made of a grade of steel similar to that of the chain assembly, except in special instances. The design of chain hooks is often characteristic of the manufacturer, rather than of the application. Materials for chains for use in acid or other corrosive environments must be specified for the particular situation.

Shafts. Misalignment of shafts resulting in failures is a common occurrence, and is difficult to eliminate when dealing with large equipment.

Frequently, 1040 or 1045 steel is specified for shafts. Failures in shafts made of these steels often can be minimized by heat treatment. In other instances, it may be necessary to make shafts from quenched-and-tempered alloy steels such as 4140 or 8640, which have excellent fatigue properties. For severe applications and large section sizes, 4340 or a comparable high-alloy steel may be used with excellent results.

Bridges and Cranes. The use of a steel having a high impact resistance at low temperatures is required for the prevention of brittle fracture of structures, especially welded ones, that are subjected to cold temperature conditions in service. Generally, use of a fine-grained, normalized, relatively low-carbon (0.20% C) steel will ensure adequate impact resistance, and freedom from high hardness in the heat-affected zone of welds. Fully quenched and tempered low-carbon steels, and similarly treated alloy steels, also are used for such applications.

Miscellaneous Equipment. Lifting booms, coil hooks, lugs and rings, boxes and containers, trunnions and miscellaneous attachments should be made of either normalized or quenched-and-tempered fully killed fine-grained steels. For equipment operated at temperatures below 20 C (68 F), transition temperature of the material also must be considered; the material selected should have a transition temperature below the operating temperature. When the weight of these components is a limiting factor, plain carbon steels may not be suitable. A high-strength low-alloy steel may be used instead, the grade and fabrication depending on the requirements of the specific application.

Flame-cut parts and welded components, insofar as possible, should be stress relieved at 600 to 650 C (about 1100 to 1200 F); flame cutting may produce hard edges that are deleterious to machining and may act as stress raisers in a weldment. Inspection of welded assemblies by nondestructive methods is highly recommended. In the fabrication of a member, the material should be oriented so that the rolling direction will be parallel to the direction of principal service stress.

Bolts, nuts and washers should be made in accordance with ASTM A325 or other recognized specifications for applications in which they are used only as fasteners. Pins and bolts used as pivots should be of fully killed fine-grained steels of compositions that will satisfy processing and application requirements. Rivets should be made in accordance with ASTM A502. Particular designs or service conditions may require the use of heat treated alloy steels.

Steel Wire Rope

Many factors must be considered when investigating a failure of steel wire rope used on lifting equipment. Environment is of obvious concern, because wire rope may be subjected to corrosive atmospheres such as water, acid and various chemicals, or to elevated temperatures. Another important factor that must be considered is the flexibility of wire rope. When sheaves or drums are involved, and they almost always are, the diameter of the sheave or drum has a direct relation to the flexibility of the wire rope. The degree of flexibility of a wire rope is determined by its construction.

Strength and Stretch. The ultimate breaking strength of a wire rope is by design less than the aggregate strength of all the wires and will vary depending on the construction of rope and grade of wire used. All manufacturers of wire rope publish catalogs that list minimum breaking strengths for the various sizes, constructions and grades of ropes. The proper design factor for a wire rope demands consideration of all loads. These loads should include, when applicable, acceleration, deceleration, rope speed, rope attachments, number and arrangement of sheaves and drums, conditions producing corrosion and abrasion, and length of rope.

Cold drawn high-carbon steel wire, the type generally used in wire rope, has a modulus of elasticity of approximately 28 to 29 million psi, which is the measure of the degree to which it will stretch under increasing load. The amount of rope stretch caused by the relative movement of all the wires in their attempt to adjust their positions to a stable condition corresponding to the load imposed, varies with the construction of the rope. Generally, the more flexible ropes, which are the ones containing the greatest number of wires and ropes with fiber cores, will stretch more than the all-metal ropes having fewer wires and as a result less flexibility.

Stretch resulting from the movement of the wires is of two types: constructional and elastic. When a rope is first placed under load, the resulting slight rearrangement of the wires will cause a permanent lengthening, known as constructional stretch, and a recoverable lengthening, which is elastic stretch.

The constructional stretch, depending to some degree on the magnitude of the load imposed, amounts to approximately 0.5 to 0.75% of the length of the rope, for six-strand ropes with fiber core. For six-strand ropes with steel core, the corresponding value is 0.25 to 0.5%; and for eight-strand ropes with fiber core, 0.75 to 1%.

All of the preceding remarks apply to bright ropes of a type intended to operate over sheaves and drums, and presuppose that the ends of the rope are restricted against rotation, are free from corrosion and have not deteriorated appreciably either internally or externally. Corrosion and other kinds of rope deterioration have a marked effect on stretch properties.

Sheaves. The size of a sheave is expressed in terms of its diameter measured at the base of the groove. This is its tread diameter. It can be expressed in inches or feet, or as a ratio determined by dividing the tread diameter (in inches) by the nominal rope diameter.

As sheave size is decreased, the stresses resulting from bending and the contact pressure between rope and sheave are increased. Higher bending stresses cause more rapid fatigue of the wires in the rope. Increased pressure also accelerates rope deterioration, and at the same time increases sheave wear.

As sheave size is increased, rope-to-sheave pressure is decreased and bending becomes easier. If bending alone were involved, an increase in rope life could be obtained by increasing sheave size up to a limit of about 90 to 100 times the rope diameter, considering a 6x19 classification rope. However, except on some shaft hoist installations, sheaves this large seldom are in actual use, for two reasons:

1 Bending is seldom, if ever, the only factor involved. Large, expensive sheaves would be unnecessary if the abrasion or scrubbing encountered by the rope on some other part of the installation were the determining factor in its ultimate service.
2 Most machines would not be practical with such large sheaves, and many would never have been designed if sheaves of this size were mandatory.

In practice, many factors other than bending influence rope life, such as repeated stressing, abrasion, pounding, impact, vibration, twisting, speed, drum-winding abuse, corrosion and lack of maintenance. For many applications, one or more of these factors affects rope life more than sheave size alone.

Determination of the best sheave size is found by evaluating the factors affecting safe economical operation. On high-speed, mobile-type equipment and equipment requiring low initial cost, it is customary to use smaller sheaves. The need for more frequent rope replacements is outweighed by the high speed and flexibility of movement provided by the more compact equipment.

Although no definite minimum sheave size can be established for all types of installations, one important factor must not be overlooked. The heavy pressures between the wires at the contact points in the rope, combined with the high bending stresses resulting from operation over small sheaves, have a definite effect on the type of rope deterioration. Under such adverse conditions, wire breakage often occurs at and between the points where the strands contact each other and contact the core of the rope. Broken wires in these sections are difficult and sometimes impossible to detect.

Therefore, where men are hoisted, or where for other reasons a high degree of safety is essential, sheaves should be liberal in size to provide better assurance that the wires will deteriorate progressively on the surface of the rope where they can readily be seen and evaluated. Extremely small sheaves should be limited to those types of equipment on which such usage is in line with acceptable practice.

Sheave size is such an important factor in wire-rope life that many laboratory bending or fatigue tests have been conducted to evaluate this relationship. Laboratory bending life can be found; however, field service life can seldom be judged by these results. There are too many factors existing under actual field conditions to be simulated under controlled laboratory tests.

Laboratory tests have their value for research and development, particularly to the wire-rope engineer. It also may be important at times to show how bending alone, as performed in such tests, affects wire rope.

One series of tests was made on ⅝-in.-diam wire-rope specimens in the 6x7, 6x19, 6x37 and 8x19 classifications. The sheaves ranged from 8 to 20 in. in diameter. The load approximated a design factor of 5, and specimens were operated until they broke. The number of cycles of operation was the measure of bending life.

The laboratory tests showed that as the ratio of sheave diameter to rope diameter was reduced, there was a reduction in bending life, with the reduction in bending life showing the same trend for all specimens tested, and that the reduction in bending life was faster than the reduction of the sheave-to-rope-diameter ratio.

Sheave Grooves. To allow wire rope to perform the maximum amount of useful work, it is essential that sheave grooves be of sufficient diameter to provide and maintain proper rope clearance.

All wire rope, when new, is slightly oversize to allow for some pulling down while becoming adjusted to its normal working tensions.

The recommended groove clearances for the usual sheave applications are given in Table 1. In some instances, departures from these recommendations are advisable. For example, with some deflectors or equalizers, smaller clearances can be used, or with conditions involving large fleet angles, larger clearances may be necessary.

The diameter of a sheave groove does not remain constant. Its change is influenced by the rope, and to a great extent by the sheave material and the pressures involved. Because a groove of the recommended size becomes worn to a smaller diameter by the time a rope is taken out of service, the question arises as to whether or not a sheave should be regrooved every time a new rope is installed. In theory, best service will be obtained when a new rope starts with all sheave grooves exactly proper for the conditions involved. In practice, it would be false economy in the majority of installations to change sheaves with every rope replacement. In most instances, the economical procedure is to allow the new rope to take extra wear at first, even at the expense of some rope life. For most installations, the limit below which a sheave should be regrooved is a clearance value in excess of the nominal rope diameter equal to half the clearance listed in the second column of Table 1.

When a sheave is regrooved, generally it is necessary to dress the flanges and cut the base of the groove to the proper diameter. If only the base is machined, the throat angle near the base may be left too small to provide proper clearance where the rope makes a fleet angle to one side or the other.

Rope Pressure. In addition to the bending stresses introduced by operation over sheaves, wire rope is subjected to radial pressure by its contact with the sheave. This pressure sets up shearing stresses in the wires, distorts the rope structure and affects the rate of wear of the sheave grooves. Therefore, the magnitude of the pressure and the wear resistance of the sheave material should be considered when selecting the most suitable rope construction.

The radial pressure, in pounds per square inch of projected area of the rope, can be determined from the equation:

$$P = 2T/Dd$$

where P is radial pressure, in psi; T is tension in the rope, in lb; D is tread diameter of the sheave, in in.; and d is diameter of the rope, in in.

Table 1. Groove Clearance in Sheaves, Based on Nominal Wire-Rope Diameter

Nominal rope diameter, in.	Groove clearance, in. (a)
$\frac{1}{4}$ to $\frac{5}{16}$	$\frac{1}{64}$
$\frac{3}{8}$ to $\frac{3}{4}$	$\frac{1}{32}$
$\frac{13}{16}$ to $1\frac{1}{8}$	$\frac{3}{64}$
$1\frac{3}{16}$ to $1\frac{1}{2}$	$\frac{1}{16}$
$1\frac{9}{16}$ to $2\frac{1}{4}$	$\frac{3}{32}$
$2\frac{5}{16}$ to 3	$\frac{1}{8}$
Over 3	$\frac{5}{32}$

(a) Recommended groove diameter equals nominal rope diameter plus groove clearance.

Table 2. Allowable Pressures on Sheaves of Cast Iron, Cast Steel and 11-13% Mn Steel for Various Classifications of Wire Rope(a)

Rope classification	Allowable pressures, psi, on sheaves made of: Cast iron	Cast steel	11-13% Mn steel
6x7	300	550	1500
6x19	500	900	2500
6x37	600	1075	3000
8x19	600	1075	3000
Flattened strand	800	1450	4000

(a) Values are for regular-lay rope; for lang-lay rope, these values may be increased 15%, except for flattened-strand rope — which normally is lang lay.

Just as is true for bending stresses, the magnitude of the stresses resulting from the radial pressure increases as the size of the sheave decreases. High bending stresses generally indicate the need for flexible rope constructions. However, the resulting relatively small-diameter wires have less ability to withstand heavy pressures than do the larger wires in the less flexible rope constructions. The selection of the most suitable type of wire rope should consider both factors.

Furthermore, the pressure of the rope against the sheave tends to flatten the rope structure. This type of rope distortion can be controlled to a large extent by proper sheave-groove contour.

Contact of the rope with the sheave results in wear, not only to the rope but to the sheave groove itself. The rate of wear is influenced by the magnitude of the rope pressure against the sheave groove.

Sheave Material. If the material of which the sheave groove is composed has insufficient wear resistance, the groove will wear to the diameter of the rope operating in it. When a new, full-size rope is installed, the groove worn small by the previous rope will subject the new rope to unnecessary abrasion in its attempt to grind the groove to its own diameter. To avoid this condition, the sheave-groove material should be selected to resist the wear corresponding to the rope pressure that will be present.

Table 2 lists allowable radial pressures, calculated from the formula given under "Rope Pressure", for three sheave materials, all based on annealed castings. Heat treatment to improve wear resistance will permit greater pressures. The values listed in Table 2 are of necessity approximate, but do represent desirable limits for avoiding excessive groove wear. These values are for regular-lay wire rope, in which the wires are laid in the direction opposite to the twist of the strands in the rope. The values may be increased for lang-lay wire rope (wires and strands laid in the same direction).

Drums. A common method of driving a wire rope is by a drum, to which one end of the rope is fastened (or in some applications, both ends of the rope), and on which it is wound and stored as the drum revolves.

Most drums are cylindrical with flanges at the ends. Flanges may not be necessary with grooved drums where the rope will never wind in more than one layer and where the rope cannot get out of the grooves. Flanges are necessary for multiple-layer winding and for instances where the rope might slip or wind off the face.

Drum size, groove contour, pressure, and drum material relate closely to the matters previously discussed on sheaves.

The groove contour, in grooved drums, should be the same as in sheaves.

The radial pressure between rope and drum on the first layer of a properly grooved drum is calculated by the equation given in the section "Rope Pressure". For these conditions, the same limitations apply to the materials listed in Table 2.

High pressures are exerted on the face of the drum with two-or-more-layer winding. This has little influence on the choice of drum material, because the additional pressure is applied after the first-layer wraps are fixed in position on the drum.

Higher pressures, resulting from multiple-layer winding, should be considered in the structural design of the drum. A drum for two-layer winding does not have to be twice as strong as for single-layer winding, nor does one for three layers have to be three times as strong. When a second layer is wound on a drum, some tension is lost in the rope on the first layer. With the application of a third layer, additional tension is lost in the rope on the second layer. Studies have indicated that the combined rope tension with two layers is about $1\frac{3}{4}$ times the tension with one layer, with three layers about $2\frac{1}{8}$ times the tension with one, and with four layers about $2\frac{1}{4}$ times the tension with one.

With plain-faced drums, the actual radial pressures are higher because the rope does not have support around part of its circumference. On drums of this type, wear to both rope and drum would be more severe than on grooved drums, and rope deterioration, resulting from pressure, would be more pronounced.

The diameter of the drum should be influenced by considerations of safety and economy. For general conditions, the ratios for sheaves should be considered, but for some applications departures are made from these values.

Where bending is the primary factor affecting the service life of the rope, the drum may be a little smaller in diameter than the sheaves in the system, because in traveling in each direction the rope bends only once at the drum, whereas it bends twice at each sheave. In traveling over each sheave, the rope is bent the first time when it conforms to the curvature of the sheave and the second time when it straightens out and leaves the sheave. The number of bends is decreased on those machines where the rope travel is not very great and the section of rope operating on and off the drum does not reach the sheaves. The reeving diagrams shown in Fig. 2 can be used in determining the number of bends in a wire rope where multiple-pulley blocks are used.

When wire rope is wound on a drum, it exhibits a slight rotation because of the spiral lay of the strands. Standing behind the drum and looking toward an oncoming overwind rope, rotation of a right-lay rope is toward the left, whereas rotation of a left-lay rope is toward the right. This rotation is extremely small and seldom of any significance.

However, with a plain-faced drum, where the only other influence to the rope in winding on the first layer is the fleet angle, this slight rotation sometimes can be used to advantage in keeping the windings close and uniform. Right-lay rope is standard and the one most readily available from stock. Therefore, all machines or installations having plain-faced drums should be designed for use with right-lay rope.

With a plain-faced drum, a right-lay rope, and overwind reeving, the attachment should be made at the left flange. With a right-lay rope and underwind reeving, the attachment should be made at the right flange.

When grooved drums are used, there generally is sufficient control by the grooving to wind the rope properly, whether it is right or left lay. With either an overwind or an underwind installation, or a left or right flange attachment, the standard right-lay rope construction can be employed. Only in special applications should a change to left-lay rope be considered. One instance would be when opposite rotation of the rope might help in preventing open winding, or a piling up at the flange under adverse fleet-angle conditions.

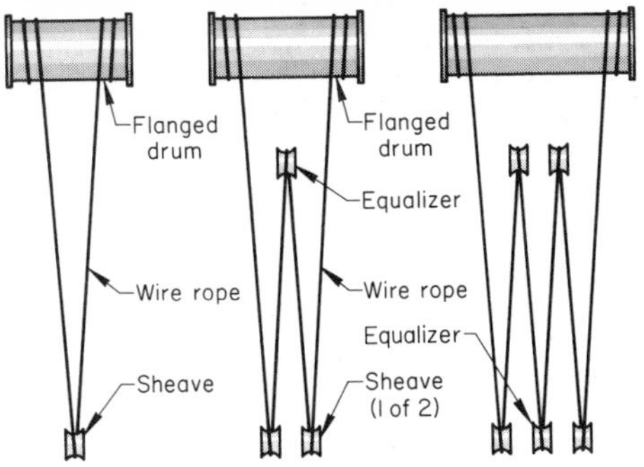

Fig. 2. Three reeving diagrams for double-drum hoists

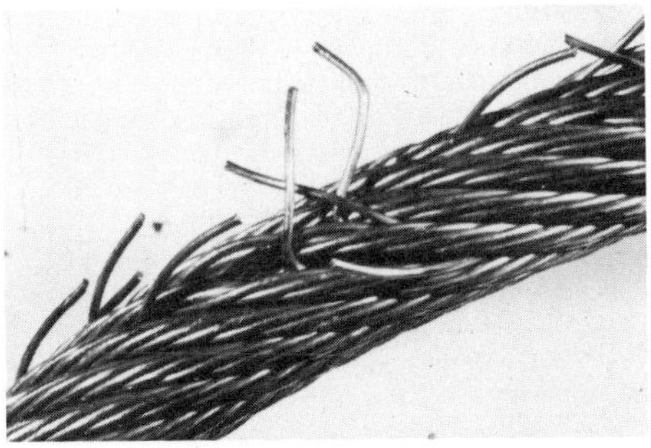

Fig. 3. A 1/2-in.-diam 18x7 fiber-core improved plow steel nonrotating wire rope that failed in bending fatigue after operating over a sheave that was too small in diameter (Example 1)

Grooved drums offer greater control and uniformity of rope winding, compared with plain-faced drums. Moreover, where several layers are involved, grooved drums also influence the winding of the second and subsequent layers, provided the change from each layer to the next is accomplished properly. Grooving also provides some degree of circumferential support for the rope, which is advantageous to drum and rope life.

Maximum support is provided by grooving having a depth equal to half the diameter of the rope, if the contour is proper. However, it is seldom possible or advisable to make the grooves this deep. For some applications, deep grooves have another advantage: they help keep the rope winding properly where a swinging load or some other condition of abnormal displacement causes the rope to lead improperly to the drum.

Deep grooves can be a disadvantage by adding to rope abrasion and restricting the freedom of movement as the rope enters the groove. In leading to the drum, there is only one point where the lead is absolutely straight into the groove. On either side of this point some fleet angle is encountered. This causes rope and groove wear if the rope is confined around too much of its circumference.

There is seldom any advantage in designing a groove to have more than 150° circumferential support at the base, and in most cases it would be disadvantageous to do so. If single-layer winding is involved, and if deep grooves are necessary, this can be accomplished best by spreading the wraps apart and providing higher ridges between grooves.

It is important that grooved drums be designed with the proper pitch or distance from center to center of grooves to allow ample but not excessive clearance between successive wraps of rope. This is essential to prevent crowding and scrubbing of the oncoming rope against the rope already on the drum. To provide proper conditions for multiple-layer winding, the pitch between center of grooves should only be enough to prevent rope contact when winding under the maximum angle of fleet. The minimum values for groove pitch shown in Table 3 are suggested for both helical and parallel grooving, expressed in relation to the nominal rope diameter. These values for pitch of drum grooving, combined with a maximum fleet angle of 1 1/2°, have been recognized generally as satisfactory to prevent contact of the lead rope against the adjacent wrap on the drum.

Examples. In the following example, a sheave that was too small in diameter for the size and type of rope led to bending-fatigue failure of the rope.

Example 1. Bending-Fatigue Failure of a Steel Wire Hoisting Rope for a Stacker Crane Because of Insufficient Sheave Diameter (Fig. 3)

A 1/2-in.-diam 18x7 fiber-core improved plow steel nonrotating wire rope broke after 14 months of service on a stacker crane. Previously, 1/2-in.-diam 6x37 improved plow steel ropes with independent wire-rope cores had been used. These ropes were in service for 12 months. The change to an 18x7 rope was made because of difficulties caused by twisting of the 6x37 rope.

Investigation. Chemical analysis of the steel wire indicated a carbon content of 0.51 to 0.55%, as specified. The tensile strength of the individual wires averaged 179,000 psi, which was above average. The quality of the steel was satisfactory, with the crown wires showing very little wear.

The hoist arrangement for this crane consisted of one rope with each end attached to a separate drum; the rope wound around

Table 3. Groove Pitch on Drums With Helical and Parallel Grooving

Nominal rope diam, in.	Groove pitch, in.	Clearance, in. (a)	Nominal rope diam, in.	Groove pitch, in.	Clearance, in. (a)
1/4	9/32	1/32	1 1/8	1 11/64	3/64
5/16	11/32	1/32	1 1/4	1 5/16	1/16
3/8	13/32	1/32	1 3/8	1 7/16	1/16
7/16	15/32	1/32	1 1/2	1 9/16	1/16
1/2	17/32	1/32	1 5/8	1 23/32	3/32
9/16	19/32	1/32	1 3/4	1 27/32	3/32
5/8	21/32	1/32	1 7/8	1 31/32	3/32
3/4	25/32	1/32	2	2 3/32	3/32
7/8	59/64	3/64	2 1/8	2 7/32	3/32
1	1 3/64	3/64	2 1/4	2 11/32	3/32

(a) Clearance equals groove pitch minus nominal rope diameter.

Fig. 4. Steel wire rope with heavy corrosion and broken individual wires, resulting from intermittent underwater service (Example 2)

two 12-in.-diam sheaves in the block and back up and around an equalizer sheave (see Fig. 2b). The section of the rope that had been in contact with the sheaves was found by measurement checks. Reverse bending of the section of the rope normally subjected to this flexing revealed the presence of broken wire ends (shown in Fig. 3), which indicated that the rope failed by fatigue. Handbook tables indicated the minimum sheave diameter for a ½-in.-diam 18x7 wire rope should be 17 in. Thus, the 12-in.-diam sheaves were too small.

Conclusion. Failure of the wire rope occurred by bending fatigue. Continually running the same section of the rope over a sheave too small in diameter had resulted in excessive bending stresses.

Corrective Measures. The sheave diameter could not be increased, thus the flexibility of a 6x37 rope was required. The ½-in.-diam 18x7 rope was replaced by two ½-in.-diam 6x37 steel-core ropes stranded side-by-side, one with left lay and the other with right lay. The twisting problem was eliminated by the use of the two counterstranded cables.

Corrosion is a common cause of wire-rope failure. The corrosive atmospheres in which wire ropes operate are created by blast furnaces, cleaning tanks, plating tanks, and exposure to outdoor elements. The rope in the following example broke after being submerged in water throughout most of its service life.

Example 2. Corrosion Failure of a Steel Wire Rope After Intermittent Submersion in Water (Fig. 4)

A 1⅛-in.-diam 6x19 fiber-core improved plow steel wire rope that operated the crop car in a blooming mill broke in service. The break occurred a few feet from where the rope was connected to the car. When the car was at the bottom end of the track for loading, the end of the rope was under several feet of water.

Investigation. Visual examination of the rope disclosed heavy deposits of iron oxide (rust) between strands and between the wires in strands, as shown in Fig. 4. Metallurgical examination of the frayed wires showed the quality of the wire to be satisfactory.

Conclusion. Failure of the rope was the result of heavy corrosion (rusting).

Corrective Measure. Greasing of the rope provided a moisture barrier and improved service life.

Shock loading of a wire rope can cause it to vibrate, producing high-frequency cyclic bending stresses in the rope. Vibration is most severe at the connection end of the rope, and can result in fatigue failure, as in the following example.

Example 3. Fatigue Failure of a Steel Wire Rope Resulting From Shock Loading (Fig. 5)

The wire rope on a cleaning-line crane broke while lifting a normal load of coils. This rope, which was specified for the application, was ⁷⁄₁₆-in.-diam 8x19 fiber-core rope of improved plow steel wire. Service life of the rope was five weeks; average expected life was six weeks. The rope was inspected weekly.

Investigation. Visual examination of a section of the wire rope adjacent to the fracture revealed several broken wires and fraying of the fiber core, as shown in Fig. 5(a). The construction and mechanical properties of the rope were as specified.

Metallurgical examination of several wires revealed a uniform cold drawn microstructure with no evidence of severe abrasion or of martensite. Microscopic examination of a longitudinal section of a wire revealed fatigue cracks originating from both sides of the wire, as shown in Fig. 5(b). One crack changed direction and propagated parallel to the centerline of the wire. The diameter of the sheave on the bale,

(a)

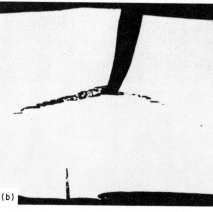

(b)

(a) Section of the wire rope adjacent to the fracture, at about 1½×. (b) Micrograph, at about 75×, of an unetched longitudinal section of a wire from the rope, showing fatigue cracks originating from both sides.

Fig. 5. Steel wire rope, used on a cleaning-line crane, that failed from fatigue resulting from vibration caused by shock loading (Example 3)

Fig. 6. Micrograph, at 265×, of a 5%-nital-etched transverse section through 0.102-in.-diam steel wire. Light-etching surface layer (at top) is untempered martensite; adjacent dark-etching zone is self-tempered martensite. The matrix was composed of deformed pearlite.

10⅝ in., was slightly below that specified for the ⁷⁄₁₆-in.-diam rope.

Observation of the crane in operation revealed that in rolling the coils over the edge of the rinse tank after pickling, the hook received a sudden shock load, which was transmitted to the rope, causing vibrations. The vibrations were most severe at the clamped end of the rope.

Conclusion. Failure of the rope was attributed to fatigue, resulting from vibration caused by shock loading.

Corrective Measures. Pitched roll plates were installed between the tanks where rolling of coils was required. The plates reduced the free fall of the coils and aided in rolling. Also, the diameter of the sheave was increased to 13 in.

Scrubbing of a wire rope against a foreign object can cause excessive heating of the crowns of the outside wires. Because these regions are small in comparison to the total area of the wire, they may be rapidly quenched to a martensitic structure by the adjacent and underlying cooler metal. Martensite has very little ductility and will readily crack under the slightest bend.

Martensite is more easily formed in rope made of the higher-carbon grades of steel wire. Two ropes were analyzed that had operated under similar conditions as main lines in a logging machine. The ropes were 1¼ in. in diameter and of 6x19 IWRC (independent wire rope core) construction. One of the ropes had a carbon content of 0.685% and a manganese content of 0.607%, whereas the other rope had a carbon content of 0.751% and a manganese content of 0.607%.

Both ropes developed martensite on the crowns of the outside wires. The martensite was caused by the friction and heat generated by the action of the rope sliding against the sides of the sheave. The outside wires were rapidly heated and then rapidly quenched by the adjacent metal. The difference in carbon contents demonstrated itself in that the layer of martensite formed was greater in the wires containing the greater amount of carbon. Figure 6 is a micrograph showing the martensite layer developed by the wires having 0.685%

carbon content. The ropes containing the 0.751% C wires displayed a deeper layer of martensite. The rope made of the lower-carbon wires had a life of about three times the other; however, this life was not considered satisfactory. Once the martensite had been formed by the same abusive conditions, the rope with the least amount of martensite (or lower carbon content) was the one that lasted longer. However, the formation of martensite must be avoided, which means that the cause of failure was the abuse the ropes received and not necessarily the carbon contents or the martensite formation.

The following example describes the failure of a wire rope on which a brittle layer of martensite formed on the crowns of the outside wires.

(a) Crushed rope, at 1.8×, showing abraded wires and crown wear. (b) Micrograph, at 500×, of nital-etched specimen, showing martensite layer (top) and uniform, heavily drawn microstructure.

Fig. 7. Wire rope, made of improved plow steel and a fiber core, that failed because of heavy abrasion and crushing under normal loading (Example 4)

Example 4. Fatigue Fracture of Individual Steel Wires in a Hoisting Rope Originating in a Martensitic Layer Formed by Heavy Abrasion (Fig. 7)

The wire rope on a crane in a scrapyard broke after two weeks of service under normal loading conditions. Expected life of the wire rope was two months. The rope was 5/8-in.-diam 6x37 fiber-core improved plow steel. This type of rope is made of 0.71 to 0.75% C steel wires, with a tensile strength of 246,000 to 278,000 psi.

The rope became damaged while it was attached to a chain for pulling jammed scrap from the baler. The chain broke during this operation, skipping the cable up on the edge of the sheave. The rope then apparently seated itself in a kink on the flange of the sheave.

Investigation. As shown in Fig. 7(a), the rope was heavily abraded (scrubbed) and crushed. Also, several of the individual wires were broken.

Metallographic examination of several of the broken wires revealed a uniform cold drawn microstructure, with patches of untempered martensite in regions of severe abrasion and crown wear.

Chemical analysis of the wire showed a carbon content of only 0.46%, whereas 0.71 to 0.75% C was specified. The tensile strength (235,000 psi) was below specification.

A hard layer of martensite (see Fig. 7b) was formed on the wires as a result of abrasion. This surface layer, being very brittle, was susceptible to fatigue cracking while bending around the sheave.

Conclusions. The wire rope failed in fatigue because of the brittle layer of martensite on the wires. Both the carbon content and the tensile strength of the wires were below specifications.

Corrective Measures. Because of a record of poor service life on this wire rope, 6x19 rope was substituted because it withstands abrasion and drum crushing to a greater degree than 6x37. Service life was doubled after this change in rope construction.

Exposure of a wire rope to excessively high temperatures in service, with resultant loss of tensile strength, caused the failure described in the next example.

Example 5. Failure of Steel Wire Rope Because of Overheating

A 1½-in.-diam 6x37 rope of improved plow steel wire broke in service during dumping of a ladle of hot slag.

Investigation. Examination of the rope showed a heavy blue oxide extending 2 to 3 ft back from each side of the break. The broken ends of the rope showed tensile fractures. Microscopic examination of the wires adjacent to the break revealed that the steel had been recrystallized. The rope had thus been heated in excess of 700 C (about 1300 F). The tensile strength of the wires in the rope that broke was 130,000 psi, whereas the specification required 250,000 psi.

Conclusion. Failure of the wire rope was attributed to overheating, which resulted in a 50% loss of tensile strength.

Recommendation. Wire ropes must not be subjected to extremes of heat, such as exposure to hot slag, except for brief, intermittent periods of time. Prolonged or continuous exposure will cause a rapid deterioration of service life.

Fracture of elevator cables resulting from fatigue under varying conditions of cyclic torsional and tensile stresses is described in the next example.

Example 6. Fatigue Fracture of a Steel 8x19 Elevator Cable Resulting From Varying Cyclic Torsional and Tensile Stresses (Fig. 8)

Fracture occurred in one of six cables on a passenger elevator. The elevator continued to operate on the remaining five cables until routine inspection discovered the broken cable. The cable was made of 5/8-in.-diam steel wire rope designated as 8x19 G Preformed Extra High Strength Special Traction Elevator Cable with fiber core. The cables had been in service for 1½ years. The end of the wire rope was sealed into a conical shape (see Fig. 8a) in a low-melting alloy. Fracture occurred at the shackle where the end of the cable was socketed.

The fractured end, a length of wire rope away from the fracture, and several mounted specimens of various wires from

the rope were examined. Samples of wire received were: 0.0456-in.-diam heart wire, 0.0405-in.-diam outer wire and 0.023-in.-diam inner wire.

Investigation. Close examination of the wire rope under a stereomicroscope revealed two general types of fracture:

1 A flat-type fracture in the samples of larger-diameter (0.0456 and 0.0405 in.) wires
2 A cup-and-cone type of fracture in the samples of smaller-diameter (0.023 in.) wire.

Generally, the larger wires, which failed with a flat-type fracture, were rusted; the smaller wires were oxidized but were not as heavily rusted. Figure 8(b) illustrates the fractured ends typical of the larger wires as received, and Fig. 8(c) after removal of the rust. Arrow A in Fig. 8(c) locates what appeared to be a nick in the side of the wire; at arrow B is a bright, smooth area containing beach marks radiating inward, which indicated fatigue cracking. Flat-type fractures were believed to result under cyclic stresses with the major stress component being torsional.

The nature of ductile behavior in the 0.023-in.-diam wires is illustrated in Fig. 8(d) as a reduction in area in a necked-down region under excessive tensile stress without fracture. The fracture surfaces of the smaller-diameter wires were slightly oxidized; however, some bright regions could be seen, which indicated that the smaller wires broke later than the larger-diameter wires.

Numerous specimens were examined microscopically on a longitudinal plane at the failed ends. The typical microscopic characteristics of the larger wires are shown in Fig. 8(e). The important features shown in Fig. 8(e) are the cleanness of the material, microstructure, and the nature of the failure. No evidence of material or processing defects could be associated with the failure. It appears that as transverse cracking occurs under cyclic torsional stresses, longitudinal cracking follows as the transverse cracking progresses, placing the maximum torsional fiber stress below the surface. Because of the fibrous nature of cold drawn materials, longitudinal crack propagation would be expected under conditions of cyclic torsional loading with transverse

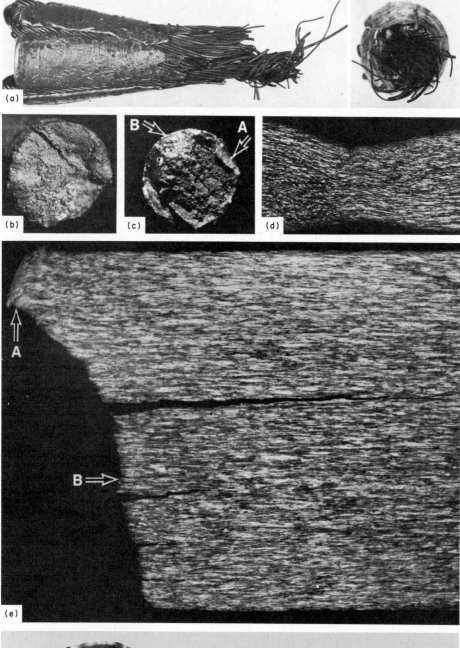

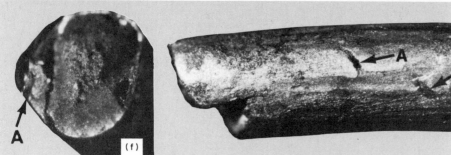

(a) Conical shape in a low-melting alloy at end of cable, and end of broken cable. (b) Fractograph, at 25×, of 0.0465-in.-diam wire as received. (c) Fractograph, at 25×, of 0.0465-in.-diam wire after cleaning with a cold aqueous solution of 10% HCl. At A is a nick in side of wire; at B is a bright, smooth area containing fatigue marks. (d) Micrograph, at 55×, of longitudinal section of 0.023-in.-diam wire etched in 2% nital, showing necked region. (e) Micrograph, at 100×, of 2%-nital-etched longitudinal section through 0.0465-in.-diam wire, showing cold working at A, flat-type fracture surface at B, and longitudinal cracks. The microstructure contained cold worked fine pearlite with some ferrite. (f) The fractured end (left) and longitudinal view (right), both at 34×, of 0.0405-in.-diam wire. Arrows at A's point to nick in a region showing cold working and wear in service. At B is a secondary crack origin.

Fig. 8. Fatigue fracture of an 8x19 steel wire rope used as an elevator cable. The fracture resulted from cyclic torsional and tensile stresses. (Example 6)

crack propagation. Restriction of free movement of the socket-end in the shackle would be expected to promote fracture by increasing the magnitude of the torsional stress under cyclic loading.

Evidence of torsional stress also was observed in the 0.0405-in.-diam wires. Nicks and cold working on the surfaces of the wire in the region of fracture are shown in Fig. 8(f). This particular wire probably failed under greater tensile stress after the heart wires (0.0465 in. diam) broke. Ductility of this wire is indicated by some necking down and cup-and-cone characteristics in the fracture surface. Most of the wires examined showed essentially flat-type fractures. The cleanness of the wire in the region of fracture also is illustrated in Fig. 8(f).

Conclusions. Mechanical damage to the surfaces of the wires was sufficient to nucleate fatigue cracking under the stresses encountered in service.

The wire rope was composed of several sizes of wire, and fracture of the larger-diameter wires appeared to have occurred earliest as denoted by the amount of rust present on the fracture surfaces. The smaller-diameter wires behaved in a ductile manner under excessive loads prior to ultimate failure. The degree of oxidation on the fracture surfaces indicated that ductile fracture of the smaller-diameter wires occurred after fracture of the larger-diameter wires. The microstructure and cleanness of the material appeared normal for the application and could not be associated with the broken wires examined.

Stress-corrosion cracking frequently occurs in terminals that have been roll swaged on ends of wire ropes for marine use. In the following example, rolling lines were evident after swaging, which acted as stress raisers. Cracks developed along these stress raisers, and corrosion by seawater occurred in the cracks.

Example 7. Stress-Corrosion Cracking of a Type 303(Se) Stainless Steel Wire-Rope Terminal by Seawater Along Hairline Cracks Produced in Swaging (Fig. 9)

An eye terminal made of type 303(Se) stainless steel that was roll swaged on the end of a ⅜-in.-diam wire rope was found to have cracked extensively after one year of service. The terminal was sectioned and specimens were mounted for metallographic examination.

Investigation. Examination of one specimen revealed that a hairline crack had initiated at the inner surface of the fitting. Holes in the region adjoining the crack and rough texture of the crack surface, as shown in Fig. 9, indicated that a corrosive medium (presumably seawater) had entered the crack from the inner surface of the fitting and, coupled with the hairline crack, developed crevice corrosion. High residual stresses in the swaged metal caused the crack to propagate toward the outer surface, followed closely by corrosion. The last 0.012 in. of metal thickness failed in pure tension as evidenced by the smooth appearance of the crack surface in this region.

Swaging creates a few small cracks in the surface of the hole in a terminal, particu-

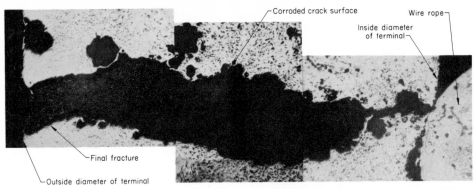

Fig. 9. Composite micrograph, at 75×, of a transverse section through a type 303(Se) stainless steel eye terminal for a wire rope, showing corroded crack surface and final-fracture region (Example 7)

larly when swaging onto stranded wire rope. Residual stresses plus load stress and corrosion frequently result in stress corrosion.

Conclusion. The terminal failed by stress-corrosion cracking as a result of residual stresses from swaging, load stresses and corrosion by seawater.

Recommendations. Rotary swaging or swaging in a punch press are recommended instead of roll swaging. Roll swaging is accomplished by nonsymmetrical radial metal deformation. The size of internal cracks is likely to be greater under these conditions than when swaging is accomplished in a more uniform symmetrical reduction, such as by rotary swaging or by press swaging. Corrosion then combines with the internal stress-strain condition to cause stress-corrosion cracking.

Chains

Chains made of resistance welded plain, low-carbon steel are in wide use and generally are acceptable. However, to ensure safety and to minimize chain failures, heat treated alloy steel chains with a hardness range of 302 to 352 Bhn should be used. This hardness range is recommended to reduce the frequency of brittle fractures and to avoid premature wear and excessive stretching. However, it is much more desirable for a chain to stretch, or to exhibit wear, than to be so hard that it can fail by brittle fracture from a small fatigue crack, as often happens to chains with a hardness of 375 Bhn and higher.

Fatigue cracks in chains usually are initiated at one of the following origins:

1 A heavily cold worked zone resulting from misuse of the chain
2 A weld zone with entrapped inclusions, or with inadequate weld penetration
3 The portion of a weld at the inside surface of a link, which, because of its position, cannot be planed smooth as can the outside surface.

In the investigation of chain failures, the following possibilities must be considered in determining the cause of failure:

1 Subjection of the chain to sudden impact loads or unbalanced loads

2 Kinks, twists or knots in the chain, which create severe stresses that can bend, weaken and break chain links
3 Deterioration of the chain by strain, usage, corrosion, or operation at elevated temperatures. The specified load limit should be reduced when alloy steel chains are used at temperatures above 260 C (500 F). Chains should be replaced when wear has exceeded the manufacturer's specified limit.
4 Stretching of the chain, which usually is indicative of overloading and which can be avoided by the use of proper chain size. Stretch often is expressed in terms of percentage of over-all length. This is not recommended, because often individual links may be severely elongated and thus only a small portion of the entire chain is stretched. Inspection of a chain to determine degree of stretching should be done link by link.
5 Improper repair. Alloy steel chains should always be identified as such to ensure that any repairs (for example, replacement of damaged sections or joiner links) are made properly. Usually, alloy steel chains are returned to suppliers for repair and proof testing.

Regular inspection of chains is imperative. Where many chains are in service, inspection is usually done by visual means. There are critical applications, however, where magnetic-particle or liquid-penetrant inspection should be utilized. Inspection of individual links by these methods is a slow and tedious process and is carried out only when chain failure would cause injury to personnel and damage to equipment.

Weld defects are common causes of chain failures, as described in the following example.

Example 8. Fracture of a 4615 Steel Chain Link Because of a Weld Defect (Fig. 10)

A resistance-welded chain link made from ⅝-in.-diam 4615 steel broke while lowering a ten-ton load of billets into a rail car. The acceptable load limit of the chain was approximately 15 tons. The chain had been in service for 13 months. Because of the large number of chains in service and the fact that chains were left around billets in storage, no routine inspection was carried out.

Observations. The link broke at the weld. Beach marks, typical of fatigue, originating at the inside of the link, are shown at the arrow in Fig. 10(a). Metallographic examination of a section through the fracture surface revealed cracks (at A's in Fig. 10b) in the weld zone, which were up to 0.049 in. deep. Examination of this region at a magnification of 65 diameters showed that the

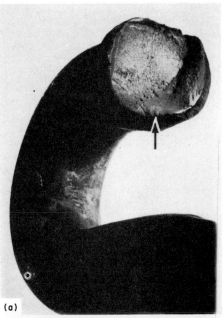

(a) A fracture surface of the chain link, at 2×, showing fatigue beach marks progressing across the surface from the inside of the link.

(b) View at 5× of a nital-etched longitudinal section through the link, showing fracture origin, at O, and weld cracks, at A's. Weld cracks at top were approximately 0.049 in. deep.

Fig. 10. Resistance welded 4615 steel chain link that broke because of a weld defect (Example 8)

cracks were filled with scale, indicating that they had formed during resistance welding of the link. The chain was made of fine-grained, quenched-and-tempered 4615 steel with a hardness of 285 Bhn, as specified.

Conclusion. Failure of the chain link was attributed to weld defects, which acted as stress raisers from which fatigue cracks originated.

Corrective Measures. Inspection revealed welding laps in all chains in service. All such chains were removed from service and replaced with defect-free chains. The chain manufacturer changed the method of welding to ensure defect-free chain links.

Ductility of the material from which chain links are made has a marked effect on chain life, as in the following example.

Example 9. Brittle Fracture of Alloy Steel Chain Links Because of Excessive Hardness

Over a one-year period, chain-link fractures occurred in many of several thousand ⅝-in.-diam alloy steel sling chains used for handling billets. Several shipments of new chains had been acquired because of expansion of production facilities. No failures had occurred prior to delivery of the new chains.

Observations. The links broke at the weld, with the breaks originating at the inside of the link. The breaks often were undetected because the broken links opened only slightly at the fracture line. There had been no fracture-related damage to the links. Metallographic examination revealed no weld irregularities. All failures occurred in links having hardness values in the range of 375 to 444 Bhn.

Upon contacting the supplier it was learned that the hardness level of the new chain links was 375 to 444 Bhn, a change from the previous hardness level of 302 to 375 Bhn. This increase in hardness was done in order to minimize wear, but it made the links notch sensitive, resulting in fractures that initiated at the butt-weld flash on the inside surfaces of the links. It is believed that most of the fractures occurred during the winter months; the low temperatures undoubtedly caused a further reduction in ductility.

Conclusions. The chain links failed in a brittle manner because the high hardness of the material made it notch sensitive, particularly at low temperatures.

Corrective Measures. All chains were visually inspected, and those with broken links were returned to the supplier for repair. All chains were retempered to a hardness range of 302 to 375 Bhn.

All new alloy steel sling chains were subsequently ordered to a hardness of 302 to 352 Bhn. No failures of this type were reported to have occurred since the chains were retempered and the hardness requirement of 302 to 352 Bhn was introduced.

Hooks

Hooks are designed for individual applications to suit the type of load, the size and weight of the load, the intended service environment, and the degree of versatility required.

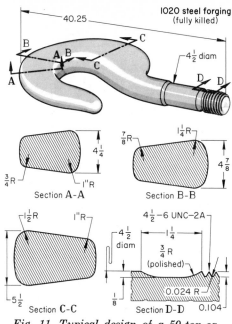

Fig. 11. Typical design of a 50-ton-capacity 1020 steel C-hook, with a stress-relief groove at end of threads and well-proportioned radii in body

Failures of hooks commonly occur, and hooks are continually being altered in order to avoid future failures. Among these alterations are changes in method of fabrication, grade of steel, heat treatment, and design. In general, the most important features required of a hook material are excellent fatigue properties and resistance to brittle fracture. It is desirable for a hook to exhibit wear rather than to fracture in a brittle manner, because of the possible serious injury and damage that can result. Such a hook should be evaluated visually while in service, and if signs of excessive wear are found, the hook should be removed from service for repair or replacement. If worn in the saddle region, a hook may be ground smooth within the specified reduction limit (usually, a maximum of 20% of the cross-sectional depth), renormalized if originally in a normalized condition (or otherwise thermally treated, depending on its prior treatment), and returned to service. If fatigue cracks are found by magnetic-particle inspection, it may be possible to eliminate these cracks by grinding within the specified limits; if not, the hook should be scrapped.

Welding on crane hooks is to be discouraged. When welding must be done for attaching safety devices or joining of laminated sections, the welding should be followed by a heat treatment that will eliminate any hard spots or residual stresses in the heat-affected zone.

Frequently, hooks that have been in service for a considerable length of time are given a stress relief to eliminate the effects of cold working from repeated lifting contacts by chains or rings.

Materials for Crane Hooks. C-hooks, pin hooks, coil hooks and sister hooks usually are forged from fully killed, fine-grained carbon or alloy steels. Extremely large ladle hooks and coil hooks are made of laminated plate sections (see Fig. 13c). Specifications governing forgings for industrial use are given in ASTM A235 and ASTM A237; the user may augment these specifications as required.

Low-carbon (1018, 1020 or 1025) and medium-carbon (1045) steels are widely used in either the normalized or the quenched-and-tempered condition. Alloy steels used include the 8620, 4320, 4130 and 4140 grades, generally in the quenched-and-tempered condition. The low-carbon steels usually have greater resistance to crack propagation.

Other alloy steels, or other materials, may be required in certain corrosive atmospheres, or because of weight limitations placed on the hook.

Some hooks have been made of cast steel. Derrick hooks, for example, may be of quenched-and-tempered 4140 cast steel. This heat treated steel has excellent fatigue properties. L-shape hooks, such as coil hooks, are usually constructed of low-alloy steel. Hooks that are torch cut from plate often fail because of cracks initiated in the torch-hardened zone. Such items should be thermally treated to eliminate this condition. A riveted, laminated L-shape hook is much more desirable.

Depending on their ultimate service requirements, hooks are frequently magnetic-particle inspected or ultrasonically tested during processing and at final inspection.

Design of C-Hook. The design of the hook shown in Fig. 11 has been developed from years of experience, and since its employment in a large steel complex, no failures of hooks of this design have occurred. The hook design may be adjusted to accommodate any load limit, such as 5 tons, 20 tons or 50 tons. The hook is forged from fully killed fine-grained 1020 steel, and is normalized after forging. This steel exhibits excellent fatigue properties and will wear rather than fail in a brittle manner.

Many hooks break at large changes in section, or at poorly blended radiused section changes in the shank. The design shown in Fig. 11 avoids severe section changes. An important feature of this hook is the stress-relief groove at the end of the threads. If the nut is turned past the last thread, as it should be so as not to concentrate the stress at the bottom of the exposed thread groove, the stresses will be distributed over the length of the stress-relief groove, minimizing stress concentrations. The depth of a properly designed groove exceeds that of the thread roots. The thread design illustrated also has been found to be op-

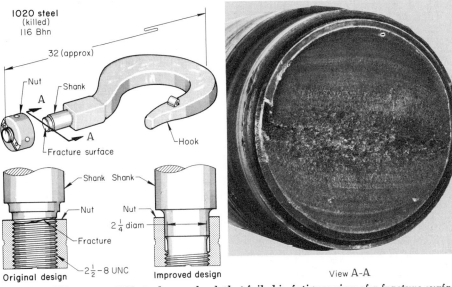

View A-A

Fig. 12. Fifteen-ton 1020 steel crane hook that failed in fatigue; view of a fracture surface of the hook, showing beach marks; and original and improved designs for the nut and the threaded end of the hook (Example 10)

timum. It is important, as with all hooks, to avoid rough-machining marks in the threads. Also, the nuts should be individually fitted to hooks.

Control and Testing. All hooks must be clearly identified, and accurate records must be kept of their characteristic features and location in the plant. Hooks should be inspected at least once a year, if not more often, depending on the predicted service life and the severity of the application. Magnetic-particle and liquid-penetrant inspection are common methods of inspecting hooks. If feasible, new hooks should be checked by magnetic-particle inspection and spark tested to ensure that the correct grade of steel has been used.

Examples. In the following example, a poorly designed stress-relief groove and chatter marks on thread flanks acted as stress raisers, causing failure of a hook.

Example 10. Fatigue Fracture of a 1020 Steel Crane Hook (Fig. 12)

The crane hook shown in Fig. 12 broke in the threaded shank while lifting a load of 10 tons. The crane was nominally rated at 15 tons. Service life of the hook was not known. The nut, still threaded on the broken shank, and the hook were sent to the laboratory for failure analysis.

Investigation. Chemical analysis of the metal in the hook showed that it was killed 1020 steel; the steel had a hardness of 116 Bhn and was judged to be satisfactory for the application.

Visual examination disclosed that fracture had occurred at the last thread on the shank. Rough-machining marks and chatter marks were evident on the threads. The fourth thread from the fracture had a small crack at the root. Beach marks emanating from the thread-root locations on opposite sides of the fracture surface (see view A-A in Fig. 12) identified these locations as the origins of the fracture.

Metallographic examination revealed a medium-coarse, slightly acicular structure, indicating that the material was in the as-forged condition. Light segregation and nonmetallic inclusions were present, but the material was considered sound.

Conclusions. Fracture of the hook resulted from fatigue cracking that originated at stress concentrations in the root of the last thread.

Life of the hook was shortened considerably because the material was in the as-forged condition, which resulted in low fatigue strength.

Corrective Measures. The crane hook was normalized after forging to produce the most desirable structure. A stress-relief groove with a diameter slightly smaller than the root diameter was placed at the end of the thread, and a large-radius fillet was machined at the change in diameters of the shank. Also, the nut was redesigned to extend beyond the threaded portion to relieve the stresses (see "Improved design" in Fig. 12).

Undercutting the last thread, using large-radius fillets, and ensuring that all crane hooks were properly normalized prevented additional failures for a period of about 16 years.

Heat-affected zones produced by torch cutting of hooks from plate can be initiation sites for cracks, as described in the example that follows.

Example 11. Fatigue Fracture of a 12-Ton 1040 Steel Coil Hook Because of Hardened Zone at Torch-Cut Surface (Fig. 13)

A 12-ton coil hook failed after eight years of service while lifting a load of 15 tons. The hook had been torch cut from 1040 steel plate.

Investigation. The inner surface of the hook exhibited the normal ironing (wear) marks. Visual examination of the fracture surface indicated that cracking had originated at the inside radius of the hook, as shown in Fig. 13(a). Beach marks, typical

of fatigue fracture, extended over approximately 20% of the fracture surface. The surface containing the beach marks was stained; the surface of the final-fracture region was bright.

Macroscopic examination of the torch-cut surfaces revealed numerous cracks. Figure 13(b) is a macrograph of an etched section through the hook, showing cracks that were initiated in a hardened martensitic zone at the torch-cut surface. One crack is shown

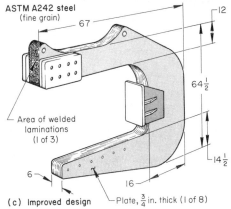

(a) Original design

(b)

(c) Improved design

Fig. 13. (a) Fracture region of a 12-ton coil hook that was torch cut from 1040 steel. (b) Macrograph at 7½× of a nital-etched section, showing cracks propagating from the surface (top), which was hardened and embrittled during torch cutting. (c) Replacement hook of laminated design made of ASTM A242 fine-grain steel plate (Example 11)

Fig. 14. Fatigue-fracture surface and keyway of a broken 1030 steel pinion shaft (Example 13)

extending into the coarse pearlite structure beneath the martensitic zone.

Conclusion. The hook fractured by fatigue that originated at the brittle martensitic surface produced in torch cutting. The 25% overload contributed to the failure. The hook should have been normalized after torch cutting.

Corrective Measure. The coil hooks were remade to a laminated design (see Fig. 13c); these hooks were flame cut from ASTM A242 fine-grain steel plate, then ground to remove the material damaged by flame cutting. The hooks were stress relieved at 620 C (1150 F) after welding but before riveting the wear pads. No failures were reported to have been encountered since adoption of the laminated design.

A forging defect and a medium-coarse, acicular as-forged structure were responsible for failure of the chain-sling hook described in the following example.

Example 12. Failure of a Forged Semikilled 1015 Steel Hook on a ½-In.-Diam Chain Sling

A hook on a two-leg chain sling broke while lifting an 11,000-lb load. The included angle between the two ½-in.-diam chains was 60°. The service life of the sling was 2½ years.

Investigation. The safe load limit for each leg of the sling was 5800 lb. The hook broke at the junction of the eye and shank. The diameter of the hook at this junction was approximately ⅞ in.

Visual examination of the fracture region revealed light intergranular oxidation at the surface on the side of the hook where cracking started. Approximately 50% of the fracture surface contained beach marks; the remainder contained cleavage facets.

Metallographic examination showed a medium-coarse, acicular as-forged structure. The internal cleanness and soundness of the metal were satisfactory. Chemical analysis showed the metal to be semikilled 1015 steel.

Conclusion. Fatigue fracture was initiated at a region of intergranular oxidation that developed during forging. The acicular as-forged structure provided poor fatigue and impact properties, which contributed to failure of the hook.

Corrective Measure. The chain-sling hook was replaced by one made of normalized, fully killed, fine-grained 1020 steel.

Shafts

The most common or recurring initiation sites for fatigue fractures in shafts are: (*a*) section changes with insufficient fillet radii; (*b*) roughly machined keyways and section changes; (*c*) intersections of keyways with section changes; (*d*) improperly located grease holes; and (*e*) fretting corrosion from connecting attachments.

Shafts usually are subjected to bending or torsional loading, or both. Careful visual examination of the fracture surfaces can provide the information necessary to identify the actual manner of loading. Bending stresses are largely the result of misalignment of bearings, fittings or couplings, and usually are difficult to eliminate completely. Although a particular steel may be satisfactory for a certain application under normal conditions, misalignment will impose further stresses that result in the shaft being unsuitable for the application.

To provide a greater margin of safety, which is justified for lifting equipment, it is recommended that the shaft material

Fig. 15. Change in section in a 1040 steel main hoist shaft, where a fatigue crack (arrow) was initiated at rough-machining marks and a break in a fillet (Example 14)

be upgraded from the normally used hot rolled medium-carbon steel to quenched-and-tempered carbon or alloy steel. Such shafting, particularly alloy steel when properly heat treated, displays superior fatigue properties and is much less susceptible to service failures. The danger and downtime resulting from a shaft failure make upgrading by heat treatment or a change in material economically feasible. It is presumed, of course, that any required improvement in design, such as increasing fillet radii or removing keyways from shoulders, also would be considered prior to or incorporated with any change in processing or material.

For a more complete discussion of shaft failures, see the article that begins on page 373 in this volume.

Rough-machining marks, chatter marks, and sharp corners serve as initiation sites for fatigue fractures of shafts. The next example describes a crane shaft that failed by fatigue that originated at a sharp corner at the end of a keyway.

Example 13. Fatigue Fracture of a 1030 Steel Crane Shaft Originating at a Sharp Corner (Fig. 14)

A drum pinion shaft, part of the hoisting gear of a 20-ton-capacity crane operating in a blooming mill, broke while the crane was lifting a 10-ton load. Specifications indicated that the shaft was made of 1030 steel in the as-rolled condition.

Investigation. The end of the broken shaft containing the keyway was visually examined (see Fig. 14). The keyway extended into a shoulder at a change in diameter; chatter marks, rough-machining marks, and sharp corner radii were visible in the keyway. Also, at each end of the keyway was a circular recess below the normal keyway surface — an outdated method of machining a keyway that is used infrequently. Both the bottoms and the sides of the recesses contained tool marks.

Examination of the fracture surface, shown in Fig. 14, revealed that the origin of fracture was a sharp corner at the end of the keyway. Beach marks radiated from the origin over a large portion of the fracture surface. The final-fracture zone, a small ductile shear lip, was approximately 30° off-center, indicating low stress and rotational bending. (See Fig. 12 on page 102 in the article on Fatigue Failures, and Fig. 5 on page 377 in the article on Failures of Shafts.)

The shaft material was 1030 steel as specified, and had a slightly acicular, fine-grained structure.

Conclusion. The shaft failed by fatigue fracture, which originated at a sharp corner at the end of a keyway at a change in section.

Corrective Measures. A replacement shaft was made of 4140 steel, quenched and tempered to a hardness of 286 to 319 Bhn. The keyway was moved away from the change in section and was machined with a 1/16-in. radius in the bottom corners. A larger-radius fillet was machined at the change in section.

In the following example, improper blending of the fillet at a change in section created a stress raiser at which cracking was initiated.

Example 14. Fatigue Cracking of a 1040 Steel Main Hoist Shaft Originating in Fillet at Change in Section (Fig. 15)

The 5½-in.-diam main hoist shaft of a mobile shovel was found to have multiple crack indications when ultrasonically inspected in the field. A crack indication located approximately 6 in. from the gear end extended around the shaft at a change in section adjacent to the bearing surface. The shaft, of 1040 steel, was removed for further examination. It had been in service for three years. A previous shaft had failed after a short service life.

Investigation. Magnetic-particle inspection of the shaft showed a crack around the entire circumference at the change in section, as shown in Fig. 15. The fillet at the change of section where the crack was located was well polished and generally free of rough-machining marks. However, the crack coincided with the junction of the fillet and the smaller diameter (4¼ in.) at this change in section. A slight step, or break, in the continuity of the ⁵⁄₁₆-in.-radius fillet and some heavy machining marks were noted at this junction. Microscopic examination of a section through the crack indication revealed a fine crack extending 0.10 in. from the surface, originating at the machining marks.

Chemical analysis of the shaft indicated that it was made of 1040 steel. Hardness was 170 Bhn. Metallographic examination revealed a fine, uniform, normalized structure.

Conclusion. The shaft failed by fatigue; the step at the base of the fillet was the point of initiation of the fatigue crack. The shaft was underdesigned from a material standpoint; 1040 steel with a hardness of 170 Bhn was too low in fatigue strength.

Corrective Measures. Shaft material was changed to 4140 steel oil quenched and tempered to a hardness of 302 to 352 Bhn. All discontinuities related to fillet machining were also removed. With the above changes, no further failures were encountered.

Lubrication holes and grooves that interrupt the surface of a shaft are sources of stress concentration, as described in the following example.

Example 15. Fatigue Fracture of a 4140 Steel Pin at Intersection of Grease Hole and Surface Groove (Fig. 16)

A 3½-in.-diam, 13-in.-long pin (see Fig. 16a) that connected the holding shoe to the pressure lever in a 20-ton bail was found on inspection to be broken. The pin, of 4140 steel, had been in service for 2½ years.

Investigation. Visual examination of the fracture surface (Fig. 16b) of the pin revealed that fracture had initiated at the intersection of a ¼-in.-diam grease hole and the surface lubrication groove. Beach marks extended over 90% of the fracture surface. The position of the final-fracture region indicated that the pin had been subjected to a unidirectional bending load. There was a sharp corner where the surface lubrication

(a)

(b)

(a) Fractured pin, showing the roughly machined surface of the lubrication groove and the drilled center grease hole. (About 0.3×)

(b) A fracture surface of the pin, showing beach marks originating at the intersection of the groove and the drilled hole. (About 0.6×)

Fig. 16. Pin, of 4140 steel, that fractured by fatigue at intersection of a grease hole and a lubrication groove (Example 15)

groove intersected the ¼-in.-diam hole. The surface of the groove contained rough-machining marks, as shown in Fig. 16(a). Chemical analysis of the material indicated that the pin was made of 4140 steel. The pin had a hardness of 285 Bhn.

Conclusion. The pin failed in fatigue from unidirectional bending. The sharp corner at the intersection of the grease hole and the surface groove was the initiation site of the fatigue crack.

Corrective Measures. The lubrication hole was chamfered for better stress dis-

tribution, and machining marks in the grease groove were avoided. No further failures were encountered after these measures were instituted.

Shafts used in lifting equipment are frequently subjected to reversed torsional loading. Insufficient fillets at the roots of spline teeth act as stress raisers, and when the shaft is subjected to torsional loading, fracture frequently occurs, as in the example that follows.

Example 16. Fatigue Fracture of a 4140 Steel Cross-Travel Shaft as a Result of Reversed Torsional Loading (Fig. 17)

The horizontal cross-travel shaft on a derrick broke after two years of service. Specifications required the shaft to be made of 4140 steel quenched and tempered to a hardness of 302 to 352 Bhn.

Investigation. Examination revealed that the shaft had fractured approximately ½ in. from the change in section between the splined end and the shaft proper. At this point, the cracks propagated in the longitudinal and transverse directions until failure occurred, as shown in Fig. 17(a). A transverse section through the spline (see Fig. 17b) showed that the longitudinal cracks had been initiated at the sharp corners at the roots of the spline teeth. The cracks visible in Fig. 17(b) were highlighted by techniques used in magnetic-particle inspection. Operation of the derrick had subjected the shaft to reversed torsional loading.

Conclusion. The shaft fractured in fatigue from reversed torsional loading; the sharp corners at the roots of the spline teeth acted as initiation sites for fatigue cracks.

Corrective Measures. The fillets at the roots of the spline teeth were increased in size and polished, to minimize stress concentrations in these areas, and no further shaft failures occurred.

Cranes and Related Members

Failures resulting in the immobilization of cranes most often are related to shafts (which have been discussed pre-

(a)

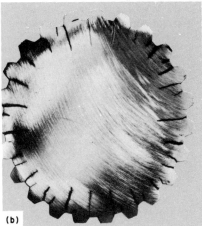
(b)

Fig. 17. (a) Broken end of a 4140 steel cross-travel shaft from a derrick, showing the star-type fracture that results from reversed torsional loading. (b) Transverse section through the spline, showing cracks initiated at sharp corners at the roots of the spline teeth. (Example 16)

viously), structural members (as related primarily to grade of steel and fabrication practice), crane wheels, and rail runways. The most common cause of failure is poor welding practice. Poor welding practice, such as a lack of preheat or postheat or use of the wrong filler metal, often results in hardening from the heat of welding, weld porosity, incomplete fusion, inadequate joint penetration, and weld cracks. Poor welding practice may occur not only during repair, but also in initial fabrication or assembly.

The most common method of repairing structural members is welding. The part must be welded properly, or it may fail soon after being returned to service. Faults such as microcracks and macrocracks, mechanical gouges and excessive wear may be corrected by welding. If a crack is present, it preferably should be removed by grinding. Magnetic-particle or liquid-penetrant inspection should be done to ensure complete removal of the crack before repair welding. Generally, all parts should be preheated prior to welding in order to prevent hardening from the heat of welding. This is most critical in medium-carbon and high-carbon steels because of their sensitivity to hardening by welding heat. It is essential that the correct welding filler metal be used. After welding, low-carbon steel members may be air cooled if they have been preheated correctly. To prevent hardening from the heat of welding, the cooling rate of medium-carbon and high-carbon steel members should be controlled — for example, by wrapping them in asbestos.

The susceptibility of a crane to failure also is enhanced by a poor choice of material. In general, structural members of a crane should be designed so as not to fail in a brittle manner. The members should be made from impact-resistant, fine-grained steels so as to resist brittle fracture and to exhibit excellent fatigue properties. This becomes more critical in cold-temperature applications.

Crane members should be inspected periodically for fatigue cracks, to ensure that a failure is not imminent. A standard specification covering all items related to cranes is difficult to establish, because of the wide variety of associated items. Those specifications that do exist must be viewed as a minimal guideline.

Examples. The tram-rail assembly described in the next example cracked in the weld region because of improper preheating and postheating.

Example 17. Fracture of a Steel Tram-Rail Assembly Because of Poor Welding Practice (Fig. 18)

A hoist-carriage tram-rail assembly fabricated by shielded metal-arc welding the leg of a large T-section 1020 steel beam to the leg of a smaller T-section 1050 steel rail

(a) Section of tram rail as fabricated; T-section beam (1020 steel) is at top, T-section rail (1050 steel) is at bottom. (b) Enlarged view of welded area, showing crack at toe of weld (arrow). (c) Crack in rail initiated in heat-affected zone produced by feathering of the weld deposit. (d) Crack in rail initiated in heat-affected zone caused by weld spatter.

Fig. 18. Tram-rail assembly that fractured because of poor welding practices (Example 17)

is shown in Fig. 18(a). Several of the welds failed in one portion of the assembly. Cracks in weld regions of other portions of the assembly were found by magnetic-particle inspection.

Investigation. The entire weldment was inspected using the magnetic-particle method. This inspection revealed four weld cracks and several indefinite indications. All cracks were located at the toes of welds that joined the rail to the beam, such as the crack shown at the arrow in Fig. 18(b).

Metallographic examination of longitudinal sections through the welds re-

vealed, in every instance, that cracks originated in heat-affected zones in the rail section. A crack (at arrow in Fig. 18c) was initiated in a localized heat-affected zone produced by feathering the weld, which left a thin deposit of weld metal on the upper edge of the rail. Cracks were also found in heat-affected zones resulting from weld spatter, as illustrated in Fig. 18(d). Additional macrographs (not shown in Fig. 18) revealed cracks in welds and in heat-affected zones resulting from arcing the electrode adjacent to the weld.

A relatively broad heat-affected zone containing tempered and untempered martensite was present at each of the weld beads because of multiple-pass welding. The rail and beam both exhibited normal as-rolled steel structures with no irregularities. Chemical analysis revealed the rail to be made of 1050 steel and the beam of 1020 steel.

Hardness surveys revealed the following values: beam, 132 Bhn; rail, 255 Bhn; weld metal, 285 Bhn; tempered martensite, 321 Bhn; and untempered martensite, 578 Bhn.

The size and shape of heat-affected zones adjacent to welds indicated that the assembly had been neither preheated nor postheated during the welding operation. Welding workmanship generally was very poor. There was excessive feathering of weld metal and careless arcing during welding, which resulted in heat-affected zones containing hard untempered martensite. Thus, vibration of the tram rail by movement of the hoist carriage on the rail could easily initiate and propagate fatigue cracking in the heat-affected zones.

Conclusion. The tram-rail assembly failed by fatigue cracking in heat-affected zones. The assembly was not preheated or postheated, as is necessary for medium-carbon and high-carbon steels. Welding workmanship was poor; feathering of weld metal and careless arcing produced zones of hard, untempered martensite.

Corrective Measures. Welding procedures were improved and the replacement rail assemblies were both preheated and postheated.

Notches produced by flame cutting and welding resulted in brittle fracture of the crane-runway stop-block guide described in the next example. Dropping the stop block in place had created shock loading.

Example 18. Brittle Fracture of a 1020 Steel Stop-Block Guide on a Crane Runway Because of Metallurgical and Mechanical Notches Developed During Flame Cutting and Welding (Fig. 19)

A section broke from a stop-block guide (Fig. 19) on a crane runway and fell to the floor. A system consisting of wire ropes, pulleys, a counterweight and a lever was used to raise the stop block from the crane runway to permit the crane to pass. When the crane was to be isolated within an area, the stop block was returned to the down position. Because the weight of the stop block and guide was about 30% greater than that of the counterweight, there was some impact against the rail each time the block was returned to the down position.

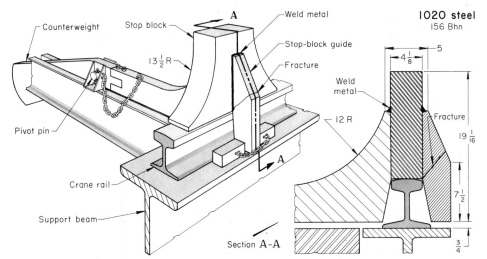

Fig. 19. Welded stop-block assembly for a crane runway, showing stop-block guide that failed by brittle fracture (Example 18)

One section of the fractured guide was sent to the laboratory so that the cause of failure could be determined.

Investigation. Examination of the fracture surface disclosed a brittle, crystalline-type break. The point of initiation was in a hardened, heat-affected layer that developed during flame cutting and welding. Hardness of the heat-affected layer was 248 Bhn.

Chemical analysis showed the metal to be 1020 steel. The base metal (hardness, 156 Bhn) had a coarse, as-rolled structure and a grain size of ASTM 00 to 4. The coarse grain size indicated that the weldment (stop block and guide) had not been normalized.

Conclusions. The stop-block guide failed in a brittle manner. Failure was initiated at a metallurgical and mechanical notch that was produced by flame cutting and welding.

Corrective Measures. New stop-block weldments were made from fully silicon-killed 1020 steel with a grain size of ASTM No. 5 or finer. The weldments were normalized at 900 C (1650 F) after flame cutting and welding, to improve microstructure and impact strength. All flame-cut surfaces were ground to remove notches.

Stop-block weldments in service were checked for grain size and heat treatment, and normalized where required.

Use of an improper filler metal and poor welding practice resulted in fracture of the aluminum alloy sling member described in the next example.

Example 19. Brittle Fracture of an Aluminum Alloy Lifting-Sling Member Caused by Use of Improper Filler Metal (Fig. 20)

The T-section cross member of the lifting sling shown in Fig. 20(a) broke in service while lifting a 2130-lb load. The L-section sling body and the cross member were made of aluminum alloy 5083 or 5086 and were joined by welding using aluminum alloy 4043 filler metal. Design load for the sling was 6000 lb.

Investigation. Visual examination of the sling showed that fracture occurred at the weld joining the sling body and the cross member. Examination of the ends of the failed cross member showed that a rotational force had been applied on the cross member, causing it to fracture near the sling body. The fracture surfaces of the sling body and the cross member are shown in Fig. 20(b). Macrographic examination of the weld disclosed inadequate joint penetration and porosity, as shown in Fig. 20(c).

Chemical analysis showed that the metal was within specifications for aluminum alloy 5083 or 5086. Analysis of the weld metal indicated that aluminum alloy 4043 filler metal had been used. The silicon content was lower, and the magnesium and manganese contents were higher, than normal for alloy 4043 filler metal. These differences were attributed to dilution of the weld metal by the base metal.

A similar sling was fabricated in the laboratory, set up in a test fixture and subjected to three-point loading duplicating that intended for the sling that failed. The yield strength of the test sling (stress causing permanent deflection in the cross member) was 7800 lb, and the ultimate load was 15,500 lb.

The initial break in the test sling started at the welded joint between the sling body and the edge of the flange of the cross member and propagated through the body to failure. The cross member of the sling that failed in service sustained permanent deformation whereas there was no evidence of deformation in the same member of the test sling.

Conclusions. The sling failed in brittle fracture at the weld when the cross member was overloaded. Overloading was attributed to misalignment of the sling during loading, which concentrated the entire load on the cross member.

Recommendations. In welding of aluminum alloy 5083 or 5086, aluminum alloy 5183 or 5356 filler metal should be used to avoid brittle welds.

Aluminum-silicon filler metals such as alloy 4043 should not be used to weld aluminum alloys in which the magnesium content exceeds 3%, because an excess of Mg_2Si produces brittle welds.

Forging defects in crane-bridge wheels were the causes of the failures described in the two examples that follow.

Example 20. Fracture of a 1055 Steel Crane-Bridge Wheel Because of Forging Defect (Fig. 21)

A bridge wheel on a crane fractured after one year of service. The wheel was forged from 1055 steel. The wheel fractured in the web between the hub and the rim.

Investigation. Visual examination of the fracture surface revealed a small area containing beach marks that originated in a heavily burned area on the web surface. Metallographic examination of a section taken through the region that contained the beach marks showed surface burning to a depth of approximately 0.030 in. (see Fig. 21). The degree of decarburization and oxide dispersion that were visible indicated a forging defect.

Conclusion. Failure occurred because of surface burning during the forging opera-

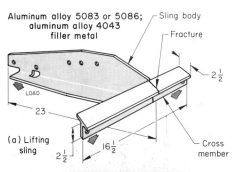

Fig. 20. (a) Aluminum alloy lifting sling that fractured because of improper welding of the cross member to the sling body. (b) Fracture surfaces of the sling body (at top) and the cross member (at bottom). (c) Enlarged view of a fracture surface of the sling body, showing weld defects. (Example 19)

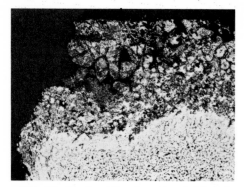

Fig. 21. Surface burning that initiated fracture in the web of a crane-bridge wheel forged from 1055 steel. 2% nital etch; about 35×. (Example 20)

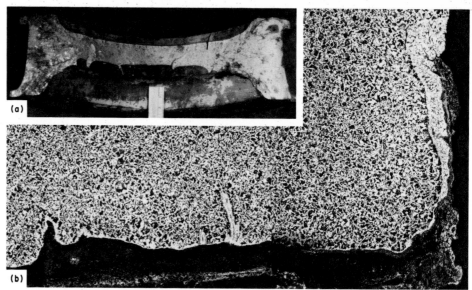

Fig. 22. (a) Fracture surface of a forged 1055 steel crane-bridge wheel that failed in fatigue originating at forging defects; dark areas are fatigue beach marks. (b) Micrograph, at 35×, of a nital-etched section through the fatigue origin, showing a gross forging defect along the fracture surface, at right, and decarburized web surface, at bottom. (Example 21)

tion. To prevent this type of failure, heating practice during forging should be more closely controlled to eliminate surface burning. If burning does occur, the burned region, if not too severely damaged, should be removed by machining.

Example 21. Fatigue Fracture of a Forged 1055 Steel Crane-Bridge Wheel Because of a Forging Defect (Fig. 22)

A bridge wheel from a 300-ton stripper crane failed after 1½ years of service. The wheel was forged from 1055 steel and the tread, hub faces, and hub bore were machined. The wheel fractured in the web near the rim.

Investigation. Macroscopic examination of the fracture surfaces revealed beach marks indicative of fatigue at ten locations. Fatigue cracking extended across about 15% of the surface before final fracture occurred. The dark areas on the fracture sur-

face shown in Fig. 22(a) are the portions that failed by fatigue. The surface of the web was heavily scaled and decarburized.

Chemical analysis showed that the material was equivalent to 1055 steel. Metallographic examination revealed that the wheel had been normalized and that the tread had been hardened to a depth of 0.200 in. The tread was tempered martensite; the core was fine pearlite.

Examination of a micrograph of a section through one of the fatigue origins

showed a gross forging defect extending about 0.072 in. along the fracture surface (at right in Fig. 22b). Shallower forging defects and the decarburized surface were visible along the web surface (at bottom in Fig. 22b).

Conclusion. Fatigue cracking of the wheel initiated at forging defects in the web.

Corrective Measures. Replacement wheels were machined all over, and magnetic-particle inspected to detect any cracks that could act as stress raisers.

Failures of Mechanical Fasteners

By WALTER L. JENSEN*

THE PRIMARY function of a fastener system is to transfer load. Many types of fasteners and fastening systems have been developed for specific requirements, such as high strength, increased fatigue life, reduced weight, easier maintenance, better corrosion resistance, greater reliability at high or low temperatures, or lower material and manufacturing costs.

The choice and satisfactory utilization of a particular fastener are dictated by the design requirements and conditions under which the fastener will be used. Consideration must be given to the purpose of the fastener, the type and thickness of materials to be joined, the configuration and total thickness of the joint to be fastened, the operating environment of the installed fastener, and the type of

*Research Group Engineer, Metallurgy and Failure Analysis Group, Lockheed-Georgia Co.

loading to which the fastener will be subjected in service. A careful analysis of these requirements is necessary before a selection of a satisfactory fastener can be made. The selection of the correct fastener or fastener system may simply involve satisfying a requirement for strength (static or fatigue) or for corrosion resistance. On the other hand, selection may be dictated by a complex system of specification and qualification controls. The extent and complexity of the system needed usually is dictated by the probable cost of a fastener failure.

Types of Mechanical Fasteners. For descriptive purposes, mechanical fasteners have been grouped into threaded fasteners, rivets, blind fasteners, pin fasteners, and special-purpose fasteners. Rivets, pin fasteners, and special-purpose fasteners are usually designed for permanent or semipermanent installation.

Threaded fasteners are considered to be any threaded part that, after assembly of the joint, may be removed without damage to the fastener or to the members being joined.

Rivets are permanent one-piece fasteners that are installed by mechanically upsetting one end.

Blind fasteners are usually multiple-piece devices that can be installed in a joint that is accessible from only one side. When a blind fastener is being installed, a self-contained mechanism, explosive, or other device forms an upset on the inaccessible side.

Pin fasteners are one-piece fasteners, either solid or tubular, used in assemblies where the load primarily is shear. Sometimes, a malleable collar is swaged or formed on the pin to secure the joint.

Special-purpose fasteners, many of which are proprietary, such as retaining rings, latches, slotted springs, and studs, are designed to allow for easy, quick re-

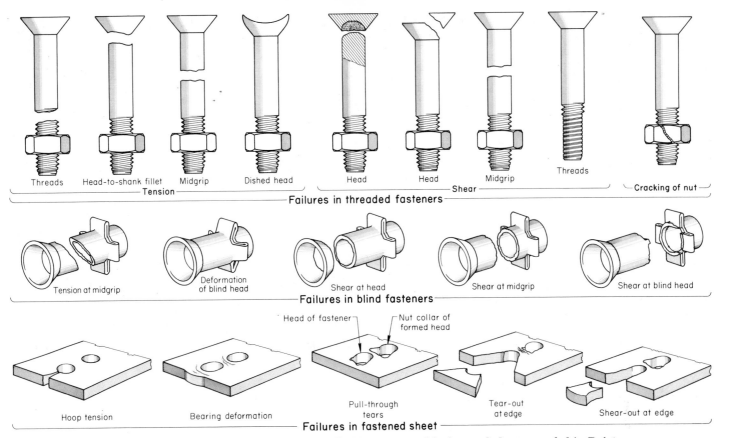

Threads | Head-to-shank fillet | Midgrip | Dished head | Head | Head | Midgrip | Threads | Cracking of nut
— Tension — | Shear | Cracking of nut

Failures in threaded fasteners

Tension at midgrip | Deformation of blind head | Shear at head | Shear at midgrip | Shear at blind head

Failures in blind fasteners

Head of fastener | Nut collar of formed head

Hoop tension | Bearing deformation | Pull-through tears | Tear-out at edge | Shear-out at edge

Failures in fastened sheet

Fig. 1. Types of failures in threaded and blind fasteners and in fastened sheet, as coded in Ref 1

moval and replacement and show little or no deterioration with repeated use.

Specifications are used to outline fastener requirements, to control the manufacturing process and to establish functional or performance standards. Their goal is to assure that fasteners will be interchangeable, dimensionally and functionally. The most common fastener specifications are product specifications that are set up to govern and define the quality and reliability of fasteners before they leave the manufacturer's plant. These specifications (a) determine what material to use; (b) state the objectives for tensile strength, shear strength, and response to heat treatment; (c) set requirements for environmental temperature or atmospheric exposure; and (d) define methods for testing and evaluation. To assure proper utilization of fasteners, additional specifications are necessary as a guide to proper design application and installation.

All ASTM and SAE specifications covering threaded fasteners require that the heads be marked for grade identification. Grade markings are a safety device that provides a positive check on selection, use and inspection. The markings reduce the possibility of selecting and using a bolt of insufficient strength, which might lead to a failure and cause damage to equipment or injury of personnel. Failure analysts should be familiar with the different grade markings

required by the specifications. The most common grade markings for steel bolts, screws and studs, together with corresponding grades, materials, sizes, proof loads and tensile strengths, are given in ASTM A307, A325, A354 and A490, and in SAE J429f. Most threaded fasteners also have a manufacturer's identification mark.

In an effort to standardize the reporting of fastener test failures, a failure-identification code has been established for reporting the failure of each fastener resulting from tests under MIL-STD-1312. Failures of threaded and blind fasteners, and of fastened sheet, covered by this identification code are illustrated in Fig. 1 (Ref 1).

Failure Origins

The most common locations for fastener failure are in the head-to-shank fillet or, on threaded fasteners, through the first thread inside the nut or at the transition from the thread to the shank. Sources of failure origins are imperfections in the work metal caused by segregation in the form of inclusions such as sulfides and oxides in the ingot, or by folds, laps or seams that have formed because of faulty working either in the semifinishing or finishing mills.

Seams are crevices in the surface of the metal that have been closed, but not welded, by working the metal. Seams

seldom penetrate to the core of bar stock. Seams may cause additional cracking in hot forging and quench cracking during heat treatment. Oxides in a seam can be the result of oxidation during tempering.

Seams are sometimes difficult to detect in an unused fastener but, as described in the following report, are readily apparent after a fastener has been subjected to installation and service stresses:

During periodic inspection of an airplane, a longitudinal crack was found in one of the wing-attachment bolts. The bolt was 7/8 in. in diameter and 3½ in. long, and conformed to National Aerospace Standard 634. Chemical analysis verified that the bolt material was 4340 steel as called for in specifications, and hardness measurements indicated that it had been heat treated to a tensile strength of 200,000 psi.

As indicated by the arrows on the photograph of the bolt in Fig. 2(a), the crack extended almost the full length of the bolt shank, but it branched circumferentially at the head-to-shank fillet (shown by arrows in Fig. 2b) and extended about halfway through the bolt-head diameter, as shown by arrows in Fig. 2(c). The bolt was sectioned to expose a portion of the crack surface, which was found to be heavily oxidized (see Fig. 2d). Figure 2(e) is a micrograph of a cross section transverse to the crack that shows the thickness and uniformity of the oxide coating. This heavy oxide coating and the longitudinal direction of the crack indicated that a seam was present in the bolt bar stock. Hot heading had disrupted

(a) Bolt showing crack along entire length, indicated by arrows. (b) Branching cracks (at arrows) at head-to-shank radius. (c) Head of bolt showing cracking (at arrows) about halfway through bolt-head diameter.

(d) Section through bolt, showing heavy oxidation on crack surface (between arrows). (e) Micrograph, at 1000×, of 2%-nital-etched section through the crack, showing thickness and uniformity of oxide coating.

Fig. 2. Wing-attachment bolt made of 4340 steel that cracked along a seam

the linear direction of the seam in the bolt-head areas so that the crack branched in a circumferential direction. Installation and service loads apparently opened the seam, which made it visually detectable.

Corrective action was not deemed necessary, because the periodic scheduled inspection of the aircraft was considered adequate to identify any faulty part for replacement, and thus prevent failure of any safety-of-flight components.

Causes of Fastener Failures

In a well-designed, mechanically fastened joint, the fastener may be subjected to either static loading (overload) or dynamic fatigue loading. Static load may be tension, shear, bending, or torsion — either singly or in combination. Dynamic forces may result from impact or from cyclic fatigue loading, including vibration. Pure shear failures are usually obtained only when the shear load is transmitted over a very short length of the member, as with rivets, screws and bolts. In instances where the ultimate shear stress is relatively low, a pure shear failure may result, but in general a member subjected to a shear load fails under the action of the resulting combined stresses. In addition to fatigue and overload, other common causes of fastener failures include the following: environmental effects, manufacturing discrepancies, and improper utilization or incorrect installation of fasteners.

A threaded fastener may be either a male or a female threaded cylinder — both of which are necessary as a two-element device for applying force, primarily to clamp two members together.

Bolts, screws and studs are male threaded cylinders; nuts or tapped holes are female threaded cylinders. For the purpose of discussion here, bolts and nuts are considered representative of the two. The primary force in the bolt is tension, which is set up by stretching the bolt during tightening, whereas the most important stress in the nut is the shear stress in the threads. If both the bolt and the nut had perfectly matched threads and both elements were inelastic, the torque load would be evenly distributed over all of the engaged threads. However, because the economy of mass production of fasteners requires that all fasteners be produced with practical dimensional tolerances, and because all fastener materials are elastic, all threaded fastener devices experience nonuniform distribution of load over the threads. The bolt tension causes elongation, which results in more load on the threads near the bearing face of the nut, and the compression load of the nut is likely to have the same load-concentrating effect. To obtain a more uniform distribution of load along the threaded cylinder and thus minimize the chance of failure, a softer material must be provided for one of the

elements. The usual combination is to provide material with high tensile strength for the bolt and material with good plasticity for the nut (Ref 2).

In the theory of joint design, the ideal application can be represented as a situation in which there is a rigid structure and a flexible or elastic fastener. The bolt then behaves like a spring, as is schematically represented in Fig. 3(a). When the bolt is preloaded, or the spring is stretched, a stress is induced in the bolt (and a clamping force in the structure) before any working load is encountered. As the working load is applied, the preloaded bolt does not encounter an additional load until the working load equals the preload in the bolt, as shown in Fig. 3(b). At this point, the force between members is zero. As more load is applied, the bolt must stretch. Only beyond this point will any cyclic working load be transmitted to the bolt.

For schematic representation of an actual condition, the structural material also would be represented by springs. The bolt also would be preloaded, but before application of the working load, the bolt encounters a slight increase in load, because of the elasticity of the structural members. Actually, some of the additional load is encountered before the working load equals the preload. As the dynamic working load cycles, a fatigue condition is established.

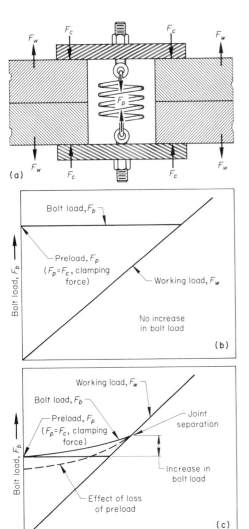

(a) Schematic arrangement showing load condition for an elastic fastener and a rigid structure (theoretical condition). (b) Relation of bolt load to working load with an elastic fastener and a rigid structure (ideal condition). (c) Relation of bolt load to working load with both fastener and structure elastic (actual condition).

Fig. 3. Schematic of the springlike effect of loading conditions on bolted joints

When the bolt encounters an increase in load, being elastic, it stretches. If this stretch (strain) exceeds the elastic limit, the bolt yields plastically, taking a permanent set. The result is a loss in preload or clamping force, as shown by the dashed curve in Fig. 3(c). With a fluctuating load this situation can cycle progressively, with continued loss of preload and possibly rapid fatigue failure. (The effect of preload on steel automotive wheel studs, and the fracture that resulted from the preload, are described in Example 1 in this article.)

To eliminate fatigue problems that occur at room temperature, the designer should specify as high an initial preload as is practicable. The optimum fastener-torque values for applying specific loads to the joint have been determined for many high-strength fasteners. However, these values should be used with caution, because the tension produced by a selected torque value is directly dependent on the friction between the contacting threads. The use of an effective lubricant on the threads may result in overloading of the fastener, whereas the use of a less effective lubricant may result in a loose joint. With proper selection of materials, proper design of bolt-and-nut bearing surfaces, and the use of locking devices, the assumption is that the initial clamping force will be sustained during the life of the fastened joint. This same assumption cannot be made in elevated-temperature design.

At elevated temperature, the induced bolt load will decrease with time as a result of creep, even if the elastic limits of the materials are not exceeded, and this can adversely affect fastener performance. Therefore, it is necessary to compensate for high-temperature conditions in advance when assembling the joint at room temperature. Failures that occur at elevated temperatures necessitate evaluation of the properties of the fastener material with respect to the applied loads, operating temperature, and time under load at temperature.

Fatigue in Threaded Fasteners

Fatigue is one of the most common failure mechanisms of threaded fasteners. Insufficient tightening of fasteners can result in flexing, with subsequent fatigue fracture. Higher clamping forces make more rigid joints and thus increase fastener fatigue life. The fatigue origin usually is at some point of stress concentration, such as an abrupt change of section, a deep scratch, a notch, a nick, a fold, a large inclusion, or a marked change in grain size; however, fatigue failures most frequently are located at the washer face of the nut, at the thread runout, or at the head-to-shank fillet. The following example describes a typical fatigue fracture in the thread runout.

Example 1. Fatigue Fracture of 4520 Steel Wheel Studs Because of Nonuniform and Improper Tightening of Wheel Nuts (Fig. 4)

Each of the ten studs on one wheel of a semitrailer that was used to haul coal broke in half while the trailer was in operation. Both halves of each of three studs were sent to the laboratory to determine the cause of failure.

Investigation. Visual examination of the fracture surfaces of the studs disclosed beach marks, indicative of fatigue cracking, starting at opposite sides of each stud, with final fracture occurring across the stud, as shown in Fig. 4(a). Each failure occurred in the first thread of the stud. Figure 4(b) is a micrograph of a cross section of the stud at the thread next to the one that failed; it shows that cracking also was present at the root of this thread.

The studs were ¾ in. in diameter. Spectrographic analysis revealed that the studs were made from a steel containing molybdenum, such as 4520 steel, and heat treated to a hardness of Rockwell C 30 and that the wheel nuts were made of carbon steel.

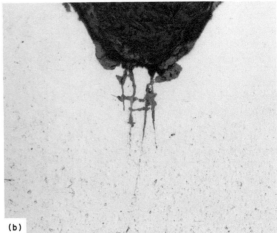

Fig. 4. (a) Fracture surfaces of three 4520 steel semitrailer-wheel studs that failed by fatigue because of improper and nonuniform tightening of wheel nuts. (b) Micrograph, at 100×, of a cross section of a stud, showing cracking at a thread root away from the failure area (Example 1)

Fig. 5. Section through the forged head on a threaded fastener showing uniform grain flow that minimizes stress raisers and unfavorable shear planes (Ref 3)

Because all ten of the wheel studs fractured, the opinion was that the wheel nuts were not tightened adequately and uniformly on the wheel. If the wheel were not secured snugly by the studs, a slight movement of the wheel relative to the studs could initiate fatigue cracking. Each time the wheel made one revolution, reversed bending would occur on the studs. After fatigue started, the loosening of any stud would increase the stress on the remaining studs, until they all failed.

Conclusion. Fracture of the wheel studs was by reversed-bending fatigue.

Corrective Measures. To minimize the possibility of a recurrence of this type of failure, the wheel nuts were tightened with an air-impact wrench to a torque of 450 to 500 ft-lb dry. All wheel studs were checked at normal maintenance periods to ensure uniform and proper loading, and no further failures occurred.

The bolt-thread root immediately adjacent to the edge of the nut on the washer side is a common fatigue-initiation site in threaded fasteners. This stress-concentration site occurs because the bolt elongates as the nut is tightened, thereby producing increased loads on the threads nearest the bearing face of the nut, which add to normal service stresses. This condition is alleviated to some extent by using nuts of a softer material that will yield and distribute the load more uniformly over the engaged threads. Significant additional improvement in fatigue life also is obtained by rolling (cold working) the threads rather than cutting them, as suggested in Example 5 in this article. It is important that the rolling operation follow, rather than precede, heat treatment.

The head-to-shank fillet is another site for fatigue fracture of tension-loaded fasteners. Several techniques can be used for avoiding failure at this location. The heads of most fasteners are formed by hot or cold forging, depending on the type of material and size of the bolt. In addition to being a relatively low-cost manufacturing method, forging provides smooth, unbroken metal flow through the head-to-shank fillet, which closely follows the

external contour of the bolt (see Fig. 5) and thus minimizes stress raisers, which promote fatigue cracking. In hot forging of fastener heads, temperatures must be carefully controlled to avoid overheating, which may cause grain growth. Several failures of 1-in.-diam type H-11 airplane-wing bolts quenched and tempered to a tensile strength of 260,000 to 280,000 psi have been attributed to stress concentration that resulted from a large grain size in the bolt head and a normally fine grain size in the shank. Other failures in these 1-in.-diam bolts, as well as in other, similarly quenched-and-tempered steel bolts, were the result of cracks in untempered martensite that formed as a result of overheating during finish grinding.

The shape and size of the head-to-shank fillet also have an important influence on fatigue performance. In general, the radius of this fillet should be as large as possible while at the same time permitting adequate head-bearing area. This requires a design tradeoff between the head-to-shank radius and the head-bearing area to achieve optimum results. Cold working of the head fillet is another common method of preventing fatigue failure, because it induces a residual compressive stress and also increases the material strength. And finally, fatigue resistance can be improved by changing to a material with higher strength and endurance limit, as shown by the following example.

Example 2. Fatigue Fracture of Modified 1035 Steel Cap Screws Because of Inadequate Strength for the Application (Fig. 6)

The drive-line assembly shown in Fig. 6(a) failed during vehicle testing. The mileage on the vehicle at the time of failure was 5606 miles. Both the intact and frac-

(a)

(b)

(c)

(a) Drive-line assembly showing fractured components. (b) Macrograph, at 4×, of the fracture surface of one of two cap screws that failed, showing beach marks typical of a fatigue-type failure. (c) Macrograph, at 4×, of the fracture surface of the other cap screw that failed, showing beach marks typical of high-stress reversed-bending fatigue failure.

Fig. 6. Drive-line assembly that failed because of fatigue fracture of two cap screws that were made of modified 1035 steel instead of the specified medium-carbon alloy steel (Example 2)

tured parts of the assembly were sent to the laboratory to determine the cause and sequence of failure.

Specifications for the threaded fasteners in the assembly called for ³⁄₈–24 UNF, SAE grade 8 hexagon-head cap screws made of medium-carbon alloy steel, quenched and tempered to a hardness of Rockwell C 32 to 38 and a minimum tensile strength of 150,000 psi.

Investigation. Visual examination of the assembly showed that three of four bearing caps, two cap screws and one universal-joint spider had fractured.

Examination of the three fractured bearing caps and the spider showed no evidence of fatigue but showed that fracture occurred in a brittle manner. The bearing cap that was not destroyed still contained portions of the two fractured cap screws.

Examination of macrographs of the fracture surfaces of the screws revealed beach marks typical of fatigue-type failures. One of the screws (see Fig. 6b) showed a single origin of cracking, a concave crack front symmetrical with the origin, and a small zone of final rupture — all of which suggested a low nominal stress. This screw apparently was the first to fracture.

The fracture surface of the other cap screw (see Fig. 6c) contained two diametrically opposite origins of cracking, from which extended two crack fronts of similar size and shape that exhibited beach marks characteristic of high-stress reversed-bending-fatigue failure. The width of the final-rupture area was slightly less than half the screw diameter. Fracture of this screw followed that of the first screw. Fracture of the two cap screws allowed the adjacent bearing cap (the unfailed cap) to become free from the spider. As a result, the bearing cap on the opposite side of the spider was overloaded, and fractured. With the two screws and the bearing cap fractured, the drive shaft was free at one end. The effect of the free drive shaft was to overload the universal joint at the opposite end of the shaft, resulting in failure of the spider and the two remaining bearing caps.

Chemical analysis and hardness determinations were made of the bearing-cap, spider and screw materials. The bearing caps were made of 1144 steel and had a hardness of Rockwell A 55. The spider was made of 8620 steel and had been carburized and hardened to Rockwell C 62 to 63. The screws were made of a steel containing 0.36% C, 1.09% Mn, 0.01% P, 0.017% S, 0.21% Si, 0.01% Ni, and 0.16% Cr, which is a modified 1035 steel. The screw material had a tensile strength of 124,000 psi, a yield strength of 92,000 psi and an approximate endurance limit (smooth specimen) of 62,000 psi at a hardness of Rockwell C 36.

Microscopic examination of a longitudinal section through one of the screws revealed the structure to be tempered martensite. Micrographs at magnifications of 200 and 400 diameters revealed cracks extending from the thread root.

Conclusions. The two cap screws failed in fatigue under service stresses. The three bearing caps and the universal-joint spider broke in a brittle manner.

The properties of the material in the cap screws did not fulfill the specifications. The modified 1035 steel was of insufficient al-

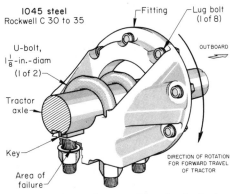

Fig. 7. Fitting, for attaching dual wheels to a tractor axle, in which 1045 steel U-bolts failed from overstress because of poor hardenability in relation to the diameter of the bolts (Example 3)

loy content. Also, the tensile strength and endurance limit were lower than specified, and were inadequate for the application.

Corrective Measure. The material for the cap screws was changed from modified 1035 steel to 5140 steel.

Upgrading of cyclically loaded parts without evaluating the load characteristics of the material can result in fatigue fracture, as in the following example.

Example 3. Fatigue Fracture of 1045 Steel U-Bolts on a Tractor Fitting Because of Overstress (Fig. 7)

When a farm tractor is to be used on sticky or wet soils, it is common practice to attach dual driving wheels to the rear axles of the tractor, using fittings like that shown in Fig. 7. SAE grade 5 U-bolts are used to fasten the dual wheels to the axles and under typical farm usage are expected to have infinite life. However, several U-bolts made of 1⅛-in.-diam rod broke in less than 100 hr of service.

The material for the U-bolts was commercial quality, cold finished 1045 steel bar, 1⅛ in. in diameter. The bar stock was cut to length, threads were cut on both ends, and the parts were bent to the specified shape. The U-bolts were then austenitized, oil quenched, and tempered to a hardness of Rockwell C 30 to 35 at the surface to obtain a uniform tempered-martensite microstructure. Oil quenching, rather than water quenching, was employed to avoid cracking of the bolts through the cut threads.

Investigation. The bolt legs in which the failures occurred all were in the same position relative to the direction of wheel rotation. This leg was designated as the "leading" leg of the U-bolt. Visual examination showed that the break was a fairly flat transverse fracture in the threaded section between the washer and the nut. The appearance of the fracture surfaces was characteristic of failure by low-cycle fatigue, with a smooth matte fatigue-failure region showing beach marks and generally extending over about 40 to 60% of the fracture surface, which indicated severe overload. The point of initiation of fatigue was at the root of the last thread at the edge of the nut on the side toward the washer.

Metallographic examination (at 100 to 1000 diameters) of cross sections of broken

U-bolts (polished, and etched in 1% nital) showed that the structure of the outer surface of the bolts, to a depth of about ¼ in., was tempered martensite. The structure of the interior of the bolts was pearlitic. Microhardness measurements on the polished surfaces of the metallographic specimens showed the hardness of the surface layer to correspond to the specified range of Rockwell C 30 to 35 and that of the interior to be about Rockwell C 25.

The observed microstructure was not that specified for this application — namely, uniformly tempered martensite with a hardness of Rockwell C 30 to 35. The design and processing for the fractured bolts had been based on a similar arrangement in which ¾-in.-diam and ⅞-in.-diam U-bolts made of 1045 steel and heat treated by the same procedure had not broken after being in service on smaller tractors for several years. When the 1⅛-in.-diam U-bolts had been selected for service on the larger tractors, it had not been considered that oil quenching instead of water quenching would require them to be made of a higher-hardenability steel.

The sequence of failure was based on the assumption that the loading of the U-bolt in service included three main components: (a) tension caused by the tightening of the nuts during assembly (by the farmer) of the bolt and hub to the axle, (b) cyclic tension and release from supporting the weight of the tractor as the wheels turned, and (c) a somewhat random tension in the leading leg of the U-bolt, caused by driving the axle and wheels. Superposition of the stresses from the three major components of loading resulted in a net cyclic stress (which was always tensile) on the U-bolts during normal operation of the tractor. The net stress was greater on the leading leg of the bolt.

Conclusions. The U-bolts fractured in fatigue because the bolt material had poor hardenability in relation to the diameter of the bolts. The oil-quench hardenability of 1045 steel was adequate for ¾-in.-diam and ⅞-in.-diam bolts, but not for 1⅛-in.-diam stock.

Corrective Action. The bolt material was changed from 1045 steel to 1527 steel, a warm-finished low-alloy steel. The diameter of the bolts was reduced to 1.070 in. and the threads were rolled rather than cut. The 1527 steel was sufficiently ductile as received to permit bending into the U shape, yet strong enough not to need heat treatment.

No failures of the improved bolts had been reported four years after the indicated changes were made. Manufacturing cost of the bolts was reduced by about 30%.

Fretting

Fretting results from a very small movement of one highly loaded surface over another. The slight movement prevents the formation of, or destroys, any protective oxide film. Thus, continually clean surfaces become available for oxidation. Also, since there is no oxide film to prevent true metal-to-metal contact, local bonding of microscopic areas can occur, ultimately resulting in dislodgment of extremely small metal particles from the surfaces. Because of their relatively small size, these metal particles are then rapidly oxidized by the ambient atmosphere.

Bolted machine parts that are subjected to vibration are most susceptible to fretting. Fretting can be prevented by minimizing clearance in boltholes and by using high-strength fasteners properly tensioned to prevent relative motion of contacting surfaces. (See also the article on Fretting Failures, which begins on page 154 in this volume.)

Corrosion in Threaded Fasteners

Corrosion is electrochemical in nature; therefore an electrolyte must be present. Water is an excellent electrolyte, especially if it contains dissolved minerals. Temperature also is important, because little reaction occurs below 5 C (about 40 F). Oxygen is required and is present in the atmosphere and, to a lesser extent, underwater and underground.

Types of corrosion, which are discussed below, include atmospheric corrosion, liquid-immersion corrosion, crevice corrosion, galvanic corrosion, stress-corrosion cracking, and hydrogen damage.

Atmospheric Corrosion. Atmospheric contaminants vary widely with location, and thus rates of atmospheric corrosion vary widely. Generally, for ferrous materials, because of sulfur and chloride compounds, most severe corrosion occurs in highly industrialized and severe marine locations, with rural exposure being much less corrosive.

Liquid-Immersion Corrosion. Both fresh water and salt water are corrosive. Usually, salt water is more severe than fresh water, because salt water is a better electrolyte and the electrochemical current generated by inhomogeneities in the same metal or by different metals is greater. Also, the chloride ions present break down the protective oxide film and corrosion products. Completely submerged locations are not so corrosive as those at the water line or splash zone, where more oxygen is present and the surface is alternately wet and dry.

Crevice Corrosion. Every bolted connection offers the possibility for crevice corrosion. Corrosion may be of two types, depending on the tightness of the joint or crevice opening. If there is a gap or opening, dirt can collect and retain moisture and thus enhance corrosion. On the other hand, in a correctly made tight joint, corrosion can result because of an oxygen deficiency or oxygen-starvation cell. The area of low oxygen becomes an anode and the high-oxygen area becomes a cathode; thus, corrosion occurs. Fortunately, ferrous metals most used for fasteners are not highly susceptible to the second type of crevice corrosion. Stainless steels and other metals that, in the presence of

Table 1. Results of Stress-Corrosion Tests of 12% Cr Steel Bolts in a 3.5% NaCl Solution To Determine Effect of Antiseizure Coating (Example 4)

Bolt No.	Hardness, Rockwell C	Surface	Visual appearance(a)	Tensile strength, psi(a)	Remarks
1	41 to 42	Uncoated	Localized pitting, no cracks	220,600	No corrosion attack on fracture surface
2	18 to 20	Uncoated	Localized pitting, no cracks	124,530	No corrosion attack on fracture surface
3	20 to 22	Coated(b)	Heavy pitting, no cracks	129,720	No corrosion attack on fracture surface
4	41 to 42	Coated(b)	Bolt completely failed in test fixture	Not applicable	Heavy corrosion on fracture surface

Bolt No. 1   2   3   4

(a) After 3 months of intermittent dipping in a 3.5% NaCl solution. (b) Coated with an antiseizure compound consisting of metallic copper flakes in a silicone vehicle.

oxygen, form protective passive surface films are much more susceptible as the film breaks down and creates an active metal area.

Galvanic Corrosion. When dissimilar metals are in contact or electrically connected together, galvanic corrosion results because of the different electrical potential existing between the two metals. Current thus produced has a great effect on metal corrosion and must be considered whenever different metals are to be fastened together.

Galvanic corrosion particularly should be kept in mind at all times when designing structures using fasteners. Too often errors are made, such as using ferrous fasteners for joining more noble metals like copper alloys. Here, not only is galvanic corrosion involved, but also the size effect, as described below.

For a structure to be well designed, the anode or corroding-metal area should be large in relation to the cathode or protected metal so as to assure reasonable anode life. With fasteners, this sometimes is difficult to do, because fasteners are always smaller than the structure they join. An example of size effect was the use of iron nails to fasten copper sheathing to the bottom of wooden ships to prevent marine growth. At the end of each voyage most of this sheathing had fallen off because of the accelerated corrosion of the iron nails.

Galvanic corrosion can be avoided by using the same metal for both fastener and structure. Several alternatives exist when this is impractical or impossible: (a) the structure may be painted, (b) the fastener may be isolated by nonconducting materials or plated with a more noble metal, (c) moisture may be prevented from contacting the couple, or (d) fasteners may be made of a metal that will be protected by sacrificial corrosion of the much larger mass of the metal being fastened.

Stress-corrosion cracking is an intergranular fracture mechanism that sometimes occurs in highly stressed fasteners after a period of time, and is caused by a corrosive environment in conjunction with a sustained tensile stress above a threshold value. An adverse grain orientation increases susceptibility of some materials to stress corrosion. Consequently, stress-corrosion cracking can be prevented by excluding the corrodent, by keeping the static tensile stress of the fastener below the critical level for the material and grain orientation involved, or by changing to a less susceptible material or material condition (for example, aluminum alloy 7075 is less susceptible to stress-corrosion cracking in the T73 or T76 temper than in the T6 temper). In some instances, the corrodent can be the seemingly innocuous ambient atmosphere, whereas in others it can be unwittingly added — as in the following example.

Example 4. Stress-Corrosion Cracking of Stainless Steel Bolts (Table 1; Fig. 8)

Stainless steel bolts broke after short-time exposure in boiler feed-pump applications. Specifications required that the bolts be made of a 12% Cr high-strength steel with a composition conforming to that of type 410 stainless steel.

Several bolts from three different installations were sent to the laboratory for examination. One lot consisted of ten 1–8 UNC 4-in.-long bolts, the second lot of nine 1–8 UNC 4-in.-long bolts, and the third lot of five 5/8–11 UNC 2 3/4-in.-long bolts. An antiseizure compound consisting of metallic copper flakes in a silicone vehicle had been applied to the bolts during assembly.

All of the bolts had fractured in the threaded portion, but not all at the same thread. None of the 1-in.-diam bolts had fractured under the head, but some of the 5/8-in.-diam bolts had broken under the head as well as in the threads.

Visual Examination. The 1-in.-diam bolts exhibited external damage, which varied in degree depending on the time that had been required to shut down the unit. No external damage was observed on the ⅝-in.-diam bolts.

The first lot of 1-in.-diam bolts exhibited flat fracture surfaces with chevron patterns. The second lot was similar in fracture-surface appearance; however, the fracture surfaces were badly stained by the corrosive boiler feedwater. The fracture surfaces of the ⅝-in.-diam bolts exhibited stained brittle-fracture features in starlike patterns.

Examination of bolts in all three lots also disclosed a copper-colored residue adhering to the threads. This residue was from the antiseizure compound that had been applied during assembly.

Accelerated Corrosion Testing. Laboratory corrosion tests were conducted on four bolts taken from stock. The purpose of the tests was to determine the effects of the anti-seizure compound in acidified 3.5% NaCl solution on bolts at two hardness levels.

Two bolts, one with a hardness of Rockwell C 41 to 42 and the other of Rockwell C 20 to 22, were coated with the antiseizure compound. Another bolt that had a hardness of Rockwell C 41 to 42, and a bolt having a hardness of Rockwell C 18 to 20, were left uncoated for the test. All four bolts were assembled in a static test fixture and tightened to a torque value equal to 90% of their yield strength and then intermittently dipped in an acidified solution of 3.5% NaCl. Intermittent dipping consisted of 10-minute total immersion and 50-minute air dry for 8 hours per day, 5 days per week for 3 months.

After three months' testing, the coated bolt having a hardness of Rockwell C 41 to 42 fractured completely across at the third thread from the head. The three other bolts had not fractured but were tensile tested to destruction. The results of the test and appearance of the fracture surfaces are presented in Table 1.

This test demonstrated the damaging effects of the metallic copper antiseizure compound to high-hardness 12% Cr steels in the presence of a corrosive medium.

Microscopic examination showed that the microstructure of the metal in the bolts of lot 1 (see Fig. 8a) contained tempered martensite. The metal in the two other lots (see Fig. 8b) showed a two-phase structure, consisting of tempered martensite, ferrite and nonmetallic stringers of sulfide. Ferrite content of the matrix was about 38%.

The examination also showed that the threads on some of the bolts had been produced by cutting, and on others by rolling. Both types of threads had fractured on the bolts in service.

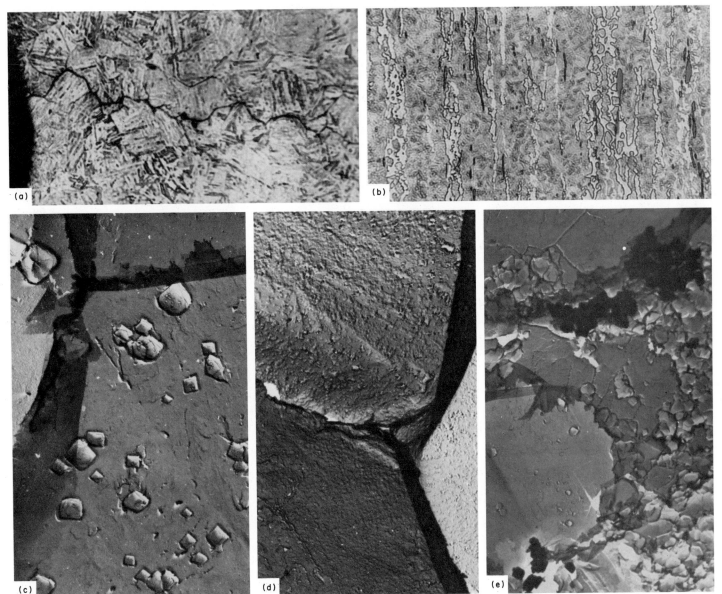

(a) Micrograph showing microstructure and branched intergranular cracking in a type 410 stainless steel bolt from lot 1 (250×; etched in picral plus HCl). (b) Micrograph showing microstructure in a type 416 stainless steel bolt typical of those in lots 2 and 3 (100×; etched in picral plus HCl). (c), (d) and (e) Electron fractographs of typical fracture surfaces of the bolts, showing, respectively: carbide particles, intergranular fracture, and intergranular fracture with corrosive residue (all at 6500×; specimens were not etched).

Fig. 8. Micrographs and electron fractographs of stainless steel bolts from three lots that failed from stress-corrosion cracking (Example 4)

Longitudinal sections were taken through the fractured bolts and examined microscopically. Branched intergranular cracking at the thread root next to the fracture, similar in appearance to the crack shown in Fig. 8(a), was found in several of the bolts. Intergranular cracking and oxide entrapment were found under the bolt heads and at the fracture surfaces.

Fractographic examination by electron microscopy disclosed evidence of corrosion products on the fracture surfaces with localized pitting and second-phase carbide particles. The carbide particles (probably chromium carbide, $Cr_{23}C_6$) and evidence of intergranular fracture are shown in Fig. 8(c). The fractograph in Fig. 8(d) shows brittle intergranular fracture with corrosive residue on the surface. Large clusters of carbide particles and evidence of intergranular fracture are shown in Fig. 8(e). No fatigue indications were in evidence. The branching intergranular cracks shown in Fig. 8(a) and the intergranular fracture surface with corrosion products shown by the electron fractographs in Fig. 8(d) and (e) are evidence of stress corrosion.

Chemical analysis of the metal in a fractured bolt from each lot revealed the following compositions:

| Element | Composition, %, for— | | | |
	Lot 1	Lot 2	Lot 3	Nominal(a)
C	0.140	0.058	0.061	0.15
Mn ..	0.560	0.370	0.410	1.00
P	0.010	0.017	0.018	0.04
S	0.016	0.251	0.241	0.03
Si ...	0.392	0.437	0.395	1.00
Cr ...	12.09	12.54	12.14	11.5 to 13.5

(a) Nominal composition for type 410 stainless steel (to which bolts were specified to conform). Percentages, except for Cr, are maximums.

Although the bolts from none of the three lots conformed to specification, the most severe deviations from prescribed chemical composition were found in lots 2 and 3, which also contained a sulfur addition to enhance machinability.

Conclusions. Fracture of the bolts was by intergranular stress corrosion. A metallic copper-containing antiseizure compound on the bolts in a corrosive medium set up an electrochemical cell that produced trench-like fissures or pits for fracture initiation. Because the bolts were not subjected to cyclic loading, fatigue or corrosion fatigue was not possible.

Corrective Measures. Bolts were required to conform to the specified chemical composition. The hardness range for the bolts was changed from Rockwell C 35 to 45 to Rockwell C 18 to 24. Petroleum jelly was used as an antiseizure lubricant in place of the copper-containing compound.

As a result of these changes, bolt life was increased to more than three years.

High static tensile stresses above the threshold for stress-corrosion cracking may be minimized by introducing compressive stresses on the fastener surfaces where stress-corrosion cracking is most likely to originate. Cold rolling and shot peening are two means of keeping static tensile stresses at the operating surface below the safe maximum. However, the beneficial effects of either of these would

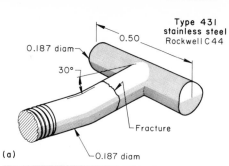

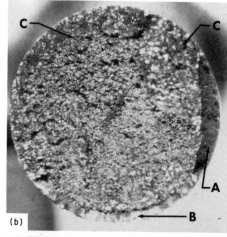

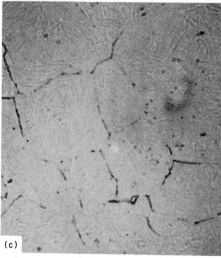

(a) T-bolt showing location of fracture. (b) Fractograph, at about 13×, of the fracture surface showing shear lip (at A), fine-grain region (at B), and oxidized regions (at C's). (c) Micrograph of a longitudinal section through the T-bolt showing severe intergranular carbide precipitation (540×; 1½-min electrolytic etch in 10% NaCN).

Fig. 9. Type 431 stainless steel T-bolt that failed by stress-corrosion cracking (Example 5)

be negated if the fastener were subsequently heat treated, if the normal service temperature were above the tempering or aging temperature of the material, if the fastener were loaded above its yield point, or if general corrosion removed the compressively stressed layer.

In the next example, stress-corrosion cracking of a stainless steel bolt was prevented by changing to a material that

was less susceptible to sensitization and by cold working the fastener to minimize the high bending stress.

Example 5. Stress-Corrosion Cracking of a Type 431 Stainless Steel T-Bolt Because the Operating Temperature Was in the Sensitizing Range (Fig. 9)

The T-bolt shown in Fig. 9(a) was part of the coupling for a bleed air duct of a jet engine on a transport plane. Specifications required that the 3/16-in.-diam T-bolt be made of type 431 stainless steel and heat treated to Rockwell C 44. The operating temperature of the duct was 427 to 538 C (800 to 1000 F), but that of the bolt was lower. The T-bolt broke after three years of service. The expected service life was equal to that of the aircraft.

The bolt was made by cold upsetting bar stock to a T-shape, chasing the threads, bending to the specified curvature, then heat treating. Heat treatment consisted of heating to 1010 to 1038 C (1850 to 1900 F) and oil quenching, tempering at 275 to 415 C (about 525 to 575 F) for 2 hr and retempering for the same time and temperature. In the manufacture of similar bolts, the threads were rolled after heat treatment, and the bolt shank was shot peened.

Investigation. Visual examination of the fracture surface revealed intergranular cracking and evidence of brittle fracture.

Macrographs were taken of the outer surface of the bolt and of the fracture surface. The outer surface contained circumferential cracks on the lower (tension) side of the T-bolt. The fracture surface (Fig. 9b) exhibited three distinct fracture areas — a shallow 45° shear-lip section along one side (at A in Fig. 9b), a thin region containing fine grains along part of the surface that could have been the result of stress corrosion or of fatigue (at B in Fig. 9b), and regions that appeared to be oxidized as the result of a prior crack (at C's in Fig. 9b).

Hardness of the T-bolt was found to be Rockwell C 44, as specified.

Examination of micrographs of longitudinal sections through the T-bolt revealed the basic microstructure to be acicular martensite with no delta ferrite present. However, there was evidence of severe intergranular carbide precipitation (see Fig. 9c), which indicated that the material had been subjected to the sensitizing-temperature range after the bolt had been manufactured.

The micrographs also showed some intergranular surface and subsurface cracking near, but not at, the primary fracture.

Although not confirmed, chlorine or chlorides in some form could have been present around the duct.

Conclusions. The bolt broke as a result of stress-corrosion cracking. Thermal stresses were induced into the bolt by intermittent operation of the jet engine. Mechanical stresses were induced by tightening of the clamp around the duct — which, in effect, acted to straighten the bolt. The action of these stresses on the carbides that precipitated to the grain boundaries resulted in fracture of the bolt.

Corrective Measures. Because of the operating temperatures of the duct near the bolt, the material was changed to A286, which is a heat-resisting alloy and is less susceptible to carbide precipitation. The bolt was strengthened by shot peening the shank and rolling the threads after heat treatment.

Avoidance of heating in the sensitizing range would have been desirable, but difficult to ensure because of the application.

When zinc alloys of correct composition are placed in service, they withstand normal atmospheric conditions and are not susceptible to stress-corrosion cracking or to corrosion fatigue. However, when the zinc alloy contains excessive impurities or has an insufficient magnesium content, there are indications that stress-corrosion cracking becomes active, resulting in failure.

In the next example, the zinc die-casting alloy used for a plumbing nut was susceptible to stress-corrosion cracking.

Example 6. Stress-Corrosion Cracking of a Nut Made From a Zinc Alloy Die Casting (Fig. 10)

The two nuts shown in Fig. 10(a) and (b) were used to secure the water-supply pipes to the threaded connections on hot-water and cold-water taps. The nut used on the cold-water tap (Fig. 10a) fractured about one week after installation.

The cold-water tap and fractured nut were submitted to the laboratory for examination to determine the cause of failure. The mating hot-water tap was forwarded for comparison examination.

Investigation. Visual examination of the two taps indicated that they were of similar design. As shown in Fig. 10(a) and (b), the two nuts on the threaded connections were of a different style although they had the same size of thread. The two nuts did not exhibit any evidence of installation abuse, such as stripping of the threads. Various other marks and indentations were found on the flats of the nuts, particularly on the hot-water nut, such as would be made during normal installation.

Examination of the fracture surfaces of the cold-water nut did not reveal any obvious defects to account for the fracture, but there were indications of excessive porosity in the nut. The fracture had occurred through the root of the first thread that was adjacent to the flange on the tap.

Metallographic examination of the cold-water nut revealed evidence of considerable corrosive attack, mainly intergranular, extending into the material from the surface. This was present over the whole surface, including the threads, and extended into the material as deep as 0.010 in. Chemical spot tests indicated that the nut had been zinc plated.

Microscopic examination of the fracture surfaces of the cold-water nut indicated that considerable intergranular corrosion also had occurred at both sides of the fracture surface to a substantial depth, somewhat more than at the zinc-plated outer surface. Considering that this was a recent fracture, it would appear that corrosion on the fracture surface occurred prior to the failure rather than afterward.

Visual and microscopic examination of the hot-water nut also revealed some evidence of corrosion, but only in isolated areas mainly associated with the threads.

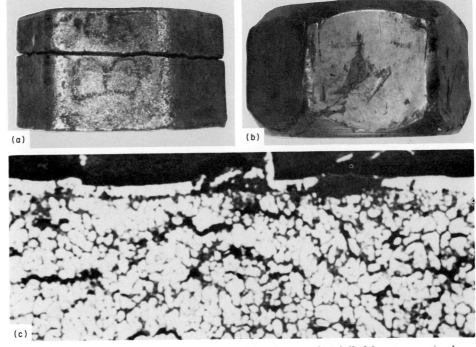

Fig. 10. (a) *Die-cast zinc alloy nut for a cold-water tap that failed by stress-corrosion cracking.* (b) *Mating nut for a hot-water tap that showed only isolated areas of corrosion.* (c) *Micrograph, at 600×, of an unetched section showing metal in the cold-water nut after corrosion testing.* (Example 6)

This nut was plated with a copper-nickel coating. Corrosion was present only at breaks in the plating and then only to a limited extent.

Radiographic examination indicated that both nuts had excessive porosity in similar amounts and distribution. Metallographic examination revealed that both nuts had a cast structure and were of a similar basic composition of zinc-aluminum die-casting alloy.

Corrosion Testing. It appeared that the cold-water nut was highly susceptible to corrosive attack; the hot-water nut did not exhibit this characteristic to the same degree. Samples of nuts of both styles were subjected to a corrosion test designed to indicate whether a particular zinc-alloy casting was susceptible to intergranular attack in atmospheric service. The test consisted of exposing the nuts in air saturated with water vapor at a temperature of 90 C (194 F) for ten days.

If the metal was attacked during this test, it indicated that there were deficiencies in magnesium content or that the content of the impurities, lead, cadmium and tin, were above 0.004%, 0.003% and 0.002%, respectively. In either instance, fracture during the test would indicate that the parts are likely to fail in service.

After four days of testing, the cold-water nut was noted to be severely cracked and was therefore removed for further examination. Slight pressure between the fingers caused the nut to crumble into several fragments. Metallographic examination of the material in the cold-water nut indicated that it had completely disintegrated, as shown by the cracks and corrosion network in the micrograph in Fig. 10(c). The zinc plating on the outer surface appeared to be relatively unattacked.

The corrosion test for the hot-water nut was run for the full ten days without any outward signs of attack. Metallographic examination revealed that there had been some additional corrosion but not to as great an extent as in the cold-water nut.

Conclusions. The nut from the cold-water tap failed by stress-corrosion cracking. Apparently, sufficient stress was developed in the nut to promote this type of failure by normal installation, because there was no evidence of excessive tightening of the nut.

Corrosion testing of the nuts indicated that the fractured nut was highly susceptible to intergranular corrosion, because of either a deficiency in magnesium content or excessive impurities, such as lead, tin or cadmium.

The primary cause of failure of the fractured nut was, therefore, an incorrect alloy composition.

Corrective Action. This composition problem with zinc alloys was recognized many years ago and particular attention has been directed toward ensuring that high-purity zinc is employed. This corrective action was reported to have resulted in virtual elimination of this type of defect.

Hydrogen Damage. Many fasteners require some kind of protective coating against corrosion. Sometimes this need is satisfied by an electrodeposited coating, such as cadmium or zinc. An acid pickling bath usually is employed to clean ferrous fasteners prior to plating. This pickling bath and the subsequent plating operation both supply nascent hydrogen to the fastener surface, and some of the hydrogen is absorbed by the steel. In high-strength steel components that have been electroplated but have not been baked for expulsion of hydrogen,

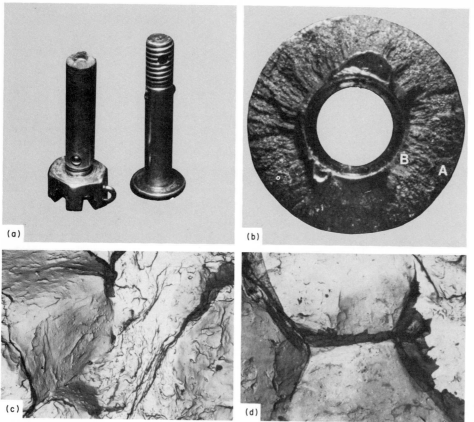

(a) Fractured and unused intact bolt. (b) Fractograph, at 13×, of fractured bolt; brittle-fracture surface is indicated by A and B. (c) and (d) Electron fractographs, at about 5000×, of surfaces A and B, respectively, showing brittle, intergranular fracture surfaces.

Fig. 11. Cadmium-plated alloy steel self-retaining bolts that fractured because of hydrogen damage (Example 8)

hydrogen diffuses to the area of the highest triaxial stress, such as at a notch. After an incubation period, a crack initiates and, with time, propagates through the section. A characteristic of this phenomenon is that there is a stress value below which hydrogen-induced delayed failure will not occur. This is sometimes referred to as the static-fatigue limit.

This difficulty, resulting from hydrogen charging during the pickling or electroplating process, can be eliminated without appreciable change in hardness by baking after plating at about 205 C (400 F) in air for a suitable time at temperature, depending upon the size and finish of the fastener. In the next two examples, cadmium-plated high-strength steel bolts that had not been properly baked failed when normally stressed in service.

Example 7. Delayed Failure of an Electroplated 8735 High-Strength Steel Bolt Because of Hydrogen Embrittlement

Cadmium-plated high-strength steel bolts were used to facilitate quick disassembly of a vehicle. One bolt was found fractured across the root of a thread after being torqued in place for one week. The bolts were made of 8735 steel heat treated to a tensile strength of 180,000 to 200,000 psi with a hardness of Rockwell C 39 to 43, followed by cadmium plating.

The bolt that failed and several that did not were sent to the laboratory so that the cause of failure could be determined. It was reported that the bolts that did not fail were stressed less than the specified torque level when attached to the assembly.

Investigation. It was assumed that the bolts had not been given a baking treatment for removal of hydrogen. Because there is no nondestructive test that will confirm such an assumption, two of the bolts were baked at 205 C (400 F) for 24 hr, then a series of tests were performed on both the baked and the as-plated bolts.

First, short-time tensile tests were performed on one of the as-plated bolts and on one that had been baked. The two bolts exhibited similar notched tensile strengths (209,750 psi for the as-plated bolt; 219,220 psi for the baked bolt), and thus this test did not disclose the presence of hydrogen. Therefore, the remaining bolts were tested under static loading.

The bolts were static loaded in tension on a creep frame. Delayed failure occurred in the as-plated bolts, but no failure occurred in the other bolt that was baked to remove the hydrogen. Test results were as follows:

Condition	Applied stress, psi	Time to failure, hr
As-plated	100,000	5.1
As-plated	75,000	5.6
As-plated	75,000	1.1
As-plated	50,000	67(a)
Baked(b)	75,000	598(a)

(a) No failure occurred; tests were concluded after time shown. (b) 24 hr at 205 C (400 F).

These results indicated that the static-fatigue limit was between 50,000 and 75,000 psi for the as-plated (hydrogen-charged) bolts. The properly baked bolt did not fail when it was subjected to a torque stress of 75,000 psi.

Conclusion. Failure of the bolts was the result of time-dependent hydrogen embrittlement. Had the remaining bolts been torqued to the normal stress levels, all would have failed within two weeks.

Corrective Measures. The bolts were baked as specified by ASTM B242, at 205 C (400 F) for ½ hr. No further failures occurred. Baking for ½ hr is the minimum baking time; however, baking times up to 24 hr are recommended for absolute safety.

Example 8. Hydrogen Embrittlement of Cadmium-Plated Alloy Steel Self-Retaining Bolts in a Throttle-Control Linkage (Fig. 11)

Two clevis-head self-retaining bolts used in the throttle-control linkage of a naval aircraft failed on the aircraft assembly line. (A failed bolt is compared with an unused bolt in Fig. 11a.) Specifications required the bolts to be heat treated to a hardness of Rockwell C 39 to 45, followed by cleaning, cadmium electroplating, and baking to minimize hydrogen embrittlement. The bolts broke at the junction of the head and shank. The nuts were, theoretically, installed fingertight.

Investigation. Inspection of the bolts and nuts showed excessive burrs in the threads at the cotter-pin holes and the nut slots, which made it necessary to use a wrench in assembly. This obviously had set up a tensile stress, which caused the bolts to fail. The fillet at the junction of the head and shank was undesirably sharp, but met the manufacturer's specification of 0.005 to 0.010 in. for the fillet radius.

Macroscopic examination of the fracture surface (Fig. 11b) gave no evidence of corrosion, fatigue marks, or rapid ductile failure. Electron fractographs of the fracture surface (Fig. 11c and d) showed a typical brittle, intergranular fracture, suggestive of hydrogen embrittlement. The microstructure was found to be sound and normal, and the hardness was within specifications.

Considerations of the event of failure before actual service and the possibility of hydrogen embrittlement that is inherent in cleaning and electroplating procedures led to the question of whether the bolts had been adequately baked after plating and whether postplating treatment had been performed as specified. To explore this, bolts from the same lot as the failed bolts were tested in prolonged tension in three conditions: as received, baked at 205 C (400 F) for 4 hr, and baked at 205 C (400 F) for 24 hr. The bolts in the first two conditions failed under a sustained tensile load, but the bolts baked for 24 hr did not, indicating that baking by the manufacturer had either been omitted or had been insufficient.

Conclusions. The failure was attributed to hydrogen embrittlement (resulting from cleaning or cadmium plating, or both) that had not been satisfactorily alleviated by subsequent baking.

The presence of the burrs on the threads prevented assembly to fingertightness and the consequent wrench torquing caused the actual fractures. The very small radius of the fillet between the bolt head and the shank undoubtedly accentuated the embrittling effect of the hydrogen.

Remedial Action. The cleaning and cadmium-plating procedures were stipulated to be low-hydrogen-contributing in nature, and an adequate postplating baking treatment at 205 C (400 F), in conformity with ASTM B242, was specified.

A minimum radius for the head-to-shank fillet was specified at 0.010 in. All threads were required to be free of burrs. A ten-day sustained-load test was specified for a sample quantity of bolts from each lot.

For additional information on hydrogen damage, the reader is referred to the article "Hydrogen-Damage Failures", which begins on page 230 in this volume.

Corrosion Protection

The most commonly used protective metal coatings for ferrous metal fasteners are zinc, cadmium and aluminum. Tin, lead, copper, nickel and chromium also are used, but only to a minor extent and for very special applications.

In many instances, however, fasteners are protected by some means other than metallic coatings. Sometimes they are sheltered from moisture or covered with a material that prevents moisture from making contact, thus drastically reducing or eliminating corrosion. For fasteners exposed to the elements, painting is universally used. The low-alloy, high-strength steel conforming to ASTM specification A242 forms its own protective oxide surface film. This type of steel, although it initially corrodes at the same rate as plain carbon steel, soon exhibits a decreasing corrosion rate, and after a few years, continuation of corrosion is practically nonexistent. The oxide coating formed is fine textured, tightly adherent, and a barrier to moisture and oxygen, effectively preventing further corrosion. Plain carbon steel, on the other hand, forms a coarse-textured flaky oxide that does not prevent moisture or oxygen from reaching the underlying noncorroded steel base.

Steels conforming to ASTM A242 are not recommended for exposure to highly concentrated industrial fumes or severe marine conditions, nor for use where they will be buried or submerged. In these environments, the highly protective oxide does not form properly, and corrosion is similar to that for plain carbon steel.

Zinc Coating. Zinc is the coating material most widely used for protection of fasteners from corrosion. Hot dipping is the most often used method of application, followed by electroplating and, to a minor extent, mechanical plating.

Hot dipping, as the name implies, is immersing parts in a molten bath of zinc. Hot dip zinc coatings are sacrificial by

electrochemical means. These coatings for fasteners meet ASTM specification A394, which specifies an average coating weight of 1.25 oz per square foot (2.2-mil thickness).

Zinc electroplating of fasteners is done primarily for appearance, where thread fit is critical, where corrosion is not expected to be severe, or where life expectancy is not great.

ASTM specification A164 for electrodeposited zinc coatings on steel specifies three coating thicknesses: GS, 0.0010 in.; LS, 0.0005 in.; and RS, 0.00015 in. — corresponding to coating weights of 0.59, 0.29, and 0.09 oz per square foot, respectively. Often, these electrodeposited coatings are given supplemental phosphate or chromate coatings to develop a specific color and, to a minor extent, enhance corrosion resistance. Corrosion life of a zinc coating is proportional to the amount of zinc present; thus, the heaviest electrodeposited coating (GS) would have only about half the life of a hot dip galvanized coating.

Mechanical (nonelectrolytic) barrel plating is another method of coating fasteners with zinc. Coating weight can be varied by varying the amount of zinc used and the duration of barrel rotation. Such coatings are quite uniform and have a satisfactory appearance.

Cadmium coatings also are applied to fasteners by an electroplating process similar to that used for zinc. These coatings meet ASTM specification A165. The specification for cadmium plating of high-quality aircraft fasteners is QQ-P-416. As is true for zinc, cadmium corrosion life is proportional to the coating thickness. The main advantage of cadmium over zinc is in marine environments, where the corrosion life of cadmium is longer. Chromate coatings also are used over cadmium coatings for the reasons given for zinc-plated fasteners.

Aluminum coating on fasteners offers the best protection of all coatings against atmospheric corrosion. Aluminum coating also gives excellent corrosion protection in seawater immersion and in high-temperature applications.

Aluminum coatings are applied by hot dip methods at about 675 to 705 C (1250 to 1300 F). Usually, aluminum alloy 1100 is used because of its general all-around corrosion resistance.

As with any hot dip coating, a metallurgical bond is formed that consists of an intermetallic alloy layer overlaid by a coating of pure bath material.

Aluminum coatings do not corrode uniformly, as do zinc and cadmium coatings, but rather by pitting. In some instances, these pits may extend entirely through the coating to the base metal; in others, only through the overlay to the intermetallic layer. Pits, which may occur in a part soon after exposure, some-

times discolor the coated surface but cause little damage. The complex aluminum and iron oxide corrosion product seals the pits and, because the seal is tightly adherent and impervious to attack, corrosion is usually limited. There is little tendency for corrosion to continue into the ferrous base, and none for undercutting and spalling of the coating.

Aluminum coatings will protect steel from scaling at temperatures up to about 540 C (1000 F); the aluminum coating remains substantially the same as when applied, and its life is exceptionally long. Above 650 C (about 1200 F), the aluminum coating diffuses into the steel to form an aluminum-iron alloy, which is highly protective. This diffusing or alloying is time-temperature dependent; the higher the temperature, the faster the diffusion. However, scaling will not take place until all the aluminum is used up, which may take a thousand or more hours even at temperatures as high as 760 C (1400 F).

Prevention of galling at elevated temperatures is another characteristic of aluminum coatings. Stainless steel fasteners for use at 650 C (1200 F) have been aluminum coated just to prevent galling. Coated nuts can be removed with an ordinary wrench after many hours at these high temperatures, which is impossible with uncoated nuts.

Fastener Performance at Elevated Temperatures

The temperature, the environment and the materials of the structure are normally fixed; therefore, a design objective is to select a bolt material that will give the desired clamping force at all critical points in the joint. To do this, it is necessary to balance the three time-and-temperature-related factors (relaxation, thermal expansion, and modulus) with a fourth factor — the amount of initial tightening or clamping force.

Modulus of Elasticity. As temperature increases, the modulus of elasticity decreases; thus, less load (or stress) is needed to impart a given amount of elongation (or strain) to a material than at lower temperatures. This means that a fastener stretched a certain amount at room temperature to develop preload will exert a lower clamping force at higher temperature. The effect of reducing the modulus is to reduce clamping force, whether or not the bolt and structure are of the same material, and is strictly a function of the bolt metal.

Coefficient of Expansion. With most materials, the size of the part increases as the temperature increases. In a joint, both the structure and the fastener increase in size with an increase in temperature. If the coefficient of expansion of the fastener is greater than that of the joined material, a predictable amount of clamping force will be lost as temperature increases. Conversely, if the coefficient of expansion of the joined material is greater, the bolt may be stressed beyond its yield or even fracture strength, or cyclic thermal stressing may lead to thermal fatigue failure. Thus, matching of materials in joint design can assure sufficient clamping force at both room and elevated temperatures, without overstressing the fastener.

Relaxation. At elevated temperatures, a material subjected to constant stress below its yield strength will flow plastically and permanently change dimensions in the direction of the stress. This phenomenon is called creep. In a joint at elevated temperature, a fastener with a fixed distance between the bearing surfaces of the male and female members will produce less and less clamping force with time. This characteristic is called relaxation. It differs from creep in that stress changes because the elongation or strain remains constant. Such elements as material, temperature, initial stress, manufacturing method, and design affect the rate of relaxation.

Relaxation is the most important of the three time-and-temperature-related factors. It is also the most critical consideration in design of fasteners for service at elevated temperature. A bolted joint at 650 C (about 1200 F) can lose as much as 50% of preload. Failure to compensate for this could lead to fatigue failure or a loose joint, even though the bolt was properly tightened initially.

Other Considerations. Bolt preloading is not the only aspect of joint design that must be considered for elevated-temperature service. Other considerations include time, environment, serviceability, coatings, manufacturing methods, fastener design, and material stability.

The element of time that is introduced with exposure to heat requires an assessment of the service life of the structure — or at least of the fastener — and of the amount of this life that will be spent at elevated temperature.

Galling and seizing are serious considerations if there is to be subsequent disassembly, which is usually necessary for threaded connections. Many of the materials with desirable elevated-temperature properties, such as the stainless steels, are inherently prone to galling during sliding contact of one member over another, even at room temperature. These materials require protective lubricating coatings. Additional problems of seizing of mating materials develop after exposure to temperature. Ease of disassembly requires that a suitable coating be used, and sometimes that clearance be provided at the pitch diameter.

At moderate temperatures, where cadmium and zinc anticorrosion platings

might normally be used, the phenomenon of stress-alloying becomes an important consideration. Conventional cadmium plating, for example, is usable only to 230 C (about 450 F). At somewhat above that temperature, the cadmium is likely to melt and diffuse into the base material along the grain boundaries, causing cracking by liquid-metal embrittlement, which can lead to rapid failure. For corrosion protection of high-strength alloy steel fasteners used at temperatures between 230 and 480 C (about 450 and about 900 F), special nickel-cadmium coatings such as that described in AMS 2416 often are employed.

At extremely high temperatures, coatings must be applied to prevent oxidation of the base material, particularly with refractory metals. These must be selected on the basis of the environments. In static air, suitable coatings are available. However, at partial pressure or in dynamic air, there will be a significant reduction in service life.

Fastener-manufacturing methods can also influence bolt performance at elevated temperature. The actual design and shape of the threaded fastener also are important — particularly, the root of the thread. A radiused thread root is a major consideration in room-temperature design, being a requisite for good fatigue performance. But at elevated temperature, a generously radiused thread root also is beneficial in relaxation performance. Starting at an initial preload of 70,000 psi, a Waspaloy stud with square thread roots lost a full 50% of its clamping force after 20 hr, with the curve continuing downward, indicating a further loss. A similar stud made with a large-radiused root lost only 36% of preload after 35 hr.

Selection of fastener material is perhaps the single most important consideration in elevated-temperature design. Most materials are effective over a limited temperature range. No fastener material is suitable for service at temperatures ranging from cryogenic to ultrahigh.

Standard high-strength bolts of medium-alloy steel have a usable temperature range up to about 230 C (450 F). The medium-alloy Cr-Mo-V steel conforming to ASTM A193, grade B16, is a commonly used bolt material in industrial turbine and engine applications to 480 C (about 900 F). An aircraft version of this steel, AMS 6304, is widely used in fasteners for jet engines.

For many industrial applications, corrosion- and heat-resistant stainless steels are usable to 425 C (about 800 F). Stabilized grades, such as types 321 and 347, can be used at slightly higher temperatures, at lower strength levels.

The 5% Cr tool steels, most notably H11, are used for fasteners having a

tensile strength of 220,000 to 260,000 psi. They retain excellent strength through 480 C (about 900 F).

From 480 to 650 C (about 900 to 1200 F), corrosion-resistant alloy A-286 is used. Alloy 718, with a room-temperature tensile strength of 180,000 psi, has some applications in this temperature range.

The nickel-base alloys René 41, Waspaloy and alloy 718 can be used for most applications in the temperature range of 650 to 870 C (about 1200 to 1600 F). Between 870 and 1095 C (about 1600 to 2000 F) is a transition range in which the nickel-base and cobalt-base alloys do not retain sufficient strength to give satisfactory service.

Mechanical fasteners for short-time exposure at ultrahigh temperature are available. Some refractory-metal fasteners are in service, in carefully controlled applications at temperatures of 1095 to 1650 C (about 2000 to 3000 F).

Rivets

Solid, tubular and split rivets are among the most commonly used fasteners for assembled products. Rivets are used as mechanical fasteners because they have a favorable relative cost and weight, because they are available in a wide variety of materials, head styles, and sizes, or because they have excellent hole-filling ability. To achieve these benefits, however, a product must be designed for riveting from the beginning, with consideration given to production as well as product design. The five basic types of rivets used are shown in Fig. 12.

Rivet Positioning. The location of the rivet in the assembled product influences both joint strength and clinching requirements. The important dimensions are edge distance and pitch distance.

Edge distance is the interval between the edge of the part and the centerline of the rivet and is controlled by the bearing strength of the material being joined. Maximum bearing strength is obtained with an edge distance equal to twice the diameter of the rivet shank. At less than this distance, the bearing strength of the joint decreases approximately directly with edge distance under some shear loadings. Even in the absence of shear load, edge distance of twice rivet-shank diameter should be specified to avoid buckling of the material while clinching. The recommended edge distance for plastic materials, either solid or laminates, is between two and three diameters, depending on the thickness and inherent strength of the material.

Pitch distance, which is the interval between centerlines of adjacent rivets, should be determined by the load to be carried across the joint and by the size of the fastener. Unnecessarily high stress concentrations in the riveted material

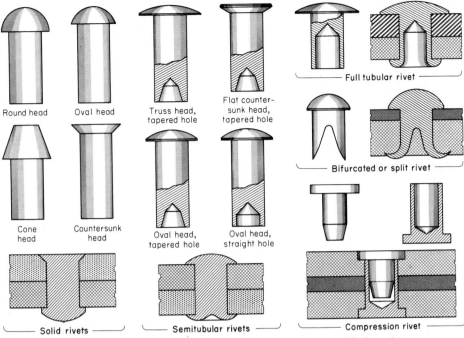

Round head | Oval head | Truss head, tapered hole | Flat countersunk head, tapered hole

Cone head | Countersunk head | Oval head, tapered hole | Oval head, straight hole

Full tubular rivet

Bifurcated or split rivet

Compression rivet

Solid rivets — Semitubular rivets

Fig. 12. Five basic types of rivets used for fastening assembled products

and buckling at adjacent empty holes can result if the pitch distance is less than three times the diameter of the largest rivet in the assembly. The maximum pitch distance is limited by the tendency of the sheet to buckle between rivets. Multiple rows of rivets, sometimes staggered, frequently are necessary to provide the desired joint strength.

Types of Rivet Failures. Standard design analyses of riveted joints consider two primary types of failures: (a) shear in the shank of the rivet, and (b) bearing or crushing failure of the metal at the point where the rivet bears against the joined members. The load per rivet at which each of these two types of failures may occur is separately calculated, and the lower value of the two calculations governs the design. However, the practical goal should be to design all riveted joints as "bearing critical". This can be accomplished by selecting the correct material composition, condition and thickness. For optimum performance, the rivet and the members being joined should have the same properties, but from the driving standpoint, it is often necessary to have a softer rivet.

In addition to the design considerations, rivets also may be susceptible to failure by many of the same failure mechanisms experienced by threaded fasteners. For instance, rivets are especially susceptible to fatigue failure when used in the same joint with threaded fasteners. This is because rivets fill the holes more nearly completely than threaded fasteners and thus are subjected to more than their proportionate share of the load.

Shear in Shank. The number of planes on which a rivet fails in shear depends on the type of joint that is riveted. Rivets normally are used in single or double shear. For design purposes, the load required to shear a rivet can be assumed to increase directly with the number of planes on which shear loading occurs; thus, in double shear, a rivet is approximately twice as strong as in single shear. However, if the members being joined are relatively thin and have significantly greater hardness than the rivets, the rivets will fail at a lower value of shear stress than that determined in tests with thicker material.

Machine-countersunk flush-head rivets are subject to failure of the sheet or to shear and tension failure of rivet heads. Riveted joints with thin outer sheets are critical because of the instability of the outer sheet, which can buckle around the rivet before full bearing stress is developed, as shown in Fig. 13.

Bearing-Surface Failure. In riveted joints involving sheet of moderate thickness, the controlling factor is the strength of the rivet head, because induced shear and tension in the rivet head are more critical than shear through the shank. Determining factors are magnitude of the induced loads in the rivet head, deflection of the rivet head and sheet under load, and bearing of the knife-edge of the countersunk hole in the top sheet on the rivet. Typical loading of a riveted joint is shown in Fig. 14(a); failure generally occurs as shown in Fig. 14(b). Because of these inherent limitations of flush-head rivets, protruding-head rivets are preferred. Flush-head rivets should be used only when a clean surface is required for appearance or for aerodynamic efficiency, or where clearance for an adjacent structure is inadequate to accommodate protruding-head fasteners.

Stress-Corrosion Cracking. In aluminum alloys containing more than 4% magnesium, the introduction of plastic deformation followed by aging at a slightly elevated temperature, such as might occur in the tropics, can lead to stress-corrosion cracking. A rivet of Alcan aluminum alloy B54S-O, shown in cross section in Fig. 15(a), failed during a stress-corrosion test in the laboratory and illustrates this effect. The rivet was heated for seven days at 100 C (212 F) prior to testing. The residual deformation from the heading operation, followed by the treatment at elevated temperature, resulted in failure from stress-corrosion cracking. The path of the fracture along the grain boundaries is illustrated in Fig. 15(b). The specimen was etched in dilute phosphoric acid, which, on alloys of this type, outlines the grains in a material that is sensitive to stress corrosion. Electron-microscope investigation has shown that this type of grain-boundary attack prevails when a fine, closely spaced precipitate is present at the grain boundary (Ref 4). If the precipitate is coarser and more widely spaced, as when treated at 230 C (446 F) for 6 hr, small etch pits that resemble a string of pearls at the grain boundaries

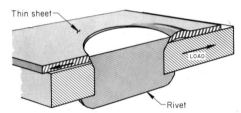

Thin sheet

LOAD

Rivet

Fig. 13. Schematic representation of failure of thin sheet in a riveted joint because of buckling. Note that countersinking the top sheet formed a sharp edge at the faying surface.

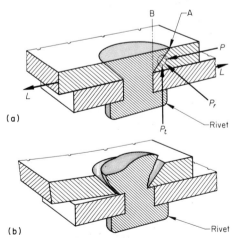

(a) Loading of rivet. A is bearing area of upper sheet; B, bearing area of lower sheet; L, load; P, shear component; P_t, tension component; P_r, resultant of shear and tension components. (b) Shear and tension failure mode.

Fig. 14. Schematic representation of typical behavior characteristics of flush-head rivets

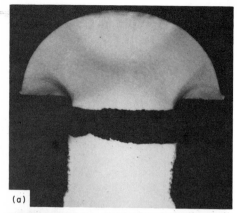

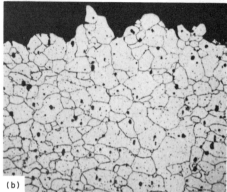

(a) Macrograph, at 5×, of section through rivet showing shape of fracture surface. (b) Micrograph, at 450×, showing an intergranular fracture path.

Fig. 15. Rivet made of Alcan aluminum alloy B54S-O that fractured by stress corrosion after being heated for seven days at 100 C (212 F)

can be seen with the optical microscope. Such a structure is not susceptible to stress-corrosion cracking.

Blind Fasteners

Blind fasteners are mechanical fasteners that can be installed in a joint that is accessible from one side only. When a blind fastener is set, a self-contained mechanical, chemical or other device forms an upset on the inaccessible, or blind, end of the fastener and also expands the fastener shank, thereby securing the parts being joined.

Blind fasteners are classified according to the methods with which they are set, either pull-mandrel, threaded, drive-pin, or chemically expanded. Rivets that conform to these classifications are illustrated in Fig. 16.

A blind-fastened joint is usually in compression or shear, both of which the fasteners can support somewhat better than tensile loading. The amount of loading that blind fasteners subjected to vibration can sustain is influenced by minimum hole clearance and such installation techniques as applying compression to the assembly with clamps before the fasteners are set.

Some blind fasteners can be used in material as thin as 0.020 in. if the heads are properly formed and shank expansion is carefully controlled during setting. However, in joining sheets that are dissimilar in thickness, it is best practice to form the blind head against the thicker sheet. Also, if one of the components being joined is of a compressible material, rivets with extralarge-diameter heads should be used.

Tolerances applied to blind-fastener holes vary according to the type of rivet used. Ordinarily, it is more economical to select a fastener that clamps against the surfaces of the components being joined, rather than to select one that depends only on hole filling.

Pin Fasteners

Pins are effective fasteners where loading is primarily in shear. They can be divided into two groups: semipermanent pins and quick-release pins.

Semipermanent Pins

Semipermanent pin fasteners require the application of pressure for installation or removal. The two basic types are machine pins and radial-locking pins.

General rules that apply to all types of semipermanent pins are:

1 Avoid conditions where the direction of vibration is parallel to the axis of the pin.
2 Keep the shear plane of the pin a minimum distance of one pin diameter from the end of the pin.
3 Where the engaged length is at a minimum and appearance is not critical, allow pins to protrude at each end for maximum locking effect.

Machine Pins. The four important types of machine pins are: dowel pins, taper pins, clevis pins and cotter pins.

Machine pins are used either to retain parts in a fixed position or to preserve alignment. Under normal conditions a properly fitted machine pin is subjected to shear only, and this occurs only at

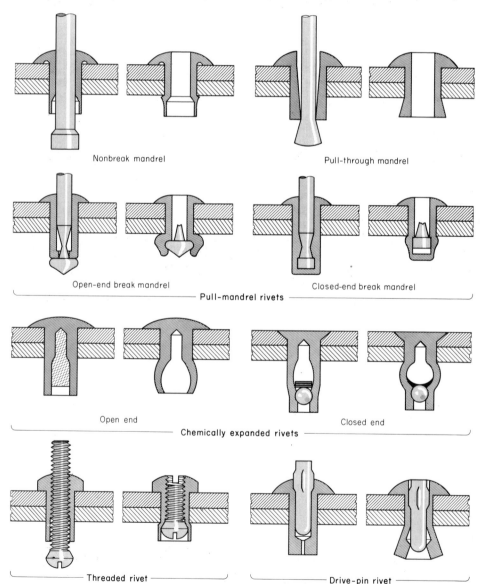

Fig. 16. Types of blind fasteners used in fastening of assembled components

the interface of the surfaces of the two parts being fastened.

Taper pins are commonly used for fastening parts that are taken apart frequently, where the constant driving-out of the pin would weaken the holes if a straight pin were used.

A loose fit between the drive wheel and shaft of the assembly described in the next example resulted in fatigue fracture of a taper pin that held the two components together.

Example 9. Fatigue Fracture of an 1141 Steel Taper Pin in a Clutch-Drive Assembly Because of Loose Fit Between Components (Fig. 17)

The drive wheel on the clutch-drive support assembly shown in Fig. 17(a) was slightly loose and caused clutch failures in service after 6,800,000 cycles. After failure, removal of the taper pin holding the drive wheel on the shaft was difficult, indicating that the pin was tight in the assembly.

The taper pin was made of 1141 steel, the shaft of 1117 steel, and the drive wheel of 52100 steel.

Investigation. On removal from the assembly, the taper pin was found to be broken at the small end (see section A-A, Fig. 17). In assembly, the fracture occurred near the interface of the shaft and the drive wheel. As shown in Fig. 17(b), the surface of the taper pin contained axial grinding marks, some of which were partly obliterated by movement of the components during operation, before and after the pin broke. Evidence of fretting also was found on the pin. Surface finish on the pin was 45 micro-in.; specifications required 32 micro-in. The fracture surface of the pin contained ductile tears, fatigue striations, and shear lips.

Examination of the clutch shaft revealed that fretting had occurred on the portion of the shaft covered by the drive wheel (see Fig. 17c). It did not appear that fretting alone had impaired machine operation.

During the investigation, a second clutch-drive support assembly was received at the laboratory. This second assembly exhibited a loose fit similar to the first. The assembly was sectioned transversely at the taper pin, and the pin was found to be fractured in the same area as the first. There was a tight line-to-line fit between the shaft and the taper pin. However, there was a maximum clearance of 0.003 in. between the drive wheel and the large end of the pin, and a lesser amount at the small end. Also, the clearance between the shaft and the drive wheel was 0.0015 in. (specifications permitted a maximum clearance of 0.001 in.). Because of the excessive clearance between the shaft and the drive wheel, alternating stresses were transmitted to the pin.

Conclusion. Failure of the clutch-drive support assembly occurred as a result of fatigue fracture of a taper pin. A loose fit between the drive wheel and the shaft, and between the drive wheel and the pin, permitted movement that resulted in fatigue failure. Fretting of the pin and drive shaft was observed but did not appear to have contributed to the failure.

Recommendations. The assembly should be redesigned to include an interference fit

between the shaft and the drive wheel. The drive wheel and the shaft should be taper reamed at assembly to ensure proper fit.

In addition, receiving inspection should be more critical of the components and accept only those that meet specifications.

In the next example, drive pins (a type of dowel pin) used to secure jackscrews failed by stress-corrosion cracking because overdriving caused damage, in the form of cracking and chipping, to the protective chromium plate on the pins.

Example 10. Stress-Corrosion Cracking of 300M Steel Jackscrew Drive Pins Because the Protective Chromium Plating Was Damaged (Fig. 18)

Both jackscrew drive pins on a landing-gear bogie failed suddenly when the other bogie on the same side of the airplane was kneeled for a tire change. The pins were smooth, cylindrical tubes that fastened the top tubular ends of the jackscrews to the plane. The primary service stress on the pins was shear. The pins had nominal dimensions of 1.6-in. OD, 1-in. ID, and 7-in. length, and they had a smooth push fit with a hole tolerance of +0.0015 to +0.0040 in. They were shot peened and chromium plated on the outside surface, and cadmium plated and painted with polyurethane on the inside surface. The pins were made of 300M steel heat treated to a tensile strength of 280,000 to 300,000 psi. The top of the jackscrew was of 6150 steel heat treated to a tensile strength of 180,000 to 200,000 psi.

Investigation. After the retrieved portions of the fractured pins had been reassembled (see Fig. 18a and b), it was evident that they had sustained prior mechanical damage. Both ends of the pins were dented where the jackscrew had pressed into them, probably as a result of overdriving the jackscrew at the end of an unkneeling cycle. The one end of the forward pin was noticeably bent (see Fig. 18c). The chromium plating was missing from the dented areas, and these areas were heavily corroded.

Chromium-carbon replicas of the areas of fracture origin showed a heavily corroded intergranular fracture mode, as shown in Fig. 18(e) and (f). Subsequent metallographic examination revealed deep corrosion pits adjacent to the fracture origins and directly beneath cracks in the chromium plate, as shown in Fig. 18(d). Intergranular cracks that had propagated from several of the pits under the cracks in the chromium plate are shown in Fig. 18(g).

The dimensions, surface finish and composition of the pins were within the specified limits. Microhardness traverses and metallographic examination of sections through the pins confirmed that neither carburization nor decarburization had occurred on the surface of either pin. Alkaline chromate etching confirmed that no intergranular oxidation products were present. The microstructure was typical of tempered martensite and was satisfactory.

Conclusions. Overdriving the jackscrew dented the drive pins and caused cracking and chipping of the chromium plate. The unprotected metal rusted, and stress-corrosion cracks grew out of some of the rust pits. The terminal portion of the fracture resulted

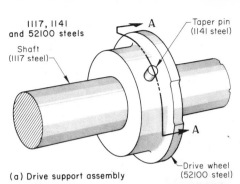

(a) Drive support assembly

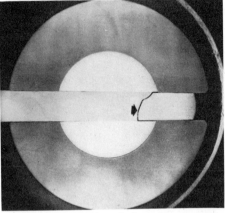

Section A-A

(b)

(c)

(a) Drive support assembly. Section A-A shows break in the small end of the taper pin (at arrow). (b) Fractured pin; note axial grinding marks on surface. (c) Fretting on the portion of the shaft covered by the drive wheel.

Fig. 17. Steel clutch-drive support assembly that failed in service because a loose fit between components caused the taper pin to fracture (Example 9)

from overstress when the remaining uncracked cross section was not adequate to carry the load.

Corrective Action. The jacking-control system was modified to prevent overdriving and subsequent damage to the drive pins. The pin material was changed from 300M steel to PH 13-8 Mo stainless steel, which is highly resistant to rusting and stress-corrosion cracking. The inside diameter of the pins was reduced to compensate for the lower strength of the PH 13-8 Mo steel. The protective plating and paint were eliminated because of the good corrosion resistance of the new material.

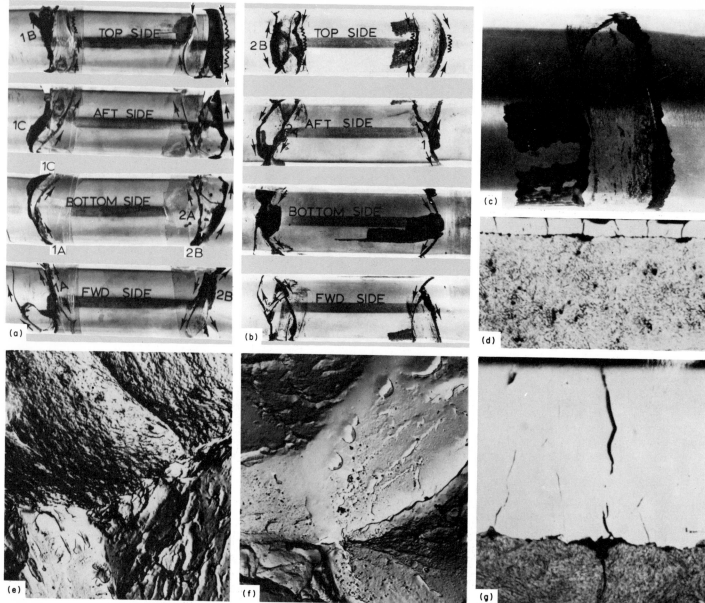

(a) Four views of aft-pin locations of individual origins (numbers), directions of fracture (arrows), and final fracture regions (wavy lines). (b) Same as (a) except for forward pin. (c) Top surface of forward pin showing slight bend at left end. (d) Micrograph, at 100×, of specimen etched in nital, showing pits in base metal at cracks in chromium plating. (e) Electron fractograph, at 4000×, showing corroded intergranular fracture surface at origin 1 on forward pin (see b). (f) Same as (e) except at 6500× and origin 1A on aft pin. (g) Micrograph, at 400×, of specimen etched in nital, showing intergranular crack in base metal propagating from corrosion pit adjacent to crack beneath chromium plating.

Fig. 18. Jackscrew drive pins made of 300M steel that fractured by stress-corrosion cracking (Example 10)

Radial-locking pins are of two basic styles: solid, with grooved surfaces; and hollow spring pins, which may be either slotted or spiral wound. In assembly, radial forces produced by elastic action at the pin surface develop a friction-locking grip against the hole wall. Spring action at the pin surface also prevents loosening under shock and vibration.

Locking of the solid grooved pins is provided by parallel, longitudinal grooves uniformly spaced around the pin surface. When the pin is driven into a drilled hole corresponding in size to the nominal pin diameter, elastic deformation of the raised groove edges produces a force fit with the hole wall. Best results under average conditions are obtained

with holes drilled the same size as the nominal pin diameter. Undersize holes should be avoided, because they can lead to deformation of the pin in assembly, damage to hole walls, and shearing-off of the raised groove edges.

Resilience of hollow cylinder walls under radial compression forces is the principle of spiral-wound and slotted tubular pins. Compressed when driven into the hole, the pins exert spring pressure against the hole wall along their entire engaged length to develop locking action. For maximum shear strength, slotted pins should be placed in assemblies so that the slots are in line with the direction of loading and 180° away from the point of application.

Quick-Release Pins

Quick-release pins are of two types: push-pull and positive locking. Both employ some form of detent mechanism to provide a locking action for rapid manual assembly and disassembly.

Push-pull pins are made with a solid or hollow shank containing a detent assembly, such as a locking lug, button or ball, which is backed by a resilient core, plug or spring. These pins fasten parts under shear loading, ideally at right angles to the shank of the pin.

Positive-locking pins employ a locking action that is independent of insertion and removal forces. These pins are primarily suited for shear-load applications.

However, some tension loading usually can be tolerated without adversely affecting the function of these pins.

Special-Purpose Fasteners

Special-purpose fasteners, many of which are proprietary, frequently are used in nonstructural applications to provide some unique feature, such as quick release, snap action or cam action. These fasteners are subject to the same failure mechanisms experienced by threaded fasteners and rivets.

Spring clips are a type of special-purpose fastener that perform multiple functions, are generally self-retaining and, for attachment, require only a flange, panel edge, or mounting hole. The spring-tension principle of fastening eliminates loosening by vibration, allows for design flexibility, compensates for tolerance buildup and misalignment, and minimizes assembly damage.

The basic material for spring-clip fasteners is steel with 0.50 to 0.80% carbon content. Generally, fasteners are formed in the annealed stage, then hardened and tempered to Rockwell C 45 to 50. Zinc or cadmium electroplating is specified for certain applications. Other applications may use a zinc mechanical plating to eliminate hydrogen embrittlement. In the following example, a spring clip made of zinc-electroplated 1060 steel fractured because of hydrogen embrittlement.

Example 11. Failure of a Zinc-Electroplated 1060 Steel Fastener Because of Hydrogen Embrittlement (Fig. 19)

The fastener shown in Fig. 19 was used to secure plastic fabric or webbing to the aluminum framework of outdoor furniture.

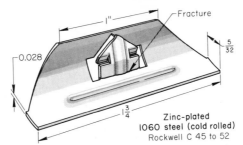

Fig. 19. Zinc-electroplated 1060 steel fastener, for securing fabric to lawn-furniture framework, that failed by hydrogen embrittlement (Example 11)

Several clips were required on each piece of furniture, and these had to hold the fabric for several seasons of varying weather conditions.

The fasteners were made in high-production progressive dies from 0.028-in.-thick cold rolled 1060 steel. They were barrel finished to remove burrs, and hardened and tempered to Rockwell C 45 to 52. The fasteners were electroplated with zinc and coated with clear zinc dichromate.

During attachment of the fabric to the furniture, approximately 30% of the fasteners cracked and fractured as they were compressed to clamp onto the framework prior to springback, which held the fabric in place. Fasteners on some of the furniture that was successfully assembled fractured in warehouses, in retail stores, and in service, allowing the plastic fabric or webbing to come off the chair.

Discussion. The heat treatment of the fasteners consisted of austenitizing at 790 C (about 1450 F) for 10 min, quenching in oil at 82 C (180 F), rinsing, then tempering at 343 C (650 F) to obtain a microstructure of tempered martensite. After being acid cleaned, zinc electroplated to a thickness of 0.0002 in. and coated with a clear dichromate, the fasteners were baked 8 hr at 163 C

(325 F) to remove the nascent hydrogen. Fasteners treated in this manner were very brittle and had a limited capability of being compressed without fracture. Low ductility at room temperature and delayed failure are characteristic of steel that has been damaged by hydrogen embrittlement.

Conclusions. The fasteners failed in a brittle manner as the result of hydrogen embrittlement. Hydrogen was induced into the surface of the steel when the hardened parts were acid cleaned prior to electroplating and during the electroplating operation. Baking at 163 C (325 F) for 8 hr failed to remove all of the nascent hydrogen that had interstitially diffused into the steel.

Corrective Measures. The heat treatment was changed from austenitizing, quenching and tempering to austenitizing at 790 C (about 1450 F) for 15 min, quenching in a potassium chloride salt bath at 343 C (650 F) for 20 min, air cooling, and rinsing. This heat treatment produced a more ductile and bainitic structure than the original heat treatment, and a hardness of Rockwell C 48 to 52.

The method of plating the fastener with zinc was changed from electroplating to a mechanical deposition process.

These two changes eliminated the possibility of hydrogen embrittlement, because acid cleaning was not needed after austempering and before plating. Also, mechanical deposition of zinc coating does not produce hydrogen embrittlement in hardened steel.

References

1. Military Handbook, "Metallic Materials and Elements for Aerospace Vehicle Structures", Vol II, Figure 9. 4. 1. 7(a)
2. J. S. Davey, Why Nuts Should Have Their Own Specification, *Fasteners*, Vol 13, No. 3, Fall 1958, Industrial Fasteners Institute
3. SPS Bolts for the Aerospace Industry, 1964-1965 edition, Standard Pressed Steel Co.
4. A. T. Thomas, Etching Characteristics and Grain Boundary Structure of Aged Aluminum-Magnesium Alloys, *J Inst Metals*, Vol 94, 1966

Failures of Springs

By James H. Maker*

SPRINGS are made in many types, shapes, and sizes, ranging from delicate hairsprings for watches to massive buffer springs for railroad equipment.

The vast majority of springs are made from one of several grades of carbon or alloy steel. However, to accommodate the broad spectrum of applications, springs have been made from a wide variety of metals and alloys, including stainless steels, heat-resisting alloys, copper alloys and titanium alloys.

*Chief Metallurgist, Wallace Barnes Div., Associated Spring Corp.

The broad range of compositions, sizes and types of springs is equaled by the required range of quality and characteristics. Quality can range from that required for low-cost ballpoint pens to the extremely high quality necessary for aerospace applications.

Ordinary springs, such as those used in noncorrosive environments and at temperatures not much higher than room temperature, are produced to high strength levels that often can be obtained entirely by severe cold working (drawing or rolling). This approach to producing springs generally dictates that no metal

be removed from the wire or strip during working, which allows any existing defects in the raw material to remain. For a great number of applications, springs produced in this manner are adequate because minor surface discontinuities are of little or no consequence.

More rigorous applications are more likely to require springs with defect-free surfaces. Such surfaces can be obtained by conditioning of billets or even by grinding of the wire or strip stock from which the springs are formed. These practices, however, significantly increase cost and decrease availability. (For more detailed information on composi- tions and characteristics of steels for springs, see the article that begins on page 160 in Volume 1 of this Handbook.)

Operating Conditions

Although most spring applications in- volve operating temperatures that are not far above or below room temperature, many applications require springs to operate over an appreciable temperature range. For instance, valve springs in in- ternal-combustion engines must operate in frigid weather for start-up and then, within minutes, must function at the nor- mal operating temperature of the spring chamber, which may approach 90 C (194 F). This temperature range, and even a range with a maximum temperature somewhat higher, can be accommodated by springs made of carbon or low-alloy steels. (For examples of springs that failed because of excessive operating tem- peratures, see the article on Distortion Failures, which begins on page 125 in this volume.) However, some springs are required to operate at much higher tem- peratures and thus must be made of heat- resisting materials. Such applications must be evaluated individually before a suitable selection of material can be made. For further information, see the article on Selection of Material for High- Temperature Springs, which begins on page 635 in Volume 1 of this Handbook.

Corrosive Environments. Most springs are not subjected to environments more corrosive than humid air; there are, how- ever, many exceptions. As for elevated- temperature service, applications that in- volve corrosive environments must be evaluated individually prior to the selec- tion of materials for springs or of suitable protective coatings.

Common Failure Mechanisms

Fatigue is the most common mech- anism of failure in springs, as demon- strated by the examples in this article. Any of the causes noted in the section on Common Causes of Failures may result in failure by fatigue; sometimes, more than one cause is involved.

Settling (relaxation) is another com- mon failure mechanism. This condition is caused by overstressing and often results from use of a grade of material that is marginal for the application.

Relaxation from operation at exces- sively high temperatures also is a com- mon failure mechanism.

Although some spring materials are quite notch sensitive and have limited ductility, brittle fracture is not a major problem in springs in the usual sense. Apparently, this is true because the sec- tion sizes are usually small, an extreme degree of working has been utilized, and

Fig. 1. Fractograph, at 10×, of the sur- face of a fracture that occurred one turn from the end of a titanium alloy spring; arrow indicates the point of contact near the end of the next coil

care in minimizing stress concentrations has been applied.

One form of brittle fracture occasion- ally encountered results from hydrogen absorption in martensitic structures, which occurs in electroplating or other finishing processes. Corrosion contributes to spring failure in much the same way as it contributes to failure of other highly stressed structures, although in springs it is most often connected with fatigue. Nevertheless, static stress-corrosion fail- ures can occur at high stresses in the presence of electrolytes.

Examination of Spring Failures

For the most part, procedures that apply to analysis of failures in other parts also apply to analysis of spring failures (see the article beginning on page 10 in this volume). Loading and other service conditions, and all details of the material, should be determined, and a preliminary visual examination should be made to identify fracture-surface features, wear patterns, contact marks, surface deposits, and temperature colors. Fracture features often are damaged by clashing of the portions of the broken spring, and thus it may be necessary to analyze several similar failures to arrive at the correct conclusion as to the cause of failure.

For small springs, a stereoscopic bench microscope is essential, because the entire cross section may be only as large as the origin of failure in many large sections.

Another important factor is lighting. Sometimes, spot lighting is required, but because of reflections into and away from the objective lens, such lighting can be misleading. What is best for fractography often is not best for stereo viewing. A small ring-type fluorescent lamp around the objective is suitable for general use if supplemented by a more concentrated source of light. By exploration at all pos- sible viewing angles with this lighting, features may be revealed that otherwise could escape detection.

Common Causes of Failures

Overstressing is a common cause of failure of springs. Settling and other types of distortion generally are caused by operation of springs at higher-than- expected stresses. It must be kept in mind, however, that the stresses a given spring can withstand are greatly affected by the operating environment. For in- stance, helical springs made of 6150 steel provided failure-free service in fuel-in- jection pumps when the fuel oil being pumped was a normal low-sulfur grade, but several of these springs failed under identical stress conditions when the fuel oil contained substantial amounts of hy- drogen sulfide.

Likewise, operating temperatures that are higher than those anticipated often result in failures of springs, without changes in stress.

Design deficiencies, material defects, processing errors or deficiencies, and un- usual operating conditions are common causes of failure of springs. In a majority of instances, these causes result in failure by fatigue.

In the remainder of this article, 19 ex- amples of specific failures of springs are presented. Although most of the springs that are discussed in these examples failed by fatigue, the fatigue cracks were initiated by a wide variety of causes. In some of the examples, more than one cause contributed to failure.

Failures Caused by Errors in Design

Rules governing design of the more common types of springs generally are well understood and closely followed. Proper distribution of stresses to prevent the spring from "going solid", and avoid- ance of sharp bends, are among the prin- cipal requirements of a well-designed spring.

Because the rules of design are gen- erally understood and followed, the num- ber of failures of springs that occur solely as the result of faulty design is comparatively small. However, there are occasional exceptions.

For instance, one of a test set of ti- tanium alloy Ti-13V-11Cr-3Al torsional (helical) springs failed by fatigue after 12 million cycles at a maximum stress of 93,000 psi. The surface of the fracture, which occurred one turn from the end, is shown in Fig. 1. Radial marks emanate from the fracture origin (arrow), which was in an area of contact with the end turn of the spring. In this area, small elongated gall marks were visible, indi- cating that there was sliding motion over a region about 0.004 in. in length. It was thus concluded that fretting in this area had lowered the fatigue strength. In this instance, and in many other instances,

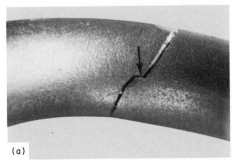

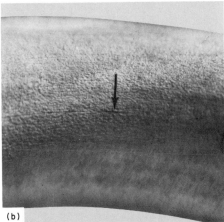

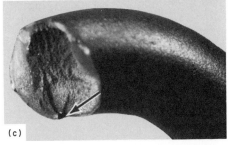

Fig. 2. (a) Macrograph, at 5×, of a fatigue fracture in a carbon steel helical spring, which originated at a seam (arrow). (b) Macrograph, at 10×, showing seam (arrow) near fracture. (c) Fracture surface, at 5×, showing distinct marks radiating from origin (arrow). (Example 1)

the proximity of one coil to another does not permit some areas to be properly shot peened, and this can contribute to a reduction in fatigue life.

Failures Caused by Material Defects

Seams frequently contribute to failures of springs, usually by initiating fatigue cracks. Pipe, inclusions and pits also may contribute to premature failures. The next three examples describe fatigue failures that resulted from material defects of these types.

Example 1. Fatigue Fracture of an Automotive Shift-Mechanism Spring Caused by a Seam (Fig. 2)

The helical spring used in an automotive shift mechanism was made from carbon steel wire similar to that used for valve springs. The wire, 0.200 in. in diameter, was hard-

ened and tempered, formed into the spring and then shot peened. Although this particular wire was restricted with respect to allowable seam depth, it was not of the highest quality obtainable. (Failure of this spring could not, however, have an adverse effect on the safety of the vehicle.)

The spring was designed for a life of 5 million cycles at a stress range of 20,000 to 120,000 psi, but fractured after only 2.4 million cycles of operation within this stress range.

Investigation. Figure 2(a) shows the fracture, which consisted of two segments, both at approximately 45° to the wire axis, connected by a short longitudinal step. Because such steps are typical of fatigue fractures originating at seams or other flaws that have been elongated by the wiredrawing process, and because a seam was found near the fracture (see Fig. 2b), it was concluded that the longitudinal step was originally a seam, which initiated the fracture. This seam had been 0.050 in. long and 0.0017 in. deep.

Figure 2(c) shows the fracture surface, which contains distinct marks radiating from the origin (arrow).

Conclusion. Fracture of the spring occurred by fatigue and originated at a tiny longitudinal seam in the wire. This example shows that a defect having a depth of no more than approximately 1% of the wire diameter can have an appreciable effect on the fatigue life of a spring.

Recommendations. Seams in springs can be eliminated by requiring either (a) better conditioning of the wire (removal of more stock in processing) or (b) nondestructive inspection of either the wire or the finished springs. However, either approach will greatly increase spring cost and therefore must be justified economically.

Example 2. Fatigue Fracture of Alloy Steel Valve Springs Because of Pipe (Fig. 3)

Two outer valve springs broke during production engine testing and were submitted for laboratory analysis. The springs were from a current production lot and had been made from air-melted 6150 pretempered steel wire. The springs were 2 in. in outside diameter and 2½ in. in free length, had five coils and squared-and-ground ends, and were made of 7/32-in.-diam wire. Because both failures were much alike, the analysis of only one is discussed here.

Investigation. The spring (see Fig. 3a) broke approximately 1½ turns from the end. Fracture was nucleated by an apparent longitudinal subsurface defect. Magnetic-particle inspection did not reveal any additional cracks or defects.

Microscopic examination of transverse sections of the spring adjacent to the fracture surfaces revealed that the defect was a large pocket of nonmetallic inclusions at the nucleus of the fracture. The inclusions were alumina and silicate particles. Partial decarburization of the steel was evident at the periphery of the pocket of inclusions. The composition and appearance of the inclusions, and the presence of the partial decarburization, indicated that the inclusions were associated with residual shrinkage pipe carried over into the finished spring wire from the ingot. The pipe was 0.03 in. in diameter (max), 1 in. long and 0.05 in. below the surface (see Fig. 3b).

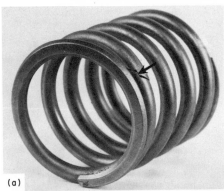

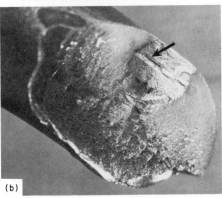

Fig. 3. (a) Alloy steel valve spring that fractured from fatigue because of residual shrinkage pipe; fracture is indicated by arrow. (b) Fracture surface; pipe is indicated by arrow. (Example 2)

The steel had a hardness of Rockwell C 45 to 46, a microstructure of tempered martensite, and a grain size of ASTM 6 or 7, all of which were satisfactory for the application. The fracture surface contained beach marks typical of fatigue and was at a 45° angle to the wire axis, which is indicative of torsional fracture.

Conclusions. The spring fractured by fatigue; fatigue cracking was nucleated at a subsurface defect that was longitudinal to the wire axis. The stress-raising effect of the defect was responsible for the fracture.

The defect was residual shrinkage pipe carried into the finished spring wire from the original ingot, possibly as the result of insufficient ingot cropping.

Example 3. Fatigue Fracture of a Carbon Steel Pawl Spring That Originated at a Delamination at a Rivet Hole (Fig. 4)

The pawl spring shown in Fig. 4(a) was part of a selector switch used in telephone equipment. Three of these springs that broke, and strip specimens of the raw material used to fabricate similar springs, were examined in order to determine the cause of failure. The springs had been blanked from 0.014-in.-thick tempered 1095 steel, then nickel plated.

Investigation. Longitudinal specimens from the three broken springs were mounted and processed, and microscopic examination of these specimens revealed numerous pits around the rivet holes. These pits can be seen readily in Fig. 4(b), which is a close-up view of one rivet hole, because their surfaces were covered with nickel plating that was not removed during grinding and etch-

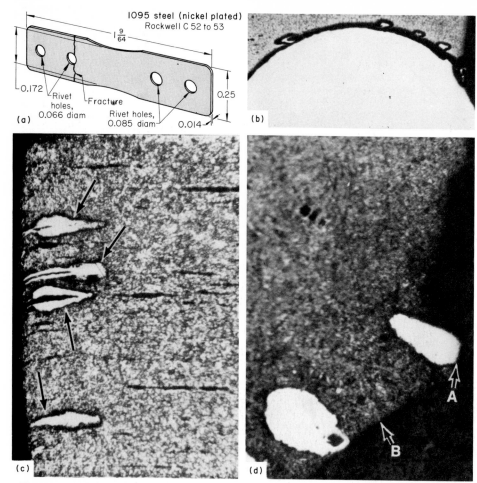

Fig. 4. (a) Nickel-plated 1095 steel pawl spring that fractured by fatigue. (b) Micrograph, at 45×, showing pits at edge of rivet hole. (c) Micrograph, at 250×, of area adjacent to rivet hole, showing delaminations (arrows) filled with nickel plating. (d) Micrograph, at 250×, showing delamination, at A, that initiated fracture; edge of rivet hole is at B. (Example 3)

ing of the specimen. The pits, and other defects found at the rivet holes and at the bottom end of the spring, were produced by a dull blanking-and-punching tool.

A longitudinal section through a rivet hole is shown in Fig. 4(c). This micrograph reveals delaminations that were formed at inclusion sites during punching of the rivet holes and that were filled with nickel during the plating operation. Each of the delaminations acted as a stress raiser, and one of them initiated the fracture, as shown in Fig. 4(d).

Longitudinal specimens were sectioned from the raw material and slightly bent for mounting purposes. Examination of the stock revealed numerous long, narrow sulfide stringers, which probably were the main cause of delamination in this spring material.

The broken springs and the specimens of raw material all had a hardness of Rockwell C 52 to 53, which was acceptable because specifications required a hardness of Rockwell C 45 min. However, the hardness was higher than normal and may have contributed to delamination.

Conclusions. Fracture of the springs occurred by fatigue and originated at delaminations around the rivet holes. The fatigue was caused by stresses from blanking and from rivet compression, and by use of poor-quality spring material.

Failures Caused by Fabrication

Fabrication errors or deficiencies often result in spring failures. The most common of these errors or deficiencies are:

1 Split wire, usually caused by overdrawing of the wire
2 Tool marks
3 Arc burns, sometimes occurring during welding and sometimes during plating; either can cause hard, brittle spots
4 Hydrogen damage, usually resulting from improper pickling or plating practice
5 Improper winding, which may allow formation of flats or scratches
6 Improper heat treating practice
7 Improper relation of spring index and hardness. A small index and high hardness may result in incipient cracks

The ten examples that follow demonstrate how improper fabrication can result in failure.

Example 4. Failure of Carbon Steel Springs During Testing Because of Split Wire (Fig. 5)

The springs shown in Fig. 5 failed to comply with load-test requirements. These springs were formed from 0.148-in.-diam cold drawn carbon steel wire.

During load testing, most of the springs from a production lot supported a load of 200 lb without going solid. However, the springs shown in Fig. 5, which were from the same lot, supported only 130 to 150 lb.

Investigation revealed split wire, as shown in the spring at top in Fig. 5. The spring at bottom in Fig. 5 is intact except for what appears to be a seam (at arrow) that runs the entire length of the spring. The upper spring (originally similar to the lower) has been deliberately distorted to expose the split interfaces. The fracture shows two longitudinal zones — a smooth, heat tinted one, which was the original split, and a rougher, bright-appearing one, which resulted from tearing during testing and examination. The course of the defect can be followed for a full turn in Fig. 5.

Conclusion. The springs failed the load test because of split wire. This condition can vary from the extreme demonstrated here to occasional short lengths of one or two turns that have no visible or magnetically detectable opening to the surface and that cannot be detected until the spring is stretched out of shape. The cause of this condition is overdrawing, which results in intense internal strains, high circumferential surface tension, and decreased ductility.

Example 5. Fatigue Fracture of a Phosphor Bronze Spring Because of Tool Marks (Fig. 6)

Premature failure of a copper alloy 510 (phosphor bronze, 5% A) spring occurred during life testing of several such springs. As shown in Fig. 6(a), the fracture occurred in bend 2, which had an inside radius of 0.015 in. The wire used for the springs was 0.018 in. in diameter and was in the spring temper condition (tensile strength, 145,000 psi).

Test Procedure. These springs were formed and then assembled and tested as shown in Fig. 6(a) for up to 50 million cycles. During testing, the springs were subjected to cyclic loading, mainly in the horizontal and vertical planes, with displacements of approximately 0.127 and 0.020 in., respectively. A certain amount of torsional loading also resulted. The vertical loading was applied by means of a typical cantilever arrangement. Near bend 3 the springs were sub-

Fig. 5. Split wire in a 0.148-in.-diam carbon steel spring (at top). The spring at bottom appears to have a seam along its entire length, as indicated by the arrow. (Example 4)

jected to impact loading by a plastic loading member, which moved a driven member approximately 0.020 in. This complex loading system developed very complicated stress patterns along the length of the springs.

The springs were examined by high-power microscopy at various intervals during testing to note the time at which cracks were initiated. After approximately 150,000 cycles, a crack was observed at the inside of bend 2 in one of the springs, as shown in detail A in Fig. 6(a).

Investigation. Microscopic examination of the surface of the fractured spring revealed an indentation at the inner surface of the bend, where fracture occurred (see Fig. 6b). This indentation was presumed to have been made by the bending tool during forming. Spiral marks and other surface defects such as those shown in Fig. 6(c) were observed on the surfaces of all the springs being tested. These spiral marks are similar to those that can be produced on springs during rotary straightening.

The indentation and the other marks were, in effect, notches and would have some detrimental effect on fatigue life because of the reduced cross-sectional area in those zones.

Microscopic examination of the fracture surface (see Fig. 6d) revealed two areas of prominent characteristics. One area was smooth, discolored and rippled, indicating the gradual propagation of a crack from one or more origins. The indentation developed by the bending tool is also shown in Fig. 6(d). The remainder of the surface (see Fig. 6e) had either a crystalline or a fibrous appearance, which indicated final fracture.

A longitudinal section was taken through bend 2. A micrograph of this section (see Fig. 6f) revealed a crack that had originated at the surface at the inside bend and had propagated outward. The crack had been initiated at a spiral mark where the fatigue limit had been decreased by a weak skin.

The small bend radius could create a condition that would result in straining at the bend zone and therefore render the section weak. It is difficult to determine to what extent the small bend radius contributed to spring fatigue, but this condition is recognized as an important factor in fatigue life.

The microstructure of the metal appeared normal for drawn wire and contained no nonmetallic inclusions that would act as stress raisers.

Conclusions. The spring failed by fatigue that was initiated at a bending-tool indentation and at spiral rotary-straightener marks. The small bend radius at the fracture zone contributed to the failure.

Recommendations. The springs should be made of wire free from straightener marks, and the bending tool should be redesigned so as not to indent the wire. The small bend radius should be increased, particularly at bend 2, which is the area of maximum stress.

Example 6. Fatigue Fractures of Stainless Steel Toggle-Switch Springs That Originated at Tool Marks (Fig. 7)

Several electrical toggle switches failed by fracture of the conical helical spring sealed within each switch enclosure. The springs were fabricated from 0.017-in.-diam

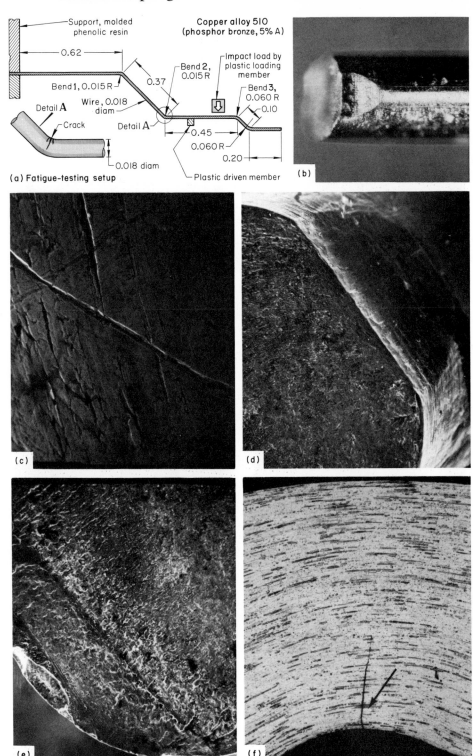

(a) Fatigue-testing setup

(a) Setup for fatigue testing, and detail of the spring showing location of crack at bend 2. (b) A broken end of the spring, at 40×; the tool mark (indentation) is just to right of fracture surface. (c) Spiral marks on spring surface, at 450×.

(d) and (e) Two areas of the fracture surface, at 225×; flat along edge of surface in (d) is tool mark. (f) Micrograph, at 145×, of a longitudinal section through spring at bend 2; arrow points to crack that originated at surface at inside of bend.

Fig. 6. Phosphor bronze spring that broke prematurely during fatigue testing, because of the presence of a tool mark (indentation) at a bend (Example 5)

type 302 stainless steel wire to the configuration shown in Fig. 7(a). In qualification testing of the springs at room temperature, fractures occurred after 11,000 to 30,000 switching cycles. Two broken springs and two unbroken springs were submitted for laboratory examination.

Investigation. Inspection of a fracture surface of one of the broken springs revealed a typical fatigue fracture that originated at a tool mark on the wire surface. This fracture surface is shown in Fig. 7(b); the fracture origin is indicated by the arrow at the right edge of the fracture surface. Scanning-electron-microscope (SEM) fractographs showed regions displaying beach marks around the fracture origin and parallel striations within the beach-mark regions. Outside the area containing beach marks (the area of slow crack growth), the fracture surface was dimpled in a fashion characteristic of overload and rapid ductile fracture. Figure 7(c) is an SEM fractograph of the fracture origin in Fig. 7(b). An appreciable amount of scale was observed on the fracture surfaces of both broken springs.

The inner surfaces of one unbroken spring and both broken springs had coarse textures and contained tool marks (see Fig. 7d); the tool marks had been formed during the spring-winding operation. The other unbroken spring had a relatively smooth-textured surface and no tool marks. The microstructure of the wire in all four springs was normal. Chemical analysis of the material established that its composition was in conformity with specifications for type 302 stainless steel.

Conclusions. Fracture of the springs was caused by fatigue and was initiated at tool marks.

Corrective Measure. The spring-winding operation was altered to eliminate the tool marks. No further fatigue failures of the toggle-switch springs occurred.

Example 7. Fatigue Fracture of a Stainless Steel Torsion Spring Because of Arcing During Welding (Fig. 8)

The torsion spring in the assembly shown in Fig. 8 broke after the assembly had operated for 450 hr in a main fuel control for an aircraft engine. The expected life of the spring was in excess of 5000 hr.

The spring was formed from 0.0525-by-0.0595-in. AMS 5673 (17-7 PH, condition C, stainless steel) wire, heat treated at 482 C (900 F) for 1 hr, shot peened to improve fatigue life, and then stabilized at 232 to 246 C (450 to 475 F). The assembly was made by electron beam welding a type 17-4 PH stainless steel connector to each end of the spring.

Observations. Fracture occurred approximately one complete turn away from the weld that joined the end of the spring to a connector, at a location in the spring that was close to the weld area (see Fig. 8). The weld extended about 0.22 in. from the end of the spring. The surface of the fracture was generally transverse to the axis of the wire and showed indications of dual fracture mechanisms. Although there were no beach marks on the fracture surface, there were several straight marks associated with fatigue that generally pointed toward the area of initiation. The remainder of the fracture was at an angle of about 45° to the wire axis and had the irregular appearance of a ductile tensile fracture. Fatigue-fracture indications extended across about one-fourth of the fracture surface.

Examination of the surface of the spring through a wide-field stereomicroscope disclosed a dark-blue spot on either side of the fracture at the point of initiation. This point was directly opposite the weld that joined the two components. The coloration on the original surface at the point of fracture initiation was suggestive of oxidation by intense localized heating such as would be caused by inadvertent arcing during welding.

The hardness of the metal at the darkened spot adjacent to the fracture was 484 to 496 Knoop. Hardness of the metal away from the fracture ranged from 595 to 604 Knoop. The reduced hardness at the point of fracture was indicative of local overaging caused by intense heat concentration and shortened the fatigue life of the spring.

Conclusion. The spring broke in fatigue. The fracture was caused by a local loss of the beneficial effects of shot peening, which resulted from inadvertent heating during welding and loss of strength due to overaging. A fatigue crack developed over about one-fourth of the section; final fracture was a ductile tensile rupture.

Recommendation. The use of a heat shield between the weld zone and the adjacent coil of the spring was recommended.

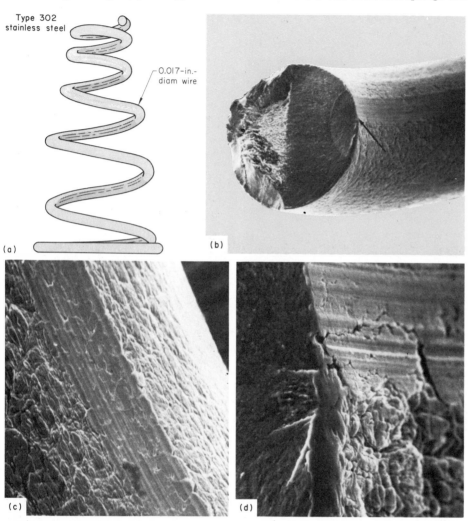

Fig. 7. (a) Stainless steel toggle-switch spring that fractured by fatigue originating at a tool mark. (b) Fracture surface, at 85×; fracture origin (arrow) is at lower edge of tool mark. (c) SEM fractograph, at 1000×, of fracture origin. (d) SEM micrograph, at 300×, of surface of an unbroken spring, showing area around a tool mark. (Example 6)

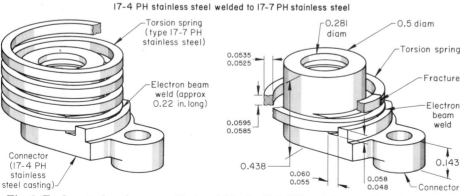

Fig. 8. Fuel-control spring assembly in which the 17-7 PH stainless steel torsion spring fractured in service because of arcing that had occurred during welding of the spring to the 17-4 PH stainless steel connector (Example 7)

Fig. 9. (a) Surface of fractured music-wire spring, at 9.2×; arrow indicates fracture origin. (b) Fracture surface, also at 9.2×; arrow indicates hard kernel that caused fracture. (Example 8)

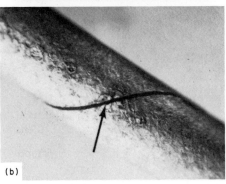

Fig. 10. Cadmium-plated spring, made from 0.250-in.-diam oil-tempered carbon steel wire, that fractured during load testing because of hydrogen embrittlement in combination with high residual stresses (Example 9)

Example 8. Fatigue Fracture of a Music-Wire Spring Caused by Poor Electroplating Practice (Fig. 9)

A cadmium-plated music-wire return spring that operated in a pneumatic cylinder was designed for infinite life at a maximum stress level of 90,000 psi. Several such springs broke after only 240,000 cycles. No flaws were revealed by visual inspection.

Investigation. Figure 9(a) shows the surface of one spring at the origin of failure. The origin was at the outside surface of the coiled spring, despite higher stress at the inside surface (due to the Wahl effect).

Figure 9(b) shows the fracture surface, which has a small kernel (arrow) at its center. This kernel shows as a circle on the surface and has the appearance of a weld deposit. Stroking this kernel with a file showed it to be extremely hard, thus indicating that the kernel may have resulted from extreme localized overheating.

It was learned that these springs had been barrel electroplated after fabrication. It is well known that barrel loads that are too small or that tangle can result in intermittent contact with the dangler (suspended cathode contact) as the barrel rotates. This allows high local currents when the last contact is broken, resulting in an arc that causes local melting of the metal being plated. Because the motion of the barrel rapidly moves the spring away from the dangler, the spot of molten metal caused by arcing is instantly quenched by the plating solution and by the mass of the cold metal of the spring.

Conclusion. Fatigue fracture of the spring resulted from a hard spot that was caused by arcing during plating.

Recommendations. Hard spots can be avoided either by resorting to rack plating, which is more expensive than barrel plating, or by using barrels that have fixed button contacts at many points instead of dangler-type contacts.

Example 9. Fracture of Carbon Steel Springs During Load Testing Because of Hydrogen Embrittlement (Fig. 10)

The spring shown in Fig. 10 was one of several that were wound from oil-tempered carbon steel wire 0.250 in. in diameter and barrel plated with cadmium. Tensile strength of the wire was 230,000 psi. During final load testing, some of the springs fractured as shown in Fig. 10. Note that in the segment at right, the portion of the fracture nearest the interior of the spring is stained darker. In the segment at left, other partial fractures show at the inner surface and are oriented nearly normal to the wire axis.

Investigation disclosed that a mixup had occurred in manufacture and that, although normal stress relief had been performed after coiling, the springs had been compressed to solid height without being stress relieved again before plating. This had resulted in high residual torsional stresses at the inside surfaces.

During pickling and plating, hydrogen had been absorbed into the spring surfaces, and it is well known that the deleterious effects of hydrogen are increased when the metal is in a state of high residual stress. The exact time of fracture could not be ascertained, but it must have been well before plating was completed, because cadmium was found on the portions of the fracture surfaces nearest the interiors of the springs.

Conclusion. Omission of the stress-relief treatment between compressing and plating left residual tension stresses. The combined effect of the absorbed hydrogen and the unrelieved stresses caused the fracture.

Example 10. Fatigue Fracture of a Carbon Steel Counterbalance Spring Caused by Hydrogen Damage (Fig. 11)

During fatigue testing, the power-type counterbalance spring shown in Fig. 11(a) fractured at the two locations indicated by the arrows. The spring had been formed from hardened-and-tempered carbon steel strip and subsequently subjected to a phosphating treatment. In the normal manufacture of these springs, winding to solid is performed to take out set (provide stable torque output) before phosphating. Al-

though this operation creates residual tensile stresses in the interior surfaces of the coils, phosphating of this spring had not produced sufficient hydrogen absorption to cause embrittlement.

Investigation disclosed a dark band at the inside edge of the fracture surface, as indicated by the arrow in Fig. 11(b). This dark band was rust colored and extended through about 20% of the spring thickness. Examination of the cleaned surface revealed etch pits 0.002 to 0.004 in. deep (Fig. 11c). Such pits were never observed on properly phosphated springs; thus, the spring that failed must have been subjected to an abnormal acid attack, either in pickling or in phosphating. This attack resulted in considerable absorption of hydrogen by the metal.

Conclusion. The dark band in Fig. 11(b) could have been rust colored only by the chemical action of some aqueous medium, which means that the part cracked in a water-base solution — either the phosphating solution or the pickling solution.

Cracks can result from vigorous pickling. The sum of the tensile stress from setout

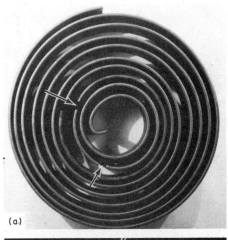

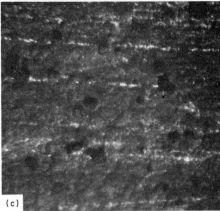

Fig. 11. (a) Carbon steel counterbalance spring, at ⅓×, that fractured at locations indicated by arrows. (b) Fracture surface, at 6×, showing dark band (arrow) that nucleated fracture. (c) Etch pits in surface, at 100×. (Example 10)

(which deforms the metal beyond the yield point) and the internal hydrogen pressure exceeds the strength of the metal. When the crack reaches the edge of the area of residual tensile stress, it stops. In normal practice, when hydrogen pickup is low, no fracture occurs. It thus was suspected that the spring had been subjected to excessive acid pickling prior to being phosphated, and that this excessive pickling was responsible

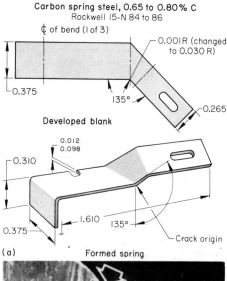

for hydrogen absorption by the spring. Normal phosphating treatments do not cause hydrogen embrittlement.

Example 11. Fatigue Fracture of a Carbon Steel Wiper Spring Because of Stress Concentration at a Sharp Corner (Fig. 12)

Parts like the one shown in Fig. 12(a) were used as grease-wiper springs for cams. The springs were formed from stampings of 0.010-in.-thick carbon spring steel (0.65 to 0.80% C) and were hardened to Rockwell 15-N 84 to 86. The springs were fracturing at the 0.001-in. radius on the stamped 135° corner at a 90° bend after 5 million cycles; normal life was 2.5 billion cycles.

Four broken springs were sent to the metallurgical laboratory to determine the cause of fracture. Three new springs from stock and six used springs from reconditioned machines also were sent to the laboratory for inspection and comparison.

The grease-wiper springs that fractured were of an old design, but they had been made in a new die.

Investigation. Visual examination of all the springs in the laboratory disclosed tool marks 0.080 to 0.090 in. from the center of the stamped bend. The fracture surfaces were nearly parallel to these marks, but the fractures had not been initiated by them.

Examination of the fracture surface by scanning electron microscopy revealed fatigue striations originating from cracks at the 0.001-in.-radius inside corner at the bend. Examination of a new part from stock

and one from a reconditioned machine also showed cracks originating at the small-radius inside corner, as shown in Fig. 12(b). This micrograph also shows the condition of the cut edge of the stamping.

On the new parts, the cracks extended approximately 0.020 in. along the width. On the used parts, the cracks extended across approximately 75% of the width and completely through the stock thickness, as shown in Fig. 12(c).

Stress calculations indicated the maximum stress at the bend, in stock of maximum thickness (0.012 in.), to be 41,000 psi without considering the stress-concentration factor in the 135° corner. The minimum stress under the same conditions would be 12,000 psi. Calculated stress as a function of the radius of the 135° corner, based on 0.012-in.-thick stock and a maximum stress of 41,000 psi, was as follows:

Radius, in.	Stress-concentration factor	Maximum stress, psi
0.001	3.0	122,000
0.015	1.82	74,000
0.025	1.56	63,000
0.030	1.52	62,000
0.035	1.46	59,000

The maximum allowable fluctuating stress for this material was 137,000 psi. Thus, the 122,000-psi maximum stress provides a very small factor of safety.

Conclusions. The wiper springs fractured in fatigue that originated at a 0.001-in. inside radius at the corner of a stamped bend. The very small radius resulted in a high

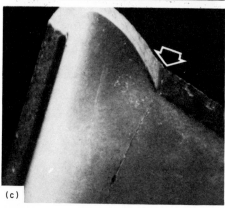

Fig. 12. (a) Wiper spring that fractured at a small-radius corner of a stamped bend. (b) SEM micrograph, at 200×, showing a forming crack (indicated by arrow) in the 135° corner on a new spring. (c) SEM micrograph, at 20×, showing a crack (indicated by arrow) that originated at the 135° corner in a used spring. (Example 11)

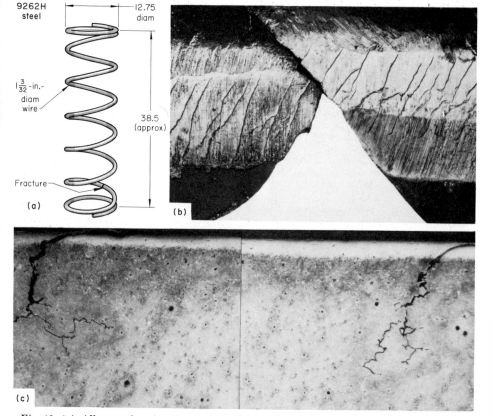

Fig. 13. (a) Alloy steel spring that fractured in fatigue from cracks in flats worn on wire surface. (b) View at 5× of typical cracks on the outer surface of the spring, as revealed by magnetic-particle inspection. (c) Micrograph, at 100×, of a section taken through cracks shown in (b), showing cracked martensite layer with shades of tempering plus original microstructure. Micrograph was spliced to conserve space. (Example 12)

stress-concentration factor in the spring, which caused the maximum applied stress to approach the allowable limit. Tool marks at the bend were not considered major causes of fracture. Cyclic loading resulted from cam rotation.

Corrective Measures. The corner radius was increased to 0.030 in., and the tools were repolished to avoid tool marks. These changes increased fatigue life of the springs to an acceptable level.

Example 12. Fatigue Fracture of Alloy Steel Springs That Initiated in Flats Worn on the Circumference (Fig. 13)

Failures of springs in a counter-recoil mechanism in a weapons system were occurring after approximately 500 cycles at $1\frac{1}{2}$ to 2 turns from the same end of each spring. Because the cylinders in which the springs operated were tapered, the springs encountered wear primarily on the first two or three coils. Also, the rapidity of cycling caused adjacent coils to hammer against each other.

The springs (see Fig. 13a) were made of $1\frac{3}{32}$-in.-diam 9262H steel wire. The winding temperature was 927 to 1038 C (1700 to 1900 F). Specified hardness was Rockwell C 48 to 53.

Investigation. Visual examination of the broken springs disclosed that rubbing of the springs against the cylinder walls had been so severe that flats had been worn on the wire surfaces and severe overheating had occurred. Magnetic-particle inspection of the wire revealed many cracks in the flattened areas (Fig. 13b). A micrograph of a section through two of the cracks visible in Fig. 13(b) is shown in Fig. 13(c). The cracks originated in the untempered-martensite zone, extended through the over-tempered zone into the original tempered-martensite structure. A hardness survey taken across a transverse section of the spring wire at the worn flat showed hardness variations from Rockwell C 60 at or near the surface to approximately Rockwell C 41 at a depth of 0.004 in. to Rockwell C 55 at a depth of 0.010 in. The microstructure and hardness values indicated that the material beneath the flat had been heated (by the extreme rubbing action) to above 800 C (1475 F) and subsequently quenched by the remaining mass of metal and by the oil in the cylinder in which the spring operated. The impact speed of compression caused the hard, brittle layer in the worn area to crack as shown in Fig. 13(b). The dominant cracks virtually paralleled the principal compression planes of the torsionally loaded wire; however, the plane of fracture was perpendicular to these planes, or parallel to the principal tension planes.

The unworn surfaces of the wire contained indications of decarburization to a depth of 0.008 to 0.010 in. Hardness of several of the springs was Rockwell C 53 to 55.

Investigation of the manufacturing procedures disclosed that the springs had not been properly cooled after winding, which resulted in a large grain size.

Conclusion. The springs fractured in torsional fatigue that originated at cracks in flats worn on the wire surfaces. The plane of fracture was parallel to the principal tension planes, but the cracks in the flats were parallel to the principal compression planes

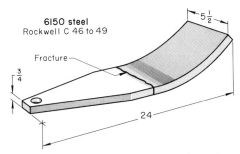

of the torsionally loaded wire. Also, hardness of the spring wire, Rockwell C 53 to 55, was greater than specified.

Corrective Measures. The manufacturing procedure was corrected so that, after being wound at 927 to 1038 C (1700 to 1900 F), the springs were properly cooled to below approximately 705 C (1300 F) to ensure fine grain size. Also, the springs were tempered to the specified hardness range of Rockwell C 48 to 53. The specifications were revised to include a required grain size of ASTM No. 7 or finer.

These corrective measures helped to delay fracture in the presence of cracks in the worn flats. The average spring life was increased from 500 to 1000 cycles.

Example 13. Fatigue Fracture of an Alloy Steel Landing-Gear Spring Because of Surface Fissures (Fig. 14)

The upper tang of an aircraft landing-gear spring (see Fig. 14) fractured during landing. The spring had been in service for 1207 hr and had been subjected to 4000 to 6000 takeoffs and landings. Two previously reported failures of similar springs resulted from fatigue that originated at the bolthole on the outboard face of the spring end adjacent to the wheel.

Specifications required that the spring be made of 6150 steel and be hardened to Rockwell C 46 to 49.

Investigation. Visual and microscopic examination of the fracture surface revealed indications of fatigue that had originated on the inboard surface of the spring at the midpoint of the tang bend line. The fatigue crack had propagated to approximately $\frac{3}{32}$ in. in depth and $\frac{5}{16}$ in. in length before final fracture occurred in a brittle manner. Secondary fatigue origins were apparent on the outboard surface at the forward edge. Magnetic-particle inspection of the spring surface did not reveal any defects. However, fissures too small to be detected by magnetic-particle inspection probably were present.

Microscopic examination of a transverse section at the origin of fatigue indicated that the fracture was transgranular. The surface was decarburized to a depth of 0.017 in. and contained 0.005-in.-deep oxide-filled fissures, scale, and localized intergranular oxidation as deep as 0.002 in.

A review of the manufacturing process indicated that the boltholes had been drilled prior to heat treatment. Examination of a section through a hole showed decarburization to a depth of only 0.003 in., and scale and localized intergranular oxidation

similar to that found on the inboard and outboard surfaces of the spring. It is apparent that surface oxidation in the hole occurred during heat treatment, most likely as a result of an improper furnace atmosphere. The greater portion of the decarburization (0.014 in.) probably was present on the material as received from the mill.

The hardness of the metal away from the surface was Rockwell C 46 to 47. Chemical analysis of the material showed that it was within specifications for 6150 steel.

Conclusions. The spring had fractured transversely by fatigue that originated on the inboard surface approximately at the midpoint of the tang bend line. Three factors contributed to the fracture:

1. The stress-raising effect of surface fissures 0.005 in. in depth, which resulted from an improper furnace atmosphere
2. Surface decarburization as deep as 0.017 in., which detrimentally affected the endurance strength of the spring
3. Cyclic bending loads due to normal aircraft operation.

Recommendations. The proper furnace atmosphere must be employed to reduce the extent of decarburization and surface oxidation, and decarburization-free steel should be purchased. Also, increasing the size of the spring would result in an over-all reduction of the stresses imposed on the part during normal operation of the aircraft.

Failures Caused by Corrosion

Corrosive environments very often are principal contributors to failures of springs. Any metal is more likely to be attacked when under stress. Consequently, springs are extremely susceptible to stress corrosion, which usually results in fatigue fracture.

Protective Coatings. Electroplated coatings of any of several metals, or organic coatings such as paint, are commonly used to protect springs that must operate in corrosive environments. These means of protection can be very effective, but either or both of two deficiencies are likely to prevail, particularly for helical springs that have closely spaced coils. The portions of springs that have the greatest need for protection (often about $1\frac{1}{2}$ to 2 coils from the ends) usually get the least protection because of the proximity of the coils to each other, and are the areas from which protective coatings are most likely to be rubbed or broken away in operation.

The two examples that follow deal with spring failures caused by corrosion.

Example 14. Fatigue Fracture of an Alloy Steel Valve Spring That Was Initiated at a Rust Pit (Fig. 15)

The gas-injection-valve spring shown in Fig. 15(a) was one of several that broke in service following an undetermined length of operating time. The spring was $2\frac{1}{8}$ in. in free length and $1\frac{11}{16}$ in. in outside diameter. Normal operating frequency was 300 cycles per minute. Each spring had broken into three pieces; the length of the center section was approximately $\frac{3}{4}$ to $1\frac{3}{4}$ coils. The ma-

Fig. 14. Alloy steel upper tang of an aircraft landing-gear spring that fractured in fatigue (Example 13)

Chromium-vanadium alloy steel (ASTM A232)
Rockwell C 45 to 58, 0.218-in.-diam wire

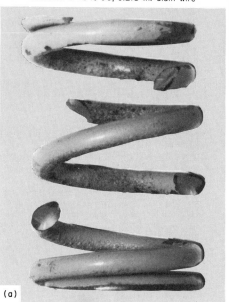

Fig. 15. (a) Alloy steel valve spring that fractured in torsional fatigue. (b) Fracture surface at approximately 6×. (Example 14)

terial specified for the springs was 0.218-in.-diam chromium-vanadium steel of valve-spring quality (ASTM A232) with a hardness of Rockwell C 45 to 58.

Investigation. Visual examination of the springs indicated that they had been coated with black paint or other protective coating and then with a coating of gray material applied over the black coating. In several places, the coating had separated from the steel and rusting was obvious.

Macroscopic examination of a fracture surface of one of the springs (Fig. 15b) revealed that fracture had started at the interior of the spring at the surface of the wire and had progressed at a 45° angle to the longitudinal axis of the wire.

The fracture had progressed in torsional fatigue by a low-stress, high-cycle mechanism over approximately 25% of the cross-sectional area and then had increased rapidly until final separation occurred over a relatively small shear lip. In all the springs examined, fracture started at a small surface pit associated with rust or scale on the lower inner surface of the wire. Rusting appar-

ently took place after the coating had been worn or chipped away rather than under the coating layer.

Microscopic examination of an unetched cross section through a spot that appeared to be typical of the site where fracture started revealed several pits 0.004 to 0.008 in. deep, or up to 3.7% of wire diameter.

Hardness surveys of two of the springs indicated ranges of Rockwell C 43.5 to 45 for one spring and Rockwell C 41.5 to 42 for the other. Although these hardness ranges are slightly lower than the specified range of Rockwell C 45 to 58, fracture was not attributed to this specific condition. Both springs showed an inclusion rating of thin series 3, type D (ASTM E45), which was suitable for this application.

Fracture characteristics usually attributable to surging, such as fractures at the inner ends of inactive coils, were not present.

Conclusions. The springs failed in torsional fatigue that was initiated at pits on the wire surface. These pits, which served as stress raisers, resulted from rusting after the protective coating had deteriorated.

Example 15. Stress-Corrosion Cracking of Inconel X-750 Springs (Fig. 16)

Springs like that shown in Fig. 16(a) were used for tightening the interstage packing ring in a high-pressure turbine. After having been in operation for about seven years, the turbine was opened for inspection, and several of the springs were found to be broken. Operation of the turbine was not impaired by the broken springs. The springs were made of 0.045-in.-diam Inconel X-750 wire. The interstage packing rings were machined from centrifugally cast leaded nickel brass (German silver). The broken springs were submitted for laboratory analysis.

There were chemical deposits in the turbine starting at about the fifth stage. These deposits were judged to have come from the water or boiler chemicals. There were no broken springs in the fifth or sixth stages. The temperatures attained in the turbine stages were: stage 1, 462 C (864 F); stage 2, 405 C (761 F); stage 3, 372 C (702 F); stage 4, 351 C (664 F); stage 5, 330 C (626 F); and stage 6, 313 C (595 F).

Investigation. Many of the springs were broken into small pieces that had a white deposit on their rustlike surface scale. The white deposit was 100% water soluble and had a pH of 9.6 (slightly alkaline). Spectrographic examination showed the surface scale to contain a high amount of sodium, a low amount of tin, a high trace of zinc and traces of lead and calcium.

Chemical analysis of the spring material showed that it was within specifications for Inconel X-750. The hardness values were within the specified range of Rockwell C 43 to 48.

Metallographic examination of a longitudinal section through the wire revealed intergranular cracks (see Fig. 16b and c) about 0.05 in. in depth and oriented at an angle of 45° to the axis of the wire. In some places, these cracks were 90° apart on the wire circumference. A light-gray phase had penetrated the grains on the fracture surfaces. A fine lacey attack was also observed along the surface of the wire to a depth of about 0.0005 in. This general attack had the appearance of liquid-metal corrosion. When bent in the laboratory, the spring wires fractured in a brittle manner along a plane 45° to the wire axis, which is characteristic of fracture from torsional loading.

Inconel X-750
Rockwell C 43 to 48
— 0.500 diam —

0.045-in.-diam wire

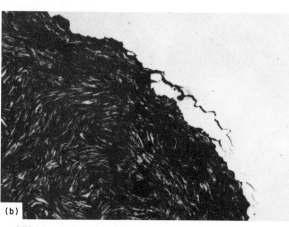

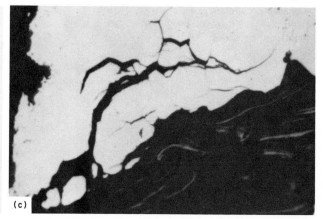

Fig. 16. (a) Inconel X-750 spring that failed by stress-corrosion cracking. (b) and (c) Unetched longitudinal sections, at 100× and 500×, respectively, showing intergranular cracking. (Example 15)

High-nickel alloys are susceptible to embrittlement by some low-melting metals and alloys. Tin, lead and zinc melt below the maximum service temperature of the turbine, which was 462 C (864 F). One tin-zinc system had a eutectic melting point of less than 204 C (400 F). Such metals can cause liquid-metal embrittlement at temperatures above their melting points.

Sodium, tin and zinc could have been present in a pigmented oil or grease used as a lubricant during spring winding and could have been left on the Inconel wire by the manufacturer. The white deposit on the surface of some of the springs was slightly alkaline and could have initiated stress-corrosion cracking by caustic penetration.

Conclusions. The springs fractured by intergranular stress-corrosion cracking during service. The cracks were promoted by the action of liquid zinc and tin in combination with static and torsional stresses on the spring wire. Stress-corrosion cracking by caustic action was a less likely mechanism of fracture.

Corrective Measures. The springs were thoroughly cleaned by the spring manufacturer before shipment, to remove all contaminants, and were cleaned again prior to installation in the turbine. Failure of the springs was thus reduced to a minimum.

Failures Caused by Operating Conditions

In some instances of spring failure the cause is not evident, even after an exhaustive examination of material, processing and design factors. When a thorough investigation in these areas does not reveal the cause, it is necessary to investigate operating conditions.

Sometimes changes in operating conditions thought to be only minor deviations from normal prove to be the causes of spring failure. For instance, certain fuel-injection pumps on diesel engines were designed for operation at 600 rpm (one-half engine speed). The coil springs in the pump were fabricated from 0.125-in.-diam 6150 steel wire. The springs were wound from annealed and ground wire, heat treated, and then 100% inspected by the magnetic-particle method. Under the conditions described, no failures were reported until several springs failed within a short period of time. Exhaustive investigation of material and processing did not reveal the cause of these failures. When operating conditions were investigated it was discovered that the engine speed had been increased by 100 rpm (50 rpm for the pump). Photographs taken with high-speed movie cameras of the springs operating at various speeds provided the answer. Harmonic vibration had developed with increased speed and had resulted in fatigue failures. In this instance it was necessary to redesign the springs.

The four examples that follow describe other spring failures that were attributed to operating conditions.

Fig. 17. Carbon steel torsion spring that fractured by fatigue because of unusual stress conditions (Example 16)

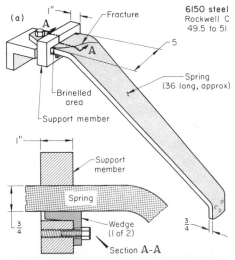

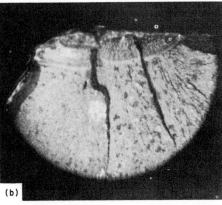

Fig. 18. (a) Landing-gear spring, of 6150 steel, that broke during a hard landing. (b) Fractograph, at 7×, showing fatigue crack that initiated the brittle fracture. (Example 17)

Example 16. Fatigue Fracture of a Carbon Steel Torsion Spring Caused by an Unexpected Mode of Stressing (Fig. 17)

The fractured torsion spring shown in Fig. 17 was used on a rake tine of an agricultural tillage tool. The spring was wound from pretempered carbon steel wire approximately 0.375 in. in diameter and was not stress relieved after winding. Torsion springs are stressed in bending, and are normally deflected in the direction of winding, to decrease the required coil diameter. Therefore, the residual compressive stress

resulting from the winding operation is beneficial in increasing load capacity and fatigue life.

This spring operated for only a few days before fracturing. It was regarded as unusual, considering operating conditions, that the fracture originated at the interior of the spring. Figure 17 shows a relatively smooth fracture surface with clamshell marks (beach marks) about midway through the wire. The remainder of the surface is dark, rough and curved, indicating that the last half of the fracture occurred as the result of a single application of stress.

Investigation did not reveal any material defects or any defects caused by processing operations. The cause of the failure was not resolved until it was learned that sometimes when the tine breaks free from a clod, it vibrates at its natural frequency. When this vibration occurs, the inside surfaces of the coils of the spring sustain a total stress consisting of the applied stress plus residual stresses, and premature failure can result.

Example 17. Fracture of a Landing-Gear Flat Spring Made From 6150 Steel (Fig. 18)

A flat spring for the main landing gear of a light aircraft broke after a hard landing had been safely executed. The spring, shown in Fig. 18(a), was submitted for laboratory examination. No information was furnished concerning design, material, heat treatment or length of service.

Investigation. Fracture occurred near the end of the spring that was inserted through a support member about 1 in. thick and attached to the fuselage by a single bolt. The required fit between the spring and the support member was obtained by inserting wedges beneath the spring at each side of the support. These wedges were bolted to the support member, and the degree of tightness of the assembly was controlled by the tension on the bolts. Details of the assembly are shown in section A-A in Fig. 18(a).

The spring had broken laterally at an angle of about 60° to its longitudinal axis, as shown in Fig. 18(a). One end of the fracture corresponded to the point where the forward edge of the spring contacted the support member. The other end of the fracture was in an unsupported area.

Brinelling (plastic flow and indentation due to excessive localized contact pressure at the faying surfaces) had occurred on the upper surface of the spring where the forward and rear edges of the spring contacted the support member. There was no evidence of brinelling on the bottom surface of the spring where it contacted the support member.

Visual examination of the fracture surface revealed that the spring had failed by mainly brittle fracture. Chevron marks indicated that fracture had started beneath the brinelled area at the forward edge of the upper surface of the spring. Figure 18(b) is a light-microscope fractograph of this corner and shows that the origin of the brittle fracture was, in fact, a small fatigue crack that had been present for a considerable period of time before final fracture occurred.

Microscopic examination of longitudinal and transverse sections near the fracture confirmed that the material had suffered extensive grain flow from cold working in

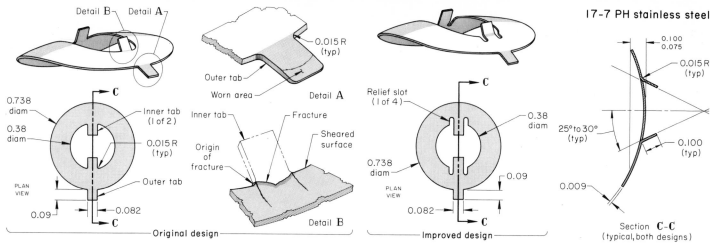

Fig. 19. *Original and improved designs of a 17-7 PH stainless steel valve-seat retainer spring. As originally designed, the inner tabs on the spring broke off as a result of fatigue, and the outer tab exhibited wear. (Example 18)*

the brinelled areas. The general microstructure was fine-grained tempered martensite of good quality. There was no surface decarburization.

Chemical analysis identified the spring material as 6150 steel. The hardness of the material was Rockwell C 49.5 to 51.

Discussion. Normal recurring vertical landing loads cause the top surface of the spring at the edge of the support to be stressed in compression. These probably were the major loads applied to the spring. On the other hand, side and drag loads produce tensile stresses at the top surface of the spring. When vertical, side and drag loads are applied simultaneously during a landing, the resultant stress at the support is compressive. However, after the aircraft has touched down and the vertical load has decreased to the static load of the aircraft, the continuing application of side and drag loads during taxiing causes a tensile stress at the top surface of the spring.

Compressive stresses in the top surface of the spring at the support generally are localized at the edges of the support by the wedges, as well as by any lack of straightness across the section that may have been introduced during fabrication or that may have occurred when the complicated loading pattern caused a torsional deflection in the region of failure. Also, it was considered probable that the assembly could have been more tightly compressed than it actually was. This would explain the brinelling observed near both the forward and the rear edges of the top surface. The localized plastic deformation under compressive loading (brinelling) created high residual tensile stresses in the deformed region, thus reducing the capacity of the material to withstand fluctuating tensile stresses due to applied loads.

Ultimately, a crack started at the corner where the fluctuating tensile stress was highest under combined side and drag loads. This crack progressed by fatigue over a relatively long period of time (many landings). Final fracture occurred when the applied stress (primarily tensile stress due to side and drag loads) exceeded the critical fracture stress for the partially cracked spring. Under normal conditions, such a cracked part might last a long time, although complete fracture would occur

eventually. An abnormal condition such as a sharp change of direction on a runway or taxiway, rolling over the edge of a runway or encountering a rut could impose a sufficient amount of additional loading to cause final, fast fracture.

Conclusions. Fracture of the landing-gear spring was caused by a fatigue crack that resulted from excessive brinelling at the support point. The fatigue crack significantly lowered the resistance of the material to brittle fracture under critical side and drag loads.

Although the loading at the time of final fracture may have been unusual, a spring that did not contain a fatigue crack similar to the one found in the failed spring probably would not have broken.

The fatigue crack had been present in the part for some time, and suitable inspection would have revealed it.

Recommendations. It was recommended that regular visual examinations be carried out to detect evidence of brinelling and wear at the support in aircraft with this configuration of landing-gear spring and means of attachment. If visual examination showed evidence of brinelling or wear, the spring should be magnetic-particle inspected for evidence of cracks. Liquid-penetrant inspection might be adequate if the amount of brinelling were minor, although care should be used in this type of inspection because brinelling can hide small cracks.

Cracked parts should be replaced. Brinelling itself need not be cause for retiring a part. The presence of a crack was considered necessary for failure to occur in the manner described in this example.

Example 18. Fatigue Fracture of Tabs on a Stainless Steel Retainer Spring Because of Cyclic Loading and Torsional Vibration (Fig. 19)

The part shown in the "Original design" portion of Fig. 19 was a valve-seat retainer spring from a fuel control on an aircraft engine. This spring was found to be broken during disassembly of the fuel control for a routine overhaul after 3980 hr of service. The two inner tabs had broken off but were not recovered. There had been no known malfunction of the fuel control.

The spring was made of 0.009-in.-thick 17-7 PH stainless steel and heat treated to

TH 1050, then passivated. The spring was thrust loaded in assembly, but there was no thrust load on the tabs. The thrust load was the primary function of the spring. The radial, or torsional, load was rotational vibration of the assembly in which the spring imparted a relatively constant thrust load. The three tabs were antirotational devices and were subjected to unintentional torsional vibrations. These torsional vibrations created the cyclic loading that resulted in fracture.

Investigation. As received at the laboratory, the spring was clean and free from corrosion products, with no evidence of chemical attack. Radial wear marks on the convex surface indicated that the part had been in relative rotation against its contacting member. The outer tab was worn in the area indicated in detail A in Fig. 19, which was evidence of slippage and apparent rotation against the contacting member. There was a wear mark on the concave surface 180° from the outer tab.

The fracture zone of an inner tab that broke off is shown in detail B in Fig. 19. Examination of the fracture surfaces of the washer in the area of the tabs revealed beach marks indicating that fatigue fracture had been initiated at the convex surface of the washer and had propagated across to the concave surface. The cracks originated in the 0.015-in.-radius fillet between the tab and the body of the washer. The fracture started at three places at radial cracks emanating from the radii at the intersections of the tab and washer, and at one place on the sheared surface of the stamping.

Microscopic examination of the radial cracks showed a slight amount of plastic deformation, with the short surface between the fractures pushed toward the concave side. The two cracks on the sides of one tab were opened by sectioning. The fractures were smooth with arc-shape crack fronts.

Analysis of this compound fracture indicated that it was composed of fatigue fractures caused by the formed tab being loaded so as to compress the part along the axis of its centerline and produce torsional vibrations. After the radial cracks had started as a result of torsional vibration, a straight bending mode of stress resulted in initiation of fatigue cracking in the concave side of the tab at the bend.

This was not an isolated failure; shortly after this part had been examined, three additional springs that had broken were returned from service. Although there were some minor variations in the type of fracture, the basic cause appeared to be the same for all the springs.

Examination of a mating part revealed worn impressions that had been generated by the torsional motion of the tabs against the walls of the mating slot.

Twelve springs from stock were inspected and were found to be in satisfactory condition except for some malformed areas that were unrelated to this problem.

Conclusion. The two inner tabs broke in fatigue as the result of cyclic loading that compressed and torsionally vibrated the spring. The fracture resulted in relative rotation between the spring and the mating parts, both the one in contact with the convex side and the one in contact with the outer tab, as evidenced by the wear on the appropriate surface.

Corrective Measures. The springs were redesigned as shown in the "Improved design" view in Fig. 19. The fillets were replaced with slots to minimize stress concentration at the corners. Fatigue testing indicated that springs of the improved design would have a service life 2½ times as long as that of springs of the original design.

Example 19. Fatigue Fracture of a Nickel-Base Alloy Differential-Pressure Spring in a Fuel-Control Valve (Fig. 20)

After approximately 240 hr of hot testing, the differential pressure across a fuel-control valve dropped sharply from 30 to approximately 18 psi. During the course of testing, differential pressure had dropped from 43 to 30 psi. Prior to the start of hot testing, this valve, and the differential-pressure spring in the valve, experienced about 7 hr of 0.6-Hz instability, or fluctuation in fuel discharge. The instability was caused by remote problems in the hydromechanical circuitry, which resulted in greater-than-normal stress in the spring. At the end of the test, the differential-pressure spring shown in Fig. 20(a) was removed and found to be broken. Fuel temperature during testing generally was 138 to 155 C (280 to 310 F), but reached 163 C (325 F) for a short period of time at the beginning of the test. The fuel used was Jet A kerosine.

The spring was formed from 0.065-in.-diam wire of a proprietary nickel-base alloy designed to provide a positive thermoelastic coefficient and was coated with an organic material to prevent corrosion.

The spring provided force against the plunger of a hydraulic pilot valve that

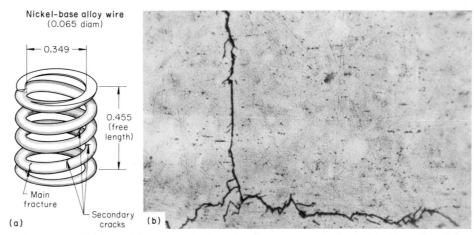

Fig. 20. (a) *Differential-pressure spring that fractured by fatigue.* (b) *View of typical secondary crack, at 100×.* (Example 19)

sensed a pressure drop across the main fuel valve. Loading was relatively constant, with a slight amplitude of stress above the mean caused by normal service. Expected service life was in excess of 20,000 hr.

Investigation. Brownish dustlike deposits on top of the organic coating were reported to be gum residues from the fuel. Small granules of this deposit could be flaked off with a scribe or penknife. The coating itself was intact and showed no flaking. No red rust or other corrosion products were present on the body of the spring. The uncoated ground ends of the spring were bright and reflective and had no evidence of corrosion.

The main fracture through the spring occurred in a plane roughly perpendicular to the wire axis, near the start of the first active coil. Three secondary cracks were found farther around the same coil, beginning at the interior of the spring and extending partly across the coil in a plane approximately perpendicular to the wire axis.

The fracture surface, with no special preparation, was examined metallographically in an area containing striations. The striations were difficult to focus for photographic purposes because of the uneven plane of fracture, but were obvious under direct metallographic observation, in which continual adjustment of focus allows clear viewing of such features on a variety of fracture facets.

The cracks in the spring were opened, and the fracture surfaces were examined metallographically. This examination showed that the cracking was generally transgranular, with abrupt shifts in orientation and a slight tendency to follow grain boundaries. There was some branching of the fine cracks, which was suggestive of stress-corrosion

cracking. However, the cracks followed generally the lines of principal stress in the spring, beginning perpendicular to the wire axis and then turning parallel to the axis, as shown in Fig. 20(b).

To gain further understanding of the fracture mechanisms of this metal, similar springs known to have developed fatigue cracks were examined metallographically. These springs were used in the study of fatigue properties and were uncoated. All testing was done in air free of corrosives. The cracks observed in these springs were essentially transgranular, with abrupt changes of direction, and had occurred in patterns similar to those in the spring that broke in service.

The reported service conditions were suggestive of a fatigue-type fracture, and this was confirmed by a cursory examination of the broken spring. In each of the four cracks, there were no significant nonmetallic inclusions, surface conditions or other characteristics that could be related to crack initiation. Experience with this metal had been generally satisfactory, with no known instances of service fatigue failure. It is statistically unlikely for four cracks to occur in one spring because of a materials problem when no other problems have been reported for that material. The possibility of stress-corrosion cracking could not be supported by the results of the investigation.

Conclusions. The spring broke in torsional fatigue as the result of cyclic compression under unusual service conditions. This conclusion was based on the similarity of this fracture to known fatigue fractures, the presence of striations, and the absence of any gross material defect to which fracture initiation may be ascribed.

Failures of Dies

INFORMATION and data presented in the forepart of this article are oriented toward dies that are used for cold working operations, although much of this information also applies to hot working dies. A section at the end of this article (see page 506) deals exclusively with dies used in hot working operations.

Die Characteristics. Dies have two characteristics that set them apart from the majority of other metal parts. First, dies are involved in the fabrication of other products. In fact, dies are involved either directly or indirectly in the manufacture of most metal products. Thus, the premature failure of a die may cause production delays that greatly increase the cost of goods. Second, dies are usually employed at higher hardnesses than the other products — very often as high as Rockwell C 60, and sometimes higher. This means that dies are more prone to sudden fracture than most other machinery components.

Everyone who makes or uses dies is faced with the problem of making them hard enough to stand up under the anticipated service conditions and tough enough not to crack, either during manufacture of the dies or after they are placed in service.

Causes of Die Failure. To attain acceptable die life and to prevent premature failures, the following conditions must be closely maintained. Most of these conditions are interrelated.

1 Design that is compatible with the die material selected and with the planned processing procedure
2 Selection of material that is compatible with the design and processing procedure
3 Selection of a heat treating procedure that is compatible with design and material
4 Control of the specified heat treating procedure
5 Control of grinding and other finishing operations
6 Control of die setup (particularly, alignment) in the equipment
7 Die operation — specifically, avoidance of overloading.

Virtually all die failures are caused by some lack of control in one of, or in a combination of two or more of, the above conditions.

Types of Failure. In addition to plain breakage, lack of control of the conditions in the foregoing list may result in one or more of the following conditions, which may be pronounced as a failure if the die is no longer capable of performing its required function: cracking, deforma-

tion, abnormal wear, erosion, pitting or etching, and exfoliation.

Influence of Design on Failure

A substantial portion of die failures can be attributed to design — either directly, or indirectly because the prescribed heat treatments or finishing procedures were not compatible with the design. Thus, good design is of great importance in failure prevention.

Design errors include sharp corners, fillets with radii that are too small, poorly located or designed grooves and notches, abrupt changes in section, location of holes so as to result in thin walls, sections that are too thin, and improper clearances.

The generally well-known rules of design that apply to at least some degree for all metal parts are usually more important for die design, because the harder-metal dies are more sensitive to design deficiencies than are parts made of softer metals.

Design factors may be generally classified as (a) those relating to heat treatment, and (b) those relating to service conditions. The former require that the type of steel, method of heat treatment, and available equipment for both heat treatment and processing be considered, along with service conditions, to forestall premature failure of properly manufactured dies.

Designing of dies for cold forming is difficult, because the service stresses usually cannot be calculated accurately. Because of the many factors involved, design is most often based on experience.

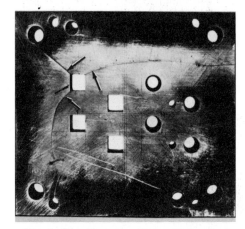

Fig. 1. Blanking die, 10 by 12 in., and made of a manganese oil-hardening tool steel (O1), that cracked through sharp corners of an opening (arrows) during heat treatment

Design faults that cause failures in heat treatment include the presence of heavy sections adjacent to light sections, sharp corners, stamp marks, blind holes, and improper spacing of holes. Design faults that cause service failures include failure to fillet corners, failure to provide proper clearance, sections that are too thin, and gross differences in section thicknesses.

All the potential failure causes are associated with stresses present in the die, which are generated during its manufacture or during its service life, or both.

Failure Due to Design. Many failures are experienced because of lack of consideration for basic design guidelines. For example, Fig. 1 shows a blanking die of a manganese oil-hardening tool steel (O1) that cracked during heat treatment. Note the sharp corners of the closely spaced die openings. If sharp corners are required, as was true for this die, an air-hardening grade of tool steel should be used. As an alternative, because of the high hardenability of O1 tool steel, the die could have been subjected to a martempering heat treatment (see page 36 in Volume 2 of this Handbook), which probably would have prevented cracking.

Shown in Fig. 2 is a coining die made of S7 tool steel, that had to be quenched in oil because of its size (6 by 8 by 20 in.). The combination of large size, blind holes, and the thin edges at the junction of the cavity with the holes, resulted in cracks during the quench. Redesign for a better balance of section thicknesses was recommended. However, for a die that is already made there are often heat treating procedures that can compensate for design deficiencies. For instance, the coining die in Fig. 2 could have been oil quenched to approximately 535 C (just under 1000 F) and then air cooled to about 60 C (140 F) before tempering. This treatment would have lessened the possibility of cracking, and probably would have met hardness requirements.

Forming dies are often made of a water-hardening tool steel, such as W2, because of the need to make repairs by welding. Dies of many designs, however, are unsuitable for water or brine quenching; for example, they may have closely spaced holes, sharp internal corners, and deep stamp marks — all of which are hazards. To try to avoid cracking, a knowledgeable heat treater will attempt to reduce quenching severity by partly quenching in brine and finishing in oil.

Service failures stemming from improper design are common. Some of these failures result from fatigue, as in the example that follows.

Example 1. Fatigue Failure of a 4150 Steel Die-Box Hold-Down Pin From Unintended Torsional Loading (Fig. 3)

The 1½-in.-diam 4150 steel hold-down pin that held the die box in position at a wiredrawing block ("bullblock") broke during the drawing of large-diameter cold heading wire.

Failure of the pin allowed the die box to be carried onto and around the bullblock, thus breaking the die and shutting down this wiredrawing unit. In addition to the loss of production time and repair costs of about $250 to make the die serviceable again, damage to the wire and the need to cut the wire at two places to remove the die box resulted in the scrapping of a 1000-lb coil of wire.

Service History. Before the failure, this equipment had been used for about 14 months to draw steel cold heading wire that varied in diameter from 0.70 to 1.00 in. No failure of the hold-down pins in two similar wiredrawing units at this plant had been reported during about 18 months of operation.

The hold-down pin that failed was on the second-stage bullblock, at which the wire rod was reduced from a diameter of 0.878 in. to a final diameter of 0.815 in.

In normal operation of the wiredrawing equipment, the pin was subjected to bending and tensile loading that resulted in stresses of approximately 95,000 psi.

Pin Composition and Properties. The hold-down pin was specified to be machined from quenched-and-tempered 4150 steel having a minimum tensile strength of 125,000 psi and a hardness of 241 to 272 Bhn. Chemical analysis of the pin showed that it was 4150 steel as specified. Hardness measurements on a cross section of the pin averaged 277 Bhn at the half-radius and 255 Bhn at the center. The hardness varied only slightly between the half radius and the surface.

Macroexamination. The fracture was flat and in a plane approximately perpendicular to the axis of the pin. There were no signs of prior mechanical damage or corrosion at or near the fracture, and no plastic deformation could be seen at the fracture.

Visual examination and examination at a magnification of 5 to 30 diameters showed the characteristic appearance of fatigue-initiated failure.

Failure originated on a broad front extending about 210° around the circumference along a thread. The fatigue-propagated crack covered about 70% of the area of the fracture surface. This region had a smooth, matte appearance and showed faint concentric beach marks indicating axial progress of the fatigue fracture. It was fairly bright and showed no signs of rust or other corrosive attack.

The region of final instantaneous fracture was much rougher than the fatigue region and had a fairly bright, many-faceted, crystalline appearance. Chevron marks that were in general aligned radially were visible in this region on examination

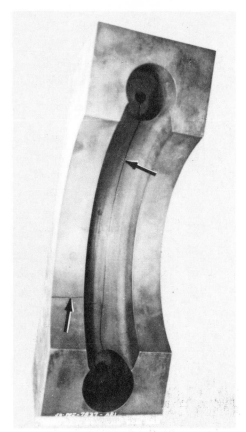

Fig. 2. Coining die, 20 in. by 6 in. by 8 in. deep, and made of S7 tool steel, that cracked (arrows) during oil quenching

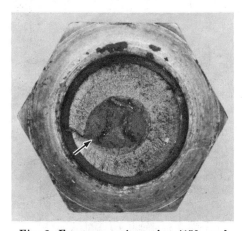

Fig. 3. Fracture surface of a 4150 steel die-box hold-down pin that failed as a result of torsional fatigue; shown at about 0.95×. Approximately 30% of the area exhibited brittle fracture (dark region indicated by the arrow). (Example 1)

at 30 diameters. Apparently, final failure was mainly by brittle fracture.

Metallographic Examination. Microscopic examination of a section through the pin at 100 diameters showed that the threads had been made by cutting and were free from defects and irregularities. No cracks were detected in threads next to the fracture.

The microstructure of the pin, as examined at 1000 diameters on polished-and-etched sections near the failure region, was normal for the specified material and heat treatment; no abnormalities were detected.

The microstructure was essentially tempered martensite and contained fairly numerous small and uniformly distributed sulfide inclusions. Occasional areas of fine pearlite and fine angular patches of ferrite were present at the center of the pin. There was no evidence of decarburization at the surface of the pin.

Preliminary Conclusions. The failure was initiated by fatigue cracking that originated along a thread that acted as a stress raiser.

Although the loading on the pin during wiredrawing (which was the basis for the design and material selection) would ordinarily consist of bending and tensile components only, the flat transverse nature of the fracture and the shape of the fracture pattern were characteristic of fatigue failure caused by purely torsional cyclic loading (Fig. 3).

Additional examination was done to determine the cause of failure. It was found that the hold-down pin had been improperly fitted in the die box. Clearances had not been specified for this assembly, and an oversize pin had apparently been forced into the pivot hole, causing peening of the edge of the pivot hole. The lack of adequate clearance caused binding of the die box so that it could not swing back and forth without exerting a twisting or torsional load on the threaded portion of the pin.

Final Conclusions. The hold-down pin failed in torsional fatigue, a rather uncommon mode of failure for fasteners, because of binding of the die box as a result of improper pin fit. As a consequence of the binding, the slight pivoting back and forth of the die box that occurs during normal wiredrawing operations produced unintended cyclic torsional loading that was sufficient to initiate and propagate a transverse fatigue crack.

The basic design of the assembly and the size and strength of the hold-down pin were completely adequate for the application, as evidenced by the results of this investigation and the prior history of satisfactory per-

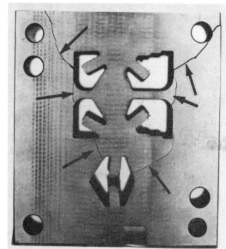

Fig. 4. Blanking die, 10 by 10 in., and made from D2 tool steel, that failed in service by cracking (arrows indicate cracks). Failure was attributed to thin-wall sections, close spacing of holes, abusive grinding, and improper electrical discharge machining.

formance of this and similar hold-down pins for wiredrawing die boxes.

Corrective Measures. The die-box pin was replaced, with special precautions being taken to ensure proper fitting. A diametral clearance of 0.010 to 0.015 in. was used in assembling the replacement pin in the die box and was specified for additional assemblies of this type. No further pin failures were reported to have been encountered during extended periods of service.

The blanking die made from D2 tool steel shown in Fig. 4 failed in service by cracking. Thin-wall sections and close spacing of holes were the main causes of failure, although in this instance a poor design was aggravated by abusive grinding and improper electrical discharge machining. Because D2 is an air-hardening steel, it is unlikely that a change in grade of tool steel would have prevented the failure. Design for better balance of section thicknesses is the best solution to problems of this nature.

Failures Caused by Poor Heat Treatment

A survey of die failures has revealed that 70% were caused by irregularities during heat treatment. This 70% is the total of 40% due to failure to control surface composition of the steel, 20% to quenching to too low a temperature or ineffective tempering, and 10% to quenching from excessively high austenitizing temperatures. Only the remaining 30% were caused by bad design, abusive grinding, service abuse, or selection of an improper grade of die steel.

Note that in this survey the greatest single cause of failures was associated with inability to control the surface composition. Ideally, most dies should be hardened in a neutral atmosphere, which will neither add carbon to nor subtract it from the surface, but perfection in this area is rarely attainable in practice. It is essential, however, to maintain the base carbon content during heat treatment to obtain the proper working hardness for the anticipated service life. Surface composition can be controlled in a variety of ways, all of which are intended to provide protection from the atmosphere. Among these are pack hardening in a neutral material to prevent contact with the furnace atmosphere, and processing in controlled-atmosphere furnaces, in vacuum furnaces, or in molten salt or lead baths.

In many instances when dies have undergone serious changes in surface composition, they fail before heat treatment is completed or fail during subsequent finishing operations. In other instances, such dies may survive until they are placed in service, but their service life is likely to be very short, as in the three examples that follow.

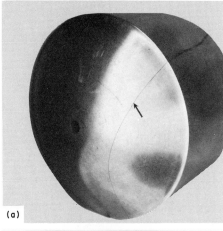

(a)

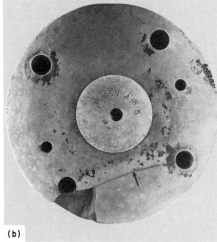

(b)

Fig. 5. Views of (a) the face and (b) the back of an A2 tool steel die, 8.090 in. in diameter, used for stamping mine covers. Arrows indicate cracks that occurred because of a carburized layer that was allowed to remain on the back surface. (Example 2)

Example 2. Fracture of an A2 Tool Steel Dome-Shaped Stamping Die That Started in an Unintentionally Carburized Layer (Fig. 5)

A stamping die with a dome-shaped face, shown in Fig. 5(a), cracked after it had produced only two mine covers from hot rolled carbon steel strip.

The die, made from A2 tool steel, had been austenitized in an atmosphere furnace, quenched in salt at 204 C (400 F) until the die had cooled to 482 to 538 C (900 to 1000 F), air cooled to room temperature, and tempered twice at 204 C (400 F). The specified hardness resulting from the above treatment was Rockwell C 60 to 62.

Investigation. One large crack intersected the surface of the die along a path down one side of the die, across the face (Fig. 5a), up the other side and across the back through two tapped holes (Fig. 5b). At one of the tapped holes, a piece of the die had broken off, and small cracks could be seen elsewhere on the back of the die at or near holes and edges.

The hardness of the face, sides and interior of the die was Rockwell C 56 to 58.5, but the hardness of the back of the die was Rockwell C 59 to 62.

Specimens were taken at the face and back surfaces; these specimens were quenched in liquid nitrogen from room temperature, and their hardness was measured. The specimen from the face had a hardness of Rockwell C 56 to 58 after the liquid-nitrogen treatment, whereas the specimen from the back had a hardness of Rockwell C 61 to 62. The increase in hardness in the latter specimen after the liquid-nitrogen quench was considered evidence that this region in the die contained a significant amount of retained austenite.

The microstructure near the back surface had a 0.06-in.-thick carburized layer consisting of tempered martensite with large quantities of carbides and retained austenite. Underneath this layer, the interior structure was mostly tempered martensite. The face and sides of the die did not have a carburized layer.

The carbon content varied from 2.24% at the back surface to 1.06% in the interior, as determined from chemical analysis at 0.005-in. increments from the back surface.

Conclusions. Fracture of the stamping die was caused by brittle cracking that started in a 0.06-in.-thick carburized layer at the back surface. Stress concentration at holes and the edge of the back surface apparently determined the location of crack origins.

The carburized layer most likely was the result of poor atmosphere control during furnace austenitization when the rough-machined die was heat treated. Finish machining after heat treatment had removed the carburized layer from the face and cylindrical sides of the die, but not from the back.

Recommendation. Proper control of the atmosphere in the austenitizing furnace to avoid heavy carburization was recommended. (Refer to the article beginning on page 85 in Volume 2 of this Handbook for a detailed discussion of control of surface carbon content.) An alternative remedy would be to machine the back surface of the die after heat treatment to remove the brittle carburized layer.

Example 3. Fracture of an S7 Tool Steel Plastics-Molding Die Caused by Unintentional Surface Carburization During Heat Treatment (Fig. 6)

A plastics-molding die, made from a 2½-in. by 3-in. S7 tool steel bar, cracked after a short service life. The die reportedly had been quenched and tempered to a hardness of Rockwell C 50 to 52.

Investigation. Figure 6 shows the fracture surface, which was located transverse to the long dimension of the bar-shaped die. The crack passed through a hole that contained a guide pin near one end of the die. The arrow in Fig. 6 points to a bright area of brittle fracture. The remainder of the fracture surface has a temper color and therefore appears darker.

Examination of an etched transverse section through the die revealed a dark surface layer, which was subsequently examined microscopically.

Specimens were taken at the surface and the interior of the die. The surface and interior hardnesses were Rockwell C 52 to 54 and Rockwell C 54 to 56, respectively. After the specimens were quenched from room temperature in liquid nitrogen and allowed to warm to room temperature again, the surface hardness was Rockwell C 61 to 63, whereas the interior hardness did not change. These data prove that the surface layer on the die contained a sizable amount of retained austenite that transformed to hard martensite upon refrigeration in liquid nitrogen.

A carburized layer extended 0.020 in. in from the surface. The structure in the carburized layer was found to be coarse martensite and retained austenite, whereas the interior structure was tempered martensite.

The carbon content varied from 0.76% at the surface to 0.51% in the interior, as determined by chemical analysis at successive incremental depths from the surface.

Conclusions. The die broke by brittle-fracture mechanism because the surface had been carburized unintentionally during the austenitizing stage of the heat treatment. Temper color, present on the fracture surface, formed during tempering; thus, the die cracked after being austenitized and quenched but before being tempered.

Recommendation. Proper control of the atmosphere in the austenitizing furnace should be maintained to prevent excessive carburization. (The article on pages 85 to 92 in Volume 2 of this Handbook discusses surface-carbon-content control in detail.)

Example 4. Fracture of an S7 Tool Steel Striking Die Caused by Retained Austenite in a Carburized Surface Layer (Fig. 7)

A jewelry-striking die, shown in Fig. 7, cracked after limited service. The die, made from S7 tool steel, reportedly was heat treated to a hardness of Rockwell C 57 as follows: austenitized at 954 C (1750 F), flash quenched in oil, and tempered at 204 C (400 F).

Investigation. The die cracked at several areas of stress concentration in fillets, recesses and corners, as indicated in Fig. 7. The cracks were opened to check for temper color; none was found on the fracture surfaces. (If present, temper color generally implies quench cracking.)

Specimens from the surface and interior of the die were checked for hardness, both before and after a refrigeration treatment in liquid nitrogen. Hardness in the interior was Rockwell C 56 to 57 before and after refrigeration, but the surface hardness was Rockwell C 50 to 55 before refrigeration and Rockwell C 62 to 65 after refrigeration, indicating the presence of a substantial quantity of retained austenite in the surface layer.

Metallographic examination of a section taken through the die cavity prior to refrigeration confirmed the presence of retained austenite in the surface layer.

Chemical analysis at increments inward from the surface of the die revealed a carbon content at the surface of 0.79% that decreased to 0.53% in the interior. The depth of carburization was 0.020 in.

Conclusions. Brittle fracture started in a carburized surface layer that contained a substantial quantity of retained austenite after heat treatment. Stress concentrations around fillets, recesses and corners appar-

The face as shown measured approximately 2¼ by 2¾ in. Failure of the die resulted from the presence of a crack that formed after austenitizing and quenching, but before tempering. The surface showed temper color everywhere except in the small area indicated by the arrow.

Fig. 6. Fracture surface of a plastics-molding die, made of S7 tool steel, that failed after a short service life (Example 3)

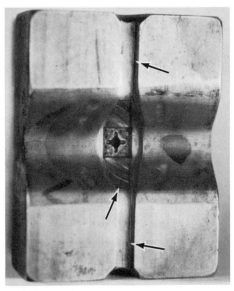

Fig. 7. Jewelry-striking die, of S7 tool steel, that failed by cracking after a short service life. Arrows show locations of cracks. Face of die measured 2⅜ by 3¼ in. (Example 4)

ently determined the location of crack origins.

Carburization probably rendered the tempered-martensite matrix in the surface layer abnormally brittle, and the soft spots of retained austenite contributed to fracture by deforming locally under service stresses.

Carburization was the result of poor atmosphere control in the austenitizing furnace.

Recommendation. Since the die cavity had been machined prior to heat treatment, proper control of the furnace atmosphere during austenitizing was recommended. (See pages 85 to 92 in Volume 2 of this Handbook for a detailed discussion on control of surface carbon content.)

Effect of Austenitizing Temperature. Die steels are extremely sensitive to overheating during austenitizing. Overheating causes grain growth and formation of coarse martensite and excessive amounts of retained austenite in the microstructure, all of which result in brittle dies that are susceptible to failure in service — especially if they are subjected to slight overloading or abusive conditions. The next example describes a die failure that was attributed to overheating during the austenitizing operation.

Example 5. Cracking of Hardened O6 Tool Steel Punches Caused by Overheating During Austenitization (Fig. 8)

Two punches, processed from hardened O6 tool steel, cracked after limited service. The larger of the two punches was made from a 1.135-in.-diam centerless-ground bar and is shown in Fig. 8; the smaller punch (not illustrated) was made from a 0.885-in.-diam centerless-ground bar.

Investigation. The crack in the larger punch can be seen in Fig. 8. The smaller punch cracked in a similar manner, but its cracking was more extensive. The cracks in both punches were opened to check for the presence of temper color on the fracture surfaces; none was found. The absence of temper color indicated that the punches did not crack upon quenching from the austenitizing temperature.

Hardness measurements were made on the surface and in the interior of both punches. After a refrigeration treatment in liquid nitrogen, hardness measurements on the surface and in the interior were repeated. Hardness increases found after the refrigeration treatment indicated that both punches contained significant amounts of retained austenite in the microstructure after heat treatment.

The microstructures of both punches consisted of coarse martensite, carbide particles,

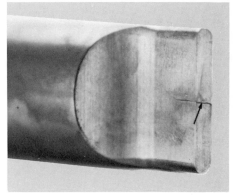

Fig. 8. Hardened O6 tool steel punch (shown at 1½×) that cracked after limited service. Crack (at arrow) was caused by overheating during austenitizing. (Example 5)

and retained austenite. The smaller punch exhibited a coarser structure and had more retained austenite than the larger punch. From this it was deduced that both punches had been heat treated together and both had been overheated during the austenitization stage of heat treatment. Being of smaller cross section, the smaller punch suffered the greater metallurgical damage from overheating.

Experimental tempering revealed that the punches had been tempered above 149 C (300 F) but below 204 C (400 F).

Conclusions. The punches cracked in service because they had been overheated during the austenitizing stage of the heat treatment. Overheating resulted in a coarse microstructure that was too brittle.

Soft spots of retained austenite probably contributed to cracking by deforming locally under service stresses, thus producing stress concentrations at the austenite-martensite boundaries.

Recommendation. Use of the proper austenitizing temperature during heat treatment would have prevented the failure. [The article on Heat Treating of Tool Steel, beginning on page 221 in Volume 2 of this Handbook, contains recommendations for heat treating all types of tool steels; pages 228 and 229 in that article contain specific data on oil-hardening cold work (O-series) tool steels.]

Quenching and Its Relation to Die Failure. Quenching mediums and quenching practices are selected with careful consideration of the steel grade and its hardenability, section thickness, and die design. In general, quenching practice is the same for dies as for production parts (see the article that begins on page 15 in Volume 2 of this Handbook). Quenching practice specifically oriented to tool and die steels is described in detail in the article that begins on page 221 in Volume 2.

Quenching practice that is inappropriate for a particular die because of its hardenability or design frequently causes die failure. For instance, the two header dies of which macroetched sections are shown in Fig. 9 were made from W1 tool steel and selectively quenched in the bores by forcing water through the bores. The die section at left in Fig. 9 gave long service life, whereas the die section at right wore excessively and then failed by cracking. As Fig. 9 shows, the die with the long service life had a uniformly hardened zone along the bore and at the ends, but the hardened zone of the die that failed was extremely nonuniform. It was concluded that this nonuniform hardening was the cause of failure.

Tempering and Its Relation to Die Failure. Dies should be tempered immediately after quenching and before they reach room temperature. When they uniformly reach about 52 to 65 C (125 to 150 F) after quenching, they should be placed in the tempering furnace. It is important that all portions of the die have reached this temperature range before

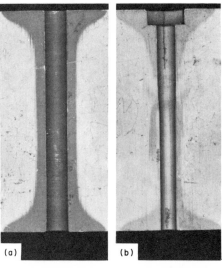

Fig. 9. At left is a macroetched section of a header die that provided acceptable life; note uniformly hardened zone (dark areas next to bore). At right is a macroetched section of a similar die that wore excessively and cracked prematurely; note nonuniform hardened zone caused by improper quenching.

tempering. Some dies have cracked from tempering too soon; that is, they had not been allowed to become uniform in temperature and some transformation was still taking place. Tempering serves to relieve residual stresses, which are often close to the tensile strength of the die material. When dies are placed in service without proper tempering, early failure is likely.

For dies made from the higher-alloy grades of tool steel, retempering (double, or sometimes triple, tempering) is required for added assurance against early failure in service. Dies made from tool steels such as the D, M or T grades retain significant amounts of austenite, which transforms to martensite during cooling from the first tempering oper-

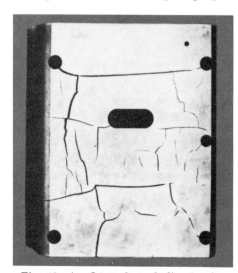

Fig. 10. An O1 tool steel die showing deep cracks that resulted from abusive grinding

ation; therefore, at least one additional tempering is necessary to relieve stresses caused by the transformation that took place during cooling from initial tempering.

Further in-process tempering may be appropriate or necessary when certain grinding operations or EDM (electrical discharge machining) have been performed (see subsequent discussion on these operations).

Failures Caused by Operations Following Heat Treatment

Several operations commonly performed after heat treatment can cause, or at least contribute to, die failure. Sometimes, identification of dies by such operations as cold stamping, or etching with an electric pencil, contribute to failure by causing stress raisers.

More often, however, grinding and electrical discharge machining are causes for premature failure of cold working dies.

Effects of Grinding. Grinding results in intense localized heating, and produces high surface stresses that can cause cracks or checks in dies. Common grinding faults are: (a) grinding burn, resulting from removing metal too rapidly; (b) grinding with a dull or loaded wheel; (c) grinding with a wheel of grit size too fine for the job; and (d) ineffective removal of the heat generated by grinding.

Damage resulting from abusive grinding may manifest itself as surface discoloration (often called grinding burn), shallow cracks (generally less than 0.004 in. deep), or deep cracks such as those in the O1 tool steel die shown in Fig. 10. Because burned areas and shallow cracks are not always evident in a visual examination, magnetic-particle testing, liquid-penetrant testing, or cold etching with dilute nitric acid may be needed to reveal this type of damage. Deeper cracks can often be detected by visual examination.

Die components must have adequate finishes for good service performance. One aspect of grinding, rarely considered in the average shop, is the direction that the die surface is ground. Regardless of how smooth the surfaces are finished by grinding, the surface will contain grinding scratches parallel to the direction of grinding. It has been proved that the direction of grinding marks on a die influences the die life, particularly of dies used for punching and deep drawing.

Grinding technique is not always the sole cause of grinding cracks; some heat treating practices produce extreme sensitivity toward grinding cracks, no matter how carefully the grinding is done. Among these heat treating practices are (a) failing to temper the die immediately after quenching; (*b*) quenching the die from an excessively high temperature; (*c*) producing a high-carbon carburized case, particularly one with a carbide network; and (*d*) use of tempering procedures that leave either untempered martensite or excessive amounts of retained austenite that transform in grinding.

Carbon and low-alloy die steels rarely give trouble in normal grinding operations. Because higher-alloy tool steels, such as the high-carbon high-chromium or the high speed grades, are more prone to grinding cracks, they usually cannot be ground with the same grinding wheels used for low-alloy grades. If reasonable precautions are taken to use a clean, coarse-grit wheel and adequate cooling fluid, however, the higher-alloy steels can be ground without difficulty when moderate amounts of metal are removed (see the article "Grinding of Tool Steel", which begins on page 367 in Volume 3 of this Handbook).

Electrical Discharge Machining. The use of electrical discharge machining (EDM) as the final metal-removing process in diemaking has progressed to a near necessity. This process can be used for machining hardened steels as well as other hard materials, such as carbides, which are difficult to shape by conventional means.

The use of EDM on hardened steels, however, can produce a shallow rehardened layer of untempered martensite at the surface, beneath which is a layer of tempered steel. This "white layer" of untempered martensite contains microcracks that can grow into serious cracks when the tool is loaded in service.

When used on hardened steel, EDM also adds surface stresses to the already established residual stresses. It is important, therefore, to relieve stresses in EDM-processed dies by retempering at a temperature slightly below the maximum tempering temperature used in the heat treatment.

Other precautionary measures are: (*a*) if low-frequency EDM was used for roughing, high-frequency EDM should be used for finishing to minimize the depth of the rehardened white layer; and (*b*) the white layer can be eliminated or minimized by light grinding or lapping, again followed by retempering.

A laboratory investigation of a failed die (of A4 tool steel) that had several holes finish machined by EDM showed the effect of poor practice. Microscopic examination (at 700 diameters) clearly revealed four distinct zones: (*a*) a surface layer possessing an as-cast dendritic structure due to the solidification of molten steel; (*b*) a hardened, untempered martensitic layer (the so-called white layer, which is highly stressed, and

Fig. 11. A2 tool steel blanking die, 2¾ in. in diameter by ⅝ in. thick, that cracked in service because of a brittle zone that had formed during electrical discharge machining of the cavity at center. Arrows point to cracks emanating from the cavity. (Example 6)

may lead to failure unless remedied); (*c*) a shallow, highly tempered zone resulting from gradient heating during EDM; and (*d*) a zone in which the base steel was not seriously affected by EDM, but had been lightly tempered.

The two examples that follow describe die failures caused by EDM, although both failures could probably have been avoided had the dies been tempered following the EDM operation.

Example 6. Cracking of an A2 Tool Steel Blanking Die Caused by a Brittle Layer Resulting From Electrical Discharge Machining (Fig. 11)

A 2¾-in.-diam by ⅝-in.-long blanking die for a small part, shown in Fig. 11, cracked from the corners of the electrical discharge machined cavity after the die had produced 20,000 pieces. The die was made from heat treated A2 tool steel.

Investigation. Four cracks emanating from the corners of the die cavity are indicated by arrows in Fig. 11; magnetic particles were used to accentuate the crack locations. Cracking apparently progressed by a brittle-fracture mechanism.

The die was sectioned transverse to the surface of the die cavity. Microscopic examination revealed three layers with different structures along the electrical discharge machined surface. The outermost layer was an as-cast structure. Next was a layer of as-quenched martensite. Underneath the as-quenched martensite layer was a dark region of overtempered martensite, which had been heated below the austenitizing temperature during the electrical discharge machining operation. The interior of the die had a normal structure of tempered martensite and carbide particles.

The various layers around the cavity were checked by microhardness testing. The as-cast structure showed hardness values equivalent to Rockwell C 58; the martensite layer had a hardness equivalent to Rockwell C 60 and the overtempered zone had a hardness equivalent to Rockwell C 55.5. The in-

terior of the die had a hardness equivalent to Rockwell C 60 to 61.

Conclusion. The die cracked by a brittle fracture mechanism; the fracture initiated in a metallurgically damaged zone caused by local overheating during the electrical discharge machining operation.

Recommendation. The undesirable brittle structures in the as-cast and as-quenched layers could have been rendered less prone to fracture in service if the die had been tempered after the electrical discharge machining operation.

Example 7. Fracture of a D2 Tool Steel Blanking Die Caused by a Brittle Martensitic Layer Resulting From Electrical Discharge Machining (Fig. 12)

A die for blanking a part for a seat-belt buckle, shown in Fig. 12(a), broke after a short time in service. The die, made of D2 tool steel, had been heat treated in a carburizing atmosphere with a dew point of −4 C (25 F); other details of the heat treatment were not reported. After hardening and tempering, the two deep recesses were electrical discharge machined in the die.

Investigation. The die cracked through the ends of the longer recess as shown in Fig. 12(a). Fracture was complete, separating the die into two pieces.

Figure 12(b) is a light-microscope fractograph of the broken die; the white arrow on the fractograph denotes the direction of brittle crack propagation, away from the surface of the recess, as determined from chevron marks. There was no temper color on the fracture surface, from which it can be assumed that the fracture occurred after the die was heat treated.

The microstructure of a section transverse to the surface of the recess is shown in Fig. 12(c). A thin layer of hard, brittle, as-quenched martensite is present at the electrical discharge machined surface. The remainder of the micrograph shows a normal structure of carbide particles in a matrix of tempered martensite.

Conclusion. The die cracked by brittle fracture that originated in a thin as-quenched martensite layer at the internal surface of a deep electrical discharge machined recess.

Recommendation. The die should have been retempered following electrical discharge machining. This would have rendered the surface layer less brittle.

Welding. Weld repair of failed dies requires experienced, skilled workmanship. When annealed, most tool steel parts can be welded without difficulty by established practices. Generally, these practices include: (*a*) matching of base-metal and weld-metal compositions; (*b*) proper preparation of the area to be welded; and (*c*) procedures that include preheating, postheating, and stress relieving or annealing. The welded die is then heat treated in the conventional manner.

Welding of hardened dies is difficult. Welds are used, for example, to repair cracked or heat-checked dies, restore spalled edges, build up worn edges or

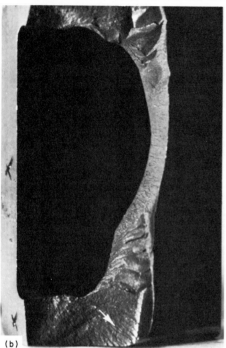

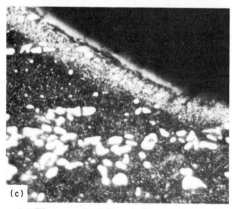

(a) Photograph of die, at about 85% of actual size. Arrows show cracks at ends of recess, which was made by electrical discharge machining.

(b) Light fractograph, at 3.4×, showing a fracture surface of the die. Arrow, at lower right, points in direction of brittle crack propagation.

(c) Micrograph, at 600×, of an etched (Marble's reagent) section taken transverse to the surface of the electrical discharge machined recess. A thin layer of hard, brittle as-quenched martensite is present at the surface; remainder of structure is normal, consisting of carbide particles in a matrix of tempered martensite.

Fig. 12. D2 tool steel die, for blanking a part for seat-belt buckles, that fractured after a short time in service (Example 7)

surfaces, make changes in die design, and correct shop errors. Because welding of hardened tools is hazardous, detailed procedures must be carefully followed (see data on welding of tool steels, pages 219 to 221 in Volume 6).

Dies Used in Hot Working

One large manufacturer of forgings made an extensive study of the causes of failure of dies used in hot working. Dies used in hydraulic forging presses and steam hammers were studied independently. Other variables considered were: die material, die position (top versus bottom), forging operation (busting, blocking, finishing), die-block size, and temperature of metal forged.

Dies Used in Hydraulic Presses. To study the failure of forging dies on large presses (35,000 and 50,000-ton), several hundred die blocks were examined, both failed and successful; from these, 72 failures were randomly chosen and analyzed. All failed dies were relatively large; some weighed as much as 20 tons. The study revealed the following:

1 A statistical analysis of the life cycle showed that the average life of a forging die was 150 forgings, with a 95% confidence range of 5 to 4400 forgings; that is, from this study, it would be expected that less than one broken die in 20 would have made fewer than five forgings or more than 4400 forgings.

2 Dies made of one proprietary die steel made more parts on the average. Although only four dies were made of this steel, the longer life proved statistically significant at the 95% confidence level. Average life was 1200 forgings, with a 95% confidence range of 300 to 400 forgings. This steel is not considered a premium grade, and was purchased as a competitive grade to the bulk of the die material in the study. (It is well understood in the industry that most hot working dies are made from proprietary die steels; see the article on The Selection of Material for Closed-Die Forging Tools, which begins on page 730 in Volume 1 of this Handbook.)

3 Fifty-eight of the 72 failures (80%) were bottom dies. Reasons for the significantly high incidence of bottom-die failure are believed to be: (*a*) the press bed for the bottom die is not as rigid as the ram holding the top die, which results in greater deflection of the bottom die; and (*b*) the bottom die is subjected to more thermal abuse and often contains the more complex cavity impression of the die set. For the 58 bottom-die failures, forging operation (blocking or finishing) was found to have no effect on the failure. The remainder (20%) of the dies that failed were top dies, and among this group finishing dies were found to be more prone to failure than blocking dies.

4 Forty-six of the failures (64%) were finish-impression dies, whereas 26 failures were preliminary-impression dies.

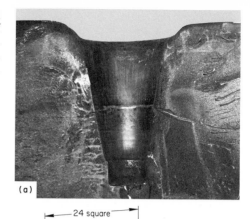

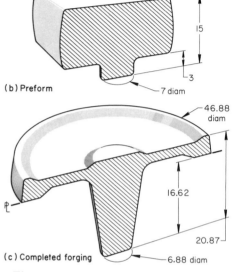

Fig. 13. (a) Cavity portion of a bottom finish-forging die that failed in a hydraulic press by circumferential and radial cracking. (b) Preform of the forging. (c) Finished forging produced in the die. (Example 8)

5 Statistical analysis of die dimensions showed thickness to be the most important size factor affecting die life. Die width had no bearing on die life.

6 Out of the 72 dies, it was noted that 66 dies (about 92%) failed while forging material requiring a high forging temperature, such as alloy steel, Waspaloy, and Inconel alloy 718. The six other dies failed while forging titanium in the temperature range of 900 to 955 C (1650 to 1750 F). A survey of forge-shop activity for a two-month period showed that the material requiring a high temperature was only 14% of the jobs forged. Thus, it appears that forging temperature is a very important factor in die life.

Details of a typical die failure are described in the example that follows.

Example 8. Cracking of a Hydraulic-Press Die for Forging Large Rotors (Fig. 13)

Figure 13(a) shows the cavity portion of a bottom finishing die used for producing the alloy steel forging shown in Fig. 13(c). This forging was produced from the preform shown in Fig. 13(b).

Die Details. This failure represents one of four similar failures that occurred within one year; all four dies were used to produce the same forging, and all failed from circumferential and radial cracks. The dies were made from proprietary prehardened die steels; die size was 75 by 56 in. by 33 in. thick. Dies No. 1, 2 and 3 were solid, one-piece dies; die No. 4 was a three-piece horizontal laminated die. Number of forgings made before failure were: die No. 1, 164; No. 2, 2000; No. 3, 256; No. 4, 287.

Operation. The preforms (Fig. 13b) were forged at 1232 C (2250 F) in an 18,000-ton hydraulic press using a load of 15,000 tons.

The finished forgings (Fig. 13c) were forged at the same temperature as that for the preforms on a 35,000 or 50,000-ton press using a load of 33,000 tons.

Investigation. All of the four failed die blocks showed the evidence of heavy die-wall erosion, interrupted circumferential cracks, and radial cracks. Further examination of these die blocks revealed that in all four dies, the circumferential crack was located at about 9 to 11 in. from the top face of the die. One of the die blocks was completely broken open for a thorough metallurgical study of the crack, especially its origin and growth. This study pointed out that a circumferential crack starting at a location about 10 in. from the top face of the

die first progressed to some distance inside the die wall. At this point a radial crack began, which brought about the die failure. The mechanics of metal flow in this type of forging operation is referred to as "extrusion forging", and consists of upsetting and extruding. Information on this type of metal flow is sparse in the literature; however, it has been shown (see paper by S. C. Jain, A. N. Bramley, C. H. Lee, and S. Kobayashi, "Theory and Experiments in Extrusion Forging", Proceedings of 11th Machine Tool Design and Research Conference, 1970, Pergamon Press) that in this type of compound metal flow, there are three well-defined flow stages. Stage 1 involves predominantly upsetting and slow extrusion; stage 2 has equalized rates of upsetting and extrusion; and stage 3 is mainly extrusion and slower rates of upsetting.

From the theoretical and experimental data presented in the above-mentioned paper, the onset of stage 3 was calculated using the dimensions of the steel forging under study. The calculation showed that stage 3 starts at about 10 in. from the face of the die. This correlation between theory and experience was a pointer to the solution of the problem. The interrelationship between the third stage of this compound metal flow and the initiation of circumferential cracks at this location is not clear. It may be that at

stage 3, a thermal and mechanical shock that is generated as a result of the change in metal flow is responsible for this phenomenon. An analysis of stress and temperature distribution along the die wall may be helpful to an understanding of the problem.

Corrective Action. On the basis of the understanding gained from this analysis, the following action was taken: The No. 4 broken die (the three-piece lamination) was successfully repaired by mechanical strapping and inserting an 8-in.-long liner of H11 die steel in the die at the problem area — that is, where the circumferential cracks initiated. This repaired die was reported to have completed over 260 forgings, with no evidence of deterioration.

Dies Used in Steam Hammers. The study of causes of failures of dies used in hot working involved 39 dies that failed on 12,000-lb, 20,000-lb and 35,000-lb steam hammers. The data, when analyzed, revealed the following:

1. Die position (top or bottom) did not show any significant influence on the incidence of die breakage in hammers. Twenty were top dies and 19 were bottom dies.
2. Out of 39 dies, 28 (72%) of the dies that broke were finishing dies.

Failures of Gears

*By the ASM Committee on Failures of Gears**

GEARS can fail in many different ways and, except for an increase in noise level and vibration, total failure often is the first and only indication of difficulty. In general, each type of failure leaves characteristic clues on gear teeth, and detailed examination often yields enough information to establish the cause of failure. In spite of the variety of ways in which gears can fail, service failures of gears are relatively rare occurrences.

This article deals primarily with the common types and causes of gear failures and the procedures employed in analyzing them. First, however, the major types of gears, and the basic principles of gear-tooth contact, are reviewed briefly.

Types of Gears

Gears are a type of machine element that transmits motion and power. The type of gear, and specific design features, determine not only the operating characteristics of a gear but also whether it may fail prematurely. The major types of gears are described in the following paragraphs. Various modifications exist for most of the major types of gears.

Spur gears (Fig. 1a) are used to transmit motion between parallel shafts or between a shaft and a rack. The teeth of a spur gear are radial, uniformly spaced around the outer periphery, and parallel to the shaft on which the gear is mounted.

Contact between mating teeth of a spur gear is in a straight line parallel to the rotational axes, lying in a plane tangent to the pitch cylinders of the gears. (A pitch cylinder is the imaginary cylinder in a gear that rolls without slipping on a pitch cylinder or pitch plane of another gear.)

Helical gears (Fig. 2a) are used to transmit motion between parallel or crossed shafts, or between a shaft and a rack, by meshing teeth that lie along a helix at an angle to the axis of the shaft. Because of this angle, mating of the teeth occurs in such a way that two or more teeth of each gear are always in contact. This condition permits smoother action

*WILSON T. GROVES, *Chairman*, Manager, Research and Development, Technical Center, Dana Corp.; L. E. ALBAN, Assistant Chief Metallurgist, Fairfield Manufacturing Co., Inc.; LYNN ARNOLD, Manager of Metallurgy, Tool Steel Gear & Pinion Co.; ROBERT M. BAKER, Chief, Metallurgy and Materials, Terex Div., General Motors Corp.

DONALD L. BORDEN, Director, Application and Special Product Engineering, Falk Corp.; DONALD P. BUSWELL, Chief Metallurgical and Chemical Engineer, Buick Motor Div., General Motors Corp.; JAMES E. DENTON, Metallurgical Project Engineer, Materials Engineering Dept., Cincinnati Milacron, Inc.; RICHARD P. EDWARDS, Manager, Manufacturing Services, Transportation Equipment Group – Automotive, Borg-Warner Corp.; J. A. HILDEBRANDT, Corporate Metallurgist, Clark

Equipment Co.; SHERWOOD W. McGEE, Director of Research, Burgess-Norton Manufacturing Co., Amsted Industries, Inc.; DANIEL F. NEWMAN, Senior Metallurgical Engineer, Curtiss-Wright Corp.; THEODORE R. WEINS, Supervisor, Metallurgical Laboratory, J. I. Case Co.; RICHARD A. WILDE, Chief Materials Engineer, Research Center, Eaton Corp.; EDWARD A. DURAND, *Secretary*, Senior Editor, Metals Handbook, American Society for Metals.

Some of the information and illustrations contained in this article were derived from the following sources: "Nomenclature of Gear-Tooth Wear and Failure", American Gear Manufacturers Assn.; "Gears and Their Lubrication", Mobil Oil Corp.; and Gear Lubrication II, Vol 53, No. 4 (1967), of *Lubrication*, Texaco Inc.

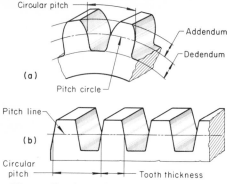

Fig. 1. Sections of (a) a spur gear and (b) a spur rack

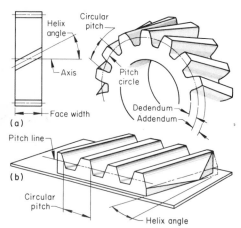

Fig. 2. Sections of (a) a helical gear and (b) a helical rack

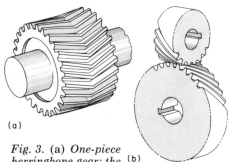

Fig. 3. (a) One-piece herringbone gear; the opposed helixes allow multiple-tooth engagement and also eliminate end thrust. (b) Mating crossed-axes helical gears.

than that of spur gears. However, unlike spur gears, helical gears generate axial thrust, which causes slight loss of power and requires thrust bearings.

Herringbone gears (Fig. 3a), sometimes called double helical gears, are used to transmit motion between parallel shafts. In herringbone gears, tooth engagement is progressive, and two or more teeth share the load at all times. Because they have right-hand and left-hand helixes, herringbone gears usually are not subject to end thrust.

Crossed-axes helical gears transmit motion between shafts that are nonparallel and nonintersecting (Fig. 3b). The action between the mating teeth has

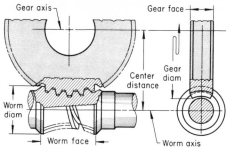

Fig. 4. Mating of worm gear (worm wheel) and worm in a double-enveloping worm-gear set

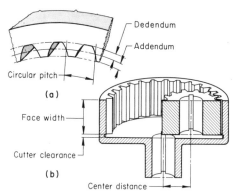

Fig. 5. (a) Section of a spur-type internal gear. (b) Relation of internal gear and mating pinion.

a wedging effect, which results in sliding on tooth flanks. These gears have low load-carrying capacity but are useful where shafts must rotate at an angle to each other.

Worm-gear sets usually are right-angle drives consisting of a worm gear (or worm wheel) and a worm. A double-enveloping worm-gear set is shown in Fig. 4. Worm-gear sets are used where the ratio of the speed of the driving member to the speed of the driven member is large, and where compact right-angle drive is required.

If a worm gear such as the one shown in Fig. 4 engages a straight worm, the combination is known as single-enveloping worm gearing.

Internal gears are used to transmit motion between parallel shafts. The teeth of internal gears are similar in form to those of spur gears and helical gears but point inward toward the center of the gear (see Fig. 5a). Common applications for internal gears include rear drives for heavy vehicles, planetary gear systems, and speed-reducing devices. Internal gears sometimes are used in compact designs, because the center distance between the internal gear and its mating pinion is smaller than that required for two external gears. The relation between an internal gear and a mating pinion is illustrated in Fig. 5(b).

Racks. A rack is a gear whose teeth lie in a straight line (pitch circle of infinite radius). The teeth may be at right angles

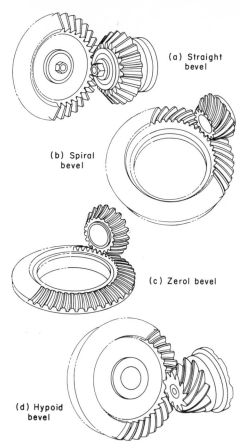

Fig. 6. Four types of bevel gears; see text for discussion

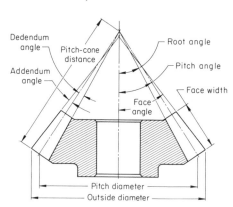

Fig. 7. Angles and terminology for straight bevel gears

to the edge of the rack and mesh with a spur gear (Fig. 1b), or may be at some other angle and engage a helical gear (Fig. 2b).

Bevel gears transmit rotary motion between nonparallel shafts that usually are at 90° to each other.

Straight bevel gears (Fig. 6a) have straight teeth that, if extended inward, would intersect at the intersection of gear and pinion axes. Thus, the action between mating teeth resembles that of two cones rolling on each other (see Fig. 7 for angles and terminology). The use of straight bevel gears generally is limited to drives that operate at low speeds and where noise is not important.

Spiral bevel gears (Fig. 6b) have teeth that are curved and oblique and that lie along a spiral at an angle to the shaft. The inclination of the teeth results in gradual engagement and continuous line contact or overlapping action — that is, two or more teeth are in contact at all times. Because of this continuous engagement, the load is transmitted more smoothly from the driving gear to the driven gear than with straight bevel gears. Spiral bevel gears also have greater load-carrying capacity than that of straight bevel gears. Spiral bevel gears usually are preferred over straight bevel gears for operation at speeds greater than 1000 sfm, and particularly for very small gears.

Zerol bevel gears (Fig. 6c) are curved-tooth bevel gears with zero spiral angle. They differ from spiral bevel gears in that their teeth are not oblique. They are used in the same way as spiral bevel gears and have somewhat greater tooth strength than that of straight bevel gears.

Hypoid bevel gears (Fig. 6d) are similar to spiral bevel gears in general appearance, the important difference being that in a hypoid-gear set the axis of the pinion is offset somewhat from the axis of the gear. This feature provides many design advantages. In operation, hypoid gears run even more smoothly and quietly than spiral bevel gears, and are stronger. However, they undergo more sliding action along the tooth-profile axes than do spiral bevel gears and, for many applications, may require extreme-pressure lubricants.

Gear-Tooth Contact

The way in which tooth surfaces of properly aligned gears make contact with each other is responsible for the heavy loads that gears are able to carry. In theory, gear teeth make contact along lines or at points; in service, however, because of elastic deformation of the surfaces of loaded gear teeth, contact occurs along narrow bands or in small areas. The radius of curvature of the tooth profile has an effect on the amount of deformation and on the width of the resulting contact bands. Depending on gear size and loading, the width of the contact bands varies from about 0.015 in., for small, lightly loaded gears, to about 0.2 in., for large, heavily loaded gears.

In a plain journal bearing, the journal continuously rubs against the same part of the bearing surface, and thus the heat that is generated (by either fluid or metallic friction) is continuously absorbed by this same area of bearing metal. This area, therefore, may overheat quickly if the load is heavy, and failure of the lubricating film may result. In contrast, gear-tooth surfaces are not continuously active. Each part of the tooth

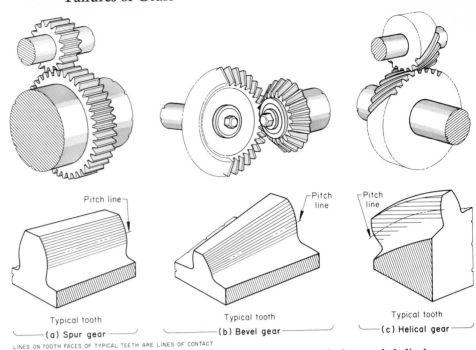

LINES ON TOOTH FACES OF TYPICAL TEETH ARE LINES OF CONTACT

Fig. 8. Tooth-contact lines on a spur gear, a bevel gear, and a low-angle helical gear

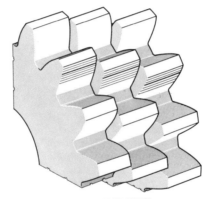

LINES ON TOOTH FACES ARE LINES OF CONTACT

Fig. 9. Lines of contact on a stepped spur gear. The heavy line on a tooth face of each gear section represents the instantaneous line of contact for that section. This offset-contact pattern is typical for helical, spiral bevel and hypoid gears.

surface is in action for only short periods of time. This continual shifting of the load to new areas of cool metal and cool oil makes it possible to load gear surfaces to stresses approaching the critical limit of the gear metal without failure of the lubricating film.

The maximum load that can be carried by gear teeth also depends on the velocity of sliding between the surfaces, because the heat generated varies with rate of sliding as well as with pressure. If both pressure and sliding speeds are excessive, the frictional heat developed can cause destruction of tooth surfaces. This pressure-velocity factor has, therefore, a critical influence on the probability of galling and scoring of gear teeth. The permissible value of this critical factor is influenced by gear metal, gear design,

character of lubricant and method of lubricant application.

For any gear, the area of surface contact and the manner in which teeth roll and slide over each other are major factors in breakdown of an oil film and, therefore, in determining the effectiveness of gear lubrication.

Spur and Bevel Gears. Spur-gear teeth are cut straight across the face of the gear blank, and the mating teeth theoretically meet at a line of contact (Fig. 8a) parallel to the shaft. Straight teeth of bevel gears also make contact along a line (Fig. 8b) that, if extended, would pass through the point of intersection of the two shaft axes. As teeth on either spur or bevel gears pass through mesh, the line of contact sweeps across the face of each tooth. On the driving tooth, it starts at the bottom and finishes at the tip. On the driven tooth, the line of contact starts at the tip and finishes at the bottom.

Helical, Spiral Bevel, and Hypoid Gears. Gear-tooth contact on these gears is similar to that developed on a stepped spur gear (see Fig. 9). Each section, or lamination, of the spur gear makes contact with its mating gear along a straight line; each line, because of the offset between sections, is slightly in advance of its adjacent predecessor. When innumerable laminations are combined into a smoothly twisted tooth, the short individual lines of contact blend into a smoothly slanted line (Fig. 8c), extending from one side of the tooth face to the other and sweeping either upward or downward as the tooth passes through mesh. This slanted-line contact occurs between the teeth of helical gears on parallel shafts, spiral bevel gears, and hypoid gears.

The greater the angle of the helix or spiral, the greater the number of teeth that mesh simultaneously and share the load. With increased angularity, the length of the slanted contact line on each tooth is shortened, and shorter but more steeply slanted lines of contact sweep across the faces of several teeth simultaneously. The total length of these lines of contact is greater than the length of the single line of contact between straight spur-gear teeth of the same width. Consequently, the load on these gears is distributed not only over more than one tooth, but also over a greater total length of line of contact. On the other hand, the increased angularity of the teeth increases the axial thrust load and thus increases the loading on each tooth. These two factors counterbalance each other so that, if the power transmitted is the same, the average unit loading remains about the same. Helical gears on crossed shafts make tooth contact only at a point. As the teeth pass through mesh, this point of contact advances from below the pitch line of the driving tooth diagonally across the face of the tooth to its top and from the top of the driven tooth diagonally across its face to a point below the pitch line. Even with several teeth in mesh simultaneously, this point contact does not provide sufficient area to carry an appreciable load. For this reason, helical gears at angles usually are used to transmit motion where very little power is involved.

Worm Gears. In a single-enveloping worm-gear set, in which the worm is cylindrical in shape, several teeth may be in mesh at the same time, but only one tooth at a time is fully engaged. The point (or points) of contact in this type of gear set constitutes too small an area to carry an appreciable load without destruction of the metal surface. As a result, single-enveloping worm-gear sets are used in applications similar to those for helical gears on crossed shafts: to transmit motion where little power is involved.

Considerable power must be transmitted by commercial worm-gear sets; therefore, the gears of these sets are throated to provide a greatly increased area of contact surface. The gear tooth theoretically makes contact with the worm thread along a line curved diagonally across the gear tooth. The exact curve and slant depend on tooth design and on the number of threads on the worm relative to the number of teeth on the gear. Usually, two or more threads of the worm are in mesh at the same time, and there is a separate line of contact on each meshing tooth. As meshing proceeds, these lines of contact move inward on the gear teeth and outward on the worm threads. To secure smooth operation from a gear of this type, the teeth of the gear, and sometimes the threads of

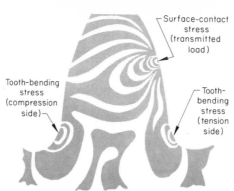

Fig. 10. Photoelastic study of the principal stress regions in a loaded gear tooth. The highest stress gradients occur where the stress patterns are close together and concentric.

the worm, usually are altered from theoretically correct standard tooth forms. These alterations result in slightly wider bands of contact, increasing the load-carrying capacity of the unit. Load-carrying capacity also depends on the number of teeth in simultaneous contact. Exact tooth design varies from one manufacturer to another, and for this reason the patterns of contact also vary.

In a double-enveloping worm-gear set, the worm is constructed so that it resembles an hourglass in profile. Such a worm partly envelops the gear, and its threads engage the teeth of the gear throughout the entire length of the worm. The teeth of both the worm and the gear have straight-sided profiles like those of rack teeth, and in the central plane of the gear they mesh fully along the entire length of the worm.

The exact pattern of contact in double-enveloping (or double-throated) worm-gear sets is somewhat controversial and seems to vary with gear design and with method of gear manufacture. It is generally agreed, however, that contact is entirely by sliding with no rolling, and that radial contact occurs simultaneously over the full depth of all the worm teeth.

Operating Loads

Gears and gear drives cover the range of power transmission from fractional-horsepower applications, such as hand tools and kitchen utensils, to applications involving thousands of horsepower, such as heavy machinery and marine drives. However, neither the horsepower rating nor the size of a gear is necessarily indicative of the severity of the loading it can withstand. For example, the severity of tooth loading in the gear train of a ¼-hp hand drill may exceed that of the loading in a 20,000-hp marine drive. Factors other than horsepower rating and severity of loading can affect gear strength and durability — notably, duration of loading, operating speed, transient loading, and environmental factors such as

extreme temperature, moisture, corrosive atmosphere and abrasive dust.

Gear Stresses. Figure 10, a photoelastic study of a loaded gear in action, emphasizes the importance of root fillets in gear loading. The areas where the stress patterns are close together and concentric indicate very high stress gradients. High stress gradients usually are indicative of high stress levels. Generous round root fillets like those shown in Fig. 10 serve to spread out, or distribute, the high stress gradients that normally are present at the base of a loaded cantilever beam. On the other hand, sharp corners at the root fillets accentuate high stress concentrations and may produce excessively high stress levels and premature failures.

Apparent in Fig. 10 are the two principal stress regions of a loaded gear tooth in service. One principal stress is the *surface-contact stress* that results where the force of loading is transmitted from one gear to another by intimate contact. This loaded area moves up and down the gear-tooth profile as the gear and the pinion proceed through mesh. The other principal stress is at the root fillet and gives rise to what is commonly referred to as the *tooth-bending stress*. Note that deflection of the beam produces similar stress patterns on both sides of the tooth. Under the conditions of loading shown in Fig. 10, the root fillet on the right is subjected to tensile stress, whereas the root fillet on the left is subjected to compressive stress. Tooth-bending fatigue failure of the teeth can be expected to originate on the side of the gear tooth that is subjected to tensile loading.

The American Gear Manufacturers Association (AGMA) has developed standards for determining gear-tooth stresses. The equations from these standards can be regrouped and summarized in general terms, and the basic formula for all stresses in gears can be related to three indexes: a load index, a geometry index, and a rating index. The load index is related to gear size and measures the load transmitted by the gear. The geometry index is related to the general characteristics of gear teeth, such as pressure angle, helix angle, tooth size, root-fillet radius, number of teeth, contact ratio and overlap ratio. The rating index (over-all rating-adjustment factor) is related to internal misalignment of gear teeth, manufacturing inaccuracies, relative velocity of mesh, duty or application of the gear unit, size of gear wheels, and temperature. Thus, the rating index is a measure of the additional capacity that must be designed into a gear drive to allow for variations in operating conditions resulting from design, manufacture, installation and environment.

In most applications, the rating index used for calculating the surface-contact stress has the same value as the rating index used for calculating tooth-bending stress. However, for industrial drive gears, the rating index used to compute surface-contact stress often must be higher than that used for tooth-bending stress. The fact that many gear drives run at relatively slow speed and must operate in the mixed-oil-film region accounts for the necessity of using a higher rating index for surface-contact stress of industrial drive gears.

Oil-Film-Thickness Ratio. The behavior of contacting tooth surfaces is closely associated with the problem of surface-contact stress and the pitting type of tooth failure that results from contact fatigue.

Most loaded gears require some form of lubrication in order to perform satisfactorily. Gears may operate with boundary, hydrodynamic, mixed or elastohydrodynamic lubrication. Over various portions of their operating life or cycle, they may be required to perform with lubrication that changes from one mode to another.

It is possible to evaluate the performance of concentrated contacts in terms of a calculated oil-film thickness; the performance is determined from the equation $R = h/\sigma$, where R is the oil-film-thickness ratio; h is the calculated film thickness; and σ is the combined surface roughness of the mating surfaces, in micro-inches (rms).

One investigator has indicated that this oil-film-thickness ratio (R) should be at least 1.4 to 1; others have suggested a ratio between 2 to 1 and 4 to 1.

Gear Materials

A variety of cast irons, powder metallurgy materials, nonferrous alloys and nonmetallic materials are used in gears, but steels, because of their high strength-to-weight ratio and relatively low cost, are the most widely used gear materials. Consequently, steel gears receive primary consideration in this article.

Among the through hardening steels in wide use are 1040, 1060, 4140 and 4340. These steels also can be effectively case hardened by induction heating. Among the carburizing steels used in gears are 1018, 1524, 4026, 4118, 4320, 4620, 4820, 8620 and 9310 (AMS 6260). Many high-performance gears are carburized. Some special-purpose steel gears are case hardened by either carbonitriding or nitriding. Other special-purpose gears, such as those used in chemical or food-processing equipment, are made of stainless steels or nickel-base alloys because of their corrosion resistance or their ability to satisfy sanitary standards, or both. Gears intended for operation at elevated temperatures may be made of tool steels or elevated-temperature alloys.

The majority of gears are made of carbon and low-alloy steels, including carburizing steels and the limited number of low-alloy steels that respond favorably to nitriding. In general, the steels selected for gear applications must satisfy two basic sets of requirements that are not always compatible — those involving fabrication and processing and those involving service. Fabrication and processing requirements include machinability, forgeability, and response to heat treatment as it affects fabrication and processing. Service requirements are related to the ability of the gear to perform satisfactorily under the conditions of loading for which it was designed and thus encompass all mechanical-property requirements, including fatigue strength and response to heat treatment as it affects these and other properties.

Because resistance to fatigue failure is partly dependent on the cleanness of the steel and on the nature of allowable inclusions, melting practice may also be a factor in steel selection and may warrant selection of a steel produced by vacuum melting or electroslag refining. The mill form from which a steel gear is machined is another factor that may affect its performance. Many heavy-duty steel gears are machined from forged blanks that have been processed to provide favorable grain flow consistent with load pattern, rather than being machined from blanks cut from mill-rolled bar.

Classification of Gear Failures

Systematic analysis of a gear failure begins with classification of the failure by type. The type of failure is determined from the appearance of the failed gear and from the process or mechanism of the failure. After the mechanism of a failure has been established, it remains to determine what caused the failure. In general, an understanding of the failure mechanism is of considerable assistance in isolating the cause or causes of a failure.

Types of gear failures have been grouped into four general classes: wear, surface fatigue, plastic flow, and breakage.* Each of these general classes has been subdivided to provide more accurate and specific identification.

Wear (for gears defined as loss of material from contacting surfaces of teeth) is further classified as normal wear (polishing in), moderate wear, destructive wear, abrasive wear, scratching (a severe form of abrasive wear), scoring, interference wear, corrosive wear, flaking, burning and discoloration. Obviously, normal wear (polishing in) does not constitute failure because it involves loss of metal

*American Standard B6.12, Nomenclature of Gear Tooth Wear and Failure

at a rate too slow to affect performance within the expected life of the gear. Nevertheless, normal wear is a useful classification in failure analysis in that it provides a basis for comparison. Interference wear may have no serious consequence other than noisy operation, or it may result in severe pitting at the point of interference or in tooth breakage.

Surface fatigue, the failure of a material as a result of repeated surface or subsurface stresses that exceed the endurance limit of the material, is further classified as initial pitting, destructive pitting, and spalling. Initial pitting may not constitute failure if it is self-corrective and nonprogressive.

Plastic flow, which is surface deformation resulting from yielding of surface metal under heavy loads, is further classified as rolling and peening, rippling, and ridging. Rippling, a wavelike formation on the tooth surface at right angles to the direction of sliding, does not constitute failure unless allowed to progress.

A type of plastic-flow failure that is accompanied by surface and subsurface cracking is referred to as "case crushing", and is limited essentially to carburized steel gears.

Breakage, defined as fracture of an entire tooth or of a substantial portion of a tooth, is further classified as fatigue breakage, breakage from heavy wear, overload breakage, quenching cracks and grinding cracks. Breakage from heavy wear, of course, is essentially a type of wear failure in which enough tooth metal is removed by wear to lower the strength of the tooth to the level at which fracture occurs.

It is not uncommon for a gear to fail by more than one failure mode — for example, by wear and breakage or by plastic flow and breakage. Failure by two or more modes may occur simultaneously, or one may be the result of the continued or progressive nature of the other. Classification of the different types of wear or failure is intended to assist in distinguishing between cause and effect, in evaluating the degree or progression of an observed condition, and in determining suitable corrective action.

In the sections that follow, the various common causes of gear wear and gear failure are related to the types of wear and failure previously classified under the general heading of wear, surface fatigue, plastic flow and breakage.

Gear Wear and Wear Failures

The term "wear", as applied to gears, primarily refers to, but is not restricted to, loss of gear-tooth surface metal and accompanying loss of profile (roughening) as a result of metal-to-metal contact through the lubricating film. The term wear, therefore, generally encompasses normal wear, or polishing in, moderate wear, destructive wear, and scoring (also called galling) — a form of wear in which gross damage to tooth surfaces occurs. The American Standard B6.12 extends the classification to include abrasive wear, scratching (a severe form of abrasive wear), interference wear, corrosive wear, flaking and burning.

For detailed information on wear and wear mechanisms, see the article on Wear Failures, which begins on page 134 in this volume.

Lubrication and Gear-Tooth Wear. In many moderately loaded gear sets operating at moderate speeds, relatively thick oil films are maintained between gear teeth and no metal-to-metal contact occurs. No wear occurs (except during starting and stopping), and original tool marks are visible on teeth even after long periods of operation.

Under full-film conditions, oil viscosity (at the temperature of the film and the pressure exerted on the film) is the property that determines load-carrying ability of gear teeth as well as resistance to motion between tooth surfaces.

In practice, it is not always possible to have full-film lubrication. When the surfaces are at rest under pressure, the thick film is squeezed out of the pressure area, because motion is necessary to establish and maintain that film.

Under conditions of low speed, heavy load, extreme temperatures, relatively rough and irregular surfaces, scanty oil supply, or use of oil too low in viscosity, there may be only a partial film present in the loaded area. Under such conditions, there will be some degree of metal-to-metal contact between the surfaces.

Gear-tooth surfaces are not smooth, but are wavy because of inherent characteristics of the machine tools used to cut and finish them; superimposed on the waves are countless minute asperities. When surfaces come together under insufficient lubrication, contact is made between crests of surface waves. A number of actions then take place: shearing of surface films; heavy rubbing and deformation of metal; plowing of asperities on the surface of the harder material through the softer material, which results in detachment of wear particles and creation of new asperities; and, finally, bonding of minute high areas that have been rubbed clean. The minute bonds break immediately as motion continues, but may bond at another location so that metal is transferred from one surface to the other. New asperities are formed, some of which are plowed off to form wear particles. These actions account for both wear and friction.

Normal wear, also called polishing in, is defined as slow loss of material from contacting gear-tooth surfaces at a rate that does not affect performance

significantly within the expected life of the gears. The loss of metal is very slow and generally quite uniform. Normal wear on steel gear teeth has an appearance ranging from dull gray to burnished. Because of an inherent lack of contrast, a normally worn surface is diffi-

Fig. 11. Hypoid pinion, made of carburized and hardened 8620 steel, exhibiting normal wear (polishing in)

Fig. 12. Helical gear, made of hardened and tempered 4340 steel, exhibiting moderate wear

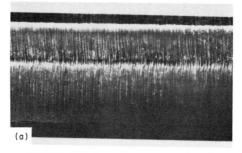

(a)

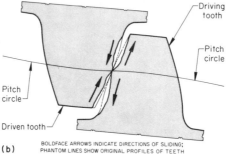

(b)　BOLDFACE ARROWS INDICATE DIRECTIONS OF SLIDING; PHANTOM LINES SHOW ORIGINAL PROFILES OF TEETH

Fig. 13. (a) Destructive wear on a gear tooth. (b) Schematic illustration of the effect of destructive wear on the tooth profile of an involute gear.

cult to photograph meaningfully. A hypoid pinion exhibiting normal wear, or polishing in, is shown in Fig. 11. This pinion was made of carburized and hardened 8620 steel and was removed from a truck rear end after many cycles of operation. The polishing was attributed to high-velocity sliding.

Although normal wear does entail a very mild form of adhesive wear, it obviously does not constitute failure. For all practical purposes, following an initial period during which wear occurs at a slow rate, normal wear ceases. In worm gears, normal wear is desirable, because some wear must occur before proper tooth contact is established. Spiral bevel gear sets often are run with a lapping compound to simulate normal wear before being placed in service.

Moderate and Destructive Wear. Moderate wear refers to a loss of metal more rapid than normal wear. Moderate wear is not necessarily destructive and may develop on heavily loaded gear teeth. It may be self-healing, or may indicate the onset of destructive wear. Moderate wear may be characterized by an increase in noise level, but generally does not constitute failure. Figure 12 exhibits moderate wear on teeth of a helical gear made of hardened and tempered 4340 steel.

Destructive wear usually results from loading that is excessive for the lubricant employed. Destructive wear on a gear tooth is shown in Fig. 13(a), and the effect of destructive wear on the tooth profile of an involute gear is depicted in Fig. 13(b). This type of wear, which is synonymous with adhesive wear, is caused by direct tooth contact, and is not related to abrasives or corrosion. Such wear occurs over most of the gear-tooth face except at the pitch line; no other form of failure is evident. In general, destructive wear, sometimes called overload wear, occurs at low speeds and high loads only. Because destructive wear destroys the gear-tooth profile, it may initiate other types of failure. Consequently, it is important to be able to determine the original cause, because other types of failure, such as pitting due to surface fatigue, may also destroy tooth profile.

Causes of Destructive (Overload) Wear. As previously noted, destructive wear generally is associated with excessive tooth loading for the lubricant being used. If the cause of wear can be traced to the lubricant, the substitution of a higher-viscosity oil, or an oil containing mild extreme-pressure (EP) additives, should be effective in controlling or eliminating wear. For example, the gears used on rolling-mill stands are subjected to a combination of heavy loads and extreme shock loads, which makes it difficult to maintain an effective oil film between driving-gear and driven-gear tooth surfaces when conventional lubricants are employed. This condition requires extreme-pressure lubricants. If an improved lubricant is not effective in controlling overload wear in this instance, the cause of wear may be attributable to design factors or use of improper gear material, or both.

There are applications in which, because of insufficient space or other limiting and unavoidable factors, gears are loaded so heavily that it is difficult to maintain an effective lubricating film between the rubbing surfaces. Hypoid gears in automotive applications typify this condition. Nevertheless, the *rate* of wear can be controlled within acceptable limits by use of special extreme-pressure lubricants that contain additives designed to prevent bonding and surface destruction.

Even when lubrication is adequate, abusive operation can result in overload wear. In the following example, abuse of a worm gear resulted in extreme overload wear and catastrophic failure.

Example 1. Catastrophic Failure of an 1113 Steel Hoist Worm Caused by Destructive Wear Resulting From Abusive Operation (Fig. 14)

A farm-silo hoist was used as the power source for a homemade barn elevator. The hoist mechanism consisted of a pulley attached by a shaft to a worm that, in turn, engaged and drove a worm gear mounted directly on the hoist drum shaft. The worm was made of leaded, cold drawn 1113 steel (hardness: Rockwell B 80 to 90); the worm gear was made of class 35-40 gray iron that had been nitrided in an aerated salt bath. Driving power was applied to the pulley, which actuated the worm and worm gear and rotated the drum to which the elevator cable was attached. After less than one year of service, the hoist failed catastrophically from destructive wear of the worm, as shown in Fig. 14. The hoist was rated at 2000 lb at 200-rpm input. It was determined that at the time of failure the load on the hoist was only 720 lb.

Investigation. When the gearbox was examined, it was found to contain fragments of the worm teeth and shavings that resembled steel wool. It was determined that both fragments and shavings were steel of the same composition as the worm, ruling out the possibility that these materials may have derived from a source other than the gearbox. The teeth of the worm had worn to a thickness of approximately 1/16 in. from an original thickness of 1/8 in. More than half of the worm teeth had been sheared off.

Further investigation revealed that the drive pulley had been replaced with a pulley of different diameter, and that consequently the pulley was rotating at 975 rpm instead of at the rated maximum of 200 rpm. By calculation, with a load of 720 lb, the gearbox was forced to develop 0.32 hp — almost twice the specified rating of 0.18 hp (2000 lb at 200 rpm).

Conclusion. Failure was caused by destructive wear of the steel worm, which resulted from operation of the gearbox at a rating

Fig. 14. Destructive wear of an 1113 steel worm used in a silo hoist (Example 1)

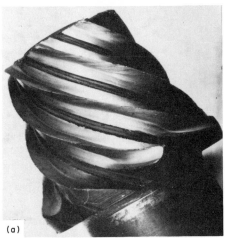

(a)

(b)

Fig. 15. (a) Steel hypoid pinion with teeth worn to a knife-edge from both sides. (b) A similar steel pinion with teeth worn completely away.

that far exceeded the maximum specified by the gearbox manufacturer.

The adhesive wear that is associated with overloading and inadequate lubrication may also result from marginal tooth design — that is, design that cannot satisfactorily withstand light or normal loads because of inadequate load-supporting surfaces. Usually, this inadequacy can be traced to load-supporting surfaces that are of insufficient size

or insufficient hardness, or both. However, poor alignment and eccentric loading can result in wear of tooth surfaces of adequate design.

Failure of the steel hypoid pinion shown in Fig. 15(a) was attributed to destructive wear resulting from a combination of factors that included marginal design, less-than-optimum mounting alignment, high surface temperatures resulting from high operating speeds, and high sliding velocity of gear teeth. The pinion operated in both forward and reverse, and the teeth were worn on both sides to knife-edges at the tips. Because there was no breakage of the severely worn teeth, it was evident that high loads had not contributed to the failure. A similar steel pinion in an even more advanced stage of destructive wear is shown in Fig. 15(b); the teeth of this pinion have been worn completely away.

Scoring. The term "scoring" is essentially synonymous with, but generally is considered preferable to, the terms "scuffing", "seizing" and "galling". Scoring entails the rapid removal of metal from tooth surfaces caused by the tearing-out of small contacting particles that have bonded together as a result of metal-to-metal contact. Scoring is a form of adhesive wear in which the damaged surface exhibits a torn or dragged-and-furrowed appearance with markings in the direction of sliding, in contrast to the smooth grooves or polish of a tooth surface worn by abrasion. In scoring, the tips and roots of the teeth are worn the most, whereas the pitch-line area generally remains in its original condition. This is because essentially there is rolling contact at the pitch line, with little or no sliding action. If gear alignment is correct and scoring is not a result of isolated high spots on the tooth surfaces, the scored areas extend across the entire width of the teeth.

Scoring is a symptom of inadequate load-carrying capacity of the lubricant;

in this respect, scoring is similar to destructive wear. Sometimes, particularly when gears are misaligned, the damage may cease and the surface may become smoother as the contact area spreads and more load-carrying face is brought into contact.

Scoring sometimes is associated with an increase in oil temperature sufficient to affect lubrication — for example, by markedly lowering oil viscosity. The increase in temperature may arise from an increase in operating speed or load or from heating of the inlet oil.

Two instances of scoring are shown in Fig. 16. Initial scoring on a wide-face helical gear is shown in Fig. 16(a). This gear was made from a 4340 forged steel blank that was hardened and tempered to 300 Bhn. The gear was finished by hobbing, and scoring was attributed to the presence of high spots on the gear teeth following the hobbing operation. Moderate scoring on a spur gear with a 20° pressure angle is shown in Fig. 16(b). This gear was made of 3310 steel and was carburized, hardened and tempered to Rockwell C 60, and finished by grinding. Scoring appears on both the addenda and dedenda but does not follow a fixed pattern. The cause of the scoring was not reported.

Interference wear occurs when gear teeth mate improperly at the start or end of contact. It is a type of localized overload wear in which the entire load is concentrated at the point of engagement low on the profile of the driving flank with the mating tip, or at disengagement of the driven flank and mating tip. Interference wear may range from a light line of wear or pitting of no serious consequence other than noisy operation to more severe damage in which the flank is gouged out and the tip of the mate heavily rolled over, usually resulting in complete failure of the pair.

Interference wear is not influenced to any degree by lubrication. Although its appearance is similar to other types of wear and scoring, it can be distinguished from them by the location of the distressed area. Interference wear usually can be traced to errors in design, tooth generation or alignment.

Abrasive wear is surface damage caused by the presence of abrasive particles in the lubricant. The particles may be dirt not completely removed from the system, sand or scale from cast gear housings, impurities in the oil, abrasive particles from the operating environment, or metal detached from tooth surfaces or bearings. Abrasive wear is much more common than overload wear. An abrasive common in automotive gearing is sand from cast iron housings. Most housings are dipped in a paint-type sealer before machining in order to seal leaks due to porosity and to bind any

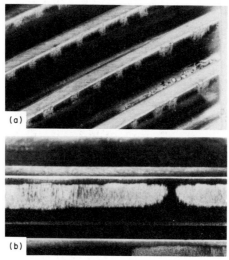

Fig. 16. (a) Initial scoring on a wide-face 4340 steel helical gear. (b) Moderate scoring on a 3310 steel spur gear with a 20° pressure angle.

residual foundry sand to the metal surfaces. Wear debris, machining chips and environmental contaminants are other types of abrasives that often are found in lubricants.

The appearance of abrasive wear depends on the particle size and nature of the abrasive contaminant. Abrasive dust, for example, forms a slurry with the lubricant that will polish gear teeth to a mirror finish; damage to tooth contours may be forestalled until an appreciable quantity of wear debris accumulates in the lubricant-slurry. Larger particles, such as particles of welding slag or machining chips, will scratch and gouge the surface.

A potentially severe form of abrasive wear is referred to as scratching; it is characterized by short scratchlike lines or marks on the contacting surfaces of gear teeth in the direction of sliding. Scratching may be caused by burrs or projections on the tooth surface, material embedded in the tooth surface, or hard foreign particles suspended in the lubricant. Scratching should be differentiated from scoring, because scratching does not result from inadequate lubrication. If the cause of scratching is removed at an early stage, scratching damage may be light and progressive destruction may be avoided.

Corrosive wear is a type of surface deterioration that is caused by chemical

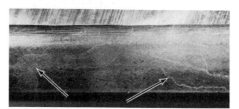

Fig. 17. Corrosive wear (patches at arrows) on a tooth of a spur gear

reaction of lubricant, or of contaminants such as water or acids, with gear-tooth surfaces. Sometimes, corrosion attacks other surfaces of a gear as well, making the cause of damage relatively easy to distinguish. Corrosive wear on a spur-gear tooth is shown in Fig. 17.

Corrosive wear may result in pitting of the contacting tooth surfaces; the evidence of such pitting may be removed by wear, in which case the contacting surfaces appear polished. The potential sources of corrosion are numerous. Acid or water in the lubricant are among the most common sources. Highly active extreme-pressure (EP) additives are also a source, especially when the gear is heavily loaded. The gear will operate without scoring but with a uniform and low rate of corrosive wear. Overheating the EP additives will accelerate corrosive action.

Often, as a result of exposure to acids or rusting, corrosion begins before the gear is assembled in a unit. Steel gears that retain a tenacious light oxide resulting from heat treatment have reasonably good resistance to rusting, even though they may have been dipped in an alkaline wash to remove quenching oils. If the light oxide is removed by dipping in a mild phosphoric acid solution, followed by conversion coating with manganese or iron phosphate, resistance to rusting can be further improved. Gears that have been ground or grit blasted after heat treatment have highly reactive surfaces and are most susceptible to rusting if stored in a humid area without the protection of a rust-preventive coating. Gears that have been washed in strong chemicals and inadvertently exposed to these chemicals for extended periods may exhibit severe corrosion and should be scrapped.

Flaking is classified as a type of wear in which material is removed from the tooth surface in the form of small, very thin wafers or flakes; initially, it is characterized by a dull and slightly rough appearance. Sometimes it can be detected only by the presence of flaked material in the lubricant. Flaking may also be a type of surface fatigue, but more often it is a type of wear associated with the action of combined rolling and sliding. In general, flaking is limited to the softer steels and gear bronzes.

Burning, although not a type of wear, can result in severe wear and surface deterioration. Burning is localized overheating to elevated temperatures caused by excessive friction from overload, overspeed or inadequate lubrication. The temperatures achieved are sufficient to cause discoloration and overtempering or rehardening of hardened steels. Burning may also have an adverse effect on fatigue properties and promote failure by surface fatigue.

Surface-Fatigue Failures

Surface fatigue is the most common mode of gear failure and is characterized by varying degrees of pitting, and sometimes spalling, of tooth surfaces. Unlike wear damage, which (except for abrasive and corrosive wear) is related to inadequate lubrication, surface-fatigue failure can occur even with proper lubrication and results primarily from repeated stressing.

Mechanism of Surface Fatigue. Each time gear teeth go through mesh, rolling and sliding on each other, the surface and subsurface metal is subjected to tensile, compressive, and shear stresses. Figure 18 is a schematic illustration of the stresses between rolls, which are similar to the stresses between gear-tooth surfaces. In Fig. 18(a), the rolls are turning at the same speed, and contact between them is comparable to contact between gear teeth at the pitch line, where there is no sliding. Contact occurs in a flattened band rather than in a line because of elastic deformation under load. The band is in compression, which is maximum at the center. Metal is displaced, forming bulges ahead of and behind the band, and this displacement results in subsurface shear and tensile stresses in the areas indicated. The magnitude of the stresses depends on the modulus of elasticity of the metals, the forces pressing the surfaces together, and the radii of the curved surfaces. The smaller the radius of either surface, the narrower the band of contact and the greater the unit stress.

Figure 18(b) illustrates contact between rolls turning at different speeds, which is comparable to contact between gear teeth away from the pitch line, where both sliding and rolling occur. Frictional forces add to the stresses shown in Fig. 18(a), imposing additional surface compressive and tensile stresses in the areas indicated. Metal at, and for some distance below, the surface is subjected to compression, tension, and shear every time it goes through contact. After what usually is a very large number of

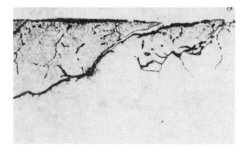

Fig. 19. Micrograph, at 1000×, of a picral-etched specimen showing fatigue cracks that joined below the surface of a steel gear tooth. The eventual result is that small bits of metal are separated from the surface, leaving pits.

Fig. 20. Initial pitting in a steel helical gear. Pitting was confined to the pitch-line area and did not worsen after many millions of stress cycles.

stress repetitions, surface failure may occur. Minute cracks form at and below the surface, grow, and join (see Fig. 19). Eventually, small bits of metal are separated and forced out, leaving pits. Surface fatigue may occur after fewer revolutions if, because of load conditions, stresses are higher than intended.

Initial Pitting. High spots or asperities on tooth surfaces of new gears are stressed highly even under normal loading, and the small areas involved may undergo fatigue in a relatively few cycles and drop out, leaving small pits. When the high spots or asperities are at a distance from the pitch line where both sliding and rolling occur, they may be worn smooth during run-in before fatigue and pitting can occur. On the other hand, at or near the pitch line, where there is rolling but little or no sliding, initial pitting frequently occurs. This often is referred to as "pitch-line pitting" (see Fig. 20). The fact that the direction of sliding reverses at the pitch line also is believed to be a factor in pitch-line pitting.

Initial pitting may be corrective, in that when asperities are removed, stresses are relieved and pitting stops. When this occurs, surfaces usually smooth up with continued operation.

Destructive Pitting. Contact stresses in dedendum areas (that is, below the pitch line) of driving-gear tooth surfaces are higher than those elsewhere because of the shorter radii of tooth curvature. From the initial point of contact, surface stresses decrease as contact moves outward because tooth radii increase. At some point, the number of teeth in contact changes from two pairs to one pair for spur gears of usual design and to a reduced number (but always more than one pair) for helical gears. Here, surface stresses increase sharply to a maximum and again start to decrease as contact moves outward. Whenever gears are overloaded, fatigue failure and destructive pitting of surface metal may occur — usually in dedendum areas of driving teeth and after long periods of operation (Fig. 21). If the overload is great enough,

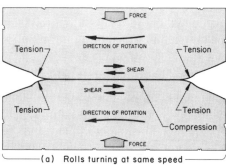

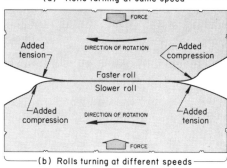

Fig. 18. Schematic illustration of the mechanism of surface fatigue; see text for discussion

Fig. 21. Destructive pitting in (a) a helical pinion and (b) a herringbone gear — both of which were driving gears. In both gears, the destructive pitting is confined to the dedendum area, which is usual for driving gears.

however, this type of pitting can develop in a relatively short period of operation.

At all times, areas of driving and driven teeth in contact with each other are subjected to the same stresses. However, pitting normally occurs first in, and may be restricted to, the dedendum areas of the driving-gear teeth. There are two reasons for this: (a) the driving gear, which usually is smaller in diameter, makes more revolutions, and its teeth, which are fewer in number, are subjected to more stress repetitions; and (b) on the driving-gear teeth, the direction of sliding is opposite to that of rolling between the surfaces, and the resulting stretching of the surface metal promotes growth of fatigue cracks and, eventually, formation of pits.

In progressive (destructive) pitting, pits continue to form and enlarge as edges crumble or as pits break into each other. Eventually, tooth shape may be destroyed, gears may become noisy and rough running, and if the condition progresses to a sufficient degree, teeth may fracture.

In certain components, failure of a critical gear by tooth fracture can have serious consequences. Such a failure in an aircraft engine — particularly during landing or takeoff — can result in loss of life and total destruction of the aircraft. Consequently, every precaution is followed to prevent destructive pitting of critical gears in service. In general, such gears are made of a high-strength, low-alloy steel of premium quality, such as AMS 6263 (AISI 9315). The gears are machined from forged gear blanks and subsequently are gas carburized, hardened and tempered to exacting metallurgical standards. After thorough inspection, they are "green tested" (operated in a test-stand engine for 4 hr under conditions of heavy loading) and then reinspected for evidence of wear, pitting, plastic flow or other abnormalities before being released for assembly in service engines. The following example concerns a pair of critical gears that exhibited evidence of destructive pitting after a 4-hr green test.

Example 2. Failure of Carburized AMS 6263 Steel Impeller Drive Gears Due to Pitting and a Wear Pattern (Fig. 22)

Two intermediate impeller drive gears were submitted for metallurgical examination when they exhibited evidence of pitting and abnormal wear after production tests in test-stand engines. Both gears were made of AMS 6263 steel and were gas carburized, hardened and tempered. The pitting and the wear pattern observed on the teeth of one of the gears (gear A) are shown in Fig. 22.

According to the heat treating specification, the gears were required to satisfy the following requirements: (a) a carburized case depth of 0.015 to 0.025 in., (b) a case hardness of Rockwell 30-N 77 to 80, and (c) a core hardness of Rockwell C 36 to 44.

Fig. 22. Pitting and wear pattern on a carburized AMS 6263 steel impeller drive gear, shown at about 2.3× (Example 2)

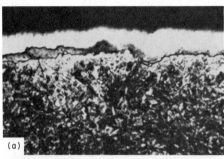

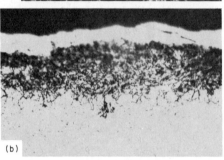

(a) Micrograph, at 500×, of a specimen etched 15 to 20 sec in 2% nital, showing a surface layer of decarburized material. (b) Micrograph, also at 500×, of same specimen repolished and etched 3 sec in 2% nital, showing a heavy subsurface layer of oxide scale. The white band immediately above the decarburized and oxidized layers is electrodeposited nickel, applied to prevent edge-rounding during polishing.

Fig. 23. Metallurgical causes of destructive pitting that occurred in a carburized AMS 6263 steel gear (Example 3)

Investigation. Sections of both gears were removed with a cutoff wheel and examined for hardness, case depth, and microstructure of case and core. Results were as follows:

	Gear A	Gear B
Hardness:		
Case, R_{30-N}	70-73	77-78
Core, R_C	40	40
Case depth, in.	0.020-0.024	0.024-0.028
Microstructure:		
Case	Lean carbon (< 0.85% C)	Normal
Core	Normal	Normal

Both the pitting and the wear pattern were more severe on gear A than on gear B.

Conclusions. Gear A failed because carbon content of the carburized case, and consequently case hardness, were below specification and inadequate for the loads to which

the gear was subjected. The pitting and wear pattern observed on gear B were relatively mild because case carbon content and case hardness were within specified requirements. Nevertheless, it was evident that case depth, as specified, was not adequate for this application — even with case carbon content and hardness being acceptable.

Recommendations. It was recommended that the depth of carburized case on impeller drive gears be increased from 0.015 to 0.025 in. to 0.025 to 0.035 in., an increase that would still allow a minimum of 30% core material across the tooth section at the pitch line. This increase would ensure better load-carrying potential and improved wear resistance. It also was recommended that hardness readings on gears be made using a 60-kg load (Rockwell A scale), and that minimum case-hardness requirement be set at Rockwell A 81, an additional safeguard to ensure adequate load-carrying potential.

Problems in furnace-atmosphere control during carburizing, and inadequate protection against decarburization during austenitizing, are relatively common causes of destructive pitting on heavily loaded gears, as described in the following example.

Example 3. Failure of a Carburized AMS 6263 Steel Generator-Drive Idler Gear by Pitting Due to Decarburization and Subsurface Oxidation (Fig. 23)

Following test-stand engine testing, an idler gear for the generator drive of an aircraft engine exhibited evidence of destructive pitting on the gear teeth in the area of the pitch line; as a consequence, the gear was submitted for metallurgical examination. The gear was made of AMS 6263 steel and was gas carburized to produce a case 0.015 to 0.025 in. deep.

Investigation. Sections of the gear were removed and examined for hardness, case depth, and microstructure of case and core. Results of the examination, and specified requirements, were:

	Required	Actual
Case depth, in.	0.015-0.025	0.024-0.028
Hardness:		
Case, R_{30-N}	77-80	74-76 (R_{15-N} 88-89)
Core, R_C	36-44	40-41

When it was determined that the case hardness of the gear was below specification, additional hardness measurements were made, using a 15-kg load. These measurements confirmed the low hardness and suggested that it had resulted from one or more surface defects.

A specimen from the pitted area of one gear tooth was prepared for metallographic examination. The results of this examination are shown in Fig. 23. When the specimen was etched in 2% nital for 15 to 20 sec, a decarburized surface layer was observed in the vicinity of pitting (Fig. 23a). When the specimen was repolished and then etched in 2% nital for only 3 sec, a heavy subsurface layer of oxide scale was observed in the vicinity of pitting (Fig. 23b).

Conclusions. Based on low case-hardness readings and the results of metallographic examination, it was concluded that pitting had resulted from a combination of surface decarburization and subsurface oxidation. Because of previous failure analyses and thorough investigation of heat treating facilities, the source of these defects was well known. The oxide layer had been developed during the carburizing cycle because the furnace retort had not been adequately purged of air prior to commencement of carburizing. Decarburization had occurred during the austenitizing cycle in a hardening furnace containing an exothermic protective atmosphere because of defects in the copper plating applied to the gear for its protection during austenitizing. These defects had permitted leakage of exothermic atmosphere to portions of the carburized surface, and, because of the low carbon potential of the exothermic atmosphere, the leakage had resulted in decarburization.

Recommendations. It was recommended that, during heat treatment, steps be taken to ensure that furnaces are thoroughly purged prior to carburizing, and that positive atmospheric pressure be maintained throughout the carburizing cycle. Further, it was recommended that more effective control be exercised over all aspects of copper plating of carburized gears, including final inspection, before releasing the gears for hardening.

Figure 24 shows destructive pitting in teeth of a cyanided 5145 steel countergear that failed during a dynamometer test. Although a complete metallurgical analysis of this gear is not available, it is apparent from the pattern of pitting and wear that loading was limited to less than half the available tooth contact surface. Pitting therefore resulted from excessive contact stress due to nonuniform loading.

Spalling. One type of spalling may be considered a type of destructive pitting — the distinction between the two being primarily one of degree. In this type of spalling, a series of small pits are joined by failure of the metal between them, and ultimately a relatively large particle of metal spalls from the surface. Such spalling occurs only after many cycles of operation. When spalling occurs after relatively few cycles, it is not related to destructive pitting, but often is the result of subsurface defects, excessive internal stress due to heat treatment, or severe eccentric overloads. This type of spalling

Fig. 24. Destructive pitting in a cyanided 5145 steel countergear, which was attributed to excessive contact stress due to nonuniform loading

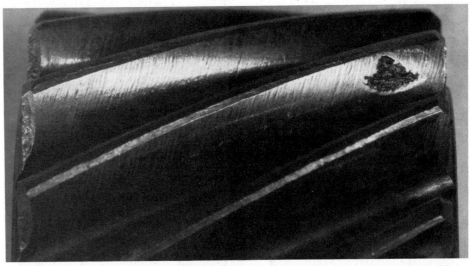

Fig. 25. Two types of spalling on the steel pinion of a hypoid-gear set: at far left, spalling due to extreme overloading at the edges of teeth; at far right (large dark patch), spalling due to destructive pitting

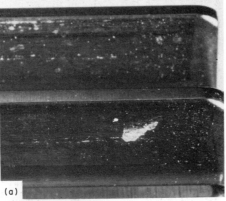

(a)

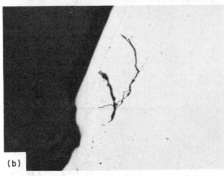

(b)

Fig. 26. (a) Spalling due to destructive pitting, on a tooth of a steel spur sun gear shaft. (b) Micrograph, at 100×, of an unetched section taken through the spalled area, showing progressive subsurface cracking.

most commonly occurs along the top edges or ends of gear teeth, and the resulting cavities often are larger, deeper, and more sharply defined than spalls associated with destructive pitting.

Only rarely are the two types of spalling encountered on the same gear. An exception, the steel pinion of a hypoid-gear set, is shown in Fig. 25. The large spall visible at upper right resulted from destructive pitting that originated at and above the pitch line. However, the spalling that occurred at the edges of the teeth (extreme left in Fig. 25) was the result of extreme overloading at one end of the pinion, later determined to have been caused by dimensional error.

Another instance of the type of spalling that is associated with destructive pitting is shown on a tooth of a steel spur sun gear shaft in Fig. 26(a). Both of the teeth shown bear evidence of pitting; spalling occurred near the pitch line of each of these teeth and on several other teeth in this gear. The gear shaft was subjected to 315 hr of testing under heavy stress loading; the general appearance of the gear teeth is indicative of good alignment, because the pattern of pitting is uniform. A micrograph of a section through the spalled area of the tooth is shown in Fig. 26(b) and illustrates the progressive subsurface cracking that precedes this type of spalling.

Extreme eccentric overloading will cause tooth-edge spalling in a relatively short period of time. The micrograph in Fig. 27 shows subsurface fatigue cracking, which subsequently led to spalling, in an aircraft-engine gear after 4 hr of operation in a test-stand engine. Spall-

This micrograph, at 500×, shows an unetched section of a carburized AMS 6260 steel gear tooth. Cracking initiated in the transition zone between the carburized case and the core.

Fig. 27. Subsurface cracking that subsequently resulted in spalling at a gear-tooth edge due to eccentric overloading

ing occurred at the tooth edge — an area remote from the normal contact area on the flank of the tooth. This gear was made of AMS 6260 steel and was gas carburized. The cracking initiated in the transition zone between carburized case and core.

Spall-Like Indications. Occasionally, spall-like indications on gear teeth (particularly on edges or lands) are attributed incorrectly to spalling on the basis of appearance alone. The carburized steel gear shown in Fig. 28 was one of several that were removed from service when spall-like indications were noted on the lands and corners of their teeth. Complete metallurgical analysis of this gear revealed that it had acceptable case depth, case hardness, core hardness and microstructure, and that the spall-like indications had been caused by flaking of an adherent oxide coating the source of which could not be determined. The coating was removed by grit blasting without damaging the gear teeth. After blasting, the remaining gears were inspected by the magnetic-particle method and were found to be free of cracks or other surface defects. They were returned to service, and their performance thereafter is reported as satisfactory.

Spalling and Plastic Flow. One type of spalling does not entail surface fatigue exclusively, but rather reflects the combined effects of surface fatigue and plastic flow. Spalling that accompanies plastic flow is discussed under "Plastic Flow and Spalling", on the next page.

Surface Fatigue and Lubrication. Although surface fatigue is associated primarily with strength and resilience of gear materials, it may not be completely independent of the lubricant. In carefully controlled experiments, it has been demonstrated that fatigue occurs earlier with some lubricants than with others.

Fig. 28. Spall-like indications (shown at 4×) on the lands of teeth of a carburized steel gear. It was determined that the indications had been caused by flaking of an adherent oxide coating and would not affect performance of the gear.

Fig. 29. An instance of rolling and peening in which the ends and top lands of steel gear teeth have been deformed to feather edges

Unfortunately, the practical significance of this research has not been resolved. Experiments with rolling disks have shown that some lubricant is necessary for a growing surface crack to form a pit. In another investigation, an increase in lubricant viscosity delayed pitting whereas use of a surface-active extreme-pressure lubricant had no noticeable effect. In general, it is agreed that surface fatigue is related primarily to gear design and material, and that the lubricant usually is a relatively minor factor.

Plastic-Flow Failures

The term "plastic flow" refers to surface deformation of gear-tooth metal as a result of yielding under heavy loads, frequently impact loads. Although more commonly associated with soft, ductile metals, failure by plastic flow also occurs in through-hardened and case-hardened steels. Plastic flow is always the result of a gear being loaded above the yield stress of the metal in the contact zone. Three major types of plastic flow in gears are rolling and peening, rippling, and ridging. Plastic flow may be accompanied by surface-fatigue damage, such as destructive pitting or spalling, although plastic flow and fatigue are distinctly different phenomena. Plastic flow also may precede or accompany breakage.

Rolling and Peening. If compressive loading is high, if vibration causes high peak loading, or if improper tooth action produces high impact loading, gear-tooth surfaces can become rolled and peened, especially if they are relatively soft. The

rolling and peening resemble what occurs when the head of a cold chisel or a rivet is peened by repeated blows. In gears, rolling and peening are characterized by fins at the top edges or ends of teeth (not to be confused with burrs from cutting or shaving), by badly rounded tooth tips, or by a depression in the surface of the driving gear at the start of single-tooth contact, with a raised ridge near the pitch line of the mating (driven) gear. The remaining portions of teeth usually are deformed to a considerable degree before complete destruction occurs. Although the cause of failure lies with gear material or loading, or both, higher-viscosity oil can help in cushioning blows and thereby extending gear life. The feather edges at the ends and top lands of the gear teeth shown in Fig. 29 resulted from rolling and peening of a gear metal that was too soft for the intended application.

Failures caused by rolling and peening are easy to recognize and, in general, easy to correct. Usually, correction consists of selecting a somewhat harder (and stronger) gear material or, for through-hardening steels, specifying a higher surface hardness or resorting to a method of case hardening, such as flame or induction hardening, to obtain a considerably higher surface hardness.

Although failure of carburized steel gears from rolling and peening is relatively uncommon, such failure can occur if the surface hardness of the carburized gear teeth is substandard. Among the common causes of low surface hardness are (*a*) a carburized case with "lean" carbon content, (*b*) surface decarburization, and (*c*) inadvertent failure to harden after carburizing — an oversight that is more likely to occur when gears are carburized and austenitized on a batch basis in different furnaces.

Damage by rolling and peening may be reduced by lowering the gear loading (and thereby reducing tooth loading) or by reducing shock loading, if shock loading is due to some external condition. In some instances, where oil viscosity has been too low (as a result, for example, of high-temperature operation), it has been possible to arrest plastic flow by changing to an oil of higher viscosity. The more viscous oil has provided better cushioning and a thicker oil film with improved friction-reducing ability.

Rippling (see Fig. 30), another type of damage that occurs by plastic flow, is a wavelike pattern on the tooth surface at right angles to the direction of sliding and is caused by shearing stresses (rather than compressive stresses) at the surface of the metal. Sometimes, these stresses can be relieved by changing to a lubricant with a lower coefficient of friction.

Rippling occurs mostly on case-hardened hypoid gears. In general, it does not lead to immediate failure, but rather is an indication of excessive loading and should serve as a warning of possible future failure. Vibration is also known to cause rippling.

Ridging, shown in Fig. 31, is the most severe form of plastic flow that may occur on case-hardened steel hypoid pinions and bronze worm gears. Usually, it appears as diagonal lines or ridges across the tooth surface, but may be characterized by a herringbone or fishtail pattern oriented in the direction of sliding. If ridging progresses, the surface metal is continually reworked, which results in pitting and ultimate fatigue-type failure. In general, ridging is associated with excessive loading or inadequate lubrication, or both.

Plastic Flow and Pitting. The carburized steel gear shown in Fig. 32(a) failed by both plastic flow and destructive pitting. The gear, approximately 4 in. in diameter and 1½ in. wide, was made of AMS 6260 steel and was carburized to a depth of 0.025 to 0.035 in. However, by an error in machining, an excessive amount of stock was removed from the drive faces of the teeth (see Fig. 32b). Stock removal reduced case depth on the drive faces to approximately 0.010 in. Because this shallow case was incapable of supporting the loads to which it was subjected, the drive faces of the gear teeth were deformed by plastic flow and severely pitted.

Plastic Flow and Spalling. The carburized steel differential side gear shown in Fig. 33 failed by a combination of plastic flow and spalling. This failure was attributed to use of a carburizing steel (4027) that produced a core hardness (Rockwell C 22 to 27) inadequate for supporting the carburized case indefinitely. The failed gear was removed from a vehicle after 18,698 miles of service. Corrective action consisted of changing the gear material to 8625 steel with a core hardness of about Rockwell C 40.

Plastic Flow and Cracking. The splined end of a tailshaft (see Fig. 34) failed as a result of excessively high torsional loads during start-up of a radial reciprocating aircraft engine. Failure occurred by a combination of severe plastic flow and cracking of the spline teeth. The tailshaft, which was about 14 in. long and 3 in. in diameter, was made of AMS 6263 steel. The splined end was carburized to a depth of 0.015 to 0.025 in. Surface hardness of the spline teeth was required to be equivalent to Rockwell C 60 to 63. Failure was attributed to torsional overloading.

Case crushing, which also combines plastic flow and cracking, is a form of plastic-flow failure that occurs in carburized gears. The most common cause of case crushing is insufficient case depth for a given core hardness and service

load, although the condition may also result from severe overloading or from a large radius of curvature on the tooth profile. In case crushing, the hard metal of the case is forced down into the softer core metal, which deforms plastically. Case crushing is accompanied by cracking. The cracks extend from the surface into the core material and often progress across most of the gear-tooth face with no evidence of pitting. In general, the cracks are not limited to the addendum or dedendum portions of the tooth, but extend over most of the tooth surface.

Case crushing is commonly corrected by increasing the depth of the carburized case. Selecting a steel with higher hardenability will permit heat treating to higher core hardness and strength, which also may eliminate case crushing.

Breakage Failures

"Breakage" usually refers to fracture of an entire gear tooth or a substantial portion of a tooth. In this discussion, however, cracking (the onset of breakage) is considered a type of breakage, because, from a practical standpoint, a cracked gear tooth is essentially as unserviceable as a broken gear tooth.

The American Standard B6.12 classifies tooth breakage as fatigue, heavy-

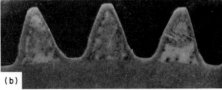

Fig. 32. (a) Damage involving both plastic flow and destructive pitting on teeth of a carburized AMS 6260 steel gear. (b) Etched end face of the gear, showing excessive stock removal from drive faces of teeth.

Fig. 33. Tooth damage involving both plastic flow and spalling. The core hardness of this carburized 4027 steel gear was not high enough to support normal loading in service.

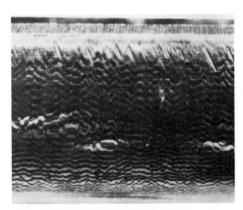

Fig. 30. Rippling, a wavelike pattern on a gear-tooth surface at right angles to the direction of sliding

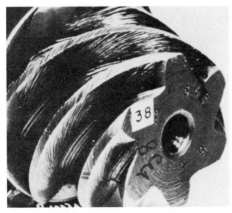

Fig. 31. Ridging on a heavily loaded hypoid gear made of case-hardened steel

Fig. 34. Splined end of AMS 6263 steel tailshaft, carburized to a depth of 0.015 to 0.025 in., showing damage involving severe plastic flow and cracking of spline teeth. Damage was caused by torsional overloading.

wear or overload breakage. It is important to be able to distinguish breakage failures due to tooth fatigue from breakage failures resulting from other initial causes.

Fatigue Breakage. Gear teeth are loaded as cantilever beams, with loading being applied along contacting surfaces. Gear teeth are shaped such that an applied load causes maximum bending stress in the root area of the tooth. Thus, any tooth that breaks off at the root has failed from bending. In some bending-fatigue failures, a crack that starts in the root may propagate upward toward the tip of the tooth. Such a crack usually can be traced to its origin by beach marks on the fracture surface. (Beach marks are circular or semicircular ripples concentric with the origin of the crack, and are reliable indicators of the site of crack initiation.)

Fatigue breakage is the most common type of breakage failure. The repeated bending stresses that exceed the endurance limit of the material and that cause fatigue breakage may result from a variety of factors, including poor design, misalignment, overload, and inadvertent stress raisers such as notches or surface or subsurface defects.

Most gears designed for maximum fatigue strength are case hardened by carburizing, a treatment intended to provide an extremely hard and wear-resistant surface layer supported by a tough core. This combination provides a surface layer that is in a state of residual compression as a result of the different rates of expansion and contraction of case and core during hardening. Because gear fatigue failures initiate at surfaces subjected to high tensile stresses, the residual compressive stresses in the carburized case, which are balanced by corresponding tensile stresses in the core, must be exceeded before a fatigue crack can be initiated. The advantages of carburizing can be canceled, however, if this optimum stress relationship is altered, as occurs in a gear designed with acute-angle intersections that, when carburized, are essentially through hardened. As described in the following example, these through-hardened areas are prone to fatigue breakage.

Example 4. Fatigue Breakage of a Carburized 4817 Steel Spiral Bevel Gear at Acute-Angle Intersections of Mounting Holes and Tooth-Root Fillets (Fig. 35)

A spiral bevel gear set was returned to the manufacturer because the gear broke into three pieces after about two years of service. Damage to the pinion was minor. The gear broke along the root of a tooth intersected by three of the six 0.875-in.-diam holes (see Fig. 35) used to mount the gear to a hub.

The intersection of the hole and root fillet created an acute-angle condition, as shown in section A-A in Fig. 35.

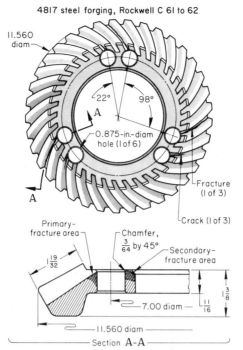

Fig. 35. Carburized 4817 steel spiral bevel gear that broke from fatigue at acute-angle intersections of mounting holes and tooth-root fillets as a result of through hardening (Example 4)

The ring gear, machined from a forged blank made of 4817 steel, had been gas carburized at 925 C (1700 F), cooled to 815 C (1500 F), press quenched in oil at 60 C (140 F) and then tempered at 175 C (350 F) for 1½ hr to produce a case hardness of Rockwell C 61 to 62, as measured at a tooth land.

Investigation. Examination of the gear revealed fatigue progression for about ¼ in. at acute-angle intersections of three mounting holes with the root fillets of three teeth. Subsequent fracture was increasingly rapid until the entire section failed. Cracking between the holes and the bore of the gear started before the tooth section failed.

Magnetic-particle inspection revealed cracks at the intersections of the remaining three mounting holes and the adjacent tooth-root fillets.

Microstructure of the carburized and hardened case was fine acicular martensite

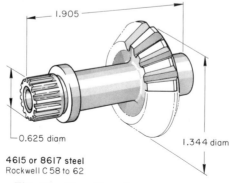

4615 or 8617 steel
Rockwell C 58 to 62

Fig. 36. Aircraft-engine governor gear that failed by fatigue because of insufficient clearance and irregular tooth form (Example 5)

with about 5% retained austenite. The core was composed principally of low-carbon martensite.

Metallographic examination revealed that the acute-angle intersections of the mounting holes and tooth-root fillets were carburized to a depth that comprised the entire cross section and, consequently, were through hardened.

Conclusions. The gear failed in fatigue; slowly to a depth of about ¼ in., then rapidly until final fracture. Design of the gear and placement of the mounting holes were contributing factors in the failure, because they resulted in through hardening at the acute-angle intersections of the mounting holes and tooth-root fillets.

The next example describes another fatigue-breakage failure involving gear design. This failure was attributed to insufficient tooth clearance and irregular tooth form, although a less-than-optimum heat treatment of the gear may have been a contributory factor.

Example 5. Fatigue-Breakage Failure of an Alloy Steel Governor Gear Because of Insufficient Clearance and Irregular Tooth Form (Fig. 36)

A governor gear from an aircraft engine (see Fig. 36), a driven gear, failed after ½ hr of operation. The engines on the aircraft had run for 500 hr, but the governors had been changed recently to improve synchronization. The mating (driving) gear on the engine, not supplied with exchange governors, also failed. At no time was the governor frozen and unable to rotate.

Both gears were returned to the laboratory to determine the sequence and mechanism of failure.

Specifications required the gears to be made of 4615 or 8617 aircraft-quality steel and to be carburized (Rockwell C 58 to 62) to a depth of 0.005 to 0.020 in.

Investigation revealed that four teeth and parts of two others were missing from the governor gear, and that six teeth and parts of two others were missing from the engine gear. The pressure faces of the engine gear were polished as a result of normal loading. There was no fatigue spalling at the pitch line, and the machining marks in the addendum were polished but still evident. On the nonpressure faces, considerable abrasion had occurred in the addendum, erasing the machining marks and slightly rounding the tip corners.

All teeth that had broken from the engine (driving) gear had fractured in the direction of normal loading, with initial fracture in tension and final fracture in shear. This mode of failure was substantiated by the brittle (case) and fibrous (core) fracture surfaces on the tension side, and the smooth, satiny fracture surface on the shear side. All of the fracture surfaces were free from discoloration. There was no evidence of cracking in the remaining teeth.

On the governor (driven) gear, a wear pattern was observed similar to that on the engine gear. Wear on the pressure face at the pitch line was moderate; but progressing toward the tip, the wear increased with severe scoring at the tip because of contact with a mating gear. On the nonpressure face, there was a general condition of pitch-line fatigue with the associated spalling. Two of the teeth that had fractured exhibited a fatigue-tension-shear type of failure. The third tooth had the appearance of fatigue-tension failure. The fourth tooth failed in tension-shear with no evidence of fatigue. The fourth tooth was the only one that failed in the direction of the normal driving force.

In each of the teeth where fatigue cracking was evident, cracking occurred at the root of the teeth on the nonpressure side. Because fatigue can occur only under conditions of tensile loading, cracking must have been the result of the force that caused the pitch-line spalling on the nonpressure face, acting to bend the tooth in the direction opposite to normal loading. One tooth that was partly broken off in the direction opposite to normal loading was removed with a hammer so that the fracture surface could be examined. A fatigue crack to a depth of 0.060 in. was observed at the root of the tooth on the nonpressure side. The fatigue portion of the surface was discolored, but the remainder of the surface was unstained. The fatigue-fracture surfaces on the other teeth exhibited a similar but faint discoloration. Of the 15 teeth on the gear, seven exhibited evidence of a fatigue crack at the root on the nonpressure side of the tooth.

The governor gear, which appeared to be brittle, had a surface hardness of Rockwell C 61 and a core hardness of Rockwell C 41. These hardness values indicated that the gear may have been direct quenched from the carburizing temperature instead of being quenched from the proper hardening temperature.

A comparison of the two gears showed that the governor gear was more brittle than the engine gear.

Two new gears from stock were checked for tooth profile, cracks and burrs. Examination at a magnification of eight diameters revealed that the tooth profile was irregular and not of the proper geometry. One gear had large burrs at the roots of two teeth. Cracks or other defects that could cause tooth failure were not evident.

Several used gears waiting to be reassembled into governors also were checked. The condition of the teeth varied from lightly to moderately worn. All of the gears had been inspected using the magnetic-particle method after being removed from the previous governor and showed no evidence of cracking. However, tool marks along the roots of the teeth could have resulted in misinterpretation of any indications.

Conclusions. Failure of the gear was caused by fatigue of the metal at the roots of the teeth on the nonpressure side. One tooth broke loose from the governor gear and caused the other teeth of the two gears to be torn out. Insufficient clearance was the major cause of failure.

With a tougher core structure, the governor gear would have been less likely to develop a fatigue crack. The condition resulting from heat treatment may have had a marginal effect on the failure. However, without the fatigue crack, gross failure would not have occurred.

Irregularities in tooth form on the gears in stock indicated that the teeth were unsatisfactory for the load. Examination at a magnification of eight diameters showed

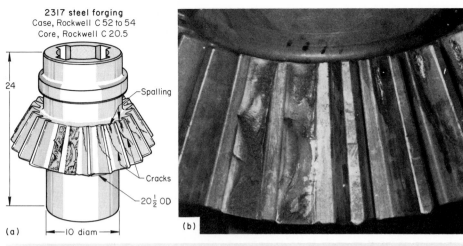

2317 steel forging
Case, Rockwell C 52 to 54
Core, Rockwell C 20.5

Fig. 37. (a) *Bevel pinion, forged from 2317 steel, that failed by fatigue breakage of teeth.* (b) *View of area where two teeth broke off at the root.* (c) *Fracture surface of a broken tooth, showing fatigue marks.* (Example 6)

that the tooth form was wavy, and revealed a drop-off of involute profile three-fourths of the distance along the cut.

The next example describes a bevel pinion used in a steel-plant edging mill, which failed by fatigue breakage caused by severe cyclic shock loading resulting from misalignment with the mating gear.

Example 6. Fatigue-Breakage Failure of a Carburized 2317 Steel Bevel Pinion Because of Misalignment (Fig. 37)

The bevel pinion shown in Fig. 37(a) was part of a drive unit in an edging mill. The pinion had been in service about three months when several teeth failed. Specifications required that the pinion be made from a 2317 steel forging and that the teeth be carburized and hardened to a case hardness of 75 scleroscope (Rockwell C 56) and a core hardness of 250 Bhn (Rockwell C 24.5).

Investigation. Chemical analysis of the metal in the pinion showed that it was 2317 steel as specified. Case hardness was 70 to 72 scleroscope (Rockwell C 52 to 54), and core hardness was 229 Bhn (Rockwell C 20.5). Both hardness values were slightly lower than specified, but acceptable.

Visual inspection of the pinion showed that two teeth had broken off at the root, as shown in Fig. 37(b). The surfaces of these fractures exhibited fatigue marks extending across almost the entire tooth, as shown in Fig. 37(c). Magnetic-particle inspection of the pinion showed that all of the teeth were cracked. Each crack had initiated at the tooth root, on the toe (small) end of the

tooth, extending to the center of the crown. Spalling was also noted on the pressure (drive) side of each tooth at the toe end. A metallographic specimen taken transversely through a broken tooth showed it to be case carburized to a depth of $\frac{3}{16}$ in., hardened and tempered.

Conclusions. The pinion failed by fatigue breakage. Some mechanical misalignment of the pinion with the mating gear caused a cyclic shock load to be applied to the toe ends of the teeth, as exhibited by the spalling. This continuous pounding caused the teeth to crack at the roots and finally break off.

Location of Tooth Breakage. In failures involving breakage of gear teeth, the location of breakage on the tooth can be of significance in helping to determine the cause of failure or in establishing the failure mechanism. Locations at which gear teeth commonly break are: root fillets or roots, corners or ends, and top lands.

Maximum contact loading in gears generally occurs at midface on the teeth, and it is possible for fractures to originate in these regions. When breakage occurs at root fillets, it generally is indicative of severe overloading. The coarseness of the root-fillet fractures shown in Fig. 38(a) indicates that they were caused by single shock loads or by relatively few high-level loads. Fatigue fractures also can originate at root fillets, which are the portions of teeth subjected to the

Fig. 38. Broken gear teeth in which fracture originated at root fillets: (a) by sudden shock loading, and (b) by fatigue

Fig. 39. Breakage at one end of a gear tooth, caused by misalignment

highest bending stress. The relatively smooth beach marks on the fracture surfaces in Fig. 38(b) are characteristic of slow crack propagation.

Figure 39 shows breakage at one end of a gear tooth, typical of breakage resulting from misalignment. Among the common causes of misalignment are an excessive deviation in lead when the gear teeth were cut, elastic deflection of the shaft or of the gear housing, excessive bearing clearance, and inaccuracies in bore alignment.

Fatigue breakage at the top lands of gear teeth, such as that shown on the pinion teeth in Fig. 40, occurs on heavily loaded gears with a tooth profile that does not allow for tooth deflection under load. The tooth top land is the first point of contact, and therefore is most vulnerable to fracture. The solution to this problem is design modification to relieve the gear addenda and the pinion dedenda.

Fatigue Breakage Caused by Stress Raisers. Mechanical notches in the form of grooves or tool marks, and metallurgical notches in the form of surface and subsurface defects, are common stress raisers that may contribute to fatigue breakage of gear teeth. In general, the source of such stress raisers usually can be traced to faulty processing or defective material, although design features such as inadequate fillet radii at the roots

of teeth also constitute mechanical notches that promote breakage failure.

Figure 41 shows a fatigue fracture that was caused by an undercut, or groove, in the root-fillet area of a spur-gear tooth. The undercut, indicated by the

Fig. 40. Breakage at the top lands of pinion teeth, which occurred because tooth profile did not allow for deflection under load

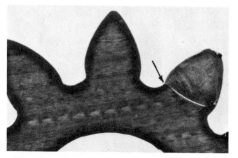

Fig. 41. Fatigue fracture in spur-gear tooth that initiated at an undercut, or a groove (arrow), in root-fillet area of tooth

arrow in Fig. 41, was generated during shaving, because the profile of the shaving tool was faulty. The spur gear, made from an AMS 6260 steel forging, was carburized, hardened and tempered after machining. However, the defective root profile was not detected in final inspection. The fracture shown in Fig. 41 occurred by bending fatigue; the origin of fracture was the notch on the loaded (left) side of the tooth. The fracture propagated transversely across the tooth.

Too small fillet radii at the roots of gear teeth resulted in the failure shown in Fig. 42. The cracks that developed at the tooth roots of this carburized steel gear progressed radially inward toward the center of the gear. Figure 42 shows a section of the gear after rough grinding.

The source of the defect that resulted in the failure shown in Fig. 43 is relatively uncommon. Breakage of this internal-spline tooth was caused by a defect developed during forging. The defect, known as a forging burst, developed well below the surface and was not detected by the nondestructive testing applied to this gear. The forging burst occupied the area bounded by the arrows in Fig. 43.

Inclusions probably are the most common metallurgical stress raisers. The fatigue failure shown in Fig. 44 originated at the large subsurface inclusion indicated by the arrow. In this instance, fatigue cracking was initiated in the rim of the gear, rather than in the gear teeth. The crack was detected by magnetic-particle inspection following engine testing.

Another type of metallurgical stress raiser that can develop in the teeth of carburized or nitrided steel gears and lead to fatigue breakage is cracking at the case-core interface, as shown in Fig. 45. The cracks shown resulted from transformation of retained austenite in this carburized steel gear when the gear was refrigerated following heat treatment. The cracks are crescent-shaped and, when subjected to loading, progress in fatigue across the tooth section until breakage occurs. These cracks are referred to as "internal" quench cracks, and may also develop as a result of quenching at too drastic a rate or quenching from too high a temperature.

Breakage From Heavy Wear. This type of breakage is more properly classified as wear failure, because the role of breakage in ultimate failure, obviously, is secondary and the contribution of wear to failure is primary. Thus, for example, heavy abrasive or corrosive wear may remove enough metal from gear teeth to reduce the tooth section and the load-bearing capacity of the tooth to the point where breakage is inevitable. Severe pitting, caused by surface fatigue, may also lead to breakage.

Fig. 42. Radial fatigue breakage initiating in the small fillet radii at the roots of teeth of a carburized steel gear

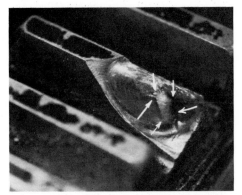

Fig. 43. Breakage of an internal-spline tooth caused by a forging burst

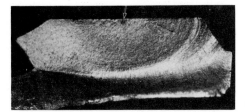

Fig. 44. Fatigue fracture that initiated in the rim of a gear at a large subsurface inclusion (arrow)

Overload breakage may or may not involve fatigue; from the standpoint of failure analysis, the distinction is very important. Overload breakage involving fatigue was discussed earlier in this article in the section dealing with fatigue breakage. Overload breakage that does not involve fatigue is not a common type of failure but may result from (*a*) sudden shock overload, (*b*) wedging of teeth due to bearing failure, (*c*) shaft bending, or (*d*) the introduction of large pieces of foreign matter between mating gears. The fracture surface produced by overload breakage does not exhibit the crack progression characteristic of fatigue failure; instead, it has a silky appearance in the harder and more brittle metals and a fibrous and torn appearance without definite pattern in the more ductile metals. When several teeth or parts of teeth break out, examination may show that the first break was the result

of fatigue and that other breaks occurred subsequently as a result of the debris and shock loading caused by the broken tooth.

In carburized steel gears, overload breakage involving impact often produces a characteristic fracture that initiates at the root fillet on the loaded side of the tooth, cracking through the carburized case, and then progresses across the more ductile core section, emerging near the root fillet on the unloaded side of the tooth. The fracture surface that is exposed with the removal of the tooth is convex and is sometimes referred to as a "hump-type" fracture.

Cracking. In an earlier section of this article dealing with damage resulting from plastic flow, it is indicated that cracking sometimes accompanies severe plastic flow. Cracking that results from abusive processing — notably, grinding cracks and quenching cracks — is a more common type of damage, and, if not detected before the gear is placed in service, it usually leads to breakage. Finally, cracking may result from a feature of gear design that contributes to an increase in internal stresses or lowers the strength of the gear, or both.

Grinding Cracks. One of the hazards of grinding cracks is that sometimes they do not appear until the affected surface has been subjected to loading; consequently, they may escape detection even when postmanufacturing inspection is rigorous. Grinding cracks are fine surface cracks that usually follow a definite pattern or network. They are developed during grinding and are caused by use of an incorrect wheel, grinding speed or feed, or — in the case of hardenable steels, especially those of high carbon content — by transformation of retained austenite to martensite as a result of the stresses imposed by grinding or by formation of untempered "white" martensite as a result of localized overheating and "self-quenching". Grinding cracks can be origins of fatigue breakage or fatigue-induced spalling.

The internal gear shown in Fig. 46 illustrates three phenomena commonly

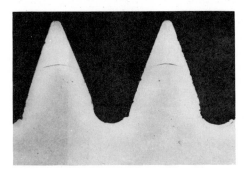

Fig. 45. Internal cracking at the case-core interface in a carburized steel gear, which resulted from transformation of retained austenite

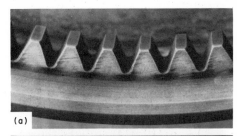

(a) Dark pattern of grinding burns, developed by etching. (b) Grinding cracks (at arrows) at roots of teeth. (c) Surface of fatigue fracture that was nucleated by a grinding crack, which is indicated by two small arrows.

Fig. 46. Damage caused by abusive grinding of a carburized AMS 6260 steel gear

associated with grinding: grinding burns, grinding cracks and fatigue breakage. This gear, approximately 6 in. in diameter and 1½ in. wide, was made of AMS 6260 steel and was subsequently carburized, hardened and tempered prior to final grinding of the end faces of the gear. When the gear was etched in an acid solution used to detect grinding burns, the dark pattern of burns shown in Fig. 46(a) was observed. Note that the most pronounced burning on the gear end face occurred at the bases of teeth.

When the gear was inspected by the magnetic-particle method, fine grinding cracks (at arrows in Fig. 46b) were observed at the roots of some of the gear teeth. These hairline cracks are accentuated markedly by the magnetic-particle fluid. The cracks were attributed to the volume change that accompanies transformation. The surface of a fatigue fracture that was nucleated by one of the grinding cracks is shown in Fig. 46(c). The grinding crack is indicated by the arrows at the upper right corner of the fracture surface.

Quench cracks result from excessive internal stresses developed during quenching from the austenitizing temperature and, like grinding cracks, can be origins of fatigue breakage. Usually they are visible hairline cracks that run across the tooth land, follow along the radius in

Fig. 47. Quench cracks extending across tooth lands and radiating from tooth roots

Fig. 48. Broken steel spur gear that fractured by fatigue. Cracking originated in the vicinity of two oil holes, which were located in a tooth root.

the tooth root, or follow a random direction at the ends of teeth. Typical quench cracks are shown in Fig. 47. If the cracks are large, the gear may fail in service after relatively few cycles in a manner similar to overload breakage. In general, quench cracks are caused by excessive austenitizing temperatures or quenching rates, uneven cooling during quenching, or undue restraint during cooling.

Design-Related Cracking. Oil holes, keyways, thin webs and sharp corners are among the design features that can contribute to cracking. In general, design-related cracking can be traced to mechanical stress raisers or inadequate strength, or both. Placement of oil holes in gears can be of critical importance to the performance and reliability of the gear. Oil holes at the roots of gear teeth can contribute to cracking and premature breakage. The steel spur gear shown in Fig. 48 developed fatigue cracks in the vicinity of two oil holes at the root of a tooth after a short period of service; the cracks propagated rapidly from the tooth root to the bore of the gear.

Fig. 49. Thin-shell steel pinion that fractured at an internal keyway

Failure of the steel pinion shown in Fig. 49 resulted from a combination of unfavorable design factors. The wall thickness of this hollow pinion was marginal, at best, for the loads imposed on the teeth. Even more critical, however, was placement of a keyway in the thin wall. The notch effect at the base of the keyway produced a fatigue crack across the width of the gear, and through fracture occurred shortly thereafter.

Statistics on Types and Causes of Gear Failure

Gear-failure statistics based on adequate sampling are of value in failure analysis because they provide an over-all view of the types and causes of gear failure and the relative frequencies with which they occur.

A leading manufacturer of steel gears has prepared a statistical gear-failure report based on a total of 931 failures that occurred over a period of 35 years. All failures were classified by both type and cause; results, in percentages, are summarized in Table 1.

Types of Failure. As shown in Table 1, breakage accounted for the largest percentage of the gear failures (61.2%), followed by surface fatigue (20.3%), wear

Table 1. Summary of a Statistical Report on Types and Causes of 931 Gear Failures Over a 35-Year Period

Types of Failure, %	
Breakage, total	61.2
Fatigue breakage, teeth	32.8
Fatigue breakage, bore	4.0
Overload breakage, teeth	19.5
Overload breakage, bore	0.6
Chipping, teeth	4.3
Surface fatigue, total	20.3
Pitting	7.2
Spalling	6.8
Pitting-and-spalling	6.3
Wear, total	13.2
Abrasive wear	10.3
Adhesive wear	2.9
Plastic flow, total	5.3

Causes of Failure, %	
Service-related causes, total	74.7
Improper assembly	21.2
Improper lubrication	11.0
Continual overloading	25.0
Impact loading	13.9
Bearing failure	0.7
Foreign material	1.4
Operator error	0.3
Abusive handling	1.2
Heat treatment, total	16.2
Excessive core hardness	0.5
Insufficient core hardness	2.0
Excessive case depth	1.8
Insufficient case depth	4.8
Improper hardening	5.9
Improper tempering	1.0
Distortion	0.2
Design-related causes, total	6.9
Improper design	2.8
Improper material selection	1.6
Specification of unsuitable heat treatment	2.5
Manufacturing-related causes, total	1.4
Grinding burns	0.7
Tool marks or notches	0.7
Material-related causes, total	0.8
Forging defects	0.1
Steel defects	0.5
Mixed steel or wrong composition	0.2

(13.2%) and plastic flow (5.3%). Most breakage failures involved gear teeth; tooth breakage by fatigue (32.8%) was more common than tooth breakage by overload (19.5%).

Causes of Failure. As shown in Table 1, the majority of the gear failures were service related (74.7%). The two principal causes of failure were continual overloading (25.0%) and improper assembly (21.2%). Faulty heat treatment was the next most common cause of failure (16.2%), followed by errors in design (6.9%), manufacturing defects (1.4%) and material defects (0.8%).

Failures of Boilers and
Related Steam-Power-Plant Equipment

By the ASM Committee on Failures of Pressure Vessels, Boilers and Pressure Piping*

FAILURES in boilers and other equipment in stationary and marine power plants that use steam as the working fluid are discussed in this article. The discussion is mainly concerned with failures in Rankine-cycle systems that use fossil fuels or a nuclear reactor as the primary heat source, although many of the principles that apply to Rankine-cycle systems apply also to systems using other steam cycles or to systems using working fluids other than steam.

Procedures for Failure Analysis

Procedures for analysis of failures in steam power plants do not differ significantly from procedures for failure analysis in general or for analysis of specific types of failure. These procedures are presented in other articles in this volume, particularly those dealing with basic mechanisms of failure, failures of specific product forms (such as castings, forgings, weldments and pressure vessels), and elevated-temperature failures. Consequently, this article discusses the main types of failure that occur in steam-power-plant equipment, with major emphasis on the distinctive features of each type that enable a failure analyst to determine cause and to suggest corrective action.

Service Records. Most power-plant operators maintain records that are relatively complete. Records of operating conditions and preventive maintenance for a component that has failed, and for the system as a whole, are relatively good sources of background information. These records can provide valuable information, such as: (*a*) operating temperature and pressure, (*b*) normal power output, (*c*) fluctuations in steam demand, (*d*) composition of fuel, (*e*) amount of excess combustion air, (*f*) type and amount of water-conditioning chemicals added, (*g*) type and amount of contaminants in condensate and make-up feedwater, and (*h*) frequency and methods of cleaning fire-side and water-side surfaces of steam generators.

Precautions in On-Site Examination. Power plants are vital to most industries, and power-plant downtime has an adverse effect on the entire operation. Thus, the individual making the on-site examination should have experience in making preliminary determinations of cause and recommending corrective action on the spot.

Certain deductions, such as the exact cause or mechanism of failure, frequently cannot be made without laboratory examination. However, some determinations — for example, which of several damaged components failed first — can be made on the basis of careful on-site examination. The relationship of the location of the failure to the locations of other system components — for instance, the location of a tube rupture in relation to those of burners or soot blowers — is an important phase of on-site examination.

It usually is helpful for the individual making the on-site examination to have an assortment of plastic bags or paper envelopes in which samples can be placed. Identification of each sample, with its location marked on photographs or sketches, is recommended, because the failed component usually must be repaired or replaced with as little delay as possible so that normal system operation can be resumed. This need for prompt return to service also may preclude a second on-site examination, and therefore the first examination should be thorough and complete.

Precautions in Sampling. Because of the massive size and the fixed, sometimes remote location of power plants, detailed examination usually cannot be carried out at the scene and must be performed on selected samples taken from the failed equipment. The methods used in obtaining samples for laboratory examination thus are of utmost importance. For instance, if the failure involves rupture of one or more boiler or superheater tubes, there is a high probability that adjacent tubes may have been degraded by the same conditions that led to the ruptures. Samples from adjacent, apparently undamaged tubes should be taken, so that the total extent of damage can be assessed.

The effect of the method of sample removal should be considered when choosing the size and location of samples. Mechanical methods of sample removal, such as cutting with a tube cutter, sawing or drilling, are less likely to alter microstructure than is flame cutting. Mechanical methods, although generally preferred, are slow and sometimes cannot be used because samples are inaccessible to the necessary tools; flame cutting may be the only reasonable alternative method. When flame cutting is used, larger samples are necessary than when mechanical methods are used, and cuts must be made farther from the location of interest.

Corrosion frequently is associated with failure in steam-power-plant equipment, but the active corrosive agent is not always obvious. Consequently, collection and preservation of corrosion products (particularly loose, flaky or powdery deposits) may be vital, because chemical analysis of corrosion products can be the key factor in determination of cause.

Characteristic Causes of Failure in Steam Equipment

Boilers and other types of steam-power-plant equipment are subject to a wide variety of failures involving one or

*G. M. SLAUGHTER, *Chairman*, Group Leader, Metals and Ceramics Div., Oak Ridge National Laboratory; PIERRE V. ANDREAE, Metallurgical and Materials Laboratory, Combustion Engineering, Inc.; JACK J. BODZIN, Principal Engineer, Engineering Research Dept., Detroit Edison Co.; D. A. CANONICO, Metallurgist, Metals and Ceramics Div., Oak Ridge National Laboratory.

JOHN F. CLAYTON, Research Metallurgist, Gulf Oil Canada Ltd.; LOUIS F. COFFIN, JR., Metallurgy and Ceramics Laboratory, Research and Development Center, General Electric Co.; E. PHILIP DAHLBERG, Group Leader – Materials Science, Corporate Research Center, Universal Oil Products Co.; J. V. GLUCK, Research Metallurgist, Research Laboratory, Tecumseh Products Co.; JESSE LE COFF, Chief Mechanical Design Engineer, Catalytic, Inc.; DONALD E. McGARRIGAN, Quality Assurance Engineer, United Engineers and Constructors, Inc.

WILTON F. MELHORN, Associate Professor, Mechanical Engineering Technology, School of Technology, Purdue University; DANIEL M. NOBLE, Technical Services Administrator, Consumers Power Co.; LEWIS H. REID, Senior Metallurgical Engineer, Sun Oil Co.; CHARLES C. SEASTROM, Research Associate, E. I. du Pont de Nemours & Co., Inc.; EDWARD A. DURAND, *Secretary*, Senior Editor, Metals Handbook.

more of several mechanisms. Most prominent among these mechanisms are corrosion (including pitting and erosion), mechanical-environmental processes (including stress-corrosion cracking and hydrogen damage), fracture (including fatigue fracture, thermal-fatigue fracture, and stress rupture), and distortion (especially distortion involving thermal-expansion effects or creep).

The causes of failure generally can be classified as design defects, fabrication defects, improper operation (including improper maintenance), and miscellaneous causes. Of these general types of causes, improper operation (which includes most incidents of overheating, corrosion and fouling) and fabrication defects (which include most incidents of poor workmanship, improper material and defective material) together account for more than 75% of all failures of steam-power-plant equipment.

Most steam-generator failures occur in pressurized components — that is, the tubing, piping and pressure vessels that comprise the steam-generating portion of the system. With very few exceptions, failure of pressurized components is confined to the relatively small-diameter tubing comprising the heat-transfer surfaces within the boiler enclosure.

Overheating is the main cause of failure in steam generators. For example, a survey compiled by one laboratory over a period of 12 years, encompassing 413 investigations, listed overheating as the cause in 201 failures, or 48.7% of those investigated. Fatigue and corrosion fatigue were listed as the next most common causes of failure, accounting for a total of 89 failures, or 21.5%. Corrosion, stress corrosion and hydrogen embrittlement caused a total of 68 failures, or 16.5%. Defective or improper material was cited as the cause of most of the remaining failures (13.3%). Although "defective material" often is blamed for a failure, this survey indicates that, statistically, it is one of the least likely causes of failure in power-plant equipment.

Defective material does not always cause a component to fail soon after being put into service. Figure 1 shows cracking at the root of a longitudinal mill defect in a stainless steel superheater tube. This tube ruptured after 18 years of service because the normal operating pressure caused stress-rupture cracking to initiate at the mill defect.

Boiler design is inherently conservative; thus, even massive defects may be present in some areas without causing fracture to occur until after a considerable period of operation. Some defects may be present without ever causing failure. Nevertheless, fabrication and repair procedures should be aimed at producing defect-free systems. In the following example, a defect in a large drum for a

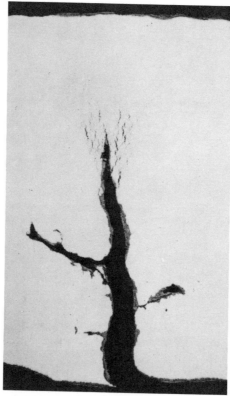

Fig. 1. Micrograph, at about 25×, showing stress-rupture cracking at the root of a longitudinal mill defect in a stainless steel superheater tube. The tube ruptured after 18 years in service.

high-pressure boiler went undetected because nondestructive inspection was not done after a stress-relief heat treatment. As a result, the drum fractured in a brittle manner during a hydrostatic test. It should be understood that this boiler was not fabricated in accordance with the ASME Boiler and Pressure Vessel Code, and therefore certain practices required by the code (such as radiographing all welded joints and hydrostatic testing with water at 21 C or 70 F, minimum) were not followed.

Example 1. Brittle Fracture of an Mn-Cr-Mo-V Steel High-Pressure-Boiler Drum, Caused by an Undetected Crack (Fig. 2)*

A 164-ton high-pressure-boiler drum with an inside diameter of 5 ft, 6 in. and an overall length of 74 ft, 9 in. failed by brittle fracture as shown in Fig. 2 during a hydrostatic test as the pressure reached 3980 psi. Water temperature in the test was 7 C (44 F). The drum had withstood three previous hydrostatic tests at the specified test pressure of 4163 psi; water temperature in these tests apparently was above 7 C (44 F). The design pressure was 2775 psi.

Fabrication History. The drum was made from annealed and cold formed 5%16-in.-thick Mn-Cr-Mo-V steel plate, and consisted of 12 half-cylindrical shells and two hemispherical drumheads. All seams were made by electroslag welding — longitudinal seams without preheating and circumferential seams with preheating. The two heads and the six cylindrical courses were normalized and ultrasonically inspected prior to circumferential welding into two subassemblies. Nozzles and other connections were attached by means of fillet welds, using manual welding with preheating, after the two subassemblies had been stress-relief annealed and ultrasonically inspected. After all connections and attachments had been welded, the weldments were magnetic-particle inspected. One economizer nozzle and the weld that attached it to the high-pressure-boiler drum were found to be defective and were replaced; the new attachment weld was inspected, and no defects were found.

The two subassemblies then were stress relieved and joined using automatic submerged-arc welding; the final joint was locally stress relieved after ultrasonic inspection. No ultrasonic or magnetic-particle inspection was performed after final stress relief of either of the two drum halves or of the final assembly weld.

*This example is a condensation of the following article: "Report on the Brittle Fracture of a High-Pressure Boiler Drum at Cockenzie Power Station", pages 2-29 in *Welding Research Abroad* (Welding Research Council Bulletin), Vol XIII, No. 8, Oct 1967.

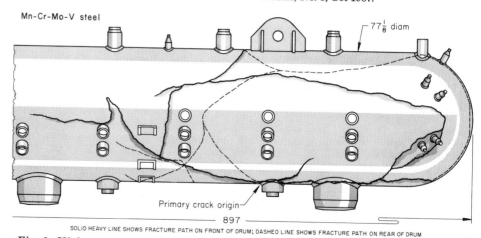

Mn-Cr-Mo-V steel

77 1/8 diam

Primary crack origin

897

SOLID HEAVY LINE SHOWS FRACTURE PATH ON FRONT OF DRUM; DASHED LINE SHOWS FRACTURE PATH ON REAR OF DRUM

Fig. 2. High-pressure Mn-Cr-Mo-V steel boiler drum that failed by brittle fracture during hydrostatic testing. Arrow indicates an undetected oxidized crack at which fracture originated. Fracture occurred because the ductile-to-brittle transition temperature of the steel was too low. (Example 1)

Investigation. Visual inspection performed immediately after failure showed that the drum had split at one end (see Fig. 2) and a section approximately 16 ft long had been detached from the rest of the shell. This section extended from a split, skewed slightly from the vertical, across the drum-door opening, and then to the drum sling. This sling lay beneath course No. 5 at a position about one-fourth of the way across the course from the end of the drum that failed. At its widest point, the detached section had a circumference about one-half that of the drum.

The initial inspection also revealed that a localized area of the fracture surface adjacent to the economizer nozzle in course No. 6 (the nozzle that had been replaced) was covered with black oxide. Later, detailed examination of the fracture surfaces identified this oxidized area as the primary origin of fracture.

Macroscopic and microscopic examination of the metallic structure at the origin showed the origin to be an oxidized transgranular crack associated with the toe of the nozzle weld but not with an adjacent bracket weld. The fracture, however, did not follow the interface between the nozzle weld and the drum, but propagated into the base metal of the drum. Although it was ultimately concluded that the oxidized crack had existed ever since final stress relief of this drum half, the fracture surface did not exhibit any evidence that subcritical crack growth had occurred during previous hydrostatic tests.

Extensive hardness, tensile and impact testing was performed, both on specimens from the fractured drum and on edge-discard samples from the original steel plates. In addition, stress-relief experiments and nozzle-replacement experiments were performed to assess the effects of these operations on the failure.

Discussion. The evidence suggested that the oxidized crack, which was the ultimate origin of the fracture, had been formed after magnetic-particle inspection of the nozzle weld (assuming that the inspection was completely thorough and effective) and may have been generated during the heat-up period of the final stress relief. The thermal stresses arising from the temperature nonuniformities involved in initial heating, when added to the residual stresses, may have been sufficient to have produced the crack. The oxidation of the surface of the crack indicated that the crack had existed during most of the soaking period of the final stress relief. If the drum had been inspected for cracks after the final stress relief, the origin probably would have been discovered.

It appears that the plate in which the crack formed was unfavorably low in impact strength. The value at room temperature was essentially one-third of the average for the entire drum. It also appears that the ductile-to-brittle transition temperature for this plate (and, in fact, for the grade of steel in general) was too high to afford maximum properties at ambient temperatures. In view of the low impact strength and the high transition temperature, it is surprising that the drum withstood the pressure of 4163 psi in three previous hydrostatic tests without propagation of the crack.

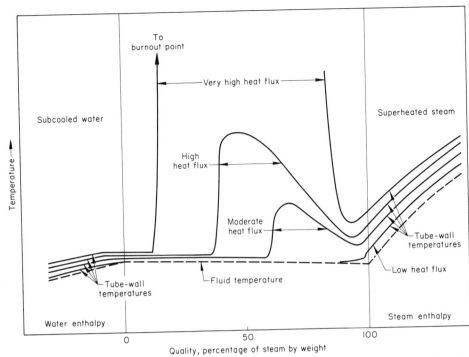

Fig. 3. Variation of fluid temperature and tube-wall temperature as water is heated through the boiling point with low, moderate, high and very high heat fluxes (rates of heat transfer). See text for discussion. (Redrawn from Ref 1)

From the standpoint of ductile-to-brittle transition, the water temperature in the final hydrostatic test, 7 C (44 F), might be considered undesirably low. However, in certain circumstances, a successful low-temperature test (4.5 C or 40.1 F minimum, to avoid freezing) is considered to provide ensurance that failure will not occur later in service. (Note that this does not apply to vessels made in accordance with the ASME Boiler and Pressure Vessel Code.)

Recommendations. To prevent cracking and consequent fracture of other boiler drums of this type, the principal remedial actions recommended were:

1 A steel with a lower ductile-to-brittle transition temperature should be substituted for the Mn-Cr-Mo-V steel.
2 Nondestructive-testing techniques should be carefully assessed to ensure that all defects of critical size or larger will be detected. Final nondestructive testing should be carried out *after* completion of final heat treatment.
3 The heating rates employed during the early stages of stress relief of such large and complex welded structures should be carefully gaged to ensure that generation of harmful levels of thermal stress will be avoided.

Failures Involving Sudden Tube Rupture

Sudden rupture of a tube in a steam generator is a serious failure, because the steam generator must be shut down immediately to minimize or avoid (*a*) erosion of adjacent tubes and furnace sidewalls by escaping steam, (*b*) overheating of other tube banks because of a loss of boiler circulation, and (*c*) damage to other components in the system resulting from loss of working fluid. The downtime resulting from boiler failure and subsequent repair may require other operations to be curtailed or shut down, with an attendant economic loss.

Tube ruptures (excluding cracks caused by stress corrosion or fatigue, which usually result in leakage rather than sudden fracture) may be classified as ruptures caused by overheating and ruptures caused by embrittlement. Each type has characteristic features, which are discussed in the following paragraphs.

Ruptures Caused by Overheating

When water is boiled in a tube having uniform heat flux (rate of heat transfer) along its length under conditions that produce a state of dynamic equilibrium, various points along the tube will be in contact with subcooled water, boiling water, low-quality steam, high-quality steam and superheated steam. A temperature gradient between the tube wall and the fluid within the tube provides the driving force for heat transfer at any point. Figure 3 indicates the effects that different heat fluxes have on tube-wall temperature. In the region where subcooled water contacts the tube (at left in Fig. 3), the conductance of the fluid film is relatively high; therefore, a small temperature difference sustains heat transfer at all heat-flux levels. However, the conductance of a vapor film in steam of low quality is relatively low; therefore, at the onset of film boiling, a large temperature difference between the tube wall and the bulk fluid is required to sustain a high heat flux across the film. The effect of the

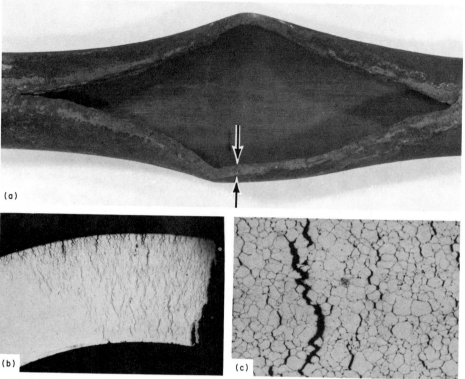

(a) Over-all view of rupture, at about ½×; a typical "fishmouth" rupture. (b) Macrograph, at about 4½×, of an unetched section from location between arrows in (a), showing extensive transverse cracking adjacent to the main fracture (at right). (c) Micrograph, at 100×, of a specimen etched electrolytically in 60% HNO₃, showing intergranular nature of cracking.

Fig. 4. Type 321 stainless steel (ASME SA-213, grade TP321H) superheater tube that failed by thick-lip stress rupture

onset of film boiling on tube-wall temperature appears as sharp breaks in the curves for moderate, high and very high heat fluxes in Fig. 3. With increasing heat flux, the onset of unstable film boiling (also known as departure from nucleate boiling, or DNB) occurs at lower steam qualities, and tube-wall temperatures reach higher peak values before stable film boiling, which requires a lower temperature difference to sustain a given heat flux, is established.

At very high heat fluxes, DNB occurs at low steam quality, and the temperature difference between tube wall and bulk fluid at a point slightly downstream from DNB is very high. Under these conditions, tube failure theoretically can occur by melting of the tube wall, although in reality the tube will rupture because metal loses its strength (and thereby loses its ability to contain pressure) before it melts. In design of fossil-fuel boilers and nuclear reactors, DNB is an important consideration, because heat flux can quickly exceed the failure point (burnout point) at local regions in a tube if the tube does not receive an adequate supply of incoming feedwater.

In superheaters and reheaters, which normally operate at temperatures that are 28 to 83 degrees C (50 to 150 degrees F) higher than the temperature of the steam inside the tubes, heat transfer is controlled primarily by the conductance of fluid films at the inner and outer surfaces. Although higher heat fluxes require higher tube-wall temperatures to sustain heat transfer, deposits have a greater effect on tube-wall temperatures and therefore on overheating.

A tube rupture caused by overheating can occur within a few minutes or can take several years to develop. A rupture caused by overheating generally involves fracture along a longitudinal path, with some detectable plastic deformation prior to fracture. Longitudinal fracture may or may not be accompanied by secondary, circumferential fracture. The main fracture usually has a "fishmouth" appearance (see Fig. 4a) and is either a "thick-lip" or a "thin-lip" rupture.

Thick-lip ruptures in steam-generator tubes occur mainly by stress rupture as a result of prolonged overheating at a temperature slightly above the maximum safe working temperature for the tube material. Fracture surfaces of such ruptures are rough (crystalline) in macroscopic appearance and usually are oxidized or hot-gas corroded because of exposure to a high-temperature corrosive environment following the rupture. The macroscopic direction of fracture is normal to the tube surface (flat-face fracture) and parallel to the tube axis, as shown in Fig. 4(a). Thick-lip rupture may or may not be accompanied by slight swelling of the tube in the region adja-

cent to the rupture, and usually there is only a small amount of reduction in tube-wall thickness at the fracture. Examination of a polished, transverse section through the tube at the center of the fracture usually reveals extensive secondary transverse cracking adjacent to the main fracture (see Fig. 4b), and, when etched, the section will exhibit intergranular separation, as shown in the micrograph in Fig. 4(c).

Thin-lip ruptures (see Fig. 5 and 6) usually are transgranular tensile fractures occurring at metal temperatures from 650 to 870 C (1200 to 1600 F). These elevated-temperature tensile fractures exhibit macroscopic and microscopic features that are characteristic of the tube alloy and the temperature at which rupture occurred. A tensile fracture results from rapid overheating to a temperature considerably above the safe working temperature for the tube material and is accompanied by considerable swelling of the tube in the regions adjacent to the rupture that have been exposed to the highest temperatures. Sometimes, as shown in Fig. 5, steam escaping at high velocity through the rupture will impose a reaction force on the tube sufficient to bend it laterally. The higher and more uniform the degree of overheating, the greater is the likelihood of lateral bending.

Ruptures caused by rapid overheating exhibit obvious tube-wall thinning adjacent to the rupture, often to a knife-edge

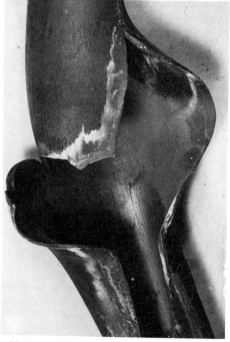

This rupture exhibits a "cobra" appearance as a result of lateral bending under the reaction force imposed by escaping steam. The tube was a 2½-in.-OD, 0.250-in.-wall boiler tube made of 1.25Cr-0.5Mo steel (ASME SA-213).

Fig. 5. Thin-lip rupture in a boiler tube, caused by rapid overheating

at the fracture surface, as shown in the inset in Fig. 6. Thinning also occurs in areas of swelling adjacent to ruptures; near the rupture shown in Fig. 6, the tube wall was 67% as thick as it was opposite the rupture, where the tube was shielded from exposure to hot gases.

Even though tube-wall thinning characterizes all rapid-overheating failures, rapid overheating is not necessarily the cause of all ruptures that exhibit tube-wall thinning. Erosion and corrosion are mechanisms that also can cause thinning and subsequent rupture. Overheating may or may not occur in tubes thinned by erosion or corrosion.

Microstructural Features. Prolonged overheating, usually at temperatures below Ac_1 in carbon and low-alloy steels, causes decomposition of pearlite into ferrite and spheroidal carbides, which weakens tube materials. If continued overheating persists, it can cause formation of voids along grain boundaries (see Fig. 7a) and eventual grain separation (see Fig. 7b), resulting in stress-rupture failure of the tube.

Austenitic stainless steels generally can exhibit three types of metallurgical instability at elevated temperatures: carbide formation or modification, ferrite precipitation, and sigma-phase or chi-phase formation. The effects of sigma phase are discussed in detail in the article on Elevated-Temperature Failures, which begins on page 249. All three types of metallurgical instability may shorten the stress-rupture life of stainless steels and can enhance the probability of tube failure with prolonged overheating. Regardless of whether metallurgical instabilities occur, tube materials can fail by stress rupture if subjected to excessive temperatures over sufficiently long periods of time.

Rapid overheating of boiler tubes made of carbon and low-alloy steels usually results in failure because of a decrease in yield strength. If rupture occurs at a temperature below the recrystallization temperature, the microstructure near the fracture will exhibit severely elongated grains, as shown in Fig. 8(a). Rupture that occurs at a temperature between Ac_1 and Ac_3 may exhibit a mixed microstructure of ferrite and upper transformation products (pearlite and bainite) resulting from the quenching effect of escaping water or steam on the partly austenitic structure existing at the instant of rupture (see Fig. 8b).

Microstructural evidence of overheating in the area of rupture is not conclusive proof that overheating occurred in service. The microstructural features discussed above may have been present at the time the tube was installed in the boiler. Thus, microstructural examination of the ruptured tube at a point some distance from the rupture, of an adjacent

Fig. 6. Thin-lip rupture in a 2½-in.-OD, 0.105-in.-wall carbon steel furnace-wall tube, caused by rapid overheating. Knife-edge wall thinning at longitudinal main rupture is shown in cross section in the inset. Note secondary, circumferential fracture at left end of the longitudinal main rupture.

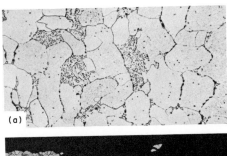

(a) Specimen, at 250×, exhibits voids (black) in grain boundaries, and spheroidization (light, globular) — both of which are characteristic of tertiary creep. (b) Specimen, at 50×, exhibits intergranular separation adjacent to fracture surface (top). Mottled areas in both specimens are regions where pearlite has decomposed into ferrite and spheroidal carbides. Both specimens were etched in 2% nital.

Fig. 7. Microstructures of specimens from carbon steel boiler tubes subjected to prolonged overheating below Ac_1

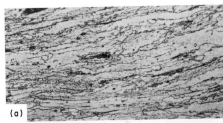

(a) Specimen exhibits elongated grains near tensile rupture resulting from rapid overheating below the recrystallization temperature. (b) Specimen exhibits mixed structure near rupture resulting from rapid overheating between Ac_1 and Ac_3 and subsequent quenching by escaping water or steam. Both specimens were etched in 2% nital and are shown at 250×.

Fig. 8. Typical microstructures of 0.18% carbon steel boiler tubes that ruptured as a result of rapid overheating

tube, or (better still) of a sample of unused tubing from the same mill lot should be performed. In the example that follows, microstructural features and measurements of deformation (swelling) of two boiler tubes that ruptured

revealed that failure had occurred as the result of rapid overheating. Other tubes in the same region of the boiler exhibited the same microstructural features, which indicated that damage was not confined to the tubes that burst.

The specimens were taken (a) adjacent to a rupture in a tube, (b) about 10 in. from the rupture in the same tube, and (c) from a nearby unruptured tube. All three structures contain martensite or other lower transformation products. (Specimens were etched in nital and are shown at a magnification of 500×.)

Fig. 9. Microstructures of three specimens taken from severely overheated carbon steel boiler tubes (Example 2)

Example 2. Rupture of Low-Carbon Steel Boiler Tubes Because of Severe Overheating (Fig. 9)

After seven months of service, two low-carbon steel boiler tubes ruptured during a start-up period, causing extensive secondary damage to a two-drum marine reheat boiler. The tubes were 2 in. in diameter and 0.220 in. nominal wall thickness, and were made to ASME SA-192 specifications.

Reports indicated that there had been sufficient water in the boiler two hours before start-up. Six hours after start-up, the center portions of two adjacent tubes in the boiling surface ruptured. The pressure and temperature of the steam at the time of failure were reported to be 1250 psi and 399 C or 750 F (boiling temperature, 300 C or 572 F).

Examination of the boiler revealed no blocked tubes, and, as determined with an audio gage, tube-wall thickness ranged from 0.185 to 0.215 in. The ruptured section of one tube and sections of two apparently unaffected tubes were submitted for laboratory examination.

Investigation. The outer surfaces of all of the tubing exhibited a general oxidized condition. The inner surfaces were covered with an evenly distributed, thin, tightly adherent scale.

Chemical analysis of the metal in the tube that ruptured indicated that it was within ASME SA-192 specifications.

Polished and nital-etched specimens of the metal in both the ruptured and the unruptured tubes were examined metallographically at a magnification of 500 diameters. Near the rupture edge in the failed tube, the microstructure consisted of ferrite and acicular martensite or bainite, as shown in Fig. 9(a). There were no indications of a cold worked structure in this area; hardness of the metal was Rockwell C 33 to 34. The microstructure and the lack of cold worked metal indicated that a temperature above the transformation temperature of 727 C (1340 F) had been reached. Examination of the microstructure opposite the rupture revealed a lesser amount of lower transformation products — an indication that the maximum temperature was lower in this area of the tube than at the rupture, but still was higher than 727 C (1340 F). The hardness of the metal opposite the rupture was Rockwell B 89.

The microstructure of the metal about 10 in. from the rupture (Fig. 9b) contained some small, randomly located areas of acicular martensite or bainite in a ferrite matrix. Hardness of the metal was Rockwell B 80 to 82. The microstructure of one of the unruptured tubes (Fig. 9c) revealed a considerable amount of martensite or bainite in a ferrite matrix (hardness was Rockwell B 82 to 85), but the other unruptured tube had a structure of spheroidized carbide in a ferrite matrix and a hardness of Rockwell B 72 to 73.

In order for lower transformation products to form in low-carbon steel, the metal must be heated above 727 C (1340 F) and rapidly quenched. The microstructure of the ruptured tube indicated that this temperature was exceeded in the general area of failure, and was greatly exceeded at the rupture, where a temperature of at least 870 C (1600 F) had been reached. Apparently, only one of the unruptured tubes had been heated above 727 C (1340 F).

Measurements of the wall thickness and outside diameter of the tubing showed that both the ruptured and the unruptured tubes were swollen. The diameter of the failed tube near the rupture ranged from 2.062 to 2.083 in., which was about 3½% greater than the diameter of the tubing as shipped from the mill (1.992 to 2.010 in.). Records indicated that the original wall thickness of the tubing was 0.226 to 0.286 in., whereas the wall thickness in the swollen regions was only 0.182 to 0.221 in.

Accurate measurement of the outside diameter of the two unruptured tubes could not be made because they had been split before being shipped to the laboratory; however, the diameter was judged to be 2.038 in. min. The wall thickness of the unruptured tubes was 0.201 to 0.225 in., which was further evidence that swelling due to overheating had occurred in portions of the tube bank where no ruptures occurred.

Conclusions. The tubes failed as the result of rapid overheating. The microstructure, hardness and tube dimensions indicated that temperatures above 727 C (1340 F) were reached in a large section of the boiler. The tubing at the rupture area had reached a temperature of about 870 C (about 1600 F).

The boiler was heated too rapidly and to an excessively high temperature, at which time two tubes burst. This released a flood of water that quenched the overheated tubes, which accounts for the martensite and other lower transformation products in the microstructure. Because no evidence of tempered transformation products was found, it was concluded that the tubes had been overheated only once — at the time of failure.

Evidence of severe overheating also was found in unruptured tubes. This indicated that widespread damage had occurred. Consequently, the entire tube bank was replaced.

Effects of Deposits. During operation, a wide variety of deposits can form on both sides of heat-transfer surfaces. (The chemical properties of these deposits and the means by which they are accumulated on heat-transfer surfaces are discussed in the section of this article that begins on page 533.) Deposits can cause overheating failures by changing the heat-transfer characteristics of a tube bank or of an individual tube.

Fuel-ash deposits on surfaces exposed to flue gases (fire-side deposits) can cause local hot spots by insulating portions of the heat-transfer surface or, if the deposits are thick enough, by changing the flow pattern of flue gases through a tube bank. In either instance, metal temperatures will be higher in regions devoid of fire-side deposits than in regions where deposits are present.

When water-side deposits are present, tube-wall temperatures increase in the region of the deposits. A local region of deposited scale on the inside surface of a boiler tube interposes resistance to heat flow between the tube wall and the working fluid, thus causing a temperature gradient across the scale and increasing tube-wall temperature in direct proportion to the thickness of the scale, as shown graphically in Fig. 10. It is important to keep water-side surfaces free of adherent scale, particularly in regions of high heat flux, because of the effect on tube-wall temperatures. For example, as can be seen in Fig. 10(d), adherent scale 0.016 in. thick or thicker can cause the maximum metal temperature at the outside surface of the tube to exceed the maximum allowable temperature for a 2.0-in.-diam carbon steel boiler tube at a heat flux of 100,000 Btu per square foot

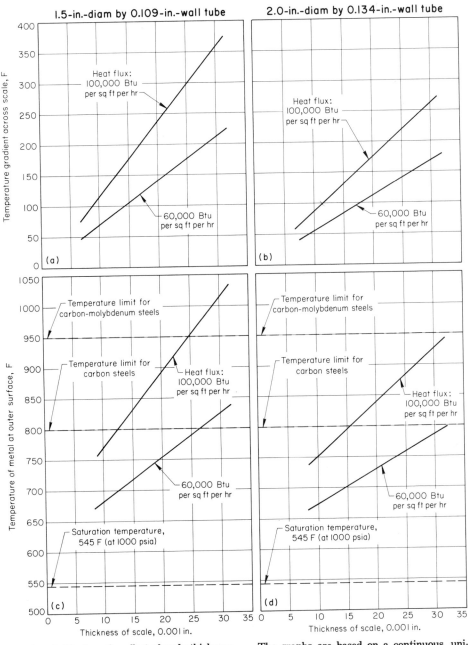

(a) and (b) show the effect of scale thickness on the temperature gradient across the scale.
(c) and (d) show the effect of scale thickness on the temperature of the metal at the outer surface of the tube.

The graphs are based on a continuous, uniform scale, with a thermal conductivity of 10 Btu/hr/sq ft/°F per inch of thickness, on tubes in the film-boiling region of a 1000-psia system (saturation temperature, 545 F).

Fig. 10. Scale thickness versus temperature, for two sizes of boiler tubes and two values of heat flux

of full-power operation, may be caused by sudden loss of circulation resulting either from general loss of circulation (such as from feed-pump failure) or from local loss of circulation affecting only a few tubes. The example that follows describes a stress-rupture failure of superheater tubes that led to loss of circulation and tensile failure of adjacent tubes.

Example 3. Rupture of Cr-Mo Steel Superheater Tubes Because of Overheating (Fig. 11)

Two instances of superheater rupture occurred about ten days apart in a stationary industrial boiler. Three tubes failed the first time, and four tubes the second. The tubes, 2½ in. in diameter and made of 1.25Cr-0.5Mo steel (ASME SA-213, grade T11), failed by two different types of rupture, and both types occurred in each instance of failure.

Visual examination of each type of rupture revealed noticeable swelling of the tubes in the area of rupture (see Fig. 11). Relatively slight scaling, probably caused by high-temperature oxidation, was visible on fire-side surfaces, and both black deposits and white deposits were found on steam-side surfaces. Subsequent analyses by scanning electron microscopy and x-ray diffraction identified magnetic iron oxide (Fe_3O_4) as the major constituent in the black deposit, and a complex sodium aluminum silicate as the major constituent in the white deposit. The nature and extent of the scale did not suggest that it was a contributory factor in the failures.

Metallographic examination indicated that the tubes with slight splits (Fig. 11a) had failed by stress rupture resulting from prolonged overheating at 540 to 650 C (1000 to 1200 F); there was extensive spheroidization and coalescence of carbides in the micro-

Fig. 11. Superheater tubes made of Cr-Mo steel (ASME SA-213, grade T11) that ruptured because of overheating. Tube in (a) failed by stress rupture, causing loss of circulation and tensile failure of tube in (b). (Example 3)

per hour. The effect of water-side scale on metal temperatures is more pronounced for smaller-diameter tubing and higher heat fluxes.

Many boilers are designed so that heat transfer at the boiling surface is controlled by fluid-film conductance. The presence of scale on internal surfaces of tubes inhibits the vaporization process and can make it difficult to maintain proper operating conditions in the boiler.

Causes of Overheating. Overheating can result from restriction of flow within a heated tube or from localized hot spots in a tube wall. Water or steam within a

tube extracts heat from the metal, thus cooling it. Mild restriction of flow favors a small degree of overheating and failure by stress rupture; a sudden or severe restriction favors rapid overheating and tensile failure. Mild restriction can result from such causes as local imbalance of flow among tubes joined to a common header, localized deposits near a tube inlet, or local variations in inside diameter because of variations in tube-installation techniques. Rapid overheating, which is most likely to occur at start-up, during periods of rapid fluctuation in steam demand, or during periods

structure. On the other hand, the larger ruptures (Fig. 11b) were tensile failures resulting from rapid overheating to 815 to 870 C (1500 to 1600 F); a completely martensitic structure existed at the edges of the ruptures in these tubes because of rapid quenching by escaping fluid.

Conclusions. Based on the evidence — especially that both types of rupture had occurred in each instance of failure — it was concluded that the prolonged-overheating failures had been the primary ruptures and that local loss of circulation had caused rapid overheating in adjacent tubes. The prolonged overheating was believed to have resulted from poor boiler circulation and high furnace temperatures.

Another frequent cause of rapid overheating involves improper operation — specifically, delivering heat to the system more rapidly than the boiler or superheater heat-transfer surface can transmit heat to the working fluid. At the beginning of this section, the phenomenon of departure from nucleate boiling (DNB) and its effect on tube-wall temperature is discussed. If a boiler is operated in a manner that causes DNB to occur in a region of high heat flux where the system cannot accommodate this condition, a rapid-overheating failure is inevitable. It also is possible that heat transfer at the boiling surface will be significantly lower than anticipated in design of the boiler, with the result that flue gases in the superheater or reheater section will be too hot and an overheating failure in the superheater or reheater may occur. Uneven firing of a multiburner furnace can cause a similar effect, especially when furnace conditions do not favor high turbulence of the flue gases.

Ruptures Caused by Embrittlement

Tube ruptures caused by embrittlement of the metal result from metallurgical changes within the tube metal that affect its ability to sustain service loads. The main mechanisms are hydrogen damage and graphitization, which make normally satisfactory alloys susceptible to brittle fracture.

Hydrogen damage in steam systems occurs primarily in steel components. At low to moderate temperatures, cracking caused by hydrogen damage often resembles stress-corrosion cracking, except that hydrogen-damage failures may exhibit little or no crack branching. At the high temperatures common in steam generators and most high-pressure piping, hydrogen damage is more likely to manifest itself as discontinuous intergranular cracking, often accompanied by decarburization (see Fig. 12).

In high-temperature hydrogen damage discontinuous cracking occurs because of the precipitation of molecular hydrogen (or methane resulting from hydrogen decarburization of the steel) along

grain boundaries. Tubes that have undergone this type of hydrogen damage often rupture as shown in Fig. 13, in which a portion of the tube wall is detached; sometimes this type of rupture is called a "window" fracture. High-temperature hydrogen damage can be confirmed by macroetching with a hot 50% solution of hydrochloric acid; regions of hydrogen damage appear black and porous (see Fig. 14).

Hydrogen is one of the normal products of the basic corrosion reaction between iron and water. Atomic hydrogen formed at a corrosion site can (a) combine with other hydrogen atoms to form molecular hydrogen, which becomes dispersed in the working fluid; (b) become dissolved as ions in surrounding liquid; or (c) pass into the metal as highly mobile atoms. Hydrogen damage results only from the last phenomenon. Most of the dissolved atoms migrate through the tube wall and pass through the opposite surface, where they are carried away by another fluid, usually flue gas. However, some of the dissolved hydrogen, the amount of which is determined primarily by the concentration of the hydrogen and by the temperature of the metal, participates in the damaging reactions.

In the following example, hydrogen damage weakened the tube not only by discontinuous grain-boundary cracking, but also by decarburization.

Example 4. Rupture of a Carbon Steel Tube Because of Hydrogen-Induced Cracking and Decarburization (Fig. 15)

A 3-in.-OD, 0.290-in.-wall carbon steel boiler tube ruptured as shown in Fig. 15. The fracture was of the brittle "window" type, without the "fishmouth" appearance characteristic of overheating failures.

Visual examination disclosed a substantial degree of corrosion on the water-side surface, leaving a rough area in the immediate vicinity of the rupture. Microscopic examination of a cross section through the tube wall at the fracture revealed decarburization and extensive discontinuous intergranular cracking (similar to the structure shown in Fig. 12).

The combination of water-side corrosion, cracking and decarburization observed in this instance led to the conclusion that rupture had occurred because of hydrogen damage involving the formation of methane by the reaction of dissolved hydrogen with carbon in the steel. Hydrogen was produced by the chemical reaction that corroded the internal tube surface.

Steel embrittled by hydrogen can be restored to its original ductility and notched tensile strength only if grain-boundary cracking or decarburization has not occurred. A low-temperature bake (3 hr or more at 175 to 205 C, or 350 to 400 F) usually is sufficient to drive dissolved hydrogen out of a steel part, thus restoring ductility. However, hydrogen damage involving internal cracking

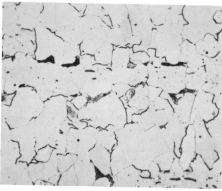

Fig. 12. Micrograph, at 250×, of an etched specimen from a carbon steel boiler tube, showing the decarburization and discontinuous intergranular cracking that resulted from hydrogen damage

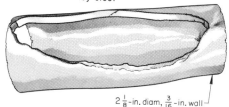

Carbon or low-alloy steel

2 ⅛-in. diam, ³⁄₁₆-in. wall

Fig. 13. "Window" fracture, a typical result of hydrogen damage in carbon or low-alloy steel boiler tubes

Fig. 14. Hydrogen damage (dark area) in a carbon steel boiler tube, revealed by macroetching a cross section of the tube with hot 50% hydrochloric acid

Fig. 15. Carbon steel boiler tube that ruptured because of hydrogen damage (Example 4)

is irreversible; material embrittled in this manner is permanently degraded and should be replaced.

Graphitization is a microstructural change that sometimes occurs in carbon or low-alloy steels that are subjected to moderate temperatures for long periods of time. Graphitization results from decomposition of pearlite into ferrite and carbon (graphite) and can embrittle steel parts, especially when the graphite particles form along a continuous zone through a load-carrying member. Graphite particles that are randomly distributed throughout the microstructure cause only moderate loss of strength.

Graphitization and the formation of spheroidal carbides are competing mechanisms of pearlite decomposition. The rate of decomposition is temperature dependent for both mechanisms, and the mechanisms have different activation energies. As shown in Fig. 16, graphitization is the usual mode of pearlite decomposition at temperatures below about 550 C (about 1025 F), and formation of spheroidal carbides can be expected to predominate at higher temperatures. Because graphitization involves prolonged exposure at moderate temperatures, it seldom occurs in boiling-surface tubing. Economizer tubing, steam piping and other components that are exposed to temperatures from about 425 to 550 C (about 800 to 1025 F) for several thousand hours are more likely than boiler-surface tubing to be embrittled by graphitization.

The heat-affected zones adjacent to welds are among the more likely locations for graphitization to occur. Figure 17(a) shows a carbon-molybdenum steel tube that ruptured in a brittle manner along fillet welds after 13 years of service. Investigation of this failure revealed that the rupture was caused by the presence of chainlike arrays of embrittling graphite nodules (see Fig. 17b and c) along the edges of heat-affected zones associated with each of the four welds on the tube. Arrays of graphite nodules also were found in the same locations on welds in several adjacent tubes, necessitating replacement of the entire tube bank.

Failures Caused by Corrosion or Scaling

The mechanisms of corrosion, specific techniques for analyzing corrosion failures, and degradation of various alloys in some of the more common corrosive media are discussed in detail in the article "Corrosion Failures", on pages 168 to 205 in this volume. In this section of the present article, only some of the more common types of corrosion and corrosion-related failures that occur in steam-power-plant components and equipment will be discussed.

Water-Side Corrosion

By far the most common corrodent encountered on water-side surfaces is oxygen. Three means by which oxygen may be admitted to the water side of a steam system are:

1 During operation, air can leak into a closed system in regions where the in-

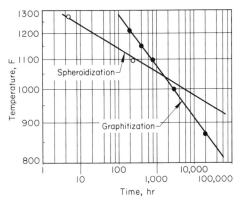

The curve for spheroidization is for conversion of one-half of the carbon in 0.15% C steel to spheroidal carbides (Ref 2 and 3). The curve for graphitization is for conversion of one-half of the carbon in aluminum-deoxidized, 0.5% Mo cast steel to nodular graphite (Ref 4).

Fig. 16. Temperature-time plot of pearlite decomposition by the competing mechanisms of spheroidization and graphitization in carbon and low-alloy steels

ternal pressure is less than atmospheric pressure — that is, in regions between the outlet of the low-pressure turbine and the boiler feed pump.
2 Usually, air is admitted to a system each time the system is opened for repair or cleaning.
3 Free oxygen is released as a product of the dissociation of water molecules.

Raw water used for initial filling and for make-up feed may contain one or more of the following: dissolved or emulsified organic substances; suspended organic and inorganic substances; dissolved inorganic solids (silica, and a wide variety of inorganic compounds); and dissolved oxygen, nitrogen and carbon dioxide. In addition, many industrial processes involve organic and inorganic chemicals that can leak into a steam system and contaminate the condensate. Many of the organic and inorganic contaminants in raw water or condensate can form scale or varnish on heated boiler tubes. Contaminants also cause foaming in vapor-generating regions. Foaming causes gross mechanical carryover, or the entrainment of water droplets in the steam. Carryover reduces turbine efficiency and may result in heavy deposition of solids from the feedwater on superheater and reheater heat-transfer surfaces, in piping and in turbines. Certain dissolved substances — especially

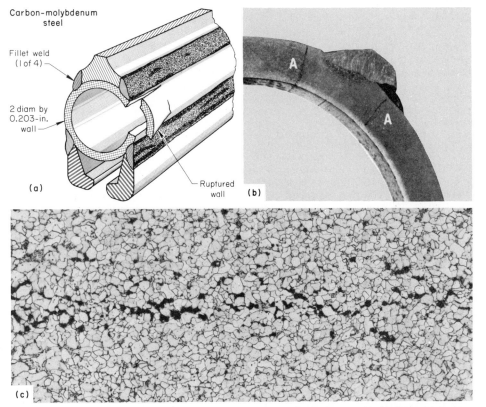

(a) View of tube showing dimensions, locations of welds, and rupture. (b) Macrograph, at 2×, showing graphitization along edges of a weld heat-affected zone (at A's); this was typical of all four welds. (c) Micrograph, at 100×, of a specimen etched in 2% nital, showing chainlike array of embrittling graphite nodules (black) at the edge of a heat-affected zone.

Fig. 17. Carbon-molybdenum steel tube that ruptured in a brittle manner after 13 years of service, because of graphitization at weld heat-affected zones

oxygen, carbon dioxide, chloride ions and hydroxide ions — can cause corrosion or stress-corrosion failures.

Because boiling-surface and economizer components are made mainly of carbon and low-alloy steel, they are corroded by water or by oxygen dissolved in the water. Make-up water usually is purified, and chemicals are added to boiler feedwater to control water-side corrosion; the type of purification and the type and concentration of the chemical additives vary with operating pressure, type of boiler, and type and concentration of contaminants in the raw water and the recirculating condensate. However, even with the most carefully controlled program of make-up purification and feedwater conditioning, water-side corrosion cannot be eliminated entirely.

Iron reacts with oxygen and water to form one of the iron oxides or hydroxides. The corrosion product that is formed depends primarily on the temperature of the metal at the corrosion site and on the concentration of oxygen in the surrounding environment. In steam systems, general corrosion rarely is a mode of failure, because water treatment is employed to prevent it. Despite all precautions, however, certain types of corrosion still can cause problems, as discussed below.

Types of Water-Side Corrosion in Boilers. In economizers and in boiling-surface components, pitting corrosion and crevice corrosion are the main types of severe corrosion that occur. Both types proceed by the same mechanism — galvanic corrosion.

In pitting corrosion, a small area is attacked because it becomes anodic to the rest of the surface, or because of highly localized concentration of a corrosive contaminant in the water. Pitting often is the direct result of local breakdown of normally passive surface films. Pitting that occurs at relatively few and scattered sites can result in rapid perforation because of the large ratio of cathode-to-anode area.

In crevice corrosion, oxygen is excluded from between two close-fitting surfaces or from beneath a deposit or particle on a surface. The area within the crevice, or beneath the deposit, is anodic to the surrounding area because of the difference in oxygen concentration. The anodic areas are subject to relatively rapid attack, mainly because they are small in relation to the surrounding cathodic area.

Corrosion of Components Exposed to Steam. Surfaces exposed to steam in superheaters, reheaters, steam piping and turbines usually do not become corroded. However, certain conditions that exist during start-up, shutdown and idle periods may cause corrosion of these components.

Fig. 18. Carbon steel superheater tube, showing pitting corrosion and perforation caused by the presence of oxygenated water during idle periods (Example 5)

The main cause of corrosion of components that normally are exposed to dry steam is moisture. When a high concentration of oxygen also is present, as often occurs when a system has been opened to the atmosphere for maintenance or repair, the potential for corrosion is enhanced. Moisture can be present in normally dry portions of the system if strict procedures for exclusion of moisture are not followed during start-up, shutdown and idle periods. It is important to balance the flow of working fluid that is required to prevent overheating of superheater and reheater tubes with the minimum flow required to maintain proper boiler circulation at low firing rates during start-up and shutdown. This balance of flow usually is obtained by use of a steam-bypass system. It is important to avoid admitting steam of excessively low quality to superheaters, reheaters or turbines, especially during shutdown, because the high moisture content can leave a film of water on normally dry surfaces. If metal surfaces are allowed to cool more rapidly than the steam inside a component, condensation will occur, leaving small pools of water at low points in the component. In the following example, pitting corrosion of a superheater tube occurred because water containing dissolved oxygen was present during idle periods.

Example 5. Pitting Corrosion of a Carbon Steel Superheater Tube Caused by Oxygenated Water Trapped in a Bend (Fig. 18)

A resistance welded carbon steel superheater tube made to ASME SA-276 specifications failed by pitting corrosion and subsequent perforation (see Fig. 18), which

caused the tube to leak. The perforation occurred at a low point in a bend near the superheater outlet header after about two years of service in a new plant.

During these two years, the plant had experienced a number of emergency shutdowns, which had resulted in the boiler being idle for periods of several days to several weeks. The superheater tubes could not be completely drained because of low points.

Investigation. When the perforated bend was cut open, water-level marks were noticed on the inside surface above the area of pitting. In addition, above the water-level marks, some slight pitting had occurred in an area where it appeared that water had condensed and run down the surface.

Microscopic examination disclosed that localized pitting had resulted from oxidation.

Conclusions and Recommendations. Water containing dissolved oxygen had accumulated in the bends during shutdown. Because the bends at low points could not be drained, cumulative damage due to oxygen pitting resulted in perforation of one of the tubes.

This type of corrosion can best be avoided by completely filling the system with condensate or with treated boiler water. Alkalinity should be maintained at a pH of 9.0, and approximately 200 ppm of sodium sulfite should be added to the water.

Alternatively, dry nitrogen should be admitted to the system after steam pressure has dropped below 75 psi. The dry nitrogen will purge the system, keeping internal surfaces dry while the temperature drops to ambient. The boiler then should be sealed under 5-psi nitrogen pressure, with the nitrogen feed line left connected to compensate for any slight loss in pressure due to leakage.

Corrosion of Condensers and Feedwater Heaters. Corrosion of components that are exposed to condensate — primarily condensers, feedwater heaters and boiler-feed piping — is caused mainly by the presence of carbon dioxide in the condensate. Carbon dioxide is produced when carbonates in the feedwater dissociate in the boiler. The carbon dioxide, being gaseous, is carried along in the steam through the turbine and into the condenser, where it dissolves in the liquid condensate. The mildly acidic solution (dilute carbonic acid) that results from contamination of condensate by carbon dioxide is corrosive to the copper alloy or low-carbon steel components in the preboiler portions of the system.

The main problem caused by corrosion of copper alloys is that soluble copper in the feedwater may be plated out on steel surfaces in the boiler or economizer, where galvanic corrosion can result in pitting of steel tubing. If soluble copper salts are present during chemical cleaning, metallic copper can be deposited readily on steel surfaces. The resultant layer of flash plating can be harmful if it covers a sufficiently large area and is continuous. Although extensive deposition of copper in mud drums, attemperators and similar components has occurred in some instances without subsequent galvanic corrosion of adjacent steel surfaces, removal of copper and copper salts from the components prior to the acid-treatment stage of chemical cleaning avoids this problem.

Condensers are subject to corrosion not only by the working fluid but also by the cooling medium. Lakes, rivers and other sources of fresh water are highly oxygenated and often contain significant concentrations of various industrial wastes; these contaminants occasionally are sources of significant corrosion. When external corrosion of condenser elements occurs, leakage of the contaminated water into the working fluid can cause severe disruption of the chemical balance in high-temperature regions of the system, leading to corrosion or fouling of boiler tubes. Marine systems and stationary plants at seaside locations are subject to special problems because of the salinity of the cooling water.

One instance of condenser corrosion involved a heat exchanger that was used during shutdowns for rapid cooling of a steam generator. During long periods between shutdowns, the heat exchanger was allowed to remain idle with highly oxygenated lake water sitting stagnant on the shell side. Pitting corrosion caused premature failure of the carbon steel tubes. The entire tube bundle was replaced using copper alloy 706 (copper nickel, 10%), which is resistant to this type of attack.

Protection From Corrosion During Operation. Control of corrosion and scaling generally involves three processes: (a) removal of dissolved solids, (b) oxygen scavenging and (c) control of pH. Solids are removed primarily by chemical treatment or demineralization of make-up feedwater. Oxygen scavenging and control of pH are accomplished mainly by chemical treatment of boiler feedwater. Feedwater treatments commonly used for control of pH include conventional phosphate, coordinated phosphate, chelant and volatile treatments. The first three also control scale-forming hardness constituents by reacting with the dissolved solids to form substances that can be removed by blow-down. In volatile treatment, which is used mainly when boiling pressure exceeds 1800 psi, pH is controlled by the addition of a volatile amine such as ammonia; total solids are maintained below 15 ppm for drum boilers, or below 50 ppb for once-through boilers, by demineralization. Conventional phosphate treatment is the least sensitive to upsets resulting from leakage of contaminants into the system. Volatile treatment cannot remove hardness constituents and thus is extremely sensitive to upsets.

Oxygen and other dissolved gases are removed primarily through the use of deaerating heaters. Typical dissolved-oxygen concentrations at the deaerator outlet seldom exceed 7 ppb. Chemical scavenging of the remaining dissolved oxygen is accomplished by addition of sodium sulfite or hydrazine in drum boilers that operate below 1800 psi, or by addition of hydrazine in once-through boilers or in drum boilers that operate at pressures above 1800 psi.

Corrosion Control in Nuclear Systems. Coolant for primary loops of pressurized-water reactors consists of high-purity water to which a rather large quantity of boric acid is added. Because the primary loop is constructed largely of stainless steel, halogen ions must be eliminated to avoid halide cracking. Oxygen is scavenged chiefly by pressurizing with hydrogen. Other contaminants are limited by using high-purity make-up feedwater and purified additives.

Secondary-loop treatment generally follows the methods used for supercritical boilers — that is, control of solids by demineralization, oxygen scavenging with hydrazine, and control of pH with ammonia.

Boiling-water reactors make use of a "sidestream loop", in which a portion of the circulating coolant in the reactor is continually purified; oxygen is removed by mechanical deaeration and no chemical scavengers are used.

Protection From Corrosion During Idle Periods. The oxygen scavengers that normally are added to feedwater during operation usually provide sufficient protection from corrosion for short idle periods, probably not exceeding 24 hr. For longer idle periods, components should be drained and filled with dry inert gas (nitrogen, helium or argon), or should be protected by "wet lay-up". Depending on the characteristics of the system, wet lay-up may consist of filling the system with (a) deoxygenated water treated with caustic to a high pH; (b) deoxygenated water treated with about 200 ppm of an oxygen scavenger; or (c) treated, deoxygenated water, plus a cover of nitrogen gas, called a nitrogen cap. Continuous recirculation of demineralized, deoxygenated water often is used for protection against corrosion during lay-up of large central-station boilers.

To a certain extent, the volatile amines used to control corrosion of surfaces contacted by steam or condensate also will help to protect these surfaces during idle periods, but use of dry inert gas is preferable for this purpose.

Scaling

In most systems, the pH of feedwater is maintained between 8.0 and 11.0. The optimum pH level, which is established by experience for each installation, is the level that keeps the amounts of iron and copper corrosion products in the boiler to a minimum. When water treatment is inadequate or control of pH is lax, there is a potential for excessive water-side corrosion in economizer and boiling-surface tubes. If thick corrosion scale forms, overheating failures can result.

The major source of water-side scale in boilers is, however, not corrosion but dissolved solids in the feedwater. Compounds containing iron, calcium, magnesium and sodium cations normally exist in most raw water; the usual anions are bicarbonate, carbonate, sulfate and chloride radicals. Calcium and magnesium compounds ("water hardness" compounds) become less soluble in water as temperature is increased. These hardness compounds separate from solution at temperatures common in economizers and boilers, and usually precipitate as tube-wall deposits, or hardness scale. As is true for corrosion scale, hardness scale is undesirable in regions of high heat transfer because it can cause rapid overheating of tube material. In addition, hardness scale may be somewhat porous. Dissolved solids in the boiler water, and strong alkalis sometimes used to treat feedwater, can be concentrated in the pores, which may lead to severe pitting corrosion of the tube surface beneath the hardness scale.

Scaling in Superheaters. Deposition of solids as scale in superheater tubing occurs primarily as the result of carryover of water droplets in wet steam. When carryover occurs, water droplets vaporize in the superheater and any nonvolatile solids present in these droplets are deposited on heat-transfer surfaces. Deposits may not be as likely to cause rapid-overheating failures in superheater tubing as in boiling-surface tubing because of the lower heat flux in superheaters. However, because superheaters operate at higher metal temperatures than boilers, scaling may lead to stress-rupture failure, or to loss of ductility because of metallurgical changes such as sigma formation or spheroidization of carbides.

Deposition in Turbines. Silica is the substance most commonly deposited in turbines, although other feedwater solids may be found as well. At the higher boiling temperatures associated with high-pressure subcritical systems and with supercritical systems, a portion of the silica in the feedwater will volatilize and be carried into the turbine along with the steam. As heat is extracted from the working fluid, steam temperature drops; volatile silica becomes nonvolatile and deposits out of the vapor stream onto turbine blades and surfaces of interstage passages. These deposits interfere with fluid flow in the turbine, resulting in a loss of power.

Silica, which is present in most raw water, is not removed by the same treatments that are used for control of water hardness; consequently, when silica deposition is excessive, special treatments must be used.

Removal of Water-Side Scale. Periodic removal of scale from internal surfaces in boilers and economizers is part of the normal maintenance of this equipment. Removal of scale can minimize unscheduled outages caused by tube rupture due to overheating. In addition, internal cleanness is an important factor in maintaining high thermal efficiency and low operating cost.

Although mechanical methods of scale removal may be used, chemical cleaning with a suitable inhibited acid offers several advantages: less downtime; lower cost; ability to clean otherwise inaccessible areas such as sharp bends, irregular surfaces, crevices and small-diameter tubes; and ability to clean internal surfaces without dismantling the unit. The particular acid and inhibitor that are appropriate for a specific situation depend on the composition and adherence of the deposits, the type of cleaning method (circulation or soaking), and the type of materials being cleaned — especially in applications that involve alloys with high chromium contents.

Chemical cleaning should be supervised by a competent chemist to ensure maximum effectiveness and safety, and to ensure that cleaning solutions do not excessively corrode base metal under deposits. In chemical cleaning of nuclear steam generators, additional precautions must be taken in disposing of the solutions and to ensure that personnel are not exposed to radioactive wastes from the cleaning process.

Chemical cleaning should always be followed by thorough flushing to remove loosened deposits and residual acid, after which the boiler should be filled with a neutralizing and passivating solution to prevent the clean metal surfaces from rusting.

Chemical cleaning is not a substitute for adequate water treatment. Corrosion and scale deposition can lead to severe deterioration of tube materials, and the chemical-cleaning process itself removes a thin layer of base metal along with the deposits.

Fire-Side Corrosion

Except for most gaseous fuels, combustion of fossil fuels produces solid, liquid and gaseous compounds that can be corrosive to structural components and heat-transfer surfaces. In addition, deposits of solid and liquid residues in gas passages can alter the heat-transfer characteristics of the system, with potentially severe effects on system efficiency and tube-wall temperatures.

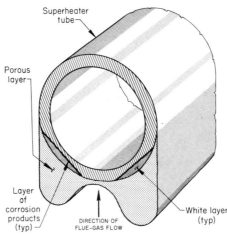

Fig. 19. Schematic illustration of the three layers formed during coal-ash corrosion of a superheater tube

Residues from the combustion process, called ash, normally comprise 6 to 20% of bituminous coals, but may run as high as 30%. The composition of coal ash varies widely, but is composed chiefly of silicon, aluminum, iron and calcium compounds, with smaller amounts of magnesium, titanium, sodium and potassium compounds.

Wood, bagasse (crushed juiceless remains of sugar cane) and other vegetable wastes used as fuel in some industrial plants contain lower amounts of ash than coal contains. In many respects, however, the compositions of these vegetable ashes resemble that of coal ash.

Fuel oils have ash contents that seldom exceed 0.2%. Even so, corrosion and fouling of oil-fired boilers can be particularly troublesome because of the nature of oil-ash deposits. The main contaminants in fuel oil are vanadium, sodium and sulfur — elements that form a wide variety of compounds, many of which are extremely corrosive.

Coal-Ash Corrosion. During combustion of coal, the minerals in the burning coal are exposed to high temperatures and to the strongly reducing effects of generated gases, such as carbon monoxide and hydrogen. Aluminum, iron, potassium, sodium and sulfur compounds are partly decomposed, releasing volatile alkali compounds and sulfur oxides (predominantly SO_2, plus small amounts of SO_3). The remaining portion of the mineral matter reacts to form glassy particles known as fly ash.

Coal-ash corrosion starts with the deposition of fly ash on surfaces that operate predominantly at temperatures from 540 to 705 C (about 1000 to 1300 F) — mainly, surfaces of superheater and reheater tubes. These deposits may be loose and powdery, or may be sintered or slag-type masses that are more adherent. Over an extended period of time, volatile alkali and sulfur compounds condense on the fly ash and react with it to

form complex alkali sulfates such as $KAl(SO_4)_2$ and $Na_3Fe(SO_4)_3$ at the boundary between the metal and the deposit. The reactions that produce alkali sulfates are believed to depend in part on the catalytic oxidation of SO_2 to SO_3 in the outer layers of the fly-ash deposit. The exact chemical reactions between the tube metal and the alkali sulfates are not well defined; nevertheless, certain characteristics of coal-ash corrosion are known:

1 Rapid attack occurs at temperatures between the melting temperature of the sulfate mixture and the limit of thermal stability for the mixture.

2 Corrosion rate is a nonlinear function of metal temperature, being highest at temperatures from 675 to 730 C (about 1250 to 1350 F).

3 Corrosion is almost always associated with sintered or slag-type deposits.

4 The deposit consists of three distinct layers, as shown in Fig. 19. The porous, outermost layer comprises the bulk of the deposit and is composed essentially of the same compounds as those found in fly ash. The innermost layer (shown as heavy black lines in Fig. 19) is a thin, glassy substance composed primarily of corrosion products of iron. The middle layer, called the white layer, is whitish or yellowish in color, often is fused, and is largely water-soluble, producing an acid solution.

5 Coal-ash corrosion can occur with any bituminous coal, but is more likely when the coal contains more than 3.5% sulfur and 0.25% chlorine.

6 None of the common tube materials is immune from attack, although the 18-8 austenitic stainless steels corrode at slower rates than lower-alloy grades.

Particles of fly ash deposit on superheater and reheater tubes in a characteristic pattern (see Fig. 19) in relation to the direction of flue-gas flow. The tube surfaces are corroded most heavily beneath the thickest portions of the deposit. When deposits are removed, shallow macropitting can be seen. Eventually, the tube wall becomes thinned to the point where the material can no longer withstand the pressure within the tube, and the tube ruptures, as in the example that follows.

Example 6. Coal-Ash Corrosion of a Chromium-Molybdenum Steel Superheater Tube (Fig. 20)

The top tube of a horizontal superheater bank in the reheat furnace of a steam generator ruptured as shown in Fig. 20 after about 7½ years of service (normal service life would have been 30 years). The tube consisted of 2½-in.-diam by 0.220-in.-wall ferritic steel tubing welded to 2½-in.-diam by 0.134-in.-wall austenitic stainless steel tubing. The rupture occurred in the ferritic steel tubing, near the welded joint.

The ferritic steel tubing, used in the low-operating-temperature portion of the tube, was made of 2.25Cr-1Mo steel (ASME SA-213, grade T22); the austenitic steel tubing was made of type 321 stainless steel (ASME SA-213, grade TP321H).

The surface temperature of the tube was 620 to 695 C (about 1150 to 1280 F), which was higher than the operating temperature in use up to about nine months earlier. At that time, the exit-steam temperature had been raised from about 520 C (970 F) to about 540 C (1000 F).

Investigation. The ferritic steel portion of the tube had split longitudinally for about 1½ in. along the top surface. Heavy corrosion had occurred in the region of the rupture (see especially the portion to the left of the rupture in Fig. 20).

The top surface of the tube in the rupture area was free of deposits, but the sides and bottom were covered with a heavy accumulation of red and white deposits that had a barklike appearance (Fig. 20). The nearby stainless steel portion was free of deposits but did show some pitting corrosion.

Spectrographic analysis showed that the ferritic tube steel contained 2.10% Cr and 1.10% Mo, both of which were within specified limits.

The white deposit was identified as sodium-potassium sulfate, $(Na,K)SO_4$, containing about 3% alkali acid sulfate, $(Na,K)HSO_4$. The red deposit was found to be mainly Fe_2O_3 plus about 5% SiO_2, 2% Al_2O_3 and 0.5% Cr_2O_3. Attack of the steel by the alkali acid sulfate, which has a low melting point, both thinned the tube wall and produced the red deposit. This type of corrosion is known to be severe on chromium-molybdenum steel at temperatures of about 595 to 705 C (about 1100 to 1300 F). Where the tube surface had been exposed to intermittent blasts of air from soot blowers, the corrosion products had been carried away. Although stainless steel also is vulnerable to this type of attack, the reaction is slower, and only a slight amount of tube-wall thinning was detected on the stainless steel portion of this tube.

The operating records showed two probable causes of the corrosion: (a) the increase in operating temperature, and (b) the use of coal with an ash-fusion temperature 28 C (50 F) lower than normal during the week immediately prior to the failure. Use of this coal could have caused severe slagging conditions in the boiler.

Sectioning of the tube through the region of failure showed that the attack by the alkali acid sulfate had significantly reduced tube-wall thickness. Metallographic examination revealed a structure that was largely normal except for marked spheroidization of the carbides, which indicated appreciable service time at temperatures close to the Ac_1 temperature.

Conclusions. Rupture of the tube was attributed to thinning of the wall by coal-ash corrosion to the point at which the steam pressure in the tube constituted an overload of the remaining wall. The attack was accelerated by the increase in operating temperature and may have been influenced by temporary use of an inferior grade of coal.

Corrective Measures. Adjacent tubes, which also showed evidence of wall thinning, were reinforced by pad welding. Type 304 stainless steel shields were welded to the stainless steel portions of the top reheater tubes and were held in place about the Cr-Mo steel portions of the tubes by steel

Fig. 20. Superheater tube, made of 2.25Cr-1Mo steel (ASME SA-213, grade T22), that ruptured because of thinning by coal-ash corrosion (Example 6)

bands. These shields were intended as a temporary expedient against coal-ash corrosion and not as a permanent solution. Because the shields would not be cooled by steam flow, their temperature was expected to be above 705 C (1300 F), the maximum at which coal-ash corrosion would occur, and little corrosion was anticipated. The replacement for the ruptured tube was left bare to permit assessment of the degree of corrosion that would ensue after the improvements in coal quality and operating temperature were adopted.

The superheater operated for about ten years with no further ruptures or additional repairs. At that time, the tubes were inspected and those that were thinned the most were replaced; this amounted to about 10% of the superheater bank.

Oil-Ash Corrosion. During combustion of fuel oils, organic compounds (including those containing vanadium or sulfur) decompose and react with oxygen. The resulting volatile oxides are carried along in the flue gases. Sodium, which usually is present in the oil as a chloride, reacts with the sulfur oxides to form sulfates. Initially, vanadium pentoxide (V_2O_5) condenses as a semifluid slag on furnace walls, boiler tubes and superheater tubes — in fact, virtually anywhere in the high-temperature region of the boiler. Sodium oxide reacts with the vanadium pentoxide to form complex compounds, especially vanadates $(nNa_2O \cdot V_2O_5)$ and vanadylvanadates $(nNa_2O \cdot V_2O_4 \cdot mV_2O_5)$. These complex compounds, some of which have melting temperatures as low as 249 C (480 F), not only foul tube surfaces but also actively corrode them.

Slag of equilibrium thickness (0.12 to 0.25 in.) has developed in experimental furnaces within periods of time as short as 100 hr. Slag insulates the tubes, resulting in an increase in the temperature of the slag, which in turn increases the rate of corrosion and also promotes further deposition of ash. Thicker slag deposits generally lead to greater corrosion, because slag temperatures are higher and more of the corrodent is present to react with tube materials. However, higher slag temperatures also make the slag more fluid so that it will flow more

readily on vertical surfaces. Consequently, slag generally builds up in corners and on horizontal surfaces, such as at the bases of water walls and around tube supports in the superheater.

Oil-ash corrosion affects all the common structural alloys. The mechanism is believed to be catalytic oxidation of the metal by reaction with vanadium pentoxide or with the complex vanadates or vanadylvanadates. Even highly corrosion-resistant materials such as 60Cr-40Ni and 50Cr-50Ni cast alloys, which sometimes are used for superheater-tube supports, are not immune. In addition, nonmetallic refractory materials used for furnace linings are attacked by vanadium slag; the mechanism of this attack appears to be a dissolution or slagging type of attack rather than the direct chemical attack that characteristically occurs with metals.

Low-Temperature Corrosion. In low-temperature zones of flue-gas passages, corrosion is caused chiefly by condensed water vapor containing dissolved SO_3 and CO_2. The dew point of sulfuric acid, which is the most active corrodent, ordinarily ranges from 120 to 150 C (about 250 to 300 F) for SO_3 concentrations of 15 to 30 ppm, which are common for coal-fired boilers. The dew point of the acidic vapors depends on (a) the amount of moisture in the fuel and in the combustion air, (b) the quantity of excess air, (c) the amount of hydrogen in the fuel, and (d) the amount of steam used for soot blowing — all of which influence the amount of water vapor in the flue gas.

Condensation of acidic vapors is most prevalent in air heaters, precipitators, stack coolers, flues and stacks, and near the inlets of economizers in units without feedwater heaters. Factors that increase the likelihood of acid condensation include: (a) low flue-gas flow, such as occurs during start-up and during periods of low-load operation; (b) excessively low flue-gas-exit temperatures during normal operation; (c) too great an amount of excess air of high humidity; and (d) very low atmospheric temperatures. Figure 21 is a graph of suggested minimum metal temperatures for avoiding external corrosion in economizers and air heaters; the temperatures are plotted as functions of the type of fuel and the amount of sulfur in the fuel.

Low-alloy steels, particularly those containing copper, have been used successfully in economizers and air heaters that are prone to low-temperature corrosion. An additional advantage of these alloys is their good resistance to pitting caused by excess oxygen in boiler water.

The deposits that form as a result of low-temperature corrosion may contain corrosion products, fly ash and the products of chemical reaction of the condensed acid with fly-ash constituents. Many of the compounds in these deposits are water soluble and thus can be removed conveniently by washing the affected areas with water. However, the deposits sometimes become difficult to remove, especially when they are allowed to accumulate until they completely plug passages or when they contain insoluble compounds such as calcium sulfate.

Low-temperature corrosion is encountered more often in oil-fired units than in coal-fired units, because the vanadium in oil-ash deposits is a catalyst for oxidation of SO_2 to SO_3, and because oil firing produces less ash than coal firing. In coal-fired units, a substantial portion of the sulfur oxides is absorbed by fly-ash deposits in the high-temperature regions, where the sulfur oxides participate in coal-ash corrosion. Furthermore, coal ash, which is composed chiefly of basic compounds, partly neutralizes the condensed acids when it deposits on moist surfaces in low-temperature regions. Oil ash, which is mainly acidic, is incapable of neutralizing condensed acids.

Control of Corrosion. Fire-side corrosion rarely can be eliminated altogether. Obviously, if alkali and sulfur could be removed from coal, or vanadium and sulfur from oil, prior to combustion, fireside corrosion would largely disappear. However, although there are some processes for removing contaminants from these fuels, they are both expensive and partly ineffective. Reduction of fire-side corrosion can be accomplished by one or more of the following methods, listed in approximately the descending order of their effectiveness:

1 Fuel selection
2 Combustion control
3 Boiler design and construction
4 Periodic ash removal
5 Use of fuel additives.

Frequently, several of these measures are required rather than just one.

Fuel Selection. Use of ashless or sulfur-free fuel is perhaps the most direct means of minimizing fire-side corrosion. Most natural and manufactured gaseous fuels are ashless, whereas most oils, coals, cokes, vegetation, residues and waste

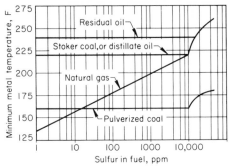

Fig. 21. Suggested minimum metal temperatures to avoid flue-gas corrosion in economizers and air heaters, plotted as a function of as-fired sulfur contents of various fuels (Redrawn from Ref 1)

gases have some ash content. Any type of fuel may contain sulfur; few coals, oils, tars, or burnable wastes are sulfur-free, whereas gases are more likely to be sulfur-free or to have low sulfur contents. Some fuels, such as the "black liquor" burned in kraft-mill recovery furnaces, have very substantial sulfur contents.

Some boilers are fitted with burners that can use more than one type of fuel; others are fitted with auxiliary burners to permit firing of secondary fuels (generally, main and auxiliary burners are not fired together). Most boilers are built to burn only one type of fuel, and thus selection of low-ash or low-sulfur fuel involves selection of a specific type of boiler as well. Boiler operators should always be aware of the composition of the fuel being burned, so that they can properly adjust operating conditions to minimize ash deposition.

Sometimes, use of a high-sulfur fuel cannot be avoided. In such instances, close control of operating conditions is mandatory. For example, in a fire-tube boiler that burned sulfur-contaminated refinery gas, leaks in the carbon steel tubes in the fifth pass caused the boiler to be taken out of service. Sulfuric acid corrosion on the internal surfaces of the tube was determined to have caused the leaks. Apparently, the operator had failed to purge the boiler by burning fuel gas with a low sulfur content for a sufficient length of time prior to several previous shutdowns, and acid had condensed in the tubes as the boiler cooled through the dew point of the acid in the flue gas. Corrosion of this type normally is not a problem, provided that clean fuel gas is burned long enough to expel all sulfur compounds from the tubes before the boiler is allowed to cool down.

Combustion control — that is, adjustment of firing rate, amount of excess air, air temperature, and amount of recirculated flue gas (applicable only to boilers equipped for gas tempering) — can be very effective in controlling the amount and composition of ash deposits. For example, in an experimental boiler burning high-vanadium, high-sulfur residual oil, it was found that reducing the amount of excess air from 7% to 1 to 2% reduced the rate of corrosion of 18-8 stainless steel superheater tubes by as much as 75%. This reduction in corrosion rate ap-

parently occurred because the low amount of excess air did not permit oxidation of vanadium and sulfur to their highest states of oxidation and thus prevented formation of the most corrosive oil-ash compounds. Low-temperature corrosion was virtually eliminated by maintaining excess air at 1 to 2%. This effect of low excess air on low-temperature corrosion has been widely substantiated, but the results are not as conclusive for high-temperature corrosion.

Boiler design and construction, including tube size and spacing, furnace configuration, size and direction of flue-gas passages, and size and location of baffles or shields, can help control ash deposition. The ability to make changes in boiler design specifically for the purpose of corrosion control is somewhat limited by the need to maintain proper gas-temperature distribution in order to facilitate efficient generation of steam.

Periodic ash removal, although less effective in controlling fire-side corrosion than procedures that reduce ash deposition, is nevertheless an important aspect of boiler operation. Ash removal prevents development of conditions that alter the distribution of metal temperatures on heat-transfer surfaces, which can lead to problems such as failure by overheating. Almost all water-tube boilers are provided with soot blowers or air lances. Soot blowers and lances direct jets of air or steam against heat-transfer surfaces to remove fire-side deposits. The effectiveness of soot blowers in performing this task depends on (a) the design and location of the soot blowers, (b) the blowing medium and its temperature, (c) the properties of the deposit, especially its friability and adherence, and (d) the frequency and duration of soot-blower operation. It is important to coordinate combustion control with the soot-blowing schedule to ensure that deposits are initially friable, or loosely adherent and powdery, and that they are removed before they are transformed into sintered masses.

Additives are used to control both coal-ash and oil-ash corrosion. Finely powdered magnesia, dolomite and alumina are injected into furnace gases or blown onto heat-transfer surfaces through soot blowers. Sometimes, additives are mixed with fuel oil prior to combustion. Additives promote the formation of ash deposits that are easily removed. Additives also reduce low-temperature corrosion by reacting with SO_3 to form innocuous sulfates. This reduces the SO_3 content of the flue gas, thus reducing the likelihood that acid will condense in low-temperature regions.

Failure by Fatigue

Fatigue often is considered the most common mechanism of service failure of mechanical devices. Basically, fatigue involves nucleation and propagation of brittle-appearing cracks under fluctuating (cyclic) loading at stresses that have peak values less than the tensile strength of the material. Macroscopic and microscopic features of fatigue fractures are discussed in the articles that begin on pages 57 and 95 in this volume. The latter article covers analysis of fatigue failures in depth. Additional information, especially on high-temperature fatigue and thermal fatigue, can be found in the article that begins on page 249.

Steam equipment may fail by fatigue if mechanical service stresses are fluctuating or vibratory, or if thermal cycles or thermal gradients impose sufficiently high peak stresses. Vibratory loads in steam equipment are fairly common — for example, as a result of (a) slight imbalance in rotating equipment; (b) rapidly fluctuating fluid pressures (water hammer); (c) vibration transmitted through settings or mountings; or (d) turbulent fluid flow, especially at high flow rates. All but a few of the various components in a steam plant are subjected to pressure and thermal cycling during start-up and shutdown. Transient thermal gradients of a lesser degree may occur during operation, especially during changes in power output.

In contrast to most mechanical stresses, thermal stresses often are difficult to avoid and, if severe, can lead to fracture in relatively few cycles. Cyclic strain is more important than cyclic stress in thermal fatigue, because nonuniform or differential thermal expansion is the usual source of the cyclic loading. Frequently, extended periods of high-temperature operation ensue between thermal cycles, and thermally activated processes such as stress relaxation, stress oxidation and second-phase precipitation may alter material properties between successive cycles, thus changing resistance to thermal fatigue and to other failure mechanisms.

Identification of Fatigue Fracture. On a fracture surface, features that indicate fatigue as the fracture mechanism include beach marks, multiple origins, ratchet marks, fatigue striations and smooth, rubbed regions. Of these five types of features, striations are the most reliable indicators of fatigue. In the following example, positive identification of fatigue by observation of striations on the fracture surface was instrumental in determining the cause of failure and the appropriate solution.

Example 7. Fatigue Failure of Carbon-Molybdenum Steel Boiler Tubes Caused by Vibration

Tubes in a marine boiler on a new ship failed after short service lives. Circumferential brittle cracking occurred in the carbon-molybdenum steel tubes near the points where the tubes were attached to the steam drum.

Visual, macroscopic and metallographic examination did not disclose the reason for the failures. There was no evidence of overheating, excessive corrosion, or metallurgical damage caused by improper fabrication.

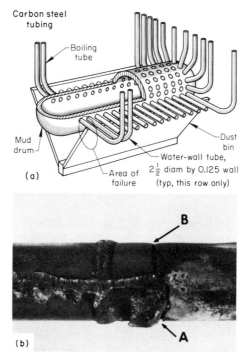

Fig. 22. (a) *Portion of a stationary boiler in which a carbon steel water-wall tube failed by fatigue fracture at the weld joining the tube to a dust bin.* (b) *Photograph of fractured tube; fatigue crack is at arrow A, and ductile fracture is at arrow B.* (Example 8)

However, when the fracture surfaces were examined by electron microscopy at high magnification, fatigue striations were found. It was concluded that the fatigue failures were caused by vibrations resulting from normal steam flow at high steam demand. The tubes were supported too rigidly near the steam drum, resulting in concentration of vibratory strain in the regions of failure.

The method of supporting the tubes was changed to reduce the amount of restraint and thus the strain concentration, and no further failures occurred. In similar circumstances, it might be necessary to lengthen or shorten tubes (or pipes), or to reduce operating load, to eliminate fatigue caused by vibrations resulting from normal fluid flow.

Mechanism of Fatigue Fracture. Fatigue results from reversed plastic strain in metallic crystals. If plastic straining is confined to microscopic or submicroscopic regions in an otherwise elastically stressed component, it is likely that a single crack will occur, originating at the point of maximum local stress and minimum local strength in the entire structure. Microstructural discontinuities such as inclusions, grain boundaries, and intersections of slip planes with free surfaces are the usual microscopic sites of crack initiation. Cracking occurs only after many cycles of loading (high-cycle fatigue), and usually there is no macroscopic evidence of plastic flow. On the other hand, when plastic straining is more extensive, there is a greater likelihood that cracks will initiate at many

discontinuities after fewer cycles of loading (low-cycle fatigue) and that there will be macroscopic evidence of plastic flow.

Fatigue-crack initiation most often occurs at structural features that concentrate macroscopic stress, such as notches, fillets, holes, joints, changes in section thickness, and material discontinuities. In addition, service-induced damage such as dents, gouges and corrosion pits frequently raise local stress sufficiently to initiate fatigue cracks. In the next example, a local stress raiser at a welded joint caused severe stress concentration, which led to fatigue failure.

Example 8. Fatigue Failure of a Carbon Steel Water-Wall Tube Because of an Undercut at a Welded Joint (Fig. 22)

In a new stationary boiler, furnace water-wall tubes were welded to the top of a dust bin for rigid support (see Fig. 22a). The tubes were 2½ in. in outside diameter and 0.125 in. in wall thickness, and were made of carbon steel to ASME SA-226 specifications. Shortly after start-up, one of the tubes broke at the welded joint.

The portion of the fracture surface adjacent to the attachment weld around the bottom half of the tube had a flat, brittle appearance. Over the remainder of the tube wall the fracture was ductile, with a noticeable shear lip and necking. Beach marks were evident on the brittle portion of the fracture surface, indicating fatigue to have been the fracture mechanism. The origin was identified as a small crevicelike undercut at the edge of the weld bead. In Fig. 22(b), the origin is shown at A and local necking opposite the origin is shown at B.

Cracking began by fatigue from a severe stress raiser. As the fracture progressed out of the region of high restraint where the tube was welded to the dust bin, the fracture changed from fatigue to ductile overload. It was concluded that the crevicelike undercut was the primary cause of the fracture and that the source of the necessary fluctuating stress was tube vibration inherent in boiler operation.

The remaining water-wall tubes in the row were inspected by the magnetic-particle method; several other tubes were found to have small fatigue cracks adjacent to the welds attaching the tubes to the dust bin. The broken tube was replaced, cracks in other tubes were repaired by welding, and the attachment welds were blended smoothly into the tube surfaces for the entire length of the dust bin. No further failures occurred after the severe undercut was eliminated.

Low-Cycle Fatigue. Pressure and thermal cycling during start-up and shutdown are the most common causes of low-cycle fatigue failures. Design factors that concentrate strain influence low-cycle fatigue as well as high-cycle fatigue; however, the effect is not quite the same. When service stresses are high enough to be conducive to low-cycle fatigue, the presence of a severe stress raiser often will cause complete fracture to occur on the first load cycle. Mild stress raisers

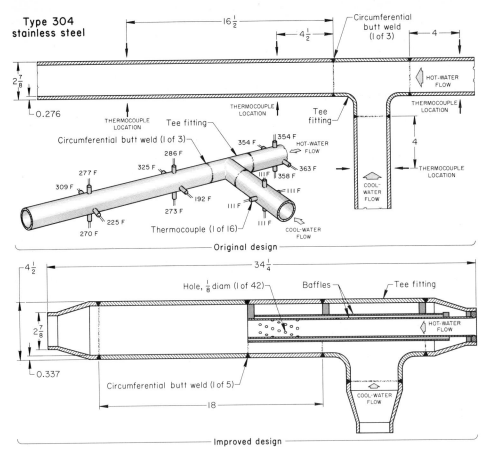

Fig. 23. Type 304 stainless steel tee fitting that failed by low-cycle thermal fatigue, as originally designed. View of original design shows locations of thermocouples used in analyzing thermal gradients, and typical temperatures at each thermocouple location. The analysis resulted in the improved design shown. (Example 9)

usually do not lead to fracture on the first cycle but only induce localized yielding. The resultant plastic flow may redistribute the stress, but usually not enough to avoid further yielding on successive cycles.

In piping exposed to high temperatures, for instance, restraint produces bending moments (and strain) in the piping system when it expands at start-up; strain reversal occurs at shutdown. Elbows and U-bends frequently undergo larger bending moments than straight sections. The mild stress concentration associated with these bends can, under certain conditions, induce plastic strain in the bends, resulting in cracking after a sufficient number of thermal cycles. The thermal expansion of the entire system is important in determining the magnitude of strain concentration, and consequently the number of cycles to failure. Lack of flexibility is a frequent cause of low-cycle fatigue in piping systems. Sometimes, major redesign of the system is required to remove or reduce restraint, thus allowing the system to accommodate thermal strains by deflecting elastically over a greater portion of the system than was possible in the original design. Major redesign was used in the following example, not to reduce re-

straint but rather to eliminate the source of a fluctuating thermal gradient.

Example 9. Low-Cycle Thermal-Fatigue Failure of a Type 304 Stainless Steel Tee Fitting (Fig. 23)

Several failures occurred in 2½-in. schedule 80 type 304 stainless steel (ASME SA-312, grade TP304) piping in a steam-plant heat-exchanger system, in the vicinity of tee fittings at which cool water returning from the heat exchanger was combined with hot water from a bypass (see "Original design" in Fig. 23). During operation, various portions of the piping were subjected to temperatures ranging from 29 to 288 C (85 to 550 F).

Visual and Metallographic Examination. Each of the failures consisted of cracking in and/or close to the circumferential butt weld joining the tee fitting to the downstream pipe leg, where the hot bypass water mixed with the cool return water. The cracking was transgranular and was located (a) within the weld, (b) adjacent to the weld or (c) in the base metal of either the pipe or the tee. Several cracks resulted in leakage. In one instance, the welds were radiographed before any leak was observed, and a long crack was found in the weld between the tee fitting and the downstream pipe leg. It was established that this crack had developed in service and had not been an original welding defect. In another instance, a crack occurred in a pipe segment

about 4 in. from the nearest weld. This crack was outside the heat-affected zone of the weld; however, additional cracks were found in the tee fitting and in the welds. Because propagation of the cracks was entirely transgranular, thermal fatigue was a more likely cause of failure than was stress-corrosion cracking, in which some intergranular cracking would be expected.

Temperature Measurements. To investigate thermal stresses, an array of thermocouples was installed in two tee fittings in the arrangement shown in Fig. 23. The temperatures at different points along the length and around the circumference of the piping also are shown for one of the two instrumented fittings; temperatures were similar for the other fitting. It was concluded that circumferential temperature gradients, in combination with inadequate flexibility in the piping system as a whole, had caused all of the failures.

Corrective Measures. To alleviate the thermal-stress pattern, the tee fitting was redesigned as shown in the "Improved design" view in Fig. 23. A larger tee fitting, made of 4-in. schedule 80S type 316H stainless steel pipe (ASME SA-312, grade TP316H), was used and an 18-in.-long extension of 4-in. schedule 80 type 316H pipe was added to the downstream leg. Two concentric tubular baffles, both made of type 316H stainless steel, were placed in the run direction of the interior of the tee fitting. The inner baffle (18 in. long, 1½ in. in outside diameter, 0.085 in. in wall thickness, and perforated at the downstream end) carried the full flow of the hot water from the bypass. The outer baffle (16 in. long, 2 in. in outside diameter and 0.085 in. in wall thickness), which was open at each end, served to insulate the inner baffle from the cool water entering the fitting from the heat exchanger and provided a region in which the cool water could form an annulus to receive the core of hot bypass water entering the downstream extension beyond the baffles. Mixing in that region was possible without generation of damaging circumferential thermal gradients.

Thermal fatigue may result in either low-cycle or high-cycle failure. Low-cycle thermal fatigue usually is associated with large plastic strains and most often is caused by large changes in temperature or large differences in thermal expansion between two structural members. If a change in temperature is especially severe, and if it occurs rapidly, it is called thermal shock; failures due to thermal shock generally occur in ten thermal cycles or less — sometimes in only one thermal cycle when the material is sufficiently brittle.

High-cycle thermal fatigue frequently results from intermittent wetting of a hot surface by water having a considerably lower temperature. In such instances, the wetted surface contracts rapidly whereas the metal below the surface does not; this produces biaxial tensile stresses in the wetted surface. As the water absorbs heat and evaporates, the temperature of the surface returns to its previous value and surface stresses are relaxed. After a sufficient number of thermal cycles, a crazed pattern of cracks appears on the surface (see Fig. 24). Eventually, one or more of the surface thermal-fatigue cracks may propagate completely through the section by fatigue, or by another mechanism, as discussed under "Multiple-Mode Failure" on page 544.

Example 14 on page 274 in the article on Elevated-Temperature Failures describes the failure of a thick-wall cast steel casing for a steam turbine. The basic mode of cracking was by thermal fatigue, although portions of the fracture surface exhibited characteristics of crack propagation by corrosion fatigue.

Cracking that is caused by thermal fatigue sometimes resembles cracking caused by corrosion fatigue or stress corrosion. However, in contrast to corrosion fatigue and stress corrosion, which can be retarded by use of inhibitors, coatings or galvanic protection, thermal fatigue will proceed regardless of what is done to alter the environment or to coat the metal to prevent direct contact with the environment. Thermal fatigue can be prevented only by eliminating excessive strain caused by thermal cycling.

Ferritic steels generally are considered to be more resistant to thermal fatigue than are austenitic steels. This has been confirmed in several instances in which parts made of ferritic steels have withstood service conditions under which austenitic steel parts have failed. One such instance involved two flanged 18Cr-12Ni austenitic stainless steel valves that were bolted to 5Cr-0.5Mo ferritic steel piping in a petroleum plant. The valves were exposed alternately to atmospheric temperature and to an elevated temperature between 595 and 620 C (1100 and 1150 F). Each valve was subjected to 1½ thermal cycles per day (that is, three cycles every two days); about eight hours elapsed between the start of the heating portion of the cycle and the start of the cooling portion, and vice versa. After ten days of operation, cracks were found radiating from the bore into the flange of one valve; the other valve failed shortly thereafter. The mating 5Cr-0.5Mo ferritic steel piping gave excellent service, as did replacement valves made of 9Cr-1Mo ferritic steel.

The superiority of ferritic alloy steel over several wrought austenitic stainless steels in applications involving thermal cycling is a result of differences in thermal conductivity and coefficient of thermal expansion between the two types of steel. The higher thermal conductivity of ferritic alloy steel results in a lower temperature gradient between the surface and the interior when the surface of a cool part is heated (or when the surface of a hot part is cooled). This lower temperature gradient results in less

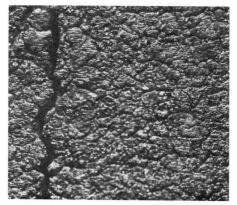

Fig. 24. Crazed pattern of thermal-fatigue cracking on the outer surface of a stainless steel tube, shown at about 4×. See also Fig. 28.

thermal stress in the surface layer. In addition, because of the lower coefficient of expansion of ferritic steel, a given temperature gradient produces less expansion, and thus less thermal stress, in ferritic alloy steel than in wrought austenitic stainless steel. The combination of these two factors can result in appreciably less thermal stress, and longer life, for ferritic steel under a given set of cyclic thermal conditions.

Corrosion fatigue is discussed in detail in the article beginning on page 240 in this volume. Strictly speaking, few service failures occur by pure fatigue. Most fatigue failures actually occur by corrosion fatigue, because most parts are exposed simultaneously to cyclic stress and to a medium that is somewhat aggressive toward the material; in this strict sense, even air can be considered an aggressive medium. In a more practical sense, however, because fatigue properties normally are determined in air, corrosion fatigue can be thought of as fatigue that takes place in an environment in which the combined action of corrosion and cyclic loading results in more rapid crack initiation and/or propagation than would occur in air. The microscopic mechanism of corrosion fatigue appears to be related to the galvanic or preferential dissolution processes that are believed to be responsible for stress-corrosion cracking. In fact, all alloys that are susceptible to stress corrosion in a given medium appear to be susceptible to rapid corrosion fatigue in the same medium. However, corrosion fatigue has been identified as a failure mechanism in alloys that are considered immune to stress corrosion (but not immune to ordinary corrosion in the same environment).

The length of time necessary for a crack to be initiated and propagated by corrosion fatigue can be increased — sometimes substantially — by reducing or eliminating either the fluctuating stress or the corrosiveness of the environment. In addition to reduction of stress

or of stress concentration, the following measures have been used successfully to combat corrosion fatigue: (a) use of corrosion inhibitors; (b) cathodic protection; (c) shielding of the surface of a part from contact with the environment by seals, by paint, plastic or other nonmetallic coatings, or by plating with corrosion-resistant metals; and (d) use of a more corrosion-resistant material. The last method should be used with care, however, because some of the ordinarily corrosion-resistant materials can be more susceptible to failure by corrosion fatigue in certain environments than the materials they replace. Coatings should be used to combat corrosion fatigue only in instances where local strains are uniform and low. The protection afforded by coatings, either metallic or nonmetallic, is only skin deep, and local breaches of this protective skin expose the metal underlying the coating to the same conditions as those that ordinarily lead to failure of uncoated parts.

Failures Caused by Erosion

Erosion involves impact of large numbers of small solid or liquid particles against a surface, or is caused by the collapse of gas-filled bubbles in a cavitating liquid. Erosion by solid particles is a form of abrasive wear, whereas liquid-impingement erosion — for example, as caused by the water droplets in wet steam — is more like cavitation erosion.

The microscopic mechanisms of material removal by erosion are discussed in the articles on Wear Failures (see page 134) and Liquid-Erosion Failures (see page 154) in this volume. Failures caused by these mechanisms can be readily recognized by visual examination.

Abrasive erosion of screen tubes or superheater tubes results from impact by particles of fly ash entrained in the flue gases. Erosion is enhanced by high flow velocities; thus, partial fouling of gas passages in tube banks by deposition of fly ash can lead to erosion by forcing the flue gases to flow through smaller passages at higher velocity. This effect, sometimes called "laning", exposes tube surfaces to a greater probability of impact by particles having higher kinetic energy, thus increasing the rate of damage. Erosion by fly ash causes polishing, flat spots, wall thinning and eventual tube rupture.

Fly-ash erosion can be controlled by coating tube surfaces with refractory cements or other hard, wear-resistant materials, although this reduces the heat-transfer capability of the surfaces. An alternative method is channeling of gas flow away from critical areas with baffles.

Liquid-impingement erosion occurs chiefly in components that are subjected

Fig. 25. Cast iron suction bell, 18 in. in diameter, from a low-pressure general-service water pump, that failed by cavitation erosion after about five years of service. Note the deeply pitted surface and the irregular shape of the erosion pattern, both of which are typical characteristics of cavitation damage.

to high-velocity flow of wet steam. Among the components most susceptible to liquid-impingement erosion are low-pressure-turbine blades, low-temperature steam piping, and condenser or other heat-exchanger tubes that are subjected to direct impingement by wet steam. Corrosion may or may not occur simultaneously with liquid-impingement erosion.

Liquid-impingement erosion in tubing or piping is most likely when fluid velocities exceed 7 ft per second. Damage first occurs at locations where direction of flow changes, such as elbows or U-bends. Large-radius bends are less susceptible to such damage; however, use of erosion-resistant materials such as austenitic stainless steel often is more effective. Erosion of heat-exchanger tubes caused by impingement of wet steam sometimes can be eliminated by redirecting flow with baffles.

Cavitation erosion occurs in regions of a system where a combination of temperature and flow velocity causes growth and subsequent collapse of large quantities of vapor-filled bubbles in a flowing stream of liquid. Damage occurs at the points of bubble collapse. In steam plants, the components most often damaged by cavitation erosion are feed lines, pump casings and pump impellers. Figure 25 shows the typical appearance of a part extensively damaged by cavitation erosion; note that the surface is deeply and irregularly pitted.

Cavitation erosion is most effectively avoided by reduction of either flow ve-

locity or temperature (reduction of flow velocity is preferable). Other measures, including selection of material and the use of erosion-resistant welded overlays, are discussed on page 166 in the article on Liquid-Erosion Failures.

Failure by Stress-Corrosion Cracking

Stress-corrosion cracking occurs in specific alloys exposed to specific environments, as discussed in detail in the article that begins on page 205 in this

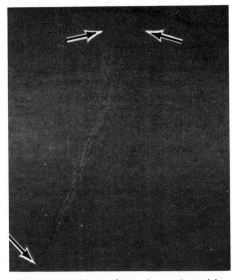

Fig. 26. Inside surface of an austenitic stainless steel superheater tube, showing a tight crack caused by stress corrosion. Arrows indicate ends of crack.

volume. Stress-corrosion cracking is a type of failure defined as fracture of a structural member under the combined effects of static tensile stress and a corrosive environment in circumstances where, if either the tensile stress or the corrosive environment were absent, fracture would not occur.

Stress-corrosion cracking can occur in boiler and superheater tubes, piping, valves, turbine casings and other parts, especially where feedwater or condensate can collect. Concentration of caustic in portions of systems that use conventional or coordinated phosphate methods of feedwater treatment is probably the most common cause of stress-corrosion (caustic) cracking in steam equipment. Aqueous solutions containing chloride ions can cause stress-corrosion cracking of austenitic stainless steel (see Example 11 on facing page), and solutions containing ammonia can cause stress-corrosion cracking of copper alloys. Stress oxidation in high-temperature regions also can occur.

Many cracks that result from stress corrosion are tight and difficult to detect visually (see Fig. 26); they are particularly difficult to detect on scaled surfaces. Liquid-penetrant examination is useful in locating tight stress-corrosion cracks but may not reveal all such cracks. Because the substances found in liquid penetrants are similar to some of the substances that cause stress-corrosion cracking, use of a liquid penetrant to detect a crack can interfere with the identification of fracture-surface deposits. Consequently, liquid penetrants should not be used without due consideration of their undesirable side effects on the over-all analysis.

Microscopic examination is required to confirm stress-corrosion cracking as the mechanism of failure. Stress-corrosion cracks may be transgranular or intergranular, depending on the alloy and the environment, but usually are extensively branched, becoming more branched as cracking progresses.

Although service conditions may produce static stress that exceeds the threshold for stress-corrosion cracking, residual stress more often is responsible. Residual stress may result from metallurgical transformations or from uneven heating or cooling, especially in weldments. Hot or cold forming processes can introduce residual stress of high magnitude, as can assembly processes such as press fitting, bolting or riveting. Incidental damage such as bending or hammering during assembly is less frequently a source of residual stress. In the example that follows, residual stress that resulted from welding with a high heat input was the primary stress that caused stress-corrosion cracking in a length of stainless steel piping in heat-exchanger service.

Example 10. Stress-Corrosion Cracking of a Type 304 Stainless Steel Pipe, Caused by Residual Welding Stresses

A 6-in. schedule 80S type 304 stainless steel pipe (6⅝ in. in outside diameter and 0.432 in. in wall thickness), which had served as an equalizer line in the primary loop of a pressurized-water reactor, was found to contain several circumferential cracks 2 to 4 in. long. Two of these cracks, which had penetrated the pipe wall, were responsible for leaks detected in a hydrostatic test performed during a general inspection after seven years of service.

On-Site Inspection. The general inspection had included careful scrutiny of all pipe welds by both visual and ultrasonic examination. Following discovery of the two leaks, the entire line of 6-in. pipe, which contained 16 welds, was carefully scanned. Five additional defects were discovered, all circumferential and all in heat-affected zones adjacent to welds. In contrast, scans of larger-diameter pipes in the system (up to 22 in. in diameter) disclosed no such defects.

Metallurgical Studies. Samples of the 6-in. pipe were submitted to three laboratories for independent examination. Inspection in all three laboratories disclosed that all the defects were circumferential, intergranular cracks that had originated at the inside surface of the pipe and that were typical of stress-corrosion attack. A majority of the cracks had occurred in heat-affected zones adjacent to circumferential welds. Some cracks had penetrated the entire pipe wall; others had reached a depth of two-thirds of the wall thickness. In general, the cracks were 2 to 4 in. long. Branches of the cracks that had approached weld deposits had halted without invading the structure (austenite plus delta ferrite) of the type 308 stainless steel welds. All heat-affected zones examined contained networks of precipitated carbides at the grain boundaries, which revealed that welding had sensitized the 304 stainless steel in those local areas.

Additional cracks, also intergranular and circumferential and originating at the inner surface of the pipe, were discovered at locations remote from any welds. These cracks penetrated only one-sixth to one-fourth of the wall thickness, through a solution-annealed structure showing evidence of some cold work at the inner surface.

Chemical Analysis. The water in this heat exchanger was of sufficient purity that corrosion had not been anticipated. The water conditions were as follows:

Temperature: 285 C (545 F)
Pressure: 1000 psi
pH: 6.5 to 7.5
Chloride content: < 0.1 ppm
Oxygen content: 0.2 to 0.3 ppm
Electrical conductivity: < 0.4 micromho/cm

Analysis of the pipe showed the chemical composition to be entirely normal for type 304 stainless steel. The material was certified by the producer as conforming to ASME SA-376, grade TP304. All available data indicated that the as-supplied pipe had been of acceptable quality.

Stress-Corrosion Tests. Several types of stress-corrosion tests were conducted. In one group of tests, samples of 6-in. type 304 stainless steel pipe were welded together

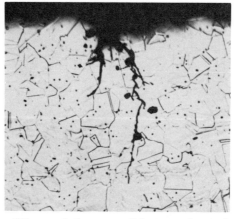

Micrograph shows a small transgranular crack that originated at a corrosion pit on the inside surface of the tubing and only partly penetrated the tubing wall. Specimen was etched in aqua regia; magnification, 250×.

Fig. 27. Section through type 316 stainless steel tubing that failed by stress-corrosion cracking because of exposure to chloride-contaminated steam condensate (Example 11)

using type 308 stainless steel filler metal. Two different welding procedures were used — one consisting of three passes with a high heat input, and the other consisting of ten passes with a low heat input. The welded samples were stressed and exposed to water containing 100 ppm dissolved oxygen at 285 C (545 F) and 1000 psi. Samples that were welded with the high-heat-input procedure, which promotes carbide precipitation and residual stress, cracked after 168 hr of exposure, whereas samples that were welded with the low-heat-input procedure remained crack-free. These results were considered significant, because service reports indicated that the cracked pipe had been welded using a high heat input and a small number of passes, and that the larger-diameter piping in the primary loop, which did not crack in service, had been welded with the use of a low-heat-input, multiple-pass procedure.

Conclusions. The intergranular stress-corrosion cracking of the 6-in. schedule 80S type 304 stainless steel pipe exposed to high-temperature, high-pressure, high-purity water in seven years of heat-exchanger service was believed to have been caused by the following factors:

1 **Stress.** The welding procedure, which employed few passes and high heat input, undoubtedly generated unacceptably high levels of residual stress in the heat-affected zones. The cold working of the internal surface in a sizing operation also set up residual stresses in areas apart from the welds. Both conditions were conducive to stress-corrosion cracking.

2 **Sensitization.** The high-heat-input welding caused precipitation of chromium carbides at the grain boundaries in the heat-affected zones. This rendered the steel sensitive to intergranular attack, which, combined with the residual stress, afforded a completely normal setting for stress-corrosion cracking.

3 **Environment.** Although the level of dissolved oxygen in the water was quite low, it was considered possible that, on the basis of prolonged exposure, oxygen in the range of 0.2 to 1.0 ppm could have provided the necessary specific ion.

Corrective Measure. All replacement pipe sections were installed using low-heat-input, multiple-pass welding procedures.

When stress corrosion is identified as the mechanism of a failure, the proper corrective action can be either a reduction in stress (or stress concentration) or an alteration of the environment. When the cause of failure is inadvertent concentration of a corrodent (or inadvertent exposure of the part to a corrosive foreign substance, such as use of a steam line to feed concentrated caustic during chemical cleaning), the preventive measure may be no more complicated than exclusion of the corrodent from that region of the system. In most instances, however, reduction of the level of residual stress is the most effective means of minimizing or preventing stress-corrosion cracking. In the example that follows, both removal of corrodent (chloride) and reduction of residual stress were recommended as measures for preventing stress-corrosion cracking.

Example 11. Stress-Corrosion Cracking of Type 316 Stainless Steel Tubing (Fig. 27)

A steam-condensate line made of type 316 stainless steel tubing 0.75 in. in outside diameter and 0.065 in. in wall thickness had been in service for five to six years when leakage occurred. The line was buried, with no wrapping, in a sandy, caustic soil. The line carried steam condensate at 120 C (250 F) with a 2-hr heat-up/cool-down cycle. No chemical treatment had been given to either the condensate or the boiler water. Two sections of the tubing, with a combined length of approximately 13 in., were submitted for laboratory analysis of the cause of the leakage.

Investigation. The outside surface of the tubing exhibited no signs of corrosion; however, on one of the sections there was a transverse crack along the edge of a ¼-in.-diam pitted area. Two adjacent areas were raised, resembling blisters, and also had transverse cracks along their edges. The cracks were irregular and had penetrated completely through the tube wall. The pitted area was believed to be a spall, and the blisters incipient spalls, resulting from stress-corrosion cracking that originated at the inner surface of the tube. The cracks, the spall and the blisters did not appear to have been related to any effect of the external environment.

The inside surface of the tubing was covered with a brown, powdery scale, was slightly rough, and contained small pits. Some cracks were found that had originated at pits on the inner surface but had not completely penetrated the tubing wall (see Fig. 27). The cracks were transgranular and branching, which is typical of chloride-induced stress-corrosion cracking of austenitic stainless steel.

To check for chlorides, the inside of the tubing was rinsed with distilled water and the rinse water was collected in a clean beaker. A few drops of silver nitrate solution were added to the rinse water, which

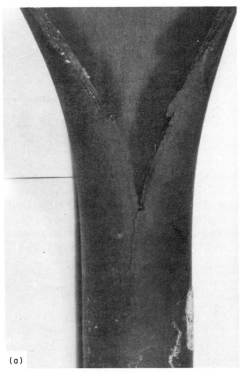

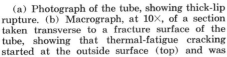

(a)   (b)

(a) Photograph of the tube, showing thick-lip rupture. (b) Macrograph, at 10×, of a section taken transverse to a fracture surface of the tube, showing that thermal-fatigue cracking started at the outside surface (top) and was followed by stress-rupture cracking in the inner half of the tube wall.

Thermal fatigue also produced cracking on the outside surface of the tube, in the crazed pattern shown in Fig. 24.

Fig. 28. Stainless steel superheater tube that failed by thermal fatigue and stress rupture

clouded slightly because of the formation of insoluble silver chloride. This test indicated that there was a substantial concentration of chlorides inside the tubing.

Conclusion. The tubing failed by chloride-induced stress-corrosion cracking. Chlorides in the steam condensate also caused corrosion and pitting of the inner surface of the tubing. Stress was produced when the tubing was bent during installation.

Recommendations. Water treatment should be provided to remove chlorides from the system. Continuous flow should be maintained throughout the entire tubing system to prevent concentration of chlorides. No chloride-containing water should be permitted to remain in the system during shutdown periods. Bending of tubing during installation should be avoided to reduce residual stress.

Multiple-Mode Failure

Many failures in steam systems involve more than one failure process — one that initiates the failure and another (or others) that eventually destroys the part. For example, fatigue failures that cause tubes or pipes to leak may start at corrosion pits. A failure that involved a combination of thermal fatigue and stress-rupture cracking is described in the following report:

The tube rupture shown in Fig. 28(a) has the macroscopic characteristics of a thick-lip rupture caused by overheating. However, as shown in Fig. 28(b), stress-rupture cracking was confined to the inner half of the tube wall. There was no microstructural evidence of overheating.

The outside surface of this 2⅛-in.-diam stainless steel superheater tube exhibited extensive crazing by thermal fatigue, as shown previously in Fig. 24. Apparently, cyclic thermal stress initiated cracking at the fire-side surface. Pressure stresses assisted in defining the preferential direction of fatigue-crack propagation (parallel to the tube axis and transverse through the tube wall), and stress-rupture cracking became the ultimate fracture process in the weakened tube.

The effects of internal and external scaling on tube ruptures caused by overheating are discussed in a previous section of this article. In tubes and other high-temperature structural components, thinning caused by corrosion or erosion also can lead to overheating-type failures. Corrosion or erosion, particularly on the fire-side surfaces of screen tubes and superheater tubes, may reduce the tube-wall thickness to the extent that the tube no longer can sustain the pressure stress without creep. Continued thinning will accelerate the onset of tertiary creep, ultimately leading to stress-rupture fracture. Because localized loss of material is responsible for increasing the local tube-wall stress, overheating-type ruptures often occur with little or no swelling. Internal grain separation will be evident in the microstructure only in the thinned region, and macroscopic examination of the fire-side surface usually is sufficient to reveal the extent of external attack. Localized overheating is not necessary for tube rupture to occur. Consequently, a lack of microstructural evidence of overheating would be a positive indicator that corrosion or erosion was a factor. Conversely, the presence of such evidence does not rule out corrosion or erosion as a cause of failure.

References

1. "Steam", 38th edition, Babcock & Wilcox Co., New York, 1972, 607 pages
2. R. W. Bailey, *Engineering,* Vol 129, 1930, p 265
3. R. W. Bailey, *Engineering,* Vol 133, 1932, p 261
4. W. L. Hemingway, "The Study of Graphitization", Edwards Valve Co., 1952, 11 pages

Selected References

H. Thielsch, "Defects and Failures in Pressure Vessels and Piping", Reinhold, New York, 1965

C. C. Osgood, "Fatigue Design", Wiley, New York, 1970

S. S. Manson, "Thermal Stress and Low-Cycle Fatigue", McGraw-Hill, New York, 1966

B. E. Gatewood, "Thermal Stresses", McGraw-Hill, New York, 1957

"Proceedings of International Conference on Fatigue of Metals", Institution of Mechanical Engineers, London, 1956

"Proceedings of Joint International Conference on Creep", Institution of Mechanical Engineers, London, 1963

H. Thielsch, Why High Temperature Piping Fails, *Metals Eng Quart,* Vol 10 (No. 1), 1970, p 7-11

O. Devereux, A. McEvily and R. Staehle (Editors), "Corrosion Fatigue: Chemistry, Mechanics and Microstructure", NACE, Houston, 1972

H. H. Uhlig, "Corrosion and Corrosion Control", 2nd edition, Wiley, New York, 1971

P. D. Stevens-Guille, Steam Generator Tube Failures: World Experience in Water-Cooled Nuclear Power Reactors During 1972, Chalk River Nuclear Laboratories (Ontario), Mar 1974

Failures of Heat Exchangers

*By the ASM Committee on Failures of Pressure Vessels, Boilers and Pressure Piping**

HEAT EXCHANGERS generally are used for the transfer of heat from combustion gases, steam or water to gases, vapors or liquids of various types. Heat exchangers are of tube, plate or sheet construction. Tubular heat exchangers generally are used for large fluid systems, whereas heat exchangers of plate or sheet construction often are preferred for smaller fluid streams. Heat exchangers usually are separate units, but sometimes can be incorporated as components in larger vessels.

In selecting materials for heat exchangers, corrosion resistance, strength, heat conduction and cost must be considered. The demand for corrosion resistance is particularly difficult to meet because the material can be exposed to corrosive attack by two different mediums. For this reason, damage to heat exchangers often is difficult to avoid.

Characteristics of Tubing

The primary function of tubes in a heat exchanger is to transfer heat from the shell side of the unit to the fluid on the inside of the tube, or vice versa. Therefore, thermal conductivity, wall thickness and resistance to scaling are extremely important. In most instances, tensile strength and yield strength of the tubes are not significant factors; loading, because it is opposed by the internal pressure, is so low that tubes with a high allowable stress are not required.

Stiffness and resistance to denting are properties of tubing important in manufacturing heat exchangers. Stiffness of a tube is proportional to the wall thickness, diameter and modulus of elasticity. Resistance to denting is related to the same factors plus the yield strength of the material.

Extended-surface (finned) tubing is sometimes used to provide the proper thermal conductance for effective transfer of heat from gas to liquid or liquid to liquid. Fins on much of the tubing used in air coolers and hydrogen coolers are applied by soldering, brazing or resistance welding; thus, the ability of the tube material to accept these processes is important. Oil coolers often use integral-finned (extruded) tubing. This type of tubing requires a material with a significant amount of ductility, in order that

*See page 525 for committee list.

the extended surface can be extruded satisfactorily.

Corrosion Resistance. To meet corrosion requirements, tubing must be resistant to general corrosion, stress-corrosion cracking, dealloying and oxygen-cell attack in whatever environments are encountered prior to service, in service and during periods in which the equipment is not operating.

The environment to which tubes will be exposed often is difficult to predict. Many heat exchangers operate with river water, seawater, brackish water or recirculated cooling-tower water in the tubes. The compositions of these waters used for cooling can change over a period of time, through seasonal variations, or from an unpredictable accident. Long lead time in power-plant erection can have a considerable effect on the tubes. Heat exchangers may be completed and sent to the field years before the remainder of the plant is completed and put into operation. Under such circumstances, the heat exchanger should be adequately protected from corrosion which might occur prior to start-up. Wet lay-up using a suitably buffered or inhibited solution can be used to retard corrosion. Another method is to keep the heat exchanger dry

Table 1. Data Needed for Analysis of Failures in Heat Exchangers

Process name and function
Unit name and function
Material size, grade, specification
Sketches of unit, failures or other
  particulars
Environment (inside and out):
  Temperatures, max and min
  Substances contacting tube:
    Common name
    Chemical composition
    Concentration
    Impurities
    pH
    Velocity
    Aeration
    Contact with other metals
Particulars of failure:
  Type
  Location
  Circumstances at time of failure
  Service life
History:
  Service behavior of other materials
  Unusual conditions before failure
  Fabricating operations, sequence
  Maintenance operations, sequence
  Heat treating operations, sequence

and, if necessary, fill it with an inert gas. The heat exchanger can then be sealed until start-up.

After start-up, consideration must be given to the many unscheduled shutdowns that generally affect the early life of any new plant. Suitable precautions must be taken to protect equipment temporarily out of service if damage is to be avoided during downtime.

Examination of Failed Parts

Full background information on a part is important for proper failure analysis. The information should describe the circumstances of failure, operation or other pertinent details. Inadequate information on the circumstances surrounding the failure often results when the investigation is not conducted at the failure site and samples are sent to the laboratory for examination. A list of the type of background information useful for a proper analysis of failures in heat exchangers is given in Table 1.

Sample Selection. The selection of samples that are representative of the failure is important. Samples should be taken not only from the actual failure area, but also from areas remote from the site of the failure so that comparisons can be made. Care should be taken in selecting and removing samples from heat exchangers. Samples that have been burned or battered in removal or have been pickled or modified during the preliminary examination do not adequately illustrate the failure and cannot be considered representative.

Visual Examination. Much information concerning a failure can be obtained from a careful visual examination. Dimensional changes reflect swelling or thinning. The pattern, extent or nature of corrosion or cracking often is an important clue to the cause of failure (consequently, the examination may be hindered by a sample that is too small). Discoloration or rusting on stainless steel may be a sign of iron contamination. Heavy deposits on a tube (such as scale or corrosion product) could be caused by overheating.

The visual examination will indicate the direction of further work; the detailed investigation should be planned at this stage. Care must be used so that evidence is not inadvertently altered or destroyed. Provision should be made for preserving some of the original samples to provide material for a fresh start if an answer to the failure is not found. Sketches and photographs prepared at this time are helpful for later reference in interpreting results.

Microscopic Examination. For metallurgical investigation, microstructural details provide much information about thermal history, operating temperatures, chemical environment, manner of attack, or cracking.

Microstructural examination of a section through the fracture surface is an aid in determining if the fracture is transgranular or intergranular. Also, variations in material between the failure area and a remote region can reveal specific local microstructural effects, such as decarburization, alloy depletion, graphitization, or precipitation of embrittling constituents at the failure area. Quality of soldered or brazed joints, depth of penetration of welds, or occurrence of gas porosity can be revealed by proper sectioning. Occasionally, a critical combination of strain and subsequent heating can cause excessive grain growth. This has occurred in copper tubing, aluminum alloy tubing, or copper-clad steel tubing used for medium-pressure duty.

Identification of the materials may be done by microstructural examination. For instance, various grades of carbon steel pipe or tubing may be distinguished according to the deoxidation practice and resulting microstructure. Similarly, seamless and welded pipe or tubing may be differentiated. A gross error in material usage, such as using low-carbon steel instead of medium-carbon steel, can be determined quickly by microstructural inspection. In low-carbon steels, rimmed steels can be distinguished from killed steels by their larger-grained rimmed zone at the surface and concentration of carbon and impurities at the center of the section. The presence or absence of inclusions also can be checked.

In failures involving a weld, careful evaluation of the heat-affected zone is necessary. In carbon and alloy steels, heat-affected zones may be abnormally hard. In austenitic stainless steels, heat-affected zones may be sites for precipitated intergranular carbides; the resulting alloy-depleted zones surrounding the precipitates may become responsible for intergranular corrosion or cracking of the weldment.

Chemical Analysis. Information on corrosive agents usually is obtained by analysis of corrosion deposits, scales, residues or metal surfaces. For example, silver nitrate tests may be performed on residues clinging to a pitted stainless steel surface to confirm the presence of chloride ions — a common cause of pitting. Wet chemical methods often are supplemented by the use of x-ray diffrac-

tion, electron microprobe or dispersive and nondispersive spectrometers for identification of compounds, which in turn may identify corrosives. These techniques often are used to analyze for the presence of contaminants on crack surfaces or at the roots of pits.

Mechanical Tests. Tensile or stress-rupture tests may be used to determine if the metal had strength characteristics that were suitable for the service conditions. Hardness tests may be used to check whether heat treatment was correct or uniform or if hardening occurred from cold working, overheating, carburization or phase changes in service. Impact tests indicate brittle tendencies.

Causes of Failures in Heat Exchangers

Failures in heat exchangers commonly are associated with methods of manufacturing pipe and tubing, handling methods during fabrication, testing methods in the shop and in the field, and the total environment to which the unit is exposed after fabrication — including conditions during shipment, storage, start-up, normal operation, and shutdown.

A major effort is made by fabricators and suppliers of pipe or tubing to minimize or eliminate latent surface or subsurface imperfections that are produced during manufacturing. Nondestructive inspection, such as by electromagnetic (eddy-current) tests, ultrasonic tests, air-under-water tests and hydrostatic tests, are used to detect these imperfections. Each test has its limitations. Hydrostatic tests and air tests are useful for detecting discontinuities extending completely through the tube wall, but they are of little use in detecting discontinuities that extend only partly through the wall. In these instances, ultrasonic and electromagnetic methods are more useful. These test methods allow the sensitivity of the test instrument to be set at a level consistent with the type and size of imperfection being sought.

Where an imperfection extends through the wall, but is very small and tight, the tube may not leak in a hydrostatic test but may leak in subsequent service. Air tests under water can be used in revealing imperfections of this type.

Fortunately, relatively few imperfections produced during manufacturing escape detection and lead to failures in service. The combination of electromagnetic testing and hydrostatic testing, whether conducted by the fabricator or tube supplier, effectively minimizes service failures that result from imperfections produced during manufacturing.

Secondary manufacturing techniques result in more service failures than do surface and subsurface imperfections produced during tubing manufacture.

The methods used to draw, clean, heat treat and straighten the tubes may be quite significant to service performance, but often are overlooked in specifications and inspection procedures. Drawing, heat treating and straightening operations determine the level of residual hoop and bending stresses induced in the tube. By varying the severity of these operations, it is possible to produce tubes with either very low residual stresses, or very high residual stresses that are near the yield strength of the metal. Low residual stresses are particularly important when tube materials must have maximum resistance to stress-corrosion cracking in service. The residual stresses on the inner and outer surfaces of the tube and through the tube wall must be low; preferably, residual stresses at the surfaces should be compressive.

Cleaning methods, control of heat treating atmospheres, and pickling operations affect the condition of the oxides on the inner surface of the tube. The oxide should be very thin and flexible, and completely cover the inner surface of the tubing, because fractures in the oxide layer create anodic and cathodic sites that can lead to pitting corrosion. If the surface oxide scale is to be removed, it should be *completely* removed, so as not to establish anodic and cathodic sites, which are starting points for corrosion during service. The inner surfaces of some tubes are abrasive blasted to remove the oxides produced during heat treatment and thus to eliminate anodic and cathodic sites. The strip stock from which welded tubing is made can be inspected just before forming and welding, and can be rejected if it does not meet quality requirements.

Alignment and drilling of tube sheets and tube-support plates to reasonable tolerances will ease tube insertion and will minimize stresses induced during the fabrication of heat exchangers. Overrolling the tube past the tube sheet will also introduce residual stresses. Tubes rarely fail within the tube sheet, but failure behind the tube sheet because of overrolling is a relatively common occurrence. To minimize overrolling, it is important to (a) locate the tube-expander cage properly and (b) control the rolling process.

Effects of Inspection Procedures. All heat-exchanger tubes purchased to ASTM specifications are hydrostatically tested at the mill; sometimes the purchaser specifies that a nondestructive test also be used. Hydrostatic testing also is performed after the heat exchanger has been fabricated. One advantage of not hydrostatic testing at the tube mill is that tubes can be kept dry during shipment and storage prior to installation in the heat exchanger. The presence of corrosives in the water used in hydrostatic testing, inadequate drying after hydrostatic testing, and improper boxing of the tubes at the tube mill can lead to corrosion. Most tube mills are aware of the problems associated with hydrostatic testing and drying, and take steps to ensure that the test water is free of corrosives and that tubes are dry prior to boxing.

Hydrostatic testing of heat exchangers in the shop must be conducted with water that is free of any material that can decompose and form a corrodent that will pit the tubing or cause stress-corrosion cracking. Also, it is important to drain,

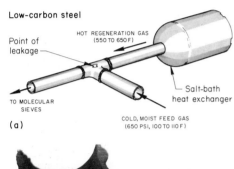

Low-carbon steel

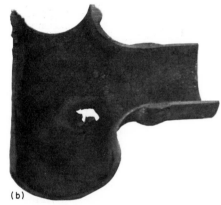

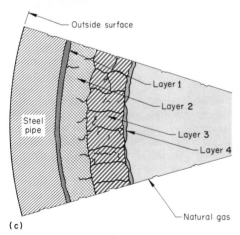

(a) Arrangement of piping (3-in. diam, schedule 40), showing point of leakage in the tee fitting. (b) Inner surface of the tee fitting, showing corrosion deposit and area of complete penetration through the tube wall. (c) Positions of layers of corrosion product on inner surface of piping (see Table 2 for compositions of corrosion product).

Fig. 1. Low-carbon steel tee fitting in a line leading to a natural-gas dryer that failed from corrosion because of high hydrogen sulfide content in the gas (Example 1)

flush and dry the finished heat exchanger prior to shipment. Frequently, filling the heat exchanger with an inert gas is desirable.

Failure to remove shop-hydrostatic-test water that contained contaminants has caused tubing failures to occur prior to start-up. The type of water used for hydrostatic testing of units in the field also is important, as is the method used to drain the units after field hydrostatic testing.

Some copper alloys are very sensitive to stagnant water conditions — especially if the water contains biological material or chemicals that can generate or decompose into ammonia. Hydrostatic-testing procedures that permit water to become stagnant in the tubes can result in serious pitting and stress-corrosion cracking.

Boxing of tubing for shipping should be done with care. All tubes should be wrapped in waterproof paper or plastic to resist corrodents that may be present in the air during shipping, or that may be present in outdoor storage and be washed through the tubes by rainwater. It also is possible for preservatives in wooden boxes to leak out and wash over the tubes.

A problem with an airborne corrodent occurred in one instance in which packing boxes became contaminated with calcium chloride from road-deicing and dust-control operations. The corrodent washed over stainless steel condenser tubes, causing ferric chloride pitting, which perforated the tubes before they were removed from the boxes. Wrapping with waterproof paper probably would have prevented corrosion of these tubes. In another instance, a zinc chloride wood preservative leached out of wooden boxes containing tubes and caused pitting of the tubes prior to their installation in a heat exchanger. Exposure to ammonia or other atmospheric contaminants in industrial areas could result in damage to stored components.

Corrosion

General corrosion resulting in uniform wall thinning causes considerable damage to heat-exchanger tubes. However, the principal corrosion damage in heat exchangers usually is from localized attack. Stray electrical currents also may contribute to significant corrosion of heat exchangers. Localized corrosive attack may occur as pitting, impingement, thinning, or dealloying.

For more information on corrosion, the reader is referred to the article that begins on page 168 in this volume.

General corrosion may be the result of deliberately designing a heat exchanger with a limited life. Otherwise, it can be the result of a mistaken choice of materials, or miscalculation of the corrosive effect of the medium the heat exchanger is subjected to.

In the following example, general corrosion occurred in piping between a salt-bath heat exchanger and a bed used for drying natural gas.

Example 1. Corrosion Failure of a Low-Carbon Steel Tee Fitting Caused by Hydrogen Sulfide in Gas (Fig. 1; Table 2)

Wet natural gas was dried by being passed through a carbon steel vessel that contained a molecular-sieve drying agent. The gas, which contained 15% H_2S, was passed through the vessel at a pressure of 650 psi and at a temperature of 38 to 43 C (100 to 110 F). After several hours, the drying agent became saturated, and was taken off the line and regenerated by gas heated to 290 to 345 C (about 550 to 650 F) in a salt-bath heat exchanger. The arrangement of the 3-in.-diam schedule 40 piping for the dehydrator system is shown in Fig. 1(a). After 12 months of service, the tee joint failed and a fire resulted.

Investigation. Inspection of the piping between the heat exchanger in the salt bath and the molecular-sieve bed revealed a hole in the tee fitting (see Fig. 1a and b) and a corrosion product (scale) on the inner surface of the piping. This scale occurred in four subtle layers, which are shown in Fig. 1(c).

Chemical analysis of the scale revealed it to be iron sulfide of various compositions in four distinct layers. The probable composition and thickness of each layer are given in Table 2. The subtle-layered structure of the scale indicated hydrogen sulfide attack on the carbon steel. The sulfur content was lowest in the layer in contact with the inner surface of the carbon steel pipe.

For several months prior to the failure, the temperature of the gas heated by the

Table 2. Compositions and Thicknesses of Layers of Corrosion Product Found on Inner Surface of Low-Carbon Steel Gas-Dryer Piping Shown in Fig. 1 (Example 1)

Layer (see Fig. 1c)	Carbon, %(a)	Sulfur, %(b)	Stoichiometric ratio	Probable composition	Thickness, in. (approx)
1	10	36.9	$FeS_{1.08}$	$FeS_{1.1}$	0.020
1 and 2 (composite)	...	41.7	$FeS_{1.15}$	$FeS_{1.1} + FeS_{1.2}$	...
2	...	...	...	$FeS_{1.2}$(c)	0.080
2 and 3 (composite)	6	45.0	$FeS_{1.46}$	$FeS_{1.2} + FeS_2$	...
3	...	...	...	$FeS_{1.2} + FeS_2$(c)	0.080
4	...	...	...	FeS_2(c)	(d)

(a) Determined by combustion methods. (b) Determined by gravimetric methods. (c) Determined by x-ray diffraction. (d) Layer too thin and fragile to measure its thickness.

salt-bath heat exchanger was below 290 C (about 550 F) and was about 232 C (450 F) at the molecular sieves.

Corrosion of carbon steel by hydrogen sulfide occurs only at temperatures above 260 C (500 F). At 315 C (600 F), 15% H_2S would cause rapid attack on carbon steel. However, the carbon and sulfur found in the scale on the piping and in the molecular sieves indicated that oxygen was present in the system. At pressures of 300 psi or more, the presence of small amounts of oxygen promotes hydrogen sulfide corrosion of carbon steel, even at room temperature. Thus, oxygen combined with moisture produces conditions for attack of hydrogen sulfide on carbon steel at temperatures below 260 C (500 F).

Failure in the wall of the tee fitting probably was the result of turbulence, with some effect from the coarse grain size usually found in pipe fittings. Grain size usually has an effect on corrosion rate.

Conclusion. The piping failed by corrosion in the tee fitting because of the presence of hydrogen sulfide, moisture and oxygen in the natural gas that was dried in the system. Turbulence in the tee fitting and coarse grain size both contributed to the corrosion.

Corrective Measures. The piping material was changed from carbon steel to type 316 stainless steel, which is readily weldable and resistant to corrosion by hydrogen sulfide at temperatures up to 400 C (about 750 F). Chloride concentration in the plant was very low; however, postweld stress relief was used to minimize residual stresses and avoid the possibility of stress-corrosion cracking.

A less expensive alternative would have been to use a 5% Cr steel or a 9% Cr steel, neither of which is susceptible to stress-corrosion cracking in the presence of chlorides. However, these steels are susceptible to corrosion by hydrogen sulfide, although much less so than carbon steel.

In the next example, oil with a high sulfur content was pumped through heat-exchanger pipes made of low-carbon steel. Sulfur attack caused thinning of the pipe walls and embrittlement of the metal.

Example 2. Rupture of a Low-Carbon Steel Heat-Exchanger Pipe Because of Erosion by Sulfide Attack (Fig. 2)

One of the pipes in a heat exchanger ruptured in service, and an investigation was conducted to determine the cause. The pipe was 4½-in.-OD pipe with a ¼-in. wall, and was made of ASTM A106, a low-carbon steel for high-temperature service. The failure, shown in Fig. 2(a), was near one end of the 36-in.-long sample of pipe submitted for analysis. In operation, oil was pumped through the pipes in the heat exchanger at 75 psi; the inlet temperature was 135 C (275 F), and the outlet temperature was 288 C (550 F).

Investigation. Visual examination indicated that failure had occurred as a longitudinal split accompanied by swelling and bulging, as shown in Fig. 2(a). The fracture surface of the pipe wall had been thinned to almost a knife edge.

Metallographic examination of specimens taken near the fracture and at the opposite

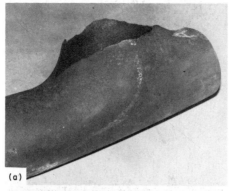

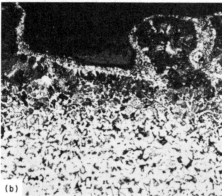

(a) End of pipe sample, showing bulge and rupture at failure area. (b) Micrograph, at 85×, of an unetched section through the pipe, showing carburized areas (dark) and areas of sulfide attack (light skin and channels).

Fig. 2. Heat-exchanger pipe of low-carbon steel (ASTM A106) that ruptured as a result of sulfide attack from oil having a high sulfur content (Example 2)

end of the pipe showed some light scaling and decarburization on the outer surface. The microstructure near the center of the pipe wall was typical of a 0.2% carbon steel, consisting of ferrite and pearlite, with the carbide in the pearlite being slightly spheroidized. There was no microstructural evidence of a hot spot or of cold work in the material near the fracture.

The inner surface of the pipe showed evidence of carburization (dark areas in Fig. 2b) and sulfide penetration (light skin and channels in Fig. 2b) through the remaining wall thickness at the edge of the fracture. Channels near the fracture suggested that the sulfide attack had caused continuous erosion of the inner surface during service.

Conclusion. The pipe ruptured after the wall had been eroded by sulfide attack to such a thickness that it could no longer withstand the service pressure of 75 psi. Sulfide attack and carburization of the inner surface resulted from reaction of sulfur and carbonaceous compounds in the oil with the steel at the elevated operating temperature.

Recommendation. Because of the apparently high sulfur content of the oil, a pipe made of a ferritic chromium-molybdenum steel, such as one of the grades of ASTM A335, would offer greater resistance to sulfide attack and provide longer service life.

Crevice Corrosion. A common cause of deterioration in tubing containing water is corrosion pitting caused by differential aeration or concentration-cell corrosion (crevice corrosion). This type of corrosion occurs frequently, but often is not identified as crevice corrosion.

Corrosion by differential aeration arises from regional differences in the concentration of dissolved gases (principally oxygen), or of soluble contaminants (such as chlorine, fluorine or sulfur), in water that is in contact with a part or component. The result is the establishment of an electrochemical cell, with the surface in the region of lowest concentration becoming anodic with respect to the surrounding surface. This situation can develop under conditions of stagnant flow between two overlapping surfaces, or beneath corrosion products or sludge on the surface. Anything that restricts free access of oxygen is likely to cause crevice corrosion. Other factors, such as gas bubbles on the surfaces, inhomogeneity of the material, cracks in mill scale, and local breakdown of protective films, may also initiate crevice-corrosion attack. Corrosion of this type often is associated with water that contains dissolved solids in comparatively small concentrations, the amounts present being insufficient, or unsuitable, to cause formation of protective films or deposits but sufficient to raise the electrical conductivity of the water so that it becomes an electrolyte. In marine boilers, crevice corrosion often is found where the boiler water has been contaminated with chlorides from seawater; in land boilers, other salts, such as sulfates, contribute to the corrosion. Invariably, the cathodic zone is larger than the anodic zone; consequently, the rate of attack at the small anodic zone is high. Corrosion extends preferentially in depth, forming pits and cavities. Sometimes, the affected part becomes completely penetrated even though the total area affected by corrosion is relatively small. The corrosion products commonly form a nodule over the cavity, increasing the crevice effect. When the corrosion is associated with elevated temperature, as at the hottest parts of heat-exchanger surfaces, the nodule that is formed is hard, and is difficult to remove until it has attained considerable size. The temperature may be sufficient to evaporate some of the liquid within the nodule; the corrosive action then becomes intermittent, and partial drying of the corrosion products occurs.

In the corrosion of iron-base alloys, dissolved oxygen in the water diffuses into the precipitated ferrous hydroxide and, in combination with the ferrous hydroxide and water, forms hydrated ferric hydroxide, commonly known as rust. If the supply of oxygen is limited, the corrosion product may be green hydrated magnetite or black anhydrous magnetite. The nodule that forms from the corrosion product is porous, so that electrochemical attack proceeds as iron enters into solution in the aqueous medium beneath the nodule. The oxygen dissolved in the water mainly is consumed over the large cathodic surface in oxidizing the hydrogen evolved there; that is, it acts as a depolarizer, with the rate of oxygen consumption determining the rate at which ions leave the metal beneath the nodule.

Because of the intense corrosive attack, it is usual to find that the corrosion nodule has a stratified structure, the composition changing from rust-colored ferric hydroxide on the outside surface of the nodule to layers of ferrous hydroxide, ferric oxide and magnetite on the inside. The ferric oxides permit the passage of hydroxyl ions as well as the diffusion of oxygen, with the result that electrochemical action is able to proceed, and the rate of attack is increased with a rise in temperature because of the consequent alteration in the nature of the corrosion products, the improved electrical conductivity of the water, and the enhanced rate of chemical reaction that follows an increase in temperature.

The following features are characteristic of crevice-corrosion attack:

1 Nodules generally will form on the corroded surfaces. The nodules will be hard if formed on a hot surface, and soft if formed on a cold surface.
2 The composition of the nodules varies from the outside surface to the inside. Externally they often present a rusty appearance. Internally they are mostly black. In some instances, the appearance may be modified by the presence of salts deposited from the water, giving various colors.

3 Generally, the nodules are isolated from one another, although they may sometimes be found in confluent groups.
4 When a nodule is removed, the cavity in the plate beneath it is quite often sharply defined and the walls may be almost perpendicular to the metal surface.
5 The metal surface between the cavities generally shows little or no corrosion, and in some instances the original mill scale may be present.

New installations are particularly vulnerable to crevice corrosion, because of insufficient time for a protective film or scale to form on the surface before the onset of corrosion.

Copper alloys also are susceptible to crevice corrosion, forming similar corrosion products and taking part in similar chemical reactions. For instance, in the corrosion of a copper alloy in an aerated-water medium, copper carbonate hydroxide $[CuCO_3 \cdot Cu(OH)_2]$ would be the expected corrosion product. Note that bicarbonate (HCO_3) and carbonate (CO_3) radicals, which are needed for the formation of copper carbonate hydroxide, are present as contaminants in most naturally occurring waters.

In the following example, dirt particles in river water that was used as a coolant in a cooler for hydraulic oil caused crevice corrosion in the copper alloy 706 tubing.

Example 3. Crevice Corrosion of Copper Alloy 706 Tubing in a Hydraulic-Oil Cooler, Caused by Dirt Particles in River Water Used as a Coolant (Fig. 3)

Leakage from the horizontal heat-exchanger tubes in one of two hydraulic-oil coolers in an electric-power plant occurred after 18 months of service. Under normal operating conditions, service life is generally about ten years in similar cooling units. In this plant, river water was used as the coolant in the heat-exchanger tubes. The tubes were ⅜ in. in diameter with a 0.025-in. wall and were made of copper alloy 706 (copper nickel, 10%). Five of the tubes that were leaking were removed and sectioned lengthwise. One section of each tube was sent to the manufacturer of the cooler, and the other was sent to the power company laboratory, for a determination of the cause of failure.

Investigation. Visual examination of the sectioned tubes revealed several nodules on the inner surface and holes through the tube wall, which appeared to have formed by pitting under the nodules. In Fig. 3(a), a pit that penetrated the wall of the tube is shown at A and a typical nodule is shown at B.

Metallographic examination was performed on tube areas that exhibited (a) no effects of corrosion, (b) pitted areas, and (c) areas containing nodules. The tubing contained several nodules and pits, but all were isolated from each other. A cross section through an unaffected area of the tube showed no corrosion on the inner surface and an undamaged microstructure. Most of the inner surface of the tube was in good condition.

A micrograph of a section through a pit that had penetrated the tube wall is shown in Fig. 3(b). The pit had steep sidewalls, which indicated a high rate of attack. A micrograph of a section through the tube beneath one of the nodules is shown in Fig. 3(c). Corrosion beneath the nodule had penetrated approximately 65% of the tube wall. The pit had a low slope angle, which indicated a low or intermittent rate of corrosion.

Spectrographic analysis of the tube metal indicated that it was copper alloy 706. A reddish deposit was removed from the inner surfaces of the tubes and analyzed. The major constituent of this deposit was iron

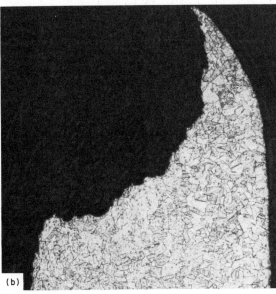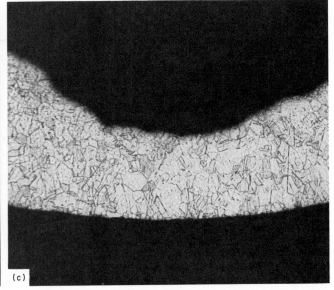

(a) Inner surface of hydraulic-oil-cooler tube containing a hole (at A), and nodules (one of which is indicated by arrow at B) formed from a corrosion product. (b) Micrograph, at 100×, of an etched section through the pit at A, which penetrated the tube wall. (c) Micrograph, at 100×, of an etched section through a pit beneath the nodule at B, with about 35% of the wall thickness remaining.

Fig. 3. Copper alloy 706 (copper nickel, 10%) tube from a hydraulic-oil cooler that failed from crevice corrosion caused by dirt particles in river water that was used as a coolant (Example 3)

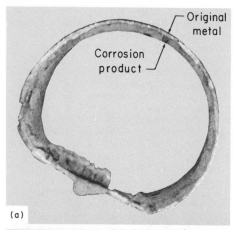

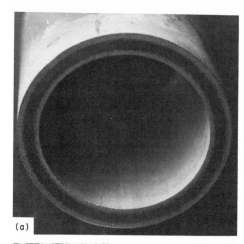

(a) Section through condenser tube, at 3½×, showing dezincification of inner surface. (b) Micrograph, at 100×, of an etched specimen from the tube, showing corroded porous region at the top and unaffected region below.

Fig. 4. Steam-turbine condenser tube made of copper alloy 260 (cartridge brass, 70%) that failed by dezincification

oxide, and less than 1% was manganese dioxide. These and other constituents present indicated that effluent from steel mills upstream was the source of most of the solids found in the tubes.

A nodule that was greenish in color was analyzed by x-ray diffraction. The major compound found in the nodule was copper carbonate hydroxide $[CuCO_3 \cdot Cu(OH)_2]$. This compound would be expected in corrosion of a copper alloy exposed to aerated natural water.

Flow of cooling water from the river through the tubes reportedly was not uniform, but ebbed and flowed in accordance with cooling demand. Under these circumstances, deposits would form on, or particles would drop on, the inner surfaces of the horizontal tubes.

Conclusions. Failure of the tubing was by crevice corrosion. Particles of dirt in the river water were deposited inside the tubes during periods of low flow. The difference in oxygen content under the deposit and on the exposed surface of the tube estab-

lished an electrolytic cell under the deposit. The end results were nodules of a corrosion product and pits that, in some instances, eventually became holes in the tube wall.

Corrective Action. The cooler was retubed, and the cooling-water supply was changed from river to city water, which contained no dirt to deposit on the tube surfaces.

After the first cooler was back in service, the second cooler was shut down and the tubes removed for investigation. Nodules, pits, and deposits were found on the inner surfaces of the tubes similar to those found on tubes removed from the first cooler. Although the tubes were not leaking, they would have been within a short time. For this cooler also, the tubes were replaced and city water was substituted for river water as the coolant. At the time of this report, both coolers had been in service for about three years with no evidence of leakage.

An alternative solution to the problem would have been to install replacement tubes in the vertical position and continue to use river water. With the tubes in the vertical position, solids would be less likely to be deposited on the tube walls during low flow of the river water.

Dealloying is localized corrosion of copper alloys that leaves a spongy, structurally weak mass of the more noble alloying element in place at the site of corrosion attack. Dealloying can occur in brasses (dezincification) and in copper-nickel alloys (denickelification). The net result of dealloying is that sound metal is gradually changed to a brittle, porous mass of copper that has little mechanical strength. Dealloying sometimes can be detected visually by the reddish appearance of the deposited copper; it is favored by waters having a high content of oxygen, carbon dioxide or chloride, and is accelerated by elevated temperatures and low water velocities.

Dezincification occurs in two forms, plug type and layer type. Plug-type dezincification is less spread out on the surface than layer type and can cause pit-like wall perforation more rapidly than layer type. An acidic environment favors layer-type attack. High-zinc brasses of the alpha variety, such as copper alloy 260 (cartridge brass, 70%), are more susceptible to dezincification than copper alloys having a lower zinc content — for example, copper alloy 240 (low brass, 80%). In copper alloys that show an alpha-plus-beta structure, such as copper alloy 280 (Muntz metal, 60%), the grains of the beta constituent (which have the higher zinc content) may suffer preferential dezincification.

A section through a copper alloy 260 steam-turbine condenser tube is shown in Fig. 4(a). Uniform dezincification of the bore extended from one-half to two-thirds through the wall of the tube. The porous nature of the affected portion of the tube is illustrated in Fig. 4(b).

Figure 5(a) and (b) show a section through a heat-exchanger tube made of

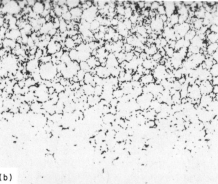

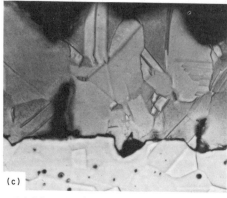

(a) Macrograph, at 3.7×, of an etched section through a copper alloy 710 (copper nickel, 20%) tube, showing dealloying (light areas) around the tube surfaces; etchant: NH_4OH plus H_2O. (b) Micrograph, at 85×, of an unetched section through the outer surface of the tube shown in (a); dark pattern shows dealloyed region. (c) Micrograph, at 375×, of an etched section through a copper alloy 715 (copper nickel, 30%) tube, showing the surface that was denickelified (at top) and unaffected base metal (at bottom); etchant: 50% nitric acid, 50% acetic acid.

Fig. 5. Heat-exchanger tubes made of copper nickel alloys that failed from denickelification as a result of attack by water and steam

copper alloy 710 (copper nickel, 20%). Water passing through the tube and steam in contact with the outer surface caused denickelification of the alloy at both inner and outer surfaces. The dealloying occurred along the grain boundaries, which have higher energy than the grains and are more susceptible to attack. Another form of denickelification is shown in Fig. 5(c) for a copper alloy 715 (copper nickel, 30%) heat-exchanger tube.

Impingement attack (or erosion-corrosion) occurs where gases, vapors or liquids impinge on metal surfaces at high velocities. The erosive action removes protective films from localized areas at the metal surface, thereby contributing to the formation of differential cells and localized pitting of anodic areas.

Impingement attack usually produces a horseshoe-shape pit. This form of attack frequently occurs in condenser systems handling seawater or brackish water that contains entrained air or solid particles and circulates through the system at relatively high velocities and with turbulent flow. The pits are elongated in the direction of flow and are undercut on the downstream side. When the condition becomes serious, a series of horseshoe-shape grooves with the open ends on the downstream side may be formed. As the attack progresses, the pits may join one another, forming fairly large patches of undercut pits.

When impingement attack occurs in heat-exchanger or condenser tubing, it usually is confined to a short distance on the inlet end of the tube where the fluid is turbulent. Impingement attack can be controlled by use of corrosion-resistant alloys such as copper alloy 715 (copper nickel, 30%).

Impingement attack has been somewhat relieved by inserting relatively short sleeves inside the tube on the inlet end of the tube bundle. Other corrective measures are to decrease the velocity, streamline the fluid flow, and decrease the amount of entrained air or solid particles. These may be attained by a streamlined design of water boxes, injector nozzles, and piping. Abrupt angular changes in direction of fluid flow, low-pressure pockets, obstruction to smooth flow, and any other feature that can cause localized high velocities or turbulence of the circulating water should be minimized as much as possible.

In the following example, impingement corrosion occurred on the outer surfaces of heat-exchanger tubes in an air cooler. An abrupt reversal of air flow caused turbulence in the water vapor that condensed on the tubes during cooling.

Example 4. Failure of Copper Alloy 443 Heat-Exchanger Tubes by Impingement Corrosion (Fig. 6)

Failure of tubes in heat exchangers used for cooling air occurred in an increasing number after five to six years of service. Air passed over the shell-side surface of the tubes and was cooled by water flowing through the tubes. Although sanitary well water was generally used, treated recirculating water also was available and was sometimes used in the heat exchanger. Water vapor in the air was condensed on

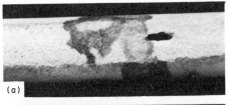

(a)

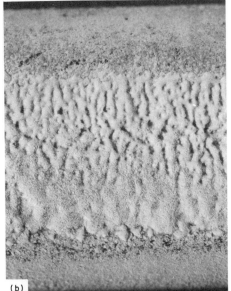

(b)

(c)

(a) Shell-side surface of tube showing damaged area. (b) Macrograph, at 4×, of damaged surface showing ridges in affected area. (c) Micrograph, at 100×, of unetched section through damaged area showing undercut pitting typical of impingement attack.

Fig. 6. Heat-exchanger tube made of copper alloy 443 (arsenical admiralty metal) that failed by impingement corrosion from turbulent flow of air and condensate along the shell-side surface (Example 4)

the tube surfaces during the cooling process. The pH of this condensate was approximately 4.5. Air flow over the tubes reversed direction every 23 in. as a result of baffling placed in the heat exchangers.

The tubes were ¾ in. in diameter with a wall thickness of 0.050 in., and were made of copper alloy 443 (arsenical admiralty metal).

Samples of the tubes were sent to the laboratory to determine the mechanism of failure.

Investigation. Visual examination of the damaged area revealed an uneven ridgelike thinning and perforation of the tube wall (Fig. 6a) on the leeward side of the tube. An enlarged view of the ridges on the surface of the tube is shown in Fig. 6(b). Metallographic examination of a cross section of the failed area (Fig. 6c) disclosed undercut pits on the outer surface of the tube. Both the ridgelike appearance of the damaged area and the undercut pitting are indicative of impingement attack.

Spectrochemical analysis of the tube confirmed that the material was copper alloy 443 (arsenical admiralty metal).

Conclusion. Failure of the tubes was caused by impingement corrosion that resulted in perforation. A combination of air and water (the condensate) was rapidly agitated by changes in direction at the metal surface and acted to accelerate impingement corrosion. This action and the low pH (4.5) of the condensate resulted in removal of the protective film that normally formed on the tube surface during initial corrosion, and ultimately produced a hole in the tube.

Corrective Action. The heat exchanger was retubed with tubes made of aluminum bronze (copper alloy 614 or 628). At the time of this report, these tubes had been in service for more than 12 years without failure.

Failure by impingement attack of tubes in a heat exchanger using seawater for cooling fresh water is described in the next example.

Example 5. Impingement Attack of Copper Alloy 442 Heat-Exchanger Tubes Because of High-Velocity Seawater Containing Solids

Shell-and-tube heat exchangers, using seawater for cooling fresh water, exhibited leakage after less than two years of service. Leakage was detected by using salinity tests of the fresh water. The temperature of the seawater at the inlet was approximately 28 C (82 F), which cooled the fresh water from approximately 50 C to 32 C (120 F to 90 F). Seawater temperature at the outlet was approximately 29 C (84 F).

Two additional heat exchangers were examined during the investigation of the one that failed. All three were operated under similar service conditions.

The heat-exchanger channels and channel covers were made of gray iron. The heat-exchanger shells were made of sheet steel. Tube sheets were made of copper alloy 280 (Muntz metal, 60%). The tubes were made of copper alloy 442 (uninhibited admiralty metal); however, two replacement-tube bundles in the heat exchanger were made of copper alloy 706 (copper nickel, 10%).

Investigation. Inspection of the heat exchanger that failed revealed that the tubes of copper alloy 442 were blocked and perforated at the tube inlets. The replacement tubes of copper alloy 706 that had been in service about six months were in good condition. Deposits of coral and other solids were lodged in most of the tube inlets.

Extensive graphitic corrosion of the gray iron inlet channels and channel covers were evident. The inlet, made of cement-lined cast iron pipe, appeared in very good condition. The cement was intact except at a few small areas. The outlet end of the heat exchanger contained much less corrosion than the inlet channel.

The two other heat exchangers had twelve ¾-in.-diam zinc anodes threaded into the channel heads. The anodes were almost completely corroded away. Some corrosion of the channels had occurred, but it was appreciably less than in the heat exchanger in which leakage occurred. The tubes in these two heat exchangers exhibited severe impingement attack and had some blockage of the tube inlets by coral and other solids, but no perforations were found.

Conclusions. Perforations in the tubes of copper alloy 442 were caused by impingement attack resulting from high-velocity impingement of seawater, coral and other solids. Heavy graphitic corrosion of gray iron components was the result of corrosive attack by seawater.

Corrective Measures. The tubes of copper alloy 442 were replaced with tubes made of copper alloy 715 (copper nickel, 30%), containing 0.5% Fe. This alloy has good resistance to impingement attack.

Zinc anodes were installed in the inlet-channel cover of each heat exchanger, with recommendations that they be inspected monthly and replaced as needed to afford protection to the gray iron channels by sacrificial corrosion of the zinc anodes.

Replaceable screens of copper alloy 443, 444 or 445 (inhibited admiralty metals), or of copper alloy 715, were suggested for installation in the inlet piping or channel to separate deposits that could otherwise lodge in the exchanger tubes. Such deposits in the tubes could result in a form of concentration-cell corrosion and pitting with failure at the point of deposit contact.

Another instance of graphitic corrosion, similar to the deterioration of the gray iron components in the preceding example, is discussed in Example 20 on page 332 in the article on Failures of Iron and Steel Castings.

Stress-Corrosion Cracking

Stress-corrosion cracking occurs as a result of corrosion and stress at the tip of a growing crack. The stress level necessary for stress-corrosion cracking is below the stress level needed for fracture without corrosion.

For more information on stress-corrosion cracking, see the article that begins on page 205 in this volume.

Evidence of corrosion, although not always easy to find, should be present on the surface of a stress-corrosion-cracking fracture up to the start of final rupture. Generally, one of several specific corrosive substances must be present for stress-corrosion cracking to occur in a given alloy. For example, ammonia compounds have been identified as agents that produce stress-corrosion cracking in copper-zinc alloys.

The arsenic, antimony or phosphorus additions for inhibiting dezincification do not prevent stress-corrosion cracking of inhibited admiralty metals (copper alloys 443, 444 and 445). Their susceptibility to ammonia cracking is about the same as that of uninhibited admiralty metal (copper alloy 442). Cracking can be transgranular, intergranular, or mixed on the same metal part, and may be accompanied by deposition of copper within the cracks. Arsenic does not prevent stress-corrosion cracking in copper

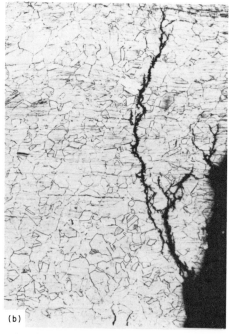

Type 304 stainless steel

(a) ——— Crack

——— ¾ diam

(b)

(a) Section of integral-finned tube showing major crack (circumferential crack between fins). (b) Micrograph, at 45×, showing branched transgranular cracking propagating from major crack.

Fig. 7. Type 304 stainless steel integral-finned tube that cracked from chlorides and high residual stresses (Example 6)

alloy 687 (arsenical aluminum brass) subjected to ammonia-dosed and copper-dosed seawater, although there can be beneficial effects of arsenic at stresses below the elastic limit. Low-temperature stress-corrosion cracking has been found in brasses. The copper nickels (copper alloys 701 to 720), despite their proved susceptibility to ammonia, are much superior in service with respect to stress-corrosion cracking in condenser-tube service than are brasses.

The austenitic stainless steels are subject to stress-corrosion cracking that is induced by acidic chlorides and fluorides. In systems where there is a possibility of chloride contamination, austenitic stainless steel tubes should be in the annealed condition. If corrosion is not so severe as to require an austenitic stainless steel, ferritic 12 or 16% chromium stainless steel, such as type 405, 410 or 430, may be used. Series 400 stainless steels, in the annealed condition, generally are not susceptible to chloride stress-corrosion cracking.

Where chloride cracking is known to be a problem but where high-alloy steels are not required by other service environments, the most economical material to use would be carbon steel. A high-nickel alloy, such as Incoloy 800, is a good material to use where chloride contamination is suspected.

The next example describes stress-corrosion cracking of type 304 stainless steel in the presence of chlorides.

Example 6. Stress-Corrosion Cracking of a Type 304 Stainless Steel Integral-Finned Tube Caused by Chlorides and High Residual Stresses (Fig. 7)

A tubular heat exchanger in a refinery reformer unit was found to be leaking after one month of service. The exchanger contained 167 type 304 stainless steel U-bent integral-finned tubes, ¾ in. in outside diameter.

Investigation. Examination revealed cracks in the tube wall about 3 in. from the tube sheet and at the first full-depth fin on the tube, as shown in Fig. 7(a). Hardness tests on a cross section of the tube showed Rockwell C 30 at the inside surface and up to Rockwell C 40 at the base of the fin midway between the roots. The fins were cold formed and not subsequently annealed, as indicated by the hardness values. Cold working without subsequent annealing made the tubes susceptible to stress-corrosion cracking because of a high residual-stress level.

Metallographic examination of a section through the tube wall established that fracture was predominantly by transgranular branched cracking (see Fig. 7b) and had originated from the inside surface.

Transgranular branched cracking of austenitic stainless steels frequently is caused by chlorides in the presence of high residual stresses.

The presence of chlorides is not unusual in a reformer unit. Chlorides often enter such systems as an additive used in water treatment. Although steam and steam condensate injected into reformer systems are normally free of chlorides, there can be accidental carryover of dissolved solids with the steam under periods of high demand.

Conclusion. The tubes failed in stress-corrosion cracking by chlorides in the presence of high residual stresses. The fins were cold formed on the tubes and not subsequently annealed.

Corrective Measure. The finned tubes were ordered in the annealed condition. This minimized the possibility of residual stresses in the tubes.

Heat exchangers sometimes fail by stress-corrosion cracking because of improper specification of materials and design. In the following instance, a heat exchanger was part of a separator, which was designed as a single combination vessel for construction economy:

The exchanger was of a vertical-tube design, located directly beneath the separator. The separator had a ¼-in.-thick type 316 stainless steel shell that extended below the partition head of the vessel, forming the shell of the heat exchanger. The designer had not provided for complete filling of the water space between the upper tube sheet and partition head. As a result, the type 316 stainless steel shell of the exchanger was constantly wetted with water in the vapor space below the partition head. Heat from the separator caused continuous flashing of water into steam inside the exchanger, building salt deposits on the hot surfaces of the shell. The deposits contained chlorides from the city water used in the exchanger. Acting in combination with the normal fabricating stresses inherent in the vessel, chloride salts caused the type 316 stainless steel shell at the vapor space to fail because of the presence of numerous small stress-corrosion cracks. Some of the cracks penetrated completely through the wall of the shell.

This problem could have been avoided by either (a) providing for complete filling of the water space above the tube sheet, or (b) providing sufficient distance between the separator and exchanger so that heat from the separator would not cause steam flashing inside the exchanger. Finally, it is not considered good practice to use austenitic stainless steels in hotwater service under conditions of alternate wetting and drying; the drying favors the accumulation of corrosive salt deposits.

As a corrective measure, carbon steel doubler plates were welded over the cracked region of the exchanger shell. The exchanger eventually was replaced with a vessel designed to eliminate the vapor space between the tube sheet and the partition head.

Corrosion Fatigue

Corrosion fatigue is the combined action of an aggressive environment and a cyclic stress, which results in premature failure of metals by cracking. Neither cyclic stress in air nor environmental attack applied separately produces the same damaging action. Thus, a precorroded specimen does not necessarily show appreciable reduction in fatigue life, nor does prefatiguing in air increase the corrosion rate of metals.

In general, corrosion fatigue should not be confused with stress corrosion. All metals that are susceptible to corrosion are susceptible to corrosion fatigue in any corrosive environment, whereas stress-corrosion cracking occurs only in alloys subjected to very specific environments, and normally occurs under conditions of static tensile stress rather than of dynamic stress. However, the application of cyclic stresses under stress-corrosion-cracking conditions also may influence corrosion-fatigue behavior.

In the chemical industry, there are more materials susceptible to corrosion fatigue than to stress corrosion. Mainly, stress-corrosion cracking affects the brasses and the series 300 stainless steels, but corrosion fatigue can occur in most metallic materials that are used in the chemical industry.

There are two general sources of stress and environment necessary for corrosion fatigue; (a) where the cyclic stress and corrosive environment result from the same sequence of events, and (b) where the cyclic stress and corrosive environment arise independently.

The first source is more common in high-temperature applications and relies on thermal transients that produce thermal cyclic stresses and corrodent concentration. In the second, cyclic stresses are usually mechanical in origin, such as rotating bending, cyclic pressurization, and start-stop centrifugal loading. Because corrosion fatigue is, by definition, restricted to the simultaneous action of a cyclically varying stress and a corrosion process, the damage mechanisms *not* covered by this term are (a) purely mechanical stress followed by a corrosive action in the unstressed state; and (b) corrosion in the nonloaded state, followed by purely mechanical cyclic stressing without interaction of corrosion.

Fracture Appearance. For carbon and low-alloy steels the corrosion-fatigue fracture surface is typically jagged, whereas the fracture surface of rust-resisting and acid-resisting steels is usually flat. The number of branch cracks has an influence on whether the fracture surface is flat or jagged; with a great number of cracks, the fracture is jagged. The jagged surface results when several cracks penetrate, very close to one another, into the interior of the material. Because the cracks are not in the same plane, the fracture jumps from one crack plane to another, causing the jagged appearance. When the distance between each crack is large, as is generally seen with a small number of cracks, the fracture cannot jump from one plane to another. Consequently, the crack that penetrates to the greatest depth into the material continues to grow until the residual cross section breaks. The flat form of fracture is, therefore, determined by the number of cracks per unit length and is not a specific property of austenitic steels.

On the other hand, the form of a fracture in an austenitic "corrosion-resistant" steel will be similar to that of a carbon steel if the rate of corrosion is increased. Tests carried out with an austenitic stainless steel that was exposed to cyclic loading and a spray of saturated sulfurous acid showed severe corrosion conditions, producing numerous surface cracks and a jagged fracture surface.

The number of cracks, which considerably influences the form of fracture, not only depends on the rate of corrosion, but also on the state of the surface from which the crack begins to propagate. On rough surfaces, a great number of cracks are formed, resulting in a jagged fracture surface. With alloys that are not corrosion resistant, the jagged form of fracture becomes more characteristic when the mechanical stress decreases. With a small stress, the life of a part is long; consequently, there is time enough for the corrosion to roughen the surface. Thus, the conditions for the formation of many cracks and a jagged fracture are created.

Thermal Stresses. Thermally generated cyclic stresses have proved more important in corrosion fatigue than mechanical stresses. Transient thermal conditions can arise when a fluid is brought into contact with a surface having a markedly different temperature or, more commonly, due to imposed system operations. Such thermal stresses result from constrained thermal expansion or contraction.

Mechanical Stresses. Mechanical cyclic stresses arise from rotating machinery and cyclic pressurization. Vessels subject to cyclic pressurization usually are penetrated by pipes welded to the vessel shell. In addition to being regions of stress concentration, these welded connections can act as sources of residual stresses, and any lack of penetration or fusion at the weld may be a site for environmentally assisted cracking. Not only are mechanical cyclic stresses superimposed on any residual stresses, but also any additional thermal stresses resulting from operational transients are similarly additive. Other significant sources of cyclic stresses are fans or pumps, which generate high-frequency vibrations in coolant circuits, and turbulent fluid flow through or over tubes, such as steam flow over condenser tubes.

Effects of Design

The shape of the components in heat exchangers is of importance in producing regions of stress concentrations. The ASME Boiler and Pressure Vessel Codes generally are used for the design of pressure vessels. These codes contain relatively simple formulas that can be used for design. If they are used properly, the vessel will withstand the operating pressures and temperatures anticipated. If used improperly, or for the wrong application, these formulas can result in designs that can cause failures. One member of the brine heater described in the next example had a high discontinuity stress that was not taken into account in the design. This discontinuity stress was greater than the tensile strength of the carbon steel shell material. Although initial cracking probably occurred during hydrostatic testing, the vessel operated at such low pressure that it was able to be used for about two years, during which time a crack propagated

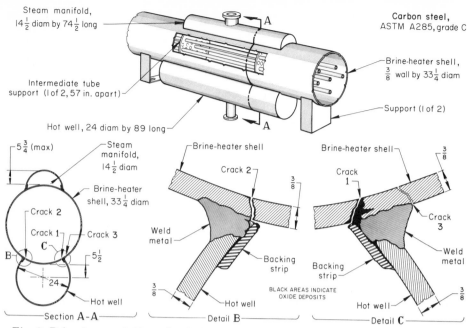

Fig. 8. Brine-heater shell, made of ASTM A285, grade C, carbon steel, that fractured at welded joints because of overstress during normal operation (Example 7)

nearly 7 ft before failure. Investigation revealed that a single welded joint, although properly made, provided a notch that acted as a crack starter.

Example 7. Fracture of an ASTM A285, Grade C, Carbon Steel Brine-Heater Shell at Welds Because of Overstress During Normal Operation (Fig. 8)

The brine-heater shell (Fig. 8) in a sea-water-conversion plant failed by bursting along a welded joint connecting the hot well to the heater shell. Failure occurred approximately two years after the plant had been brought on stream.

Specifications required the heater shell to be made of ASTM A285, grade C, steel, which has a tensile strength of 55,000 to 65,000 psi, a yield strength of 30,000 psi, and elongation in 2 in. of 27% minimum.

The tube side of the heater was designed for a pressure of 175 psi and 150 C (300 F); the shell side, for a pressure of 150 psi and 186 C (366 F). Both sides were hydrostatically tested at 150% of design pressure. The heater tubes were made of copper alloy 706 (copper nickel, 10%) per ASTM B466.

Both on-site and laboratory investigations were conducted to determine the cause of failure and to develop corrective measures to minimize future failures.

Service History. The steam supplied to the plant was normally controlled at 75-psi line pressure. For the first 18 months of service, the brine heater operated at a maximum temperature of 120 C (250 F) and a steam temperature of 130 C (265 F) with a pressure of 25 psi. One exception was during the scaling of the brine-heater tubes about one month after start-up, when the brine temperature exceeded 143 C (289 F), and steam pressure was greater than 56 psi.

During the six months before failure, the maximum brine temperature was 138 C (280 F) and the steam pressure was 48 psi. About five months before failure, a second scaling of the brine-heater tubes occurred, and the

steam pressure approached that of the steam line, or 75 psi.

There were 44 recorded pressure surges in the steam line. Most of these were minor (plus 10 psi max). However, pressures of 90 psi were recorded three times, and of over 100 psi four times. The last 100-psi pressure surge occurred about six weeks before the failure.

When the brine heater failed, the operators immediately went to the control room and found that the steam-temperature valve that admits steam to the brine heater was secured. However, the chart indicated that the brine temperature was 60 C (140 F) and that the pressure in the steam supply had increased. The steam valve was closed immediately, and within three minutes the valve in the steam line at the power plant was closed.

The relief valve on the steam-supply line at the power plant, which was set at 125 to 130 psi, was inspected and there were no indications that the valve had relieved. Also, within the power-plant control room was an alarm that sounded if the pressure upstream of the final reducing station increased to approximately 300 psi. According to the power-plant operators, this alarm did not sound.

During the day the failure occurred, the steam supply pressure at the conversion plant did not exceed 95 psi.

Visual inspection of the heater shell disclosed three cracks or failure areas in the welded joints between the heater shell and the hot well. The locations of these cracks, numbered in the probable order of occurrence, are shown in section A-A in Fig. 8.

Crack 1 may have initiated at the built-in notch (see detail C in Fig. 8), which is characteristic of welds made with a backing strip. The fracture surfaces were covered with high-temperature oxidation, indicating that the surfaces may have been separated for some time. The crack, which extended the length of the hot well, was completely internal and could not be detected from

outside the vessel. The intermediate tube supports were tack welded to the heater shell. The welds nearest the crack were broken and also covered with high-temperature oxidation, indicating that they had been broken for some time.

The heater shell burst along crack 3 (see detail C in Fig. 8), which was in the heat-affected zone of the longitudinal weld. All the fracture surfaces of this crack exhibited bright metal and there did not appear to be any one point or defect where this failure started.

Crack 2 (see detail B in Fig. 8) was on the side of the hot well that did not rip open. This crack was approximately 30 in. long and was propagating toward the ends of the hot well. These fracture surfaces also were covered with high-temperature oxidation.

The temperature-control valve was removed and inspected but no damage was noted.

Metallurgical Tests. A section was taken through the longitudinal weld on the same side of the hot well as crack 2. A crack was observed that extended from the notch formed at the root of the weld and the backing strip to about the center of the heater-shell plate. This crack terminated at what appeared to be an inclusion in the metal. The hardness of the metal in the heater-shell plate at this section ranged from Rockwell B 81.5 in the base-metal zone to Rockwell B 85 in the heat-affected zone adjacent to the weld. Hardness near the inclusion, which was in the heat-affected zone, was Rockwell B 72. The hardness value of Rockwell B 81.5 indicated that the steel should have a tensile strength of about 75,000 psi.

Tensile Tests. The tensile strength of three specimens from the brine-heater shell was 76,920 to 78,700 psi, yield strength was 54,120 to 59,950 psi, and elongation in 2 in. was 22 to 27%. Compared to the specified requirements for ASTM A285, grade C, steel, these strengths exceeded the maximum and ductility was less than, or equal to, the minimum. Chemical analysis showed silicon content of 0.48%, which indicated a killed steel. Carbon content was 0.20%.

Stress analysis was conducted on the original design of the brine heater. A very high discontinuity stress existed at the longitudinal welds between the hot well and the heater shell. A lesser discontinuity stress existed at the longitudinal weld between the brine-heater shell and steam manifold. The stress values were calculated for the heater-shell wall between the welds and the hot well outside the welds. These values exceeded the actual yield strength of the shell material at operating pressures of 48 psi and greater. The material was no longer in the elastic region and deformed plastically to relieve or transfer the stress.

It was assumed that the section of the heater shell between the welds attempted to straighten out. When this occurred, the root of the weld would have been under tension, which would create an ideal site for a crack to initiate.

Discussion. Cracks 1 and 2 probably happened during hydrostatic tests of the heater or shortly after the heater was put into operation. These cracks were internal and undetectable from the outside. During the first 18 months when the brine heater was operated at 25 psi, these cracks would propagate at a very slow rate, if at all. During the last six months the brine heater was operated at 48 psi, where the discontinuity stresses were greater than the yield strength of the material, and the cracks propagated at a more rapid rate. The brine heater was subjected to 44 recorded steam-pressure surges, which increased the operating pressure above the nominal 25 and 48 psi needed to maintain the required brine temperature. There were probably other pressure surges during plant shutdown, similar to the one that caused the final failure, which were not recorded. In addition to the high discontinuity stresses, the fact that the cracks did exist increased the stress concentrations in the heater. The loss of the support by the intermediate tube sheets at the failed portion of the shell increased the stress in the remaining shell.

Conclusions. The brine heater cracked and fractured because it was overstressed in normal operation. The two internal cracks propagated by continuing along the root of the longitudinal weld. The crack on the side that fractured had extended nearly seven feet before failure.

Corrective Measures. The heater design was modified to make the heater shell and the hot well two separate units. Also, the heater-shell expansion section was redesigned to minimize stress on the tubes and minimize the resulting distortion.

A tight shutoff valve was added to the brine-heater steam line to prevent steam from leaking into the heater.

Holes in the support plates were enlarged to allow the heater to move in any horizontal direction.

Recommendations. A relief valve should be installed in the heater or in the steam line near the heater. At the time of failure, the relief valve was some distance upstream of the brine heater.

Additional hydrostatic tests of the new brine heater should be conducted at ambient temperature and 150 psi (design pressure) at approximately six-month intervals.

Mechanical Joints. The coefficient of expansion and yield strength at high temperature of metal components used in an assembly are important design considerations. Bolted assemblies require fasteners with a yield strength that would allow the fasteners to be tightened to such a prestress value that the assembly would remain leakproof even at high temperatures. The following is a situation in which this condition existed:

Leaks developed in an assembly that consisted of a flanged bonnet bolted to the shell of a heat exchanger and that was operated at a temperature of 510 C (950 F). The bonnet was made of a ferritic steel; the tube sheet, heat-exchanger shell and studs were all made of an austenitic stainless steel. When leakage was not stopped by repeated tightening of the nuts on the studs, the joint was disassembled.

Initial inspection was done to check the surface finish on the flanges and the condition of the gasket. Both were satisfactory. The joint dimensions and metals

(a) Location and shape of collapsed tube in tube sheet. (b) Micrograph, at 75×, of a nital-etched section through tube showing carburization of outer surface of tube (at top) and the general deformation.

Fig. 9. Heat-exchanger tube made of 5% Cr − 0.5% Mo steel (ASTM A213, grade T5) that collapsed from the action of carbon formation in a crevice between the tube and tube sheet (Example 8)

used were then checked for compliance to specifications; these also were satisfactory. During the examinations and review of the design calculations, it was noted that the materials in the assembly had greatly differing coefficients of expansion and that the studs had a coeffi-

cient of expansion that matched only the components made of austenitic stainless steel. Studs made of conventional stainless steel have a low yield strength and high ductility, which leads to stud elongation because of the operating temperature and load. These differing coefficients of expansion caused the tension on the studs on the assembly to relax, permitting leakage. The joint was made tight by replacing the conventional austenitic stainless steel studs with those conforming to ASME specification SA-453, which is a high-temperature bolting material with a coefficient of expansion comparable to austenitic stainless steel but with a much higher yield strength. Using material conforming to SA-453 permitted tightening the nuts on the studs to a torque load that would maintain tightness at the operating temperature.

Crevices in rolled joints between tubes and tube sheets in heat exchangers can be a gathering place for some reaction deposits. In the following example, a carbonaceous material was deposited in the crevice between the tubes and tube sheets, causing collapse of some tubes.

Example 8. Collapse of a 5% Cr − 0.5% Mo Steel (ASTM A213, Grade T5) Heat-Exchanger Tube Because of the Buildup of Carbon in a Crevice Between the Tube and Tube Sheet (Fig. 9)

After about nine months of service, a section of a heat-exchanger tube failed by what appeared to be a crushing force. Failure occurred in the area where the tubes were rolled into the tube sheet (see Fig. 9a). The design temperature was 620 C (1150 F) on the tube side, and pressure was 100 psi on the shell side and 25 psi on the tube side. The shell side of the tubes was immersed in a mixture of ethyl benzene and water; the tube side was exposed to superheated steam.

The tubes were 1 in. in diameter with a wall thickness of 0.109 in. and were made of 5% Cr − 0.5% Mo steel (ASTM A213, grade T5). The tube sheets were 4½ in. thick and made of 1.25% Cr − 0.5% Mo steel (ASTM A387, grade C).

Investigation. Visual examination of samples of failed tubing showed complete collapse of the tubing wall (see Fig. 9a). Thick black deposits were present in the immediate area of failure on the outer surfaces of the tubes. Only those sections that had been contained within the tube sheet were collapsed; the sections of tubing extending beyond the tube sheet were unaffected.

The deposits around the collapsed area of tubing were scraped off, placed in a small crucible and heated with an oxyacetylene torch. The characteristic red glow and blue vapors of carbon, combined with the observation that there was no ash residue remaining after burning, led to the conclusion that the deposits were essentially uncombined carbon.

Microscopic examination of the tube revealed a deeply carburized microstructure, but no cracking was observed in the carburized layer. Flow lines, indicative of extensive cold working, were in the microstructure and also were well defined in the brittle carburized layer (see Fig. 9b). This indicated either that the section was deformed at high temperatures or that the steel was carburized after it was deformed.

It is probable that both high-temperature deformation of the tube and carburization of the steel after deformation occurred because the vaporizer was in operation at high temperatures. Collapsing of the tube did not cause extensive secondary damage.

Conclusions. The black carbon deposits found on the tube were produced by cracking (carbonizing) of the hot ethyl benzene on the shell side of the tubes. The ethyl benzene entered the small crevices between the tube and tube sheet and was carbonized. The pressure generated by formation of carbon from the ethyl benzene within the crevice caused swaging and collapse of the tubes.

Recommendation. The crevice could be closed by seal welding around the tube at the face of the tube sheet, provided that welding would not introduce detrimental stresses.

Effects of Welding Practices

Welding, which is commonly used to join components of heat exchangers, produces metal in the joints that is not homogeneous. The weld consists of a dendritic structure (cast metal) and intermediate zones between fused metal and unaffected base metal. In some instances, the entire heat exchanger can be normalized or annealed, and the metallurgical structure of the weld metal and base metal may become nearly identical. However, heat treating the heat exchanger is not always feasible, so generally there is a gradation in metallurgical condition from unaffected base metal through a heat-affected zone to weld metal.

In addition to this intrinsic change in homogeneity of material, other factors may provide metallurgical or mechanical stress raisers. Weld defects may include voids, porosity, slag or oxide inclusions, poor penetration and shrinkage cracks. Many welds have rough surfaces and may join the base metal with an undercut or reinforcement. If metallurgical discontinuities are minimal, if defects are eliminated, and if the external contour does not contain mechanical notches, the properties of a welded joint can be expected to approach that of the base metal.

Preparation of joint surfaces prior to welding can be a source of weld defects in heat exchangers. For instance, a pinhole leak developed in a heat-exchanger shell adjacent to a weld deposit that joined a nozzle, made of ¾-in.-diam schedule 80 pipe, to the shell. When the nozzle was removed, it was found to have been installed by torch cutting a 1½-in.-diam hole in the shell, inserting the nozzle and welding it in place. There was no evidence of cleanup after torch cutting the hole or of beveling of the wall

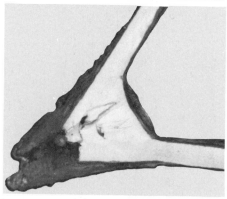

(a) Original design

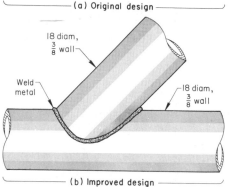

(b) Improved design

(a) Original joint design of pipe connection, and location of cracks. Photograph is an oblique view of a section through the weldment, showing the abrupt intersection of pipe walls, and voids and crevices in the weld metal. (b) Improved joint design.

Fig. 10. Carbon steel discharge line at a cooling tower that failed because of poor fit-up at Y-joint and poor-quality welds (Example 9)

edges around the hole to permit good weld penetration. Examination of the weld deposit revealed that the weld metal generally was oxidized and contained several flux inclusions. There was little or no bonding of the weld bead to the surfaces that had been cut with the torch. Examination revealed evidence that the weld was made under conditions of poor fit-up, lack of cleanness, and poor workmanship. A good joint was made by removing old weld metal and properly beveling the edges of the hole before rewelding.

Joint design can be responsible for mechanical notches at welds in heat-exchanger components. Designs that incorporate sharp corners and heavy longitudinal welds are sources of stress raisers.

In the following example, a Y-shape connection between two pieces of 18-in.-diam pipe had a sharp corner that contributed to high localized stresses.

Example 9. Fracture of an 18-In.-Diam Carbon Steel Pipe in a Cooling Tower Because of Poor Fit-Up and Substandard Weld Beads (Fig. 10)

An 18-in.-diam, 5/16-in.-wall carbon steel discharge line for a circulating-water system at a cooling tower fractured in service; a manifold section cracked where a Y-shape connection had been welded. The steel pipe was made to ASTM A53 specifications.

Investigation. Examination of the pipe revealed that cracking occurred in the heat-affected zone parallel to the weld and across the weld as shown in Fig. 10(a). The end of the branch pipe was prepared for welding by making a transverse cut, then a second cut was made at about 15° to the longitudinal axis of the pipe, resulting in a sharp corner (see Fig. 10a). The main pipe was then notched to fit the end of the branch pipe. Fitting of the saddle connection was poor and no backing strips were used even though the pipe wall was thin; as a result, condition of the root-weld bead was below standard, and numerous deep crevices and pits were in the weld area exposed to the inner surfaces of the manifold, as shown in the sectional view in Fig. 10(a).

Conclusions. The pipe failed in brittle fracture, which originated at crevices and pits in the weld area. The crevices and pits acted as stress raisers, producing high localized stresses because of the sharp-corner joint design. Abnormally high structural stresses, and stresses resulting from the pump vibrations, contributed to the fracture.

Corrective Measures. The joint design was changed to incorporate a large-radius corner (see Fig. 10b), and fitting of the components was improved, to permit full weld penetration. Backing strips were used to increase weld quality. Also, the pipe wall thickness was increased from 5/16 in. to 3/8 in.

Stiffening, which results when the weld metal is thicker than the adjacent base metal, also can lead to failure, as discussed in the following instance. The design of expansion bellows in a heat exchanger incorporated a longitudinal weld across each corrugation and a circumferential weld joining each corrugation (see Fig. 11a). The bellows had an outside diameter of 26 in. and were made of 5/32-in.-thick type 321 stainless steel. The heat exchanger was shut down when leakage occurred in the bellows. Circumferential cracks were found along the heat-affected zone of the weld and through the corrugation wall. These are areas of highest stress. Examination of the fracture surface revealed fatigue beach marks (see Fig. 11b) that initiated at the heavy weld reinforcement of the longitudinal seam weld. The unusually heavy reinforcement had a stiffening effect causing overstressing and transverse cracking of the longitudinal seam. Grinding flush the reinforcement of the longitudinal weld reduced the stiffening. As a corrective measure, the bellows were formed from a single sheet large enough to provide the proper number of convolutions without a circumferential weld in the working section. The only weld required was one longitudinal seam the full length of the bellows. This change in design eliminated the points of high stress that had led to failure.

Effects of Elevated Temperature

Failures associated with elevated temperature generally involve a material that is too weak for the service temperature or a material that develops unexpected embrittlement at or above the service temperature. Thermal cycling can cause failures where adjacent materials differ significantly in composition and coefficient of expansion. Embrittlement also may be the result of metallurgical changes that leave the material relatively ductile and tough at elevated temperature but brittle at or slightly above room temperature.

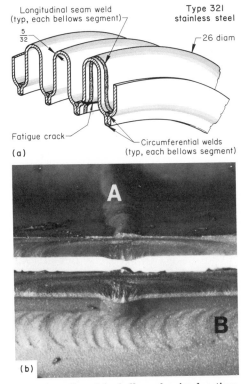

(a) A section of the bellows showing locations of longitudinal seam weld, circumferential welds, and fatigue crack. (b) Fractograph, at 2×, of mating fracture surfaces of the bellows. Crack initiated at the longitudinal seam weld (at A) and propagated circumferentially along the heat-affected zone of the circumferential weld (at B). Fatigue beach marks are present along edges (at center of fractograph). Note that the fracture surfaces are oriented to show the inner surface of the bellows (top) and the outer surface (bottom).

Fig. 11. Heat-exchanger bellows, made of type 321 stainless steel, that failed by fatigue originating at heavy weld reinforcement of a longitudinal seam weld

Another temperature-related problem that is encountered is scaling and oxidation because of excessive temperatures. Creep and stress rupture also occur because of excessive temperatures, as discussed on pages 249 to 252 in this volume. These temperature-related failure mechanisms must be accounted for in selection of material, in fabrication and in operating procedures.

In the following example, accidental overheating of leach-heater tubes resulted in embrittlement of the material.

Example 10. Embrittlement of a Titanium Heater Tube Because of Absorption of Hydrogen and Oxygen at Elevated Temperatures (Fig. 12)

A flow stoppage in a leach heater caused overheating of the 3½-in.-OD, 0.25-in.-wall titanium heater tubes (ASTM B337, grade

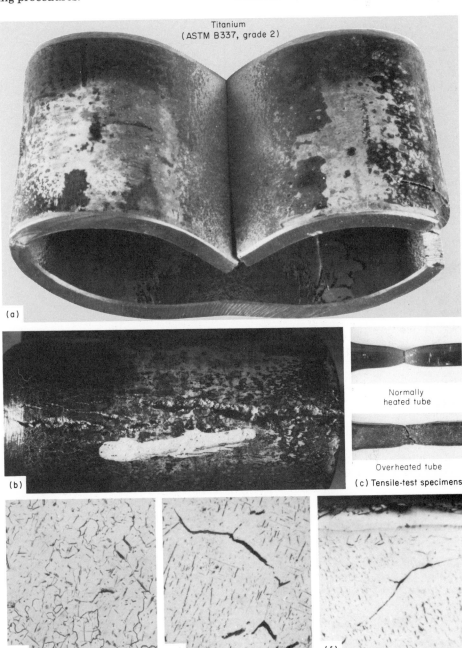

(a) View, at ¾×, of a 3-in.-long section of the titanium tube flattened as a result of test per ASTM B337; first crack was longitudinal along top inside surface. (b) Side of flattened tube section, at 1¼×, showing cracks. (c) High-temperature (370 C, or 700 F) tension-test specimens: top, specimen from normally heated tube; bottom, specimen from overheated tube. (d) Micrograph, at 200×, of normally heated tube specimen etched in Kroll's reagent, showing fine grain size and hydride particles (faint black needles). (e) Micrograph, at 200×, of overheated tube specimen etched in Kroll's reagent, showing large grain size and hydride particles (small needles). (f) Micrograph, at 200×, of transverse section of overheated tube specimen at outside surface, showing 0.002-in.-thick oxygen-embrittled layer (light band near top).

Fig. 12. Heat-exchanger tube made of titanium (ASTM B337, grade 2) that became embrittled and failed because of absorption of hydrogen and oxygen at elevated temperatures (Example 10)

2) for a brief period. Many of the tubes showed colorful surface oxides, and some sagged slightly.

A short section of an oxidized and sagged tube was sent to the metallurgical laboratory for evaluation. The purpose of the examination was to determine whether the mechanical properties of the tube had been altered by overheating — particularly, whether the tube had been embrittled, making it susceptible to fracture. A section from a similar tube removed previously from a leach heater that had not been heated above normal operating temperatures was sent to the laboratory for comparison.

Visual examination of the section of the overheated tube disclosed blue tinted areas and patches of flaky white, yellow and brown oxide scale. There was a dark-gray scale on the inside surface with no evidence of corrosion. The presence of the colored scale on the outer and inner surfaces was an indication of heating to approximately 815 C (1500 F).

Mechanical Tests. A 3-in.-long section of the overheated tube was subjected to a flattening test. ASTM B337 requires that a welded or seamless grade 2 titanium tube shall be capable of withstanding, without cracking, flattening under a load applied gradually at room temperature until the distance between the platens is seven times the nominal wall thickness — in this instance, 1.75 in. In the test, when the platens were 2.6 in. apart cracking initiated at both inner and outer surfaces of the tube; when the platens were 2.4 in. apart the tube fractured, with fracture initiating at the inner-surface cracks. Thus, the tube no longer met ASTM B337 specifications.

An end view of the flattened tube is shown in Fig. 12(a). The cracks on the outer surface are shown in Fig. 12(b).

Longitudinal tensile tests were conducted at 370 C (700 F) on specimens taken from

the overheated and normally heated tubes. The results were as follows:

Mechanical property	Over-heated tube	Normally heated tube
Yield strength, psi (0.2% offset)	14,000	14,500
Tensile strength, psi	21,200	28,500
Elongation in 2 in., %	36	38
Reduction in area, %	69	82

As shown in Fig. 12(c), the specimen from the normally heated tube necked down more than the overheated-tube specimen, although elongation was approximately the same.

Metallographic examinations were made of specimens from both the normally heated and the overheated tubes. The normally heated tube had a fine grain size and only a few faint hydride particles in the microstructure, as shown in Fig. 12(d). By comparison, the microstructure of the overheated tube (Fig. 12e) exhibited a much larger grain size and more numerous needle-like hydride particles. Also, the overheated tube had a very hard brittle surface layer approximately 0.002 in. thick (see Fig. 12f), which was present on both the inner and outer surfaces. The layer was extremely hard (Rockwell C 51) at the surface and decreased to almost normal hardness (Rockwell C 33) at 0.003 in. from the surface. At the approximate center of the tube wall, the hardness was Rockwell B 83.

The flaky white, yellow and brown oxide scale and the increased grain size indicated that the tube had been heated to approximately 815 C (1500 F). At this temperature the metal readily absorbs hydrogen and oxygen. The hydride formation and the shallow surface embrittlement were indications of hydrogen and oxygen absorption. The oxygen absorbed at the surfaces created very hard, and consequently brittle, layers

that made the tubes susceptible to cracking at ambient temperatures.

Although the high-temperature (370 C, or 700 F) tensile strength of the overheated tube was significantly lower than that of the normally heated tube, the yield strengths were about the same and the ductility of the overheated tube was slightly lower. At 370 C (700 F), there was no evidence of the severe embrittlement shown in the flattening test at room temperature. However, at temperatures below 205 C (400 F), embrittlement from hydrogen and oxygen absorption occurred, as evidenced by the poor performance of the flattening test.

Conclusions. The titanium tubes had been embrittled by being heated to a temperature of about 815 C (1500 F), which is excessive for ASTM B337, grade 2, titanium. The most serious effect of overheating the tubes was the generally embrittled condition at low temperature, and particularly the severe surface embrittlement resulting from oxygen absorption. The brittle surface layers made the overheated tubes susceptible to cracking under start-up and shutdown.

At operating temperatures of 370 C (700 F), the overheated tubes would not have been brittle but the over-all mechanical properties of the tubes would have been somewhat degraded.

Recommendations. If the overheated tubes remain in service, thermal stresses should be avoided during start-up and shutdown, particularly at temperatures below 205 C (400 F). Although at the operating temperature of 370 C (700 F) the overheated tubes are not in an embrittled condition, the tubes should be replaced because there is a possibility that cracks formed during start-up and shutdown would propagate through the tube wall under operating conditions. Replacement tubes should be made of Hastelloy C-276, rather than of titanium.

Failures of Pressure Vessels

By the ASM Committee on Failures of Pressure Vessels, Boilers and Pressure Piping*

PRESSURE VESSELS and pressure piping of the types that are exposed to the chemical environments encountered in power plants, refineries and chemical-processing plants are discussed in this article. Such equipment operates over a range of temperatures and pressures and is used in contact with a wide variety of chemical substances.

The conditions under which a pressure vessel has been fabricated, shipped and stored require consideration during failure analysis. Air and its contaminants may be corrosive and can have significant effects on failures. Fabricating practices also can have effects.

Operating temperature affects the life of a pressure vessel in two ways. When

pressure vessels are pressurized or stressed below the ductile-to-brittle transition temperature in the presence of relatively small flaws, brittle failures may occur. At elevated temperatures, corrosion, oxidation, scaling, creep, and stress rupture may become problems. These possibilities must be considered in material selection, in fabrication and in specification of operating procedures.

Operating pressure is an important design consideration and is the subject of various pressure-vessel design codes such as the ASME Boiler and Pressure Vessel Codes. Rapidly flowing streams of liquid and gas can cause erosion damage to metal surfaces. Sometimes, erosion wears away protective surface scales and oxides, resulting in increased corrosion of the freshly exposed metal.

Intermittent operation also can affect the life of pressure vessels. Long periods of inactivity greatly enhance the probability of internal or external corrosion. During long shutdown periods, the recommended practice is to fill the system with gases such as nitrogen or helium to avoid unacceptable corrosion. Wet layup using deoxygenated water, or continuous circulation of demineralized, deoxygenated water, also can be used to minimize corrosion.

Equipment sometimes is operated only during peak-demand periods; this imposes many start-ups and shutdowns, with attendant thermal stresses on pressure vessels and piping systems. When cracking occurs, it is in areas least able to accommodate severe cyclic loading; such areas are likely to be rigid or massive sections under conditions of high constraint or thermal stress.

Design of components in a system, such as valves and piping, can be affected by operating conditions. When the components are incorporated into a system, service conditions may be unacceptable for one of the components. Water hammer and vibration can damage piping systems, including hangers and supports. Heavy valves, instruments and associated components should be properly supported so that the connecting piping system is not overstressed in a manner that could lead to fatigue fracture when it is subjected to severe vibration.

Procedures for Failure Analysis

The basic procedures for analyzing failures of pressure vessels and pressure piping are not much different from those for investigating failures of other types of equipment (see article beginning on page 10). At the outset, a preliminary examination should be made, to provide a clear over-all picture of what happened. If the failure involved an explosion, a careful search should be made for all material components and fragments. The location and mass of each component or fragment should be recorded, and all burn discolorations or impact marks on surrounding objects or surfaces should be located. This ballistic information can be used to estimate launch angles and trajectories and to calculate the approximate pressure in the vessel at the instant of failure.

Because an explosive failure of a pressure vessel may result in extensive damage, system downtime, and expense, it is natural that the preliminary examination will generate considerable expression of opinions as to the possible cause of failure. Casual opinions should be avoided, and certainly not solicited. Subsequent recollections of witnesses could be colored by the offhand comments or speculation of investigators.

As in any failure analysis, it is important that the investigator gain a clear understanding of the entire system involved, including specifications, intended functions, normal methods of operation, thermomechanical history, maintenance history, manufacturing history, and operator experience. This information, plus information from subsequent examinations and from laboratory analysis of specimens, should permit accurate determination of how and why the failure occurred.

Techniques used during a preliminary examination should not affect any subsequent examinations. For instance, liquid-penetrant inspection can make it difficult to analyze for chlorides in deposits on the part surfaces or on fracture surfaces.

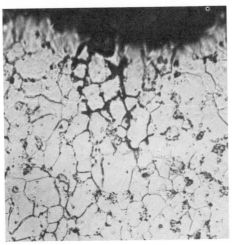

Fig. 1. Micrograph, at 80×, of a specimen from a low-carbon steel nipple, showing fissuring at grain boundaries (top) caused by hydrogen attack

Effects of Using Unsuitable Alloys

Specification of an alloy that is not suited to the application frequently is the cause of failure of a pressure vessel. The composition of the alloy may be incorrect, or the metallurgical properties may not meet requirements. This often results from a misunderstanding of the operating conditions by the designer.

A common cause of failure of pressure vessels is use of an alloy other than the one specified. Sometimes, bars or plates are not properly marked or are accidentally stored with another alloy. Mistakes can be made when care is not taken to ascertain that the alloy used complies with the alloy specified.

In one instance, several low-carbon steel nipples were inadvertently used in place of 5Cr-0.5Mo steel nipples in a pipeline containing hydrogen at 400 C (752 F). Failure occurred after approximately four years of service. The micrograph in Fig. 1, which shows a specimen from one of the low-carbon steel nipples, reveals fissuring at the grain boundaries. This phenomenon is characteristic of hydrogen attack when low-carbon steel is exposed to hydrogen at high pressures and temperatures. A complete survey of the piping system was made to ensure that only the specified metal was used. Replacements were made when the wrong metal was found.

Welding Problems. In the fabrication of pressure vessels, welding problems, such as brittle cracking in the heat-affected zone, often result from the use of steels containing excessive amounts of residual elements that increase hardenability and susceptibility to cracking. Such steels often are produced inadvertently when low-carbon steel is made in a furnace normally used to make high-alloy steels. The refractory lining of the

furnace may impart sufficient residual chromium and other alloying elements to a heat of low-carbon steel to the extent that problems may occur when components made from that heat are joined using standard welding procedures. Therefore, complete control of composition is of the utmost importance when welding is involved.

As an example of improper material specification or use, galvanized steel clips were welded to stainless steel piping. The galvanized (zinc) coating became molten during the welding process, and the liquid zinc attacked the grain boundaries in the stainless steel, causing intergranular cracks. The piping was dimpled and leaked at some of the welds. The location and depth of the cracks were related to the welding procedure and the amount of welding heat used. Excessive welding heat had caused dimpling (distortion) of the stainless steel piping and further crack penetration into the piping wall. The cracks continued to propagate during service from stresses induced in the piping during operation.

In another instance, a transfer line carrying 73% sodium hydroxide developed a leak at a weld joining a cast Monel coupling to wrought Monel piping. Metallographic examination disclosed many small microfissures in the weld metal, but no microfissures were found in the heat-affected zones of the wrought Monel. This section of line contained high thermal stresses that resulted from injection of steam a short distance upstream from the coupling. Chemical analysis revealed that the cast Monel coupling had a silicon content of 1.97% whereas the wrought Monel piping had a silicon content of 0.10%. Castings of high-silicon Monel generally have poor weldability and often are hot short — that is, sensitive to cracking in the weld heat-affected zone. Fissures in the cast coupling were formed during welding and subsequently penetrated the section when the coupling was subjected to the thermal shock of steam injection. Where welding is required, a weldable-grade casting should be specified to ensure freedom from hot fissuring.

A welded-on blank cap began leaking during a hydrostatic test because it had cracked in the weld. Analysis showed that the cap had a carbon content of 0.56%, whereas a maximum carbon content of 0.30% was specified. The excessive carbon content had resulted in a brittle heat-affected zone. It was found that construction personnel had substituted ASTM A53, type F, piping, which does not have a specification for maximum carbon content. Because the higher-carbon steel had been used on a random basis throughout the piping system, all piping was spark tested in the field to expedite repair. When a section was found with a questionable spark, a specimen was removed for chemical analysis. All sections having a high carbon content were replaced by piping with a maximum carbon content of 0.30%.

Failure of several high-pressure nipples was attributed to the occasional inadvertent use of 4140 steel instead of the specified 1035 steel. The presence of approximately 1% Cr and 0.15 to 0.25% Mo in 4140 steel enhanced the hardenability and contributed to hardness and brittleness in heat-affected zones adjacent to welds. All failures in the nipples occurred in these hardened zones. A spot test for chromium was made, and those nipples showing chromium contents in excess of 0.3% (estimated) were removed and replaced with nipples fabricated from 1035 steel. Although 4140 steel is a weldable alloy steel, welding procedures suitable for 1035 steel were not appropriate for the higher-alloy material.

Specification of the filler metal used for welding components of pressure-piping systems is important, as demonstrated in the following example.

Example 1. Brittle Fracture of a Clapper Weldment for a Disk Valve Because of Improper Filler Metal

After a service life of only a few months, the clapper in a 10-in.-diam disk valve fractured. During operation, the valve contained a stream of gas consisting of 55% H_2S, 39% CO_2, 5% H_2 and 1% hydrocarbons at 38 C (100 F) and 8 psi. Specifications required the clapper to be made of $\frac{1}{2}$-in.-thick ASTM A36 steel, stress relieved and cadmium plated.

Investigation. Fracture occurred at the welded joint between the clapper and a $\frac{3}{4}$-in.-diam support rod, also made of ASTM A36 structural steel. Examination revealed voids on the fracture surface and evidence of incomplete weld penetration. The over-all appearance of the fracture surface indicated brittle fracture, but there was some evidence of fatigue beach marks. Fracture originated at a slag inclusion in the weld metal. In some areas, particularly on the weld metal, the plating material had flaked off the clapper.

Vickers microhardness surveys across the weld area revealed very narrow bands of high hardness (400 to 650 dph) at the edges of the weld metal. The normal hardness of the base metal was 150 to 160 dph, hardness in the heat-affected zone was 150 to 180 dph, and hardness of the weld metal was 230 to 250 dph.

Chemical analysis of the material in the high-hardness bands revealed a composition of 70% Fe, 17% Cr, 9% Ni and 1.2% Mn. This composition indicated that a stainless steel filler metal had been used, which produced a mixed composition at the weld boundaries. Although the weldment may have been stress relieved as specified, stress-relief annealing apparently was incapable of reducing the high hardness of the localized bands caused by alloy mixing.

Chemical analysis of the plating material showed it to be nickel, probably electroless nickel because it had a high hardness.

Conclusions. The clapper failed in fatigue and brittle fracture because it was welded with an incorrect filler metal. Fatigue cracking was initiated at voids and high-hardness bands in the weld deposit. Also, the clapper was plated with nickel instead of cadmium.

Corrective Measure. A clapper assembly was welded with a mild steel filler metal and then cadmium plated. The new clapper was installed in the valve and subsequently provided satisfactory service.

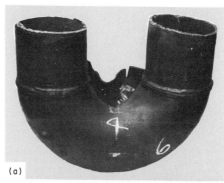

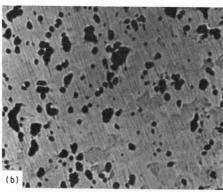

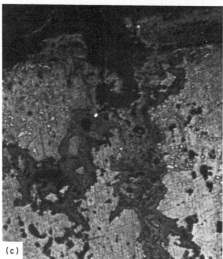

(a) Over-all view of the return bend, showing rupture. (b) Micrograph, at 400×, of an unetched specimen, showing high concentration of inclusions. (c) Micrograph, at 435×, of an unetched specimen, showing inclusions and cracks containing scale.

Fig. 2. Return bend, made of ASTM A213, grade T11, ferritic steel, that ruptured because it contained a large number of inclusions (Example 2)

Effect of Metallurgical Discontinuities

Nonmetallic inclusions, seams, laps, bursts, and pipe are common discontinuities found in wrought products that may cause premature failure. Shrinkage, gas porosity, and cold shuts are likely to occur in castings and can lead to failure, usually leakage in cast components.

Discontinuities can and sometimes do cause failures and should never be overlooked during failure analysis. However, except in fatigue, the number of failures caused by microstructural defects is relatively small compared with the number resulting from any one of several other causes.

A failure that resulted because of an excessive number of inclusions is described in the example that follows.

Example 2. Rupture of a Ferritic Steel Return Bend Because of Inclusions (Fig. 2)

After two years of service, a return bend from a triolefin-unit heater ruptured (see Fig. 2a). The bend was made from 4½-in. schedule 40 (0.237-in.-wall) pipe, of ASTM A213, grade T11, ferritic steel. The unit operated at 350 psi with a hydrocarbon feed stream (85% propylene) entering at 260 to 288 C (500 to 550 F) and leaving at 427 to 482 C (800 to 900 F). The temperature of the combustion gas was 900 C (1650 F).

This rupture occurred on the inner surface of the bend, rather than on the outer surface (as is usually the case), because of the susceptibility to erosive attack. The fracture was limited to the return bend and terminated at the welds that joined the bend to the pipeline.

Investigation. Examination of the fracture surfaces using a low-power stereomicroscope revealed that very little thinning of the metal had taken place, indicating low ductility and little corrosive attack.

Metallographic specimens were prepared from regions adjacent to the fracture and at the outer surface of the bend. The steel in the vicinity of the fracture exhibited a high concentration of both small and large inclusions (see Fig. 2b). The steel in the outer surface contained relatively few inclusions, and most of them were very small.

A micrograph of a section through the fire-side edge of the fracture surface is shown in Fig. 2(c). Branched cracks similar to those produced by stress corrosion of steel were observed. These cracks apparently had propagated between the inclusions in the steel. Scale was observed over most of the crack path, even down to the fine tip of the crack. It appeared likely that intrusion of the scale was promoted by the inclusions, which were linked together and thus provided an easy access path for oxidation. In addition, these intrusions of scale provided stress raisers in two ways:

1　The volume of the oxide was greater than that of the steel it replaced, so that the end of the intrusion put the adjacent metal in tension, thereby providing an excellent site for a stress-corrosion reaction. The metal at the sides of the intrusion was in compression, and thus the intrusion progressed longitudinally rather than laterally.

2 If any temperature cycling was involved, such as when the unit was shut down, the compressive effect was increased because of the differential thermal expansion, which was much greater for the steel than for the scale.

The high density of inclusions was assumed to be the result of improper cropping of the ingot from which the tube for the return bend was made.

Conclusions. The return bend failed as a result of stress-corrosion cracking, which propagated because of the presence of numerous inclusions in the metal. Scale deposited in the cracks, acting in combination with thermal cycling, contributed to stresses, which caused cracking.

Corrective Action. There is no general remedy for this relatively rare type of failure, which is difficult to control because of its localized nature. It would be too expensive to test every fitting. The best that can be done is draw the attention of the manufacturer to the problem in the expectation that he will exercise greater care with his steel supply in the future.

Effects of Fabrication Practices

Mechanical or metallurgical imperfections in a workpiece can be introduced, and detected, at any stage of construction, including mill processing, fabrication, shipping and erection. Imperfections do not always result in failure and are, in fact, a relatively infrequent cause of failures of pressure vessels during operation. The ASME Boiler and Pressure Vessel Codes recognize that perfection seldom is obtained in commercial materials and define acceptability standards for the producer.

Many imperfections are detected prior to actual operation. For instance, a crack indication was found in a forged nozzle by magnetic-particle inspection prior to welding of the nozzle into a pressure vessel. The nozzle manufacturer had found the crack and, instead of rejecting the part, had attempted to repair it by welding, which was not permitted in the specification.

In another instance, a piece of 2-in.-diam schedule 80 (0.218-in. wall thickness) ASTM A106 seamless carbon steel pipe that had been hydrostatically tested was about to be welded into a pipeline when the operator found a lap in the outer surface. The lap was about 3 in. long and extended through almost the entire wall. A slight ridge on the inner surface had prevented leakage through the lap during hydrostatic testing. A section across the lap showed light mill scale adhering to the sides with some decarburization. There was no evidence of branched cracking nor any indication of stress-corrosion cracking. The condition of the lap surfaces indicated that the lap had been formed at a temperature above 870 C (1600 F), which would have occurred early in the tube-

Fig. 3. Rimmed steel tube that failed by brittle fracture after being strain aged by cold swaging from 2½ to 2 in. in diameter

forming process. It was concluded that a foreign object had fallen on the tube as it was being formed and the object had passed through the rollers, producing a dent in the tube wall. Subsequent forming forced the dent inward and the lips together to produce a lap.

Heat treatment may be required subsequent to a fabricating operation. Deviations from specifications are potential causes of failure. Figure 3 shows a section of tubing made of rimmed steel that had been cold swaged from 2½ to 2 in. in diameter. Stress relief at 620 C (1150 F) after swaging was specified but was inadvertently omitted, and when the tube was expanded in a hole in a tube sheet, it broke in a brittle manner. The fracture was the result of strain aging of the steel, which can occur at room temperature and markedly decreases formability.

Repeated heat treatments, although performed at the proper temperature, may produce undesirable microstructures that can result in premature failure. For instance, a stainless steel tube was solution heat treated, straightened and then reheat treated. The light surface deformation between heat treatments caused germination of severe localized grain growth, which resulted in a coarse and less ductile grain structure. In service, grain-boundary cracking developed with relatively little swelling. Generally, this condition is harmful only when the tubing material has marginal strength or is stressed to an extent that results in measurable deformation.

An instance of improper heat treatment involved a pressure vessel made from forged HY-100 alloy steel plates and heat treated after welding. Heat treating specifications called for water quenching, with the vessel being lowered into the bath in the vertical position in order to develop uniform properties. After heat treating, six slots were machined through the vessel shell to serve as seats for wedges designed to retain a removable closure. The plugs cut from the slots in the vessel wall were subjected to mechanical tests, which showed large variations in tensile strength and impact properties depending on circumferential location in the shell. In some locations the values met specification, whereas in other locations they were considerably below specification. Investigation revealed that

the vessel had been quenched in the horizontal position instead of the vertical position because there was not enough headroom over the available quench tank to permit lowering the vessel into the tank in the vertical position. The vessel was reheated and quenched in the vertical position to develop the specified properties.

An instance in which heat treatment was required following forming involved a gas-plant debutanizer tower made of 1¼-in.-thick high-strength steel plate with properties as specified by ASTM A516, which permits, as an option, a refined normalized microstructure. Radiographic inspection of the entire vessel disclosed no imperfections. The vessel was designed to operate at 225 psi and 343 C (650 F). The vessel was hydrostatically tested using water at a temperature of not less than 16 C (60 F). When the test pressure reached 400 psi, the vessel ruptured, and about one-third of the head was torn out. Chemical analysis and tensile testing showed that the composition and tensile properties of the steel complied with ASTM A516. Charpy impact tests were made in the temperature range of 22 to 80 C (72 to 175 F) and indicated that the ductile-to-brittle transition temperature was above 38 C (100 F). Metallographic examination showed a microstructure with a grain size coarser than ASTM No. 1, which indicated that the head had not been normalized after forming. The coarse grain size contributed to reduction in fracture toughness of the steel. The vessel was completely checked ultrasonically for other plates with large grains, and the head was replaced. The vessel was hydrostatically tested again, and then returned to service. No further difficulties were encountered.

Overheating during fabrication can result in cracking of susceptible materials. Leakage was detected in the U-bend of a 2-in.-diam stainless steel tube during preoperational hydrostatic testing. The tube had been heated for bending, with a specified maximum temperature of 980 C (about 1800 F). Metallographic examination of a section through the leakage area showed evidence of partial melting, which indicated that the specified forming temperature had been considerably exceeded.

In the following example, closing the end of 1541 steel tubing by spinning caused overheating of the metal, which resulted in cracking.

Example 3. Cracking of a Fire-Extinguisher Case Because of Overheating During a Spinning Operation (Fig. 4)

The top of a fire-extinguisher case (see Fig. 4a) was closed by spinning. The case was made from 1541 steel tubing 6.75 in. in diameter and 0.165 in. in wall thickness. Leakage from the top of the case was observed during testing, and a 3-in.-long specimen was sent to the laboratory for analysis to determine the cause.

Investigation. Visual examination of the specimen did not reveal any surface cracks. However, three small folds were observed on the surface, and one was sectioned for microscopic examination. A very fine transverse fissure through the section was visible. Examination of a micrograph (see Fig. 4b) showed streaks of ferrite. Ferrite of this nature can be formed when steel is heated approximately to the melting point. Examination of specimens from other areas of the case exhibited a similar structure. The normal microstructure of 1541 steel for the specified heat treatment was annealed ferrite and pearlite.

The chemical composition was normal for 1541 steel, and no steelmaking or tubemaking defects were found in the specimen.

Conclusion. Cracking of the top of the fire-extinguisher case was the result of ferrite streaks that were formed when the metal was overheated. The initial forming temperature of the case plus frictional heat generated during spinning resulted in extreme overheating and some localized melting.

Recommendations. The temperature of the metal must be more closely controlled so that the spinning operation is done at a lower temperature, thus avoiding incipient melting and formation of ferrite streaks.

Multiple Causes. Sometimes, extensive examination of a failed vessel reveals that failure was caused not by one, but by several interrelated inadequacies in fabrication, as in the example that follows (Ref 1).

Example 4. Failure of a Thick-Wall Alloy Steel Pressure Vessel Caused by Cracks in Weld Heat-Affected Zone (Fig. 5)

A large pressure vessel (Fig. 5a) designed for use in an ammonia plant at a pressure of 5100 psi at 120 C (248 F) failed at 5000 psi during hydrostatic testing. The intended maximum test pressure was 6950 psi. The vessel weighed 183½ tons, measured 59 ft, 8⁹⁄₁₆ in. in over-all length and had an outside diameter of 6 ft, 6¾ in. It was fabricated from ten Mn-Cr-Ni-Mo-V steel plates 5⅞ in. thick, which were rolled and welded to form ten cylindrical shell sections, and three forgings of similar composition. The forgings formed two end closures and a flange for attaching one of the forged end closures to the vessel.

The failure did extensive damage to one end forging and three adjacent shell sections. Four large pieces were blown from the vessel; the largest, weighing about 2¼ tons, penetrated the shop wall and traveled a total distance of 152 ft. Pieces of the failed vessel are shown in Fig. 5(b).

Fabrication History. The cylindrical shell sections were hot formed so that the rolling direction of the plates was perpendicular to the axis of the vessel. All plates were supplied in the normalized-and-tempered condition.

The forgings were annealed, normalized, and tempered at 645 C (1193 F) to obtain the desired mechanical properties.

The longitudinal seams in the cylindrical shells were electroslag welded, and the welds

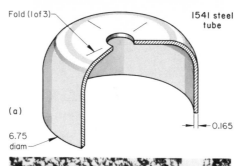

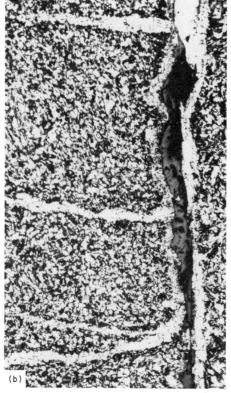

Fig. 4. (a) *Top of a fire-extinguisher case, which failed because of ferrite streaks that resulted from overheating during spinning.* (b) *Micrograph, at 150×, showing ferrite streaks.* (Example 3)

were ground to match the curvature of the shell. The cylindrical shell sections then were heated at 900 to 950 C (1652 to 1742 F) for 4 hr, rounded in the rolls within that temperature range, and then cooled in still air for examination of the seams.

Circumferential welding was done by the submerged-arc process using preheating at 200 C (392 F). Each subassembly was stress relieved by being heated to 620 to 660 C (1148 to 1220 F) for 6 hr.

Final joining of the three subassemblies followed the same welding procedures except that localized heating for stress relief was employed. During various stages of manufacture, all seams were examined by gamma radiography, automatic and manual ultrasonic testing, and magnetic-particle inspection.

Hydraulic Testing. The vessel was closed at the top, and water was admitted to the vessel through a fitting in the cover plate until the vent pipe that was within ⅛ in. of the inside surface at the top showed a full-bore discharge of water, at which time it was blanked off. The specified hydrostatic

proof test called for a pressure of 6950 psi at an ambient temperature of not less than 7 C (44.6 F).

At 5000 psi the customary halt was made, and about 30 seconds later the flange end of the vessel exploded without warning.

The flange forging was found to be cracked completely through in two locations, and the first two cylindrical sections were totally shattered. Three large fragments were flung to considerable distances from the vessel; as previously stated, one of them, weighing about 2¼ tons, actually passed through the shop wall and came to rest 152 ft away.

Metallurgical Examination. The characteristics of the fracture surfaces were those of brittle fracture and indicated that two origins had generated the crack pattern, both associated with the circumferential weld that joined the flange forging to the first shell section.

The general appearance of one fracture surface of the flange forging is shown in Fig. 5(c). The arrow near center indicates a flat facet (with major dimensions of roughly ⅜ in.) approximately ⁹⁄₁₆ in. below the outer surface of the vessel, which was partly in the heat-affected zone on the forging side of the circumferential seam weld. An enlarged view of the region containing this facet is shown in Fig. 5(d). A slightly larger facet was found on another fracture surface of the flange, near a fracture origin ⁷⁄₁₆ in. below the outer surface. This facet also was situated partly on the forging side of the heat-affected zone. Study of the portions of these facets in the heat-affected zone, both of which were flat and featureless, led to the belief that these were the true points of fracture initiation.

Metallographic examination revealed that the structure immediately below each facet in the heat-affected zone was a mixture of bainite and austenite having a Vickers hardness (1-kg load) of 426 to 460. Elsewhere, the structure of the heat-affected zone was coarse and jagged bainite with a Vickers hardness of 313 to 363.

Examination of a section transverse to the weld disclosed that the structure of the flange forging contained pronounced banding whereas the plate did not. The structure between the bands (and away from the weld) consisted of ferrite and pearlite with a hardness of 180 to 200 Vickers (10-kg load). In the bands, the structure was upper bainite with a hardness of 251 to 265 Vickers. Specimens cut from this area were austenitized at 950 C (1742 F) and quenched in a 10% solution of NaOH in water to produce pure martensite. A Vickers hardness traverse (1-kg load) across a band showed average values of 507 on one side of the band, 549 within the band, and 488 on the other side. A microprobe scan across the banded area showed the following differences in chemical composition: 1.56% Mn outside the band, 1.94% within it; 0.70% Cr outside, 0.81% within; and 0.23% Mo outside, 0.35% within. These differences indicated higher hardenability within the bands, which suggested a greater susceptibility to cracking, especially where the bands met the heat-affected zone of the circumferential weld.

The hard spots within the forging suggested that during stress relief the vessel had not actually attained the specified temperature. To check this, specimens from the heat-affected zone were accordingly heated to a variety of tempering temperatures to observe at what point softening would occur. Vickers hardness tests (1-kg load) on hard-spot specimens showed no deviation from the as-failed hardness scatter band for temperatures up to 550 C (1022 F), but gave definitely lower values after retempering at or above 600 C (1112 F). A similar behavior occurred in specimens taken outside the hard spots. It was therefore concluded that stress relief had not been performed at the specified temperature level.

Other studies of microstructure established that the mode of crack propagation was transgranular cleavage, which occurred not only in prior austenite grains but also in ferrite grains and pearlite colonies. Branching and subsidiary cracks were also found, all very close to the main fracture surface. The distance from the fracture to the crack farthest away from it was 0.020 in.

To further investigate the effect of the stress relief on the properties of the vessel, standard Charpy V-notch specimens were prepared from the flange forging, the plate, and the weld. All specimens were oriented with their length parallel to the circumference of the vessel so that all fractures would be parallel to the main fracture. Tests were performed on as-fractured material over the temperature range of −10 to +100 C (14 to 212 F), yielding impact values that met the specifications for the forging and plate, but definitely inferior impact strength for the weld metal (see the lower curve in Fig. 5e). None of the materials displayed a sufficient capacity for energy absorption (30 ft-lb for the forging, 51 ft-lb for the plate and 12 ft-lb for the weld) to have arrested the crack propagation that led to failure of the pressure vessel. Other specimens of the weld metal, which were retempered at 650 C (1202 F) for 6 hr and tested over the same temperature range as those discussed above, showed a marked improvement in impact strength at or above 20 C (68 F), as shown by the upper curve in Fig. 5(e). This confirmed the previous deduction that the stress relief of the vessel had been at a lower temperature than had been specified.

Conclusions. Failure of the pressure vessel stemmed from the formation of transverse fabrication cracks in the heat-affected zone of the circumferential weld joining the flange forging to the first shell section. The occurrence of the cracks was fostered by the presence of bands of alloying-element segregation in the forging, which had created hard spots, particularly where they met the heat-affected zone. Stress relief of the vessel had been inadequate, leaving residual stresses and hard spots and providing low notch ductility, especially in the weld.

Recommendations. The final normalizing temperature should be Ac₃ + 50 C (Ac₃ + 90 F), and the tempering temperature should be 650 C (1202 F). After completion of each seam weld, the weld preheat should be continued for a short distance along the seam. The critical flaw size for this alloy and section thickness should be determined by fracture mechanics, and the capacity of available nondestructive testing methods for detecting flaws of this size should be assessed. The possible benefits of a more

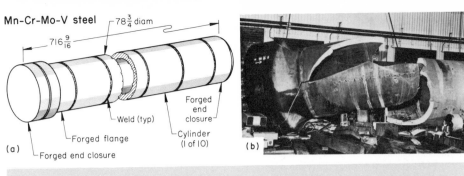

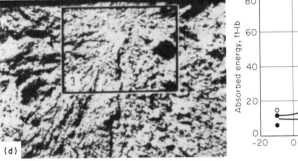

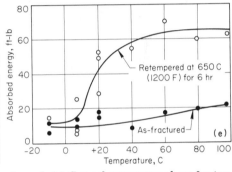

(a) Schematic illustration of vessel. (b) Shattered vessel. (c) General appearance of one fracture surface; arrow points to facet at fracture origin. (d) Enlarged view, at about 5½×, of region at arrow in (c). (e) Charpy V-notch impact-strength values of specimens from weld area, both as-fractured and after retempering at 650 C (1200 F) for 6 hr.

Fig. 5. Large, thick-wall pressure vessel that failed because of cracking in weld heat-affected zone (Example 4; Ref 1)

effective solution treatment or a revised forging practice should be explored in an effort to eliminate the banding in the flange forging.

Inspection Practices. The capability of inspection procedures to detect imperfections and discontinuities below a certain size can have an influence in preventing failure of a pressure vessel. The effectiveness of radiographic techniques depends largely on size and orientation of the discontinuity in the metal.

Touching the surface of a pressure vessel with an energized coil or probe used to magnetize a component for magnetic-particle inspection may produce an arc burn, which is a potential stress raiser.

The water used in hydrostatic proof testing and the liquid used in liquid-penetrant inspection can be sources of chlorides that later can cause cracking, unless the parts are carefully cleaned and dried after testing. For example, a type 304L stainless steel pipeline used for

transferring caustic materials was hydrostatically tested after fabrication and was found acceptable. However, after about two months of service, leaks were detected at several circumferential weld joints. The pipe had been installed in a horizontal position, and the leaks occurred predominantly at the bottom of the joints (six o'clock position), with a higher incidence of leakage at low points in the pipeline. Leakage occurred in both shop and field circumferential welds; none was observed in the longitudinal seam in the welded pipe. Investigation revealed that the leaks had resulted from chloride pitting. The source of the chlorides was determined to be the water used in hydrostatic testing of the pipeline. After the hydrostatic test had been completed, the water, which originally contained less than 100 ppm chlorides, was drained from the system. It was determined that some water had collected at low points in the pipeline and at discontinuities resulting from the weld reinforcement on the pipe inner surface. The piping was allowed to sit in this condition for about four to five months before being used to transfer caustic. Evaporation and chloride concentration, followed by corrosion and leakage, could have been eliminated if the pipeline had been completely drained after hydrostatic testing.

Pressure Vessels Made of Composite Materials

Composite materials are used in pressure vessels both to reduce cost and to conserve strategic material. Also, they provide vessels strong enough to resist deformation under pressure and surfaces that resist attack by the substance contained within the vessel.

A vessel made of a composite material usually has a carbon steel shell, which provides the necessary rigidity to resist deformation under pressure. The interior is lined with a corrosion-resistant alloy, usually stainless steel, that is compatible with the material contained within the pressure vessel.

Linings used for pressure vessels made of composite materials are applied by surface welding, roll cladding, plug welding or explosive bonding. Surface-welded linings are produced by facing the interior carbon steel surface with an overlay of a corrosion-resistant alloy, using one of several processes for surface welding. These processes include manual shielded metal-arc welding, automatic and semiautomatic submerged-arc welding, and plasma-arc welding.

Roll cladding usually is accomplished by one of two methods. In one method, stainless steel is placed on a carbon steel ingot and bonded to it by hot rolling. The other method is essentially the same, except that a flux is placed between the two materials before hot rolling.

Plug-welded linings are produced by securing roll-formed sections of a corrosion-resistant alloy to the interior surface of a carbon steel shell by plug welding.

Explosive bonding produces an excellent bond and an excellent product. The layer of cladding material is bonded to the base metal by the action of a shock wave generated in a suitable medium by a controlled explosion.

Welding. When composite materials are joined by welding, special techniques are required and metallurgical problems can arise. With roll-clad material, the overlay is machined away from the weld site and the carbon steel shell is welded by the usual methods from the outside. The inside welds are made with stainless steel filler metals such as ER308, ER309, ER310, or ER312. In plug welding, similar techniques are employed.

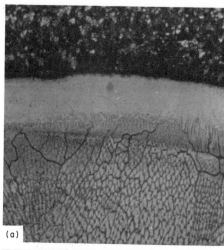

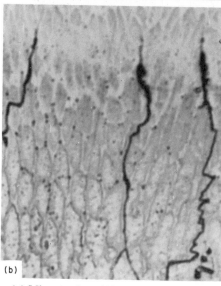

(a) Micrograph, at 100×, of specimen through weld area etched in acid cupric chloride, showing ASTM A515 carbon steel (top), interface region (center), and duplex weld structure containing fine cracks (bottom). (b) Micrograph, at 250×, of an area of the specimen in (a), showing cracks and precipitates.

Fig. 6. Cracks in pressure vessel made of ASTM A515 carbon steel lined with type 405 stainless steel. Failure occurred at plug welds because of dilution of weld metal. (Example 5; Ref 2)

Either 300 or 400 series stainless steel sheets may be used, and these sheets are welded together and to the carbon steel pressure vessel with stainless steel filler metal.

Metallurgical problems arise from the effects of dilution of the alloying constituents in the corrosion-resistant-alloy coating by the carbon steel base metal. Fully austenitic stainless steel filler metals are susceptible to microfissuring during welding. A duplex structure of austenite and a small amount of ferrite in the weld deposit prevents microfissuring. Therefore, the ferrite content usually is kept between 5 and 9%. This duplex structure may be obtained by suitably balancing the chromium and nickel contents in the weld metal. Alloy dilution

can be controlled by varying the welding technique and the electrode composition. Very little dilution can produce a fully austenitic structure, but too much produces a structure containing martensite.

Sigma phase sometimes is found in austenitic stainless steel weld metal. Although sigma phase can occur in the as-welded condition, it is more commonly encountered after long exposures at temperatures of 594 to 871 C (1100 to 1600 F). Sigma phase may embrittle austenitic stainless steel at room temperature; however, it ordinarily is not a problem at operating temperatures above 650 C (1200 F). Usually, sigma phase is associated with ferrite; alloying elements such as chromium, columbium and molybdenum, which stabilize ferrite, also promote sigma-phase formation.

Care must be used when welding Monel to carbon steel to avoid excessive dilution of the Monel with iron, such as in weld overlays. Excessive iron dilution causes the Monel to be hot short and to crack. Iron dilution can be minimized by using a barrier layer of pure nickel weld deposit, or by carefully controlling the welding procedure with the use of small-diameter electrodes and a stringer-bead technique.

In the following example (Ref 2), cracks occurred in plug welds that joined a stainless steel liner to a carbon steel pressure-vessel shell.

Example 5. Cracking in Plug Welds That Joined a Stainless Steel Liner to a Carbon Steel Shell, Because of Dilution of Weld Metal (Fig. 6)

Repeated cracking occurred in the welds joining the liner and shell of a fluid catalytic cracking unit that operated at a pressure of 20 psi and a temperature of 480 C (about 900 F). The shell was made of ASTM A515 carbon steel welded with E7018 filler metal. The liner was made of type 405 stainless steel and was plug welded to the shell using ER309 and ER310 stainless steel filler metal.

Investigation. Examination of the microstructure in the plug-weld zone revealed a good duplex structure with what appeared to be fine cracks starting inside the weld zone and spreading outward through the weld and toward the surface, as shown in Fig. 6(a). At higher magnifications, some of the fine cracks appeared to be precipitates (see Fig. 6b). When cracking had completely penetrated the plug weld, corrosion of the carbon steel occurred, spreading radially. Also, there was decarburization and graphitization of the carbon steel at the interface.

The body of the weld had a hardness of Rockwell C 45. This, combined with the decarburization of the carbon steel, was assumed to be indicative of carbon migration out of the heat-affected zone and into the weld metal, thus preventing the formation of martensite. Farther into the weld metal, the carbon level was sufficiently high to allow martensite to form. In the area where the grain-boundary precipitates appeared heaviest, between the martensite band and the duplex structure, the structure was probably austenitic. These phase changes are predicted on the Schaeffler diagram (see page 246 in Volume 6 of this Handbook).

The precipitates followed the austenitic regions into the duplex structure and eventually disappeared. They undoubtedly contributed to the cracking that occurred.

The composition of the precipitates was analyzed using an electron microprobe. Silicon was not present in significant amounts, and neither was oxygen, except in the vicinity of a filled branch crack, which also showed small amounts of carbon. Phosphorus was absent, and iron, chromium and nickel were present in amounts commensurate with the weld material. Approximately 4% sulfur was present in the filled branch crack, and the precipitates contained about 12% sulfur.

Thus, several mechanisms were operative in cracking and damaging of the vessel, many of which were the result of microstructural changes in the weld alloy at the interface caused by dilution of the alloy. Austenite was formed at a low dilution level, and the presence of sulfur gave rise to grain-boundary precipitation of sulfides, thus causing hot shortness. Further dilution produced a brittle martensitic phase, which is more susceptible to failure and is a likely source of crack initiation. This phase was not present at the interface, probably because of carbon migration into the weld, as evidenced by the decarburization and graphitization of the base material. Finally, the differential thermal expansion of the carbon and stainless steels produced the necessary internal stress to produce extensive cracking. Once the carbon steel was exposed to the contents of the pressure vessel, corrosion followed.

Conclusions. Cracking in the plug welds was the result of excessive dilution of the weld metal. Dilution of the weld metal permitted formation of a martensitic phase in which cracks initiated.

Corrective Measures. Periodic careful gouging of the affected areas followed by repair welding proved sufficient to keep the vessel in service. However, in vessels operated at higher pressures or containing more aggressive corrosive materials, such measures would not suffice, and careful selection of the filler metal and welding procedure would be necessary to prevent formation of the martensitic phase. A lower sulfur content would remove the grain-boundary precipitate. Carbon migration would still occur but in itself might not cause a major problem.

Stress Corrosion and Hydrogen Embrittlement

Very often, the materials being processed or reacted in pressure vessels are corrosive, or the impurities that they contain are corrosive. Thus, the possibility of stress-corrosion cracking must be considered. If the material being processed contains hydrogen in a certain form, hydrogen embrittlement may result. Stress corrosion and hydrogen embrittlement are closely related and frequently are indistinguishable.

Stress-corrosion cracking occurs when stress and a specific corrodent for the material are present in amounts large enough for failure to occur by the combined action of both but too small for failure to occur by either one acting alone. Characteristic of stress corrosion are highly branched, transgranular cracks; under certain conditions, intergranular cracking occurs. Equipment that fails by stress-corrosion cracking usually must be replaced, because the extent of cracking is difficult to determine and because the cracks are difficult to repair by welding.

Stress may be internal or external. Internal stress can arise from the microstructural form of the alloy — for instance, steel in the martensitic phase. Also, residual stresses produced during welding, and misalignment stresses, may be very important. Externally applied stresses arise from applied mechanical loads, vibration or pressure.

Corrosion may arise from many sources, some of which might appear to be innocuous or not aggressively corrosive. Even relatively pure water can be corrosive or can accelerate corrosion. If any concentration mechanism is at work, very small amounts of dissolved solids can be disastrous.

The embrittling effects of mercury on brass and aluminum alloys are well known. Ammonia produces "season cracking" in cold worked brass. Alkaline compounds attack high-strength aluminum alloys. Stainless steels are attacked readily by hot chlorides in aqueous solution — which even in very small amounts can cause severe damage to stressed austenitic stainless steels (see subsequent discussion under "Stress-Corrosion Cracking From Hot Chlorides"). Such steels also can be attacked by concentrated sodium hydroxide (NaOH), as can low-carbon steels. Stress-corrosion cracking of Hastelloy C-276 has occurred in environments containing organic compounds and $AlCl_3$ at 100 C (212 F). (No cracking occurred after the $AlCl_3$, which was present as an impurity, was removed.)

In the following example, a pressure vessel made of low-carbon steel failed by stress-corrosion cracking because of caustic embrittlement by potassium hydroxide.

Example 6. Stress-Corrosion Cracking of a Large Low-Carbon Steel Pressure Vessel, Resulting From Caustic Embrittlement by Potassium Hydroxide (Fig. 7)

A large pressure vessel (Fig. 7a) that had been in service for about ten years as a hydrogen sulfide (H_2S) absorber developed cracks and began leaking at a nozzle. The vessel contained a 20% aqueous solution of potassium hydroxide (KOH), potassium carbonate (K_2CO_3) and arsenic at 950 psi max and 33 C (91 F). The cylindrical portion of the vessel was 66 in. in inside diameter, 402 in. long, and $2\frac{1}{2}$ in. in wall thickness. A few months before failure occurred, portions of the exterior surface of the vessel had been exposed to a fire.

The vessel was examined at the job site and was found to be empty, but the inside surface was covered with a layer of sulfur. A sample was removed from near the end of the crack at the nozzle and was sent to the laboratory. The nozzle itself was not cracked. The vessel was returned to the fabricator and was stress relieved before repair work was begun.

The vessel wall, in which the fracture occurred, consisted of $2\frac{1}{2}$-in.-thick ASTM A516, grade 70, low-carbon steel plate. To provide a tray support, a steel angle, 3 by 3 by $\frac{3}{8}$ in., had been formed into a ring and continuously welded to the inside wall of the vessel at the heel and the toe of one leg, as shown in section A-A in Fig. 7(a).

Investigation. In the groove formed by the junction of the lower tray-support weld and the top part of the weld around the nozzle was a crack about $2\frac{1}{4}$ in. long. Each end of the crack branched into a Y, as shown in detail B in Fig. 7(a). The crack portions in the weld metal around the nozzle were arrested, and the nozzle was not damaged.

The field sample submitted for laboratory analysis contained the remote end of one of several cracks that propagated into the upper tray-support weld. The surfaces of this crack were covered by a tightly adhering dark-brown and black scale. The surfaces contained two triangular regions that were smooth and that showed no evidence of ductility, one at the top of the weld and the other at the outer surface of the wall. The remainder of the fracture surface showed cleavage planes with some evidence of ductility, indicating that failure had resulted from tensile overload.

A dirty yellow scale was found under a piece of steel angle that was part of the field sample, but no scale was noticeable elsewhere after the angle had been removed by air carbon-arc gouging. No additional cracks were found in the welds for the tray support.

Tensile and impact tests performed on specimens from the sample indicated that the physical properties, after stress relief, were adequate for the service conditions.

Because of the proximity of the crack to the nozzle, which was saved for re-use, only fragments from the tray-support side of the crack were available. How representative these were of the original microstructure was a moot question because they had been annealed during removal. Microscopic examination revealed pits and scale near the crack origin; the pits contained corrosion products. Although difficult to determine because of the small grain size, cracking was principally transgranular.

The surface of a section through a crack that started in a groove formed by the junction of the lower tray-support weld and the weld around the nozzle was examined under a microscope. The first 0.25 in. of the crack surface sloped at an angle of about 45° to the cut surface, was relatively smooth, had a thin orange-brown scale and, at higher

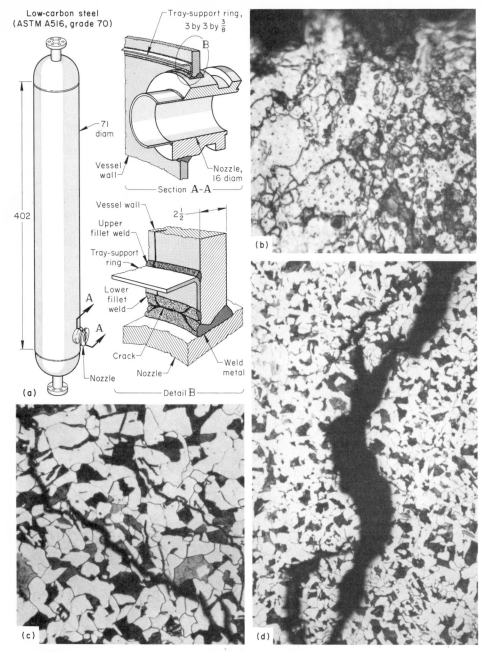

(a) View of vessel before failure, and details of nozzle and tray support. (b) Micrograph, at 600×, showing corrosion pits at edge of fracture surface, and inclusions. (c) Micrograph, at 200×, showing auxiliary cracks in tensile-overload region of main crack. (d) Micrograph, at 100×, showing auxiliary cracks in stress-corrosion zone of main crack.

Fig. 7. Large enclosed cylindrical pressure vessel that failed by stress-corrosion cracking because of caustic embrittlement by potassium hydroxide (Example 6)

magnification, exhibited plastic flow at some points and corrosion pits at others. Figure 7(b) shows corrosion pits in the edge of the fracture surface, and inclusions consisting of large dark orange-brown conglomerates and smaller gray globules that appear to have nucleated in the grain boundaries. These features suggest that periods of corrosion alternated with sudden instances of cleavage, under a tensile load, along preferred slip planes. Cracking in such a manner is typical of the stress-corrosion process according to one theory.

After the first 0.25 in., the crack progressed abruptly straight downward into the weld and was filled with a thick gray scale. The crack surface was wavy, and contained branching cracks filled with corrosion products. In this crack, corrosion had obviously predominated, with cleavage playing a lesser role or none at all. This condition is in accordance with an alternative, strictly electrochemical, theory on the mechanism of stress corrosion.

Micrographs of sections across the remote end of the crack in the field sample that propagated into the material showed both a zone that failed by tension overload (Fig. 7c) and a stress-corrosion zone (Fig. 7d). These two distinguishable fracture zones were confirmed by a gray corrosion product similar to that found near the crack origin, which was present in auxiliary cracks in the stress-corrosion zone but not present in the tension-overload zone. Cracking in both zones was clearly transgranular.

Discussion. Because the surface of the steel angle adjacent to the vessel wall had been sealed, and only one point of seepage under it had been found, the crack at the grooved area between the lower weld joining the angle to the wall and the weld around the nozzle must have formed first. Although the vessel had been postweld heat treated before being put into service, apparently there was sufficient residual stress in this grooved area for it to act as a notch or a stress raiser. With this configuration and enough time, the combination of the residual plus operating stresses and the amount of KOH present would have caused stress corrosion — in this instance, as a result of caustic embrittlement.

The fire to which the vessel had been exposed prior to failure, the only evidence of which was observable bulging of the vessel skirt, could have been instrumental in initiating cracks by any or all of the following conditions affecting the critical grooved area: (a) an increase in temperature to above 120 C (250 F), (b) an increase in concentration of the caustic solution to greater than 50%, and (c) addition of thermal stresses resulting from temperature gradients to existing residual stresses. On the other hand, cracking may have been initiated simply by the combination of existing residual stresses and normal operating conditions over a long period of time.

Caustic embrittlement appeared most plausible as the cause of failure because of the presence of KOH and the known role of KOH in stress-corrosion failures of plain carbon steel vessels. However, the presence of arsenic can induce hydrogen embrittlement under alkaline conditions. The probability of sulfur, a lesser by-product of the removal of H_2S, inducing hydrogen embrittlement under alkaline conditions is slight. Hydrogen embrittlement from arsenic may therefore have been the added influence that helped produce transgranular corrosion rather than the simpler mechanism of intergranular corrosion.

Conclusion. Failure was caused by stress corrosion, which probably resulted from caustic embrittlement by KOH.

Recommendations. The tray support should be installed higher on the vessel wall to prevent coincidence of the lower tray-support weld with the nozzle weld, thus avoiding the formation of a notch.

Stress-Corrosion Cracking From Hot Chlorides.

Equipment made of austenitic stainless steel may sustain stress-corrosion cracking when contacted by hot chlorides in aqueous solution — even in concentrations of only a few parts per million. For this reason, chloride attack generally is insidious, and operating personnel may not be aware of such a problem until failure occurs.

Chlorides commonly are introduced into pressure vessels as dissolved salts in water or wet (saturated) steam. At temperatures below about 50 C (122 F), small quantities of chloride salts create few problems. At higher temperatures in systems containing austenitic stainless steels, chlorides can be disastrous. Water is most safely introduced to pressure vessels made of austenitic stainless steel in the form of either clean steam condensate or dry superheated steam. Generally, there is no problem as long as ample quantities of condensate or dry steam are available. Unfortunately, during refinery turnarounds, superheated steam can be in short supply because the heaters are shut down. As the various units are put back on stream, the boiler plant may lack sufficient capacity to meet all immediate needs. A related problem can occur in steam methane reformers during start-up. Unless special start-up procedures are carefully followed, steam introduced to the reformer may contain water droplets with entrained chloride salts (carryover). When the wet steam subsequently flashes against a hot surface farther down the system, a residue of chloride salts remains. If the surface is hot, stress-corrosion cracking will occur quickly in some grades of austenitic stainless steel.

In one instance, stress-corrosion cracking caused failure of a type 347 stainless steel shaft in a hydrogen-bypass valve in a steam methane-reformer plant. Chloride-salt residues were found on the fracture surfaces, together with highly branched cracks typical of stress-corrosion failure (see Fig. 8). Wet steam introduced to the system during start-up operations was the source of the chlorides. The shaft had a hardness of 245 Bhn, indicating that it had been made from cold finished bar stock. Undoubtedly, the high surface residual stresses inherent to cold finishing made the shaft more sensitive to stress-corrosion cracking. The fractured shaft was replaced with an annealed type 316 stainless steel shaft having a hardness of 169 Bhn. Also, changes were made in the reformer start-up procedure, minimizing the probability of introducing wet steam.

Protection During Off-Stream Periods. When subjected to stress in aqueous chloride solutions, austenitic stainless steels fail by highly branched, transgranular cracking. When the same steels are exposed in refinery processing units to weak sulfur acids, more commonly known as polythionic acids, intergranular cracking can occur. The austenitic stainless steel must be in a sensitized condition — that is, with heavy intergranular carbides — for polythionic acids to cause cracking. Polythionic acids form directly from sulfide corrosion products inside desulfurizing, hydrotreating and hydrocracking units at ambient temperatures during refinery shutdowns, but are not a problem at operating temperatures. These types of units frequently are clad with austenitic stainless steel for on-stream corrosion protection, but the steel must be protected during off-stream periods.

Fig. 8. Micrograph, at 75×, showing chloride stress-corrosion cracking in a type 347 stainless steel shaft in a hydrogen-bypass valve

ing off-stream periods. Procedures used for this protection are as follows:

1 When a stainless-clad desulfurizer, hydrotreater or similar reactor is shut down but not opened, it should be kept under positive nitrogen pressure. If the reactor is opened but not dumped, it is recommended that it be turned over with ammonia three or four times prior to opening. It is also recommended that work be completed before the walls of the reactor reach the ambient dew point. If this is not practical, the reactor should be kept under positive nitrogen pressure during the entire downtime.

2 During dumping of the reactor catalyst, 5000 ppm ammonia should be added to the nitrogen purge. Once the catalyst is removed, a 2% solution of soda ash with 0.5% sodium nitrate should be used to fill the reactor and soak all stainless steel.

3 Any austenitic stainless steel in components such as recycle-furnace tubes, feed-heater furnace tubes, feed or effluent piping, and tubes or cladding in feed-effluent exchangers also is susceptible to intergranular cracking. Provisions should be made to keep this equipment under positive nitrogen pressure if unopened or to fill and soak with soda ash solution prior to opening.

Because polythionic acids are most likely to cause cracking in austenitic stainless steels that are in a sensitized condition, cracking can be minimized in pressure vessels of welded construction by using stabilized stainless steels such as type 321 or type 347, or by using low-carbon grades such as type 304L or type 316L.

Hydrogen Embrittlement. When corrosive reactions occur at a metal surface, hydrogen may be produced — particularly if acids or strong alkali solutions are involved. The hydrogen evolved is preferentially absorbed by steel and possibly by other metals. This absorption can cause hydrogen embrittlement. Con-

sequently, stress-corrosion cracking and hydrogen embrittlement not only are associated, but sometimes also are indistinguishable, particularly in sour-gas service where H_2S is the active corrodent.

The following example describes hydrogen embrittlement in a vessel used as a hydrogen reformer.

Example 7. Hydrogen-Embrittlement Cracking in a Large Molybdenum Alloy Steel Vessel (Fig. 9)

Figure 9(a) shows a vessel that had been in service about three years as a hydrogen reformer when cracking occurred in the weld between the shell and the lower head. As shown in detail A in Fig. 9, one crack (which was 6 in. long) developed at the bottom of the weld at the inner surface of the head (crack A), and another (which was 3 ft long) developed at the top of the weld at the outer surface of the shell (crack B). Crack B later extended to a length of 9 ft. Also, some small blisters were observed on the inner surface near the weld after attempts had been made to repair the crack.

The vessel contained ceramic balls in the lower head and a catalyst in the shell section. Temperature of the incoming gas was 690 C (1275 F), and of the outgoing gas, 620 C (1150 F). Design temperature of the vessel (which was insulated inside) was 120 C (250 F), and design pressure was 650 psi. No liquid phase was present. A temperature of 338 C (640 F) had occurred at two hot spots 4 in. in diameter on the outside surface just above the area of the failure.

The vessel was made of ASTM A204, grade C, molybdenum alloy steel. The head was 1$\frac{5}{16}$ in. thick and the shell was 2$\frac{5}{16}$ in. thick.

Metallurgical Investigation. Six samples were removed from the outside surface of the vessel at right angles to the weld, using an abrasive cutoff wheel; as shown in Fig. 9(b), three were cut across the weld line on the shell side and three on the head side. The samples were triangular in cross section, about $\frac{1}{2}$ in. wide on each surface, and 3 in. long. A sample at the end of the crack on the inner surface of the head was removed parallel to the weld. This sample was also triangular in shape, $\frac{7}{8}$ in. wide at the head surface, $\frac{5}{8}$ in. deep and 9$\frac{1}{2}$ in. long. Also, three $\frac{13}{16}$-in.-diam plugs were trepanned through the complete wall thickness, one each from the head, weld and shell.

Of the six samples taken from the outer surface, only sample 3 was visibly cracked. This crack was about $\frac{3}{16}$ in. deep and initiated at the edge of the weld in the coarse-grained portion of the heat-affected zone. Microscopic examination revealed a small crack in sample 1, which was taken from the shell side. This crack also was located in the coarse-grained portion of the heat-affected zone. No cracks were discovered in the other samples taken from the outer surface. No microfissures, decarburization or characteristics of hydrogen embrittlement were observed in any of the six samples from that surface.

Examination of a section through the sample from the inner surface of the head showed that the crack was at the edge of the weld, completely in the heat-affected zone of the head, as shown in Fig. 9(c). Fusion of the weld metal on both the head and shell sides was good on both the inner and outer surfaces. A micrograph of the start of the crack, which was at the inner surface, revealed elongated grains, indicating that the metal had undergone plastic flow prior to failure. Figure 9(d) is a micrograph of a portion of the same section farther along the crack. The microstructure was normal in appearance but was severely embrittled, as shown by the region near the fracture surfaces. Additional micrographs in the vicinity of the crack showed that the metal had become severely gassed in an area extending up to 1/8 in. on each side of the crack.

Microscopic examination of the plug trepanned from the head showed decarburization, which was present in nearly equal amounts on both inner and outer surfaces and therefore was not the result of service conditions. The inner surface was coated with a dark-brown scale. The microstructure of the metal in the head was banded, except near the surfaces, and contained spheroidal carbides, indicating that the metal had been held at temperatures above 538 C (1000 F) for a long period of time.

The plug from the shell also had a dark-brown scale on the inner surface and showed a microstructure that was uniform throughout and typical for the metal. The carbides in the pearlitic areas had lost some of their lamellar form, which indicated that the material had been held at a high temperature for some time, but the breakdown was not as severe as that observed in the head.

Hardness tests were performed on one of the samples taken from the outer surface, the sample from the inner surface, and the three trepanned plugs. Rockwell B hardness values and equivalent tensile-strength values were as follows:

Location of hardness test	Rockwell B hardness	Equivalent tensile strength, psi
Outer-Surface Sample		
Shell plate	86	85,000
Head plate	86	85,000
Heat-affected zone(a)	92 to 98	105,000
Weld metal	92 to 96	100,000
Inner-Surface Sample		
Head plate	76	67,500
Heat-affected zone(b)	89	85,000
Weld metal	90	92,500
Trepanned Plugs		
Shell:		
Inner wall	84	82,500
Center	81	75,000
Outer wall	85	84,000
Head:		
Inner wall	76	67,500
Center	78	71,000
Outer wall	79	72,500
Weld metal:		
Inner wall	96	111,500
Center	94	108,500
Outer wall	95	110,000
(a) Both shell and head sides. (b) Head side.		

Discussion. Hardness data and microscopic examination indicated that the lower head had been overheated for a sufficiently long time to reduce the tensile strength below the 75,000-psi minimum required for ASTM A204, grade C, steel. The wide difference in tensile strength between head and

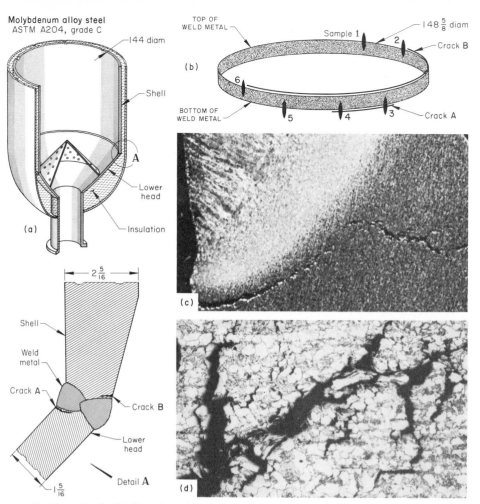

(a) Portion of tank; detail A shows locations of cracks, at welds joining shell to lower head. (b) Schematic illustration of the weld area, showing locations of cracks, and of samples removed for examination. (c) Macrograph, at about 6½×, of a nital-etched specimen from the inner surface of the head, showing a crack in the heat-affected zone. (d) Micrograph, at 100×, of a nital-etched specimen, showing normal microstructure and hydrogen embrittlement.

Fig. 9. Vessel made of ASTM A204, grade C, molybdenum alloy steel that failed as the result of hydrogen embrittlement (Example 7)

weld metal (including heat-affected zone) formed a metallurgical notch that enhanced the diffusion of hydrogen into the metal in the cracked region. The resultant embrittlement and associated fissuring led to further weakening and eventually to failure.

Because the fracture was brittle, internal cracking must have taken place prior to plastic deformation on the inner surface. Also, the major crack must have propagated internally, because it did not come out to the inside surface near its end. Cracking on the outside surface was simply the result of overloading of the embrittled material after internal failure had already occurred.

The total absence of decarburization on the trepanned plugs at the inside surface of the shell and the minor amount on the head suggest that hydrogen diffusion was limited to the head regions adjacent to the heat-affected zone or that hydrogen diffused into the metal at temperatures below 205 C (400 F). The tensile tests of the head material would have detected any embrittlement by exhibiting low ductility and low reduction of area. Had hydrogen diffusion occurred at higher temperatures, more fissuring (gassing) or considerably more decarburization would have been in evidence.

Because no serious damage was detectable in the trepanned plugs, heat treatment would relieve any embrittlement that may have occurred in the shell and head. Grains need not be separated for embrittlement to occur, and, provided no fissures have formed, the pressure can be relieved by allowing the gases to diffuse out of the metal during careful heat treatment; otherwise, blisters will result.

The damaged region adjacent to the weld on the head side should be removed, because these fissures cannot be repaired by heat treatment.

Conclusion. Failure of the vessel was chiefly the result of hydrogen embrittlement with overheating as a contributory factor.

Corrective Action. The vessel was wrapped in asbestos and heated to 455 C (850 F) at a rate of 55 C (100 F) per hour, held at 455 to 482 C (850 to 900 F) for 2¼ hr, heated to 595 C (1100 F) at a rate of 55 C (100 F) per hour and held for 2¼ hr. The vessel then was cooled at a rate prescribed by the ASME code. This treatment caused hydrogen to be diffused out of the metal, thus removing the source of embrittlement.

The weld metal on both sides of the crack, and 3/16 in. of base metal in the shell and the head, were removed. The area thus prepared was repair welded using E7018 filler metal, then stress relieved.

Brittle Fractures

Materials that ordinarily are ductile can undergo brittle fracture suddenly and without warning, depending on certain conditions and factors, which are discussed in the article on Ductile and Brittle Fractures, beginning on page 61 in this volume. Brittle fractures are most likely to occur in body-centered-cubic structures, such as ferritic steels, and in relatively thick parts that contain adequately large flaws. Strain rates required for brittle fracture depend somewhat on the temperature of the part; at low temperatures strain rates generally are low, whereas at high temperatures strain rates are higher.

The origin of a brittle fracture almost always will be a pre-existing crack, or similar type of notch or stress raiser, because the concentrated triaxial stresses developed at such points are the single most important factor in determining whether a crack can propagate under the applied load. Generally, brittle fracture happens under an applied stress that is less than the yield strength, and the energy expended in propagating the crack is low.

Most sudden brittle fractures occur by cleavage, which produces a fracture surface with a bright, granular or crystalline appearance. A characteristic herringbone (chevron) pattern, which points to the origin of fracture, often is present. Brittle fractures can be differentiated from ductile fractures by the short time required for the crack to achieve critical size and by the high rate of crack propagation. Although most brittle fractures are transgranular, intergranular brittle fracture can occur if the grain boundaries are embrittled, such as by chemical segregation or the presence of a brittle second phase.

Brittle fractures in pressure vessels often are associated with the notch-brittle behavior of carbon or low-alloy steels. Although more likely to occur at atmospheric or subfreezing temperatures, brittle fractures can occur at elevated temperatures if the metal has become embrittled by microstructural or metallurgical changes. In carbon and low-alloy steels, metallurgical characteristics imparted during manufacture may be important if they cause the ductile-to-brittle transition temperature to be near or above the ambient temperature experienced by the system during fabrication, especially during hydrostatic testing. These characteristics include chemical composition and the effects of deoxidation, forming and heat treatment. "Poor steel" or "poor welding practice" often is

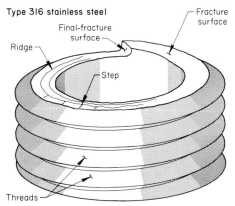

Type 316 stainless steel

Fig. 10. Representation of the surface of a brittle fracture in a type 316 stainless steel nipple (Example 8)

assumed to be the cause of brittle fracture, but superimposed mechanical factors more often are the real cause.

Corrective action that can be used to guard against the possibility of brittle fracture in pressure vessels includes attention to all the factors noted above, plus stress relief after fabrication. Metallurgical changes in the material during service should be avoided. Such changes might result if, for example, carbon steel was used instead of alloy steel in an application in which temperatures occasionally exceed the limit of operating temperature for carbon steel.

Embrittlement can result from graphitization in carbon steels and 0.5% Mo steels, development of hot shortness during welding or fabrication, exposure to atmospheres favoring hydrogen embrittlement, or formation of sigma phase in stainless steels. Thermal fatigue caused by different amounts of expansion in adjacent dissimilar metals can result in crack propagation and eventual brittle fracture. Severe and repeated temperature changes in such components as chemical-system quench tanks can result in thermal shock, the severity of which might be sufficient to cause a brittle failure.

Brittle fractures are not restricted to steels, but also have occurred in components made of other materials, such as in welded aluminum rocket-fuel tanks because of residual shrinkage stresses. These stresses were caused by weld design that was improper for the relative stiffness of the elements being joined. Microcracks that formed during cooling of the welds provided the initiating points for brittle fractures that occurred during hydrostatic proof testing.

Brittle fractures have occurred in austenitic stainless steels, as reported in the following example.

Example 8. Brittle Fracture of Type 316 Stainless Steel Nipples (Fig. 10)

Several fractures occurred in nipples on pressurized tank cars used for transportation of vinyl chloride. These schedule 40

nipples, which were used in loading and unloading the vinyl chloride, were made of type 316 stainless steel. The nipples were originally specified to be schedule 80; however, because schedule 40 nipples were sufficient for the pressure and because the nipples supposedly were protected from chance blows by being contained inside a dome, schedule 40 nipples were used.

Investigation. The fracture surface of one of the nipples was examined and found to be mainly featureless except for a partial circular ridge and a steplike pattern, both in one area as shown in Fig. 10. There were no chevron marks pointing to the origin of fracture. Fracture originated at the root of a thread, which acted as a notch. The height of the final-fracture surface (see Fig. 10) was equal to the lead of the thread.

Scanning electron microscopy was used to examine the fracture surface; this revealed a mixed brittle and ductile fracture. At the steplike area, fracture was brittle; much of the remaining surface exhibited neither ductile nor brittle fracture features. Where the thread broke, fracture was ductile. All of this indicated that fracture had resulted from a sharp blow to the side of the nipple.

This hypothesis was checked by means of hardness tests and metallography, both of which showed the material to be fully annealed. The presence of a fault such as an inclusion could have precipitated the failure, but none was found. Neither was there any trace of spidery branched cracking, which would have indicated chloride stress-corrosion cracking. Therefore, it was concluded that the failure had resulted from impact, in spite of the protection afforded by the dome.

Recommendation. Replacement of the schedule 40 nipples by schedule 80 nipples was recommended, and apparently this solved the problem.

Ductile Fractures

Ductile fracture occurs with a significant amount of macroscopic plastic deformation. It is considered to take place by a shear mechanism in which the metal is torn with considerable expenditure of energy. Even though final rupture may occur suddenly, most failures of pressure vessels or piping develop gradually, and give warning during propagation by means of a bulge or a leak.

The surface of a ductile fracture generally exhibits a dull, fibrous appearance, and there is evidence of plastic deformation, such as local bulging or distortion. A good indicator of deformation is a significant reduction in area at the fracture. When such an indicator is present, the failure may have resulted from some long-term change or deterioration of the material or from a gradual increase in the load. However, the mere classification of a fracture as ductile is not an explanation of why it occurred but only a suggestion of the factors that may have caused it. For instance, gradual reduction in wall or section thickness by corrosion, erosion or creep can render the material unable to sustain the operating load. To this extent, the classification of a failure as ductile is dependent on the time span over which the failure takes place.

Creep and Stress Rupture

Creep and stress rupture are frequent mechanisms of failure in pressure vessels, particularly when elevated temperatures are involved. Loading in pressure vessels arises mainly from fluid or gas pressures and must be sustained for long periods of time. Depending on the temperature and applied stresses, all structural metals undergo time-dependent deformation to some degree. Therefore, failure in high-temperature components is the result of excessive deformation (creep) or fracture (stress rupture), assuming that the material is not corroded, thermally fatigued or suffering from chemical or fabrication defects.

Stress rupture involves creep and migration of solute atoms to grain boundaries, where the adhesion of the grains is affected by the formation of lower-melting-point compounds at the boundaries. Inside the grains, segregation and spheroidization also may occur, the net result being localized separation at the grain boundaries and also at selected sites inside the grains. These separations grow into voids, which increase the stress and cause accelerated void growth until fracture occurs.

Figure 11(a) shows a hanger, from an ethylene furnace, that failed under a tensile load. The hanger was made of heat-resistant casting alloy HK-40 and failed in the weld zone. Tensile tears were found in the heat-affected zone adjacent to the fracture. Precipitation of a phase that appeared white in a micrograph (see Fig. 11b) had occurred. The phase had segregated to grain and subgrain boundaries and had started to spheroidize. Above the tears, voids were found that were associated with grain boundaries or with the white phase.

There were no structural defects associated with the weld, and the features discussed in the previous paragraph indi-

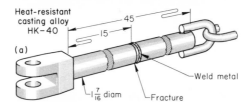

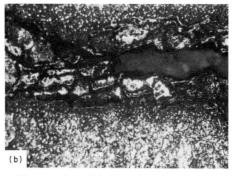

Fig. 11. (a) Ethylene-furnace hanger, made of heat-resistant casting alloy HK-40, that failed by stress rupture in weld heat-affected zone. (b) Micrograph, at 40×, showing precipitated phase (white) and voids in fracture region.

cated stress rupture. Therefore, it was recommended that the other hangers be x-rayed. Several were found to contain voids, and one was in imminent danger of failure. The cause of the stress rupture was long-term exposure of the hangers to temperatures above their maximum service temperature. Stress rupture is difficult to prevent, and therefore a regular program of radiography was instituted to reveal incipient stress-rupture failures. In addition, a tubular cover of Incoloy 800 was slipped over the hanger to allow some protection against high temperatures, and holes were drilled at the top and bottom of the tube to permit some cooling by circulation of air.

Fatigue

Fatigue fractures result from cyclic stressing, which progressively propagates a crack or cracks until the remaining section is no longer able to support the applied load. Pressure vessels and pressure piping are subject to high static stresses arising from the pressure of con-

tained liquids or gases, to stresses resulting from misalignment of components, and to residual stresses induced during welding. The cyclical component may be added mechanically — by vibration of associated equipment, pulsation from a compressor, or thermal cycling. Fatigue nucleates from a stress raiser such as a discontinuity or a notch, which produces triaxial stressing in the material.

Thermal fatigue occurs when cyclic stresses are produced by uneven heating or cooling, or when part of a vessel is restrained and cannot expand or contract uniformly.

Over a period of years, several low-carbon steel thick-wall vessels equipped with cooling jackets cracked when operated as batch reaction vessels at 400 C (about 750 F). These vessels operated with sharp thermal gradients across the walls. A small amount of sodium hydroxide could have been present in the vessels, and it was thought that cracking might have been the result of caustic embrittlement.

To increase the life of the vessels, the material was changed from low-carbon steel to a carbon-molybdenum steel. Occasional cracking still occurred. The material was then changed to 1Cr-0.5Mo steel. However, cracking occurred in a shorter time than with vessels made of carbon-molybdenum steel.

A stress analysis of these jacketed vessels indicated that cyclical stresses produced during operation might have been high enough to have caused cracking in the vessel walls. Furthermore, such stresses would be high enough to produce failure in any available grade of weldable structural steel. Thus, life of the vessels could be increased by reducing the stress but not by upgrading the material. Reducing the wall thickness would lower thermal stresses by decreasing the temperature differential in the wall.

References

1. Brittle Fracture of a Thick Walled Pressure Vessel, BWRA Bulletin, Vol 7, No. 6, June 1966
2. R. D. Wylie, J. McDonald, Jr., and A. L. Lowenberg, Weld Deposited Cladding of Pressure Vessels, paper presented at the 19th Petroleum Mechanical Engineering Conference, Sept 20-23, 1963, Los Angeles

Failures of Metallic Orthopaedic Implants

By John H. Dumbleton and Edward H. Miller*

AN ORTHOPAEDIC DEVICE is an artificial mechanical device that replaces or supports part of the skeletal structure of the human body. Applications include: (*a*) internal fixation of fractures by bone plates, nails or intramedullary rods (Fig. 1); (*b*) correction of deformities of the spine by means of the implanting of metallic rods; (*c*) external fixation or support involving a brace; (*d*) external metallic devices for halo-pelvic traction; and (*e*) arthroplasty, the surgical treatment whose aim is the relief of pain and the restoration of joint function (Ref 1). Six different types of prostheses used for joint replacement are shown in Fig. 2.

The subject of total-joint replacement is large and growing in importance. However, it is discussed in this article only insofar as metallic components are involved. External fixation or support devices are not dealt with in this article.

The hip joint is the joint most often afflicted by disease, and the loss of its function causes the severest handicap. To restore hip function, a partial joint replacement may be made in which the head of the femur is replaced by a metallic component. Usually, however, the entire joint is replaced. The most widely used total-hip prostheses consist of a metal femoral component and a plastic acetabular cup. All-metal total-hip prostheses have been used, but these devices are subject to loosening.

Total-joint prostheses are used in other locations in the body, including the knee, finger, elbow and ankle. These devices may be all-metal or metal-on-plastic, depending on the intended use of the prosthesis. For joints of the fingers, silicone rubber prostheses are often used.

Reports of Failures

An orthopaedic implant is considered to have failed when it must be prematurely removed from the body. There are two classes of failure — mechanical and biological. Mechanical mechanisms of failure include permanent deformation, overload fracture, fatigue fracture, corrosion and wear. Biological failures result from infection, inflammation or other reactions of the body to the pres-

*Dr. Dumbleton is Associate Professor, Materials Science, and Assistant Professor, Research Surgery in Orthopaedics, and Dr. Miller is Head, Division of Orthopaedic Surgery, University of Cincinnati.

ence of the implant. Only mechanical failures are discussed in this article.

If an implanted device fails, its removal can cause great expense and hardship to a patient, and thus it is highly desirable to keep the number of failures to a minimum. A good general description of failures in metallic fixation devices has been given by Bechtol, Ferguson and Laing (Ref 2). Several metallurgical analyses of failed orthopaedic implants have appeared in the literature

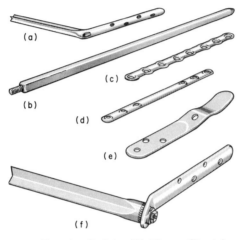

(a) Jewett nail-plate. (b) Hansen-Street intramedullary pin. (c) Sherman-type bone plate. (d) Plain-pattern bone plate. (e) Blount osteotomy plate. (f) Combination of Smith-Peterson nail and Thornton plate.

Fig. 1. Some orthopaedic internal fixation devices

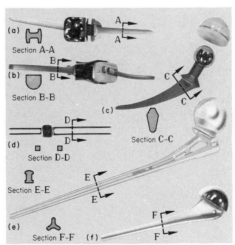

(a) Guepar total-knee prosthesis. (b) Dee total-elbow prosthesis. (c) Mueller-type total-hip prosthesis. (d) Flatt finger-joint prosthesis. (e) Moore long-stem femoral prosthesis. (f) Shoulder prosthesis.

Fig. 2. Prostheses for joint replacement

(see Ref 3 to 7), and a report on the metallurgical examination of off-the-shelf devices has been published (Ref 8).

Statistics on failed orthopaedic implants are difficult to obtain. Greene (Ref 9) estimates the percentage of failure at 3 to 20%, depending on the implant material and the type of device. The statistics of Martz (Ref 10) on implant failure are based on his own personal experiences and on those of his colleagues. Of 282 implants, 16 broke, 30 inflamed surrounding tissues, and 8 became infected. Over a period of ten years, Cohen (Ref 11) amassed 500 instances in which implants were removed prematurely for various reasons. Unfortunately, his data came from many different sources, and adequate clinical and historical details often were not supplied. Cohen has also commented on failures in the performance of surgical implants (Ref 12).

Environment Encountered by an Implant

The human body is a harsh environment in which to place even the most corrosion-resistant metal, because of the saline environment and the loads encountered. The temperature of this environment is 37 C (98.6 F). On implantation the material is placed in intimate contact with various body tissues, such as bone, muscle and tendons. Spread through and covering these tissues are complex body fluids containing numerous mineral salts, proteins, carbohydrates and lipids. The implant is continuously bathed by electrolytic fluids, such as blood, extracellular fluid, and synovial fluid.

The ionic compositions of various body fluids are given in Fig. 3. The extracellular fluid, which is the fluid implants most frequently encounter, contains large amounts of Na^+, Cl^- and HCO_3^- ions with trace amounts of other ions. Concentrations of certain gases also affect environmental composition. The oxygen content of blood is 10 to 21 vol % and the carbon dioxide content is 50 to 70 vol %, based on total gas volume (Ref 14).

The body fluids usually have a pH of about 7.4. However, when an implant is inserted, the wound normally will show an acid pH following surgery but the pH will return to normal within a few days. Hematomas may collect, and if even

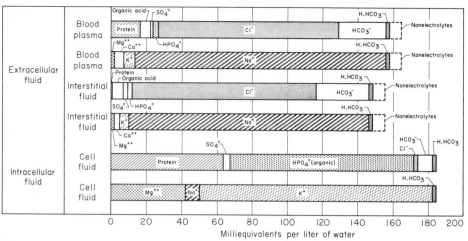

Fig. 3. Ionic compositions of blood plasma, interstitial fluid and intracellular fluid (Ref 13)

small ones contact the implant they may prevent the return to normal that accompanies healing and may maintain an acid pH for several weeks. If the hematomas are not absorbed, the tissue surrounding the implant becomes more acid, sometimes as low as pH 4, as carbon dioxide accumulates in areas of stasis. Infection will change the acid pH normally found in a wound, and the pH may then go alkaline — as high as pH 9 (Ref 15).

Tissue Reaction. The metals and alloys used must be extremely resistant to corrosion. Corrosion can have two effects. First, the implant may be weakened and premature failure may result. The second effect is tissue reaction to the implant. No metallic material is totally resistant to ionization within living tissues. In vivo studies have shown that implantation of devices of most alloys significantly increases concentrations of various ions in adjacent tissues (Ref 16). The results of a spectrochemical analysis of muscle tissue of rabbits after removal of implants of various implant materials are given in Table 1.

Once a foreign material is implanted, there are several ways in which the body may react unfavorably. The presence of

Table 1. Spectrochemical Determination of Trace Metals in Rabbit-Muscle Tissue After Removal of Implants Made From Four Different Metals (Ref 17)

	Metal concentration, ppm			
Metal	Control(a)	Type 316L stainless steel	Cast Co-Cr alloy	Wrought Co-Cr alloy	Titanium
Chromium.	3.7	76.0	67.0	74.9	...
Nickel	8.0	40.5	...	...	...
Molybdenum	1.8	8.4	11.5	...	...
Titanium	11.4	...	...	...	236.8
Cobalt	2.9	...	76.7	68.8	...
Iron	37.9	76.8	...	...	...

(a) Concentrations of metals in rabbits in which no implant was placed.

the implant may inhibit the defense mechanisms of the body, leading to infection (Ref 18), and it may be necessary to remove the implant. If infection does not occur or is overcome, the tissue response may range from mild edema to chronic inflammation. Alterations in bone and tissue structure may occur.

Materials used in making implants must be inert or well tolerated by the body. The response of the body to an implant made of such a material will be the development of a fibrous collagen sheath of low cellularity, which encapsulates the implant and separates it from normal tissue (Ref 19). The thickness of the fibrous sheath depends on the corrosion resistance of the material and on such factors as implantation site, implant size and shape, and motion of the implant relative to the surrounding tissue. Figure 4 gives results of a study on the thickness of sheaths that developed around pellets of various alloys implanted in rabbits. The materials that produce the thinnest sheaths are regarded as best-tolerated by the body. Because of the multiplicity of factors that control sheath thickness, caution should be exercised in using such studies to compare the reactivity of materials.

The fibrous sheath is not impermeable, and metallic ions can still move into surrounding tissue. Body reactions are not confined to the neighborhood of the implant, and systemic effects may occur. Spectrochemical analyses of various organs in rabbits after implantation of a series of metals have shown an increase in the concentration of various ions in the different organs several weeks after the introduction of the implant (Ref 17).

Loads. The loads encountered by an implant are quite high. An implant will be subjected to both static and dynamic loading, depending on the activity of the patient. An implant introduced for repair of a fractured bone must be able to develop, in conjunction with the bone,

sufficient strength to sustain and transmit the load actions resulting from joint and muscle forces. Simple calculations of static situations may be made to evaluate typical loading (Ref 21). For example, in a one-leg stance the load on the head of the femur is approximately 2½ times the body weight. Higher loads occur during locomotion (Ref 22). The load varies with position in the walking cycle and reaches a peak of about four times the body weight at the hip and three times the body weight at the knee. Larger loads are assumed by the hip and knee joints during activities such as running and jumping. Large loads are not confined to the so-called load-bearing members; substantial loads are developed also in the joints of the thumb (Ref 23) and fingers (Ref 24).

The frequency of loading and the number of load cycles encountered over

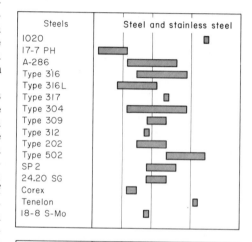

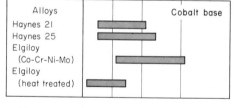

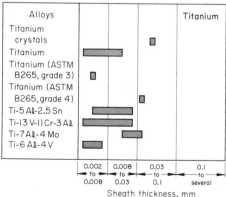

The horizontal bars give the range of sheath thicknesses found after pellets had been implanted in rabbit muscle for 24 weeks.

Fig. 4. Thickness of fibrous-tissue sheaths around implants of steel, stainless steel, cobalt-base alloys, and titanium and titanium alloys (Ref 20)

a specified time period are also important. A fast rate of walking corresponds to one complete walking cycle (two steps) per second. Typically, a person may take from one to two million steps per year. For active persons, the number of steps may be two or three times this amount (Ref 25).

Wear resistance is required of a metal used in joint prostheses. The metal must not wear excessively so that the joint surface is worn through. Normally, this is not a problem. However, wear rate must be held to extremely low levels because of interaction of the wear debris with body tissues. Wear particles have been found both in joint fluid and in tissue surrounding all-metal total-hip prostheses (Ref 26). This situation should be found for joint prostheses at other locations and is not confined to all-metal prostheses. With metal-polymer prostheses, the wear debris is predominantly polymeric.

Alloys Commonly Used in Orthopaedic Implants

Only a few alloys are in common use for implantation (Ref 15, 27 and 28). These alloys are type 316L stainless steel, cast cobalt-chromium-base alloys, and wrought cobalt-chromium-base alloys.

Titanium and titanium alloy Ti-6Al-4V also have been employed. Tantalum is occasionally used; it is limited to applications requiring low resistance to deformation.

Type 316 stainless steel was in common use until recently. This alloy has a higher carbon content than type 316L, which results in a corrosion resistance that is marginal for use in the body. Type 317 stainless steel also has been used; however, this alloy not only has a higher carbon content and lower corrosion resistance than type 316L but also has a higher molybdenum content — which may result in the formation of ferrite during processing. Inclusions in stainless steel may provide preferential sites for corrosion or may act as stress raisers for crack initiation.

The stainless steels are well tolerated by the body and are reasonably corrosion resistant. However, some corrosion is to be expected *in vivo* over long periods of time, especially if the molybdenum content is low in the allowable range. Stainless steels rely on the presence of a passive film on the surface to inhibit corrosion. This passive film may be disrupted in a crevice if the environment in the crevice is reducing.

The tissue reaction to long-term implantation of cobalt-chromium-base alloys is minimal. The cellular tissue reaction is usually somewhat less than that around stainless steel implants. The

wrought alloy is used for plates, and for components requiring ductility, such as wires. The cast alloy has excellent resistance to wear and galling, and for this reason it is used in all-metal total-hip prostheses.

Compositions of surgical stainless steels are given in ASTM F56. The cobalt-chromium-base alloys are a commercial cast alloy, the cast alloy specified in ASTM F75 and the wrought alloy specified in ASTM F90. Nominal compositions for titanium grades 3 and 4 are given in ASTM F67, and for titanium alloy Ti-6Al-4V in ASTM F136.

Mechanisms of Failure

In principle, failures of orthopaedic implants are no different from failures of components in other engineering applications. However, the *in vivo* conditions experienced by an implant are complex. The loading is a combination of static and cyclic loadings, which generates an extremely complicated stress system in the device. In addition, the implant lies in a hostile chemical environment the composition of which depends on the location of the implant in the body

and on the interaction of the body with the implant.

Deformation and overload fracture result from a single overload or from a few cycles of overload. An orthopaedic fixation device such as a bone plate or a hip nail is not designed to support, and indeed usually cannot support, the same load as can a healthy bone. The intent of using a fixation device is to hold the ends of the broken bone in close proximity so that healing is promoted. The load is to be shared between the bone and the fixation device. Even with a sharing of the load, it is necessary to limit the loading placed on the affected member until healing of the fracture is well under way and the bone is bearing most of the load.

Fracture of a fixation device because of overload is described in the following example.

Example 1. Fracture of a Co-Cr Alloy Internal Fixation Device After Overload (Fig. 5)

A 70-year-old woman fell and sustained an intertrochanteric fracture of the femur. After anatomical reduction, internal fixation was carried out using a one-piece Neufeld nail-plate device (Fig. 5a) made of ASTM

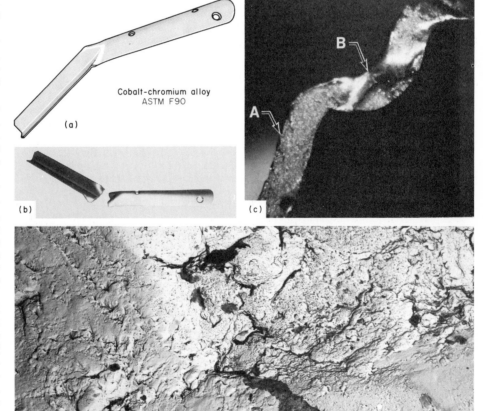

(a) Unbroken Neufeld nail-plate device. (b) Photograph of the fractured nail-plate showing location of fracture. (c) Fracture surface at 5× showing coarse texture (arrow A) and shiny obliterated surface (arrow B). (d) TEM fractograph at 5000× of a region below and to the right of arrow B in (c), showing granulated surface and evidence of corrosion.

Fig. 5. Neufeld nail-plate device, of ASTM F90 cobalt-chromium alloy, that fractured by overload (Example 1)

F90 wrought cobalt-chromium alloy. Eight weeks after the operation the device broke at the location shown in Fig. 5(b).

Investigation. The fracture surfaces were examined microscopically under reflected light. Figure 5(c) is a light fractograph of a fracture surface; areas of granularity with a coarse texture (arrow A) and a shiny region (arrow B) can be seen. The shiny region was caused by the broken ends of the device rubbing together after fracture, thereby obliterating surface detail. Optical examination did not reveal the mechanism of fracture.

Germanium-shadowed plastic-carbon replicas of several fracture-surface regions, obtained by conventional techniques, were examined in a transmission electron microscope. Figure 5(d) is a TEM view at 5000 diameters of an area in the fracture surface shown in Fig. 5(c). Note the granularity of the surface. There is evidence of corrosion, but the corrosion is not pronounced and could well have occurred after fracture of the device. Examination of other replicas and study at higher magnifications failed to reveal any clear-cut evidence of the fracture mechanism.

Conclusions. The fracture occurred at a position of maximum bending moment; other devices of the same design have broken in this same general area. In fact, failure is most likely to occur in the area that receives maximum bending, because the cross-sectional shape of the device and the abrupt changes in section can cause stress concentrations.

The fact that the device broke after only a short period of use also suggested overloading as a possible mechanism of fracture. This hypothesis received support when the patient admitted that she had borne her full weight on the leg "once or twice", in spite of instructions to the contrary.

Hence, mainly from background information, it was concluded that the mechanism of fracture was overloading and the cause of fracture was patient misuse. A device with an I or a T cross section in the nail and of a greater cross-sectional area would have given more protection against fracture.

Fatigue. In many locations in the body, implants are subjected to varying loads over a period of time. The load on a weight-bearing joint may vary from near zero to as much as 1000 lb during walking, and the joint (and implant) may have to withstand several million load cycles per year. It is not surprising, therefore, that fatigue failures of orthopaedic implants occur (Ref 4, 5 and 29).

There is a difference, at least in principle, between the intended use of a joint prosthesis and that of a fixation device. A joint prosthesis is intended to remain in place for the remaining lifetime of the patient and thus must be designed in accordance with the number of load cycles likely to be encountered. A fixation device can be removed after the fracture has healed. In fact, there is argument that removal of such a device strengthens the fracture site. However, a patient may not agree to having a fixation device re-

Fig. 6. Fracture surface of a Hansen-Street nail made from type 316 stainless steel that fractured by fatigue several years after the bone fracture healed (Example 2)

moved when all appears to be going well, and thus fixation devices also may be subjected to many load cycles over a period of years. A fixation device that has led to a successful reduction of a fracture has been known to fracture several years later (Ref 30), as described in the following example.

Example 2. Fatigue Fracture of a Type 316 Stainless Steel Fixation Device Several Years After Bone Fracture Had Healed (Fig. 6)

A 57-year-old man sustained a traumatic closed fracture of the humerus. After a six-month nonunion of the fracture, a type 316 stainless steel Hansen-Street intramedullary nail was surgically implanted. About 16 years later, the patient complained of pain in the upper arm and admitted that the implant had fractured several years earlier.

Figure 6 is a view of a fracture surface of the nail. Optical examination revealed beach marks, which indicated that fatigue fracture had occurred. Cracking began at a corner of the nail and propagated by fatigue across about 40% of the cross-sectional area before final fracture occurred. Sizable corrosion pits were visible on the surface of the nail near the corner where cracking originated.

The mechanism of fracture was clearly fatigue. The role that corrosion played is not clear. It is possible that the corrosion occurred after the nail broke (several years elapsed between fracture of the nail and removal).

The cause of the fracture is not so easy to pinpoint. The nail had been in place for more than ten years, and it is reasonable to say that it had fulfilled its function and should have been removed. Leaving the nail in place exposed it to an excessive number of

fatigue cycles. Contributing to the fracture was the sharp corner on the edge, which caused stress concentrations and was a site for nucleation of cracks. The stress concentration enhanced propagation of any existing cracks.

Corrosion. For implant applications, corrosion rate for a metal or alloy must be much lower than 0.1 mil per year to avoid tissue irritation and associated effects. Measurements indicate that the stainless steels and cobalt-chromium alloys corrode at less than 0.01 mil per year in body fluids (Ref 31).

Studies of the corrosion characteristics of metals and alloys commonly used in orthopaedic devices indicate that the isolated electrochemical potential of stainless steel in body fluids may well be in the transpassive region; under these circumstances, the corrosion resistance of a stainless steel device is impaired. In contrast, titanium should always develop potentials in the passive region and therefore should not corrode. Cobalt-chromium alloys are usually resistant to corrosion but under some conditions can develop potentials in the transpassive region. This behavior is in agreement with clinical findings, with stainless steel corroding frequently and cobalt-chromium alloys occasionally.

Scales, Winter and Shirley (Ref 32) examined a large number of implants removed from patients for various reasons. About 36% of all components showed evidence of corrosion. Colangelo and Greene (Ref 33) examined 53 single-component and multicomponent devices manufactured from type 316L stainless steel and found evidence of corrosion in 37% of the 155 components. When the frequency of corrosion of multicomponent devices was compared to that of single-component devices, it was found that 91% of multicomponent devices showed corrosion whereas corrosion was evident in only 10% of the single-component devices. Severity of attack increased with time, and 44% of the components examined showed corrosion after as little as one to four months of use.

Galvanic corrosion can result when two dissimilar metals or alloys in contact with each other are immersed in a conductive solution. A difference in potential between the two metals or alloys results in electron flow from one to the other and in accelerated corrosion of the more active material. For surgical implants, galvanic corrosion can occur if a bone plate and bone screws are of dissimilar metals. The corrosion is likely to occur between the plate and the underside of the screw heads. It is not even necessary that the two metals in contact be totally dissimilar. Small differences in composition or differences in metallurgical condition may be sufficient to set up a galvanic cell. Metal may be transferred

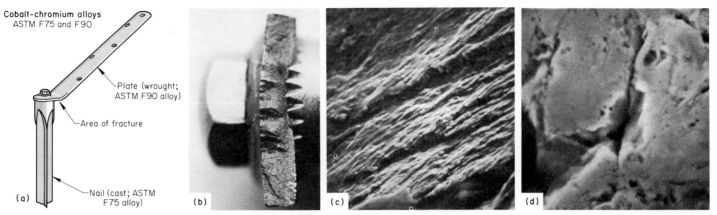

Cobalt-chromium alloys
ASTM F75 and F90

Plate (wrought;
ASTM F90 alloy)

Area of fracture

Nail (cast; ASTM
F75 alloy)

(a)   (b)   (c)   (d)

(a) The nail-and-plate device; nail was made from ASTM F75 cast Co-Cr alloy, plate was made from ASTM F90 wrought Co-Cr alloy. (b) Fracture surface of the plate, at 4×. (c) SEM fractograph, at 1325×, of an area of the fracture surface, showing striations indicative of corrosion fatigue. (d) SEM fractograph, at 3900×, of inner surface of plate at point of contact with nail, showing a microcrack nucleated by a corrosion pit.

Fig. 7. Thornton nail-and-plate device, of cobalt-chromium alloys, that fractured as a result of slightly-dissimilar-metal contact, stress concentration, and crevice corrosion (Example 3)

from a surgical instrument to an implant (for instance, from a screwdriver to a screw head); an electrochemical cell may then result at the implant (Ref 34). The problem of galvanic corrosion is well recognized in orthopaedics, and the use of dissimilar metals is not common. Sometimes, however, it is impossible to avoid mixing of metals; for instance, when an implant is replaced it is sometimes necessary to leave the shank of a screw in the bone. Alternatively, a drill may break in the bone and must be left in place.

In the next example, a nail-and-plate device made of cast and wrought cobalt-chromium alloys fractured as a result of dissimilar-metal contact, stress concentration, and crevice corrosion.

Example 3. Corrosion-Accelerated Fracture of a Nail-and-Plate Device Made of Dissimilar Cobalt-Chromium Alloys (Fig. 7)

The fracture of the left hip of a 75-year-old woman was internally fixed with a Thornton nail-and-plate device similar to that shown in Fig. 7(a). The woman never regained use of her hip and needed considerable physical assistance in walking. When the woman was 88 years old, x-rays were taken of the fracture area because motion of her hip was limited and because her fractured leg was 2 cm shorter than her other leg.

The radiograph showed that the nail in the neck of the left femur had penetrated the femoral head and eroded through the acetabulum. The plate was broken at its junction with the nail, but was still firmly fixed to the femoral shaft by the original screws. The nail, plate and screws were removed for examination.

Chemical analysis of the alloy in the broken nail-and-plate device revealed that the nail had been made of ASTM F75 cast cobalt-chromium alloy and the plate made of ASTM F90 wrought cobalt-chromium alloy. Little or no plastic flow accompanied fracture of the plate (Fig. 7b), which suggested that gross overloading was not the

prime cause of the implant failure (although an overload fracture probably would have occurred if the plate had not broken as it did). The condition of the fracture surface indicated that fracture was essentially brittle (see Fig. 7c) and that the fracture had been initiated in the region of nail-plate contact. Examination of all surfaces using a scanning electron microscope indicated corrosion fatigue as the probable cause of fracture. The fracture was initiated at corrosion pits on the surface of the plate. A microcrack nucleated by a corrosion pit is shown in Fig. 7(d). The pits were the result of electrochemical action aggravated by the dissimilar-metal contact, stress concentration, and crevice corrosion in the nail-plate contact area.

Crevice corrosion is a form of intense local attack that occurs in shielded areas on metal surfaces where the oxygen concentration is low. Generally, this type of attack occurs beneath screw heads holding a plate or in similar locations, such as the intersection of the components of a two-piece hip nail. Stainless steels and

other active-passive alloys are especially susceptible to crevice corrosion. These alloys form a passive surface film in the presence of oxygen or other oxidizers. The thickness of the protective layer is increased by a passivation treatment during manufacture of an implant. Breakdown of the passive film can occur spontaneously or be caused by relative movement between implant components, and is likely to lead to crevice corrosion.

Examples of crevice corrosion in cobalt-chromium implants have also been presented (Ref 5 and 35). Cohen and Wulff (Ref 36) found corrosion in a bone plate made of wrought cobalt-chromium alloy used with screws of cast cobalt-chromium alloy. They later showed that the wrought alloy was more susceptible than the cast alloy to localized attack.

Crevice corrosion of a type 316L stainless steel bone plate is described in the following example.

Example 4. Crevice Corrosion of a Type 316L Stainless Steel Bone Plate Augmented by Slight Difference in Composition of Screws and Plate (Fig. 8)

A 27-year-old man sustained a closed fracture of the mid-diaphysis of the femur. Initial treatment consisted of traction followed by application of a hip spica cast. The bone did not heal, and seven months following the injury the patient underwent open reduction with internal fixation, using two single-taper standard bone plates made of type 316L stainless steel. The femur united. Eighteen months later, the patient complained of pain over the lateral plate, and the plate was removed.

Examination of the bone plate showed corrosion deposits around several of the screw holes (Fig. 8). Chemical analysis of the metal in the screws and plate revealed minor differences in composition, probably because of different sources of the metal for the screws and plates. Although both components were made of type 316L stainless steel, the minor differences in composition augmented crevice corrosion.

Fig. 8. Corrosion deposits at screw hole of single-tapered standard bone plate made from type 316L stainless steel. Screws were made of same alloy but from a different source. (Example 4)

Wear is the mechanical removal of material by relative motion between contacting surfaces. The discussion here will be confined to the wear of joint prostheses. The effect of relative motion between components of a fixation device is discussed later, under "Fretting Corrosion".

Wear can affect the performance of a joint prosthesis. The device may simply wear out — that is, so much material is removed that metal contacts opposing bone. This is extremely unlikely with all-metal prostheses. A study of 18 McKee-Farrar total-hip prostheses removed after usage of up to six years has shown that, in some instances, wear was localized; in others, wear was spread over most of the bearing surface (Ref 26). Typical depth of wear was about 0.0001 in. Tests using a hip-joint simulator have also shown wear of all-metal total-hip prostheses to be low (Ref 37).

The mechanisms of wear will produce wear particles. Particles of cast cobalt-chromium alloy are hard, and if they cannot escape from the bearing surface, galling seizure may result. This has not been reported in total-hip prostheses but has been found in bench testing of this alloy for wear (Ref 38).

Wear particles can escape from a prosthesis and have been found in both joint fluid and in tissue around the prosthesis (Ref 37).

Although wear is not a problem with all-metal joint prostheses, it may result in seizure of hinge prostheses, such as those used for elbow-joint replacement and sometimes for knee-joint replacement, because it is more difficult for wear debris to escape from them. Worn bearing areas that appear polished have been reported for a total-elbow prosthesis made from cobalt-chromium alloy (Ref 5).

Interaction Between Failure Mechanisms

Seldom is only one mechanism found to have been operative in the failure of an implant. The various mechanisms influence each other in several ways. The coupling of mechanisms may lead to a failure that would not have occurred in the presence of any one of the individual mechanisms alone. For example, the imposition of stress on an implant may make a region susceptible to localized corrosion and subsequent cracking leading to fracture (stress-corrosion cracking). The same thing may happen if permanent deformation has occurred.

In the following example, a fixation device failed in a nonambulatory patient because locking nuts were improperly seated, causing internal stresses in the components.

Example 5. Stress-Corrosion Cracking of a Type 316L Stainless Steel Fixation Device Because of Improper Insertion (Fig. 9)

A 52-year-old man suffered a traumatic fracture at the neck of the femur. Open reduction and fixation were performed using a Garber nail and a Thornton side plate. Both components were of type 316L stainless steel. Four months later, the side plate broke. The patient had not been on his feet from the time of the operation to the time the device fractured.

Optical examination of the side plate showed surface damage near the fracture. Electron microscope examination showed a "mud crack" pattern (see Fig. 9). Such patterns are typically found in 300 and 400 series stainless steels that have fractured by stress-corrosion cracking.

A fatigue fracture was unexpected, because the patient was never ambulatory and thus could not have applied high-cycle fatigue loading. However, the implant would be subject to stresses even in a nonambulatory patient, and these stresses, in conjunction with corrosion, caused failure. The reason for failure was nonoptimal insertion.

X-rays taken after the operation showed that the nail was not perpendicular to the seating ring at the top of the side plate. The locking nuts were tightened eccentrically on the seating ring, causing surface damage. Improper insertion caused static stressing of the plate in the vicinity of the seating ring, which encouraged stress-corrosion cracking.

Corrosion Fatigue. Corrosion combined with fatigue is known as corrosion fatigue. This occurs when an implant is subject to time-varying stresses in a corrosive liquid environment. The liquid environment may well decrease the fatigue strength of the metal. Corrosion fatigue of type 316 stainless steel under simulated body conditions has been studied by Colangelo (Ref 39) and by Wheeler and James (Ref 40).

Fretting Corrosion. The passive film on stainless steel can be removed by wear. Fretting corrosion is the mechanical removal of the film, allowing accelerated corrosion to occur (Ref 41). Such damage occurs when metal surfaces are in contact and so is found at the contact between a bone plate and the heads of bone screws. Movement between the plate and the screw heads can occur because there is about 0.010-in. clearance between the screws and the screw holes and it is difficult to seat the screw heads firmly.

A distinction between crevice corrosion and fretting corrosion should be noted. Crevice corrosion occurs because of the local chemical conditions in a crevice leading to removal of the film; no movement is necessary. Fretting corrosion is the result of small relative movements between contacting surfaces in a corrosive medium. In the absence of a corrosive medium, fretting can lead to severe wear or fatigue. It has been argued that at least some of the reported instances of crevice corrosion were initiated by fretting. Cohen (Ref 42) examined screw-and-plate assemblies of cobalt-chromium alloys that were cyclically stressed for 10 million cycles in a saline solution over a period of three months. Similar assemblies were immersed for the same length of time without cyclic stressing. The cyclically stressed assemblies showed weight losses but the control (static) assemblies did not, which supported a conclusion of fretting corrosion rather than crevice corrosion.

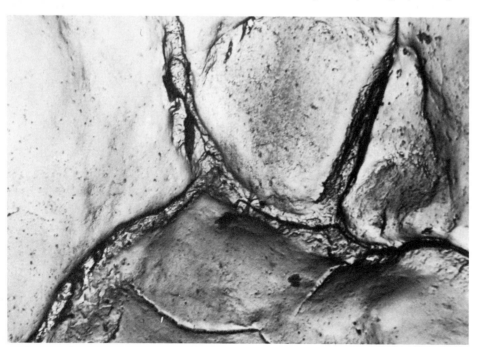

Fig. 9. "Mud crack" pattern observed on type 316L stainless steel orthopaedic side plate that fractured by stress-corrosion cracking (Example 5)

Origins of Failure

Determination of the mechanism that produced failure of an implant is important, but it is also necessary to find what event or sequence of events caused that particular mechanism to become operative. Only in this way can it be determined whether the failure was the result of an imperfection in the device or of other factors. Table 2 summarizes the common sources of failure in orthopaedic devices.

Design and Manufacture. Features in the design of an implant can lead to premature failure. For example, sharp corners act as stress raisers and lead to fracture. This has been shown for a Hansen-Street nail by Dumbleton and Miller (Ref 7) and for a nail-and-plate combination by Cahoon and Paxton (Ref 4). Cahoon and Paxton also cite an example of a bone plate in which screw holes were punched too close to the edge of the plate for it to withstand bending stresses.

To avoid corrosion, the holes in a device should be provided with a smooth finish and the countersunk portion of a screw hole should mate with the tapered section of the screw head. Crevice corrosion at screw holes, especially in stainless steel implants, often is observed. Cracks radiating from screw holes have been reported in devices removed from a body (Ref 4). It seems plausible that a significant decrease in incidence of corrosion failure could be achieved by redesigning some multicomponent surgical implants so as to minimize the number of metal-to-metal interfaces.

Colangelo and Greene (Ref 33) found instances of manufacturing imperfections such as hairline cracks originating in serrations of a device that had not seen service. Such cracks can act as sites for subsequent corrosion attack and as stress raisers. Cracking also was found on the internal surface of a Kuntscher cloverleaf intramedullary rod. On the surfaces of many devices were remnants of porosity, probably from improper electropolishing during the later stages of manufacture. It is important that surface-finish standards such as those in ASTM F86 be followed. Revie and Greene (Ref 43) have shown that electropolished surfaces corrode slowly and sand blasted surfaces are the least resistant to corrosion.

Cracks have been found to occur at a name or symbol stamped or otherwise affixed to a device. Hughes and Jordan (Ref 3) describe a case in which a titanium femoral-head replacement failed because of a crack that originated at a spark-etched identifying symbol that had been placed at a point of maximum tensile bending stress. Fractures in cobalt-chromium alloy washers due to

Table 2. Common Sources of Failure of Metallic Orthopaedic Implants

Design of implant: Notches, including holes; insufficient cross section in highly stressed areas.

Fabrication of implant: Introduction of scratches and notches, not detected in quality control; inadequate control of microstructure.

Selection of material: Dissimilar materials; material incompatible with body fluids.

Insertion and removal of implant: Introduction of gouges and scratches; installation with tools of dissimilar material. Fracture of implant during removal, due primarily to seizure by the bone. Installation of wrong implant.

Misuse by patient: Exposure of implant to stresses exceeding its design.

---

cracks originating at letters in the manufacturer's name have also been observed (Ref 8).

Little information is available on the optimum design of orthopaedic devices to accomplish a given task, although some design standards have been adopted (Ref 44).

Materials Selection and Manufacture. Materials for implants must be selected carefully because only a few alloys have the necessary combination of properties. From the available data on failed devices, it would seem that the cast cobalt-chromium alloys have the most useful combination of properties. Titanium alloy Ti-6Al-4V has not been in service long enough for a firm judgment of its suitability to be made, but initial results look promising. As mentioned in the section on galvanic corrosion, different alloys should not be employed for components of a multicomponent device. Bultitude and Morris (Ref 45) have demonstrated *in vitro* the safety of using the cobalt-chromium alloy with titanium; the potential between them is too small to cause galvanic corrosion.

Many implant failures have been ascribed to inadequacies in preparation and manufacture of materials. The inclusion content of some failed stainless steel implants has been shown to be sufficiently high to substantially reduce the fatigue strength of the implant (Ref 4). The inclusion content must be kept low; an ASTM rating of 2 is the maximum (Ref 46). Many stainless steel implants have been found to contain less molybdenum than the minimum of 2.0% specified in ASTM F55 and F56, which leaves the implant very susceptible to pitting and other forms of corrosion. Sufficient molybdenum must be present, but, on the other hand, too high a molybdenum content can cause a significant decrease in toughness, which can lead to cracking (Ref 8).

Porosity and the presence of delta ferrite have been reported in welded structures of 316L stainless steel (Ref 8). The presence of delta ferrite lowers corrosion resistance, and porosity can act to nucleate a crack. Formation of porosity during welding of stainless steel can be avoided by use of careful welding procedures. Delta ferrite can be dissolved after welding by a high-temperature heat treatment, but this leads to increased grain size. Therefore, the best means of avoiding problems associated with delta ferrite is to design a one-piece forging rather than a welded assembly.

The properties of a stainless steel of a given composition can vary over a wide range, depending on heat treatment and fabrication history. Hughes and Jordan (Ref 3) report the fracture of an osteotomy plate because of an inappropriate heat treatment that resulted in grain-boundary carbide precipitation, a sensitized condition in which intergranular corrosion is likely. Fracture of a Jewett nail occurred because the material was in the annealed condition and was too weak to withstand the loading. Weinstein *et al* (Ref 5) give an example of a fatigue fracture in a type 316L stainless steel implant that had been annealed to give too low a hardness. Another fatigue fracture resulted from a coarse-grained, recrystallized microstructure of low yield strength.

Excessive working of stainless steels can increase susceptibility to stress-corrosion cracking. Gray (Ref 6) has reported an instance in which such a situation contributed to the fracture of prosthetic pins. Cahoon and Paxton (Ref 4) give an example of a plate in which holes were punched too close to the edge. This caused plastic deformation near the edges of the plate and around the screw holes, which resulted in work hardening and the formation of martensite and led to stress-corrosion failure of the device.

Some failures of implants of cobalt-chromium alloys have been ascribed to improper manufacture of the materials. Cast cobalt-chromium alloys can have a large grain size, and a considerable amount of porosity because of shrinkage of the casting during solidification and inadequate feeding of liquid metal. Porosity can also occur by gas evolution during solidification. Inclusions and inhomogeneities in composition are also possible.

One of the final treatments of an implant made of stainless steel is passivation. As shown by Revie and Greene (Ref 47), greater corrosion will occur *in vivo* if the implant has not been passivated. These authors also demonstrate that scratching of surgical implants with a sharp edge of a device of the same metal prior to service has little effect on corrosion resistance. However, scratches should be minimized because crack initiation and propagation may occur. Revie

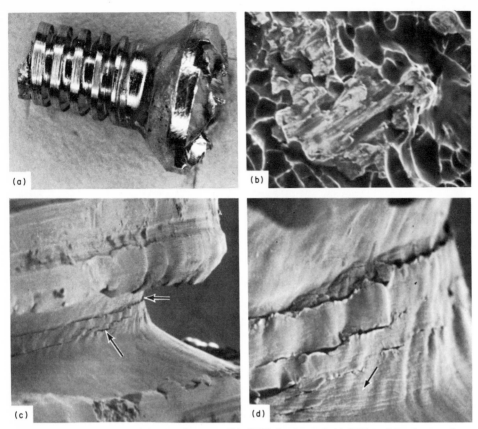

(a) Photograph at 6× of fractured screw. (b) SEM fractograph at 1000× of fracture surface, showing ductile break at center of screw. (c) and (d) SEM fractographs at 100× and 500×, respectively, of thread root, showing fissures (arrows in c) and deformed area (arrow in d).

Fig. 10. Fracture of type 316 stainless steel self-tapping orthopaedic screw that occurred because of counterclockwise torque applied during removal (Example 6)

and Greene have also shown that sterilization by steam or dry heat reduces the corrosion rate substantially for stainless steel, and that chemical disinfection has no effect on the corrosion rate. Wrought cobalt-chromium alloys are not affected, and titanium is only little affected, by sterilization.

Insertion and Removal. Failure of an implant may result from nonoptimal insertion. It is not always possible to use the most desirable device; for instance, the operating room may be out of stock of a particular item and the surgeon may be forced to improvise. Some failures can be attributed to errors in technique. In one example, a bone plate was bent at a screw hole, and the plate fractured at this location after three months of service (Ref 30). In general, implants should not be bent; however, if bending is necessary, the bend should not be made in a region of stress concentration. Other examples of errors in insertion include use of too large or too small a screw, nail or plate or use of eccentric or misaligned screws. Another possible source of failure would be the situation in which a bone screw did not extend into the lateral cortex. When both the tip end and the head end of a bone screw are in contact with bone, the holding power of the screw is increased and the screw has greater resistance to shearing at the interface of the plate and the screw.

It is very possible to apply too much torque to bone screws. Even if the head of the screw is not sheared off immediately, failure may occur later because of weakening of the screw. Failure is likely to occur if a screw is misaligned. Gray (Ref 6) has described failures of self-tapping bone screws that resulted from straight overload and from stress-corrosion cracking. In removal of an implant device, screws have been known to break because of the weakening effect of counterclockwise torque (such as in removing a screw), as described in the following example.

Example 6. Fracture of a Type 316L Stainless Steel Self-Tapping Bone Screw During Removal (Fig. 10)

After two years of service, an implanted plate and type 316L stainless steel screws were removed from a patient by an orthopaedic surgeon. The plate had served its purpose and its removal was, in the judgment of the surgeon, desirable. One screw broke (Fig. 10a) during extraction, leaving the threaded end of the screw within the bone. The fracture surface of the extracted portion of the screw appeared to be smeared at the periphery and, as shown in Fig. 10(b), exhibited a ductile break in the center of the screw. When the thread root next to the fracture was examined in a scanning elec-

tron microscope, several fissures were observed, as shown by the arrows in Fig. 10(c). These fissures continued in the root of the second thread.

Deformation resulting from the counterclockwise torque applied by the surgeon during extraction is indicated by the arrow in Fig. 10(d). A metallographic study was made of the longitudinal median plane through the screw. The assumption could be made from observing only the SEM fractographs that corrosion fatigue might have contributed to the ultimate failure. However, the median-plane view showed no indication of corrosion fatigue, so failure was attributed to excessive torque. Seizure of the screw by the bone was sufficient to produce a shear fracture in the screw where the shear stress was the highest—in the thread root nearest the bone surface.

The torque at which threads cut by self-tapping screws will strip from healthy cortical bone is approximately 30 in.-lb. Bechtol et al (Ref 2) recommended that 80% of this value (24 in.-lb) be the maximum torque exerted when inserting a screw so that the threads in the bone are not stripped. This value is to be compared with the torque required to cause plastic deformation (yielding) of the screw itself. For a $\frac{9}{64}$-in.-diam cast cobalt-chromium alloy screw the yield torque is about 35 in.-lb, whereas for a type 316L stainless steel screw of the same size the yield torque is about 50 in.-lb. ASTM F117 covers the driving torque of self-tapping bone screws.

If a screw breaks on insertion, the surgeon must decide whether to leave the shank of the screw in position or to replace the screw. It may be very difficult to remove the screw shank and, furthermore, if it is removed, an oversize screw must be used in its place and such a screw will not go through the hole in the bone plate. If the broken screw is left in place, the device will not be held by the optimum number of screws.

Breaking of bone screws is not caused solely by poor insertion technique. As with other devices, screw failures may occur as a result of an inadequacy in design, fabrication or material, or because of patient misuse.

Patient Misuse. Devices may fracture by overloading because of patient misuse. For example, if the patient falls, very high loads are placed on a fixation device. Also, the patient may ignore instructions about limiting weight bearing on a device (see Example 1). Often, the patient has little or no control over the forces that muscles exert on an implant (see Example 5). High loads may result even when a patient is confined to bed.

Interactions Between Causes. Failure of an implant may have more than one cause. For example, a design deficiency could be compounded by patient misuse. A Jewett-type intertrochanteric device underwent fatigue fracture because of incorrect heat treatment and a stress concentration at a sharp edge (Ref 5) — a design deficiency coupled with a material-fabrication deficiency.

Methods of Failure Analysis

In general, methods of failure analysis for surgical implants follow the same steps as for failures of other components. However, because there are some special difficulties in the analysis of failed implant devices, the methods of investigation described here will emphasize these points. Detailed descriptions of physical, metallurgical and other techniques of failure analysis are presented in the article beginning on page 10 in this volume.

There is no general agreement as to what constitutes failure of an implant. A patient may be pleased with a procedure that the surgeon regards as a failure. Just as often the opposite situation exists. In Ref 11, Cohen has discussed the problems that arise in the examination of failed orthopaedic implants.

In the discussion that follows, it is assumed that gross failure of the implant occurred, so that removal is required. Although there are removals of implants for reasons such as infection or tissue response, the interest in this discussion is in failures that can be analyzed using metallurgical techniques.

Because both medicine and engineering are involved, the investigation should be conducted by an orthopaedic surgeon and an engineer. When the surgeon who inserted the device is not available, an impartial orthopaedic surgeon should be approached for advice. It is fruitless to evaluate a failure from the engineering standpoint without medical input, and vice versa.

History should include general details such as age, weight, occupation and other background data on the patient. For example, a heavy person in an active occupation may place excessive loads on a device, causing failure. Also, from the background data, a judgment is sometimes possible as to the likelihood that the patient has followed the surgeon's advice on activity. Information on earlier medical problems may be pertinent to the failure.

A reasonably detailed outline of the current problem should be provided, including the treatment carried out. Was the treatment one that is generally performed for the specific condition? If not, why was the particular treatment given?

Information should be furnished regarding the manner in which the device failed. When did the device fail and how did failure occur? How long was it before the failure was reported and what course of action was then taken?

Details of Insertion and Removal. The conditions under which the device was inserted should be reported. Was the case an emergency requiring that an operation be performed quickly? The surgeon should report his recollection of any special difficulty at the time of the operation. It may be profitable for an engineering investigator to witness similar procedures.

Details regarding removal of the device should be furnished. Did damage occur during insertion or removal? It is often impossible to remove a bone screw without breaking it, because of tissue growth into the threads.

After removal, the failed device should be handled carefully. If it is broken, the ends should not be fitted together, because detail on the fracture surfaces may be destroyed. On removal, the failed device should be rinsed in distilled water and then in alcohol, dried, and wrapped carefully. All components should be wrapped separately but should be kept together in a package or container. The wrapped package should be identified, giving date of removal, name or initials of the patient, and the patient's hospital-record number. A metallic device should be sterilized in gas before being submitted for analysis. If the device is sterilized, the wrapping should clearly state this. Autoclaving is not recommended as a sterilization technique: it will change the surface and hinder failure analysis.

X-rays, preferably at three stages, should be obtained: one set of the injury, one set of the injury immediately after the implantation of the device, and one set showing the failed device still in the body. Each set should contain views from different directions. A study of the x-rays may show such conditions as nonunion or nonoptimal insertion, which may have a bearing on the failure. The device may not have been the first to be used in that location, and x-rays will show whether components from the earlier device are still in place. If the old components and the later device are of different metals, galvanic corrosion is a possibility.

Details of Device. Photographs of the device should be taken, and details of the type of device, material and usage should be collected. The device should be examined to determine any obvious design deficiencies. The literature should be searched, and advice should be sought from surgeons, as to whether there have been similar failures with that type of device.

It should be ascertained that the device used was suitable for the application. If it was an unusual choice, there may be excellent reasons why that particular device was chosen. It may be profitable to compare the failed device with other devices from the same manufacturer that the hospital has in stock.

Tissue Examination. Some hospitals routinely examine tissue taken near and adjacent to an implant. Histological examination of the tissue samples gives information on the interaction of the device with the body tissues.

Culture. Routine swab cultures should be made at the time of implant removal to determine if infection is present. Because it is sometimes difficult to distinguish between the effects of tissue reaction to an implant and infection, cultures should be made in addition to histological studies.

Optical Examination. The device should be examined using a hand lens to locate cracks, sites of corrosion, and evidence of fretting and to look at the fracture surfaces. More detailed examination of selected areas may be made at higher magnification. Similar devices that have not been implanted should be examined to determine if there are imperfections that may have occurred during manufacture. The surface preparation of the device should be compared with recommended standards, such as ASTM F86.

Electron Microscopy. Study of the fracture surfaces should be made by using a scanning electron microscope, or a transmission electron microscope and a replica of the fracture surface. Examination of the fracture surface can sometimes reveal information on the mechanisms of fracture because most mechanisms have characteristic topography or patterns (see Volume 9 of this Handbook).

Metallurgical Examination. Metallographic sections should be taken from places adjacent to and remote from the fracture surface or other point of failure. Permission should be obtained before the device is altered in any way by cutting, because it may be required to be left unaltered for various reasons.

Sections are polished and etched in ways appropriate for the specific alloy (see articles on Metallographic Techniques in Volume 8 of this Handbook) and examined in a metallurgical microscope. Information on the structure (type and distribution of phases), grain size, inclusions and porosity can be obtained.

Analytical investigation by an electron microprobe analyzer and by chemical methods will give information on the composition of the alloy, on the composition of inclusions, and on the distribution of elements in the structure; metallic wear debris and corrosion products also can be identified.

The results of metallurgical examination should be compared with existing standards, with the manufacturer's specifications, and possibly with results obtained on other devices of the same type that were purchased at the same time. Failure assignable to material inadequacy will often show up in a metallurgical examination as deviations from standards or from good metallurgical practice.

Device Evaluation. It is somtimes useful to conduct *in vitro* tests on devices to evaluate performance. A mechanical testing machine may be used to determine the deflection characteristics of an intertrochanteric device. A simulator may be used to test a total-hip prosthesis. A bone screw may be tested in torsion to determine at what torque plastic deformation occurs. *In vitro* testing of an unused implant device of the same type may try to reproduce the conditions under which an implant fractured, with the hope that fracture will occur under these controlled conditions and thus shed light on the "in service" fracture.

Integration of Inputs. Inputs from the tests, observations and history must be integrated to give as complete a picture as possible of the failure. Occasionally, a second round of tests is carried out to answer questions raised by the medical and engineering inputs. The different information must be weighed so that a rational decision may be made as to the mechanism and cause of failure.

There is little point in investigating a design deficiency in an obsolete device. Also, if the failed device has been implanted for many years, the alloy may be different from one specified by current standards. Inadequacy in a vanadium steel implant has little relevance today. On the other hand, the degree and extent of corrosion and tissue reaction may be of great interest.

The failure analysis of an implant device is not an end in itself. It is to be hoped that the results of failure analysis can be used to improve the total performance of devices.

References

1. C. M. Evarts (Ed.), "Interposition and Implant Arthroplasty", Orthopaedic Clinics of North America, Vol 4, 1973
2. C. O. Bechtol, A. B. Ferguson and P. G. Laing, "Metals and Engineering in Bone and Joint Surgery", Williams & Wilkins Co., Baltimore, 1959
3. A. N. Hughes and B. A. Jordan, Metallurgical Observations on Some Metallic Surgical Implants which Failed in Vivo, *J Biomed Mater Res*, Vol 6, 1972, p 33
4. J. R. Cahoon and H. W. Paxton, Metallurgical Analyses of Failed Orthopaedic Implants, *J Biomed Mater Res*, Vol 2, 1968, p 1
5. A. Weinstein, H. Amstutz, G. Pavon and V. Franceschini, Orthopedic Implants — A Clinical and Metallurgical Analysis, *J Biomed Mater Res Symp*, Vol 4, 1973, p 297
6. R. J. Gray, "Metallographic Examinations of Retrieved Intramedullary Bone Pins and Bone Screws from the Human Body", Report ORNL-TM-4068, Oak Ridge National Laboratory, Feb 1973
7. J. H. Dumbleton and E. H. Miller, "A Systematic Approach to the Failure Analysis of Orthopaedic Implants", presented at the 1973 meeting of the Ohio Orthopaedic Assn., Cincinnati
8. J. R. Cahoon and H. W. Paxton, A Metallurgical Survey of Current Orthopedic Implants, *J Biomed Mater Res*, Vol 4, 1970, p 223
9. N. D. Greene, "Metallic Implants — Present and Future", Map-Penntap seminar on Opportunities in Biomaterials Technology, Philadelphia, Apr 1972
10. C. D. Martz, Thesis, American Orthopaedic Assn., 1967, quoted in Abstracts of the Proceedings of a Workshop on Standardization of Metal Surgical Implants for Orthopaedic Surgery, *J Biomed Mater Res*, Vol 4, 1970, p 250
11. J. Cohen, Performance and Failure in Performance of Surgical Implants in Orthopaedic Surgery, *J Mater*, Vol 1, 1966, p 354
12. J. Cohen, Failure in Performance of Surgical Implants, *J Bone Joint Surg*, Vol 46A, 1964, p 416
13. A. C. Guyten, "Textbook of Medical Physiology", 3rd Edition, W. B. Saunders Co., Philadelphia
14. A. Wintrobe, "Harrison's Principles of Internal Medicine", McGraw-Hill Book Co., New York, 1970
15. P. G. Laing, "Compatibility of Biomaterials", Orthopaedic Clinics of North America, C. M. Evarts (Ed.), Vol 4, Apr 1973, p 249
16. A. B. Ferguson, P. G. Laing and E. S. Hodge, The Ionization of Metal Implants in Living Tissues, *J Bone Joint Surg*, Vol 42A, No. 1, 1960
17. P. G. Laing, A. B. Ferguson and E. S. Hodge, Spectrochemical Determination of Trace Metals in Normal Striated Muscle in the Rabbit, *J Bone Joint Surg*, Vol 41A, No. 4, 1959
18. J. L. Dobson, R. S. Mathews and F. H. Stelling, Implant Acceptance in the Musculoskeletal System, *Clin Orthop Relat Res*, No. 72, Sept 1970
19. C. A. Homsy, Biocompatibility in Selection of Materials for Implantation, *J Biomed Mater Res*, Vol 4, 1970, p 341
20. P. G. Laing, A. B. Ferguson and E. S. Hodge, Tissue Reaction in Rabbit Muscle Exposed to Metallic Implants, *J Biomed Mater Res*, Vol 1, 1967, p 135
21. M. Williams and H. R. Lissner, "Biomechanics of Human Motion", W. B. Saunders Co., Philadelphia, 1962
22. J. P. Paul, "Forces Transmitted by Joints in the Human Body", Institution of Mechanical Engineers, Vol 181 (3J), 1966-67, p 8
23. W. P. Cooney, E. Chao, R. L. Linscheid and F. E. Axmear, "Biomechanical Analysis of Thumb Functions", presented at the Orthopaedic Research Society, Dallas, Jan 1974
24. R. L. Linsheid and E. Chao, "Biomechanical Assessment of Finger Function in Prosthetic Joint Design", Orthopaedic Clinics of North America, C. M. Evarts (Ed.), Vol 4, 1973, p 317
25. B. B. Seedhom, D. Dowson and V. Wright, Wear of Solid Phase Formed High Density Polyethylene in Relation to the Life of Artificial Hips and Knees, *Wear*, Vol 24, 1973, p 35
26. P. S. Walker and P. G. Bullough, "The Effects of Friction and Wear in Artificial Joints", Orthopaedic Clinics of North America, C. M. Evarts (Ed.), Vol 4, 1973, p 275
27. S. Weisman, "Metals for Implantation in the Human Body", *Ann N Y Acad Sci*, Vol 146, 1968, p 80
28. S. Weisman, The Skeletal Structure of Metal Implants, in "Biomechanical and Human Factors Symposium 1967", American Society of Mechanical Engineers, New York
29. H. J. Grover, Metallic Fatigue in Some Orthopaedic Implants, *J Mater*, Vol 1, 1966, p 413
30. E. H. Miller, D. Miller, J. H. Dumbleton and E. Clark, "Failure Analysis of Orthopaedic Implant Devices", presented at the Orthopaedic Research Society, Las Vegas, 1973
31. N. D. Greene and D. A. Jones, Corrosion of Surgical Implants, *J Mater*, Vol 1, 1966, p 345
32. J. T. Scales, G. D. Winter and H. T. Shirley, Corrosion of Orthopaedic Implants, *J Bone Joint Surg*, Vol 41B, 1959, p 810
33. V. J. Colangelo and N. D. Greene, Corrosion and Fracture of Type 316 Orthopaedic Implants, *J Biomed Mater Res*, Vol 3, 1969, p 247
34. F. P. Bowden and D. Tabor, "The Friction and Lubrication of Solids, Part 2", Oxford University Press, 1964, p 108-116
35. B. O. Weightman, J. M. Zarek and A. C. Bingold, Corrosion of a Cobalt-Chromium-Molybdenum Orthopaedic Implant, *Med Biol Eng*, Vol 7, 1969, p 679
36. J. Cohen and J. Wulff, Clinical Failures Caused by Corrosion of a Vitallium Plate, *J Bone Joint Surg*, Vol 54A, 1972, p 617
37. B. O. Weightman, I. L. Paul, R. M. Rose, S. R. Simon and E. L. Radin, A Comparative Study of Total Hip Replacement Prostheses, *J Biomech*, Vol 6, 1973, p 299
38. J. O. Galante and W. Rostoker, Wear in Total Hip Prostheses, *Acta Orthopaed Scand*, No. 145, 1973
39. V. J. Colangelo, Corrosion Fatigue in Surgical Implants, *J Basic Eng (Trans ASME)*, Vol 91, 1969, p 581
40. K. R. Wheeler and L. A. James, Fatigue Behavior of Type 316 Stainless Steel Under Simulated Body Conditions, *J Biomed Mater Res*, Vol 5, 1971, p 267
41. R. B. Waterhouse, "Fretting Corrosion", Pergamon Press, New York, 1972. See p 56-59 especially.
42. J. Cohen, Corrosion Testing of Orthopaedic Implants, *J Bone Joint Surg*, Vol 44A, 1962, p 307
43. R. W. Revie and N. D. Greene, Corrosion Behavior of Surgical Implant Materials: II. Effects of Surface Preparation, *Corrosion Sci*, Vol 9, 1969, p 763
44. Annual Book of ASTM Standards, Part 7, 1973, p 1112-1122, 1132-1167
45. F. W. Bultitude and J. R. Morris, "The Corrosion of Surgical Implants. Laboratory Study of the Corrosion of Implants", United Kingdom Atomic Energy Authority, AWRE Report GRO/44/83/29, 1969
46. R. F. Hochman and L. M. Taussig, Improved Properties of Type 316L Stainless Steel Implants by Low Temperature Stress Relief, *J Mater*, Vol 1, 1966, p 425
47. R. W. Revie and N. D. Greene, Corrosion Behavior of Surgical Implant Materials: I. Effects of Sterilization, *Corrosion Sci*, Vol 9, 1969, p 755

Index

The major entries in this index are primarily failure mechanisms, fracture-mechanics terminology, fabrication processes, components or assemblies that failed, and metals from which the components or assemblies were made. The table inside the back cover of this volume directs the reader to the numbered examples of failure analysis in the book; in this table, metals and components or assemblies made from them are classified according to mechanism or cause of failure.

A few alloys designated by number are at the beginning of the index, under **Numbered Alloys**. Numbered steels are under **Steels, AISI-SAE** (or **AMS**, or **API**, or **ASME**, or **ASTM**, or **SAE**) **specific types**. Numbered stainless steels are under **Stainless steels, specific types**. Heat-resisting alloys are listed either by specification under **Heat-resisting alloys,**

specific types or alphabetically (including those with designations that include numbers) — for example, **A-286** is in the A's and **Hastelloy B** in the H's. Tool steels are listed by AISI designation under **Tool steels, specific types**. Numbered aluminum and aluminum alloys are listed under **Aluminum alloys, specific types**. Numbered coppers and copper alloys are listed under **Coppers and copper alloys, specific types**. Certain nonferrous alloys that usually are designated by name rather than by number are listed alphabetically under the name — for example, **Aluminum bronze** and **Nickel 200**.

The parenthetical letter E, F or T following an index entry means that information is in an Example, Figure or Table, respectively, and the parenthetical letter A following an entry means that the topic is the subject of an article.

Some Abbreviations and Symbols Used in This Volume

A ...... alternating-stress amplitude
A .... Angstrom (unit)
Ac$_{cm}$ ... in hypereutectoid steel, tem-
  perature at which cementite
  completes solution in austenite
Ac$_1$ .. temperature at which austenite
  begins to form during heating
Ac$_3$ .. temperature at which transfor-
  mation of ferrite to austenite
  is completed during heating
Ae$_{cm}$ .. temperature at equilibrium
  between austenite and cementite
AIME .... American Institute of
  Mining, Metallurgical and
  Petroleum Engineers
AISI .... American Iron and Steel
  Institute
amp .... ampere
AMS .... Aerospace Material
  Specification
ANSI .. American National Standards
  Institute
API .. American Petroleum Institute
Ar' .. temperature at start of trans-
  formation of austenite to
  pearlite during cooling
ASME .... American Society of
  Mechanical Engineers
ASTM .... American Society for
  Testing and Materials
at. % .... atomic per cent
atm .... atmosphere (pressure)
AWS .... American Welding Society
bcc .... body-centered cubic
Bhn .... Brinell hardness number
Btu .... British thermal unit
c .... critical; radial clearance
C .... Celsius (Centigrade)
C .... diametral clearance
CDA .... Copper Development
  Association
cm .... centimeter
conc .... concentrated

cpm .... cycles per minute
cps .... cycles per second
cs .... centistokes
cu .... cubic
d; D; diam .... diameter
dm .... decimeter
dph ...... diamond pyramid hardness
DT .... dynamic tear (test)
DWT .... drop weight test
DWTT .... drop-weight tear test
E .... modulus of elasticity
Eq .... equation
ETP .... electrolytic tough pitch
  (copper)
F .... Fahrenheit
fcc .... face-centered cubic
fpm .... feet per minute
ft .... foot
g .... gram
gal .... gallon
hcp ...... hexagonal, close-packed
hp .... horsepower
hr .... hour
Hz .... hertz
IACS .... International Annealed
  Copper Standard
ID .... inside diameter
in.; " .... inch
K .... kelvin
K .... stress-intensity factor
$K\alpha$ .... primary K-shell x-radiation
K_{Ic} ..... critical plane-strain stress-
  intensity factor (plain-strain
  fracture toughness)
K_{Iscc} ..... stress-corrosion-cracking
  threshold
K_c .... critical stress-intensity factor
  (plane-stress fracture toughness)
kg .... kilogram
kgf .... kilogram force
kgm .... kilogram-meter
ksi ...... kilopounds per square inch
K_t .... stress-concentration factor

kva .... kilovolt-ampere
kw .... kilowatt
L ...... length; load; longitudinal
lb .... pound
lbf .... pound force
ln .... natural logarithm
M ...... molar concentration
ma .... milliampere
max .... maximum
mdd .... milligrams per square decimeter per day
M$_f$ ...... temperature at which martensite formation finishes
  during cooling
mg .... milligram
min .... minute; minimum
MJ .... megajoule
ml .... milliliter
mm .... millimeter
MPa .... megapascal
mph .... miles per hour
M$_s$ ...... temperature at which transformation of austenite to martensite starts during cooling
N .. normal concentration; rotational
  speed; number of cycles
NDT .... nil-ductility transition
OD .... outside diameter
oz .... ounce
pH .... hydrogen-ion concentration
ppb .... parts per billion
ppm .... parts per million
psi ...... pounds per square inch
psia ...... pounds per square inch,
  absolute
psig ... pounds per square inch, gage
rem .... remainder
rms .... root-mean-square
rpm .... revolutions per minute
rps .... revolutions per second
S ..... alternating fatigue strength;
  short transverse; Sommerfeld
  number; stress

S_a ...... alternating-stress amplitude
SAE .... Society of Automotive
  Engineers
sec .... second
S_f .... fatigue (endurance) limit
sfm .... surface feet per minute
S_m .... mean stress
sq .... square
S_r .... stress range
S_u .... tensile strength
sus .... Saybolt universal second
S_y .... yield strength
t .... thickness
T ...... absolute temperature; long
  transverse; tangential
T_c .... ductile-to-brittle-fracture
  transition temperature
TIR .... total indicator reading
T_M ... absolute melting temperature
typ .... typical
UN .... Unified (thread)
UNC ...... Unified Coarse (thread)
UNF .... Unified Fine (thread)
vol % .... volume per cent
w .... watt
wt % .... weight per cent
μ ...... Poisson's ratio; coefficient of
  friction; magnetic permeability;
  viscosity
ν .... Poisson's ratio
σ .... normal stress
σ_y; σ_{ys} .... yield strength
τ .... shear stress
$\times$ .... diameters (magnification);
  multiplication sign
$\to$ ...... forms by chemical reaction
∞ .... infinity
$<$ .... less than
$\leq$ .... less than or equal to
$>$ .... more than
$\geq$ .... more than or equal to
$\uparrow$ ..... substance passes off as a gas
$\propto$ .... varies with

Directory of Examples of Failure Analysis in This Volume